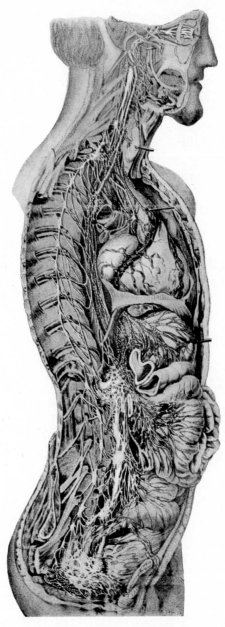

FIG. 1.—Distribution of sympathetic and parasympathetic nerves. The sympathetic nerves and ganglia are illustrated in white, the vagus and parasympathetic nerves in dotted lines, and the mixed terminal nerves in darker shade. (Modified from Müller.)

THE AUTONOMIC NERVOUS SYSTEM

BY

ALBERT KUNTZ, Ph.D., M.D.

Professor of Anatomy in St. Louis University School of Medicine

Fourth Edition, Thoroughly Revised, with 94 Illustrations

LEA & FEBIGER

PHILADELPHIA

1953

Library of Congress Catalog Card Number: 53 – 9570

Printed in the United States of America

PREFACE TO THE FOURTH EDITION

THE regulation of the visceral functions of the body and its adjustments to its internal environment are mediated in part through the autonomic nerves and in part through hormonal mechanisms. The autonomic nerves, in conjunction with the hormonal mechanisms, also play the major role in maintaining the internal environment in a steady state. An attempt is made in the present volume to give a simple but adequate account of the anatomy, the physiology, the pathology and the clinical relationships of the peripheral autonomic nerves and the centers in the central nervous system to which they are functionally related.

The data incorporated in this book are derived from a very extensive literature, including contributions of the author and his collaborators during more than three decades. Since the preparation of the third edition, significant anatomical, physiological, experimental and clinical data have been published by many investigators. Knowledge has been advanced in all aspects of the anatomical, the physiological and the clinical relationships of the autonomic nerves, and particularly with reference to their functional relationships to centers in the brain stem and the cerebral cortex. Significant new data relative to the histochemistry and the histopathology of the autonomic ganglia and nerves have been reported, but the data available do not afford an adequate basis for the complete interpretation in terms of modified functions of all the observed variations.

Adequate consideration, within the limits of a single volume, of all the anatomical, the physiological, the histopathological and the clinical data bearing directly or indirectly on the autonomic nervous system would be impossible. It is extremely difficult, furthermore, to present all the significant findings in their true historical setting. The temptation to give the most recent and the most adequately illustrated contributions undue weight is ever present. This tends to create the impression that the latest and the most detailed work is the most significant, whereas in reality the later findings have been made possible in a large measure by the original discoveries of earlier investigators. The author desires to give due credit to the pioneer investigators, but the limitations of space do not permit a complete account of the historical background of our present knowledge regarding many phases of this important subject. Some significant data have been omitted and some have been treated inadequately. An attempt has been made to maintain a proper balance between the various phases of the subject and to correlate the data selected, including the essential findings reported in the recent literature, so that clear concepts may be gained of the regulatory control of visceral functions that is exercised through the autonomic nerves, the importance of such regulatory control under normal physiological conditions and the effects of autonomic dysfunction.

The number of original papers, reports and reviews that make up the literature relative to all aspects of knowledge of the autonomic nervous system has become so great that it would be impractical to attempt to refer specifically to every important contribution. Listing of all the significant contributions in the bibliography would also be impractical since this part of the volume would be disproportionately large and the cost of publication would be correspondingly increased. In view of these considerations, many findings that have been generally accepted have been set forth without specific documentation. Direct authorship references have been limited chiefly to data that are of fundamental importance, data and points of view that have not been generally accepted and data that may be regarded as controversial. Only those contributions to which direct reference is made in the text are included in the bibliography.

In order to give the reader access to both the older and the current literature, it may be pointed out that most of the significant contributions published prior to 1945 are listed in the bibliography of the third edition of this book. Beginning with 1945 the author has every year prepared a review of the current publications relative to the anatomy, the physiology and the clinical aspects of the autonomic nervous system. These reviews, with complete lists of the publications reviewed, are published in "Progress in Neurology and Psychiatry," Volumes I to VII.

In the preparation of the fourth edition, the entire text has been revised and in part rewritten. New data bearing on certain phases of the anatomical relationships and the functional activity of the autonomic nerves have called for a critical reëxamination of some of the generally accepted concepts which, in some instances, has resulted in a new point of view. Recent clinical and experimental data also afford more adequate criteria for the evaluation of surgical procedures that involve the autonomic nerves in the treatment of patients in various categories. Some of the illustrations have been replaced by new ones in the interest of greater accuracy and clearness, and additional illustrations have been introduced.

The author wishes gratefully to acknowledge his indebtedness to Professors Kermit Christensen and C. A. Richins for valuable advice and assistance, to Dr. N. M. Sulkin for assistance in preparing the account of the histochemistry of the autonomic ganglia and that of variations in the ganglia that may be related to ageing, to Mr. P. A. Conrath for the preparation of illustrations and to the Publishers for their continued interest and courtesy.

A. K.

St. Louis, Missouri

CONTENTS

CHAPTER IV

GENERAL PHYSIOLOGY

CHAPTER V

GENERAL PHYSIOLOGY (*Continued*)

CHAPTER VI

DEVELOPMENT

CHAPTER VII

INNERVATION OF THE HEART

CHAPTER VIII

INNERVATION OF THE BLOOD VESSELS

CHAPTER IX

INNERVATION OF THE RESPIRATORY SYSTEM

CHAPTER X

INNERVATION OF THE DIGESTIVE TUBE

CHAPTER XI

INNERVATION OF THE BILIARY SYSTEM

CHAPTER XII

INNERVATION OF THE PANCREAS, SPLEEN, THYROID, ADRENALS AND BONE MARROW

CHAPTER XIII

INNERVATION OF THE URINARY ORGANS

CHAPTER XVII

Sympathetic Nerves in Relation to Skeletal Muscles

CHAPTER XVIII

Histopathology

CHAPTER XIX

Visceral Sensitivity and Referred Pain

CHAPTER XX

AUTONOMIC IMBALANCE

CHAPTER XXI

THE AUTONOMIC NERVOUS SYSTEM IN DISEASE

CHAPTER XXII

Autonomic Neurosurgery—Anatomical and Physiological Considerations

CHAPTER XXIII

Autonomic Neurosurgery (*Continued*)—Peripheral Vascular and Cardiac Diseases

CHAPTER XXIV

Autonomic Neurosurgery (*Continued*)—Other Diseases With Autonomic Factors, Visceral Pain and Pain in Extremities

The Autonomic Nervous System

HISTORICAL INTRODUCTION

THE vital physiological functions of the body, in all the higher animals, including man, are subject to nervous regulation in some degree. This involves reflex and coördinating reactions of varying degrees of complexity that are carried out through afferent and efferent conduction systems and reflex and coördinating centers. Peripheral reflex mechanisms have been demonstrated, but the chief reflex and coördinating centers involved in the regulatory control of the visceral functions are located in the central nervous system. The functional activities of these neural mechanisms are essentially involuntary, but they are not independent of regulatory influences emanating from the cerebral cortex. All the neurons located outside the central nervous system that are concerned with the innervation of the viscera, except those which are afferent components of the cerebrospinal nerves, are included in the so-called autonomic nervous system. This system also includes the neurons located within the spinal cord and the brain stem through which the outlying efferent neurons are functionally connected with the central nervous system.

The earliest anatomical description of any part of the autonomic nervous system probably is Galen's account of a nerve trunk lying along the necks of the ribs which receives fibers from the thoracic and the lumbar portions of the spinal cord and gives off branches to the viscera. Galen regarded this nerve as a branch of the vagus and advanced the hypothesis that through it the viscera receive sensitivity from the brain and motor power from the spinal cord. He obviously did not differentiate the cervical portion of the sympathetic trunk from the vagus. He observed three enlargements, or ganglia, along the course of the nerve, the first just above the larynx, the second at the entrance of the nerve into the thorax and the third at its entrance into the abdomen. The upper enlargement described by Galen undoubtedly includes the nodose and the superior cervical sympathetic ganglia. The one at the upper border of the thorax obviously is the inferior cervical or the cervicothoracic ganglion. The description of the one at the entrance of the nerve into the abdomen probably refers to the semilunar ganglion of the celiac plexus.

Galen also advanced the first widely accepted theory of "sympathy" or "consent" between different parts of the body. He rejected the teaching of Aristotle that the brain serves to cool the blood and attributed to it the function of generating "animal" spirits from the "vital" spirits in the blood. The peripheral nerves were regarded as tubular structures through which the animal spirits are distributed. It was further assumed that wherever peripheral nerves join one another communications are effected through which animal spirits may flow freely from one part of the body to

(15)

another and thus bring about "sympathy" between various parts of the body.

Galen's description of the vagi, which he regarded as the sixth pair of cranial nerves, was scrupulously followed by all the early anatomists including Vesalius; consequently, the ganglionated sympathetic trunk and the vagus nerve were regarded as a unit both anatomically and physiologically. The sympathetic trunk probably was first differentiated from the vagus nerve anatomically by Etienne (1545). Eustachio (1563) also recognized the sympathetic trunk as anatomically distinct from the vagus nerve. He illustrated it as arising within the cranium from the abducens nerve, thus emphasizing its supposedly cerebral origin. This error was not corrected until the publication of du Petit's work in 1727.

Willis (1664) called the ganglionated sympathetic trunk the "intercostal" nerve, a name which persisted until the time of Winslow. He also introduced the physiological concept of involuntary as distinct from voluntary movements, but he erroneously attributed the initiation of involuntary movements to the cerebellum. His account of a branch of the vagus nerve given off to the arch of the aorta undoubtedly is the earliest reference to the depressor nerve. He advanced the hypothesis that the nerve reacts to changes in the pulse. He recognized the vagus innervation of the heart as an important factor in its functional regulation, but discovered no specific reaction to vagus stimulation. Lower's (1669) observations on the effects of vagus section and vagus stimulation on the heart beat, which were later amplified by Ens (1745), prepared the way for the final demonstration of the inhibitory action of the vagus nerve on the heart beat by the experimental studies of Weber and Weber (1846).

The physiological concept of involuntary and voluntary movements introduced by Willis was greatly extended by Whytt (1751). His interpretation of involuntary movements on the basis of local stimulation marks the beginning of a new era in physiological thought and investigation, since it afforded a secure basis for the theory of reflex action. He envisioned reactions like the peristaltic movements of the gastro-intestinal tract and contractions of the urinary bladder as responses of the musculature to nerve stimulation due to local irritation of the mucous membrane or stretching of the muscle fibers due to distention of the organs. The idea of reflex action was thus introduced in the absence of any knowledge of reflex conduction pathways. Whytt's application of this principle to explain the responses of the pupil to light constitutes the earliest known record of light, accommodation and consensual reflexes. He later (1765) advanced the opinion that all "sympathy" or "consent" presupposes feeling and, consequently, must be mediated through the nerves, but, since in many instances the sympathy occurs between parts of the body whose nerves make no connections with one another, its mediation cannot involve the flow of any substance through anastomosing channels. Sympathy, therefore, must be referred to the brain and the spinal cord which are the source of all nerves. Although he probably had no adequate conception of nerve conduction, he drew attention to nerve fibers as functional units in contradistinction to the older concepts of anastomosing channels.

The erroneous conception of the origin of the "intercostal" nerve from the brain was corrected by du Petit (1727) who pointed out, on the basis of careful dissection and the results of experimental section of the vago-sympathetic trunk in dogs, that this nerve is not directly connected with the brain. Although the significance of this work was not fully appreciated until the time of Gaskell and Langley, investigators following du Petit recognized that the communicating rami constitute the only pathway from the central nervous system to the sympathetic ganglia.

Winslow (1732) accepted du Petit's findings, but regarded the sympathetic ganglia as independent nerve centers. He discarded the term "intercostal" nerves, which had been commonly applied to the sympathetic trunks. In accordance with his opinion that they are primarily concerned with the "sympathies" between various organs, he designated them the "great sympathetic nerves."

Johnstone (1764) advanced the hypothesis that the sympathetic ganglia represented mechanisms through which the movements of the heart and the intestine are rendered involuntary, since they intercept the "determinations of the will" and prevent them from reaching certain parts of the body. He also advanced the opinion that the ganglia interrupt sensory impressions from the viscera, which accounts for the relative lack of sensitivity in the visceral organs. His descriptive accounts of the ganglia in relation to the nerves led to the use of the terms "ganglionic nerves" and "ganglionic nervous system." He supported Winslow's view of the relative independence of the ganglia and thus contributed to the propagation of this concept.

Meckel (1751) advanced the opinion that the ganglia serve to divide nerves into many fibers, to arrange these fibers according to their course and termination and to reunite them in bundles. He observed that the volume of the fibers emerging from a ganglion is greater than the volume of those which enter it, but apparently he did not surmise that fibers arise within the ganglia.

The anatomical and physiological studies of Bichat (1800, 1801, 1802) contributed significantly to knowledge of the autonomic nervous system and stimulated further research. He conceived of life as made up of animal life (*la vie animale*) and organic life (*la vie organique*), a distinction which finds expression in the current concepts of "somatic" and "visceral" functions. He correlated the ganglionic nervous system with metabolic functions and pointed out the continuity of action apparent in the organic life in contrast to the intermittent activity apparent in the animal life. In pursuance of this point of view, he regarded the sympathetic ganglia as nerve centers entirely independent of the central nervous system. He noted the difference in the appearance of the white and the gray communicating rami and regarded the former as components of the central nervous system, but failed clearly to recognize their true significance. He also observed that the fibers which emerge from the sympathetic ganglia enter the organs chiefly along the courses of their arteries. Although Bichat commonly used the term, ganglionic nervous system, he may properly be regarded as the originator of the name, "organic nervous system," because of his emphasis on the relation of the ganglionic nerves to organic life.

2

Reil (1807) introduced the term "vegetative nervous system." Like Bichat, he regarded the sympathetic ganglia as independent nerve centers. He interpreted the communicating rami as connections between the animal and the vegetative nervous systems which serve as semiconductors. According to his view, sensory impressions from the viscera do not ordinarily reach the brain, but in disease sensory impressions from the vegetative sphere may be transmitted through the communicating rami and thus reach the level of consciousness. This view is strikingly reminiscent of the one advanced by Johnstone nearly half a century earlier.

The earliest description of nerve cell bodies in sympathetic ganglia probably is that of Ehrenberg (1833), who also recorded some observations on the microscopic structure of nerve fibers. Valentin (1836) described the histologic structure of sympathetic ganglia, including the ganglion cells, in greater detail. He recognized the fibers of the white communicating rami as arising in the spinal cord and entering the sympathetic ganglia, and distinguished between fibers which terminate in the ganglia and those which pass through them, but he failed to recognize the neural nature of the unmyelinated fibers which Remak (1838) described as arising from the sympathetic ganglion cells and which he called "organic" fibers.

Bidder and Volkmann (1842) also opposed Remak's view of the "organic" fibers. The neural nature of these fibers gradually became established as Remak's observations were confirmed by other investigators. In 1854 Remak published a more extensive account of the structure of the sympathetic ganglia and their connections, particularly the communicating rami. Although Beck (1846) had observed that the sympathetic ganglia are connected with the cervical and the sacral nerves only through gray communicating rami, Remak maintained that all the spinal nerves possess both white and gray communicating rami. In spite of this error, Remak's account afforded the basis for a better understanding of the functional significance of the communicating rami.

At the middle of the nineteenth century the relationships of the vagus nerves to the "ganglionic" or "organic" nervous system remained obscure, although a vagus influence on cardiac activity had been demonstrated. The ciliary, the sphenopalatine, the otic and the submandibular ganglia were regarded as components of the ganglionic nervous system, but their relationships also remained uncertain. The submucous plexus in the intestine was described by Meissner in 1857 and the myenteric plexus by Auerbach in 1864. The significant anatomical and physiological studies leading up to Claude Bernard's discovery of the vasomotor function of the sympathetic nerves to the blood vessels, which was confirmed by Brown-Séquard (1852), had already been accomplished.

The early studies of the vasomotor nerves gave rise to the concept of a universal vasoconstrictor action of sympathetic nerve fibers. Vasodilator effects of nerve stimulation were not reported until Bernard (1858) observed dilatation of the arteries supplying the submandibular gland on stimulation of the chorda tympani. Dastre and Morat (1883) later demonstrated the existence of vasodilator fibers in the cervical portion of the sympathetic trunk.

In the light of advancing knowledge of the nature of the communicating rami, reflex activity and reflex centers in the central nervous system, Bichat's theory, according to which the sympathetic ganglia represent nerve centers which function independently of the central nervous system, could no longer be supported. On the basis of extensive physiological data, Bernard advanced the hypothesis that all sympathetic reflexes are mediated through the spinal cord. He also demonstrated the existence of centers in the brain stem which on stimulation discharge impulses that are conducted through sympathetic nerves. The search for higher centers which exert their influence through the autonomic nerves was thus initiated.

The early anatomical and physiological studies of Gaskell (1886) contributed greatly to a better understanding of the autonomic nervous system. His account of the white communicating rami and their distribution represents the earliest account of these nerves that is based on adequate anatomical and histological observations. He pointed out that the efferent fibers in these rami arise in the spinal cord in cell columns which are interrupted by the development of the nerves to the limbs, that corresponding fibers occur in certain of the cranial nerves, and that there exist three outflows of medullated nerve fibers of small caliber, the bulbar, the thoracolumbar and the sacral, through which the peripherally located efferent ganglion cells are connected with the central nervous system. Gaskell classified the ganglia in question as (1) proximal or vertebral and (2) distal. The former category included only the ganglia of the sympathetic trunks from the lower cervical segments caudad. The latter included (a) the prevertebral ganglia, *i.e.*, the superior cervical, the celiac and the superior mesenteric, and (b) the terminal ganglia, *i.e.*, those located within the visceral organs or in proximity to them.

In his later work, Gaskell (1916) used the term "involuntary nervous system" to designate the efferent neurons located outside the central nervous system that supply fibers to involuntary structures. He conceived of the involuntary nervous system as purely motor or efferent and referred to the outflows from the central nervous system as the "connectors." His terminology presented certain obvious difficulties; consequently, it has never been widely used.

Langley and Dickinson (1890) discovered in the action of nicotine on the ganglia a new method of investigating the relationships of nerve fibers to peripheral ganglion cells. The results obtained by the use of this method led Langley (1898) to propose a new terminology for the system of nerves in question. He called it the "autonomic nervous system," although he was not unmindful of its anatomical and functional relationships to the cerebrospinal nervous system.

When the term "autonomic" was introduced by Langley, it was well known that the thoracolumbar outflow through the sympathetic trunks supplies fibers to all parts of the body. The cranial and the sacral outflows, on the other hand, were known to supply fibers only to parts of the body. It was also known that the functional effects of the thoracolumbar outflow, in general, are the opposite of those of the cranial and the sacral outflows. Langley, therefore, regarded the thoracolumbar outflow as a system distinct from the rest of the autonomic nerves. He regarded the part of the cranial outflow supplying the eye as distinct from the bulbar part of this outflow, which with the sacral outflow constitutes a system that innervates the alimentary canal and parts developmentally connected with it. On this basis, he (1898) divided the autonomic system into tectal, bulbosacral and sympathetic systems. Following the discovery that the effects produced by adrenin apparently are similar to those produced by stimulation of sympathetic nerves, and that certain other drugs produce effects apparently identical with those produced by stimulation of the tectal and the bulbosacral nerves, he (1904) grouped the tectal and the bulbosacral autonomic nerves together as the parasympathetic system. Langley (1900) had previously pointed out that the neurons in the myenteric and the submucous plexuses might conceivably be postganglionic neurons in bulbar and sacral efferent chains, but, since the data available afforded no clear proof of the central connections of these cells, and histological evidence had convinced him that they differ structurally from other peripheral neurons, he placed the myenteric and the submucous plexuses in a separate system which he called the enteric nervous system.

Although Langley's classification of the nerves in question cannot be regarded as final, and he himself recognized the inadequacy of the terminology that he proposed, it is the most satisfactory terminology in use at the present time. Accordingly, the terms autonomic, sympathetic and parasympathetic will be used in the present volume in the sense in which he used them. Such minor deviations from Langley's classification and terminology as are introduced will be discussed in their proper connections.

Chapter I

MORPHOLOGY AND DISTRIBUTION OF THE AUTONOMIC NERVOUS SYSTEM

DEFINITION AND TERMINOLOGY

THE visceral organs, including the vascular and the glandular systems, are subject to functional regulation through the nervous system in some degree. Their neural regulation is accomplished in a large measure through reflex and correlating mechanisms of varying degrees of complexity. They consist of afferent nerves, *i.e.*, nerves that conduct impulses from receptive organs, or receptors, into the spinal cord and the brain, reflex and correlating centers in the spinal cord and the brain; and efferent nerves, *i.e.*, nerves that conduct impulses from the spinal cord and the brain to the viscera. The spinal cord and the brain make up the central nervous system. All neural structures outside the spinal cord and the brain may be designated as peripheral. Some reflex neural activity that is not carried out through the central nervous system has been demonstrated, but the chief reflex and coördinating mechanisms concerned with the regulatory control of visceral functions are located in the spinal cord and the brain stem. The neural regulation of the visceral functions is essentially involuntary, but it is not independent of impulses emanating from the cerebral cortex.

The efferent neurons through which the visceral organs are innervated are designated as autonomic. They constitute the major portion of the autonomic nervous system. This system is neither anatomically separate from nor functionally independent of the central nervous system. It includes all neurons located outside the central nervous system and the cerebrospinal ganglia, except the peripheral afferent neurons associated with the special sense organs. It also includes the efferent neurons located within the spinal cord and the brain stem through which the outlying autonomic neurons are functionally connected with the central nervous system. With certain exceptions, the autonomic neurons outside the central nervous system are arranged in aggregates known as ganglia, the autonomic ganglia. Some of these ganglia are located along the ventrolateral aspects of the vertebral column. These series of ganglia, with the longitudinal interganglionic nerve fibers, constitute the paired sympathetic trunks. Other autonomic ganglia are incorporated in nerve plexuses located in proximity to the thoracic, the abdominal and the pelvic viscera or within their walls. Still others are located in the cephalic region in relation to certain of the cranial nerves.

The neurons through which the autonomic ganglia are anatomically and functionally connected with the central nervous system are visceral efferent components of the cerebrospinal nerves. They are commonly known as preganglionic neurons. Their cell bodies are located in the intermediolateral cell column in the spinal cord and the visceral efferent nuclei in the brain stem. Their axons traverse the corresponding spinal and cranial nerves and make synaptic connections with ganglion cells in the autonomic ganglia. The axons of the autonomic ganglion cells reach their destinations through either visceral or somatic nerves and terminate in relation to the tissue elements which are innervated through the autonomic nerves.

The afferent neurons through which visceral impulses are conducted into the central nervous system are the general visceral afferent components of the cerebrospinal nerves. Their cell bodies, like those of the general somatic afferent neurons, are located in the cerebrospinal ganglia. Their peripheral processes traverse the autonomic ganglia without interruption and are not known to make direct functional connections with neurons outside the central nervous system. Both visceral and somatic afferent neurons make reflex connections with preganglionic visceral efferent neurons and, consequently, are functionally related to the autonomic nerves. Afferent neurons that terminate in the central nervous system may not be regarded as constituents of the autonomic nerves, however, since both somatic and visceral afferents also make reflex connections with somatic efferent neurons. They are properly classified as somatic and visceral afferent components respectively of the cerebrospinal nerves.

The autonomic, or visceral, reflex arcs with central connections in the central nervous system differ anatomically from the somatic reflex arcs in that the preganglionic efferent components of the former make synaptic connections with ganglion cells in the autonomic ganglia, whereas the efferent components of the latter terminate in direct relation to effector organs (Fig. 2). The efferent limb of the autonomic reflex arc, consequently comprises two neurons, whereas that of the somatic reflex arc comprises but one. The portion of either the autonomic or the somatic reflex arc that is located within the central nervous system may be confined to a single segment or it may involve two or more segments. The preganglionic component of the autonomic reflex arc likewise may make synaptic connections in one or more autonomic ganglia.

The afferent components of the cerebrospinal nerves which make reflex connections with preganglionic neurons probably do not terminate in direct relation to these neurons but make synaptic connections with intercalated neurons which in turn make synaptic connections with the preganglionic neurons. The preganglionic component of an autonomic reflex arc, consequently, may not be regarded as comparable to an intercalated neuron in the somatic reflex arc.

The distribution of the preganglionic visceral efferent neurons is limited to certain regions of the spinal cord and the brain stem. Some of the cerebrospinal nerves, consequently, include no visceral efferent components. On the basis of the distribution of preganglionic visceral efferent nerve components, the autonomic nervous system may be divided into (1) the cranial division, the preganglionic components of which emerge in the third, the seventh, the ninth, the tenth and the eleventh cranial nerves, (2) the thoracolumbar division, the preganglionic components of which emerge in the thoracic and the upper lumbar nerves, and (3) the sacral division, the preganglionic components of which emerge in the second, the third and the fourth sacral nerves (Fig. 3).

The preganglionic components of the thoracic and the lumbar nerves traverse the visceral rami of these nerves and join the sympathetic trunk. Some of them terminate in the sympathetic trunk ganglia. Others traverse these ganglia without making connections in them and extend, via the splanchnic nerves, to ganglia located in closer proximity to the abdominal and the pelvic viscera. Preganglionic fibers that make synaptic connections in the sympathetic trunk ganglia, unless they terminate in the segment in which they join the trunk, run either rostrad or caudad in it. None appear to bifurcate and send one branch rostrad and the other caudad. Rostral to the midthoracic level, therefore, nearly all the preganglionic fibers in the sympathetic trunk run rostrad, and caudal to this level nearly all run caudad. The preganglionic components of the cranial and the sacral nerves

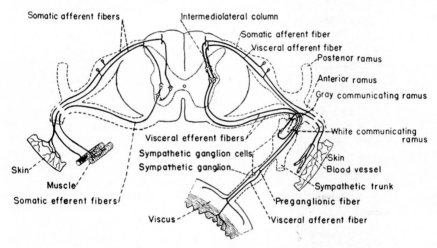

Fig. 2.—Diagrammatic illustration of visceral (right) and somatic (left) reflex arcs.

do not traverse the sympathetic trunk but extend through rami of the respective nerves to the ganglia in which they terminate. The cranial and the sacral divisions of the autonomic nervous system also react to certain drugs according to the same mode, but differ in this respect from the thoracolumbar division. On the basis of the anatomical relationships of their preganglionic components and their pharmacological peculiarities, in which the cranial and the sacral divisions are similar, but differ from the thoracolumbar division, the former two divisions have been grouped together as the craniosacral autonomic system in contrast to the thoracolumbar. The former is the parasympathetic nervous system, the latter the sympathetic nervous system, according to the common usage of these terms.

The neural structure in the wall of the alimentary canal includes two plexuses, the myenteric and the submucous, which are intimately interconnected and include numerous small ganglia. These plexuses are ontogenetically, anatomically and physiologically related to the parasympathetic division of the autonomic nervous system, but possess the capacity for independent functional activity in a greater degree than other parts of the autonomic system. Their capacity to carry out coördinated reflex activities in the absence of impulses that emanate from the central nervous system is well known. The relationships of some of the neurons in the

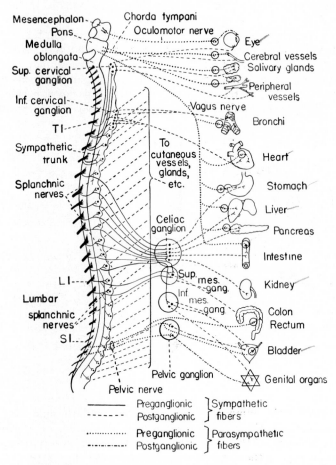

Fig. 3.—Diagrammatic illustration of the distribution of sympathetic and parasympathetic nerves.

enteric ganglia, therefore, must differ from those of the neurons in other parts of the autonomic system, *e. g.*, those in the sympathetic trunk ganglia and the autonomic ganglia in the cranial region, which probably function only as terminal neurons in visceral efferent chains. It is advantageous because of their anatomical and functional relationships as well as for descriptive purposes to retain the term, enteric nervous system, as proposed by Langley, to designate the plexuses in the wall of the alimentary canal.

STRUCTURE AND RELATIONSHIPS

Sympathetic Trunks.—Each sympathetic trunk extends from the base of the cranium to the coccyx along the anterolateral aspect of the vertebral column. It is made up of a series of ganglia (vertebral ganglia) connected by longitudinal fibers. The ganglia are connected with the spinal nerves through *communicating rami*. The latter include the visceral components of the spinal nerves that are functionally related to the sympathetic system and the sympathetic fibers that join the spinal nerves for distribution to the tissues to be innervated. The spinal nerve components contained in the communicating rami, most of which are myelinated, constitute the *white* communicating rami. The sympathetic components, most of which either are unmyelinated or but thinly myelinated, constitute the *gray* communicating rami. Visceral components are absent in the cervical, the caudal two or three lumbar and the first sacral nerves. The communicating rami of these nerves, therefore, include only sympathetic fibers. The visceral nerves through which the internal organs receive their sympathetic innervation arise from the sympathetic trunks. They include visceral afferent, preganglionic and sympathetic fibers.

Duncan (1943) has called attention to the erroneous practice of designating the aggregates of sympathetic fibers that join the spinal nerves as rami. Since these fibers join the spinal nerves for their peripheral distribution, they constitute roots, according to the common usage of this term. In the present volume the term, sympathetic root, will be used in preference to the term, gray communicating ramus. The sympathetic root commonly joins the ventral primary division of the spinal nerve. The sympathetic fibers that join the dorsal primary division, consequently, extend centrad for a short distance in the ventral primary division (Dass, 1952).

The cervical portion of each sympathetic trunk lies ventral to the transverse processes of the cervical vertebræ and dorsal to the carotid vessels. It includes the superior, the middle, the intermediate, and the inferior cervical sympathetic ganglia and contains both myelinated and unmyelinated fibers. The superior cervical, usually the largest of all the sympathetic ganglia, is a somewhat spindle-shaped body located at the base of the skull between the internal carotid artery and the jugular vein and in front of the transverse processes of the second, the third and the fourth cervical vertebræ. The middle cervical ganglion, frequently absent, usually is situated about the level of the body of the sixth cervical vertebra. Frequently it occupies a lower position. It usually lies ventral to the inferior thyroid artery as this artery passes behind the carotid sheath. The intermediate cervical ganglion is relatively small and is located on the medial side of the vertebral artery approximately at the level of the eighth cervical nerve. It is connected with the inferior cervical ganglion by a large ramus which passes behind the vertebral artery and usually by a smaller one which passes in front of this artery. In most cases it is also connected with the inferior cervical ganglion through the ansa subclavia, which forms a loop around the subclavian artery (Fig. 4). The inferior cervical ganglion commonly is situated dorsal to the subclavian artery at

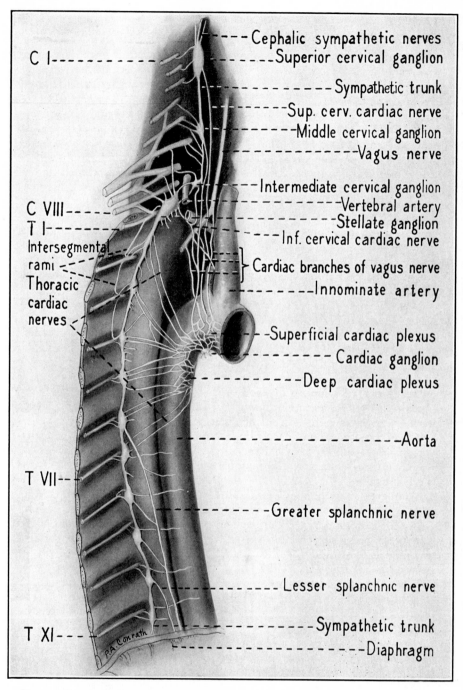

FIG. 4.—Drawing from a dissection of a human cadaver to illustrate the cervical and the thoracic segments of the right sympathetic trunk and the nerves arising from them.

the point of origin of the vertebral artery. It frequently is fused with the first thoracic ganglion. When fused, the two constitute the stellate ganglion (Fig. 4), situated ventral to the head of the first rib and covered by the pleura.

The *superior cervical* sympathetic ganglion is an elongated body which varies in size within a relatively wide range. It gives rise to sympathetic roots that join the first, the second, usually the third and in some instances the fourth cervical nerves. It also sends sympathetic roots to the hypoglossal nerve, the jugular and the nodose ganglia of the vagus, and the petrosal ganglion of the glossopharyngeal nerve. The connections between the superior cervical sympathetic and the nodose ganglia usually consist of one or two stout rami and several more slender ones. A peripheral ramus passes behind the carotid sheath to the wall of the pharynx where it joins the ascending pharyngeal plexus. This plexus also receives a few smaller rami from the superior cervical ganglion. One or two small rami also are supplied to the esophagus. The superior cardiac nerve arises near the caudal end of the ganglion and descends dorsal to the large vessels, but usually ventral to the superior thyroid artery, and joins the superficial cardiac plexus on the left and the deep cardiac plexus on the right side. It is connected by slender rami with the carotid and the external maxillary plexuses and, in some instances, with the sympathetic trunk below the superior cervical ganglion. Rarely it also sends a ramus to the recurrent nerve. This ramus is joined by one from the ansa subclavia. A ramus from the superior cervical ganglion also joins the phrenic nerve. Another joins the common trunk of the superior laryngeal nerve before the latter divides into its internal and external branches. In some instances a ramus that arises from the superior cervical ganglion with the internal carotid nerve also joins the superior laryngeal nerve. The several peripheral rami of the superior cervical ganglion that join the internal carotid artery constitute the internal carotid nerve and give rise to the internal carotid plexus. Other rami join the external carotid artery on which they form a plexus. The plexuses on the carotid arteries represent the major portion of the extension of the sympathetic nerves into the head.

The *middle cervical* ganglion (Fig. 4), when present, is most frequently located opposite or rostral to the transverse process of the sixth cervical vertebra. It usually is connected by sympathetic roots with the fifth and the sixth and sometimes also the fourth and the seventh cervical nerves. The middle cervical cardiac nerve arises from this ganglion or, in its absence, from the cervical sympathetic trunk, descends dorsal to the large vessels, either separately or with the other cervical cardiac nerves, and joins the deep cardiac plexus on both sides. Slender rami arising from this ganglion also accompany the inferior thyroid artery to supply the blood vessels in the thyroid gland. In the absence of the middle cervical ganglion, these rami arise directly from the interganglionic cord.

The intermediate cervical ganglion is connected with the brachial plexus by few sympathetic roots. Frequently one joins the sixth cervical nerve and, rarely, another joins the fifth or the seventh. In instances in which the eighth cervical nerve has a white communicating ramus, some of its preganglionic components probably enter the intermediate cervical ganglion (Kirgis and Kuntz, 1942).

The *inferior cervical* ganglion is connected by sympathetic roots with the seventh and the eighth cervical and sometimes with the sixth cervical and the first thoracic nerves. In general, the cervical sympathetic roots lie ventral and lateral to the vertebral artery, but there exists at least one ramus, the vertebral nerve, which lies dorsal to the vertebral artery. The inferior cervical cardiac nerve, arising from the medial side of the ganglion, joins the deep cardiac plexus. Slender rami join the plexuses on the subclavian, the internal maxillary and the vertebral arteries. Offsets from the plexus on the vertebral artery join the lower cervical nerves, frequently as high as the fourth. The vertebral rami of the inferior cervical gagnlion, therefore, may be regarded as sympathetic roots. Frequently a ramus arising from this ganglion joins the recurrent nerve. In some instances, rami accompany the common carotid artery and, joining the plexus on the internal carotid artery, contribute to the sympathetic innervation of the head. The subclavian plexus, derived chiefly from the ansa subclavia, sends rami to the internal mammary artery and the phrenic nerve.

Distal to the nodose ganglion, numerous connections exist between the vagus nerve and the sympathetic trunk, but they exhibit no regular arrangement. The relationship between the vagus nerve and the sympathetic trunk is more intimate on the right side than on the left, particularly in the lower cervical region.

In the thorax the sympathetic trunk lies behind the pleura and ventral to the necks of the ribs from the first to the tenth. This portion includes ten or eleven ganglia joined together by longitudinal fibers. In most instances the first thoracic ganglion, rarely also the second, is fused with the inferior cervical to form the *stellate* ganglion. As observed by Jamieson *et al.* (1952) in 100 cadavers, fusion of the first thoracic with the inferior cervical ganglion occurred in 82 per cent. Frequently other thoracic ganglia are fused so that the number is still further reduced. The thoracic sympathetic ganglia usually are irregularly angular or fusiform, but they vary greatly with respect to form and size. In general, they are arranged segmentally.

Every thoracic ganglion is connected with the corresponding spinal nerve by a white communicating ramus and a sympathetic root. Sometimes the communicating ramus and the sympathetic root are separate. The communicating ramus usually arises from the spinal nerve distal to the point at which the sympathetic root joins it. Sometimes the communicating ramus and the sympathetic root are intimately fused. Frequently the sympathetic ganglion is connected with the spinal nerve by more than two rami. Occasionally a sympathetic trunk ganglion is connected with more than one spinal nerve.

In a large percentage of cases, an intrathoracic ramus arising from the second thoracic nerve joins the first, usually proximal to the origin of the first intercostal nerve. Frequently a sympathetic root from the second thoracic sympathetic ganglion joins this ramus. In other cases, a sympathetic root joins the second thoracic nerve in proximity to the origin of the intrathoracic ramus to the first (Fig. 4). The latter ramus receives sympathetic fibers through the sympathetic root of the second thoracic nerve; consequently, it constitutes a pathway through which sympathetic fibers that leave the sympathetic trunk below the first thoracic ganglion enter the brachial plexus (Kuntz, 1927). In a somewhat smaller percentage of cases, a ramus arising from the third thoracic nerve just distal to its communicating ramus joins the second thoracic nerve in proximity to the origin of the ramus of the latter nerve that joins the first thoracic (Kirgis and Kuntz, 1942). This ramus was demonstrated bilaterally in 15, and unilaterally in 18 of 44 cadavers examined. It includes unmyelinated fibers undoubtedly of sympathetic origin which enter it through the sympathetic root of the third thoracic nerve. In some instances such fibers could be traced from this ramus directly into the ramus of the second thoracic nerve that joins the first. These rami, consequently, constitute a pathway through which sympathetic fibers that arise in the third thoracic segment or lower may reach the brachial plexus without traversing the more rostral thoracic sympathetic trunk ganglia (Fig. 4). In some bodies the fourth and the third thoracic nerves are also interconnected by a slender ramus that parallels the sympathetic trunk. It probably also conveys sympathetic fibers (Ehrlich and Alexander, 1951).

Peripheral rami arising from the upper five thoracic ganglia supply the upper part of the aorta. The second, the third and the fourth thoracic ganglia also send rami into the cardiac and the dorsal pulmonary plexuses. The *splanchnic* nerves consist mainly of visceral afferent and preganglionic visceral efferent fibers that join the sympathetic trunk *via* the communicating rami and merely traverse it on their way to more peripheral ganglia incorporated in the prevertebral plexuses or located in proximity to the viscera. The *greater splanchnic* nerve is formed by the union of several rami arising from the sympathetic trunk between the fifth and the ninth or the tenth thoracic ganglia (Fig. 4). In some instances a ganglion is present in the course of this nerve. Descending in the posterior mediastinum, it pierces the diaphragm and joins the celiac ganglion. A slight enlargement, the splanchnic ganglion, occurs on this nerve opposite the eleventh or the twelfth thoracic vertebra. Rami that arise both from this ganglion and the nerve join the plexuses on the esophagus and the descending aorta. The *lesser splanchnic* nerve is formed by the union of several rami arising usually from the ninth and the tenth thoracic ganglia. It pierces the diaphragm in proximity to the greater splanchnic nerve and, entering the celiac plexus, terminates in the aorticorenal ganglion. The *lowest splanchnic* nerve (sometimes absent) arises from the most caudal thoracic ganglion or the lesser splanchnic nerve, pierces the diaphragm and terminates in the renal plexus.

Passing from the thorax into the abdomen, the sympathetic trunk usually lies between the lateral and the medial crura of the diaphragm. At this level it is very slender and tends ventrad until it reaches the ventrolateral surface of the body of the second lumbar vertebra. Throughout the remaining lumbar segments it lies upon the bodies of the vertebræ, ventral to the lumbar vessels and medial to the origin of the psoas major muscle. Frequently one or both trunks are separated into two or more strands for varying distances. The lumbar portion of each trunk usually includes four

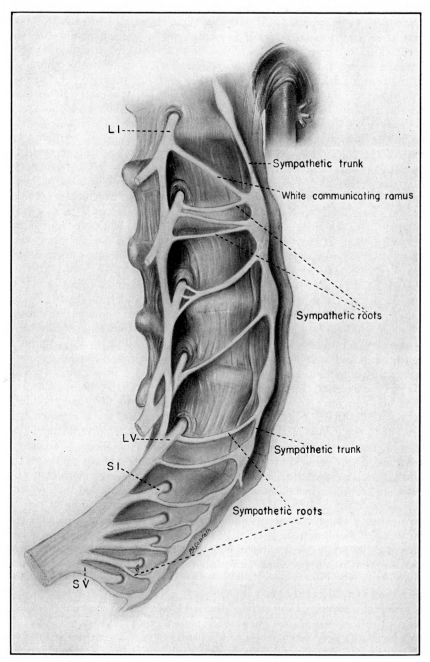

Fɪɢ. 5.—Drawing from a dissection of a human cadaver to illustrate the lumbar and the sacral segments of the right sympathetic trunk and its connections with the lumbar and the sacral spinal nerves.

ganglia, but the number varies from two to eight. Occasionally the lumbar ganglia are fused to such an extent that individual ganglia cannot be recognized. The first and the second lumbar spinal nerves, frequently the third and sometimes the fourth, send communicating rami obliquely into this portion of the sympathetic trunk. The occurrence of preganglionic fibers in the fourth lumbar nerve in man in some instances has been demonstrated experimentally (Randall *et al.*, 1952). In a study of the pre- and the postganglionic vasomotor outflows to the dog's hind foot, with the aid of the photoelectric plethysmograph, Cox *et al.* (1952) found that the preganglionic outflow, in some animals, extended caudad to the sixth lumbar nerve. The postganglionic fibers concerned arise in the sympathetic trunk ganglia from the fourth lumbar to the first sacral. The lumbar por-

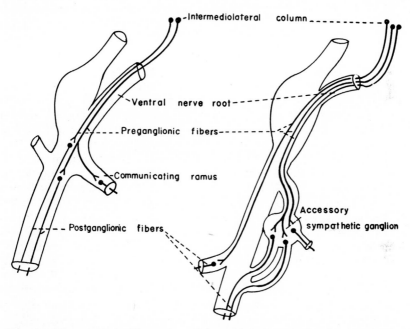

Fig. 6.—Diagrammatic illustration of synaptic relationships of accessory sympathetic ganglion cells with preganglionic fibers (left), and diagrammatic illustration of location of an accessory sympathetic ganglion and synaptic relationships of the ganglion cells based on a study of serial longitudinal secions of a twelfth thoracic nerve (right).

tion of the sympathetic trunk also contains myelinated fibers that enter it through the communicating rami of the caudal thoracic nerves. Sympathetic roots that arise from the lumbar portion of the sympathetic trunk join all the lumbar nerves. They take courses that are more nearly horizontal than those of the communicating rami. They also vary in number. A single root may bifurcate and join two adjacent spinal nerves, or several (two to five) may join a single spinal nerve.

In the pelvis, the sympathetic trunk lies on the ventral surface of the sacrum medial to the anterior sacral foramina (Fig. 5). Both trunks converge toward the median plane and terminate in the ganglion impar, or coccygeal ganglion, on the ventral surface of the coccyx. The sacral portion of the sympathetic trunk usually includes four ganglia, but the number may vary from two to six. The ganglia are small and gradually diminish in size rostrocaudally. Like the cervical and the caudal lumbar portions of the sympathetic trunk, this portion receives no communicating rami. The third and the fourth sacral nerves and occasionally the second or the fifth include visceral components that enter the pelvic plexus through the visceral rami of these nerves without passing through the sympathetic trunk. Sympathetic roots that arise from the pelvic portion of the sympathetic trunk join both the sacral and the coccygeal nerves. Visceral rami of small size also join the pelvic plexus. A few small parietal rami from both sides form a plexiform network over the ventral surface of the sacrum.

Accessory Sympathetic Ganglia

According to current concepts, all ganglion cells that are synaptically related to preganglionic fibers that traverse thoracic and lumbar nerve roots are located in the sympathetic trunk ganglia and ganglia that are located in relation to the abdominal and the pelvic viscera. According to this structural plan, all peripheral sympathetic conduction pathways should traverse the sympathetic trunk. Certain anatomical and physiological data indicate the existence of some peripheral sympathetic conduction pathways that are independent of the sympathetic trunk.

Groups of ganglion cells located in communicating rami and sympathetic roots have been described in the lumbar (Hirt, 1921; Gruss, 1932; Wrete, 1941), the cervical and the rostral thoracic segments (Skoog, 1947). Most of them, as reported, have been located in relation to sympathetic roots. Occasional ones have been observed adjacent to spinal nerves near the origins of the communicating rami. Both Wrete and Skoog have suggested the possibility that in some instances ganglion cells located in relation to a spinal nerve may be synaptically related to preganglionic fibers that reach them through the ventral root of the nerve and in turn send their axons distalward in its peripheral rami. Such anatomical relationships of ganglionic and preganglionic neurons would result in peripheral sympathetic conduction pathways which do not traverse the sympathetic trunk.

In an extensive study of human material, Alexander *et al.* (1949) have observed aggregates of ganglion cells, which may be called accessory sympathetic ganglia, located adjacent to spinal nerves or partially or completely imbedded in nerve trunks, usually near the site of origin of the communicating ramus, particularly in the first and the second thoracic and the twelfth thoracic to the third lumbar segments. Accessory ganglia have also been observed in communicating rami, usually near a sympathetic trunk ganglion, in sympathetic roots and in rami that interconnect spinal nerves. Most of them are so small that they can only be detected microscopically. Some are large enough to be observed in dissection. The largest ones observed have been located in close relation to spinal nerves.

An accessory ganglion located in a sympathetic root probably receives only preganglionic fibers that pass through the sympathetic trunk. The postganglionic fibers that arise in it join the spinal nerve. Conduction pathways formed in this manner, since they traverse the sympathetic trunk, do not differ essentially from those with synaptic connections in sympathetic trunk ganglia.

An accessory ganglion that is imbedded in a nerve trunk or is located in part in a nerve trunk and in part in its communicating ramus receives preganglionic fibers chiefly or exclusively that approach it directly through the ventral nerve root. In favorable histological preparations, fibers of ventral root origin may be traced directly into such a ganglion. Fibers that appear to arise in the ganglion may also be traced distad in the nerve trunk. Conduction pathways formed in this manner are independent of the sympathetic trunk (Fig. 6). The axons of ganglion cells that are located in a communicating ramus some distance from the nerve trunk probably extend into the sympathetic trunk.

Prevertebral Plexuses

The prevertebral autonomic plexuses are situated in the thorax, the abdomen and the pelvis. Four of these, the *cardiac*, the *celiac*, the *hypogastric* and the *pelvic* plexuses may be regarded as the great prevertebral plexuses, to each of which smaller plexuses are subsidiary.

The Thoracic Plexuses.—**The Cardiac Plexus** is situated at the base of the heart and consists of a superficial and deep part. It is connected with the sympathetic trunks through the superior, the middle and the inferior cervical and a variable number of thoracic cardiac nerves, and receives branches of both vagi. The structure and the peripheral distribution of this plexus will be described in Chapter VII.

The Pulmonary Plexuses are continuous with the cardiac plexus, but not subsidiary to it. They are intimately related to the vagus nerves, through which they receive preganglionic fibers. They will be described in detail in Chapter IX.

Mediastinal Ganglia.—In addition to the ganglia incorporated in the cardiac and the pulmonary plexuses, minute aggregates of ganglion cells occur scattered in the mediastinum. In some instances, one or more larger aggregates of ganglion cells are located in the posterior mediastinum ventral to the descending aorta and just caudal to the roots of the lungs. They may be connected with the vagi and send branches to the trachea, the bronchi and the esophagus. Ganglion cells in the mediastinum which are not incorporated in the cardiac and the pulmonary plexuses probably should be regarded as sympathetic.

The Abdominal and Pelvic Plexuses.—The celiac, the hypogastric and the pelvic plexuses are closely associated with the abdominal aorta and the hypogastric arteries. The subsidiary plexuses extend along the branches of these arteries and in the main are named after them. They are made up largely of the fibers that arise from their intrinsic ganglia and peripheral rami from the lower thoracic, the lumbar and the rostral segments of the upper sacral portions of the sympathetic trunks. Branches of the right vagus nerve also contribute to the celiac plexus, and the visceral rami of the third and the fourth sacral nerves join the pelvic plexus without traversing

3

the sympathetic trunk. The hypogastric plexus is continuous with the celiac plexus rostrally and with the pelvic plexus caudally. Nerves are distributed through these plexuses to the viscera and the vessels of the abdominal and the pelvic cavities.

On the basis of a comparative study of the prevertebral plexuses in man and other primates, Hartmann-Weinberg (1926) pointed out that the series of plexuses along the abdominal aorta, although they exhibit a relatively wide range of variation, fundamentally consist of two paired chains: a central and a lateral pair. Each chain is made up of a metameric series of ganglia connected with one another by interganglionic rami. The several chains are connected with one another and with the sympathetic trunks in a more or less regular manner. They also receive branches of the right vagus and give rise to branches that supply the abdominal and the pelvic viscera. The visceral rami of each chain have a more or less definite distribution. Those arising from the central chain supply the liver, the pancreas, the spleen and the digestive tube from the abdominal portion of the esophagus to the rectum. The lateral chain gives rise to rami which supply the adrenals and the urogenital system. Some of these rami also supply fibers to the large intestine. The aorta and the proximal portions of the paired arteries arising from it that extend into the body wall receive their nerve supply directly from the sympathetic trunks.

The Celiac (Solar) Plexus is the most extensive of the prevertebral plexuses. It is closely associated with the aorta and surrounds the celiac artery. It comprises a dense meshwork of fiber bundles, two large aggregates of ganglion cells, the celiac ganglia, and a number of smaller ganglia. The right and the left celiac ganglia lie on the right and the left crura of the diaphragm respectively. They receive the greater splanchnic nerves and constitute the chief ganglionic centers of the celiac plexus. The lesser splanchnic nerves enter the aortico-renal ganglia which may be regarded as partially detached portions of the celiac ganglia at their caudal poles.

The celiac plexus (Fig. 7) invests the celiac artery throughout its entire length and is continuous with the subsidiary plexuses along its branches. The latter include the *left gastric* plexus, from which rami extend to the esophagus and the stomach, the *hepatic plexus*, from which rami extend to the liver, the gall bladder, the stomach, the duodenum and the pancreas, and the *splenic plexus*, from which rami extend to the spleen, the pancreas and the stomach.

Nerves arising from the celiac ganglia and plexus form subordinate plexuses on the aorta and its branches. The *phrenic* plexus accompanies the inferior phrenic artery. It supplies the diaphragm and gives off rami to the adrenal plexus. On the left side it also supplies rami to the esophagus; on the right, to the inferior vena cava. The *adrenal* plexus accompanies the adrenal artery and sends rami into the substance of the adrenal gland. The *renal* plexus extends laterad along the renal artery to the hilum of the kidney. It is connected with the adrenal plexus and also receives the lowest splanchnic nerve. The *pancreatic plexus* is closely associated with the head and the body of the pancreas. In part it is derived directly from the celiac plexus. It is also connected with the superior mesenteric, the aortic, the hepatic and the duodenal plexuses. The *duodenal plexus* is a delicate meshwork of fibers without macroscopic ganglia located in the retroperitoneal tissue behind the pancreas. It is derived chiefly from the pancreatic and the superior mesenteric plexuses. The *superior mesenteric* plexus accompanies the superior mesenteric artery and forms subordinate plexuses on its branches, through which fibers are supplied to the small intestine, the cecum, the vermiform appendix and the ascending and transverse portions of the colon. This plexus includes the superior mesenteric ganglion and is continuous caudally with the aortic plexus. The *aortic* plexus invests the abdominal aorta. It may be regarded as a continuation of the celiac plexus caudad, but it also receives rami from the

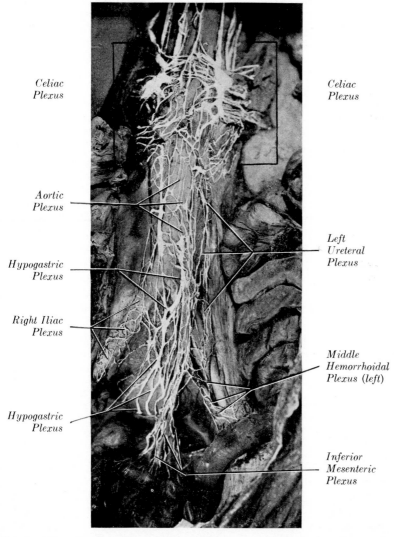

Fig. 7.—Photograph of human dissection. (By permission of Dr. J. D. Humber.)

lumbar sympathetic trunk and is connected with the hypogastric plexus by the hypogastric nerves. It contributes rami to the adrenal and the renal plexuses and gives rise to the spermatic (or ovarian) and the inferior mesenteric plexuses. The *spermatic* plexus also receives rami from the renal plexus and extends along the spermatic artery into the spermatic cord and the testis. The *ovarian* plexus accompanies the ovarian artery into the pelvis. It supplies rami to the ovary and the uterine tube and, through its communication with the uterine plexus, to the uterus. The *inferior mesenteric* plexus invests the inferior mesenteric artery and is continuous with the subordinate plexuses on its branches, the colic, the sigmoid and the superior hemorrhoidal plexuses, through which rami are supplied to the descending colon and the proximal portion of the rectum (Fig. 7).

The Hypogastric Plexus connects the celiac and the pelvic plexuses. As the hypogastric nerves extend into the pelvis, they break up into numerous bundles which form a plexiform meshwork ventral and dorsal to the bifurcation of the aorta and the region of the common iliac arteries and over the promontory of the sacrum (Fig. 7). At the level of the promontory it bifurcates and extends caudad on either side of the pelvic viscera and joins the pelvic plexuses. It conveys both sympathetic preganglionic and afferent fibers into the pelvic plexuses.

The Pelvic Plexuses are located in relation to the lateral surfaces of pelvic viscera. Each pelvic plexus is made up of an extensive meshwork of nerve fiber bundles that spread out between the visceral organs and the pelvic wall, and numerous ganglia. Its regional parts are named according to the organs to which they are anatomically and functionally related, but the parts are not sharply delimited. Two of them, the vesical plexus and the middle hemorrhoidal plexus are common to both sexes. From the vesical plexus, situated on the lateral surface of the urinary bladder, rami extend along the ureter and along the urethra. The middle hemorrhoidal plexus invests the middle hemorrhoidal artery and is connected with the superior hemorrhoidal plexus. In the male, the prostatic plexus is located in relation to the dorsolateral surface of the prostate gland. In addition to rami that supply the prostate it gives off rami that join the plexus on the ductus deferens. It is also continuous with the cavernous plexus. In the female, the uterovaginal plexus is located in relation to the cervical portion of the uterus and the vagina. Rami that arise from it penetrate into the walls of these organs where they are distributed to the musculature and the blood vessels, including the vessels in the cavernous tissue of the clitoris.

The ganglia in the pelvic plexuses include both parasympathetic and sympathetic ganglion cells. The preganglionic parasympathetic fibers are components of the sacral nerves that reach the pelvic plexus through the pelvic nerve. The sympathetic preganglionic fibers are splanchnic nerve components. They reach the pelvis through the hypogastric plexus. Both the parasympathetic and the sympathetic preganglionic fibers concerned in the innervation of the pelvic viscera are accompanied by visceral afferent spinal nerve fibers that are concerned with the afferent innervation of these viscera. Those associated with the parasympathetic nerves are sacral nerve components. Those associated with the sympathetic nerves are components chiefly of the tenth thoracic to the second lumbar nerves.

The Enteric Plexuses extend throughout the length of the alimentary tract from a level 3 to 4 cm. aboral to the larynx to the anal canal. They comprise the myenteric plexus situated between the longitudinal and the circular muscles, and the submucous plexus in the submucosa. These plexuses are intimately connected with each other through numerous connecting rami. Postganglionic fibers derived from the prevertebral plexuses traverse the enteric ganglia and contribute to the plexuses. The preganglionic fibers to the enteric ganglia are components of the vagus and the sacral nerves. The enteric plexuses will be described in detail in Chapter X.

Cephalic Sympathetic Plexuses

The cephalic sympathetic plexuses represent the extension of the sympathetic nerves into the cephalic region. Rami arising from the superior cervical sympathetic ganglion extend along the internal and the external carotid arteries respectively as the internal and external carotid nerves. The internal carotid rami become applied to the internal carotid artery as it enters the carotid canal in the temporal bone. As they continue rostrad they become separated into lateral and medial divisions. The lateral division gives rise to the *internal carotid* plexus which invests the internal carotid artery. The medial division gives rise to the *cavernous* plexus associated with the cavernous sinus. The external carotid rami form the plexus on the external carotid artery (Fig. 8). The preganglionic fibers concerned emerge from the spinal cord in the rostral three or four thoracic nerves. Most of them extend rostrad in the sympathetic trunk to the superior cervical ganglion. Some join the plexus on the common carotid artery from the middle and lower cervical sympathetic trunk ganglia. Some also join the plexus on the vertebral artery.

The Common Carotid Plexus is made up chiefly of sympathetic fibers derived from the inferior, the intermediate and the middle cervical sympathetic trunk ganglia. It also includes some afferent thoracic nerve fibers (Kuntz, 1934). Many of the afferent fibers extend rostrad in the plexuses that invest the internal and the external carotid arteries and their branches, through which they are widely distributed in the cephalic region.

The Vertebral Plexus is a relatively simple plexiform structure that invests the vertebral artery. It includes postganglionic fibers derived from all the cervical sympathetic trunk ganglia, many of which join cervical nerves through slender rami. Some extend rostrad in the plexus on the basilar artery, which is continuous with the vertebral plexuses, to be distributed to blood vessels of the brain stem. They probably account for only a minor portion of the innervation of the cerebral blood vessels.

The Internal Carotid Plexus is continuous with the plexus on the common carotid artery. It invests the internal carotid artery and gives rise to subsidiary plexuses on its branches. This plexus is made up chiefly of fibers derived from the superior cervical sympathetic ganglion, but it includes some sympathetic and some afferent fibers derived from the common carotid plexus and some afferent vagus nerve fibers (Kuntz, 1934).

A short distance from the superior cervical ganglion, some sympathetic fibers deviate from the internal carotid plexus and enter the middle ear as the inferior caroticotympanic nerve. Those which continue rostrad traverse the tympanic plexus, then emerge from the middle ear and enter the cranium lateral to the nerve of the pterygoid canal to join the cavernous plexus. The deep petrosal nerve, which joins the greater superficial petrosal to form the nerve of the pterygoid canal, also arises from the internal carotid plexus. The nerve of the pterygoid canal terminates in the spheno-palatine ganglion.

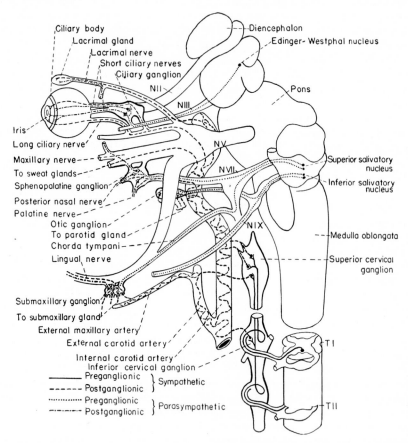

Fig. 8.—Diagrammatic illustration of the relationships of the sympathetic and para-sympathetic nerves in the cephalic region.

The Tympanic Plexus is situated on the medial wall of the middle ear. It consists chiefly of fibers derived through the inferior caroticotympanic nerve and fibers derived from the petrosal ganglion of the glossopharyngeal nerve. It supplies fibers to the mucous membranes of the tympanum, the mastoid cells, and the auditory tube. A slender ramus, made up chiefly of fibers derived from the petrosal ganglion that enter the tympanic plexus, joins a ramus from the geniculate ganglion of the facial nerve to form the lesser superficial petrosal nerve. This nerve traverses the temporal bone and joins the otic ganglion.

The Cavernous Plexus is situated in relation to the cavernous venous sinus located in part in the middle and in part in the anterior cranial fossa. It includes chiefly fibers derived from the superior cervical sympathetic ganglion through the internal carotid plexus. Sympathetic fibers extend from the cavernous plexus into the orbit through the superior orbital fissure. Some traverse the sympathetic root of the ciliary ganglion and the short ciliary nerves. Some reach the eye through the long ciliary nerves, which bypass the ciliary ganglion. Some also join the trochlear and the ophthalmic nerves, and some extend into the hypophysis along its blood vessels.

The External Carotid Plexus invests the external carotid artery and is continuous with subsidiary plexuses on its branches. This plexus is also continuous with the common carotid plexus, but it is made up chiefly of fibers derived from the superior cervical sympathetic ganglion. Fibers derived from it supply the glomus caroticum. Rami that arise from the subsidiary plexus on the middle meningeal artery join the otic ganglion, and rami that arise from the subsidiary plexus on the external maxillary artery join the submandibular ganglion.

Cephalic Autonomic Ganglia

The major autonomic ganglia in the cephalic region are located in relation to the oculomotor nerve and the several divisions of the trigeminal nerve (Fig. 8). They are anatomically and functionally connected with the brain stem through the nerves through which they receive preganglionic fibers.

The Otic Ganglion is located on the medial aspect of the mandibular nerve just below the foramen ovale and at the posterior border of the pterygoid muscle. The preganglionic neurons through which it is connected with the brain stem are located in the inferior salivatory nucleus. Their axons emerge from the brain stem in the glossopharyngeal nerve and reach the ganglion through the lesser superficial petrosal nerve. The latter nerve also conveys afferent fibers that traverse the ganglion. Sympathetic fibers derived from the plexus on the middle meningeal artery also traverse the otic ganglion. Rami derived from it join the auriculotemporal nerve, the corda tympani and the nerve of the pterygoid canal. It also sends rami to the tensor tympani and the tensor veli palatini muscles.

The Submandibular Ganglion is a small reddish body located between the lingual nerve and the duct of the submandibular gland. The preganglionic neurons that connect it with the brain stem are located in the superior salivatory nucleus. Their axons traverse the facial nerve and join the lingual nerve through the chorda tympani, which also conveys afferent components of the facial nerve. Both preganglionic and afferent fibers enter the submandibular ganglion through slender rami of the lingual nerve. Sympathetic fibers derived from the plexus on the external maxillary artery also traverse this ganglion. It supplies fibers to the submandibular gland

and its duct, and to the lingual nerve, through which they are distributed to the sublingual gland and the distal portion of the tongue.

The Sublingual and the Lingual Ganglia are located respectively in relation to the lingual nerve in proximity to the sublingual gland and in the proximal portion of the tongue. Like the submandibular, the sublingual ganglion receives preganglionic fibers from the superior salivatory nucleus via the chorda tympani and the lingual nerve. Fibers derived from it are distributed to the sublingual gland and adjacent tissues. Most of the lingual ganglia, which include numerous small aggregates of ganglion cells, are located between the intrinsic muscles of the tongue within the range of distribution of the glossopharyngeal nerve. Some are located adjacent to branches of the lingual nerve. Those within the range of distribution of the glossopharyngeal nerve receive preganglionic fibers through it that arise in the inferior salivatory nucleus. Those that are located within the range of distribution of the lingual nerve probably receive preganglionic fibers derived from the superior salivatory nucleus that emerge in the facial nerve. Fibers that arise in the lingual ganglia are distributed chiefly to lingual glands.

The Sphenopalatine Ganglion is a small reddish body located in the pterygopalatine fossa, close to the sphenopalatine foramen and at the peripheral end of the nerve of the pterygoid canal, through which it receives both preganglionic (motor root) and sympathetic (sympathetic root) fibers. The preganglionic fibers are components of the facial nerve. They are conveyed to the nerve of the pterygoid canal through the greater superficial petrosal nerve. The sympathetic fibers are derived from the plexus on the internal carotid artery. They join the nerve of the pterygoid canal through the deep petrosal nerve. Branches of the maxillary nerve join the sphenopalatine ganglion and constitute its sensory roots.

Peripheral rami that arise from the sphenopalatine ganglion are distributed as follows: A *pharyngeal* ramus, passing backward through the pharyngeal canal, supplies the mucous membrane of the roof of the pharynx. Three palatine nerves reach the palate through the palatine canals. The *anterior*, or *great*, *palatine* nerve gives rise to anterior filaments that reach the incisor teeth and communicate with branches of the nasopalatine nerve. In the palatine canal it gives rise to a small ramus, the *posterior inferior lateral nasal* nerve, that supplies the mucous membrane of the inferior concha. The *middle*, or *external*, *palatine* and the *posterior*, or *small*, *palatine* nerves supply the mucous membrane of the soft palate, the uvula and the palatine tonsil. A small ramus, the *posterior superior lateral nasal* nerve, supplies the mucous membrane of the middle and the superior conchæ. The *nasopalatine* nerve supplies the mucous membrane of the hard palate and the roof and septum of the nose. One or more *orbital* rami also extend from the sphenopalatine ganglion to the periosteum of the orbit. Some fibers of these rami also join terminal branches of the ophthalmic nerve.

The Ciliary Ganglion is a small reddish ganglion located in the posterior portion of the orbit, between the lateral rectus muscle and the optic nerve, and in proximity to the ophthalmic artery. It is connected with the inferior division of the oculomotor nerve by a short *motor* root through which it receives preganglionic fibers, and with the nasociliary branch of the ophthalmic nerve by a long *sensory* root. It also receives a slender ramus, the *sympathetic* root, derived from the cavernous plexus. This ramus may join the ciliary ganglion as an independent root or it may be incorporated in the long root from the nasociliary nerve. Twelve to fifteen slender rami, the *short ciliary* nerves, arise from the ciliary ganglion and, passing forward above and below the optic nerve, convey fibers to the eye, its extrinsic muscles and the blood vessels.

The Ganglion Terminale is situated in relation to the nervus terminalis. It appears to be made up only in part of autonomic ganglion cells. The sources of the preganglionic fibers through which these ganglion cells are connected with the brain have not been definitely localized. They probably emerge in the nervus terminalis. The postganglionic fibers that arise in the ganglion terminale are distributed through the nervus terminalis chiefly to Bowman's glands, the vomeronasal organ, the mucous membrane of the nasal septum, the blood vessels of the olfactory mucosa and the anterior cerebral artery and its branches. Afferent fibers derived from bipolar ganglion cells associated with the nervus terminalis are distributed to the olfactory epithelium.

Other Ganglia.—An accessory sympathetic ganglion located in relation to the internal carotid artery and in the course of the internal carotid nerve has been described in man. A ganglion located in the corresponding position and in the course of the internal carotid nerve has also been observed in the cat. It probably consists of nerve cells which have been displaced from the primordium of the superior cervical sympathetic ganglion. Several small ganglia in the portion of the internal carotid plexus which passes through the cavernous sinus have also been reported. The fibers arising in these ganglia, with other fibers of the internal carotid plexus, join the ophthalmic nerve.

An aggregate of ganglion cells located at the junction of the greater superficial petrosal nerve with the internal carotid nerve has been described in man. It probably receives preganglionic fibers through the greater superficial petrosal nerve; consequently, it appears to be a parasympathetic ganglion. Scattered ganglion cells, some of which are incorporated in sympathetic and others in parasympathetic efferent conduction pathways, occur along the internal carotid and the cerebral arteries. Small ganglia associated with the pineal body have also been reported.

Other Ganglia Associated with the Cranial Autonomic Nerves

The geniculate ganglion of the nervus intermedius, the petrosal ganglion of the glossopharyngeal and the jugular and the nodose ganglia of the vagus nerve are intimately associated with the cranial autonomic nerves and have been regarded by some as in part autonomic.

The *geniculate* ganglion is situated in the facial canal at the genu of the facial nerve. From it arise three slender rami: (1) The greater superficial petrosal nerve contains chiefly preganglionic fibers to the sphenopalatine ganglion and sensory fibers which traverse this ganglion to be distributed through the middle and posterior palatine nerves to the mucous membrane of the soft palate. (2) The geniculotympanic nerve enters the tympanic plexus and, continuing through the latter, joins the small superficial petrosal nerve. (3) The external superficial petrosal nerve is an inconstant ramus which joins the sympathetic plexus on the middle meningeal artery. The *petrosal* ganglion is situated in the lower part of the jugular foramen. It receives a ramus from the superior cervical sympathetic ganglion and gives off a ramus which passes into the tympanic plexus and emerges as the small superficial petrosal nerve. The *jugular* and the *nodose* ganglia of the vagus are intimately associated with the superior cervical sympathetic ganglion. Their connections with the latter ganglion are described above.

All of these ganglia are traversed by preganglionic fibers and include afferent neurons which are functionally related to the autonomic nerves. Certain histological findings have been interpreted as supporting the assumption that they include autonomic ganglion cells. Synaptic connections within the ganglia, however, have not been demonstrated. In view of all the data available, these ganglia, like the other cerebrospinal ganglia, must be regarded as comprising only sensory ganglion cells.

COMPONENTS AND STRUCTURE OF THE
SYMPATHETIC TRUNKS

Each sympathetic trunk is made up of a series of ganglia, the vertebral ganglia, and the connecting interganglionic rami. The latter consist primarily of visceral afferent and preganglionic visceral efferent fibers which enter the sympathetic trunk through the white communicating rami. The preganglionic neurons are located in the intermediolateral cell column and adjacent parts of the gray matter throughout the thoracic and the upper lumbar regions of the spinal cord. Their axons enter the sympathetic trunk via the white communicating rami and either terminate in one of its ganglia in synaptic relationship to sympathetic ganglion cells or traverse the trunk for a shorter or longer distance and continue peripheralward in one of its branches to terminate in a sympathetic ganglion lying nearer a visceral organ. The visceral afferent neurons which send fibers into the sympathetic trunk are components of the posterior nerve roots. These fibers enter the sympathetic trunk through the communicating rami and traverse it without making synaptic connections with sympathetic ganglion cells. Throughout the greater part of the sympathetic trunk the interganglionic rami also contain some fibers which arise from sympathetic ganglion cells and run longitudinally for some distance before entering the nerves through which they are conveyed to their peripheral destinations. Every sympathetic root probably receives fibers from one or two sympathetic trunk ganglia above and below as well as from the one from which it arises.

The preganglionic and the visceral afferent fibers that make up the cervical interganglionic rami enter the sympathetic trunk through the communicating rami of the rostral five or six thoracic nerves. The rostral portion of the cervical sympathetic trunk contains no afferent fibers; consequently, the most rostral interganglionic ramus consists almost exclusively of preganglionic fibers which terminate in the superior cervical sympathetic ganglion. In sections of the sympathetic trunk taken just below the superior cervical ganglion, fascicles of unmyelinated fibers frequently are observed at the periphery of the interganglionic ramus. These fibers do not degenerate following section of the trunk in the lower cervical levels. They obviously are postganglionic fibers that arise in the superior cervical ganglion and extend in the interganglionic ramus for a short distance before entering a peripheral ramus of distribution. The possibility that some of these fibers may be the axons of commissural neurons is not precluded, but evidence that commissural neurons occur in the sympathetic trunk is wanting. Exclusive of such inconstant peripheral fascicles of postganglionic fibers, nearly all the fibers in this portion of the sympathetic trunk are myelinated. They are of relatively small caliber and closely aggregated. Preganglionic fibers probably do not pass through the superior cervical ganglion into the nerves arising from it except to reach the sympathetic ganglion on the internal carotid artery and such scattered sympathetic ganglion cells as may occur along the internal carotid and the cerebral arteries.

Caudal to the middle cervical ganglion or the origin of the middle cardiac nerve, the cervical sympathetic trunk contains both preganglionic and visceral afferent fibers. The majority of the latter are conveyed to their peripheral destination through the middle and the inferior cervical sympathetic cardiac nerves and rami arising from the ansa subclavia to be distributed to the heart and lungs.

Throughout the thoracic and the lumbar regions, the sympathetic trunk includes both preganglionic and visceral afferent fibers. These fibers, most of which are myelinated, are arranged in a compact bundle, usually oval in cross-section. Unmyelinated fibers occur only in small numbers rostral to the fourth thoracic ganglion. Caudal to this level they are more abundant and are arranged in a crescent-shaped fascicle at the periphery of the larger oval fascicle of myelinated fibers. The crescent-shaped fascicle is made up of fibers which arise in the ganglia of the sympathetic trunk and run longitudinally for some distance before entering a ramus of distribution.

Rostral to the sixth thoracic ganglion, most of the fibers in the sympathetic trunk are ascending preganglionic fibers which terminate in the more rostral thoracic and the cervical ganglia. The most caudal source of preganglionic fibers to the superior cervical ganglion is the seventh thoracic nerve. Fibers which enter the sympathetic trunk through communicating rami as far caudad as that of the ninth thoracic nerve are known to reach the inferior cervical ganglion. From the sixth thoracic ganglion to the ninth the sympathetic trunk contains both ascending and descending preganglionic fibers. Caudal to the tenth thoracic ganglion it contains chiefly descending preganglionic fibers from the lower thoracic and the lumbar nerves to the more caudal ganglia of the trunk and the splanchnic nerves. The most rostral source of preganglionic fibers that enter the splanchnic nerves is the fifth, possibly the fourth, thoracic nerve. Fibers that enter the sympathetic trunk through a given white ramus may be distributed to from five to ten successive ganglia, although any one preganglionic fiber probably does not give off branches to so large a number of ganglia.

The visceral afferent fibers that traverse the sympathetic trunk are chiefly myelinated ones of large and medium sizes, but small myelinated and unmyelinated visceral afferent fibers also occur. The latter are not easily distinguished from the preganglionic fibers. Large and medium-sized myelinated fibers are present in varying numbers in the sympathetic trunk at various thoracic levels. They are relatively few rostral to the sixth thoracic segment, and gradually increase in number caudal to this level until the roots of the greater splanchnic nerve are reached, through which a large proportion of these fibers is conveyed to the viscera. Afferent components of the splanchnic nerves enter the spinal cord through the communicating rami of all the spinal nerves from the third thoracic to the first lumbar inclusive. Large and medium-sized myelinated fibers are present in relatively small numbers in the sympathetic trunk caudal to the roots of the splanchnic nerves. Some of them extend caudad into the sacral region.

In the sacral region, the sympathetic trunk includes both myelinated and unmyelinated fibers. A crescent-shaped fascicle like the one described in the thoracic region does not occur here but the unmyelinated fibers run in bundles among the myelinated ones. Most of them are descending components of the lower thoracic and the upper lumbar nerves. They include both preganglionic and visceral afferent fibers.

Experimental anatomical data reported by Kuntz and Farnsworth (1928; 1931) support the assumption that the sympathetic roots that join the brachial and the lumbosacral plexuses include myelinated fibers of relatively large, medium and small sizes in addition to the unmyelinated ones. The myelinated fibers of large and medium sizes undergo degeneration following section of both roots of the thoracic and the upper lumbar nerves distal to the spinal ganglia or section of the communicating rami and the sympathetic trunk proximal to the ganglia from which the sympathetic roots in question arise. Since no efferent fibers are known to pass through the sympathetic trunk into the sympathetic roots, the fibers in the sympathetic roots that undergo degeneration following the sections indicated above must be regarded as components of the dorsal roots of the thoracic and the upper lumbar nerves which traverse the sympathetic trunk and sympathetic roots to join the somatic rami of the spinal nerves for peripheral distribution. The afferent fibers which enter the brachial and the lumbosacral plexuses respectively through the sympathetic trunk and the sympathetic roots probably arise in the spinal ganglia connected with the segments of the spinal cord from which the corresponding preganglionic efferent fibers emerge.

RATIO OF PREGANGLIONIC TO GANGLIONIC NEURONS

Quantitative studies of various autonomic ganglia and the preganglionic fibers which enter them indicate that the neurons in the ganglia outnumber the preganglionic fibers. A single preganglionic axon, consequently, must make synaptic connections with more than one autonomic ganglion cell.

In some instances all the ganglion cells which are synaptically related to a given preganglionic neuron are included in the same ganglion. In other instances a single preganglionic neuron makes synaptic contacts with ganglion cells in more than one ganglion. The ratio of preganglionic to ganglionic neurons varies throughout the body. It also varies in the same pathways in different individuals. Actual counts of the preganglionic fibers in sections of the sympathetic trunk just caudal to the superior cervical ganglion and of the ganglion cells in this ganglion, as reported by Wolf (1941), indicate a ratio of eleven ganglion cells to one preganglionic fiber in one cat and a ratio of seventeen ganglion cells to one preganglionic fiber in another. The ratio of preganglionic fibers in the motor root of the ciliary ganglion to the ganglion cells in this ganglion, in the same animals, was found to be approximately one to two.

Every autonomic ganglion cell probably is synaptically related to more than one preganglionic neuron. The ratio of the preganglionic and the ganglionic neurons determined on the basis of actual counts of the preganglionic fibers and the ganglionic cells in question in any part of the body, therefore, does not indicate the number of synaptic contacts made by individual preganglionic neurons. The anatomic relationships of the preganglionic and the ganglionic neurons which facilitate the discharge of impulses from a single preganglionic neuron into mutliple ganglion cells and the discharge of impulses from multiple preganglionic neurons into a single ganglion cell are physiologically significant.

Chapter II

AUTONOMIC GANGLION CELLS AND GANGLIA

GENERAL MORPHOLOGY OF GANGLION CELLS

THE autonomic ganglion cells are multipolar neurons with variable numbers of dendritic processes. In general they are aggregated in ganglia which are more or less definitely delimited and enclosed in connective tissue capsules. In all the larger ganglia the perikaryon, or cell body, of every ganglion cell is enclosed in a delicate cell capsule which is penetrated by all the longer dendrites.

The autonomic ganglion cells vary in form and size within relatively wide limits. In mammals, including man, the cell bodies of some of these neurons are oval in outline. Those of others are pyriform, globose or polygonal. In some instances the form of the cell body depends on the character of the larger cytoplasmic processes. In others it is modified by its relationships to adjacent neurons or other tissue elements. The autonomic ganglion cells naturally fall into three categories on the basis of the volumes of their cell bodies: large, medium-sized and small. In man the maximum diameters of the large ganglion cells vary from 35 to 55 or even 60 microns; those of the medium-sized ones from 25 to 34 microns, and those of the small ones from 15 to 24 microns (de Castro, 1932). The ganglia are not all comparable with respect to the sizes of the ganglion cells. The cells of the several volume categories also vary in proportion to those of the other categories in different ganglia. According to de Castro, the largest of all autonomic ganglion cells occur in the superior and the middle cervical sympathetic trunk ganglia. Ganglion cells of medium sizes predominate in most of the autonomic ganglia except those of the sympathetic trunk. In the latter, large and small ganglion cells occur in approximately equal numbers, except in the superior cervical ganglion in which large ones predominate. In the prevertebral ganglia, the ganglion cells exhibit greater uniformity in volume. The maximum diameters of most of these cells fall within a range of 35 to 42 microns. The greatest cytometric variations undoubtedly occur in the ganglia that are most complex structurally and functionally.

All the cytoplasmic processes of a ganglion cell except one, which represents the axon, may be regarded as dendrites. The length of the axon is determined by the anatomical relationships of the neuron, but whether it be short or relatively long it represents only a relatively small percentage of the cytoplasm of the neuron. The dendrites vary in numbers, lengths and calibers within relatively wide limits. They may therefore represent a relatively large percentage of the cytoplasm of the neuron or only a small portion of it.

CYTOLOGY AND HISTOCHEMISTRY

Neurofibrils. — Neurofibrils are constant constitutents of autonomic ganglion cells. They are present throughout the cytoplasm, including the axon and the dendrites (Fig. 9), but vary within a wide range in abundance, distribution and arrangement. Preparations of ganglia in which the neurofibrils are abundant in most of the ganglion cells, and well stained, reveal some cells in which these structures may be observed only in the cytoplasmic processes and the peripheral zone of the cell body, but not in the perinuclear zone. In such cells the neurofibrils appear to be more delicate than in those in which the neurofibrillar structure is more abundant. In many ganglion cells the neurofibrils seem to run singly or in small bundles

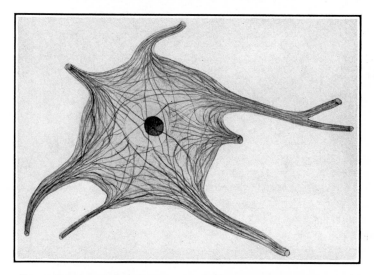

Fig. 9.—Sympathetic ganglion cell (human) drawn from a pyridine silver preparation to illustrate the neurofibrillar structure.

through the cell body in various directions. In others they appear to interlace with one another, the deeper fibrils forming a perinuclear plexus. The neurofibrils in the deeper portion of the cytoplasm appear to be arranged with reference to the nucleus. Those in the superficial portion are arranged with reference to the periphery of the cell body and the dendrites. In many ganglion cells the deep and the superficial complexes of neurofibrils are quite distinct but not independent of one another. In preparations in which the neurofibrillar structure is well differentiated, neurofibrils lying parallel to one another may be observed in the axons and the dendrites throughout the greater part of the length of these processes. Frequently individual neurofibrils may be traced from the axon or a dendrite into the cell body where they take part in some particular configuration pattern.

The exact nature of the neurofibrils is as yet unknown. Since they have been demonstrated in living neurons they may not be regarded as artifacts. They are not homogeneous but possess a central core which is less rigid than the peripheral layer. They probably are functionally related to intracellular metabolism (Parker, 1929), but the evidence on which this hypothesis is based cannot be regarded as conclusive.

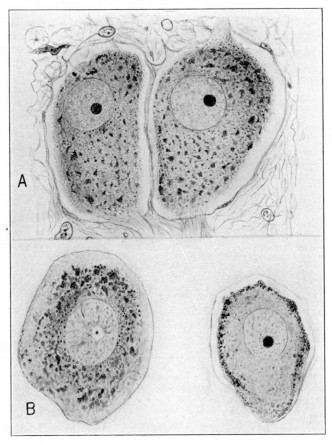

Fig. 10.—Sympathetic ganglion cells (cat). *A*, Selected to illustrate normal distribution of chromidial substance in resting cells. *B*, Selected to illustrate variations in the distribution of the chromidial substance.

Chromidial Substance.—Autonomic ganglion cells, like other neurons, possess chromidial substance (Fig. 10). It appears relatively early in man and is fairly abundant in most of the autonomic ganglion cells before birth. In the newborn the autonomic ganglion cells exhibit approximately the same range of variation in the sizes of the chromidial bodies and in their distribution as in the adult. In the largest cells in the superior cervical sympathetic ganglion of the albino rat studied from birth to maturity,

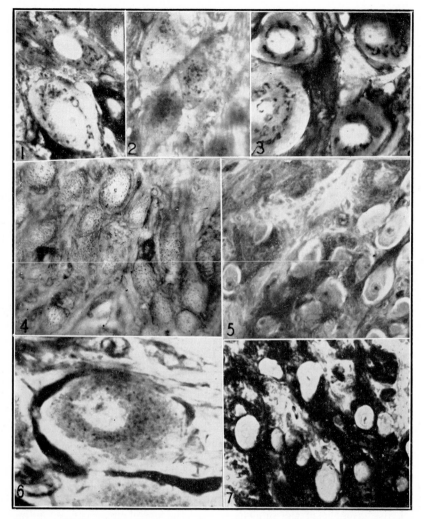

Fig. 11.—(1) Ganglion cells from superior cervical sympathetic ganglion of cat, showing Golgi apparatus in form of network.

(2) Ganglion cells from superior cervical sympathetic ganglion of cat, showing Golgi apparatus consisting of granules.

(3) Nodose ganglion cells of rat, showing Golgi apparatus in form of network.

(4) Section of a sympathetic trunk ganglion of cat, showing distribution of ascorbic acid in the ganglion cells.

(5) Section of superior cervical sympathetic ganglion of cat treated for alkaline phosphatase activity.

(6) Section of superior cervical sympathetic ganglion of cat prepared to demonstrate the distribution of mitochondria in the ganglion cells.

(7) Section of superior cervical sympathetic ganglion of cat after prolonged preganglionic stimulation treated for alkaline phosphatase activity.

Ping (1921) observed progressive changes in the quantity of the chromidial substance and in the character and the distribution of the chromidial bodies. During the first twenty days of postnatal life, the chromidial substance is fairly uniformly distributed throughout the cytoplasm, and the chromidial bodies are relatively small, but, before the close of this period, a beginning of aggregation of the chromidial granules is apparent in some of the cells. The chromidial bodies later become larger and stain more intensely. Before the sixtieth day of postnatal life, the chromidial substance in the majority of these cells is aggregated either in the peripheral or in the perinuclear zone. The same modes of distribution of the chromidial substance are also apparent in many of the ganglion cells following this period. In the dog the chromidial substance in the ganglion cells shows a gradual increase in abundance until the age of approximately forty days when a level is reached that is maintained until senility sets in (Sulkin and Kuntz, 1952). It consists essentially of ribonucleoproteins.

Golgi Apparatus.—The Golgi apparatus can be studied under more favorable conditions in autonomic ganglion cells in laboratory animals than in those of man, since human ganglia obtained at autopsy usually have undergone post-mortem alterations, and those removed in the surgical treatment of peripheral vascular disease, hypertension, etc., usually do not exhibit the Golgi substance in its normal state.

In the autonomic ganglion cells of the cat, the Golgi apparatus typically consists of a loosely woven network of osmophilic substance that may be quite uniformly distributed throughout the cell body or aggregated in the perinuclear zone (Fig. 11: 1, 2, 3). In some instances the Golgi apparatus consists of small spherical bodies that do not appear to be joined by threads. In cells of this type the Golgi substance is usually massed adjacent to the nucleus. In still other instances, both a Golgi network and discrete Golgi bodies occur in the same cell. In cells in this category, the net work is less extensive than in those in which the Golgi apparatus consists only of a network. All preparations studied included some cells that appeared to be devoid of Golgi apparatus (Sulkin and Kuntz, 1948).

The volume of the Golgi material and its distribution in the ganglion cells appear to be correlated with the functional states of the cells. In ganglia in which a large percentage of ganglion cells exhibit chromatolysis and displacement of the nucleus toward the periphery, a correspondingly large percentage of the ganglion cells exhibit Golgi substance in the form of discrete bodies, and some appear to be devoid of it.

Prolonged preganglionic stimulation of the superior cervical sympathetic ganglion in the cat, as observed by Sulkin and Kuntz (1947), results in changes in the Golgi apparatus in the ganglion cells that involve either a breaking up of the Golgi network to form discrete Golgi bodies or the complete disappearance of the Golgi substance.

Ascorbic Acid.—Ascorbic acid has been demonstrated by histochemical methods in both the ganglion cells and the neuroglial supporting cells in the autonomic ganglia of the cat, the guinea pig, the rabbit, the dog and man (Sulkin and Kuntz, 1948, 1952). The ascorbic acid, which is visualized as black granules following treatment of the tissues with acidified silver nitrate, may be distributed quite uniformly throughout the cytoplasm of the ganglion cells or it may be limited to the zone occupied by the Golgi apparatus (Fig. 11: 4). In most animals the quantity and the distribution of ascorbic acid in the cytoplasm of the ganglion cells is highly consistent. In man and the guinea pig it varies within a wide range depending in a large measure on the diet.

In cats, ganglion cells that have been subjected to prolonged stimulation exhibit a decreased ascorbic acid content. Following section of the preganglionic fibers for one week or longer the ascorbic acid content remains approximately at the normal level in some of the ganglion cells and is increased in others. In rabbits with hypercholesteremia and atherosclerosis the ascorbic acid in the ganglion cells is decreased. In guinea pigs a high vitamin C diet results in an increase, and a diet deficient in vitamin C results in a decrease in the ascorbic acid in the autonomic ganglion cells. In human ganglia removed surgically in the treatment of patients with hypertension or peripheral vascular disease the ascorbic acid content of the ganglion cells undoubtedly is altered. It appears to be concentrated in small areas of the cytoplasm.

The rôle of ascorbic acid in autonomic ganglion cells as yet is not fully understood. In a preliminary study (Weatherford and Sulkin, 1952) it has been demonstrated that following removal of ascorbic acid from the diet of guinea pigs the autonomic ganglion cells undergo cytological and histochemical alterations that are similar to changes that are observed in ageing and in certain pathological conditions. In scorbutic animals that recover following intraperitoneal and oral administration of vitamin C the autonomic ganglion cells, except those that have become completely necrotic, revert to their normal conditions with respect to vitamin C.

Phosphatases.—The cytoplasm of the autonomic ganglion cells in the cat shows positive alkaline phosphatase activity (Fig. 11: 5). Little variation is observed in the cells of the same ganglion or in those of ganglia of different cats. The activity of this enzyme is greater in the neuroglial elements than in the ganglion cells (Sulkin and Kuntz, 1950, 1952). Following prolonged preganglionic stimulation, the alkaline phosphatase activity in the cytoplasm of the ganglion cells is greatly diminished, but that in the neuroglial elements is increased (Fig. 11:7). This increase may be associated with the proliferation of neuroglial elements that takes place under similar experimental conditions (Kuntz and Sulkin, 1947). An increase in alkaline phosphatase activity in other actively proliferating tissues has also been reported by other investigators. The alkaline phosphatase activity in the ganglion cells is much more variable in man than in laboratory animals. This probably is due to the greater variability in the functional states of the cells (Sulkin and Kuntz, 1952).

The acid phosphatase activity varies within a wide range in the autonomic ganglia of different cats. The variation observed is not due to faulty technic since the sensory ganglia of different cats show no comparable variability in acid phosphatase activity even when they are fixed together with the autonomic ganglia and sections of both autonomic and sensory ganglia are incubated together on the same slide.

Glycogen.—Sections of autonomic ganglia of the cat (Sulkin and Kuntz, 1950), the dog and man (Sulkin and Kuntz, 1952) treated with periodic acid followed by the Schiff reagent show a variety of staining reactions in the ganglion cells. The amount of periodic acid-Schiff positive material varies in different cells of the same ganglion as well as in ganglia of different animals. Many of the ganglion cells in all the species studied show a positive reaction, and in some of them the reaction is of high intensity. The number of cells showing reactions of high intensity varies in different ganglia. Following digestion with a 1 per cent buffered solution of malt diastase, the reaction completely disappears from the ganglion cells. The positive reaction therefore demonstrates the presence of glycogen. The neuroglial elements, the nerve fibers and the connective tissue also show a positive reaction which appears uniform, but which is resistant to the enzymatic digestion.

Following prolonged preganglionic stimulation in the cat, there is a sharp increase in the number of ganglion cells that show a positive reaction and an increase in its intensity. Under these conditions, the ganglion cells also are negative following enzymatic digestion. The positively reacting material in the neuroglial cells, the nerve fibers and the connective tissue that resists digestion with diastase remains unaltered following prolonged stimulation.

Metachromasia.—In sections of the superior cervical ganglia fixed in lead subacetate and stained with toluidin blue, the different elements show different staining reactions. The ganglion cells appear metachromatic, due to the staining reaction of the chromidial substance. The other cytoplasmic constituents remain unstained. The nucleoli of the ganglion cells appear highly metachromatic. When a yellow filter is used to accentuate the staining reaction, the neuroglial nuclei remain blue, the chromidial substance in the ganglion cells appears purple and their nucleoli appear red. Prolonged preganglionic stimulation results in no apparent alteration in the staining reaction of any of these elements.

Plasmalogen Reaction.—In frozen sections of autonomic ganglia treated with mercuric chloride and stained with the Schiff reagent, the cytoplasm of the ganglion cells shows a weak but positive "plasmal" reaction while the nuclei are completely negative. The myelin sheaths of the nerve trunks show a much stronger reaction than the ganglion cells. Prolonged preganglionic stimulation results in no apparent change in this reaction.

Pigment.—The occurrence of pigment in autonomic ganglion cells is of peculiar interest in relation to intracellular metabolism. The presence of pigment in the ganglion cells of the sympathetic trunk and the prevertebral plexuses in human fetuses of six or seven months has been reported. Its presence in the newborn and during the early years of life has been observed by various investigators. Pigment which is resistant to fat solvents is rarely present in abundance before the age of thirty years except in the presence of chronic infection or malignant disease. In the dog it appears to be definitely associated with ageing (Sulkin and Kuntz, 1952).

The stable pigment in autonomic ganglion cells has quite generally been regarded as melanin. This point of view seems to be supported by the observation that the pigment is blackened by diamine silver compounds or silver nitrate. Preliminary data obtained in a study of the pigments in autonomic ganglion cells strongly suggest that they are fundamentally similar to ceroids (Sulkin and Kuntz, unpublished data). They are insoluble in ordinary fat solvents and exhibit a strong affinity for Sudan black B and for osmium tetroxide, the ability to reduce silver diamine compounds, a strong alkaline phosphatase activity, a strong periodic acid-Schiff positive reaction which can be inhibited by acetylation and the presence of ethylenic groupings as demonstrated by performic acid or peracetic acid oxidation. The last reaction can be inhibited by prior bromination of the sections. According to Lillie (1952), the positive Schiff reaction following oxidation with performic acid and its inhibition by bromination demonstrates the presence of ethylenic groupings in ceroids. Gatenby and Moussa (1950) have advanced the opinion that the pigment is derived from broken-down parts of the Golgi apparatus.

Nucleus.—The nuclei in the autonomic ganglion cells are similar in appearance to those in the neurons in the central nervous system. They usually are relatively large, rounded or oval in outline and contain relatively little stainable material except one or more nucleoli. In most of the cells the nucleus is centrally located, but in many it occupies an eccentric position. In favorable preparations, the nucleus exhibits a reticular structure and is separated from the cytoplasm by a distinct nuclear membrane.

In man the autonomic ganglion cells, with few exceptions, are uninucleated. The observation that binucleated ganglion cells occur quite commonly in the autonomic ganglia in young persons, but only rarely in the aged, led Spiegel and Adolf (1922) to advance the opinion that these cells retain the capacity to undergo division without further nuclear changes, and that such division occurs even during adult life. De Castro (1923) also regarded the binucleated autonomic ganglion cells as reserve cells which may still undergo division. The occasional occurrence of two ganglion cells in a common cell capsule lends support to this theory. In certain mammals, particularly rodents, binucleated autonomic ganglion cells occur in relatively large numbers.

Axon.—The axon of the autonomic ganglion cell commonly arises from an implantation cone, or axon hillock, which, as in the neurons in the central nervous system, is free from chromidial substance but is less conspicuous in the former cells than in the latter. Neurofibrils may be traced through the implantation cone into the axon where they lie closely aggregated and parallel to one another. In most instances the axon is a slender unmyelinated fiber, but ganglion cells with myelinated axons are not uncommon. Autonomic fibers with very thin myelin sheaths throughout at least a portion of their length probably occur throughout the autonomic nervous system. The nucleated neurilemma of an unmyelinated autonomic fiber lies in intimate contact with it. Even in the cases of those fibers which are covered by a thin layer of myelin, the neurilemma invests the axon so closely that nodes and incisures usually are not apparent. In mammals, the axons of autonomic ganglion cells rarely are myelinated throughout their entire length. Those which are invested by myelin acquire their myelin sheaths at unequal distances from their origin. Myelinated autonomic fibers are more abundant in proportion to the unmyelinated ones in some parts of the body than in others. The ratio of myelinated to unmyelinated autonomic fibers also varies in the different classes of vertebrates and in different species in the same class.   The sympathetic fibers that join the spinal nerves through sympathetic roots, particularly in mammals, probably are myelinated in greater proportion than those which supply the visceral organs, although myelinated fibers also exist among those that arise in the prevertebral sympathetic ganglia.

Autonomic End-formations and the Neuron Theory.—The axons of autonomic ganglion cells which terminate in relation to smooth muscle commonly form delicate plexuses around individual muscle fibers or groups of fibers.   Those that terminate in relation to gland cells, according to most observers, form a plexus adjacent to the membrana propria, from which arise fibers which penetrate the membrana and terminate in relation to the gland cells.

The results of extensive, painstaking histological studies in which attention has been focussed on the terminal neural structure in the tissues innervated through the autonomic nerves and the so-called interstitial cells have raised pertinent questions regarding the validity of the neuron theory.

Terminal structures in smooth muscle have repeatedly been described as end-rings or end-nets, but many investigators, using the specialized methylene blue and silver technics, have been impressed with the difficulty of obtaining preparations in which terminal structures of this kind can be demonstrated.   Preparations in which the nerve fiber bundles are successfully impregnated frequently fail to reveal free terminal structures, but show well-impregnated fibrillar networks in intimate relationships with smooth muscles and glands which have been variously interpreted as nerve and as connective tissue.

Stoehr, Jr. (1932, 1935, 1950) and Reiser (1933) have described a delicate fibrillar structure, the "terminal reticulum," in autonomically innervated tissues which they have regarded as continuous with the axons of autonomic ganglion cells and with the protoplasm of the innervated tissue elements. As described and illustrated by them, this structure resembles a meshwork of connective tissue fibers.   Since certain connective tissue elements may be impregnated in silver preparations or stained with methylene blue, certain investigators, particularly Nonidez (1936, 1937), have been unable to accept the conclusions of Stoehr and Reiser regarding the relationships of the so-called terminal reticulum to the autonomic nerves, but regard it as a connective tissue structure without continuity with the nerves.

In an extensive series of studies, Boeke (1933–1949) has described a fibrillar structure associated with the autonomic nerves which he has called the "ground plexus." This structure, which consists of unmyelinated nerve fibers arranged in strands or flattened bands of very delicate neurofibrils, is present throughout the body. It is commonly associated with the smaller blood vessels, including the capillaries, and is intimately related to smooth muscle and gland cells. He regards this structure as the mechanism through which impulses conducted through the autonomic nerves reach the effector organs.   In an extensive discussion of the structure of the nerve cells, the nature of the neuro-neural and the neuro-effector junctions and the bearing of his own observations and those of other investigators on the neuron theory, Boeke (1949) has pointed out that the so-called interstitial cells of Cajal, which presumably form a syncytium, may be the connecting link between the postganglionic nerve fibers and the effector cells. He regards the problem of the interstitial cells and the synapse as of fundamental importance in further investigations in this field. Jabonero (1951), on the basis of an extensive series of studies, has supported a point of view relative to the autonomic neuro-effector mechanisms similar to that of Boeke.

The interstitial cells of Cajal are particularly abundant in the wall of the gastro-intestinal canal. They have been variously interpreted as neurons and as connective tissue cells. Cajal consistently regarded them as primitive neurons. Numerous other investigators have supported this point of view. Li (1940) advanced the hypothesis that in the small intestine the inner zone of the circular muscle with the interstitial cells in it constitutes a neuromuscular mechanism that bears a definite relationship to irritability, conduction and rhythmic contractions and, consequently, plays a rôle in the ordinary activities of the gastro-intestinal tract. As observed by Spoerri (1949), the neural nature of the interstitial cells in the gastric mucosa is indicated by the demonstration of neurofibrils and chromophil substance in the cytoplasm. She also traced processes of interstitial cells to epithelial cells of the several types, and concluded that these cells represent terminal links in the enteric nerves.

If the anatomical structure through which the autonomic nerves are functionally related to the effector organs is a syncytium which actually invades the protoplasm of the tissue elements, as Boeke has maintained, the axons of the autonomic ganglion cells cannot be regarded as separated from the effector cells by a limiting membrane, as required by the classical neuron theory. If the so-called interstitial cells, furthermore, are primitive neurons which are syncytially connected with one another and with the axons of ganglion cells, it cannot be maintained that all neurons are morphologically independent units separated from one another by surface limiting membranes. Although the results of careful histological studies carried out by certain investigators of undoubted ability fail to support the assumption that either the ground plexus or the so-called interstitial cells are of neural origin, it must be conceded, particularly in view of the doctrine of the chemical mediation of nerve impulses, that a formation such as the ground plexus described by Boeke, which affords relatively large areas of junctional tissue, seems to meet the physiological requirements for the transmission of nerve impulses more completely than minute free terminal structures lying here and there on the surface of the effector elements or an indifferent terminal reticulum which surrounds them.

The neuron theory has played a more important rôle in the advancement of neurology than the doctrine of the continuity of nerve cells. The physiological concept of the synapse undoubtedly is valid. The anatomical demonstration of synapses in the autonomic nerves also is not wanting. On the basis of an intensive investigation of the synapses in autonomic ganglia by the use of the methylene blue and silver technics, Hillarp (1946) concluded that the pericellular fibers are synaptic structures and that there is no continuity of the preganglionic fibers and the autonomic ganglion cells. The neuron theory in its classical form obviously does not take adequate account of the more modern concepts of the minute structure of the organism and the arrangement of its nerves. It should therefore be modified but not abandoned. Even though the structure through which impulses are transmitted from the autonomic axons to the effector cells should have to be regarded as syncytial, a synaptic arrangement of autonomic neurons would still remain necessary.

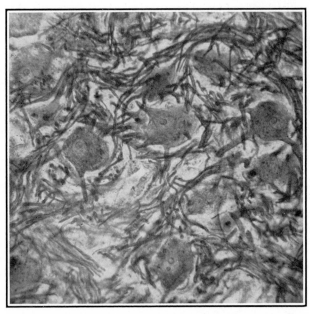

Fig. 12.—Photomicrograph from a section of a celiac ganglion (human) prepared by a modification of Cajal's silver technic.

Dendrites.—The autonomic ganglion cells vary within wide limits in the numbers and the morphological characters of their dendrites. These processes may be broad at the base and taper distalward or they may be of nearly uniform diameter throughout the greater part of their lengths. They commonly give rise to branches and frequently exhibit varicosities and other irregularities. They also include neurofibrils which, in favorable preparations, may be traced into their terminal branches. The broader proximal portions also include chromidial bodies. Many of the short dendrites lie wholly within the ganglion cell capsule. The longer ones usually penetrate the ganglion cell capsule and ramify more or less widely within the ganglion (Fig. 12). In some instances long dendrites extend beyond the border of the ganglion in fiber bundles associated with it.

Two ganglion cells joined together by a cytoplasmic bridge have been observed particularly in the myenteric plexus. In most instances the cells joined in this manner lie close together. In some, they are removed from one another by a distance equal to several times the diameter of a ganglion cell body. Anastomosing ganglion cells probably are relatively uncommon. They probably belong to the same category as binucleated ganglion cells.

CLASSIFICATION OF GANGLION CELLS

The morphological characters and the distribution of the dendrites have been used as criteria for classification of the autonomic ganglion cells. De Castro (1932) adopted a classification that is based on the morphological characters of the dendrites, but it also takes into consideration their distribution and their relationships to adjacent ganglion cells. It includes cells of the following five types:

Type I. Cells with Primordial or Long Dendrites.—Ganglion cells of this type vary in sizes and forms, but their dendrites are mainly long processes which may arise from all parts of the cell body or from limited areas of its surface. In man and other large mammals, during adult life, some of the dendrites of these cells branch only sparingly and are of approximately uniform thickness throughout the greater part of their length. Others give rise to many branches, some of which remain relatively short. Dendrites with thickenings from which branches arise that have greater diameters than the main stem are common. Fenestrated dendrites also occur.

In the primates, including man, the autonomic ganglion cells are chiefly of the long dendrite type during late fetal life and childhood. The condition of the dendrites which obtains in adult life is attained by a gradual process in which the most conspicuous changes take place from the sixth or the eighth to the twenty-fifth year. During adult life, ganglion cells with long dendrites abound in the sympathetic trunk ganglia and are most numerous in the prevertebral ganglia. In their mature condition many of the ganglion cells with long dendrites also have shorter, accessory dendrites. Many dendrites exhibit "collateral twigs" which are either simple or sparsely branched. These twigs, according to de Castro (1923), constitute receptive mechanisms, the so-called "receptor plates and collateral glomeruli."

Throughout the autonomic nervous system the terminal arborizations of the long dendrites and their collateral twigs are arranged in characteristic configurations in definite areas of the ganglia. The terminal branches of dendrites commonly arborize around the cell bodies of other ganglion cells, forming the so-called pericellular dendritic nests of Cajal (Fig. 13). These are not accidental arrangements but mechanisms through which the dendrites in question make synaptic contacts with preganglionic fibers whose terminal branches arborize around the same ganglion cell bodies.

In some instances the terminal branches of long dendrites ramify among those of one or more ganglion cells with shorter dendrites the terminal branches of which form a glomerular structure that may be enclosed in a common capsule. This probably is not a common arrangement.

Most of the long dendrites are arranged in fasciculi or tracts of various sizes, the protoplasmic tracts of de Castro. Dendrites of numerous ganglion cells are intimately associated with one another in such tracts. According to de Castro (1932), some protoplasmic tracts traverse a ganglion without receiving dendritic terminations. Others receive such terminals in large numbers. The latter appear as triangular or olive-shaped swellings bearing small divergent processes articulated with preganglionic fibers.

The most common mode of termination of the dendrites of autonomic ganglion cells, according to de Castro, is that which he has designated the "receptor plate." Such a structure involves terminal arborizations of some dendrites and short collateral twigs of others. All the dendrites involved in such a formation probably receive impulses conducted by the same preganglionic axons.

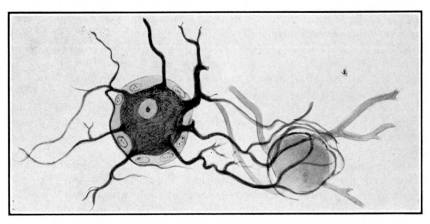

Fig. 13.—Drawing from a preparation of a sympathetic ganglion (human) illustrating arborization of dendrites around the body of an adjacent ganglion cell.

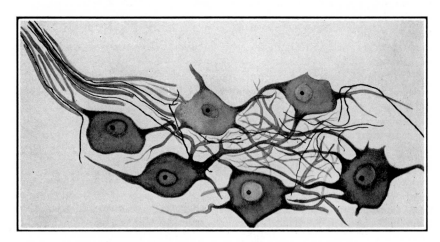

Fig. 14.—Drawing from a preparation of a celiac ganglion (human) showing ganglion cells in glomerular arrangement. Dark fibers represent preganglionic axons (Kuntz, 1938, courtesy of Jour. Comp. Neurol.).

Type II.   Monocellular and Pluricellular Dendritic Glomeruli.—A glomerulus which involves but a single ganglion cell is a relatively simple structure. Most of the dendrites arise from the cell body in a limited area.

They are mainly short processes which give rise to numerous branches that form a glomerular plexus near the cell body. If a glomerulus consists of two ganglion cells most of the dendrites of each are directed toward the other, their branches forming a glomerular plexus between the two cell bodies. If several ganglion cells are involved in a glomerulus they usually are arranged at the periphery of the group (Fig. 14). Most of the dendrites of these cells are directed toward the center of the group where they form a glomerular plexus. In larger glomeruli ganglion cell bodies also appear in the central area. Not all the dendrites which become involved in a glomerulus terminate within it. Some emerge from it and enter a protoplasmic tract or another glomerulus. Glomeruli also receive long dendrites of ganglion cells which are not incorporated in it. Dendrites of a ganglion

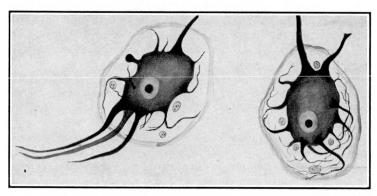

Fig. 15.—Sympathetic ganglion cells (human) with long and short (accessory) dendrites. The short dendrites are mainly intracapsular.

cell incorporated in a glomerulus which do not enter the general glomerular plexus may terminate in pericellular nests around the cell bodies of adjacent ganglion cells within the same glomerulus or in small accessory glomeruli involving one or more dendrites of adjacent ganglion cells. Glomerular arrangements of ganglion cells, according to de Castro (1923), are less common in the smaller mammals than in the larger ones, including man.

From the functional point of view, according to de Castro (1932), a glomerulus may be regarded as an intraganglionic nucleus made up of neurons which are isodynamically associated with one another, all of which receive impulses through the preganglionic fibers that terminate in it. Glomeruli arise early in embryonic development and persist throughout life, becoming more complex with advancing age.

Type III. Cells with Short or Accessory Dendrites.—This category includes ganglion cells with only short dendrites and ganglion cells with short and long dendrites. In the human fetus and the very young infant, according to de Castro (1932), the short dendrites under discussion either are absent or present in very small numbers. They arise during postfetal life and develop slowly. Many ganglion cells which at first have only long dendrites gradually develop short ones. Most of the budding and the growth of accessory dendrites takes place from the eighth to the fourteenth year. Short processes which were already present also increase in thickness and may give rise to branches during this period.

Many of the accessory dendrites do not penetrate the ganglion cell capsule (Fig. 15). They may be thick or thin. Some are unbranched. Others give rise to few or a larger number of branches which end in small knobs or spherical enlargements of variable sizes. Some terminal branches exhibit tuberosities or bead-like structures. Still others taper to a sharp point. Ganglion cells with short dendrites are less common in the smaller mammals than in the larger ones, including man.

Type IV. Fenestrated Ganglion Cells.—Fenestrated ganglion cells occur in small numbers particularly in the cephalic autonomic ganglia of man and other large mammals. In some cases the fenestrations appear as simple tracts resembling cup-handles or as fibers which anastomose with one another near their origins. In others they are more elaborate and involve stout dendritic branches which anastomose repeatedly. Ganglion cells with perforations in the peripheral zone of the cell body have also been observed.

Type V. Small Ganglion Cells.—Some of the small ganglion cells, particularly in the sympathetic trunk ganglia, retain the general appearance of young cells throughout life. They do not attain the degree of differentiation reached by the other ganglion cells and fall within a range of 15 to 24 microns in maximum diameter. The cell bodies may be ovoid or pyriform and possess few dendrites nearly all of which are long but only of moderate length. Although fairly numerous in the sympathetic trunk ganglia, cells of this type occur only rarely in the celiac and mesenteric ganglia.

STRUCTURAL CHARACTERISTICS OF AUTONOMIC GANGLIA

The autonomic ganglia vary within a wide range with respect to size, form and number and arrangement of ganglion cells. Every ganglion, with the possible exceptions of some of the smaller ones, is enclosed in a connective tissue capsule that is continuous with the epineurium of the nerves connected with it. The supporting tissue within the ganglion typically includes but little connective tissue associated with the blood vessels. Both the ganglion cell capsules and the interstitial tissue between them are made up of neuroglia.

In sections of ganglia prepared by the ferric gallate technic, the ganglion cell capsules appear to be made up of cells with spheroid or ovoid nuclei and irregular cytoplasmic bodies with irregular processes (Fig. 16, A). These cells form complete capsules that are penetrated by the ganglion cell processes. Non-cellular components of the capsules are not apparent. In areas of sections of young human ganglia and ganglia of normal animals in which the relationships of the capsule cells have not been disturbed they lie in intimate contact with the adjacent tissue. Many ganglion cell capsules lie in such intimate proximity to one another that no interstitial tissue can be observed between adjacent capsules in the contact areas (Fig. 16, B).

In sections prepared with specific neuroglia stains both the capsule cells and the interstitial cells exhibit the staining reactions and the structural characteristics of the oligodendroglia in the central nervous system (Fig. 17, A, B). In sections prepared by the silver carbonate technic or by Cajal's gold chloride sublimate technic, both of which are specific for astrocytes, they remain unstained. The capsule cells and the interstitial cells, therefore, appear to be identical with the oligodendroglia in the central nervous system (Kuntz and Sulkin, 1947).

Both the capsule cells and the interstitial supporting cells in the autonomic ganglia exhibit morphological variations comparable to those known

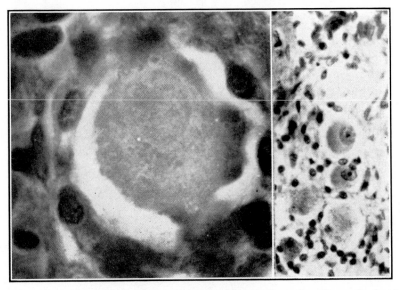

Fig. 16.—Photomicrograph from a ferric gallate preparation (human) showing ganglion cell capsule made up of a single layer of cells with irregular processes (left). Photomicrograph from a Van Gieson preparation (human) showing ganglion cell capsules with no extracapsular tissue between them in the area of contact (right). (Kuntz and Sulkin, 1947, courtesy of Jour. Comp. Neurol.)

to occur in the oligodendroglia in the central nervous system. Some are essentially spherical and exhibit no processes. Cells of this morphological type occur both in the capsules and in the extracapsular supporting tissue. Oligodendroglia of the same morphological type in the central nervous system have been called "adendroglia." Preparations in which spheroid cells are present in ganglion cell capsules may also include cells that are intermediate in form between the flat capsule cells and the spheroid ones (Fig. 17). The spheroid cells and those of intermediate form undoubtedly belong to the same category as the flatter cells in the unmodified capsules.

Preparations of most of the human ganglia in our series exhibit supporting cells in greater abundance than the preparations of ganglia taken from laboratory animals. This observation and the occurrence of cells in the process of amitosis supports the assumption that, under some conditions, the supporting tissue may undergo hyperplasia. This assumption is also supported by experimental data. In ganglia of the cat and the dog removed after prolonged faradic stimulation of the preganglionic fibers both the capsule cells and the extracapsular supporting cells were found to be more abundant than in ganglia removed from the same animals before the experimental stimulation. The preparations of the stimulated ganglia also showed some supporting cells in the process of amitotic division (Fig. 17, C).

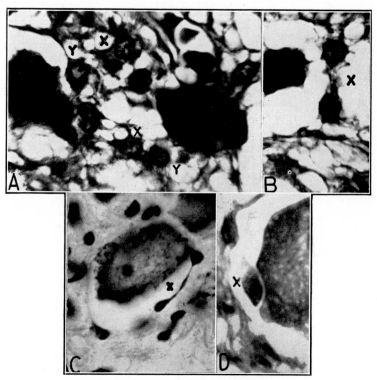

Fig. 17.—Photomicrographs from sections of sympathetic ganglia: *A*, Ferric gallate preparation (human) showing interstitial cells (x) and capsule cells (y); *B*, ferric gallate preparation (human) showing 2 capsule cells (x); *C*, preparation (cat) showing capsule cell undergoing amitotic division (x); *D*, preparation (human) showing cell (x) detached from capsular wall in early phase of change to spheroid form.

In sections of ganglia stained to demonstrate the Golgi substance in the ganglion cells, the supporting cells also exhibit a well developed Golgi apparatus. It consists typically of a dense perinuclear ring from which lines of granular material extend into the cytoplasmic processes. In the spheroid cells devoid of processes, the Golgi apparatus is limited to the perinuclear zone.

Among the conspicuous structural features in sections of a ganglion are the nerve fibers that enter it and those that arise within it. The bundles of nerve fibers which enter a ganglion pursue more or less regular courses in some instances, but exhibit no regular arrangement in others. These bundles consist predominantly of preganglionic fibers that terminate in the ganglion and preganglionic and afferent fibers that traverse it. In general the long dendrites of the ganglion cells are arranged in dendritic tracts or fasciculi. Some of the short dendrites become associated with these tracts, particularly through their terminal branches. Others give rise to glomerular structures in which dendrites of two or more adjacent ganglion cells intertwine with one another. In sections, groups of ganglion cells with long dendrites commonly appear to be separated from one another by the dendritic tracts. Ganglion cells whose dendrites intertwine in dendritic glomeruli constitute more or less definitely circumscribed glomerular groups (Fig. 14). Ganglion cells with both long and short dendrites may be associated with adjacent neurons both through dendritic tracts and dendritic glomeruli.

Most of the autonomic ganglia include ganglion cells of diverse morphological types, but some exhibit greater diversity than others in this respect. The superior cervical sympathetic ganglion includes ganglion cells that differ widely in their morphological characters, including size. Most of them have both long and short dendrites. Ganglion cell glomeruli occur frequently. They consist of one or more ganglion cells and may be regarded as small isodynamic ganglion cell centers. Ganglion cells of large and medium sizes, some of the dendrites of which end in dendritic plexuses which are less highly differentiated than the dendritic glomeruli, also are characteristic of this ganglion. Many of the long dendrites present are arranged in stout dendritic tracts in which receptor plates occur only in limited areas. Most of the short dendrites do not penetrate the ganglion cell capsule. These, according to de Castro (1932), probably represent specific receptors differentiated for the purpose of receiving individualized nerve impulses. The stellate ganglion exhibits certain structural characteristics in common with the other sympathetic trunk ganglia and others in common with the prevertebral ganglia. The thoracic sympathetic trunk ganglia exhibit greater uniformity with respect to the morphological characters of their constituent ganglion cells. Slender dendritic tracts are common but there are few pluricellular glomeruli. Most of the ganglion cells have both long and short dendrites. Many of the latter do not extend beyond the ganglion cell capsules. Others penetrate the capsule and terminate in receptor plates near by. The lumbar and the sacral sympathetic ganglia also exhibit uniformity with respect to the morphological characters of their ganglion cells in a relatively high degree. Most of these cells have both long and short dendrites. Most of the long ones lie in dendritic tracts. Most of the short ones are relatively straight. They penetrate the ganglion cell capsule and terminate in arborizations outside the capsule. In some instances their terminal branches interlace with those of similar dendrites of adjacent ganglion cells to form dendritic "brushes" and accessory glomeruli.

The prevertebral ganglia are characterized by ganglion cells of medium sizes and a high degree of uniformity in their morphological characters. Most of them are stellate and have long dendrites. Very small and very large ganglion cells occur only rarely in these ganglia. In addition to the long dendrites, many of the cells have short accessory dendrites, which penetrate the ganglion cell capsule and invade the dendritic tracts or, with short dendrites of adjacent cells, form dendritic brushes and accessory dendritic glomeruli. A striking feature in sections of these ganglia is the occurrence of extensive groups of ganglion cells surrounded by slender dendritic tracts.

The cranial autonomic ganglia include chiefly ganglion cells of medium sizes, appreciable numbers of large ones and few small ones. Most of the ganglion cells have both long and short dendrites. The long ones give rise to relatively few branches, most of which are short. Many of the short ones do not extend beyond the ganglion cell capsule. Frequently the axon arises from the proximal portion of a dendrite.

The visceral ganglia, particularly those in the enteric canal, include chiefly ganglion cells of two or three morphological types. Most investigators who have studied these ganglia have recognized ganglion cells characterized by either short or long dendrites. Some also have recognized a third category for cells with dendrites of intermediate lengths. In general the short dendrites give rise to numerous short branches, and the long ones branch only sparingly. Short dendrites of contiguous ganglion cells frequently form dendritic brushes or glomeruli. Terminal branches of long dendrites, in some instances, also end in such structures. Long dendrites frequently terminate in pericellular dendritic nests in the same ganglion or in an adjacent one.

NERVE FIBERS IN AUTONOMIC GANGLIA

The nerve fibers in autonomic ganglia include the axons of the autonomic ganglion cells, preganglionic axons that make synaptic connections in the ganglia and afferent cerebrospinal nerve fibers that traverse them. The axons of the ganglion cells commonly emerge from the ganglia and join the nerves through which they are conveyed to the effector tissues. They have been designated the postganglionic fibers. The preganglionic axons arise from visceral efferent neurons in the brain stem and the spinal cord and reach the autonomic ganglia through the efferent roots of the corresponding cerebrospinal nerves. They constitute the conductors through which impulses emanating from the central nervous system reach the autonomic ganglia. The afferent cerebrospinal nerve fibers merely traverse the autonomic ganglia without making functional connections with ganglion cells in them.

There are no certain criteria on the basis of which the axon of an autonomic ganglion cell may be differentiated from the dendrites in all cases. In many instances the axon arises, not directly from the cell body, but from the proximal portion of a dendrite. It is usually unmyelinated, but in some instances it may be sheathed with a very thin layer of myelin. Collateral branches occur only rarely if at all (de Castro, 1932), but terminal branches are common. In many instances the axons of the ganglion cells take long, tortuous courses through the ganglion before emerging from it. In others they emerge quite directly.

The preganglionic outflow from the central nervous system includes (1) fibers of relatively large caliber with thick myelin sheaths in small numbers, (2) fibers of medium caliber with thinner myelin sheaths in somewhat larger numbers, and (3) fibers of small caliber with thin myelin sheaths in much greater numbers. Preganglionic fibers of the thoracolumbar outflow terminate in the sympathetic trunk ganglia and the abdominal and pelvic prevertebral ganglia. Many of those that make synaptic connections in the superior and the middle cervical ganglia traverse one or more sympathetic trunk ganglia without making any connections in them. Those which reach prevertebral ganglia through the splanchnic nerves also traverse sympathetic trunk ganglia without making connections in them.

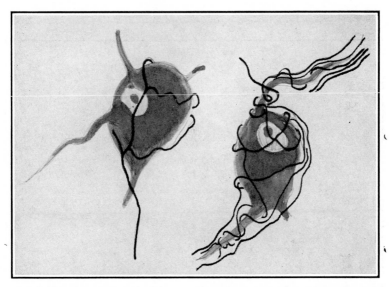

Fig. 18A.—Drawings from preparations of sympathetic ganglia (human) to illustrate synapses effected by terminal branches of preganglionic axons (dark), arranged in simple pericellular and peridendritic nests.

Some preganglionic fibers give off terminal branches in one ganglion and continue rostrad or caudad in the sympathetic trunk and give rise to terminal branches in one or more other ganglia. Others end in few or many terminal branches in only one ganglion. The terminal branches of the preganglionic fibers ramify widely within the ganglion. Those of a single fiber may make synaptic connections with many ganglion cells of identical or similar function, but there is no rigid architectural plan or typical localization. Synaptic connections are established chiefly between the terminal arborizations of the preganglionic axons and the receptive structures of the long and the short dendrites and of the cell bodies. The following types of synaptic mechanisms have been recognized:

Pericellular and Peridendritic Nests.—One or more preganglionic axons or terminal branches approach a ganglion cell body by spiral courses around dendrites, penetrate the ganglion cell capsule and arborize around the cell, forming a more or less complex pericellular nest in contact with the short accessory dendrites or, in the absence of accessory dendrites, in more or less intimate relation to the cell body (Fig. 18, A). The terminal branches end typically in minute rings, loops or bulbous enlargements, some of which lie in contact with the surface of the cell body or of a dendrite. Pericellular fiber terminations of this kind constitute a striking feature of some preparations of human ganglia but are less striking in others. In some instances only fragments of relatively simple pericellular nests may be observed in sections, in addition to slender darkly stained fibers which approach the cell along one or more dendrites. Synapses of this type are less apparent and probably less common in our animal material than in the human.

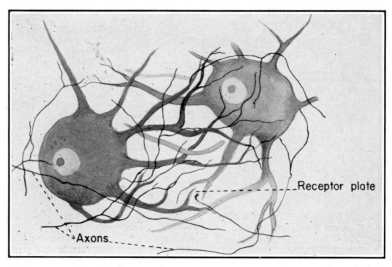

Fig. 18B.—Drawing from a preparation of a sympathetic ganglion (human) to illustrate terminal arborizations of preganglionic axons in a dendritic glomerulus (Kuntz, 1938).

Arborizations in Dendritic Cellular Glomeruli and Dendritic Brushes.— In the glomerular complexes formed by the dendrites of adjacent ganglion cells the terminal arborizations of preganglionic axons make contacts with the dendritic branches (Fig. 18, B). All the ganglion cells involved in such a glomerulus probably are synaptically related to the same preganglionic fibers. Axon terminations of the same kind also occur in glomeruli formed by the dendrites of a single ganglion cell and in dendritic brushes formed by dendrites of one or more ganglion cells.

Axon Terminations in Dendritic Tracts.—In preparations of ganglia in which dendritic tracts are well differentiated, the terminal branches of preganglionic axons may be traced among the dendrites. Many of these branches terminate in receptor plates (de Castro, 1932) scattered along the tract and at the intersections of bundles of dendrites. Others probably terminate in relation to the dendrites in the absence of specialized receptor plates (Fig. 19). In view of the large percentage of ganglion cells some dendrites of which are incorporated in dendritic tracts, synaptic connections made in these tracts must abound in many of the autonomic ganglia.

Centripetal Fibers.—Many visceral afferent components of the cerebrospinal nerves, as stated above, traverse autonomic ganglia, but make no connections with their ganglion cells. Impulses of visceral origin

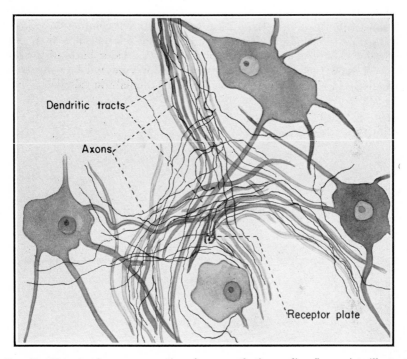

Fig. 19.—Drawing from a preparation of a sympathetic ganglion (human) to illustrate relationships of terminal branches of preganglionic axons to dendrites in dendritic tracts (Kuntz, 1938, courtesy of Jour. Comp. Neurol.).

probably reach the central nervous system only through afferent cerebrospinal nerve components. In general, reflex responses through autonomic nerves involve afferent conduction into the central nervous system through cerebrospinal nerve fibers and efferent conduction from the central nervous system through pathways consisting of preganglionic neurons and autonomic ganglion cells synaptically related to one another. Most of the reflex responses in visceral organs can be explained on this basis, but the autonomous activity of certain viscera, particularly the gastro-intestinal tract, seems to require reflex mechanisms which do not involve centers in the central nervous system.

Local enteric reflexes carried out through neurons limited to the myenteric and the submucous plexuses have long been recognized on the basis of experimental physiological studies.   Anatomical evidence for the existence of synaptic relationships between enteric neurons is not wanting, but the exact anatomical structure of the enteric reflex arcs as yet is unknown. Axons of enteric origin also traverse the mesenteric nerves and make synaptic connections in the celiac and the inferior mesenteric ganglia (Kuntz, 1938, 1940).   Reflex responses mediated through the decentralized inferior mesenteric (Kuntz, 1940; Kuntz and Saccomanno, 1944) and the celiac (Kuntz and Van Buskirk, 1941; Warkentin *et al.*, 1943; Kuntz and Saccomanno, 1944) plexuses also have been demonstrated.   The current teaching that autonomic ganglion cells are essentially efferent in function and constitute the peripheral units in visceral efferent conduction pathways has aided materially in explaining the functional relationships of the autonomic nerves and undoubtedly is correct for the major parts of the autonomic system, but exceptions to this point of view must be recognized particularly in the enteric, the celiac and the mesenteric ganglia.

Chapter III

CENTRAL AUTONOMIC CENTERS AND CONDUCTION PATHWAYS

AUTONOMIC NUCLEI IN THE SPINAL CORD

THE preganglionic fibers of the thoracolumbar autonomic outflow arise chiefly from cells in the intermediolateral cell column and in part from cells in the intermediate zone between the anterior and the posterior gray columns from the first thoracic to the second or the third lumbar segment inclusive. The extent of the intermediolateral column coincides fairly accurately with that of the thoracolumbar outflow. The preganglionic fibers of the sacral autonomic outflow arise in the intermediate zone, particularly in the nucleus myoleioticus medialis, from the second sacral segment caudad. This outflow usually is limited to the third and the fourth sacral nerves in man, but occasionally some preganglionic fibers are included in the second or the fifth. The visceral afferent spinal nerve fibers, like the somatic afferent ones, make connections in the posterior gray column and in the intermediate zone of the gray matter, including reflex connections with preganglionic neurons. The latter connections probably involve intercalated neurons.

SPINAL AUTONOMIC CENTERS

Centers through which vasomotor activity, pilo-erection and perspiration are regulated are present throughout the thoracic and the rostral lumbar segments of the spinal cord. These functions in the head, the neck and the upper extremities are regulated through centers in the rostral four or five thoracic segments. The rostral two or three thoracic segments also include preganglionic neurons that are concerned with the sympathetic innervation of the lacrimal glands. Vasomotor activity, pilo-erection and perspiration in the upper trunk region are regulated through centers in the fourth to the ninth thoracic segments. In the trunk below the umbilicus these functions are regulated through centers in the ninth or the tenth thoracic to the second lumbar segment. In the lower extremities they are regulated through centers in the twelfth thoracic to the second lumbar segment inclusive.

The pupillodilator, or ciliospinal, center is located in the eighth cervical and the first and second thoracic segments of the cord. Cardiac accelerator centers are present in all the thoracic segments of the spinal cord from the second to the fifth or sixth inclusive. Complete elimination of the cardiac accelerators in the cat requires interruption of the visceral rami or extirpation of the thoracic sympathetic trunk as far caudad as the sixth or the seventh thoracic segment. In man cardiac rami have been traced from the sympathetic trunk as low as the sixth thoracic segment. The abdominal viscera receive impulses through the splanchnic nerves from centers in the fourth thoracic to the second lumbar segment of the spinal cord. The sympathetic genito-urinary and recto-anal centers are located in the first and the second lumbar segments. The parasympathetic centers are located in the second, the third and the fourth sacral segments.

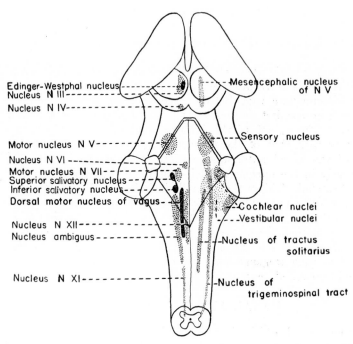

FIG. 20.—Dorsal view of the human brain stem with the nuclei of the cranial nerves projected on the surface. The motor nuclei are represented on the left side; the sensory nuclei on the right side.

GENERAL VISCERAL EFFERENT NUCLEI IN THE BRAIN STEM

The general visceral efferent fibers of the cranial nerves arise from cells in the dorsal motor nucleus of the vagus, the salivatory nucleus and the Edinger-Westphal nucleus, which constitute the general visceral efferent column in the brain stem (Fig. 20). These cells are of small and medium sizes and have relatively large nuclei. The chromidial substance is only poorly developed and exhibits an irregular distribution.

The dorsal motor nucleus of the vagus lies subjacent to the ala cinerea of the rhomboid fossa and dorsolateral to the hypoglossal nucleus. The efferent fibers that arise in it are widely distributed to the parasympathetic ganglia in relation to the thoracic and the abdominal viscera for the innervation of the involuntary musculature of the heart, the respiratory passages, the esophagus, the stomach, the small intestine, the biliary system, the pancreas, etc. According to Malone (1913) the dorsal motor nucleus of the vagus in the lemur and the monkey includes neurons of two distinct types (Fig. 21). The oral portion is composed of small neurons with relatively large nuclei and a meager supply of chromidial substance. The middle portion is composed of medium-sized neurons with a more abundant supply of chromidial substance. The nucleus-plasma ratio of these cells, as compared with that of the small ones, favors the cytoplasm. As compared with that of the somatic motor neurons, it favors the nucleus. The caudal portion is composed chiefly of small neurons, but it contains

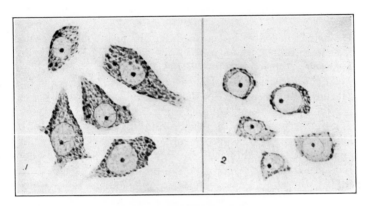

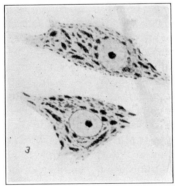

FIG. 21.—Efferent nerve cells from the medulla oblongata of the lemur: *1* and *2*, visceral efferent cells from the dorsal motor nucleus of the vagus; *3*, somatic efferent cells from the hypoglossal nucleus. (Malone.)

some which are similar to the large ones in the middle portion. The axons of the small neurons supply smooth muscle and glands. Those of the medium-sized ones supply heart muscle.

The nucleus salivatorius lies in the reticular formation, at the junction of the pons and medulla oblongata between the genu of the facial nerve and the nucleus of the hypoglossal nerve. It extends from the median plane laterad and ventrad through the reticular formation. The efferent fibers arising from the more caudal portion, or *nucleus salivatorius inferior*, are conveyed through the glossopharyngeal nerve to the otic ganglion

Those arising from the rostral portion, or *nucleus salivatorius superior*, are conveyed through the chorda tympani to the submandibular ganglion.

The Edinger-Westphal nucleus is situated in the rostral portion of the nucleus of the oculomotor nerve. It is composed of small neurons whose axons traverse the oculomotor nerve as preganglionic fibers to the ciliary ganglion for the innervation of the intrinsic musculature of the eye.

OTHER AUTONOMIC CENTERS IN THE MEDULLA OBLONGATA AND THE PONS

A vasoconstrictor center in the medulla oblongata has long been recognized. In the rabbit it is located in the floor of the upper part of the fourth ventricle, approximately 2.5 mm. from the median plane, in a position coinciding with that of the superior olive. In other laboratory animals it has been localized in the substantia reticularis grisea in the rostral portion of the medulla oblongata.

In experiments carried out on decerebrated animals, Yi (1938) observed that reflex lowering of the blood pressure, elicited by stimulation of various afferent nerves, was not abolished by cauterization of the vasoconstrictor center, but was abolished by destruction of an area adjacent to the obex. He concluded, therefore, that there is an independent reflex center in the medulla oblongata through which vasoconstriction may be inhibited. Downman *et al.* (1939) also reported experimental data which indicate the existence of a depressor reflex center in the medulla oblongata.

Experimental data reported by Claude Bernard and by later investigators indicate the existence of a center in the medulla oblongata which exerts a regulatory influence on sugar metabolism. In attempting to localize this so-called sugar center, Brugsch *et al.* (1922) observed that puncture of the rostral portion of the dorsal motor nucleus of the vagus resulted in hypoglycemia, while puncture of the caudal portion of this nucleus resulted in hyperglycemia and glycosuria. In view of the existence in the diencephalon of a center which exerts a regulatory influence on carbohydrate metabolism, it has been suggested by some investigators that the above results of puncture of the floor of the fourth ventricle could be explained most satisfactorily on the assumption that descending fibers from the sugar center in the diencephalon and not a specific group of neurons in the medulla oblongata were stimulated. Brooks (1931), however, demonstrated reflex hyperglycemia following transection of the brain stem below the mesencephalon. On the basis of his experimental findings, he concluded that there exists, in the floor of the fourth ventricle just below the middle of the brachium pontis and in close proximity to the vasomotor center, a neural mechanism through which reflex rises in blood sugar may be brought about by stimulation of an afferent nerve, at least in anesthetized cats. In spite of the existence of this center the diencephalic center probably must be regarded as the chief center for the neural regulation of carbohydrate metabolism.

The existence of a center in the medulla oblongata that plays a rôle in the regulation of respiration has long been known. According to data reported by Pitts (1940) and Beaton and Magoun (1941) relative to cats and monkeys, an inspiratory center is located dorsal to the rostral half of the inferior olivary nucleus. It includes the inferior reticular nucleus. In the monkey it extends from the median plane 4 mm. laterad. At its caudal extremity it is somewhat narrower and lies adjacent to the hypoglossal nucleus. The area involved in the expiratory center is somewhat more extensive and surrounds the inspiratory center. Experimental data reported by Wyss (1947) also support the assumption that the inspiratory and the expiratory centers do not coincide with one another. According to his findings, the internuncial neurons concerned in both centers are located in the nucleus of the tractus solitarius. Those concerned with expiration, *i. e.*, inspiratory-inhibitory reflexes, are situated rostral to those concerned with inspiratory-excitatory reflexes. The inspiratory moto-neurons appear to be controlled directly through these two groups of internuncial neurons, but certain phenomena of respiratory control probably require reflex integration at higher levels.

The pons includes a center that is functionally related to the respiratory center in the medulla oblongata and is functionally connected with it through descending fibers. This center has been designated the "pneumotaxic" center. It is located bilaterally in the ventral portion of the tegmentum, close to the median plane in the rostral few millimeters of the pons. In the cat, according to Ngai *et al.* (1952), an additional respiratory regulating mechanism is located in the caudal two-thirds of the pons. When released from the influence of the pneumotaxic and other pontile centers and afferent vagus nerve impulses the medullary respiratory centers have an autonomous rhythm.

AUTONOMIC CENTERS IN THE DIENCEPHALON

Hypothalamus. — Nuclear Configuration. — The diencephalic nuclei that are known to be functionally related to the autonomic nerves are located in the hypothalamus and the walls of the third ventricle. They are included in the paleothalamus, *i. e.*, the older portion of the diencephalon. The hypothalamus occupies the ventral portion of the diencephalon. It includes 15 to 20 nuclear aggregates of gray matter not all of which are clearly delimited, the optic chiasm, the supraoptic commissures and the hypophysis. All the hypothalamic nuclei probably are functionally related, although not exclusively, to the autonomic nerves. Certain adjacent nuclear aggregates in the preoptic area, which does not properly belong to the hypothalamus, also subserve autonomic functions.

For purposes of description, the hypothalamus in man may conveniently be subdivided into four regions: the supraoptic middle region located above the optic chiasm and rostral to it, the tuberal or infundibular middle region located in relation to the infundibulum, the mammillary middle region which occupies the caudal portion of the hypothalamus including the mammillary bodies, and the lateral region.

The supraoptic middle region includes the nuclei supraopticus, paraventricularis, suprachiasmaticus, supraopticus diffusus and the anterior hypothalamic area. The nucleus supraopticus overlies the proximal portion of the optic tract and usually is incompletely separated by the latter into a relatively large anterolateral and a small posteromedial portion. Its constituent neurons are mainly cells of relatively large sizes. The nucleus paraventricularis, as observed in transverse sections of the hypothalamus, lies in intimate relation to the wall of the third ventricle and medial to the column of the fornix. In sagittal sections (Fig. 22) it appears triangular with the base of the triangle dorsad. Most of its constituent neurons are comparable to those of the nucleus supraopticus, but they are less closely aggregated. Between the larger neurons are some small ones comparable to the small neurons of the periventricular system. The nucleus suprachiasmaticus is a small nucleus located against the dorsal surface of the optic chiasm and adjacent to the beginning of the supraoptic recess of the third ventricle. Its constituent neurons are relatively small cells. It

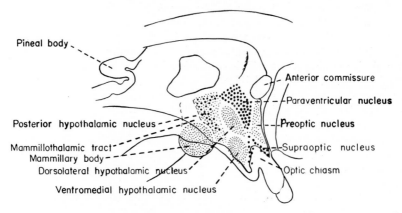

Fig. 22.—Diagram of the hypothalamic nuclei in man as viewed from the ventricular surface (redrawn from Clark).

probably is a portion of the periventricular system. The nucleus supraopticus diffusus consists of a poorly defined band of small neurons lying adjacent to the supraoptic commissures. The anterior hypothalamic area is located between the supraoptic nucleus and the ventral end of the paraventricular nucleus. It includes chiefly small neurons.

The tuberal, or infundibular, middle region (Fig. 23, *A*) includes the nuclei hypothalamicus ventromedialis, and hypothalamicus dorsomedialis and the dorsal and posterior hypothalamic areas. The nucleus hypothalamicus ventromedialis is located adjacent to the ventricular surface of the tuber cinereum and immediately behind the nucleus supraopticus. Its constituent neurons are relatively small and closely aggregated. The nucleus hypothalamicus dorsomedialis lies adjacent to the dorsal border of the nucleus hypothalamicus ventromedialis and in essentially the same relation to the ventricular surface of the tuber cinereum. It is continuous dorsally with the dorsal hypothalamic area and rostrally with the dorsal part of the anterior area. Medially it can hardly be differentiated from the periventrricular system. Its constituent neurons are mainly small and not closely aggregated. The dorsal hypothalamic area lies dorsal to the nucleus hypothalamicus dorsomedialis and extends from the dorsal part of the anterior hypothalamic area to the posterior area. It comprises relatively few small neurons. The posterior hypothalamic area occupies the border zone between the tuber cinereum and the mammillary body. It is bounded laterally by the fornix and the mammillothalamic tract and

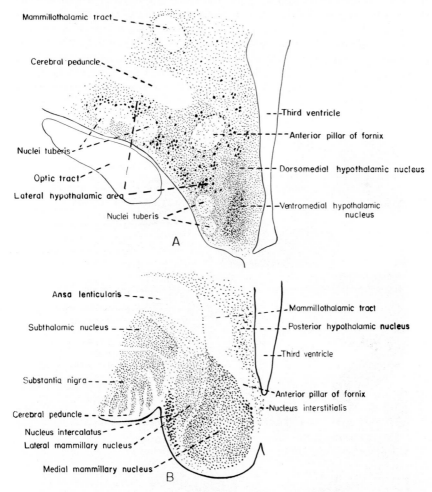

FIG. 23.—Transverse sections of the human hypothalamus through (*A*) the tuber cinereum and (*B*) the mammillary bodies.

is continuous dorsally with the midline nuclei of the thalamus. It includes the nucleus hypothalamicus posterior which is characterized by closely aggregated small neurons among which larger ones are dispersed either singly or in small groups.

The caudal or mammillary region comprises mainly the corpora mammillaria, a pair of rounded bodies, one on either side of the median plane, situated in the interpeduncular fossa immediately in front of the posterior perforated area.   Each mammillary body includes three nuclei, the nuclei mammillaris medialis, mammillaris lateralis and intercalatus (Fig. 23, B). The nucleus mammillaris medialis comprises a relatively large, homogeneous aggregate of small neurons and is sharply delimited by a capsule of mye-linated fibers.   Immediately in front of this nucleus and between it and the nucleus hypothalamicus ventromedialis is an aggregate of small neurons, the nucleus premammillaris.   The nucleus mammillaris lateralis is compara-tively small in man.   Its constituent neurons are smaller than those of the nucleus mammillaris medialis and more closely aggregated.   The nucleus intercalatus is relatively large in man and occupies a lateral position in the mammillary body.   It is continuous at its rostral border with the lateral hypothalamic area.   Its constituent neurons are larger than those of the other mammillary nuclei.

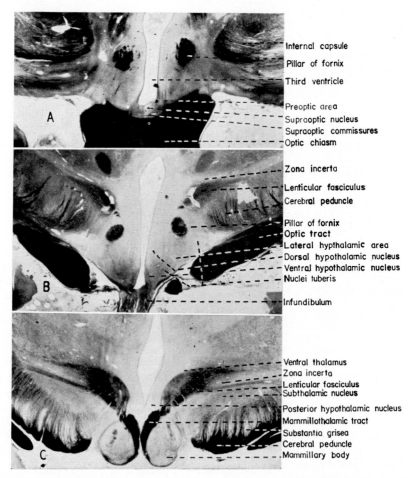

FIG. 24.—Transverse sections of the human hypothalamus through (A) the supraoptic region, (B) the infundibular region and (C) the mammillary region.

The lateral region is situated lateral to the plane of the anterior pillar of the fornix and is continuous rostrally with the lateral preoptic area. Its caudal portion is relatively narrow but extends to the tegmental portion of the midbrain. The lateral area is traversed by the medial forebrain bundle and includes scattered groups of relatively large neurons. In addition to these scattered neuron groups it includes two or three aggregates of small neurons in the lateral portion of the tuber cinereum, known as the nuclei tuberis (Fig. 24, *B*).

Hypophysis.—The hypophysis is a small rounded or ovoid glandular structure lodged in the hypophyseal fossa in the floor of the cranium. It is attached to the hypothalamus by means of the infundibulum which arises from the floor of the third ventricle in the region of the tuber cinereum. The hypophysis comprises an anterior and a posterior lobe. The posterior lobe is the smaller of the two. It is continuous with the infundibulum. Like the latter structure, it is derived from the neural tube. The anterior lobe arises from the buccal ectoderm. Nerve fibers most of which arise in the supraoptic region and the tuber cinereum extend into the hypophysis where they terminate chiefly in the posterior lobe. Collectively they constitute the hypothalamico-hypophyseal tract (Fig. 25).

Neuron Classification.—On the basis of an intensive cytological study of the hypothalamic nuclei and their known fiber connections in the cat, Kirgis (1940) advanced the hypothesis that the neurons in these nuclei may be classified in four categories according to their anatomical and functional relationships. These have been designated peripheral visceral efferent, central somatic efferent, central visceral efferent and associational. The peripheral visceral efferent neurons are large spherical or polyhedral cells with coarse chromidial granules aggregated in the peripheral zone and some chromidial substance in dust-like particles in the perinuclear zone. The central somatic efferent neurons are comparable in sizes and forms to those of the previous category and exhibit coarse, discrete chromidial bodies which are fairly uniformly distributed throughout the cell body. The central visceral efferent neurons are cells with spheroid or polyhedral cell bodies, mainly of medium sizes. Their chromidial bodies are smaller than those in the neurons of either of the preceding categories. These bodies frequently occur aggregated in the peripheral zone, but sometimes they appear in clumps in certain portions of the cell body. The associational neurons are relatively very small fusiform or spheroid cells with fine chromidial granules distributed chiefly in the perinuclear zone.

The functional requirements of the hypothalamus obviously demand neurons of these four categories, but it must not be assumed that all hypothalamic neurons can be recognized as belonging to one or another category, since many which, on the basis of their anatomical relationships, belong to one category are cytologically similar to some of the neurons of another category. In the hypothalamus of the cat, according to Kirgis, most of the neurons are central visceral efferent. Associational neurons apparently are next in abundance.

In view of the known afferent fiber connections in the hypothalamus and the efferent conduction pathways which arise in it, to be described presently, most of the hypothalamic nuclei must include central visceral efferent and associational neurons. Some of them must also include central somatic efferent neurons. The neurons whose axons enter the hypophysis through the hypothalamico-hypophyseal tract obviously must be classified as peripheral visceral efferent neurons, since their axons terminate directly in relation to the effector tissue.

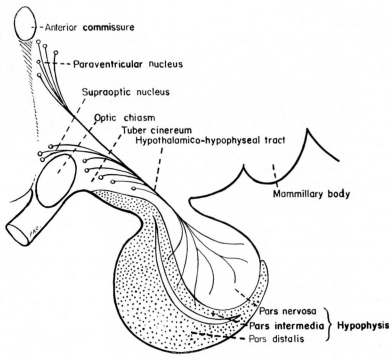

Fig. 25.—Diagram illustrating the hypothalamico-hypohyseal tract (redrawn from Clark).

Fiber Connections.—The hypothalamic nuclei are intimately interconnected with one another and with adjacent thalamic nuclei through abundant internuclear fibers. They are also connected with more remote parts of the nervous system through afferent and efferent conduction systems (Fig. 26). Most of the internuclear connections are essentially diffuse and have not been completely analyzed. The paraventriculo-supraoptic system is a fairly compact aggregate of fibers which seems to be efferent with respect to the paraventricular nucleus, but convincing proof that its fibers terminate in the supraoptic nucleus is wanting. Fibers arising in the paraventricular nucleus also enter the tuber cinereum but their sites of termination remain unknown. Another recognizable aggregate of fibers extends into the supraoptic nucleus along the optic tract, but the origin and the destination of its fibers have not been determined. The longer fiber tracts connected with the hypothalamus may be described as afferent and efferent conduction systems, but it must be recognized that in some of these systems the direction of conduction has not been fully established but only suggested on the basis of theoretical considerations.

Afferent Systems.—The medial forebrain bundle is composed of both ascending and descending, fine unmyelinated fibers. It is located in the lateral hypothalamic area and includes septo-lateral cortico- strio- tuberculo-parolfacto- and olfacto-hypothalamic tracts and an olfacto-mammillary

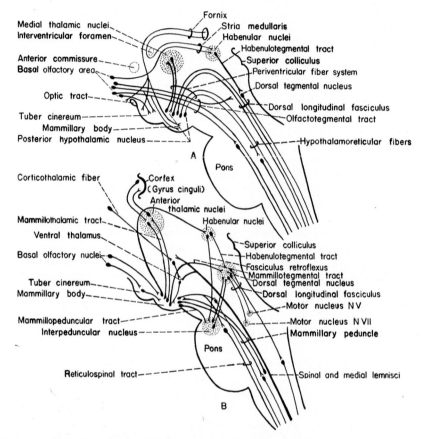

Fig. 26.—Diagrams illustrating the chief connections of the hypothalamic nuclei and descending conduction pathways.

tract. The bundle is quite apparent in the human brain, but it cannot readily be resolved into its component parts. Some of its fibers extend from the hypothalamus into the tegmentum of the mesencephalon. The septo-hypothalamic fibers probably arise from neurons that are synaptically related to neurons in the frontal lobe of the cerebral cortex.

The Cortico-Hypothalamic and Thalamo-Hypothalamic Tracts.—Conduction pathways from the neocortex to the hypothalamus are more abundant than the results of earlier studies seemed to indicate. They include projections from various parts of the frontal lobe, particularly the pre-frontal area, that make connections in widespread portions of the hypothalamus. They probably include synaptic relays in the dorsal thalamus. Other fibers of cortical origin terminate in various parts of the dorsal and the ventral thalamus where they make synaptic contacts with neurons that conduct into the hypothalamus. Thalamo-hypothalamic fibers are incorporated in the periventricular system and the mammillothalamic tract. Other fibers of thalamic origin which enter the hypothalamic nuclei are not aggregated in well defined bundles. Some of the fibers passing between the zona incerta and the hypothalamus probably are afferents which terminate in the hypothalamus. The thalamo-hypothalamic fibers provide not only for the conduction of impulses emanating from the cerebral cortex but also relay into the hypothalamus somatic and visceral sensory impulses that reach the thalamus from all parts of the body.

The **Fornix**, which arises in the hippocampus, may be regarded as a direct conduction pathway from the paleocortex to the hypothalamus. It probably also conveys some fibers from cortical areas on the medial surface of the cerebral hemisphere. Most of its fibers terminate in the mammillary nuclei and the tuber cinereum.

The **Stria Terminalis** consists mainly of fibers that arise in the amygdaloid nucleus. Many of them terminate in the preoptic and adjacent hypothalamic areas as far caudad as the premammillary nucleus. Most of the hypothalamic nuclei receive afferent fibers through this bundle.

Lenticulo-hypothalamic connections probably are made chiefly through the ansa peduncularis and the ansa lenticularis. Most of the fibers concerned arise in the globus pallidus and terminate in the ventromedial hypothalamic nucleus (Fig. 24).

The mammillary peduncle (Fig. 26) is not easily demonstrable in man, but it undoubtedly includes both afferent and efferent fibers. The ascending fibers which reach the hypothalamus through this tract arise at various levels in the brain stem, particularly the mesencephalon. It may be regarded as one of the important afferent pathways to the hypothalamus.

Vago-supraoptic connections have not been demonstrated anatomically but the assumption that there is a conduction pathway from the vagal centers to the supraoptic nuclei is supported by experimental data. This pathway seems to be directly related to the supraoptico-hypophyseal tract.

Efferent Systems.—The mammillothalamic tract is a well defined fasciculus that arises in the mammillary body, chiefly in the medial mammillary nucleus, and terminates in the anterior thalamic nuclei, particularly in the anteroventral nucleus (Figs. 24, C and 26). It is an important link in one of the chief hypothalamo-cortical connections since some of the anterior thalamic neurons in relation to which its fibers terminate send their axons into the cortex of the gyrus cinguli. The mammillothalamic tract probably reaches its highest development in man.

Diffuse hypothalamo-thalamic connections undoubtedly exist, but specific information regarding them is wanting. The anatomical data regarding the scattered fibers which connect hypothalamic and thalamic nuclei afford little information regarding the direction of conduction in them.

The mammillotegmental tract is closely related in its origin to the mammillothalamic tract (Fig. 26). Most of its fibers appear to terminate in the nucleus profundus of the tegmentum. Certain data support the assumption that it also makes connections with the central and the dorsal tegmental nuclei. In man fibers of the mammillotegmental tract mingle with descending fibers from other parts of the hypothalamus as they extend caudad in the capsule of the red nucleus.

The periventricular system and the dorsal longitudinal fasciculus are intimately associated with one another. The dorsal longitudinal fasciculus was originally described as an aggregate of fibers in the central gray matter around the aqueductus cerebri which receives contributions from the hypothalamus, all parts of the dorsal thalamus, the subthalamic nucleus and the ansa lenticularis. The hypothalamic components of the periventricular system which join the dorsal longitudinal fasciculus arise throughout the hypothalamus but most abundantly in the posterior area. The sites of termination of these fibers are not definitely known. They probably make connections at various levels in the tectal and the tegmental nuclei in the brain stem.

Diffuse descending fibers probably arising in all parts of the hypothalamus extend caudad in large numbers particularly in the lateral hypothalamic area where they mingle with those of the medial forebrain bundle. This system includes some fibers of the periventricular system. Physiological data support the assumption that below the level of the hypothalamus these fibers lie widely scattered in the lateral portion of the tegmentum. They constitute an important part of the efferent conduction system from the hypothalamus.

AUTONOMIC CENTERS IN THE MESENCEPHALON

The existence of a reflex center in the mesencephalon through which tonic responses of the musculature of the urinary bladder may be elicited has been demonstrated experimentally by Langworthy and Kolb (1938). Langworthy and Rosenberg (1939) also demonstrated the existence in the mesencephalon of reflex mechanisms through which the tonicity of the smooth muscle of the rectum is regulated. Transection of the brain stem at the rostral border of the mesencephalon, in their experiments, resulted in hyperexcitability of the rectum to stretch stimuli. Transection of the medulla oblongata, on the other hand, resulted in abolition of the response to stretch stimuli and partial loss of the normal tonus of the rectal musculature.

AUTONOMIC REPRESENTATION IN THE CORPUS STRIATUM

Experimental data which seem to indicate that impulses emanating from the corpus striatum exert an influence on visceral functions are not wanting. For example, changes in the state of contraction of the smooth muscle of the pupil, the intestine, the bladder, the uterus and the blood vessels have been observed following stimulation of this portion of the brain. Lesions of the corpus striatum may result in increased body temperature, but the chief centers for the regulation of body temperature are located in the hypothalamus. Puncture of the head of the caudate nucleus may result not only in fever but also in polyuria and an increase in the specific gravity of the urine. Experimental data also support the assumption that the anterior portion of the corpus striatum exerts an influence particularly on the water-salt balance of the body through its fiber connections with the tuber cinereum.

AUTONOMIC REPRESENTATION IN THE CEREBRAL CORTEX

The functional activities of the visceral organs are regulated and controlled through centers in the brain stem and the spinal cord, but they are also influenced by impulses that emanate from the cerebral cortex. The influence of the cortex in the regulation of visceral functions is exerted chiefly through the hypothalamus and other autonomic centers in the brain stem. It is carried out through both the sympathetic and the parasympathetic nerves, but no circumscribed cortical areas have been recognized which are functionally related to one of these systems and not to the other. Stimulation of a given cortical area, furthermore, may affect various autonomic functions equally. Certain data support the assumption that the major cortical influence in the regulation of given visceral functions emanates from areas that are closely related to the cortical areas respectively that influence the corresponding somatic functions.

AUTONOMIC CONDUCTION PATHWAYS IN THE BRAIN STEM AND THE SPINAL CORD

In the caudal levels of the diencephalon the fibers that conduct impulses from the hypothalamic centers lie widely scattered. Most of them emerge from the lateral hypothalamic areas and traverse the central and the tegmental portions of the mesencephalon and the tegmental portion of the pons. Experimental lesions in certain of the hypothalamic nuclei are followed by descending degeneration into the spinal cord. Some of the fibers in question appear to terminate in the reticular formation of the brain stem. Others extend into the intermediolateral cell column in the spinal cord. Some of the descending fibers cross the median plane, but most of them are incorporated in pathways that are uncrossed. They become concentrated in the ventral portion of the posterior longitudinal bundle and the dorsal portion of the reticular formation of the medulla oblongata. According to Allen (1932), the reticulospinal tracts are in part visceral. Since many of the short fibers that descend from the hypothalamus terminate in the reticular formation in relation to neurons whose axons descend in the reticulospinal tracts, the latter play a rôle in the conduction of visceral impulses from the hypothalamus as well as from the reticular formation of the mesencephalon and the pons.

The pathways through which autonomic impulses are conducted caudad in the brain stem and the spinal cord include some long fibers and an extensive system of short ones arranged in relays. In the medulla oblongata most of the descending autonomic pathways lie in the lateral portion of the reticular formation. In the spinal cord most of them lie in the ventral portion of the lateral funiculus. Most of the fibers are limited to one side, but some cross the median plane in the brain stem or in the spinal cord. The descending pathways which conduct vasomotor impulses from the hypothalamus include crossed and uncrossed fibers. Some vasomotor impulses that cross in the brain stem probably cross again in the spinal cord. Pathways through which impulses of hypothalamic origin reach the urinary bladder include decussations in the brain stem and in the caudal lumbar segments of the spinal cord, but none in the intervening portions of their courses. The pathways which conduct impulses from the respiratory centers in the medulla oblongata traverse the anterior funiculus and the ventral portion of the lateral funiculus in the spinal cord. The descending pathways that subserve heat elimination appear to be concentrated in the intermediate and the lateral portions of the dorsal tegmentum in the mesencephalon and the pons. Those that subserve heat conservation appear to be located in the lateral tegmental region. In certain cases the heat elimination functions are abolished by appropriately placed lesions, while heat conservation activities are maintained, thus indicating a dual temperature regulating system (Beaton *et al.*, 1943). These results also support the assumption that tegmental pathways are of greater importance than the periventricular system in efferent conduction from the hypothalamus. In the monkey the conduction pathways for sweating are located in the lateral and anterior funiculi in the spinal cord and are completely or almost completely crossed (Beaton and Leininger, 1943). The crossing takes place close to the level at which the fibers in question terminate in the intermediolateral cell column. The pathways for pilo-erection and shivering appear to be located in the anterior funiculus. Some of their fibers cross the median plane, but most of them terminate on the same side.

Chapter IV

GENERAL PHYSIOLOGY

FUNCTIONAL CONNECTIONS OF THE AUTONOMIC WITH THE CENTRAL NERVOUS SYSTEM

THE neurons in the autonomic ganglia and plexuses are functionally related to the central nervous system through the general visceral efferent, or preganglionic, components of the cerebrospinal nerves. The normal physiological activity of the autonomic nerves, with certain exceptions, requires the integrity of the preganglionic neurons. Certain experimental data strongly suggest that, in connection with peripheral tissues, the sympathetic ganglion cells are capable of some independent activity (Tower and Richter, 1932). In cats in which the superior cervical ganglion had been decentralized for one week, as reported by Meyer and Grimson (1950), the isolated ganglion cells seemed to exert a buffering influence against contraction of the nictitating membrane induced by adrenin after blocking the autonomic ganglia with 2,6-dimethyl diethyl piperidinium bromide. The enteric plexuses are dependent upon their functional connections with the central nervous system to only a limited extent. An account of their independent functional activity is given in Chapter X.

According to current teaching, the preganglionic neurons cannot function in the absence of autonomic ganglia. The axons of preganglionic neurons appear to be incapable of making functional connections in tissues in which efferent connections are normally made only by postganglionic fibers. The capacity of preganglionic fibers to make direct functional connections with skeletal muscles has been demonstrated (Ballance, 1931; Beattie et al., 1932). Their capacity to reëstablish synaptic connections in autonomic ganglia is also demonstrated. If their course is not blocked by scar tissue, the axons of preganglionic neurons grow along their former pathway into the ganglion and reëstablish functional connections with the ganglion cells in a relatively short time. Kirgis and Ohler (1944) reported functional restoration of the sympathetic innervation of the iris and the nictitating membrane in the cat four months after section of the preganglionic fibers and removal of the stellate and the rostral thoracic sympathetic trunk ganglia. In bilaterally adrenalectomized cats that were kept alive by transplants of adrenal cortex, as reported by Kirgis and Pearce (1950), no sympathetic function could be demonstrated in the eye ten months after preganglionic sympathectomy. In cats that were subjected to inferior cervical sympathectomy unilaterally one month after bilateral adrenalectomy, fright and anger 14 months later caused dilatation of the pupil bilaterally, but it was most marked on the control side. The results of certain experimental studies involving artificial anastomosis of the distal portion of the cervical sympathetic trunk and the proximal portion of the

(84)

vagus, the phrenic or a convenient somatic nerve also indicate that the interrupted fibers of these nerves may grow into the superior cervical ganglion and make synaptic connections with the ganglion cells. The results of experimental studies involving interruption of postganglionic fibers do not indicate that these fibers possess the capacity for regeneration (Tower and Richter, 1932; Kirgis and Ohler, 1944).

FUNCTIONAL SIGNIFICANCE OF GANGLION CELLS

Individual preganglionic neurons make synaptic connections with more than one ganglion cell. Individual ganglion cells likewise are synaptically related to more than one preganglionic neuron. Ganglion cells, consequently, receive impulses which probably differ qualitatively, but they are essentially relay stations in visceral efferent conduction pathways. The impulses relayed apparently are not altered by passing through the ganglion cells. Effective stimulation of postganglionic fibers requires a stimulus of greater intensity than effective stimulation of the corresponding preganglionic fibers. Impulses discharged through preganglionic fibers that are not of sufficient intensity to activate the ganglion cells may by summation reach the threshold of stimulation. The difference in the thresholds of stimulation of the pre- and the postganglionic fibers probably is correlated with their difference in caliber.

The character of the response elicited by stimulation of a postganglionic nerve, as demonstrated by Bronk *et al.* (1938), is not modified by separation of the nerve from the ganglion; consequently, there is no evidence of backfiring from the ganglion cells or of reflex connections within the ganglion. According to their findings, a volley of impulses conducted by preganglionic fibers initiates a single, temporarily dispersed volley of postganglionic impulses. The individual ganglion cells each discharge a single impulse in response to a preganglionic volley. The temporal dispersion exhibited by the postganglionic volley is due to the differences in the conduction rates of the postganglionic fibers.

At frequencies of not over 10 to 20 per second, either maximal or submaximal stimulation of a preganglionic nerve results in discharges of constant magnitude in the postganglionic fibers, showing activation of a constant number of ganglion cells. If the circulation through the ganglion is stopped, the numbers of ganglion cells that respond to single preganglionic volleys decrease progressively. Perfusion of a ganglion with acetylcholine results in a marked increase in the number of ganglion cells that respond to a submaximal preganglionic volley. It also induces either a random discharge of ganglion cells or a rhythmic discharge of single ganglion cells or closely synchronized ones. Further data advanced by Bronk (1939) support the assumption that the frequency of impulses emanating from the central nervous system is modified by the autonomic ganglion cells.

AFFERENT NEURONS FUNCTIONALLY ASSOCIATED WITH THE AUTONOMIC NERVES

The afferent neurons that conduct visceral impulses into the central nervous system, like the peripheral somatic afferent neurons, are components of the cerebrospinal nerves; consequently, they are not included in the autonomic nervous system. The afferent limb of an autonomic reflex arc may be either a visceral or a somatic afferent cerebrospinal nerve component.

Afferent impulses arising in any part of the body may elicit reflex reactions carried out through autonomic nerves. The question regarding the existence of autonomic neurons that are essentially afferent in character has been much discussed. Data available at present do not indicate the existence of autonomic neurons that are incorporated in pathways through which afferent impulses are conducted into the central nervous system. In general the autonomic neurons are efferent in function. There is no clear evidence that either the ganglia of the sympathetic trunks or the cranial autonomic ganglia either include afferent neurons or constitute reflex centers in the ordinary sense. On the contrary, both anatomical and physiological data are available that demonstrate quite clearly that certain of the peripheral plexuses, e. g., the myenteric and the submucous plexuses, include reflex mechanisms and are capable of carrying out coördinated reflex activities independently of the central nervous system (see Chapter X). Reflex reactions mediated through the celiac and the inferior mesenteric ganglia have also been demonstrated (see Chapter II).

AXON REFLEXES

Although the autonomic ganglia (except the enteric and prevertebral) do not constitute reflex centers in the ordinary sense, physiological data are not wanting which strongly suggest that reflex reactions may, under certain conditions, be carried out through them. This was known to Claude Bernard as early as 1864.

In experiments carried out on animals in which the spinal cord was completely destroyed or the preganglionic fibers connecting the portion of the sympathetic trunk in question with the spinal cord were severed so that no reflexes could be carried out through spinal centers, Langley (1900) found that when the sympathetic trunk was divided and its central end was stimulated, contraction of the erector pili muscles and constriction of the cutaneous blood vessels took place in an area corresponding to the distribution of from one to four sympathetic roots rostral to the level at which the stimulus was applied. These responses were abolished by intravenous injection of nicotine or its application to the sympathetic ganglia in question, and could not be elicited after the preganglionic fibers in the sympathetic trunk had undergone degeneration. It appeared to be evident, therefore, that the reactions in question were mediated through preganglionic fibers and neurons in the ganglia of the sympathetic trunk. On the basis of these findings, Langley concluded that every preganglionic fiber that enters the sympathetic trunk gives rise to a number of branches through which it makes synaptic connections with several, perhaps many, ganglionic neurons. Some of them make synaptic connections in only one ganglion even though, like those that reach the superior cervical ganglion, they traverse the more caudal cervical ganglia. Those which enter a segmental ganglion commonly traverse more than one ganglion and may give off collaterals which terminate in all. In the caudal thoracic, the lumbar and the sacral portions of the sympathetic trunk in the cat, according to Langley, most of the preganglionic fibers terminate through collaterals in three or more ganglia. When such preganglionic fibers are stimulated distally, under experimental conditions, the impulses travel centrad in the fiber and peripherad in its collateral branches and may activate all the ganglionic neurons in relation to which these branches terminate. Langley explained all reflex phenomena elicited by stimulation of the preganglionic fibers following destruction of their connections with the central nervous system on this basis. Since they could not be regarded as reflexes in the ordinary sense, he called them pseudo-reflexes. Inasmuch as they depend on afferent conduction through preganglionic fibers, he also called them preganglionic axon reflexes.

Postganglionic axon reflexes, i. e., reflexes which are carried out through a single axon and its branches, have also been described. It has been assumed that stimulation of the peripheral portion of an axon or an axon collateral may give rise to impulses that are conducted centrad through the division of the fiber stimulated and peripherad through its other divisions, thus calling forth a localized response in the end organ in question.

Preganglionic axon reflexes have been observed almost exclusively under experimental conditions. Reactions which have been interpreted as postganglionic axon reflexes have been observed under both experimental and apparently normal physiological conditions. To what extent either preganglionic or postganglionic axon reflexes play a rôle in the normal functional activity of the autonomic nerves as yet is unknown.

ANTAGONISTIC AND SYNERGIC ACTIONS OF SYMPATHETIC AND PARASYMPATHETIC NERVES

The autonomic nervous system, as described in Chapter I, is made up of the sympathetic and the parasympathetic divisions. The preganglionic neurons of the former division are components of the thoracic and rostral lumbar nerves. Those of the latter are components of certain of the cranial and the sacral nerves. The internal organs are innervated through both sympathetic and parasympathetic nerves; consequently, they receive efferent impulses from widely separated centers in the central nervous system, the effects of which in general are antagonistic. For example, impulses that reach the heart through the parasympathetic nerves tend to inhibit, and impulses that reach it through the sympathetic cardiac nerves tend to accelerate the heart rate. On the contrary, vagus impulses usually exert an excitatory influence on the gastro-intestinal musculature, and impulses conducted through the sympathetic nerves usually inhibit gastro-intestinal motility. The influence of the pelvic nerves on the large intestine is the same as that of the vagi on the more proximal parts of the alimentary canal. With regard to the genital organs, impulses conducted through the hypogastric nerves exert a vasoconstrictor effect and impulses conducted through the pelvic nerves exert a vasodilator effect. Similar conditions also obtain in the cephalic region. Constriction of the pupil is brought about by impulses emanating from the midbrain through the preganglionic components of the oculomotor nerve and neurons in the ciliary ganglion.

Impulses conducted through preganglionic fibers that arise in the rostral thoracic segments of the spinal cord and neurons in the superior cervical sympathetic ganglion cause dilatation of the pupil.

All blood vessels probably are innervated through sympathetic nerves. In certain parts of the body blood vessels probably are also innervated through parasympathetic nerves. With certain exceptions, vasoconstriction is mediated through sympathetic nerves. The sympathetic nerves to the peripheral blood vessels also include vasodilator fibers. There are no known pathways by which fibers included in either the cranial or the sacral autonomic outflows could reach the vessels of the extremities or of the somatic portions of the trunk. Certain investigators have assumed that groups of parasympathetic cells are present in the spinal cord throughout the cervical and the thoracic regions and that these cells send their axons out through the dorsal roots of the spinal nerves to be distributed to the peripheral blood vessels, but anatomical proof of the existence in the dorsal spinal nerve roots of efferent fibers distributed to the peripheral blood vessels is not forthcoming.

The so-called antagonistic action of the sympathetic and the parasympathetic nerves may be compared with the reciprocal action of the cerebrospinal nerves which supply the flexor and the extensor muscles respectively that act on a given joint. When either the flexors or the extensors contract in response to nerve impulses the opposing group undergoes a degree of relaxation, but it is not wholly devoid of tonus since impulses are received through its efferent innervation. In like manner, the sympathetic and the parasympathetic nerves supplying a given organ maintain a functional balance. For example, an increase in cervical sympathetic tonus, resulting in dilatation of the pupil, is accompanied by a simultaneous diminution of tonus in the parasympathetic nerves that innervate the sphincter pupillæ muscle. Dilatation of the pupil in response to cervical sympathetic stimulation probably is brought about, not only by contraction of the dilator pupillæ muscle, but in part also by relaxation of the sphincter pupillæ, due to diminished parasympathetic tonus. Splanchnic stimulation, likewise, brings about relaxation of the gastric musculature, a result which could not be obtained without simultaneous diminution of the tonic influence of the vagi. In general, it may be assumed that increased sympathetic tonus is accompanied by a corresponding diminution of parasympathetic tonus and *vice versa*.

Although the sympathetic and the parasympathetic nerves that supply a given organ usually produce opposite effects, stimulation of either a sympathetic or a parasympathetic nerve sometimes elicits a response that is the opposite of the usual one. This probably is determined by the initial tonic condition of the tissue involved or the hormonal content of the blood at the moment. On the other hand, certain autonomic nerves include both excitatory and inhibitory fibers. For example, the parasympathetic fibers that innervate the bronchial and the gastro-intestinal musculature exert an excitatory, and those that innervate the heart exert an inhibitory influence, whereas the sympathetic fibers that innervate the bronchial and the gastro-intestinal musculature exert an inhibitory, and those that innervate the heart exert an excitatory influence.

REGULATION OF AUTONOMIC FUNCTIONS THROUGH DIENCEPHALIC CENTERS

The diencephalic autonomic centers, most of which are located in the hypothalamus, exert a significant regulatory influence in all autonomic functions. They may be regarded as functionally superimposed on the lower autonomic mechanisms. These centers undoubtedly are capable of integrating complex autonomic reactions independently of influences from higher levels, but they are functionally related to the cerebral cortex.

Temperature Regulation.—The control of body temperature in warm blooded animals, including man, involves regulation of heat production and regulation of heat elimination. Hypothalamic centers undoubtedly play major rôles in both these functions, although other central mechanisms are also concerned. Experimental data support the assumption that mechanisms in the corpus striatum play a significant rôle in the regulation of body temperature. Extirpation of the cerebral hemispheres, including the corpora striata, in experimental animals, however, is not incompatible with the maintenance of body temperature within the normal range, but the capacity to maintain normal body temperature is lost following destruction of the hypothalamus. This capacity is also greatly impaired by transection of the spinal cord in the cervical region, due to interruption of the descending conduction pathways from the hypothalamus to the preganglionic autonomic nuclei.

The end organs through which the neural regulation of body temperature is brought about include the blood vessels, the sweat glands, and the internal organs whose metabolic processes tend to increase or inhibit heat production. The glands of internal secretion also play a significant rôle. Through their secretory activity they may exert a direct influence on the metabolic processes through which heat is generated. The temperature-regulating centers may also be activated directly by endocrine products in the blood. In view of the many factors which influence the production and the elimination of heat, it is obvious that the organs involved in heat production and heat elimination must receive excitatory and inhibitory impulses from the temperature-regulating centers more or less constantly. These centers in turn are influenced by every variation in temperature, both at the periphery and in the internal organs, in part through nerve conduction, but chiefly through the direct effect of the circulating blood on them.

The reactions of the temperature-regulating centers to the temperature of the blood flowing through them probably are of greater importance in the regulation of the body temperature than the reflex responses to thermal stimulation of the peripheral receptors. Elevation of the temperature of the blood in the carotid artery results in peripheral vasodilatation, perspiration and heat dyspnea, all of which are common symptoms of overheating. On the contrary, cooling of the blood supplying the hypothalamus results in increased metabolism in the internal organs and a consequent rise in body temperature. Exposure of the body to cold ambient temperature also results in increased metabolism and an increase in the volume of intercellular liquid throughout the body while the reflexes concerned are intact. If the central nervous system is chilled to the level at which general muscular relaxation occurs these responses are abolished (Barbour *et al.*, 1943).

In view of the physiological relationships of the temperature-regulating centers, we should expect that any pathological condition that affects them directly, initiates strong afferent impulses which reach the thalamus, or gives rise to toxic substances which circulate in the blood, might give rise to pathological changes in body temperature. Most of the stimuli that give rise to fever probably exert a direct effect on the temperature-regulating centers. Fever may also be produced by a variety of mechanical, chemical and physicochemical stimuli. This knowledge affords a basis for the explanation of the constant occurrence of fever in which infection is not a factor in certain cases of brain injury or other pathological lesions of the brain substance in proximity to the temperature-regulating centers. Such conditions as internal hydrocephalus and hemorrhage in the third ventricle, likewise, may give rise to fever due to mechanical pressure exerted on the hypothalamus. High fever accompanying apoplexy, in many cases, is due at least in part to the effect of pressure on the temperature-regulating centers brought about by the hemorrhage which caused the disorder. Pathological conditions which result in great pressure on the hypothalamus, *e. g.*, certain cases of hydrocephalus, also may cause a fall in body temperature due to paralysis of the temperature-regulating mechanisms.

In summarizing the results of extensive experimental investigations of hypothalamic functions, carried out by his collaborators and himself, Ranson (1940) concluded that the hypothalamic mechanisms concerned with the regulation of body temperature are arranged rostrocaudally. The results of more recent studies indicate that the heat sensitive portions of the hypothalamus coincide with the preoptic and the anterior middle regions and the dorsomedial and the ventromedial nuclei (Eliasson and Ström, 1950).

The hypothalamic neural mechanisms concerned in the protection of the body against hyperthermia are localized in the region in front of the optic chiasm and below the anterior commissure. Local heating of this region in experimental animals results in an increased respiration rate, panting, secretory activity of the sweat glands and cutaneous vasodilatation. Superheated blood circulating through this region probably initiates the same reactions. Localized lesions in this portion of the hypothalamus result in impairment of the ability of the body to protect itself against overheating. In cats with localized lesions in this area, panting does not occur even though the body temperature reaches 106° F. This is not due to damage to the motor mechanisms through which coördinated panting movements are brought about, since the latter are located farther caudad, probably in the mesencephalon. These centers receive hypothalamic impulses through fibers which descend in the lateral hypothalamic area. Cats in which they are freed from the regulatory influences emanating from higher levels by transection of the brain stem in the caudal portion of the diencephalon may exhibit decerebrate panting even though the body temperature is subnormal. Electrical stimulation of the rostral portion of the hypothalamus and the cortex of the frontal cerebral lobe results in cutaneous vasoconstriction. Simultaneous electrical stimulation and heating of the rostral portion of the hypothalamus results in cutaneous vasodilatation. Decortication of the frontal lobe does not abolish the vasomotor effect of either electrical stimulation or heating of the hypothalamus (Ström, 1950).

The hypothalamic mechanisms concerned in the protection of the body against hypothermia appear to be coëxtensive with the hypothalamic nuclei that are functionally related to the sympathetic nerves. Protection of the body against chilling is not seriously impaired by lesions of moderate size unless they are located bilaterally in the lateral hypothalamic area and near the caudal border. Large lesions in other parts of the hypothalamus, particularly in the caudal portion, result in impairment of this function to some extent. The neurons concerned probably are at least in part identical with those which subserve vasoconstriction, pilo-erection and certain other functions of the sympathetic nerves.

From the clinical point of view, impairment of the hypothalamic temperature-regulating mechanisms commonly results in grave autonomic disturbances. Paralysis of temperature regulation due to lesions in the vicinity of the third ventricle may result in hyperthermia produced by peripheral vasoconstriction and cessation of perspiration, frequently accompanied by hyperpnea and tachycardia (Penfield and Rasmussen, 1949).

Carbohydrate Metabolism.—The assumption that carbohydrate metabolism is influenced by impulses that emanate from the hypothalamus is supported by abundant experimental data. There appears to be located in the rostral portion of the hypothalamus a center that is especially important for carbohydrate metabolism. Electrical stimulation of this center, the pituitary body or the cervical sympathetic trunk results in an increase in the glucose level in fasting animals (Reiss, 1950). Hyperglycemia associated with lesions of the hypothalamus or following hypothalamic stimulation has been observed frequently. Although a hypothalamic factor in carbohydrate metabolism is demonstrated, the available data do not prove that hypothalamic mechanisms play a predominant rôle in this phase of the general metabolism. In evaluating the data bearing on this problem, Long (1940) has pointed out that the weight of evidence supports the assumption that the major part of the regulation of carbohydrate metabolism is effected through the activity of endocrine glands.

Water Metabolism.—The assumption that the hypothalamus plays a significant rôle in water metabolism has been advanced on the basis of both experimental and clinical data. The production of polyuria by stimulation of the hypothalamus was reported by Eckhart as early as 1876. Polyuria and polydipsia are not uncommon phenomena associated with hypothalamic lesions, particularly in the rostral area. Some of the most significant studies bearing on the general problem of water metabolism have been carried out in an effort to determine the etiology and the pathology of diabetes insipidus. This disease is now known to be associated with a deficiency in the production of the antidiuretic hormone by the pars nervosa of the hypophysis, but it is causally related to the hypothalamus in so far as the changes in the hypophysis resulting in the arrest or retardation of the production of the antidiuretic principle are related to hypo-thalamic lesions. Extirpation of the pars nervosa of the hypophysis or its atrophy due to interruption of the supraoptico-hypophyseal tract com-monly result in retardation or complete arrest of the production of the diuretic hormone and consequent diabetes insipidus (Fisher et al., 1938).

The results of more recent studies, particularly those of Ranson and his collaborators, have provided the basis for a more complete evaluation of the neurogenic factors in the causation of polyuria and polydipsia as observed in diabetes insipidus and in the regulation of water metabolism. The regulation of water exchange is mediated through hormonal agents, but the production of the antidiuretic hormone is regulated through the supraoptico-hypophyseal tract. Interruption of this tract results not only in arrest of the production of the antidiuretic hormone in the pars nervosa of the hypophysis but also in atrophic changes in this part of the gland. The hypothalamus, consequently, exerts a significant influence in water metabolism through the supraoptic nuclei and the supraoptico-hypophyseal tract. This point of view is also supported by the work of Ingraham et al. (1939) in which they consistently failed to recover antidiuretic substance from the urine of cats in which the nerve fibers extending from the hypo-thalamus to the pars nervosa of the hypophysis had been interrupted.

The displacement of water from the blood plasma to the tissues in a cold environment and from the tissues to the blood plasma in a warm environ-ment is correlated with the regulation of body temperature. In an ex-tensive study of the control of water movement in response to environ-mental temperature, Barbour (1940) found that in cats transection of the brain stem in the anterior region of the hypothalamus may result in ab-normally high osmotic pressure levels with reduction in the specific gravity of the blood. The normal osmotic pressure and specific gravity responses to cold persist only when injury to the hypothalamus involves the rostral portion. The control of osmotic pressure and the specific gravity of the blood, therefore, seem to be localized in the rostral portion of the hypo-thalamus. The control of osmotic pressure concerns a somewhat more extensive portion of the hypothalamus than the control of the specific gravity of the blood.

In the monkey osmotic pressure and the specific gravity of the blood are also regulated through the anterior thalamic nuclei, but this animal exhibits the capacity to utilize pathways for vicarious regulation of tem-perature and water shifting in a remarkable degree. Temperature regu-lating and osmotic and specific gravity reactions recover within a period of approximately eight days even after complete transection of the brain stem at the level of the roots of the oculomotor nerves.

Fat Metabolism.—Disturbances in fat metabolism have been observed frequently in association with either hypothalamic or hypophyseal lesions. The assumption that both these structural entities influence this important function has been supported by experimental data. Some of the data probably have been interpreted erroneously. As observed by Hetherington (1943), neither partial nor total hypophysectomy alone results in adiposity or prevents its occurrence after hypothalamic damage. It appears prob-able, therefore, that obesity associated with damage to structures in the vicinity of the hypophysis is due solely to hypothalamic dysfunction. Marked adiposity due to hypothalamic damage usually is associated with a lesion in the region of the tuber cinereum. Lesions that damage or destroy the ventromedial hypothalamic nucleus bilaterally probably result in the most extreme fat storage. Extreme emaciation is sometimes associated with a lesion of the hypothalamus located farther caudad. In some instances adiposity associated with a hypothalamic lesion is followed by emaciation. In patients with hypophyseal disease, the fatty acid and the cholesterol contents of the blood serum frequently are abnormally high (Gildea and Man, 1940).

The available experimental data emphasize the importance of the rostral portion of the hypothalamus in the regulation of fat metabolism, but they do not warrant the conclusion that this function is localized in any particular nucleus or group of nuclei. All hypothalamic lesions that cause obesity interrupt some nerve fibers. The interruption of longitudinal fibers located in the ventral portion of the hypothalamus probably is more important in the production of adiposity than interruption of the hypothalamico-hypophyseal tract. (Hetherington and Ranson, 1940.)

Animals that become obese following hypothalamic damage usually exhibit increased appetite and increased food consumption. The hyperphagia exhibited by rats with hypothalamic lesions, according to Kennedy (1950), represents a primitive urge to eat, which is hunger. In the normal animal this urge is inhibited by a hypothalamic satiety mechanism that is sensitive to changes in the blood that result from ingestion of food. Appetite and food consumption alone, however, do not account fully for hypothalamic obesity. Animals that have become obese following hypothalamic lesions exhibit metabolic disturbances. Chemical analysis of the tissues shows marked depletion of both their calcium and their phosphorus contents and irregular reduction in the iron content.

The mechanism through which the hypothalamic influence in fat metabolism is exerted is not fully understood. This influence may be mediated secondarily through the hypophysis or through neural connections with the liver and possibly other glands.

Protein Metabolism.—The hypothalamus undoubtedly exerts a regulatory influence in protein metabolism, but the mechanism through which this is accomplished as yet is unknown. Data bearing on this problem are relatively meager. Hypothalamic stimulation apparently inhibits protein metabolism, whereas elimination of the hypothalamic influence by transection of the spinal cord in the cervical region results in its acceleration.

Sexual Functions.—In certain species the gonadotropic functions of the hypophysis are known to be influenced by impulses emanating from the hypothalamus. Secretion of the gonadotropic hormones may take place independently of direct nerve impulses, but the rate of their secretion appears to be regulated through hypothalamic mechanisms (Dempsey and Uotila, 1940). Electrical stimulation of the hypothalamus close to the infundibulum, in the female rabbit, as observed by Nowakowski (1950), resulted in ovulation in 85 per cent of the trials. The same stimulation did not elicit ovulation after transection of the spinal cord. Ovarian function appears to be impaired following transection of the spinal cord to the extent that the luteinizing hormone does not exert its full effect on the ovary.

Sexual behavior undoubtedly depends on both neural and hormonal regulation. In certain species the full pattern of mating behavior can be elicited after complete decortication. Component parts of this pattern can also be elicited in animals with the brain stem transected caudal to the diencephalon. Large lesions of the hypothalamus caudal to the optic chiasm may result in abolition of mating behavior due to interference of the lesion with the neural integration of the mating reflexes. On the basis of our present knowledge, the existence of a center in the diencephalon for the regulation of sexual behavior must be regarded as problematical.

Emotional Behavior.—The assumption that neural mechanisms in the hypothalamus play a significant role in emotional behavior is supported by data obtained in many experimental investigations. As early as 1892, Goltz described signs of rage in a decorticated dog. The reactions were similar to rage reactions in a normal dog, but they were elicited more easily. The results of more recent investigations indicate that the reactions that simulate rage in decorticated animals in general conform to those that Cannon and Britton (1927) designated as "sham rage." They are essentially undirected and do not continue after the stimulus has subsided.

The chief central neural mechanisms through which emotional behavior is mediated are now known to be located in the hypothalamus. This division of the diencephalon also includes neural mechanisms concerned with emotional experience. Centers located in the brain stem caudal to the hypothalamus undoubtedly play a rôle in emotional expression, but the complete expression of emotional reactions probably requires the integrity of the hypothalamic mechanisms. The subcortical mechanisms concerned with emotion are connected with the cerebral cortex through both ascending and descending conduction pathways, consequently, they are subject to cortical influences. Under certain conditions they appear to function quite independently of the cerebral cortex.

Experimental data support the assumption that interruption of the cortico-diencephalic fiber connections liberates the subcortical emotional mechanisms from the inhibitory influences of cortical origin. The uninhibited behavior of decorticated animals frequently simulates rage. Such behavior has been called sham rage. In cats bilateral lesions in the ventromedial hypothalamic nuclei, i.e., in the infundibular region of the hypothalamus, have resulted in enduring behavior of this kind (Wheatley, 1944). Only a limited portion of the cortico-hypothalamic fiber connections can be interrupted by lesions in this region, but they interrupt portions of the columns of the fornix as well as the large pallido-hypothalamic tracts. Sham rage has been induced in cats by ablation of the corpora striata and the rostral half of the diencephalon, by radical removal of both frontal lobes and by removal of only the orbital surfaces of these lobes, but the entire neocortex in cats may be removed bilaterally without causing sham rage (Bard and Mountcastle, 1948). Animals decorticated in this manner, but with the rhinencephalon intact, showed no signs of anger or emotion even when subjected to severe nociceptive stimulation. They usually exhibited behavior similar to that of animals responding to pleasurable stimulation, even though the stimulus used would in normal animals elicit unpleasant reactions. Removal of the rhinencephalic cortex in animals which, after removal of the neocortex had exhibited pleasurable reactions, resulted in immediate exhibition of sham rage in response to stimulation of any kind. On the basis of these findings the assumptions that the subcortical mechanisms of emotional expression are normally influenced by the rhinencephalon and that they become free from cortical control when their fiber connections with this part of the brain are interrupted appear to be warranted. The manner in which the activities of the centers of autonomic representation in the neocortex are correlated with those of the rhinencephalon, on the one hand, and with those of the hypothalamus, on the other, is as yet unknown. The distribution in the hypothalamus of the fibers which project from the rhinencephalon also is not fully known. It is significant, however, that the portions of the rhinencephalic cortex that are concerned in emotional expression also influence visceral functions.

The hypothalamus receives afferent impulses from all parts of the body including the cerebral cortex. It discharges impulses through both autonomic and cerebrospinal nerves and to the cerebral cortex. Hypothalamic impulses that are discharged through the sympathetic nerves arise in all parts of the hypothalamus, but chiefly in its caudal and lateral portions. Those that are discharged through the parasympathetic nerves arise chiefly in its rostral portions. The integrative mechanisms in the hypothalamus that are concerned with emotional expression have the capacity for coördinated activity independent of impulses emanating from the cerebral cortex, but they are subject to cortical influences. Subjective emotional experience probably requires both diencephalic and cortical integration. The integration required for crude awareness probably can be completed in the diencephalon. The appreciation of various qualities of experience and their association with states of feeling undoubtedly requires integration at the cortical level.

Waking State and Sleep.—Patients with hypothalamic tumors frequently exhibit somnolence in a marked degree. The results of studies of encephalitis lethargica, particularly those of von Economo (1931), also afford evidence of subcortical factors in sleep. This investigator reported cases in which somnolence was associated with inflammation of the gray matter at the junction of the diencephalon and the mesencephalon, and cases in which initial choreic unrest and tormenting insomnia were associated with lesions located farther rostrad in the walls of the third ventricle. The results of other clinical studies, many of which have been reviewed by Harrison (1940), afford further evidence of the association of somnolence with hypothalamic lesions. Clinical data reported by Davison and Demuth (1946) indicate that somnolence due to hypothalamic damage is most frequently associated with bilateral lesions in the caudal portions of the lateral areas. They also found somnolence associated with damage to the ascending and descending fiber tracts that connect the hypothalamus with the mesencephalon.

Since decortication results in increased excitability and direct stimulation of the hypothalamus elicits intense excitement, whereas appropriately placed bilateral hypothalamic lesions result in somnolence, it seems reasonable to assume that somnolence results from suppression of hypothalamic activity and that, under normal conditiou, the hypothalamic drive exerting its influence on lower neural centers is an important factor in maintaining the waking state. Elimination of this influence results in relaxation of the body and thus favors sleep. The central mechanisms through which the sleep-waking rhythm is regulated, therefore, do not constitute a "sleep center," but a center the integrity of which is required for the maintenance of the waking state (Ranson, 1940).

The occurrence of somnolence following localized hypothalamic lesions has been interpreted by some investigators as indicating that sleep results from a preponderance of parasympathetic over sympathetic nerve activity. Certain phenomena associated with sleep, such as the decrease in the pulse rate and the blood pressure and the constriction of the pupils seem to support this point of view, but the common observation that depression of the parasympathetic nerves does not prevent sleep is incompatible with it. The assumption that the relaxation of the body which is associated with somnolence sets in when the emotional drive of the hypothalamus is suppressed or eliminated appears to afford a satisfactory explanation of sleep. The hypothalamic drive is exerted on the cerebral cortex through the thalamus as well as on the somatic parts of the body and the viscera through the brain stem and the spinal cord. The hypothalamic discharge toward the cortex undoubtedly is a factor in maintaining the waking state, but it does not appear to be essential. The activity caused by the hypothalamic discharge through the somatic and the autonomic nerves probably is the major factor in maintaining wakefulness, due to the afferent impulses that are conducted to the brain from both somatic and visceral receptors.

Most of the theories that have been advanced to account for the rhythmic recurrence of intervals of wakefulness and sleep have been based on the assumption that afferent impulses conducted from both somatic and visceral receptors tend to maintain wakefulness and that diminution of these streams of impulses is conducive to somnolence, but the cerebral cortex has generally been regarded as the chief central structure concerned. The demonstration of mechanisms in the hypothalamus that are essential for the maintenance of the waking state does not minimize the importance of afferent impulses, but it emphasizes the importance of efferent discharges from the hypothalamus and the responses elicited by them. Conduction from the hypothalamus toward the cerebral cortex probably is accomplished chiefly through the mammillothalamic tract. The downward discharge concerned with the hypothalamic drive appears to take place through pathways that traverse the lateral regions of the hypothalamus. In addition to the discharge of impulses from the hypothalamus to the cortex, facilitation by afferent impulses that do not influence the hypothalamus directly may be required to keep cortical activity above the threshold of consciousness (Harrison, 1940). Somnolence is favored by reduction in this stream of afferent impulses, but normal sleep appears to be closely associated with decreased hypothalamic activity. Salmon (1952) has emphasized the metabolic functions of the hypothalamic nuclei concerned in maintaining the waking state, and the facilitation of sleep by their functional depression.

General Visceral Functions.—The regulatory influence of the hypothalamus in the various bodily functions referred to above is exerted on visceral organs, but in part also on somatic tissues. Since the efferent innervation of the visceral organs is solely autonomic, impulses that emanate from the hypothalamus reach them only through the autonomic nerves. The somatic tissues receive hypothalamic impulses directly through extrapyramidal somatic efferent conduction pathways. Somatic tissues may also be influenced through hormonal agents liberated in consequence of autonomic stimulation. The synthesis of autonomic and cerebrospinal nerve activity into definite patterns appears to be mediated through mechanisms located in the rostral portion of the hypothalamus (Hess, 1944).

The functional regulation of the cardiovascular system, under normal physiological conditions, is mediated mainly through centers in the medulla oblongata. These mechanisms are subject to regulatory influences from higher centers and probably require such influence, particularly from the hypothalamus, for the adequate adjustment of the blood flow under various conditions of bodily activity and external temperature. The magnitude of the effect of impulses that emanate from the hypothalamus on the cardiovascular centers in the medulla oblongata is conditioned by other influences acting on these centers at the moment, such as afferent impulses from the aorta and the carotid sinuses. The hypothalamic influence is decreased during concurrent afferent stimulation from these sources and increased during afferent stimulation which tends to excite the vasomotor centers to produce a rise in blood pressure. Conversely, the effect of afferent stimulation on cardiovascular centers may be modified by impulses from the hypothalamus. Afferent impulses from the carotid sinuses and the aorta inhibit the discharge of efferent impulses through the cardiac accelerator and the vasoconstrictor nerves less effectively during a concurrent discharge of excitatory impulses from the hypothalamus, whereas the effect of peripheral afferent stimulation is increased. Hypothalamic activity, therefore, may either augment or decrease the effectiveness of afferent impulses in the reflex regulation of the cardiovascular system.

Cardiovascular responses to hypothalamic stimulation commonly are accompanied by responses in other visceral organs. Appropriate stimulation of the hypothalamus in an anesthetized animal results in increased blood pressure, dilatation of the pupils, acceleration of the respiratory movements and increased depth of respiration, increased tonus of the musculature of the urinary bladder, *etc.* Dilatation of the pupils and contraction of the vascular musculature are mediated through sympathetic nerves. Contraction of the bladder musculature is mediated through parasympathetic nerves. Both these responses are frequently associated with acceleration and increase in depth of respiration during hypothalamic stimulation.

The particular combination of responses elicited by stimulation of the hypothalamus is determined in a large measure by localization of the stimulus. Contractions of the urinary bladder associated with a decrease in the rate and depth of respiration, sometimes accompanied by a decrease in

7

blood pressure and retardation of the cardiac rate, may be elicited in cats by direct stimulation in the region just in front of the hypothalamus (Ranson, 1940). These results support the assumption that most impulses that emanate from the rostral portion of the hypothalamus reach the visceral organs through the parasympathetic nerves. Stimulation of the hypothalamus farther from the rostral border commonly elicits visceral responses mediated through sympathetic nerves, e.g., inhibition of gastro-intestinal motility and acceleration of cardiac rate, but may also result in contraction of the urinary bladder or other parasympathetic responses due to stimulation of descending pathways arising in centers the stimu-lation of which normally elicits parasympathetic responses. In general the regulatory influence of the hypothalamus on the visceral organs that is mediated through the parasympathetic nerves seems to emanate from the rostral portion and that which is mediated through the sympathetic nerves emanates from the more caudal portions, including the lateral hypothalamic regions.

A hypothalamic mechanism for the release of adrenin has long been recognized. Certain data also indicate the existence of a mechanism in the hypothalamus through which the release of adrenin is inhibited (Rogoff *et al.* 1946). Certain important differences in the responses to peripheral and to direct hypothalamic stimulation have been pointed out (Brücke, 1950), but the secretion of the adrenal medulla during rest does not differ materially from that produced during carotid sinus stimulation.

The assumption that hypothalamic mechanisms are concerned in the regulation of hemopoesis is supported by experimental data. Neutrophil leucocytosis with markedly increased phagocytic activity of the white cells due to hypothalamic stimulation has been reported (Benetato *et al.* 1945). The increased phagocytic activity appeared to be due to the release of an activating substance from the spleen. Electrical stimulation of the pos-terior region of the tuber cinereum or the mammillary bodies in unanes-thetized, unrestrained rabbits, as reported by Colfer *et al.*, (1950), resulted in lymphopenia comparable in magnitude and time relations to that caused by emotional stress.

The hypothalamic influence in sudomotor and pilomotor activity is indi-cated by the responses of the sweat glands and the erector pili muscles to emotional stimulation. The interrelationships of the hypothalamic and the hormonal influences on gastric, pancreatic and biliary functions are also recognized.

Fragmentary observations on the autonomic reactions elicited by direct stimulation of the hypothalamus in man indicate that they are com-parable to those observed in experimental animals. As reported by White (1940), electrical stimulation, under local anesthesia, of the wall of the third ventricle in the region of the paraventricular nucleus elicited abrupt acceleration of the cardiac rate and a rise in blood pressure in five conscious patients. Similar stimulation in the region of the preoptic nucleus resulted in retardation of the cardiac rate in one patient. Operative manipulation in this region regularly resulted in sudden bradycardia in seven conscious patients but no retardation of the cardiac rate in patients under atropine or ether anesthesia. Of eight patients in whom stimulation or operative manipulation of the hypothalamus resulted in bradycardia, four exhibited abrupt depression in the level of consciousness ranging from drowsiness to coma.

Hypophyseal Function.—The hypophyseal hormones play a significant rôle in the regulation of visceral functions both through their neurogenic effects and their direct influence on the activities of other endocrine glands. The functions of the posterior hypophyseal lobe are influenced directly through the hypothalamico-hypophyseal tract. The fibers of this tract terminate chiefly in the posterior lobe, but presumptive evidence that nerve impulses conducted through it also reach the anterior lobe is not wanting. Some fibers of hypothalamic origin have been traced into the anterior lobe in certain animals. In man the number of these fibers appears to be negligible.

The anterior lobe of the hypophysis seems to have a basic secretory rhythm which is regulated through hormonal products of peripheral endocrine glands. Under certain environmental conditions this rhythm may be modified by impulses that reach the hypophysis through the hypothalamico-hypophyseal tract and, probably to a lesser extent, through the cervical sympathetic nerves. The production particularly of the thyrotropic and the gonadotropic hormones is known to be influenced through these conduction pathways. The hypothalamic regulation of these hormones may be of considerable biological significance since it provides for hypothalamic regulation of certain autonomic functions through the hypophysis as well as through the peripheral autonomic nerves.

Certain functions of the hypophysis that are subject to hypothalamic regulation are not abolished by separation of the gland from the brain. For example, the adrenal cortical response to acute stress is not abolished by section of the infundibulum. The prompt release of adrenocorticotropic hormone in the hypophysis, therefore, is not dependent on nerve impulses of hypothalamic origin (Cheng *et al.* 1949).

The neurosecretory function of the hypothalamus has been recognized by various investigators. Data reported by Bargmann (1949) appear to support the assumption that the hypothalamico-hypophyseal tract serves as a pathway for the displacement of secretory granules from the supraoptic nucleus into the hypophysis and the third ventricle.

CORTICAL INFLUENCE IN AUTONOMIC FUNCTIONS AND EMOTIONAL BEHAVIOR

The concept of general autonomic representation in the cerebral cortex rests on the results of many experimental studies involving both stimulation and ablation of cortical areas in animals, including primates, and abundant clinical observations. Certain parts of the cerebral cortex, including the premotor area, the frontal eye fields and limited areas in the parietal and the occipital lobes, appear to subserve both visceral and somatic functions. They undoubtedly serve to correlate visceral and somatic activities. Other cortical areas appear to be concerned chiefly or exclusively with visceral functions. They include the hippocampus, the amygdaloid area, the rostral portion of the temporal lobe, the rostral portion of the insula and the subcallosal and the cingulate gyri. These areas form a continuous cortical ring on the medial and the inferior surfaces of each cerebral hemisphere. They have been collectively designated the mesopallium (Yakovlev, 1948). They undoubtedly exert their influence chiefly through the hypothalamus and other subcortical autonomic centers. They probably play a major rôle in determining the patterns of visceral activity and the visceral components of emotional behavior.

In general cortical areas that are chiefly concerned with specific autonomic functions are functionally related to cortical areas through which corresponding somatic functions are regulated. For example, stimulation of the motor area for the face and the tongue elicits salivation, and stimulation of the motor eye fields elicits lacrimation.

The influence of the cerebral cortex on visceral functions appears to be predominantly inhibitory. Direct stimulation of the cortex in intact animals sometimes elicits autonomic activation, but more commonly it elicits autonomic inhibition. The exaggerated autonomic activity commonly observed following cortical lesions or ablation of cortical areas that are concerned with visceral functions undoubtedly is due to the release of the subcortical autonomic centers concerned from the inhibitory influence of the cortex. Cats deprived of all cortex except that which is concerned primarily with visceral functions are extremely docile. When major portions of the cortex on the medial and the inferior surfaces of the hemispheres, including the hippocampus, are removed the animals exhibit behavior resembling sham rage even in response to relatively mild stimulation. If only the hippocampus and the amygdala are removed, leaving the remaining cortex intact, the rage reactions which ensue give evidence of voluntary direction (Bard and Mountcastle, 1948). In primates, ablation of the rostral portion of the cingulate gyrus results in behavior which exhibits reduced reactions of fear and anger and a lack of consciousness of the social consequences of actions (Ward, 1948). Such behavior is somewhat analogous to that which has been observed in some human subjects following undercutting of this cortical area. The alterations observed in the functioning of various visceral organs in human subjects following frontal lobotomies emphasize the importance of the frontal cortex in the regulation of visceral functions. The observed alterations in emotional reactions also emphasize its influence in determining behavior patterns. On the basis of a study of schizophrenic patients who had been treated by frontal lobotomy, Buck *et al.* (1951) concluded that the preoperative abnormalities in these patients represented the disturbing influence of the prefrontal cortex on subcortical autonomic centers.

On the basis of an extensive study of the visceral effects of direct cortical stimulation in man, Penfield and Rasmussen (1950) concluded that the digestive functions, including swallowing and gastro-intestinal motility, taste and gastro-intestinal sensitivity are extensively represented in the cortex on the convex surfaces of the cerebral hemispheres and the insula. The cardiovascular, the sudomotor and the pilomotor systems do not appear to be strongly influenced by impulses that arise in these cortical areas. Stimulation of the rostral portion of the cingulate gyrus bilaterally in man, according to Pool and Ransohoff (1949), resulted in alterations in respiration, pulse rate and blood pressure.

The cingulate and pyriform cortical areas constitute a significant part of the neural substratum of emotional behavior that involves both visceral and somatic reactions. Both areas are intimately related to the hippocampus through abundant fiber connections. These connections provide an anatomical basis for the assumption that the hippocampus and the fornix form part of a circuit through which a functional cycle is maintained between the hypothalamus and the neocortex. As outlined by Clark and Meyer (1950), this circuit appears to be made up of the hippocampus, the fornix, the mammillary body, the mammillothalamic tract, the anterior thalamic nuclei, the cingulate gyrus and the cingulum (Fig. 27).

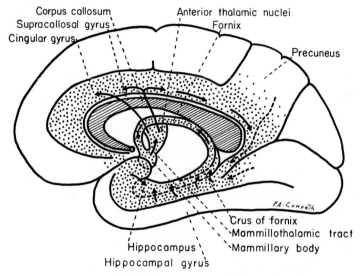

Corpus callosum   Anterior thalamic nuclei
Supracallosal gyrus   Fornix
Cingular gyrus
Precuneus
Crus of fornix
Mammillothalamic tract
Mammillary body
Hippocampus
Hippocampal gyrus

Fig. 27.—Diagram illustrating anatomical relationships of components of a functional cycle including hippocampus, fornix, mammillary body, mammillothalamic tract, anterior thalamic nuclei, cingulate gyrus and cingulum.

Although this circuit is anatomically and functionally complete, it is not to be regarded as closed since the neuron aggregates included in it receive impulses from various sources. For example, the mammillary body is connected through the mammillary peduncle with various levels in the brain stem, and through internuclear fibers with adjacent parts of the hypothalamus and the thalamus. It is also connected with the frontal cortex through direct fronto-hypothalamic pathways. Impulses conducted into the cingulate cortex may also be influenced through associational connections by the activity of other cortical areas. The abundant connections of the hypothalamus with both the paleocortex and the neocortex that have been demonstrated appear to be ample to provide for the integration of primitive neural processes, such as those that are associated with instinctive urges and emotional reactions, with cortical activity carried out at the highest functional levels.

Chapter V

GENERAL PHYSIOLOGY (Continued)

THE AUTONOMIC NERVOUS SYSTEM IN RELATION TO THE ENDOCRINE GLANDS

FUNCTIONAL interdependence of the autonomic nervous system and the endocrine glands is demonstrated by many physiological phenomena. This relationship is deep seated and may be regarded as a result of long-continued evolutionary processes. The most primitive forms of animal life respond chiefly to chemical stimuli. Such responses are inadequate to meet the needs of higher animals. The development of a nervous system through which rapid conduction and widespread coördination can be accomplished is a comparatively late event in evolution. In all the higher animals, reactions to environmental factors and the regulatory control of the internal organs are dominated by the nervous system, but chemical stimulants play an important rôle in the functional regulation of the internal organs. As differentiation advanced, the chemical stimulants became concentrated and specialized in the ductless glands and there arose a reciprocal relationship between these glands and the innervation of the internal organs through which a delicate balance of the vital functions is maintained. The first purpose for which rapid conduction and coördination became vital is self-preservation. By virtue of the wide distribution of efferent impulses made possible by the synaptic connections of a single preganglionic fiber with many ganglionic neurons and the chemical mediation of nerve impulses, particularly at the neuro-effector junctions (see p. 108), the autonomic nervous system is adapted for rapid and widespread reactions. In these reactions the endocrine glands are stimulated through the autonomic nerves. The endocrine secretory products in turn augment the responses called forth through the autonomic nerves.

The Adrenals.—Langley's generalization that the effect of adrenin on any part of the body is the same as the effect of stimulation of its sympathetic nerves expresses one of the fundamental reciprocal relationships of nervous and chemical stimuli. Although there are certain exceptions to this generalization, it may be stated that sympathetic stimulation commonly excites the secretion of adrenin and augments the reactivity of the sympathetic nerves to stimulation.

The amount of adrenin in the circulating blood is increased by sympathetic stimulation. It is also increased during emotional stimulation. The influence of adrenin on the resistance of voluntary muscle to fatigue has long been known. It does not lower the threshold of stimulation for normal muscle, but it promptly increases the irritability of fatigued muscle even when a rise in blood pressure is prevented. It also plays an essential rôle in mobilizing stored carbohydrate, thus increasing the sugar content of the blood. The distribution of the blood to the heart, the lungs, the central nervous system, the limbs and the abdominal organs is strongly influenced by the secretory activity of the adrenal glands. In general, an increase in the volume of blood flowing through the skeletal muscles is accompanied by a decrease in the volume supplied to the abdominal viscera. This reciprocal relationship, according to Cannon (1915), "is associated with some of the most primitive experiences in the life of higher organisms, experiences common to all, both man and beast, the elementary experiences of pain, fear and rage, that come suddenly in critical emergencies."

In a study of the influence of motion and emotion on the secretion of adrenin, Cannon and Britton (1927) confirmed the conclusion, based on the results of earlier studies of Cannon and his associates, that muscular activity and emotional excitement result in an increase in the output of adrenin. Taking the increased rate of the denervated heart as a rough measure of the increase of adrenin in the blood, they found that the output of adrenin was increased by even minor bodily movements. Extending the limbs or turning the body of a cat with denervated heart, in their experiments, was accompanied by an increase in the heart-rate of 5 to 10 beats per minute. Walking increased the rate 10 to 20 beats. When the adrenal glands were inactivated, the same activities were accompanied by only slight acceleration or no change in the heart-rate. Emotional excitement resulted in an even greater increase in the rate of the denervated heart. The same excitement of the same animals, following inactivation of the adrenal glands, resulted in only slight acceleration or no change in heart-rate. Great emotional excitement plus vigorous activity, in cats with denervated heart, caused an increase in the heart-rate of 30 to 80 beats per minute while the adrenals were intact, but usually only 8 beats or less followed inactivation of the adrenal glands. In view of these results, they suggested that "the increased secretion of adrenin accompanying incidental and routine muscular movements such as walking, its greater concentration in the blood during muscular exercise and its abundant outpouring as a consequence of vigorous struggle emphasize the probable significance of adrenin for efficient use of muscles in the body."

An augmenting effect of adrenin on the discharge of glycogen from muscle tissue has been amply demonstrated. The amount discharged due to large doses of adrenin usually exceeds the amount discharged due to sympathetic stimulation. The data relative to the effect of adrenin on the discharge of glycogen from skeletal muscles support the assumption that the discharge due to sympathetic stimulation is mediated through the adrenin-like substance, sympathin, liberated as a result of sympathetic nerve stimulation. Summation of the effects of sympathetic nerve impulses, adrenin and sympathin has also been demonstrated.

The injection of adrenin into the blood stream usually results in a rise in blood pressure, but in high dilutions it may, under certain conditions, result in a fall in blood pressure. Elimination of the normal output of adrenin by ligation of the adrenal vessels does not necessarily result in an appreciable fall in blood pressure for a period of at least several hours, as should be expected if the sympathetic nerves were kept in tonus by adrenin. In certain animals (cats and dogs), the administration of adrenin in appropriate dosage may result in inhibition of gastro-intestinal peristalsis without causing a rise in blood pressure.

If the blood pressure were maintained by a constant minimal discharge of adrenin, as has been assumed by many, any increase in the quantity of this substance should result in a rise in blood pressure. Very dilute solutions may be injected without any effect on blood pressure. When the rate of injection of such a dilute solution is increased, the threshold of stimulation is reached and the blood pressure, instead of rising, falls. On the basis of this observation, Hoskins and McClure (1912) advanced the opinion that if the adrenals exert a constant effect by continuous secretion of adrenin it must be a depressor effect.

On the basis of extensive experimental data, Hoskins (1927) advanced the opinion that adrenin "consistently and generally exerts a biphasic effect as it has been shown to do in cases of intestinal peristalsis, uterine contractions, and blood vessels in muscles. In that case it would serve, under ordinary conditions, if present at all, as a sympathetic sedative, as does calcium, another normal constituent of the blood. Under other conditions its stimulating effect would come into play." Although this view may seem paradoxical, it is not incompatible with the experimental data which indicate only a stimulating effect of adrenin. It also conforms to Verworn's theory that inhibition is due to subminimal stimulation. Inhibitory effects of adrenin on reactions mediated through sympathetic nerves, under experimental conditions, have also been reported by other investigators.

Some of the observed inhibitory reactions to adrenin probably can be explained most satisfactorily on the basis of the known inhibitory effects of adrenin on cholinergic mechanisms. For example, the reflex inhibition of parasympathetic tonus in the reflex dilatation of the pupil elicited by afferent nerve stimulation is increased by the presence of adrenin. The inhibitory effects of reflex stimulation on the parasympathetically innervated sympathectomized pupil also are increased, and the secretory activity of the normally innervated sweat glands is diminished. The assumption that the transmission of nerve impulses due to submaximal stimuli applied to preganglionic fibers is facilitated by small amounts of adrenin and depressed by larger amounts is supported by abundant experimental data. The liberation of adrenin in small amounts in autonomic ganglia due to preganglionic stimulation has also been demonstrated. The potentiating effect on acetylcholine transmission in autonomic ganglia of the adrenin liberated due to preganglionic stimulation has been emphasized by Burn (1945) on the basis of an exhaustive review of the literature bearing on the relation of adrenin to acetycholine in the nervous system.

The Thyroid Gland.—Functional interrelationships of the thyroid gland and the autonomic nerves, including the hypothalamic autonomic centers, have been amply demonstrated, but the mechanisms through which the thyroid is influenced by autonomic nerve impulses and those through which the thyroid influences autonomic nerve activity are not fully known. Certain anatomical data support the assumption that sympathetic nerve fibers actually make functional contacts with thyroid cells, but there is no complete agreement on this point. Thyroid activity is known to be influenced by stimulation of the cervical sympathetic nerves. It is also subject to hypothalamic influences due to the effect of impulses emanating from the hypothalamus on the production of the thyrotropic hormone secreted in the anterior lobe of the hypophysis. The integrity of either the peripheral autonomic nerves or the hypothalamico-hypophyseal tract is not essential for continued thyroid function, but the response of the thyroid to certain conditions of stress, such as exposure to cold, is impaired following bilateral extirpation of the cervical portion of the sympathetic trunk and completely abolished following section of the hypophyseal stalk. The thyrotropic activity of the hypophysis is also influenced by thyroxin produced in the thyroid gland. This influence appears to be exerted through the hypothalamus. Compensatory hypertrophy of the thyroid tissue following subtotal thyroidectomy is diminished in animals in which the hypophyseal stalk has been sectioned. Under normal physiological conditions the thyrotropic hormone undoubtedly plays a more significant rôle in the regulation of thyroid function than impulses conducted through the cervical sympathetic nerves. The influence of these nerves in the regulation of the flow of blood through the thyroid gland undoubtedly is a factor in its secretory activity. The functional state of the thyroid gland is a major factor in determining the basal metabolic rate. Its functional state in turn is influenced by the activity of the adrenal glands and the sympathetic nerves. Stimulation of the cervical sympathetic nerves frequently, but not consistently, results in elevation of the basal metabolic rate. Bilateral extirpation of the cervical portion of the sympathetic trunk in experimental animals usually results in depression of the basal metabolic rate. Repeated injections of adrenin increasingly augment the irritability of the sympathetic nerves regardless of the functional condition of the thyroid. The administration of thyroxin in large doses results in sympathetic hyperirritability due to an increased output of adrenin. The effect of the thyroid secretion on sympathetic irritability, particularly under conditions of hyperthyroidism, appears to be due to its stimulating effect on the adrenal glands. Certain data support the assumption that thyroxin in the circulating blood may also exert a direct influence on the tissue elements. The elevation of the metabolic rate that occurs in response to cold disappears after thyroidectomy, but not immediately. The response, furthermore, may be restored by the administration of thyroxin. It may be concluded, therefore, that temperature regulation does not require an active thyroid that reacts to instant cold stimulation by increased secretory activity (Gregeley, 1943).

The Parathyroid Glands.—The neural regulation of the secretory activity of the parathyroid glands has not been demonstrated. An effect of the parathyroid hormone on the reactivity of the sympathetic nerves is suggested by certain experimental data. Dogs that had developed typical parathyroid tetanus following parathyroidectomy, as reported by Hoskins and Wheelon (1914), exhibited unmistakable evidence of increased sympathetic irritability in their reactions both to adrenin and to nicotine. The visceral manifestations of parathyroid deficiency, such as anorexia, diarrhea and cardiovascular disturbances also suggest a functional interrelationship of the parathyroids and the autonomic nerves. These phenomena, like the neuromuscular hyperirritability that results from para-thyroid insufficiency probably are causally related to faulty calcium metab-olism. The major functions of the parathyroids appear to be concerned with the regulation of calcium metabolism.

The Pancreas.—The internal secretory activity of the pancreas may go on independently of nerve impulses. The assumption that the production of insulin is subject to neural regulation in some degree is supported by experimental data. Such regulatory control is exerted chiefly through the parasympathetic nerves. A greater influence appears to be exerted on the islet tissue through the right vagus nerve than through the left. The pro-duction of insulin may also be influenced through the sympathetic nerves due to their regulatory control of the flow of blood through the pancreatic islets. The existence of centers in the brain stem that are concerned with the neural regulation of carbohydrate metabolism and of the blood sugar level does not imply the existence of a specific center for the regulation of insulin production.

An influence of insulin on the reactivity of the parasympathetic nerves is amply demonstrated. Injection of insulin commonly results in decreased cardiac and respiratory rates and increased susceptibility to shock. These effects cannot be explained as the results of hypoglycemia since they also occur when glucose is administered simultaneously with the insulin. Sali-vation, increased gastric secretory activity and gastro-intestinal motility, following the administration of insulin, also indicate increased para-sympathetic irritability. No marked effect of insulin on sympathetic nerve activity has been demonstrated.

The Hypophysis.—The dependence of certain of the functions of the pars nervosa of the hypophysis on impulses emanating from the hypo-thalamus is evidenced by the effects of hypothalamic lesions or interruption of the hypothalamico-hypophyseal tract particularly on carbohydrate and water metabolism. (See p. 91). Certain of the hormones produced in the pars nervosa also influence autonomic nerve functions.

The effect of pituitrin on the contractions of smooth muscle is well known. A direct action of posterior hypophyseal hormones on the auto-nomic nerves has not been demonstrated beyond question, but it may be inferred from the antagonistic effects of posterior hypophyseal extract and insulin. The administration of posterior hypophyseal extract tends to bring about hyperglycemia or reduce the hypoglycemia resulting from the administration of insulin. Since insulin must be regarded as a para-sympathetic stimulant, these facts suggest that the posterior hypophyseal secretion includes a sympathetic stimulant. The augmenting effect of posterior hypophyseal hormones on basal metabolism and the mobilization of sugar also supports this assumption.

The assumption that impulses emanating from the hypothalamus play a rôle in the functional regulation of the pars distalis of the hypophysis is supported by both clinical and experimental data. Appropriate electrical stimulation of the hypothalamus results in the release of gonadotropic hormone from the anterior hypophyseal lobe. Section of the hypophyseal stalk also results in slight disturbances of anterior hypophyseal functions, but the integrity of the hypothalamico-hypophyseal tract is not essential for adequate functioning of the anterior lobe in animals living under ordinary conditions. Cytological changes in the anterior lobe following stalk section have been reported, but identical changes have also been observed following thyroidectomy and after injections of thyroxin or oestrin. The regulatory control of the anterior lobe is mediated chiefly through hormonal substances, but its functional rhythm may be modified, due to certain environmental situations, by impulses which reach it through the hypophyseal stalk and through the cervical sympathetic nerves.

Sympathetic nerve activity is influenced indirectly by several hormones of hypophyseal origin through their stimulating effects on the adrenal medulla. The adrenotropic hormone appears to act directly on the adrenal medullary tissue to increase the output of adrenin which in turn results in increased sympathetic nerve reactivity. The thyrotropic hormone by its stimulating effect on thyroid activity tends to increase the output of thyroxin which in turn exerts a stimulating effect on the adrenal medulla. Adrenergic neurohumoral links between the hypophysis and the sex glands have also been pointed out.

The Gonads.—The assumption that there is a special functional interrelationship between the ovaries and the autonomic nerves, although long prevalent, is supported by little direct evidence. It is based chiefly on the assumption that the well-known vasomotor instability that often arises at the climacteric is due to the subsidence of the ovarian hormones and the clinical observation that the vasomotor instability in question, in many instances, has been ameliorated by the administration of ovarian preparations. Experimental data also indicate that in dogs the responses to sympathetic stimulation are materially increased following removal of the ovaries (Hoskins and Wheelon, 1914). In experiments reported by Nowakowski (1950) hypothalamic stimulation close to the infundibulum in female rabbits caused ovulation in 85 per cent of the trials. The same response was not obtained following transection of the spinal cord.

During every cycle in the activity of the female reproductive system there is a phase of relatively slow growth of the uterine mucosa, during which the basal metabolism remains at a more or less constant low level, and a phase during which the basal metabolic rate is higher. The former phase seems to be dominated by the activity of the corpus luteum. The latter is initiated with the regression of the corpus luteum. If the assumption that the parasympathetic system subserves conservative functions be correct, it may be assumed that the corpus luteum acts synergistically with the parasympathetic nerves.

A functional interrelationship between the male sex glands and the autonomic nerves is suggested by certain experimental data. The results of quantitative studies on rats reported by Hoskins (1925) and Richter and Wislocki (1928) show that castration actually results in three- to fourfold psychomotor retardation. The direct effect of castration on either division of the autonomic system is not brought out by the results of these studies. The results of experiments carried out on dogs, reported by Wheelon (1914) and Wheelon and Shipley (1916), show clearly that the sympathetic nerves become materially less sensitive to stimulation following castration and that sympathetic irritability is restored in a large measure following successful testicular grafts.

CHEMICAL MEDIATION OF AUTONOMIC NERVE IMPULSES

The Chemical Mediators.—The concept of chemical mediation of nerve impulses is based on the results of numerous experimental studies. The humoral substances are liberated at the neuro-effector junctions or near them and at the synaptic junctions in the autonomic ganglia and within the central nervous system.

The possibility of chemical mediation of nerve impulses was suggested by the pioneer work of Elliott (1905) on medulli-adrenal secretion. Little progress was made in this field until Loewi (1921) reported the results of experiments on frogs in which he demonstrated that a perfusion fluid passing through the heart acquires a new property depending on the character of the nerve impulses dominating the heart at the moment. This new property was indicated by the effect of the perfusion fluid on a second frog's heart through which it was passed in the absence of nerve stimulation. When the first heart was under the influence of sympathetic stimulation, the second was also accelerated. When the first was under the influence of parasympathetic stimulation, the second also was inhibited, *i.e.*, the perfusion fluid acquired the capacity to transmit to the second heart the effect of the nervous stimulation of the first prevailing at the moment. The substances liberated into the circulating medium by which these effects are brought about also exert the typical sympathetic and parasympathetic effects respectively on other visceral organs. In experiments reported by Finkleman (1930), Ringer's solution allowed to flow over a pulsating piece of rabbit's intestine, still supplied with its mesenteric nerves, acquired a new property when the nerves were stimulated which could be demonstrated by allowing the solution to flow over a second piece of pulsating intestine. If the first piece is inhibited by sympathetic stimulation, the second piece also is inhibited by the action of the Ringer's solution flowing over it. In experiments in which the heart and the adrenal glands have been denervated and the spinal cord severed in the cervical region, according to Bacq and Brouha (1932), peripheral stimulation of the sciatic or the brachial nerves regularly is followed by acceleration of the cardiac rate due to the direct action on the heart of a substance which is liberated at the periphery, due to nerve impulses set up in the postganglionic sympathetic fibers, and reaches the heart through the circulating blood. Stimulation of the hepatic nerves or the abdominal sympathetic trunks also results in the liberation of a sympathomimetic substance which elicits responses in the denervated heart. These findings have been corroborated by experimental data reported by other investigators.

Stimulation of preganglionic fibers results in the liberation in the ganglia in which they make synaptic contacts of a chemical substance that has the capacity to activate the ganglion cells. The assumption that the transmission of nerve impulses in the central autonomic centers is mediated by chemical substances liberated at the synapses is amply supported by experimental data. On the basis of the pertinent data, Rosenblueth (1934) advanced the following hypothesis: "Nerve impulses impinging on a neuron give rise to *quanta* of excitatory (c.e.s.) or inhibitory (c.i.s.) substances, according to the differential structures within the cell on which they act.

Both c.e.s. and c.i.s. are destroyed at a rate proportional to the concentration. For a steady input and at equilibrium the concentrations of c.e.s. and c.i.s. are proportional to the rate of bombardment of the neuron by nerve impulses. C.e.s. attains supraliminal values; this explains after discharge. The rate of discharge of impulses by the neuron is proportional to the concentration of c.e.s. The output from a center is, therefore, proportional to the excitatory input. C.i.s. combines with c.e.s., inactivating the latter."

The chemical mediator liberated at the periphery in response to sympathetic stimulation exhibits properties similar to those of adrenin, but it is not identical with that hormone. Since it is produced under the influence of sympathetic nerve stimulation in tissues other than the adrenal medulla and other chromaffin cells, Cannon (1932) proposed that it be called "sympathin." Having determined the threshold stimuli for sympathin and for medulli-adrenal secretion respectively, using the nictitating membrane as an indicator, Rosenblueth and Cannon (1932) found that the simultaneous discharge of both sympathin and adrenin, in response to the threshold stimuli, produced a greatly augmented contraction of the nictitating membrane. The effects of the two substances, consequently, are additive. Cannon (1932) also demonstrated that sympathin enters the blood stream and is carried to distant organs in the circulating blood. According to his account, stimulation of the sympathetic fibers distributed to the erector pili muscles in the tail caused a slow increase in blood pressure and heart-rate which reached its maximum in two or three minutes and then gradually returned to the former level in a preparation in which the heart was denervated and the adrenals and the liver were excluded from action.

Certain data reported by Rosenblueth (1932) seem to support the hypothesis that every quantal autonomic nerve impulse results in the liberation of a quantal amount of chemical mediator substance; consequently, the concentration of this substance depends on the frequency of the nerve impulses. Since its destruction takes place at a limited rate, it may diffuse to other structures whenever its concentration exceeds this limit. He further advanced the hypothesis that the substance in question combines with some substance in the effector and that the response is proportional to the concentration of the combined substances.

In an effort to explain the difference between sympathin and adrenin and between the sympathins derived from different sources, and to account for the excitatory and the inhibitory effects of adrenin in organs that are similar in structure and in function, Cannon and Rosenblueth (1933) advanced the theory of two sympathins. The substance liberated in smooth muscle while it is contracting in response to sympathetic stimulation they called sympathin E. The one liberated in smooth muscle that is inhibited by sympathetic stimulation they called sympathin I. They postulated that the chemical mediator is modified in one of two ways at the neuro-effector junction. Effectors that are activated by adrenin contain a receptive substance that leads to the formation of sympathin E. Effectors that are inhibited by adrenin contain a receptive substance that leads to the formation of sympathin I. The concept of two sympathins has been a fruitful one, but certain data available at present appear to be incompatible with the hypothesis of purely excitatory and purely inhibitory sympathins (von Euler, 1951).

The chemical substance liberated in the frog's heart due to vagus nerve stimulation in Loewi's early experiments was designated by him the "vagus substance." Since the same substance is commonly liberated at the neuro-effector junction when parasympathetic nerves are stimulated, it has been called parasympathin. It has the properties of acetylcholine and probably is identical with that substance. Its action is strictly local since it is promptly inactivated by the blood. It cannot, therefore, reach distant effectors through the circulating blood. The concept of the localized action of parasympathin is compatible with the assumptions that as a rule the parasympathetic nerves distribute directly to the tissues innervated and that they are organized for relatively localized action rather than for such diffuse effects as are elicited by sympathetic stimulation, particularly when the sympathetic nerves are activated by discharges from the hypothalamus.

Certain organs whose efferent innervation is solely sympathetic react to certain chemical agents as would be expected if they were innervated through parasympathetic nerves. The chemical mediator liberated as a result of stimulation of the sympathetic nerves concerned also possesses the properties of parasympathin. Stimulation of certain parasympathetic nerves also results in the liberation of a chemical substance probably identical with sympathin. These facts seemed to call for a classification of autonomic nerve fibers based on the nature of the chemical mediators associated with them rather than on their anatomical connections. Accordingly, Dale (1933) proposed that fibers whose stimulation results in liberation of sympathin, or an adrenin-like mediator, be designated as adrenergic, and that those whose stimulation results in liberation of parasympathin, or an acetylcholine-like mediator, be designated as cholinergic. The almost universal adoption of these terms may be regarded as evidence of their appropriateness and the need which they have met. In view of the rôle of the chemical mediators in the transmission of nerve impulses and the finding that adrenergic neurons contain adrenin but not acetylcholine, whereas cholinergic neurons contain acetylcholine but not adrenin, the classification of autonomic nerve fibers in adrenergic and cholinergic categories is more significant than their classification according to sympathetic or parasympathetic origin.

The hypothesis that autonomic nerve impulses result in the liberation of chemical mediators, that these mediators act upon the autonomic effectors to evoke characteristic responses, and that the intensity of the response is proportional to the concentration of the mediator is quite generally accepted. There is no general agreement relative to the mode of action of the mediators or whether transmission by chemical mediators is the only mode of transmission at the neuroeffector junctions. The adrenergic and the cholinergic mediators appear to act independently on the effector organs, but when adrenergic and cholinergic nerves that tend to produce opposite effects are stimulated simultaneously the response is the resultant of the two influences (Rosenblueth, 1950).

The chemical mediator liberated in the autonomic ganglia when the preganglionic fibers are stimulated exhibits the properties of acetylcholine. It probably is identical with the substance liberated at the neuroeffector junctions when cholinergic postganglionic fibers are stimulated. The hypothesis that this substance is acetylcholine and that it is concerned in the transmission of impulses from the preganglionic fibers to the ganglion cells is amply supported by experimental data. The theory of chemical transmission at the synaptic junctions implies that the amounts of acetylcholine released at the synapses by the nerve impulses are sufficient to activate the ganglion cells. If the stimuli are applied to the preganglionic fibers at frequencies much higher than the threshold rate, the output of acetylcholine per nerve impulse decreases progressively. Prolonged stimulation of preganglionic fibers at moderate frequencies results first in a decrease but later in an increase in the ouptut of acetylcholine per nerve impulse. The acetylcholine liberated is destroyed by cholinesterase rapidly enough so that its concentration at the end of the refractory period of the ganglion cell is below the threshold. The time required for the destruction by cholinesterase of the acetylcholine released by a nerve impulse is longer than the refractory period of the postsynaptic unit. If a nerve impulse arrives at the synapse before the acetylcholine released by the preceding impulse is completely destroyed, the new quantum of the mediator is summated with that which remains of the previous output. The concentration of the mediator will, therefore, be increased by a series of impulses at relatively high frequency. If an anticholinesterase has been administered, the concentration of the mediator may be increased even during stimulation of relatively low frequency.

Certain electrical phenomena associated with synaptic transmission are not fully explained by the chemical theory of nerve transmission. Certain aspects of transmission at the synapse cannot be explained satisfactorily by either the chemical or the electrical theory. On the basis of the available data, Rosenblueth (1950) has advanced the conclusion that the phenomenon of synaptic transmission can be accounted for more completely on the basis of the chemical theory than on that of the electrical theory. Either theory alone appears to be inadequate. Acetylcholine appears to be the essential transmitter, but K ions appear to play an accessory role. Certain of the electrical phenomena also appear to be concerned in determining the release of acetylcholine.

Sensitization of Denervated Tissues to Chemical Mediators. — Tissues that have been deprived of their normal innervation become increasingly sensitive to chemical stimuli. On the basis of extensive studies of his own and those of other workers, Cannon (1939) formulated the law of denervation as follows: "When in a series of efferent neurons a unit is destroyed, an increased irritability to chemical agents develops in the isolated structure or structures, the effect being maximal in the part directly denervated."

This law is well illustrated in the sensitivity changes that take place in smooth muscles and glands following section of either the postganglionic or the preganglionic sympathetic fibers. For example, Meltzer and Auer (1904) observed, in rabbits and cats, that one or two days after removal of the superior cervical ganglion a selected dose of adrenin caused marked dilatation of the pupil and constriction of the blood vessels of the ear on the operated side but had no effect on the other side. Sensitization of the vascular musculature in a sympathectomized extremity to adrenin in the circulating blood has been reported by various investigators. In cases of Raynaud's disease sympathetic denervation by means of ganglionectomy may abolish vascular spasm but the vascular musculature becomes exquisitely sensitive to adrenin in the circulating blood. The sensitization is less marked if paralysis of the vasomotor nerves is effected by section of the preganglionic fibers, leaving the ganglion cells with their axons intact, than when the vascular musculature is denervated by extirpation of the sympathetic ganglia. The increased sensitivity of the vascular musculature following sympathectomy reaches its maximum in 8 to 10 days and then gradually subsides and may disappear completely (Simmons and Sheehan, 1939).

Smooth muscle which is normally inhibited by sympathetic stimulation undergoes a corresponding change in sensitivity to adrenin following interruption of its sympathetic innervation. For example, a portion of the intestine long deprived of its sympathetic nerves is more persistently inhibited by adrenin than a freshly denervated portion. The musculature of the sympathectomized non-pregnant cat's uterus reacts in a similar manner.

Interruption of the parasympathetic innervation of smooth muscle likewise is followed by increased sensitivity of the muscle to parasympathomimetic substances. Smooth muscle innervated by cholinergic sympathetic fibers becomes hypersensitive to acetylcholine following degeneration of these fibers. Glands, the functional activity of which is regulated through their innervation, also exhibit increased responsiveness to chemical stimuli following denervation.

Both smooth muscles and glands become more highly sensitive, following autonomic denervation, to certain other chemical agents as well as to hormonal substances which are their natural stimulants. The autonomic ganglion cells likewise exhibit increased sensitivity, following section of the preganglionic fibers, to acetylcholine and other cholinergic substances. The mechanism of sensitization of denervated effector organs to adrenin or acetylcholine is not fully understood. The most plausible explanation that has been advanced is based on the assumption that the permeability of the surface membranes of the effector cells is increased following interruption of their nerve supply. This point of view is supported by the fact that the increased sensitivity is not absolutely specific for adrenin and acetylcholine but also exists in some degree to other stimulating agents. For example, the denervated nictitating membrane is sensitized not only to adrenin but also to acetylcholine, pilocarpine, histamine and potassium ions. It is further supported by the fact that the electrical potential accompanying the contraction of smooth muscle is decreased following denervation, probably due to diminished polarization of the cell membranes resulting from increased cell permeability.

ACTION OF DRUGS IN RELATION TO THE SYMPATHETIC AND THE PARASYMPATHETIC NERVES

Studies involving the action of various pharmacological agents on the organs innervated through the autonomic nerves have contributed greatly to our knowledge of the functional relationships of these nerves. Certain poisons, *e.g.*, nicotine, affect both the sympathetic and the parasympathetic nerves in essentially the same manner. Other pharmacological agents exert a specific action on tissues innervated by either adrenergic or cholinergic fibers, but they do not influence both adrenergic and cholinergic functions. Adrenin and certain other substances produce effects that, with certain exceptions, are similar to the effects produced by stimulating adrenergic nerves. Pilocarpine, muscarine, physostigmine and choline usually produce effects that are similar to those produced by stimulating cholinergic nerves. Ergotoxine and ergotamine first stimulate adrenergic nerves, then block conduction to the effector organs innervated by them. Atropine exerts the same effect on effector organs innervated through cholinergic nerves. These facts indicate a fundamental chemical difference between adrenergic and cholinergic neurons. They also have an important bearing on the action of hormones on the tissues.

The essential functional relationship between the preganglionic and the ganglionic neurons was discovered by the use of nicotine. Langley first observed that when a nicotine solution is applied to an autonomic ganglion, regardless of whether it belongs to the sympathetic or the parasympathetic division of the autonomic system, stimulation of the preganglionic fibers is no longer effective, although stimulation of the postganglionic fibers still elicits the characteristic response. Similar results were also obtained when a weak solution of nicotine was injected into the blood stream. He, therefore, concluded that nicotine acts on the synaptic connections of the preganglionic axons with the ganglionic neurons to prevent conduction through these neuron junctions. Bayliss and Starling (1899) observed the same effect of small doses of nicotine on the visceral efferent chains that supply the gastro-intestinal musculature. This result led them to conclude that all effects of the vagus nerves on the enteric musculature are completely abolished by minimal doses of nicotine (0.3 cc. of a 1 per cent solution). This observation has been corroborated by many later investigators. As reported by Thomas and Kuntz (1926), when nicotine is administered in gradually increasing doses stimulation of the vagus nerves again becomes effective when 25 to 50 mgm. per kilo. of body weight has been administered. In their experiments, still larger doses of nicotine (50 to 500 mgm. per kilo.) further augmented the responses of the intestinal muscle to vagus stimulation so that the amplitude of the contractions in response to the same stimulus became greater than before nicotine was administered. Massive doses of nicotine (2000 mgm. or over per kilo.) finally caused paralysis of the intestinal vagi from which they did not recover during the period of observation.

Pharmacological agents that influence autonomic functions act primarily on the tissues innervated by the autonomic nerves either to stimulate or to depress the functions of the effector cells. These substances are

8

so numerous and their actions are so complex that their classification and an analysis of their actions cannot be undertaken in this connection.

HOMEOSTASIS

The living tissues of the body are not directly exposed to the external environment. They exist in a liquid matrix, the internal environment, which is normally maintained in a more or less constant state. The constancy of the internal environment, or homeostasis, requires the functional integrity of the sympathetic division of the autonomic nervous system (Cannon, 1930). Elimination of the sympathetic nerves is not incompatible with life under favorable conditions, but it results in certain functional defects that are more marked in some species than in others. Animals have been kept alive and apparently in good health for many months following complete surgical removal of both sympathetic trunks. The functional defects resulting from complete sympathetic denervation are apparent particularly in the decreased capacity of the animals to withstand high and low external temperatures, lowering of the basal metabolic rate, diminished resistance to anoxemia, increasing sensitivity to injected insulin and diminished capacity for compensatory reactions to successive hemorrhages.

Cats that have been subjected to complete sympathetic denervation exhibit a greater rise in body temperature than normal animals when placed in a superheated environment (40° C.). When placed in a cold room their body temperature is markedly decreased, whereas normal animals in the same environment usually respond with a slight rise in body temperature. In atmosphere in which the oxygen tension is reduced to 6 to 8 per cent, sympathectomized animals collapse much earlier than normal ones. In experiments reported by Sawyer *et al.* (1933), both sympathectomized and normal cats responded to large doses of insulin (0.5 unit per kg.) with a rapid decrease in blood sugar to nearly the level at which the symptoms of hypoglycemia appear. The normal animals then began to show an increase in blood sugar and spontaneous recovery, whereas the sympathectomized ones underwent further decrease in blood sugar until the convulsive stage was reached and spontaneous recovery did not take place. Sympathectomized animals showed only a slight compensatory reaction to a single removal of 13 to 15 per cent of the total blood volume, whereas normal ones withstood three or four bleedings of equal intensity before the compensatory vasoconstrictor reaction failed to raise the blood pressure.

Completely sympathectomized dogs are not abnormally sensitive to heat and cold. Neither is their capacity for vigorous muscular exercise materially reduced. In an intensive study in which dogs that had been subjected to complete extirpation of the sympathetic trunks were compared with normal dogs with respect to their reactions to heat and cold, anoxemia and insulin hypoglycemia, McDonough (1939) found no significant difference in the maximum decrease in body temperature in the two groups when subjected to low environmental temperature and no noteworthy difference in the rise in body temperature or the rate of panting when subjected to high environmental temperatures. In cold environments shivering began earlier and continued at a faster rate in the sympathec-tomized dogs than in the normal ones. The sympathectomized dogs seemed to be able to endure an oxygen tension of 6 per cent for five hours as well as the normal ones. In an atmosphere in which the oxygen tension was reduced to 4 per cent, respiratory failure occurred in both groups of animals, but earlier in the sympathectomized than in the normal ones. The former showed hypersensitivity to injected insulin by a greater decrease in the percentage of blood sugar and more frequent occurrence and greater severity of the symptoms of hypoglycemia than the latter which received the same insulin dosage. The fasting blood sugar level was the same in both groups of animals.

The remarkable capacity of completely sympathectomized dogs, as com-pared with completely sympathectomized cats, to endure unfavorable environmental conditions probably is attributable to various accessory physiological mechanisms, not controlled by the sympathetic nerves, which the dog possesses as a running animal. Among these may be men-tioned larger lungs and heart per kilogram of body weight, greater blood volume, higher hemoglobin content, abundant production of saliva and a tongue with a large surface area for elimination of heat. These mechanisms are of no avail in insulin hypoglycemia, with respect to which dogs and cats react in essentially the same manner.

Total or subtotal extirpation of the sympathetic trunks in man, carried out in several stages, as reported by Grimson *et al.* (1941), is not incom-patible with a relatively normal existence. Following operation the pa-tients showed postural hypotension and decreased heart rate, but no marked changes in gastro-intestinal, urinary and respiratory functions. The capacity for adjustment to changes in environmental temperature obviously is decreased since the denervated sweat glands are no longer functional and the cutaneous vessels do not respond reflexly to thermal stimulation.

Constancy of the internal environment requires continuous adjustments in the dynamics of the circulatory and the respiratory organs, the metabolic processes and general visceral activity. Visceral and somatic functions do not represent precisely delimited spheres of activity, but activities that are closely interrelated. Every motor or tonic response of skeletal muscles probably is accompanied by visceral responses. Somatic reactions are also conditioned by visceral activity. For example, the reduction in the volume of the blood flowing through the skeletal muscles during digestive activity tends to limit muscular capacity. Such interdependence of visceral and somatic functions in the peripheral fields is implied in the concept that the central control of somatic and visceral functions is exerted through neural mechanisms that are located at common levels in the spinal cord, the brain stem, the diencephalon and the cerebral cortex.

The visceral adjustments tend to maintain a physiological state that is adequate for the needs of the tissues. The reactions through which they are brought about are more complex and indirect than those concerned in the ordinary chemical and physical adjustments. They are essentially physiological reactions regulated through the autonomic nerves. For example, the increased return of venous blood due to muscular exercise is accompanied by reflex cardiac acceleration and peripheral vasoconstriction, but a simultaneous rise in blood pressure is prevented by increased activity of the aortic and the carotid sinus reflexes. A marked increase in body temperature due to elevation of the environmental temperature likewise is prevented by peripheral vasodilatation and sweating, with consequent increase in heat elimination.

The discharges through the sympathetic nerves of impulses that emanate from the higher autonomic centers, particularly the hypothalamus, are diffuse and influence all the viscera, including the vascular system. These nerves, which are chiefly adrenergic, consequently, are highly efficient in bringing about adjustments to external and internal environmental factors. The discharges through the parasympathetic nerves, which are chiefly cholinergic, usually are limited to a single organ or body region. They tend to disturb the constancy of the internal environment. Homeostasis, therefore, is promoted by the normal functional balance of the adrenergic and the cholinergic components of the autonomic nerves.

Under various conditions, including hypoxia, loss of body liquids, and emotional stress, the output of adrenin that results from adrenergic nerve stimulation is an important homeostatic reaction. In the absence of adequate controls it tends to disturb the internal environment rather than to maintain it in a constant state. The inhibitory action of adrenin on the autonomic centers of the brain stem, including those in the hypothalamus, tends to avert this danger. Other endocrine glands are also concerned in the maintenance of homeostasis. Disturbances in the functional balance of the endocrine system are always reflected in the functional balance of the autonomic nerves and in the state of the internal environment.

Chapter VI

DEVELOPMENT

HISTORICAL SURVEY

THE autonomic ganglia and nerves are related developmentally to the cerebrospinal nervous system. The primordia of the ganglia arise relatively early in embryonic development. They are made up of cells that are displaced from the neural tube and the cerebrospinal ganglia. Most of the early investigators supported the theory that the cells which make up the primordia of the ganglia of the sympathetic trunks and the prevertebral plexuses are derived exclusively from the spinal ganglia or the neural crests. The development of the autonomic plexuses that are more intimately associated with the thoracic and the abdominal viscera, e.g., the cardiac, the pulmonary and the enteric plexuses, was not studied intensively by the early investigators, but it was assumed quite generally that the nerve cells in all the autonomic ganglia except those in the head were derived from the same cerebrospinal sources.

The early data bearing on the development of the autonomic ganglia in the head, except the ciliary ganglion, are fragmentary. Carpenter (1906) described the early primordium of the ciliary ganglion in the chick as composed of cells that are displaced from the mid-brain along the oculomotor nerve. According to his account, this primordium later also receives cells from the semilunar ganglion via the ophthalmic nerve. In the absence of adequate data bearing on the development of the other autonomic ganglia in the head, it was quite generally assumed that the sphenopalatine, the otic and the submandibular ganglia arise from primordia composed exclusively of cells derived from the semilunar ganglion.

Froriep (1907) traced cells of medullary origin into the primordia of the sympathetic trunks via the ventral nerve roots and the communicating rami and advanced the opinion that the sympathetic ganglion cells are derived chiefly from the neural tube. Cajal (1908) concurred in this opinion. The results of the early studies of Kuntz (1909–1914) corroborated the findings of Froriep and showed clearly that the autonomic ganglia bear the same histogenetic relationship to the cerebrospinal nervous system in all classes of vertebrates, although they may differ somewhat in their morphogenesis in the several classes. Cells were also traced from these primordia of the sympathetic trunk ganglia into those of the prevertebral plexuses, but not into those of the plexuses that are functionally related to the vagi, i.e., the cardiac, the pulmonary and the enteric plexuses. On the contrary, the cells composing the primordia of the latter plexuses were traced distalward along the vagi and their branches. This finding was corroborated by Abel (1912) in embryos of the chick, and by Stewart (1920) in embyros of the rat. The primordia of the autonomic ganglia in the head (Kuntz, 1920) include both cells which are displaced from the brain stem along the nerves that convey the preganglionic fibers to the several ganglia respectively and cells which advance along the respective divisions of the trigeminal nerve. The displacement of cells from the neural tube into the primordia of the autonomic ganglia both in the trunk and the head regions has been amply confirmed by more recent investigators. On the basis of extensive experimental studies carried out on chick embyros, Jones (1937–1942) has supported the assumptions that only cells of medullary origin become differentiated into autonomic ganglion cells and that those which become sympathetic and parasympathetic ganglion cells respectively are displaced along the efferent roots of the nerves that convey the corresponding preganglionic outflows. This point of view has been opposed by Müller and Ingvar (1923), Van Campenhout (1927–1932) and Yntema and Hammond (1945–1952). The point of view that the sympathetic ganglion cells represent chiefly or exclusively cells that are displaced from the neural tube along the paths of ventral spinal nerve roots has been supported particularly by Kuntz and Batson (1920), Kuntz (1922), Raven (1937), Jones (1937–1942), and Brizzee and Kuntz (1950).

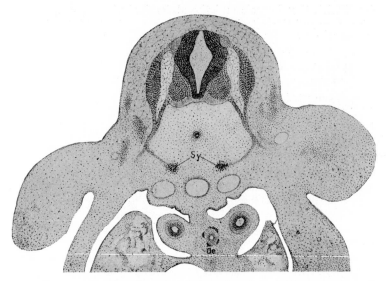

Fig. 28.—Transverse section through the thoracic region of a human embryo 7 mm. in length (No. 617, Carnegie Embryological Collection). *Sy.*, Sympathetic trunks; *Oe.*, esophagus.

EMBRYOLOGICAL DATA

Sympathetic Trunks.—The primordia of the ganglia of the sympathetic trunks appear earliest in the caudal thoracic and the rostral abdominal regions. They are composed of aggregates of cells of neural origin lying along the dorsolateral aspects of the aorta (Fig. 28). These cells are somewhat scattered and may be differentiated from the cells of the mesenchyme by the somewhat larger size and more intense staining reaction of the nucleus (Fig. 29). Such aggregates of cells may be observed from the caudal cervical to the sacral region in human embyros 6 mm. in length. They are arranged segmentally, but, due to the marked curvature of the embryo, they lie so close together that they constitute a continuous column of loosely aggregated cells. This condition obtains until the embryos have attained a length of 9 to 10 mm. The sympathetic primordia are then present from the rostral cervical to the sacral region. The segmental character of the sympathetic primordia gradually becomes apparent, as development advances, and the cell aggregates become connected by longitudinal fibers. In the cervical and the rostral thoracic segments, the sympathetic primordia lie along the dorsolateral aspects of the descending aortæ and in close proximity to them. The positions of the sympathetic primordia appear to be determined, at least in part, by the positions of the

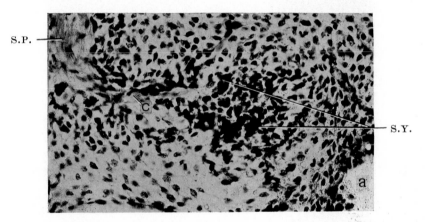

Fig. 29.—Transverse section through lower thoracic region of a human embryo 7 mm. in length, showing spinal nerve and sympathetic trunk. *a*, Aorta; *C*, communicating ramus; *S.P.*, spinal nerve; *S.Y.*, sympathetic trunk.

paired descending aortæ. Inasmuch as these vessels lie at an appreciable distance from the median plane and converge toward the unpaired dorsal aorta, the sympathetic trunks lie farther from the median plane in the cervical and the rostral thoracic than in the caudal thoracic and the lumbar segments.

The primordia of the sympathetic trunk ganglia are apparent before the fibers of the communicating rami can be traced into them in sections prepared by the ordinary methods. In preparations of human embryos 7 mm. and more in length, the fibers of the communicating rami extend into the sympathetic primordia throughout the greater part of the thorax and the abdomen (Fig. 29). In preparations of embryos that are somewhat farther advanced, fibers tend ventrad from the primordia of the sympathetic trunks and enter the primordia of the ganglia of the prevertebral plexuses, which are represented by scattered aggregates of cells along the ventrolateral aspects of the abdominal aorta (Fig. 30). These primordia arise by the ventral displacement of cells from the primordia of the sympathetic trunks.

Most of the cells in the sympathetic primordia in early embryos are identical in appearance with the cells in the spinal ganglia and the indifferent cells in the mantle layer in the neural tube. Cells of the same character are present in the paths of the dorsal and the ventral nerve roots and the communicating rami. Occasionally an individual cell the nucleus of which lies partly within and partly without the external limiting membrane may be observed in a ventral nerve root. Cells in this position

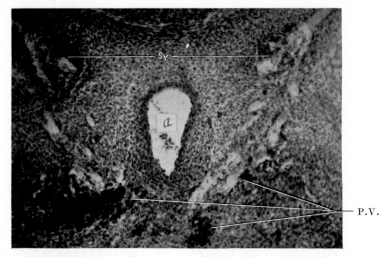

Fig. 30.—Transverse section through the abdominal region of a human embryo 10.1 mm. in length, showing primordia of sympathetic trunks and prevertebral plexuses. *a*, Aorta; *P.V.*, prevertebral plexuses; *Sy*, sympathetic trunks.

obviously are in the process of emerging from the neural tube. Cells also become separated from the distal ends of the spinal ganglia and advance along the dorsal nerve root. Since the cells of medullary and of spinal ganglion origin appear identical in early embryos, it is impossible to distinguish between the cells derived from these two sources distal to the junction of the dorsal and the ventral nerve roots. Cells from both these sources enter the sympathetic primordia.

In sections of human and other vertebrate embryos stained by the ordinary methods, cells of neural origin appear in the sympathetic primordia before fibers of the communicating rami can be traced into these locations. Various investigators have expressed the opinion that many of the cells that enter the sympathetic primordia migrate into them in advance of the growing nerve fibers. Since it is known that the distal portions of growing nerve fibers are not brought out clearly by the ordinary staining methods, it may be assumed that fibers of the communicating rami extend well into the sympathetic primordia somewhat earlier than the recorded data seem to indicate, but the earliest cells probably enter the primordia of the sympathetic trunks somewhat in advance of the growing nerve fibers.

In preparations of human embryos 9 to 10 mm. in length, cells of cerebrospinal origin remain abundant in the spinal nerve trunks and the communicating rami, indicating that the peripheral displacement of these cells is still going on. It probably does not continue long beyond the stage of embryos 11 or 12 mm. in length. The cells in the sympathetic primordia are also more numerous and are arranged more compactly than in the earlier embryos. Mitotic figures in the sympathetic primordia also indicate that the cells increase in number by local proliferation.

The primordia of the sympathetic trunks arise somewhat later in the cervical than in the thoracic region. This fact was noted by all the earlier investigators who made special mention of the development of the cervical portion of the sympathetic trunks in the embryos of the higher vertebrates. Some of them also observed that these primordia gradually extend cephalad from the rostral thoracic level as continuous columns of cells until they reach the most rostral cervical segments. In human and other mammalian embryos the primordia of the sympathetic trunks grow cephalad in the cervical region both by the displacement of cells along the dorsal aspects of the descending aortæ and by cell proliferation. They do not appear segmented in early embryos, but remain continuous cell columns until segmentation of these columns takes place, resulting in delimitation of the cervical sympathetic ganglia.

The segmental character of the sympathetic trunks is apparent throughout the greater part of their extent in human embryos 10 mm. in length. The ganglionic primordia are more compact at this stage than in the earlier stages, but some cells of neural origin remain somewhat scattered; and, although the ganglionic masses in adjacent segments are connected by longitudinal fibers, these connecting rami are nowhere devoid of cells. As the curvature of the embryo becomes less marked, with advancing development, the ganglia of the sympathetic trunks become more widely separated and more sharply delimited. In human embryos 15 mm. in length, the segmental character of the sympathetic trunks is well marked below the cervical region. The segmentation of the cervical portion, which results in the cervical sympathetic ganglia, is also well advanced. Fibers may now be traced rostrad from the superior cervical ganglia along the internal carotid arteries. In embryos 20 to 22 mm. in length, the ganglia of the sympathetic trunks have taken definite form and are sharply delimited, the fiber bundles connecting them with one another are relatively free from cells, and the trunks have assumed a definite relationship to the vertebral condensations.

Prevertebral Plexuses.—The primordia of the ganglia of the prevertebral plexuses in the abdomen arise along the ventrolateral aspects of the aorta. In the rostral abdominal region of human embryos 6 mm. in length, cells may be traced in small numbers from the primordia of the ganglia of the sympathetic trunks ventrad along the lateral aspects of the aorta. The primordia of the sympathetic trunk ganglia in this region are not sharply delimited. Cells apparently become detached from them and advance ventrad into the primordia of the prevertebral ganglia. In embryos that are somewhat farther advanced, fibers may also be traced from the primordia of the thoracic sympathetic ganglia below the fourth or the fifth thoracic segment toward the primordia of the prevertebral ganglia in the upper abdominal region. They are chiefly fibers that join the sympathetic trunks through the communicating rami of the thoracic nerves and, continuing toward the prevertebral plexuses, give rise to the splanchnic nerves. In human embryos 10 mm. and more in length, the aggregates of cells that make up the primordia of the prevertebral ganglia are conspicuous along the abdominal aorta. Some cells have already become displaced from these cell masses toward the primordia of the adrenal glands and along the renal arteries. The greatest accumulation of sympathetic cells ventral to the abdominal aorta occurs at the origin of the celiac artery. The prevertebral plexuses as yet are not clearly delimited, and fibers cannot be traced from their primordia into the mesentery. The several plexuses become more clearly delimited, as development advances, and the ganglionic cell aggregates become more compact.

The primordia of the pelvic plexuses first appear in human embryos approximately 12 mm. in length. The earliest cells of neural origin in them are displaced from the central nervous system along the visceral rami of the sacral nerves. Somewhat later cells displaced from the primordia of the prevertebral plexuses in the abdomen enter the primordia of the pelvic plexuses along nerve fiber bundles in the hypogastric plexus. The ganglia in the pelvic plexuses, consequently, include cells derived from the sacral segments of the central nervous system via the pelvic nerves and cells derived from thoracolumbar segments via the hypogastric plexus. The cells derived via the sacral nerves greatly exceed in numbers those derived via the hypogastric plexus (Kuntz, 1952). These findings are consistent with the demonstration in the pelvic ganglia of both parasympathetic and sympathetic ganglion cells and with the evidence that the pelvic organs are innervated more abundantly through the parasympathetic than through the sympathetic nerves.

Chromaffin System.—The chromaffin system includes the adrenal medulla and the paraganglia. Most of the paraganglia are located close to the aorta and are related to sympathetic ganglia. Human embryos exhibit a wide range of variation in the number of paraganglia and the quantity of chromaffin tissue outside the adrenal bodies. Much of the chromaffin tissue outside the adrenals undergoes retrogressive changes during postnatal life, but the paraganglia do not wholly disappear.

The cells destined to become chromaffin cells cannot be differentiated from the other cells of neural origin in the sympathetic primordia in early embryos. They assume the characteristic appearance of chromaffin elements relatively late during embryonic development. The displacement of cells from the adjacent sympathetic primordia into the adrenal capsules begins in human embryos about 15 mm. in length. Their differentiation into chromaffin cells and the formation of chromaffin bodies outside the adrenals is initiated at a somewhat earlier stage. Well organized chromaffin bodies are not found in human embryos until they have attained a length of about 30 mm.

The carotid body which, at least in some animals, is made up in part of chromaffin tissue is situated at the bifurcation of the common carotid artery. The chromaffin cells in this body appear to be derived chiefly from the cervical sympathetic primordia. Certain data appear to support the assumption that some cells derived from the parasympathetic primordia in the head are displaced into it along branches of the glossopharyngeal and the vagus nerves. In certain mammalian species, *e.g.*, the rat, the carotid body probably includes no chromaffin tissue.

Plexuses Related to the Vagi.—The cardiac, the pulmonary and the enteric plexuses, except in the distal parts of the intestine, arise from primordia composed of cells of cerebrospinal origin that are displaced along the paths of the vagi. This conclusion was first based on a study of mammalian (pig) embryos (Kuntz, 1909) and confirmed later by the results of studies based on embryos of types of the other classes of vertebrates.

In early human embryos, the vagus nerves, like the spinal nerves, contain cells of neural origin. In favorable sections through the vagus roots, continuous lines of cells of medullary origin may be observed extending from the wall of the hind-brain into these roots. In sagittal sections, lines of cells also extend from the distal ganglion on the vagus nerve into the nerve trunk. Cells identical in appearance with those in the ganglia are also present in abundance in the more distal parts of the growing vagi. Vagus branches bearing small aggregates of such cells may also be traced toward the esophageal wall.

In embryos 6 mm. in length, vagus branches may be traced to the stomach and for a short distance along its lesser curvature, toward the roots of the lungs and toward the bulbar region of the heart. Associated with all these branches are many cells of neural origin. In embryos 7 to 9 mm. in length, the pulmonary branches have reached the roots of the lungs and the cardiac branches may be traced close to the base of the heart. The cardiac branches are accompanied by numerous cells of neural origin that tend to become aggregated near the growing tips of the nerves to give rise to the primordia of the cardiac ganglia. The esophageal plexus is already well formed over the dorsal aspect of the heart where it lies close to the walls of the atria. Vagus branches with their accompanying cell aggregates form a plexiform meshwork around the lower portion of the esophagus (Fig. 31A). Caudal to the bifurcation of the trachea, vagus branches including cells of neural origin may be traced into the roots of the lungs where masses of such cells occur in proximity to the bronchi and the pulmonary vessels (Fig. 31B). These neural complexes which constitute the primordia of the pulmonary plexuses are continuous with the esophageal plexus and with the portion of the cardiac plexus that is associated with the walls of the atria.

In human embryos 7 to 9 mm. in length, many cells of vagus origin have advanced into the wall of the esophagus, but a definite concentric arrangement of these cells as yet is not apparent. In embryos 10 mm. in length, vagus branches accompanied by migrant nerve cells may be traced along the wall of the stomach. Many of these cells penetrate the stomach wall with the terminal vagus branches and become incorporated in the primordia

of the enteric plexuses.   As development advances, the primordia of these
plexuses also become apparent in the intestine.   As the cells of neural
origin in the wall of the digestive tube gradually become more numerous,
they become aggregated in minute ganglionic masses that assume a con-

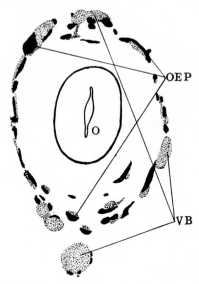

Fɪɢ. 31*A*.—Esophageal plexus in transverse section, human embryo 10.1 mm. in length.
O, Esophagus; *OEP*, cell masses in esophageal plexus; *VB*, vagus branches.

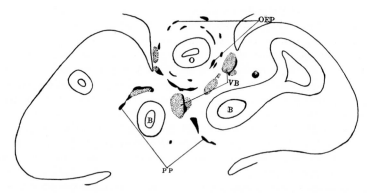

Fɪɢ. 31*B*.—Esophageal and pulmonary plexuses in transverse section, human embryo
10.1. mm. in length. *B*, Bronchus; *O*, esophagus; *OEP*, cell mass in esophageal plexus;
P P, cell masses in pulmonary plexuses; *VB*, vagus branches.

centric arrangement in two zones.   Those in the other zone become the
ganglia of the myenteric plexus.   Those in the inner zone become the
ganglia of the submucous plexus.   The enteric ganglia in the portion of the
large intestine that derives its parasympathetic innervation through the
pelvic nerves sustain a histogenetic relationship to the sacral nerves com-

parable to that which the ganglia in the more proximal parts of the enteric canal sustain to the vagi.

It is significant that no paths along which cells advance from the sympathetic trunks into the pulmonary, the cardiac and the enteric plexuses are established during the early stages of development. The early development of these plexuses goes on simultaneously with that of the sympathetic trunks. Sympathetic nerves grow into the cardiac and the pulmonary plexuses later, but not until the primordia of the ganglia of these plexuses are well established.

Cranial Autonomic Ganglia. — **Submandibular Ganglion.** — The primordium of the submandibular ganglion arises in human embryos 10 to 11 mm. in length in the path of the lingual division of the mandibular nerve. The cells of neural origin that reach this site earliest advance into it along the lingual nerve. They appear to be displaced from the semilunar ganglion. Some probably advance directly from the brain stem along the motor root of the trigeminal nerve. After the chorda tympani has joined the lingual nerve some cells of medullary origin may reach the submandibular ganglion along this course. This branch of the facial nerve does not reach the lingual nerve until the primordium of the submandibular ganglion has attained considerable size. Most of the cells that make up this primordium obviously are cells of trigeminal origin. On the basis of his own studies, Stewart (1920) concluded that the submandibular ganglion arises exclusively from cells that are displaced along the chorda tympani, although he admitted that, due to the intimate relationship of the primordium of this ganglion with the lingual nerve, direct observations lend little support to this conclusion.

Sublingual and Lingual Ganglia. — The primordium of the sublingual ganglion arises in the path of the lingual nerve somewhat distal to the primordium of the submandibular ganglion. Cells of neural origin also advance along the branches of the lingual nerve and give rise to small ganglionic masses in the tongue. These minute ganglia remain associated with the branches of the lingual nerve. The cells that give rise to the sublingual ganglion and the smaller ganglia in the tongue associated with the branches of the lingual nerve obviously are derived from the same sources as those that give rise to the submandibular ganglion.

Minute ganglia also occur in the posterior portion of the tongue. They are associated with the lingual ramus of the glossopharyngeal nerve and probably include only cells which are displaced distalward along this nerve. As the glossopharyngeal nerve grows into the tongue groups of cells accumulate near its growing extremity. Some of these cell groups remain closely associated with the nerve trunk. Others give rise to minute ganglia throughout the portion of the tongue that is innervated by the glossopharyngeal nerve.

Otic Ganglion. — The primordium of the otic ganglion arises at the growing tip of the lesser superficial petrosal nerve as an aggregate of cells that are displaced distalward along this nerve. It is first apparent in human embryos 9 to 10 mm. in length. In sagittal sections of embryos 8 mm. in length, the tympanic ramus of the glossopharyngeal nerve may be traced to the level of the geniculate ganglion. Its fibers are accompanied by cells of neural origin, giving it the appearance of an early migration path. The primordium of the otic ganglion may usually be recognized when this ramus has reached a point a little below the level of the semilunar ganglion. It increases in size rapidly and becomes elongated. Its rostral pole soon extends beyond the caudal level of the semilunar ganglion and lies close to this ganglion. During the early phases of its development, the primordium of the otic ganglion is not connected with the semilunar ganglion, but in embryos 13 mm. in length it is apparent that cells derived from the semilunar ganglion become incorporated in the primordium of the otic ganglion. The otic ganglion now lies in contact with the proximal portion

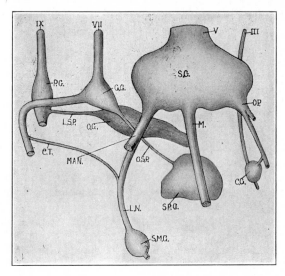

Fig. 32.—Diagrammatic reconstruction of the larger cranial autonomic ganglia and the nerves to which they are genetically related in a human embryo about 20 mm. in length. *C.G.*, Ciliary ganglion; *C.T.*, chorda tympani; *G.G.*, geniculate ganglion; *G.S.P*, greater superficial petrosal nerve; *L.N.*, lingual nerve; *L.S.P.*, lesser superficial petrosal nerve; *M.*, maxillary nerve; *MAN.*, mandibular nerve; *O.G.*, optic ganglion; *OP.*, ophthalmic nerve; *P.G.*, petrosal ganglion; *S.G.*, Semilunar ganglion; *S.M.G.*, submaxillary ganglion; *SP.G.*, sphenopalatine ganglion.

of the mandibular nerve. This nerve, like the other divisions of the trigeminal, contains numerous cells of neural origin, some of which deviate from its course along the slender rami that join the otic ganglion. Inasmuch as the mandibular nerve has a motor as well as a sensory root, it is not improbable that a portion of the cells which advance distalward along its course are derived directly from the hind-brain, but it is quite apparent that many of the cells of trigeminal origin that enter the otic ganglion are derived directly from the semilunar ganglion. Some earlier investigators have supported the theory that the cells which give rise to the otic ganglion are derived exclusively from the semilunar ganglion. On the contrary, Stewart (1920), who studied preparations of embryos of the pig and rat, maintained that the otic ganglion arises solely from cells that are displaced distalward along the lesser superficial petrosal nerve.

Sphenopalatine Ganglion.—The primordium of the sphenopalatine ganglion arises at the growing tip of the greater superficial petrosal nerve as an aggregate of cells that are displaced distalward along this nerve. It first becomes apparent in human embryos 10 to 11 mm. in length. The geniculate ganglion is not sharply delimited during early development. Cells apparently become separated from it and advance along the path of the greater superficial petrosal nerve. This nerve has the appearance, during early development, of a narrow migration pathway. Many of the cells that are displaced along its course undoubtedly are cells of medullary origin.

The primordium of the sphenopalatine ganglion lies medial to the maxillary nerve but not in contact with it. In embryos 12 to 15 mm. in length, rami of the maxillary nerve accompanied by cells derived from the semilunar ganglion may be traced into the sphenopalatine primordium. Most of the cells in this primordium advance into it along the greater superficial petrosal nerve, but it also receives cells from the semilunar ganglion via the maxillary nerve and its sphenopalatine rami. On the basis of his observations on embryos of the pig and the rat, Stewart (1920) concluded that the primordium of the sphenopalatine ganglion contains only cells that are displaced distalward along the greater superficial petrosal nerve.

Ciliary Ganglion.—The primordium of the ciliary ganglion arises in the path of the oculomotor nerve by the displacement of cells along this nerve. It also receives cells that are displaced along the ophthalmic nerve. Cells of neural origin in the oculomotor nerve are not very apparent in early human embryos, but such cells can be observed at the site of the primordium of the ciliary ganglion before cells can be traced to it from the ophthalmic nerve. In sections of human embryos 12 to 14 mm. in length, continuous lines of cells identical with those in the semilunar ganglion extend from this ganglion along the ophthalmic nerve. Cells also become aggregated very early in the path of this nerve at a point just proximal to the origin in the nasociliary ramus. This aggregate of cells gradually extends toward the oculomotor nerve until it becomes continuous with the cell aggregate on the latter nerve (Fig. 33). At this stage (14 mm.), nerve fibers may be traced from the oculomotor nerve into the primordium of the ciliary ganglion. As development advances, this ganglionic cell mass gradually becomes separated from the ophthalmic nerve, but it remains in contact with the oculomotor nerve until relatively late. It includes the primordium of the ciliary ganglion and is relatively large in early human embryos. Most of the cells in it appear to be derived from the semilunar ganglion, but the number contributed via the oculomotor nerve is not insignificant. On the basis of these observations, the ciliary ganglion appears to be genetically related to both the oculomotor and ophthalmic nerves.

The findings of some earlier investigators appear to support the assumption that the ciliary ganglion cells are derived in part via the oculomotor nerve and in part via the ophthalmic nerve. Those of others have been interpreted as indicating that the ciliary ganglion cells are derived exclusively from the semilunar ganglion. In embryos of the chick, as re-

ported by Jones (1942), the primordium of the ciliary ganglion is represented by a relatively large aggregate of cells in the path of the oculomotor
nerve before any connections with the trigeminal nerve can be observed.
In his experiments, removal of the cephalic neural crests prevented the development of trigeminal ganglia, but did not prevent the development of
the primordia of the ciliary ganglia. On the other hand, removal of the
mid-brain, including the oculomotor nuclei, but leaving the cephalic
neural crests intact, did not prevent the accumulation of cells at the sites
of the primordia of the ciliary ganglia.

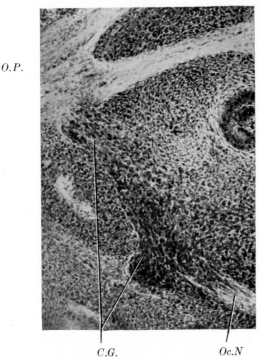

O.P.

C.G.   *Oc.N*

Fig. 33.—Sagittal section through primordium of ciliary ganglion, human embryo 14 mm.
in length. *C.G.*, Ciliary ganglion; *Oc.N.*, oculomotor nerve; *O.P.*, ophthalmic nerve.

Histogenic Relationships.—The assumption that the cells which become
differentiated into ganglion cells in the ganglia of the sympathetic trunks
and the prevertebral plexuses are derived from the neural tube via the
ventral roots of the spinal nerves represents a wide departure from the
older teaching, but it is in full accord with our present knowledge of the
functional relationships of the sympathetic nervous system. The neurons
in the ganglia of the sympathetic trunks and the prevertebral plexuses are
essentially efferent in function. In the central nervous system, efferent
neurons arise chiefly in the ventral, or basal, plate and afferent neurons
arise in the dorsal, or alar, plate; consequently, it seems more probable

that the sympathetic neurons are derived from the ventral portion of the neural tube, which is a source of efferent neurons, than from the spinal ganglia or the neural crest, which is a source of afferent neurons. Certain investigators, particularly Müller and Ingvar (1923), Van Campenhout (1927–1932) and Yntema and Hammond (1945–1952) have maintained that the sympathetic primordia are composed of cells that are derived exclusively from the spinal ganglia or the neural crests. They have contended that no cells of medullary origin become displaced into the ventral roots of the spinal nerves.

The existence of cells of medullary origin in the ventral spinal nerve roots has been observed in embryos of all classes of vertebrates. The evidence that these cells are displaced from the ventral part of the neural tube along the ventral nerve roots is especially clear in elasmobranch

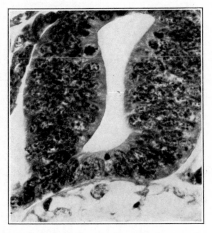

Fig. 34.—Section through the ventral root of a spinal nerve in an embryo of Squalus acanthias. A column of cells of medullary origin extends into the nerve root.

embryos. Balfour (1877) described the early ventral nerve root in these embryos as "an elongate cellular structure with a wide attachment to the spinal cord." His illustrations indicate continuity of this cellular structure with the mantle layer in the wall of the neural tube. This condition is illustrated in Figure 34, taken from a cross-section of an embryo of S. acanthias in our collection. Continuous lines of cells extending from the mantle layer of the neural tube into the ventral nerve roots may also be observed occasionally in preparations of embryos of birds and mammals. This condition, as observed in preparations of an embryo of the chick, is illustrated in Figure 35. Individual nuclei partly within and partly without the external limiting membrane in the ventral roots of the spinal nerves and the motor roots of the cranial nerves occur frequently in preparations of embryos of all the higher vertebrates, including the human species. The importance, in the establishment of the primordia of the autonomic ganglia, of the cells of medullary origin that are displaced distalward along

9

the efferent nerve roots has been emphasized by so many investigators that it cannot be disregarded.

In an investigation undertaken to determine more exactly the rôle of cells of medullary origin in the development of the sympathetic ganglia, embryos of the chick were subjected to an operative procedure, before the close of the second day of incubation, by which the neural crests and the neural tube were destroyed in varying degrees throughout a series of segments. These embryos were killed about the close of the fifth day of incubation and prepared for study (Kuntz and Batson, 1920; Kuntz, 1922).

In some of the embryos, as became apparent on microscopic examination of the sections, the spinal ganglia and dorsal nerve roots were absent on one or both sides through a series of segments, while the ventral portion of the neural tube remained intact, and the ventral nerve roots were apparently of normal size. In other embryos nearly all the nerve tissue

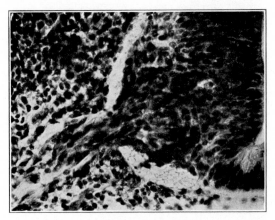

Fig. 35.—Section through the ventral root of a spinal nerve in an embryo of the chick about the close of the fourth day of incubation. Cells of medullary origin are present in the ventral nerve root.

was destroyed in a series of segments, leaving only a small ventral portion of the neural tube intact. In nearly all these cases, ventral nerve roots were present but diminished in size in proportion to the degree of destruction of the basal plate of the neural tube. Visceral rami were present wherever a part or all of the portion of the mantle layer which gives rise to the intermediolateral cell column remained intact, but absent wherever this portion of the mantle layer was completely destroyed. Preparations of embryos in which all the nerve tissue was destroyed throughout a series of segments showed no traces of spinal nerves in these segments.

An aggregate of cells representing the sympathetic primordium was present in every instance in which there was a ventral nerve root with a visceral ramus, even though there was no spinal ganglion or dorsal nerve root; but no sympathetic primordium was observed in any segment in which there was no visceral ramus, even though there was a small ventral nerve root, except in one instance in which very small sympathetic primordia were present in the rostral thoracic segments in complete absence of spinal ganglia and neural tube in these segments. Some cells obviously had been displaced peripheralward in the segments in question in this embryo before it was subjected to operation. Sections through the caudal thoracic segments in the same embryo revealed no sympathetic primordia, since the peripheral displacement of cells of neural origin had not yet been initiated in the caudal thoracic segments. Most of the preparations used showed no evidence of the peripheral displacement of cells of neural crest origin before the operative procedure was carried out.

Van Campenhout (1927–1932), as stated above, denied the displacement of cells of medullary origin along the efferent nerve roots, but maintained that the cells of neural origin that enter the primordia of the autonomic ganglia are derived exclusively from the neural crests. In criticizing our findings, Van Campenhout suggested that the sympathetic primordia observed by us in segments devoid of dorsal nerve roots represents the extension of sympathetic structures connected with spinal nerves a few segments rostrad or caudad. The validity of this criticism cannot be admitted, since Jones (1937) has shown that cells in the sympathetic primordia do not migrate from more caudal segments into adjacent segments from which the neural tube has been removed and that such cells do not migrate caudad more than three segments from segments farther rostrad.

Similar findings have been reported by Brizzee and Kuntz (1950). In their investigation, the neural crest and variable portions of the neural tube were removed unilaterally or bilaterally in a series of successive segments in chick embryos of 16 to 22 somites. The eggs were further incubated for 3 to 6 days or longer. The embryos were then fixed and sectioned serially. Extension of the sympathetic trunk primordia caudad from the first segment rostral to a series of segments in which dorsal and ventral nerve roots were absent did not exceed two segments. Extension of the sympathetic trunk primordia rostrad from the first segment caudal to such a series did not exceed one segment.

In all the experimental embryos in this series sympathetic trunk primordia were present in every segment throughout the sympathetic preganglionic outflow in which ventral nerve roots were present, although spinal ganglia and dorsal nerve roots were absent in six or more successive segments. The neuronal nature of some of the cells in these primordia is demonstrated by the presence of recognizable neuroblasts. In some instances multipolar nerve cells were also present in segments devoid of spinal ganglia and dorsal nerve roots that were so far removed from segments in which neural crest derivatives were present that displacement of neural crest cells into the sympathetic primordia in them could be ruled out. The derivation of sympathetic ganglion cells from the neural tube, therefore, appears to be demonstrated. Strudel (1952) also traced cells from the neural tube along ventral nerve roots into the sympathetic trunk primordia in chick embryos in which the neural crests had been completely excised in a series of segments, and there was no evidence of neural crest derivatives in the segments in question.

In the light of these findings in experimental embryos of the chick we cannot avoid the conclusion that the primordia of the ganglia of the sympathetic trunk may arise in complete absence of cells derived from the neural crest or the spinal ganglia. Under these conditions, the cells of neural origin in the sympathetic primordia must be derived exclusively from the neural tube along the ventral spinal nerve roots. The fact that such primordia do not arise in segments in which the portion of the mantle layer that gives rise to the intermediolateral cell column is destroyed, even though a small ventral nerve root is present, suggests that the cells which enter the sympathetic primordia via the ventral nerve roots, under normal conditions, are derived mainly from this portion of the neural tube.

Under normal conditions, the sympathetic primordia include many cells of neural crest origin that are displaced from the spinal ganglia along the dorsal nerve roots. Most of these cells become differentiated into neuroglia and neurilemma cells. The neuroglial nature of the supporting tissue in the autonomic ganglia, including the cells that make up the ganglion cell capsules, has been amply demonstrated. In embryos of the chick the neuroglial cells in the sympathetic trunk ganglia are derived in part from the neural crest via the dorsal nerve roots and in part from the neural tube via the ventral nerve roots (Brizzee, 1949). The cells of neural crest origin that enter the sympathetic primordia, therefore, can be accounted for without the assumption that any of them become differentiated into ganglion cells.

The parasympathetic ganglia sustain a histogenetic relationship to the nerves that include the parasympathetic preganglionic outflow comparable to that of the sympathetic ganglia to the thoracic and the upper lumbar spinal nerves. The conclusion advanced by Kuntz, on the basis of extensive studies of preparations of normal embryos of species of all classes of vertebrates, that the thoracic prevertebral ganglia and the enteric ganglia, except in the distal portion of the enteric canal, are made up of cells which are displaced distalward along the vagus nerves, has been corroborated by the findings reported by Jones (1942) that these ganglia fail to arise in embryos of the chick in which the hind-brain had been removed at approximately the forty-second hour of incubation. Jones also reported that the ganglion coli and the enteric ganglia in the distal portions of the enteric canal failed to arise in embryos in which the caudal portion of the neural tube was removed at the forty-eighth hour of incubation. This experimental finding supports the hypothesis that the cells which become differentiated into ganglion cells in the distal portion of the enteric canal are displaced distalward from the sacral segments of the neural tube along the sacral nerve roots. The observation that the earliest cells of neural origin to appear in the pelvic plexuses in mammalian embryos are derived via the visceral rami of the sacral nerves (Kuntz, 1952) also supports this hypothesis.

Segregation of the cells of medullary origin from those of sensory ganglion origin along the paths of the vagus, the glossopharyngeal and the facial nerves is beset with peculiar difficulties. The sensory ganglia associated with these nerves are not derived exclusively from the neural crests. Consequently, they cannot be eliminated by removal of the cephalic portions of the latter structures alone. Since these ganglia are traversed by the preganglionic components of the respective nerves, their removal after complete differentiation of their primordia can hardly be accomplished without damage to the preganglionic outflow. Removal of the portions of the hind-brain which include the efferent nuclei of these nerves without destroying the primordia of the sensory ganglia probably can be accomplished.

In the experiments on chick embryos reported by Jones (1942) in which the hind-brain and the corresponding portions of the neural crests were removed at the forty-second hour of incubation, this operation did not prevent the development of the nodose ganglion of the vagus nerve. Fibers growing rostrad and caudad from this ganglion also were present. Those growing rostrad did not grow into the residue of the brain stem. Those growing caudad could be traced into the wall of the stomach, but there were no neuroblasts associated with them. The nodose ganglia obviously contribute no neurons to the parasympathetic ganglia related to the vagus nerves. The parasympathetic ganglia probably sustain a histogenetic relationship to the brain stem and the sacral segments of the spinal cord comparable to that of the sympathetic ganglia to the thoracic and the rostral lumbar spinal cord segments.

Yntema and Hammond (1952) have advanced certain data obtained from experimental embryos of the chick which they have interpreted as indicating that the cells of neural origin that are displaced from the hind-brain region along the vagus nerves are derived, not from the neural tube, but from the neural crests. These findings are in direct disagreement with those of Jones. In view of Jones' findings in chick embryos in which the portion of the hind-brain in which the motor nuclei of the vagus nerves become differentiated was destroyed, and in view of all the data that support the hypothesis that cells of neural tube origin become differentiated into ganglion cells in the sympathetic trunk ganglia, the point of view that the ganglion cells in the plexuses that are cytogenetically related to the vagus nerves are derived solely from the neural crests cannot be accepted without further verification.

The concept of the development of the autonomic nervous system here set forth does not imply that all the cells that become differentiated into neurons in its ganglia actually migrate from the neural tube. In a critical study of cell differentiation in the central nervous system, Schaper (1897) pointed out that the cells which arise by the mitotic division of the "germinal" cells in the ependymal layer do not all become neuroblasts. He described them as "indifferent" cells, some of which become differentiated into neurons and others into neuroglia. He also pointed out that in the higher vertebrates many of the indifferent cells retain the capacity for further propagation by mitotic division and give rise to daughter cells of the same indifferent type which may become differentiated either into neurons or into supporting cells. Most of the cells of neural origin which are displaced distalward along the cranial and the spinal nerves conform to Schaper's description of the indifferent cells. In preparations of embryos that are sufficiently advanced in their development, a neuroblast may be observed occasionally along the path of migration, but most of the cells that develop into neurons in the autonomic ganglia cannot be identified as neuroblasts before they have entered the primordia of these ganglia. Many migrant cells, apparently of the indifferent type, do not become differentiated into neuroblasts, but give rise to neurilemma and neuroglial supporting tissue. In preparations of early embryos of the higher vertebrates, mitotic figures occur in both the nerve trunks and the autonomic primordia. It may be assumed, therefore, that many of the cells that become differentiated into neurons in the autonomic ganglia arise by the mitotic division of migrant cells either before or after they have become incorporated in the primordia of these ganglia. The neurons in the autonomic system, consequently, may be regarded as homologous with the neurons in the cerebrospinal nervous system.

The cells in the autonomic primordia that are destined to become ganglion cells do not differentiate simultaneously or at the same rate. Preparations of ganglia taken from human fetuses during the sixth or the seventh month of gestation show cells in all phases of differentiation from bipolar or unipolar neuroblasts to young multipolar ganglion cells of large sizes. The earliest dendritic processes at first are unbranched, but branching is initiated relatively early and continues for an indefinite period. The dendrites of individual ganglion cells which arise earliest, according to de Castro (1932), are longer and of greater diameter than those which arise later. They may, therefore, be recognized in the adult as the primary dendritic processes. Many of the short dendrites arise relatively late.

Chapter VII

INNERVATION OF THE HEART

EXTRINSIC NERVES

THE heart is innervated through the sympathetic cardiac nerves, the cardiac branches of the vagi and the cardiac plexus. Its sympathetic innervation includes the superior, the middle and the inferior cervical cardiac nerves, arising from the superior, the middle and the inferior cervical sympathetic ganglia respectively, and several rami that arise from the sympathetic trunk caudal to the inferior cervical or the stellate ganglion. The cardiac nerves that arise from the sympathetic trunk caudal to the inferior cervical have been called the thoracic cardiac nerves. Credit for their discovery, as has been pointed out by Mitchell (1949), is due to Weber (1815) and Swan (1830). Nerves that join the cardiac plexus have been traced from the sympathetic trunk as far caudad as the sixth thoracic segment in certain mammals, including man. In man the thoracic cardiac nerves include approximately twice as many fibers that enter the cardiac plexus as the cervical sympathetic cardiac nerves (Saccomanno, 1943). The thoracic cardiac nerves are more abundant in the fourth and the fifth thoracic segments than in the more rostral ones. The efferent fibers in the sympathetic cardiac nerves arise in the sympathetic trunk ganglia. They are, therefore, postganglionic and make no synaptic connections in the cardiac ganglia. The preganglionic fibers to which they are synaptically related are components of the first to the fifth or the sixth thoracic nerves.

The parasympathetic innervation of the heart commonly involves three rami of the vagus nerve on either side. The superior cervical ramus arises from the vagus trunk just distal to the origin of the superior laryngeal nerve. The inferior cervical, the largest cardiac ramus of the vagus, usually arises from the recurrent nerve. The third, or thoracic, cardiac ramus arises from the vagus trunk within the thorax. The efferent components of the vagus branches to the heart are preganglionic fibers that make synaptic connections with ganglion cells in the cardiac plexus. Most of them are unmyelinated. As the vagus fibers approach the cardiac plexus, they mingle with the cardiac sympathetic fibers, a large percentage of which is also unmyelinated. There are no morphological criteria by which the fibers of sympathetic and those of parasympathetic origin can be certainly identified within the cardiac plexus unless they have been differentially stained. By the use of appropriate silver technic, according to Nonidez (1939) and Cheng (1950), the parasympathetic fibers become more heavily impregnated than the sympathetic fibers, particularly in young animals. By means of electrical stimulation and action potential records, Marguth et al. (1952) found that nearly all the vagus branches to the heart include vagus efferent, vagus afferent and some sympathetic fibers.

All the extrinsic nerves of the heart, except the superior cervical sympathetic, convey both efferent and afferent fibers. The afferent fibers associated with the sympathetic nerves, like the corresponding preganglionic fibers, are components of the first to the fifth or the sixth thoracic nerves. The so-called depressor nerve is a branch of the vagus. It consists chiefly of afferent fibers that are connected with receptors in the proximal parts of the aorta and the adjacent cardiac wall.

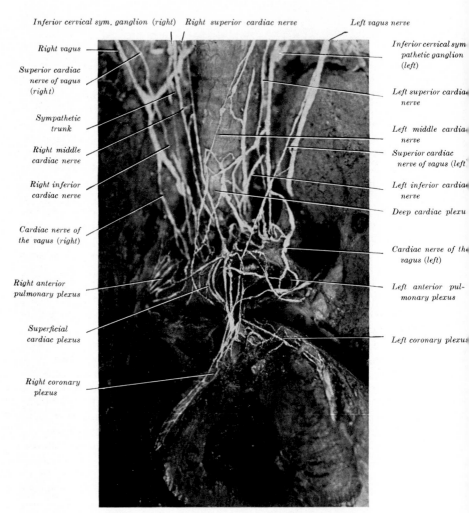

Inferior cervical sym. ganglion (right) Right superior cardiac nerve   Left vagus nerve

Right vagus

Superior cardiac nerve of vagus (right)

Sympathetic trunk

Right middle cardiac nerve

Right inferior cardiac nerve

Cardiac nerve of the vagus (right)

Right anterior pulmonary plexus

Superficial cardiac plexus

Right coronary plexus

Inferior cervical sym pathetic ganglion (left)

Left superior cardia nerve

Left middle cardia nerve

Superior cardiac nerve of vagus (left

Left inferior cardia nerve

Deep cardiac plexu

Cardiac nerve of th vagus (left)

Left anterior pul monary plexus

Left coronary plexu

Fig. 36.—Photograph of dissection of the nerves to the heart in the human cadaver. (By permission of Dr. J. D. Humber.)

THE CARDIAC PLEXUS

Location and Distribution.—The cardiac plexus is situated at the base of the heart and is composed of a superficial and a deep part. The superficial cardiac plexus lies superficial to the pericardium in the concavity of the aortic arch. It is made up largely by the left superior sympathetic cardiac nerve and the inferior cervical cardiac branch of the left vagus. These nerves approach the heart by passing over the arch of the aorta. They

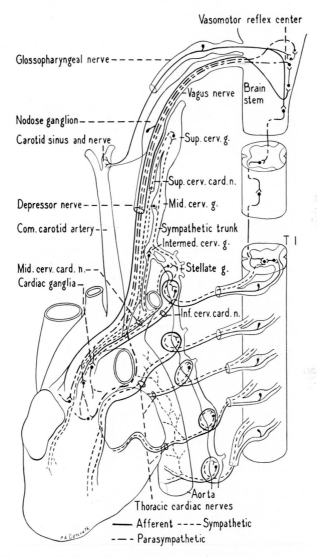

FIG. 37.—Diagrammatic illustration of the sympathetic, parasympathetic and afferent innervation of the heart, (Kuntz, 1944).

meet on the right side of the ligamentum arteriosum where there usually is located a small ganglion, the cardiac ganglion of Wrisberg.

The deep cardiac plexus is situated behind the arch of the aorta and in part between the aorta and the pulmonary veins. It is a large plexus consisting of two lateral parts joined together by numerous fibrous communications. These two parts are unlike in composition and distribution. The one on the right side receives contributions from the right superior, middle and inferior cervical and the thoracic sympathetic cardiac nerves and all the cardiac branches of the right vagus. The one on the left side receives contributions from the left middle and inferior cervical and the thoracic sympathetic cardiac nerves and the superior cervical and the thoracic cardiac branches of the left vagus. Thus, all the extrinsic nerves that contribute to the innervation of the heart, except the inferior cervical cardiac branch of the left vagus and the left superior sympathetic cardiac nerve, enter the deep cardiac plexus. It also receives rami from the superficial cardiac plexus.

The superficial cardiac plexus sends branches of distribution along the pulmonary artery to join the anterior (right) coronary plexus. It also sends branches along the left branch of the pulmonary artery to the anterior pulmonary plexus and between the aortic arch and the bifurcation of the pulmonary artery to the left portion of the deep cardiac plexus.

The right portion of the deep cardiac plexus contributes largely to the right, or anterior, coronary plexus. The latter also receives fibers from the superficial cardiac plexus. It supplies the substance of the heart along the course of the right coronary artery. The right portion of the deep cardiac plexus also contributes to the posterior coronary plexus and communicates with the right anterior pulmonary plexus. Reinforced by fibers from the superficial cardiac plexus, the left portion of the deep plexus gives rise to the left, or posterior, coronary plexus which supplies the substance of the heart along the course of the left coronary artery. This portion of the deep cardiac plexus also contributes to the left anterior pulmonary plexus.

The deep cardiac plexus in man has been further subdivided into six more or less distinct plexuses, the anterior and posterior atrial and the right and left anterior and right and left posterior ventricular plexuses. Corresponding subdivisions of the deep cardiac plexus have been described in the calf, the cat and the dog. The plexuses named above appear to be constant components of the cardiac nerve supply, although they anastomose freely with one another and vary within relatively wide limits in different individuals. Beneath the epicardium the larger nerve trunks accompany the coronary vessels. Smaller nerves deviate from the larger ones, usually at right angles to the courses of the vessels, and form a simple subepicardial network. The fibers of these nerves interlace in a complex manner beneath the epicardium both in the atria and the ventricles. Many of them come into relation to ganglion cells. Others penetrate the myocardium. Some of the latter reach the subendocardial tissue where they form a plexus.

Distribution of the Cardiac Ganglia.—The intrinsic innervation of the heart has been studied by many investigators, but there is no general agreement regarding the number and the distribution of nerve fibers in the several layers of the cardiac wall. Ganglia have been reported in all parts of the heart in mammals, including man, and in lower vertebrates. The results of most of the more recent investigations indicate a limited distribution of cardiac ganglia in most mammals. Perman (1924), who investigated 30 human hearts, found numerous ganglia on the dorsal surfaces of the atria and the roots of the great vessels. These ganglia, according to his account, are always interpolated in the nerve trunks. He divided them into two groups: one in proximity to the aorta and the pulmonary artery and extending to the proximal ventricular wall; the other on the posterior surfaces of the atria and extending to the proximal parts of the ventricles. The first group is associated with the nerves that pass ventral to the transverse sinus and supply the ventral surface of the heart. The

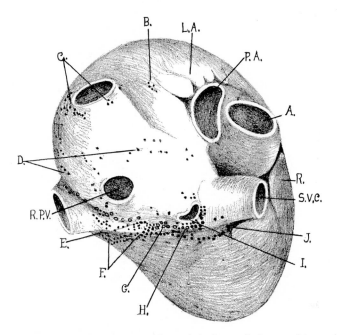

Fig. 38.—Distribution of ganglia at the base of the heart of a human fetus. *A.*, Aorta; *B.*, ganglia in the sulcus between the left atrium and left auricle; *C.*, ganglia at the mouth of the pulmonary vein; *D.*, ganglia in the esophageal sulcus of the left atrium; *E.* and *F.*, ganglia in the caudal portion of the sulcus terminalis; *G.*, ganglia in the interatrial septum; *H.*, ganglia in the sulcus terminalis; *I.*, ganglia at the mouth of the right superior pulmonary vein; *J.*, superior group of ganglia in the sulcus terminalis; *O.A.*, left auricle; *R.P.V.*, right pulmonary vein; *S.V.C.*, superior vena cava. (Redrawn from Francillon.)

other is associated with the nerves that pass dorsal to the transverse sinus to supply the atria and the greater part of the dorsal surfaces of the ventricles. Woollard (1926), who combined intravital methylene blue staining and the process of clearing used in the Spalteholtz method, studied transparent preparations of the superficial layers of the entire heart, including the visceral pericardium and a stratum of the underlying muscle of various vertebrates, including the snake, the rabbit, the cat and the dog. He described ganglia in abundance on the ventral and the dorsal surfaces of the left atrium and extending to both auricular appendages, a chain of ganglia extending along the interatrial septum, several large ganglia in the region of the atrio-ventricular sulcus, numerous smaller ones adjacent to the base of the pulmonary artery and along the proximal portion of its course.   No ganglia were found on the ventricular side of the atrio-ventricular sulcus, except in the heart of the snake, where collections of ganglia occur in the region of the posterior interventricular sulcus.   Isolated observations suggest the occasional occurrence of ganglia in the walls of the ventricles in various mammals.   In the Cetacea and the Artiodactyla, according to Davies *et al.* (1952), ganglion cells are widely distributed in the epicardium and the endocardium of the ventricles.   They have also

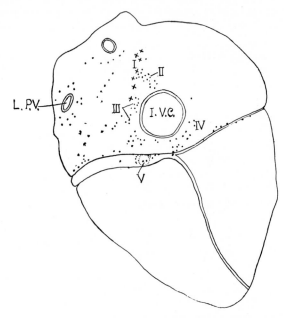

Fig. 39.—Distribution of ganglia on the diaphragmatic aspect of the heart of a human fetus. *I*, Ganglia in the interatrial septum; *II*, ganglia in the sulcus terminalis; *III*, ganglia in the wall of the right atrium; ganglia adjacent to the mouth of the inferior vena cava (*I.V.C.*); *L.V.P.*, left pulmonary vein; *V*, projection of the mouth of the coronary sinus in the right atrium. (Redrawn from Francillon.)

reported bipolar and unipolar as well as multipolar ganglion cells in the cardiac plexus.   On the basis of all the available data it appears that ganglion cells occur only rarely, if at all, in the ventricular walls in the hearts of most mammals.

The intramural cardiac ganglia vary greatly in size.   The larger ones may be observed macroscopically in transparent preparations.   The smaller ones can only be detected microscopically.   As observed by Francillon (1928) in an advanced human fetus, the individual ganglia contain 8 to 150 ganglion cells.   Most of them lie in the subepicardial connective tissue. Their distribution, as observed by Francillon, is illustrated in Figures 38 and 39.

Cardiac Ganglion Cells.—In general the cardiac ganglion cells are comparable to those in the intramural ganglia of other viscera, *e.g.*, the enteric ganglia. They include some with only short dendrites, some with only long dendrites, and some with both long and short dendrites. According to de Castro (1932), ganglion cells with numerous short, frequently branching dendrites are very common. Those of adjacent ganglion cells frequently terminate in dendritic brushes in which some branches of long dendrites also terminate. The ganglion cells with only long dendrites usually show 5 to 10 of these processes, which branch infrequently. They commonly terminate within the same ganglion in pericellular nests or dendritic brushes or glomeruli. Some extend into adjacent ganglia. The ganglion cells with both long and short dendrites vary widely with respect to the numbers of their processes. Many of the short ones terminate close to the cell bodies.

Terminations of Incoming Fibers.—As the extrinsic nerves enter the cardiac plexus the fiber bundles gradually undergo changes in composition as they subdivide, intermingle with one another and enter the cardiac ganglia. The cardiac branches of the vagi include preganglionic and visceral afferent components most of which are myelinated. The sympathetic cardiac nerves include postganglionic fibers, some of which are myelinated, and visceral afferents most of which are myelinated. Components of the vagus and the sympathetic nerves, therefore, cannot be identified on the basis of their condition with respect to myelinization. In general, preganglionic fibers are larger than postganglionic ones, but this does not afford a useful criterion, since many of the vagus fibers are actually smaller than the largest of the sympathetic fibers. There are no known morphological criteria by which pre- and postganglionic fibers can certainly be separated from one another in the terminal plexuses. Woollard recognized three distinct types of fibers in the extrinsic cardiac nerves. Some are myelinated and exhibit nodes of Ranvier. They may be regarded as visceral afferent. The depressor nerve includes fibers of this type. Some unmyelinated fibers with smooth contour may be traced into the cardiac ganglia. The preganglionic character of these fibers is strongly suggested. On the other hand, fibers of this type may often be identified as arising from cells in the cardiac ganglia. They obviously are postganglionic. As they approach their terminal distribution, they become exceedingly fine and exhibit the varicosities characteristic of postganglionic fibers. The third group consists of varicose fibers of very much smaller caliber than those of the other two types. Fibers of this type were observed in the incoming nerves and throughout the cardiac plexus. They were greatly reduced in numbers in the incoming nerves following extirpation of the stellate ganglia. This observation suggests that they are postganglionic components of the sympathetic nerves. Woollard observed no alterations in the intraganglionic fiber terminations in the cardiac plexus or changes in the cardiac ganglion cells following removal of a large percentage of the sympathetic fibers by extirpation of both stellate ganglia.

Terminal Distribution of Nerve Fibers.—Efferent.—An abundant efferent innervation of the cardiac musculature is generally conceded, but there is no general agreement regarding the terminal distribution of the nerves in the heart and the relative importance of the sympathetic and the parasympathetic cardiac nerves. A nerve plexus composed chiefly of unmyelinated fibers is present in the subepicardial tissue in all parts of the heart. The intracardiac ganglia are associated with this plexus. It is most abundant in the areas of distribution of the ganglia and throughout the interatrial septum. Fiber bundles that arise from it penetrate the musculature and ramify throughout the myocardium, forming a loose meshwork between the fascicles of muscle cells and around the blood vessels.

In transparent preparations of the hearts of cats and guinea-pigs, Woollard (1926) traced nerve fiber bundles along the posterior surface of the left atrium which bear no ganglia and receive no fibers derived from ganglia in the cardiac plexus. These bundles probably are composed of sympathetic fibers that reach the ventricular wall without interruption in ganglia. In no instance could he trace fibers directly from the ganglia into the ventricles. Both fibers of sympathetic origin and fibers derived from cardiac ganglia could be traced into the atrial walls. After degeneration of the severed sympathetic fibers, following extirpation of both stellate ganglia, the distribution and the abundance of fibers was altered much more profoundly in the ventricles than in the atria. The intramuscular plexus, so prominent in Woollard's preparations of normal ventricular muscle, could hardly be demonstrated in preparations of the ventricles of the operated animals. His findings strongly suggest that the atria and the atrio-ventricular bundle are innervated through both sympathetic and parasympathetic fibers and that the ventricular muscle is innervated chiefly through sympathetic fibers. The entire atrio-ventricular conduction system is abundantly supplied with unmyelinated nerve fibers. In silver preparations of the hearts and adjacent structures in very young animals (cats, dogs), Nonidez (1939) found that the preganglionic components of the vagi and the axions of the cardiac ganglion cells were more heavily impregnated than the fibers derived from the sympathetic trunk ganglia. He could trace axons of the cardiac ganglion cells to their terminations in the atrial and auricular musculature and the nodes of the conductive system, but not into the ventricular musculature. The less heavily impregnated sympathetic fibers could be traced into the ventricular musculature as well as into the atrial and auricular muscle and the conductive system.

According to Woollard's account, the fibers that supply the cardiac muscle form delicate plexuses around the muscle fibers. Nerve fibers from these plexuses ultimately penetrate the individual muscle cells and, running in the sarcoplasm, sometimes extend through the protoplasmic bridges into adjacent muscle fibers, giving off occasional terminal twigs which end in small bulb-like enlargements or loops. Jones (1927) also described intracellular terminal structures in the ventricular muscle of the cat. According to Boeke (1933), nerve fiber terminations of this character, which usually lie in proximity to the nucleus of the muscle cell, occur only in relatively small numbers in the myocardium. He emphasized the importance of the terminal plexus in the cardiac muscle, which he regards as comparable to the terminal plexus in smooth muscle, through which, according to his point of view, the autonomic fibers make functional connections with the muscle cells.

The innervation of the conductive system in the heart has been described in part by various investigators, but it has not generally been regarded as a major factor in the innervation of the cardiac muscle. According to the account of Stotler and McMahon (1947), the sinu-atrial and the atrio-ventricular nodes receive an exceedingly abundant nerve supply. The sinu-atrial and the atrio-ventricular bundles are also abundantly innervated. Relatively few nerve fibers extend directly into the atrial and the ventricular walls. The data reported have been interpreted as indicating that the motor innervation of the heart is mediated through the elements of the conductive system that intervene between the nerves and the cardiac muscle. The fibers of the conductive system that radiate from the sinu-atrial and the atrio-ventricular nodes carry their innervation with them, but the nerve fibers do not extend to the zones of transition of these fibers into the cardiac muscle. The efferent nerve fibers that extend into the cardiac muscle are distributed in relation to the blood vessels. The conductive tissue appears to retain in a high degree the primitive protoplasmic functions of irritability, conductivity and contractility.

These findings may afford a basis for the explanation of some of the discrepancies in the accounts of various investigators relative to the distribution of sympathetic and parasympathetic nerve fibers in the myocardium. The neural regulation of the functional activity of the cardiac muscle undoubtedly can be accounted for satisfactorily without the assumption that nerve fibers make direct functional contacts with cardiac muscle cells.

Afferent.—Structures that appear to be receptors connected with afferent nerve fibers have been described in the epicardium and in the subepicardial connective tissue. A nerve plexus, probably made up chiefly of afferent fibers, is present throughout the atria and the ventricles and extends onto the atrio-ventricular and the semilunar valves. It is most highly developed over the inferior portion of the interatrial septum. The fibers in this plexus are unmyelinated or thinly myelinated, but they are derived from heavily myelinated ones. Its afferent nature is demonstrated by the observation that it undergoes extensive degeneration following section of the vagus nerves distal to the nodose ganglion. Ablation of the spinal ganglia in the rostral thoracic segments resulted in no extensive degeneration of the endocardial plexus except near the apices of the ventricles (Nettleship, 1936). Lipp (1951) has described the plexuses on the ventricular surfaces of the semilunar valves at the base of the pulmonary artery as particularly abundant. He has advanced the opinion that these structures may be stimulated by pressure and that they may serve to indicate differences in pressure between the cardiac and the pulmonary circulation.

Well-defined terminal structures associated with the endocardial plexus are relatively rare. The simplest ones, as described by Nettleship, are uncomplicated twigs that terminate in dot-like expansions which may be single or double. The more complex fiber terminations involve more or less elaborate arborization of the terminal branches. These terminal structures probably do not represent the only receptive areas. Not infrequently nerve fibers within the plexus split, interweave, coil and twist upon themselves, forming structures which Nettleship has designated "sensory nodal points.'"

Encapsulated sensory nerve endings lying between bundles of muscle fibers, muscle spindles of varying complexity, and simpler configurations of terminal branches on the surface of muscle fibers have been observed in the myocardium (King, 1939). Structures similar to tactile corpuscles have also been observed in the atrio-ventricular bundle. All of these receptors are connected with relatively large myelinated nerve fibers.

Nettleship (1936) also described a plexiform structure surrounding the basal portions of both the aorta and the pulmonary artery which in part lies adjacent to the adventitia of these great vessels. It is derived from the subepicardial network at the base of the heart but is quite distinct from the endocardial plexus. This plexus underwent extensive degeneration following section of the vagus nerves distal to the nodose ganglia, but not following vagus section proximal to these ganglia, extirpation of the stellate ganglia or ablation of the spinal ganglia in the rostral thoracic segments; consequently, it must be regarded as made up mainly of the terminal branches of afferent vagus fibers.

Innervation of the Coronary Arteries.—The coronary arteries are abundantly innervated. Large fibers of vagus origin terminate in the adventitia apparently without penetrating the media. These undoubtedly are afferent. The media is richly supplied, chiefly through unmyelinated fibers of small caliber. Most of these probably are sympathetic, but fibers that arise in the cardiac ganglia may also be traced directly to the coronary arteries. This abundant nerve supply also extends along the branches of the coronary arteries as far as the arterioles.

Following extirpation of both stellate ganglia, Woollard (1926), found that a large percentage of the nerve fibers in the media of the coronary arteries and their larger branches underwent degeneration, but the nerves of the smaller branches and the arterioles were affected to a lesser degree. He, therefore, concluded that the coronary arteries are innervated through both sympathetic and parasympathetic nerves, but the smaller branches and the arterioles are innervated mainly through parasympathetic nerves. This finding is corroborated by experimental data reported by Nettleship (1936). In his experiments, bilateral extirpation of the stellate ganglion in the cat resulted in degeneration of one-half to three-fourths of the plexus on the coronary arteries, but the finer nerve fibers supplying the coronaries and the plexuses on the arterioles and the capillaries remained intact. These findings are of particular interest in view of the widely divergent results of physiological studies involving coronary vasodilatation and vasoconstriction.

In Nettleship's experiments, ablation of the spinal ganglia in the rostral thoracic segments resulted in degeneration of some of the larger fibers in the coronary plexuses, indicating their afferent character. Section of the vagi distal to the nodose ganglia, on the other hand, resulted in but little degeneration in the coronary plexuses. These results indicate that the major portion of the afferent innervation of the coronary vessels is effected through spinal nerve components.

FUNCTIONAL RELATIONSHIPS OF THE CARDIAC NERVES

Intrinsic Nerves.—The regulatory control of the heart that is exercised through the visceral components of the cerebrospinal nerves obviously is mediated through its intrinsic nerves, but to what extent the various activities of the heart depend on impulses emanating from the central nervous system is not fully known. The capacity for rhythmic contraction is inherent in cardiac muscle, but this does not necessarily imply that rhythmic cardiac activity may go on independently of the intrinsic cardiac nerves.

Various investigators have maintained that the cardiac plexus includes a system of local reflex mechanisms. Morphological evidence for the existence of intracardiac reflex arcs must be regarded as inconclusive. The fact that rhythmic contractions of the heart may continue after its connections with the central nervous system are severed, or even after it is removed from the body, does not warrant the assumption of an intrinsic reflex mechanism. It only shows that the isolated heart possesses automaticity, *i.e.*, the heart with its intrinsic nerves possesses the capacity to initiate and carry out the various phases of cardiac activity in the proper sequence to bring about coördinated contractions of its various parts.

The normal sequence of contraction of the cardiac musculature probably involves differentiated conduction systems and graded differences in the degree of responsiveness to stimulation. The cycle of contraction is initiated in the region adjacent to the entrance of the superior vena cava into the right atrium, *i.e.*, the area which corresponds to the sinus venosus in the more primitive vertebrate heart. This area, in which the contraction phase also continues longest, may be regarded as the seat of the pacemakers for the entire heart.

In all vertebrate embryos the heart arises as the so-called cardiac tube. The remains of this primitive tube are not apparent in the mammalian heart on superficial examination, but it has been shown by careful anatomical studies that it exists in the specialized tissue that makes up the atrio-ventricular bundle. This tissue is histologically distinct from the rest of the cardiac tissue and is disposed in a manner which suggests that it is the pathway along which the heart beat is propagated.

At the upper end of this bundle, in the mammalian heart, is the atrio-ventricular node. This structure, situated near the dorsal margin of the interatrial septum, consists of an aggregate of peculiar primitive cells and fibers. It extends into the interventricular septum, and, at a point a little ventral to the attachment of the septal valve, it bifurcates into right and left branches that extend toward the apex of the heart just beneath the endocardium on either side of the interventricular septum. Each branch ultimately gives rise to an intricate system of smaller branches which become reflected over the inner surfaces of the ventricles. These branches are made up of the so-called Purkinje fibers many of which ultimately terminate in close relationship to the papillary muscles.

10

The evidence available strongly favors the conclusion that the heart beat actually originates in the sinu-atrial node. From this point it probably spreads through the muscular tissue of the atrial wall until it reaches the atrio-ventricular node. It is then transmitted to the ventricles along the atrio-ventricular bundle. This fact has been most clearly demonstrated by experiments involving heart-block. If, in the mammalian heart, a clamp is so arranged that it compresses practically nothing but the atrio-ventricular bundle, partial or complete heart-block may be produced at will. When moderate pressure is applied, ventricular contraction follows regularly every second, third or fourth atrial contraction. When the pressure is extreme, the rhythm of the ventricle becomes entirely independent of that of the atrium. When the pressure is relieved the heart-block usually disappears and the normal sequence of atrial and ventricular contractions is reëstablished. Additional data in support of the theory that the impulses for ventricular contraction are conducted through the atrio-ventricular bundle have been reported by Davies and Francis (1952).

From the atrio-ventricular bundle, the impulse is propagated along its many branches which terminate in close association with the papillary muscles. These muscles are the first part of the ventricular musculature to contract. This obviously is significant in connection with the function of the papillary muscles in putting the chordæ tendinæ under tension, so as to keep the atrio-ventricular flaps from bulging into the atria when, at the beginning of ventricular contraction, high intraventricular pressure is brought to bear on their ventricular surfaces. After being initiated at these points in the ventricle, the wave of contraction seems to spread through the muscle at a fairly uniform rate.

The atrio-ventricular bundle is abundantly innervated through both sympathetic and parasympathetic nerve fibers. Conduction through the atrio-ventricular bundle is known to be subject to alteration by impulses reaching it through the cardiac branches of the vagi, particularly those of the left vagus. Experimental data support the assumption that vagus stimulation does not exert a direct effect on the cardiac musculature, but results in the liberation of an acetylcholine-like substance in the sinus area the effect of which is transmitted to the musculature through the atrio-ventricular bundle.

Extrinsic Nerves.—The control exercised through the extrinsic innervation of the heart on cardiac activities is primarily regulatory. In general, cardiac inhibition is mediated through the vagi and cardiac acceleration through the sympathetic cardiac nerves. The extrinsic cardiac nerves also mediate impulses that modify the force of the heart beats and the conductivity of the cardiac muscle.

Cardiac acceleration due to impulses conducted by the vagi has been demonstrated experimentally. Cardiac accelerator fibers appear to be more abundant in the right vagus than in the left. The chemical mediator liberated in the heart when its rate is accelerated due to vagus stimulation appears to be sympathin. This response cannot be elicited reflexly by stimulation of the carotid sinus or afferent vagus fibers (Kabat, 1940). In totally sympathectomized dogs, as reported by Brouha *et al.* (1939), the cardiac acceleration that occurred in response to muscular exercise and emotional excitation could be consistently abolished by intracranial, bilateral vagus section. Cardiac acceleration due to muscular exercise could be recognized in totally sympathectomized dogs fourteen days after the operation, but it did not reach its maximum until approximately one year after sympathectomy. The cardiac acceleration observed in these animals obviously represents a shift of function to potential mechanisms which normally are not brought into play. This shift requires a certain length of time. The sensitivity of the mechanisms involved apparently develops gradually after the normal accelerator mechanisms are destroyed. Okinaka *et al.* (1951) also found that cardiac accelerator fibers in the vagus nerves could be demonstrated with greater facility following extirpation of the stellate ganglion.

Cardiac acceleration due to muscular exercise could be recognized in totally sympathectomized dogs fourteen days after the operation, but it did not reach its maximum until approximately one year after sympathectomy. The cardiac acceleration observed in these animals obviously represents a shift of function to potential mechanisms which normally are not brought into play. This shift requires a certain length of time. The sensitivity of the mechanisms involved apparently develops gradually after the normal accelerator mechanisms.

In mammals, as in cold-blooded vertebrates, the right vagus acts chiefly on the sinu-atrial node and the left vagus on the atrio-ventricular bundle. Stimulation of the right vagus always results in retardation and weakening of both the atrial and the ventricular beats. Stimulation of the left vagus sometimes has little effect on the atrial beat, although it may bring about a condition of partial heart-block. If the atrio-ventricular bundle is clamped so that a condition of partial heart-block already exists, stimulation of the left vagus may result in complete heart-block. The left vagus also exerts a direct influence on the ventricles that affects the force of contraction rather than the rate.

The various ganglion cell groups in the vicinity of the sinu-atrial junction are related to both vagi. The left vagus is distributed predominantly to the superior caval ganglia and the ganglia at the head of the sinu-atrial node. The right vagus is distributed chiefly to the intercaval ganglia and those at the tail of the sinu-atrial node. The ganglia in the coronary sinus usually receive only fibers of the left vagus. The greater inhibitory power of the right vagus noted above appears to be directly related to its more extensive distribution to the ganglia associated with the sinu-atrial node. The quantitative distribution of both vagus nerves to the ganglia associated with the sinu-atrial node varies widely in different animals.

Stimulation of the sympathetic cardiac nerves on the right side results in greater acceleration of the heart-rate than equal stimulation of the sympathetic cardiac nerves on the left side. It also augments the force of the atrial contraction, but has no marked effect on the force of the ventricular contraction. It does not alter the interval between atrial and ventricular contractions. Stimulation of the left sympathetic cardiac nerves exerts no marked influence on atrial contraction, but augments the force of ventricular contraction. It also tends to shorten the interval between atrial and ventricular contractions. Section of the sympathetic cardiac nerves results in no marked depression of the basal heart-rate.

Afferent impulses from any part of the body may influence the heart through the vagi. Impulses conducted by certain afferent nerves elicit more marked cardiac responses than those conducted by others. Stimulation of the pulmonary branches of the vagi usually results in marked cardiac inhibition. Stimulation of trigeminal fibers through the mucosa of the upper respiratory passages, as by inhalation of irritating vapors, likewise, brings about strong cardiac inhibition. Profound cardiac inhibition is also elicited by violent stimulation of the mesentery, as by a blow on the abdomen, or by irritation of the sensory nerves of the gastro-intestinal canal either mechanically or by disease.

In anesthetized dogs, as reported by Owen (1933), distention, sudden collapse or irritation of the hollow viscera rarely elicited cardiac arrhythmias. In dogs which had been jaundiced due to obstruction of the flow of bile, distention of the bile duct caused either ectopic atrial beats or heartblock which usually was associated in time of occurrence with the appearance of retching or vomiting. Crittenden and Ivy (1933) also reported that nausea, retching and vomiting produced by the subcutaneous injection of apomorphine in dogs may elicit cardiac irregularities, such as heartblocks, cardiac arrests and atrial or ventricular ectopic beats. In their experiments, nausea usually was accompanied by tachycardia, and retching by bradycardia.

Retardation of the heart-rate in man may be caused by direct stimulation of the vagus center, as by the pressure of a blood clot or a tumor in the medulla or by the reaction of this center to some unusual hormone in the blood. The vagus center is also stimulated by a general increase in intracranial pressure. A rise in general cerebral pressure causes slowing of the heart-rate. Various other conditions that result in direct stimulation of the vagus center, likewise, cause temporary or prolonged retardation of the cardiac rate.

An increase in the blood pressure in the carotid arteries, under normal conditions, results in retardation of the heart-rate. External pressure in the vicinity of the bifurcation of the common carotid artery likewise may elicit reflex bradycardia. The afferent limbs of the reflex arcs concerned in this reaction are components of the carotid sinus nerves. The inhibitory impulses are conducted to the heart through visceral efferent components of the vagi. The reflex connections undoubtedly are made in the nucleus of the vagus nerve. Blocking the vagus nerves, according to Kjellberg *et al.* (1951), resulted in increased heart-rate, decreased duration of systolic contraction, increased amplitude of the first and the second heart sounds and a rise in arterial pressure. Blocking of the sympathetic cardiac nerves resulted in a reversal of these effects.

Cardiac acceleration is mediated through the sympathetic cardiac nerves, but it does not involve the entire sympathetic supply. The cervical sympathetic nerves do not appear to be concerned with cardiac acceleration. In man the cardiac accelerator nerves appear to be limited to the second to the fifth thoracic segments, bilaterally. Those on the right side are slightly more important than those on the left (Smithwick *et al.*, 1949).

Bilateral section of these nerves results in a decrease in the heart-rate, but not necessarily in untoward effects. In addition to bringing about cardiac acceleration, sympathetic stimulation also modifies the conductivity and the contractile power of the cardiac musculature.

Sympathetic stimulation differs from vagus stimulation of the heart in that a longer latent period elapses before it becomes effective. The effect of sympathetic stimulation also continues longer than that of vagus stimulation after the stimulus has subsided. When the vagus and the sympathetic nerves are stimulated simultaneously the vagus effect is observed first and is usually followed, after the removal of the stimulus, by the sympathetic effect. If stimulation of both nerves is continued for a long time, the vagus becomes fatigued and permits the sympathetic to become effective earlier than it would if the vagus alone were stimulated. The sympathetic influence, however, is never as strong as the vagus influence. Vagus and sympathetic nerves, therefore, are not antagonistic in the sense that the influence of the one is neutralized by that of the other, but when both are stimulated simultaneously the heart responds first to the vagus and later to the sympathetic. This difference in the response of the heart to vagus and sympathetic stimulation probably is an important factor in the normal functioning of the organ. It also lends support to the theory that the vagus center is dominant in the regulatory control of the heart that is mediated through its extrinsic nerves.

Acceleration of the heart-rate may be brought about either by diminution of impulses from the vagus center or by increase in impulses from the spinal accelerator centers. Reflexes carried out through the spinal centers, that influence the heart-rate, may be demonstrated under experimental conditions. If both vagi are cut and the peripheral end of one of them is stimulated sufficiently to keep the heart beating at almost its normal rate, stimulation of certain sensory nerves may elicit acceleration of the heart beat. Under normal conditions reflex control of cardiac rate through the spinal accelerator centers probably is much less important than reflex control through the vagus center.

A rise in body temperature or application of heat to the skin elicits reflex cardiac acceleration through the spinal accelerator centers. Reflexes initiated in the cutaneous thermal receptors probably are more significant in the regulation of cardiac rate than changes in body temperature. Accelerator reflexes are initiated more readily by a hot water bath than by dry air-radiant heat applied to the skin. Muscular activity may elicit reflex cardiac acceleration even though the general body temperature is not increased. This reaction appears to be due to the stimulating effect of metabolites which accumulate in the active skeletal muscles.

Afferent impulses that arise in the heart and the proximal portion of the aorta reach the central nervous system through both the vagus and spinal nerves. The afferent impulses conducted from the heart and the aorta through the vagi probably do not reach the threshold of consciousness, but elicit reflex vasomotor responses. Impulses of cardiac origin that eventuate in pain are conducted into the central nervous system through afferent fibers associated with the sympathetic cardiac nerves.

The so-called depressor nerve plays an important rôle in the regulatory control of the heart through its influence on both the cardio-inhibitory and the vasomotor centers. Whenever the blood pressure rises above its normal limits the depressor fibers are stimulated, probably by the mechanical effect of the increased intracardiac pressure, and conduct impulses to the medulla which tend to bring about reflex inhibition of the heart through the vagus center and inhibition of vascular tonus through the vasoconstrictor center. In addition to the depressor fibers, the vagus nerves include some cardiopressor fibers at least in some cases.

The heart is protected against variations in arterial pressure and blood supply not only by depressor reflexes initiated in the cardio-aortic pressoreceptive zone but also through other pressoreceptive reflex mechanisms. The coronary blood flow depends in part on the pressure in the aorta. The pressures in the aorta, the left atrium and the left ventricle depend chiefly on the pressoreceptive sensitivity of the left ventricle, the aortic arch and the pulmonary artery. The venous pressure and the pressure in the pulmonary artery and, consequently, the pressure in the right atrium and ventricle are regulated at least in part by the pressoreceptive sensitivity of the pulmonary arteries and veins, the venæ cavæ and the right atrium.

Chemoreceptive reflexes play a significant rôle particularly in the regulation of the cardiac output. When the human subject, on a tilting board, is tilted passively to the upright position the pulse rate is increased and the cardiac output is diminished. These changes are correlated with the shift of blood from the trunk to the lower extremities (Asmussen *et al.*, 1939). Cutaneous vasoconstriction is also indicated by a reduction in skin temperature. The cardiac acceleration and the vasoconstriction which occur on tilting undoubtedly are reflex responses to stimulation of the pressoreceptors in the cardio-aortic pressoreceptive zone and the carotid sinus which tend to maintain the blood pressure at normal levels, but do not tend to increase the cardiac output. If the subject on the tilting board, whose cardiac output is decreased, breathes air low in O_2, the volume of the blood issuing from the heart is increased, which indicates that stimulation of the chemosensitive receptors initiates reflexes which tend to increase the cardiac output. Similar reflexes are also initiated by the onset of work (Asmussen and Knudsen, 1942).

The literature bearing on the regulation of the coronary circulation is voluminous and records many conflicting observations. In a comprehensive review of this literature Anrep (1926) pointed out that the weight of evidence favors the hypothesis that constriction of these vessels is mediated through the parasympathetic nerves, their dilatation through the sympathetic nerves. The results of certain later studies also support this assumption, and those of others support the opposite point of view. In experiments reported by Kountz *et al.* (1934), vagus stimulation resulted in retarding the rate of contraction of the normal human heart and increasing the flow of blood through the coronary vessels, and sympathetic stimulation resulted in accelerating the heart-rate and reducing the coronary flow. In perfusion experiments on the revived human heart, vagus stimulation reduced the coronary flow, and sympathetic stimulation increased it while there was dissociation of atrial and ventricular contractions, and the rate of contraction was not influenced by nerve impulses. The action of drugs which, in the beating heart, increase muscular activity and decrease coronary flow simulated the effects of sympathetic stimulation. The action of drugs which cause dilatation of the beating heart and increased coronary flow simulated the effects of vagus stimulation. No comparable similarity was noted between effects of nerve stimulation and the action of drugs which exert their influence primarily through the constrictor and the dilator fibers to the coronary vessels. On the basis of these experimental results, the conclusion was advanced that in man the cardiac nerves exert their influence on the coronary flow primarily through changes in the state of the cardiac muscle. The results of experiments carried out on the dog's heart in a state of ventricular fibrillation, reported by Katz and Jochim (1939), seem to support the assumption that the vagi include only cholinergic coronary vasodilator fibers which are tonically active, and the sympathetic cardiac nerves include both adrenergic coronary vasodilator and adrenergic coronary vasoconstrictor fibers which are tonically active. The action of the sympathetic nerves is predominantly vasoconstriction. Certain data reported by Hirsch (1952) seem to indicate that increased coronary blood flow elicited by administration of adrenin or by sympathetic stimulation is not due to dilatation of the coronary arteries.

In a study of the effect of the activity of skeletal muscles on the coronary circulation, Greene (1941) found that the coronary flow is sharply augmented at the beginning of muscular activity and the coronary dilatation persists into the after period. He advanced the opinion that reflex coronary dilatation associated with muscular activity is a major factor in the nutrition of the heart during the added strain incident to the activity of skeletal muscles. In experiments reported by Essex *et al.* (1943), the effects of exercise on coronary flow did not differ essentially in dogs that had been subjected to sympathetic denervation of the heart and normal control animals. In the absence of marked cardiac acceleration and elevation of blood pressure the coronary flow was not modified by exercise. In animals with vagotomized or totally denervated hearts the coronary flow appeared to be influenced mainly by the blood pressure.

Chapter VIII

INNERVATION OF THE BLOOD VESSELS

ANATOMICAL DATA

Source of the Nerve Supply. — The innervation of the blood vessels includes both efferent and afferent nerve fibers. The efferent nerves include both vasoconstrictor and vasodilator fibers. The former are chiefly sympathetic. The latter include both sympathetic and parasympathetic components. The afferent fibers distributed to the blood vessels are components of the sensory cerebrospinal nerve roots. Certain vascular areas, particularly (1) the proximal portion of the aorta including the aortic arch and the aortic bodies, the proximal portion of the pulmonary artery and the cardiac walls adjacent to the great vessels, and (2) the carotid sinuses and the carotid bodies are supplied with special afferent nerves. Those that supply the former area, which may be called the cardio-aortic zone, are branches of the vagi that constitute the depressor nerves. The carotid sinuses and the carotid bodies are supplied through branches of the glossopharyngeal nerves known as the carotid sinus nerves (Fig. 40). The carotid sinus may also receive an afferent branch of the vagus. These vascular areas, with their afferent nerves, may be regarded as pressoreceptive and chemo-receptive mechanisms.

The large blood vessels of the trunk, *e.g.*, the aorta and the inferior vena cava, are innervated quite directly through the autonomic nerves nearest to them. In the thorax, these vessels receive fibers directly from the sympathetic trunks and the cardiac plexus. In the abdomen, they are innervated through rami from the plexuses along the aorta. The arteries and the veins supplying the abdominal organs in the main are innervated in the same manner. The vessels in the neck and the head derive their efferent innervation chiefly from the cervical sympathetic ganglia. Rami from the inferior cervical and the upper thoracic ganglia form a plexus on the vertebral artery which extends rostrad. This plexus also receives fibers through rami of all the cervical nerves. Rami from the superior cervical ganglion form a rich plexus on the internal carotid and a lesser plexus on the external carotid artery through which the sympathetic system is extended into the head. Rami from the inferior cervical and the rostral thoracic sympathetic trunk ganglia also give rise to a plexus on the common carotid artery which is continuous with those on the internal and the external carotid arteries. The peripheral vessels are supplied by sympathetic fibers that join them through the somatic nerves that lie in closest proximity to them. Afferent nerve fibers in general reach the blood vessels via the nerves through which they receive efferent fibers.

The subclavian and the axillary arteries derive their efferent innervation directly from the sympathetic trunk, but all the more distal arteries in the upper extremity are innervated through sympathetic fibers that traverse the spinal nerves and are distributed to the various blood vessels at irregular intervals. The vessels in the more distal parts of the limbs, particularly those in the hands, are joined by branches of the adjacent nerves at more frequent intervals than those in the proximal parts of the limbs.

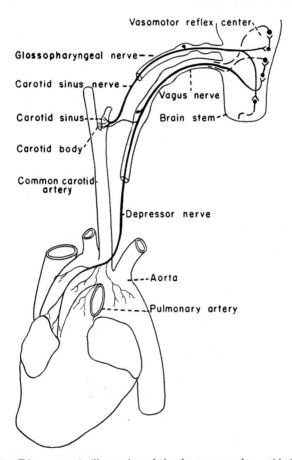

Fig. 40.—Diagrammatic illustration of the depressor and carotid sinus nerve.

The plexus on the abdominal aorta gives rise to a subordinate plexus on the common iliac artery, from which some fibers extend to the proximal portion of the femoral artery, but the more distal portions of the femoral artery and the other vessels of the lower extremity, like those of the upper extremity, are supplied with sympathetic fibers that traverse the somatic nerves and are distributed to the vessels at irregular intervals. The distribution of nerves to the large arteries of the lower extremity, as observed in a careful dissection, is illustrated in Figure 41.

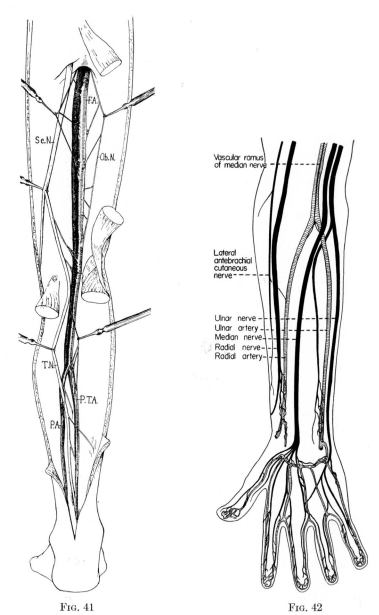

Fig. 41   Fig. 42

Fig. 41.—Drawing from a dissection of the lower extremity, showing the distribution of nerves to the large arteries. *F.A.*, Femoral artery; *Ob.N.*, obturator nerve; *P.A.*, peroneal artery; *P.T.A.*, posterior tibial artery; *Sc.N.*, sciatic nerve; *T.N.*, tibial nerve. (Dissection by Mr. I. Levy.)

Fig. 42.—Drawing from a dissection of the upper extremity, showing the distribution of nerves to the arteries of forearm and hand.

Nerve fibers derived from the aortic plexus accompany the peripheral arteries only short distances. Only a few fibers that extend onto the common iliac artery from the aortic plexus become definitely related to this artery. The external iliac artery is innervated through rami from the genito-femoral nerve. The femoral artery is innervated chiefly through branches of the femoral and the saphenous nerves.

The subclavian and the proximal part of the axillary artery are commonly innervated through fibers derived directly from the sympathetic trunk. The axillary and the proximal part of the brachial artery also receive fibers from the brachial plexus. Farther distad the brachial artery is supplied by branches of the several nerves that lie in proximity to it. In the proximal part of the arm it is supplied mainly by branches of the radial and the cutaneous nerves of the forearm. The distal half of the brachial artery is supplied chiefly through branches of the median nerve. The musculocutaneous nerve does not regularly supply branches to the brachial artery. The ulnar nerve occasionally supplies a few branches to its middle and distal parts.

The innervation of the blood vessels in the distal portions of the extremities is particularly abundant. Many of the smaller nerves that join them are so delicate that they cannot be detected by the ordinary methods of dissection. These finer rami are regularly imbedded in connective tissue. In general, they run nearly parallel to one another from the nerve trunk to the vessel, but frequently they exhibit more or less complex intercommunications. As they enter the adventitia, some of their fibers become incorporated in the adventitial plexus. Others pass through the adventitia and form a plexus at the surface of the media.

According to Woollard and Phillips (1933), the peripheral vasomotor and other sympathetic fibers have the same distribution as the nerves that convey them, e.g., the sympathetic fibers in the median or the ulnar nerves are limited to the areas supplied by the somatic components of these nerves, respectively, although the lines of demarcation are not as sharply drawn as those of the cutaneous nerves. Telford and Stopford (1933) have pointed out that the profound vasodilatation succeeding irritative lesions of such nerves as the median and the ulnar is not confined to the cutaneous territory of the affected nerve. They have also advanced certain evidence in support of the view that the innervation of the deep vessels of the palm is less simple than that of the cutaneous vessels. The distribution of nerves to the arteries of the forearm and hand is illustrated in Figure 42.

The blood vessels in the vertebral canal, including the intramedullary vessels of the spinal cord, are supplied with sympathetic nerve fibers segmentally from the sympathetic trunks through rami that traverse the intervertebral foramina. These rami also include afferent components of the corresponding spinal nerves.

The intracranial vessels, including the dural sinuses, are supplied with sympathetic nerve fibers chiefly from the plexuses on the internal carotid arteries. Some of the preganglionic fibers concerned with the sympathetic innervation of these vessels terminate in relation to ganglion cells located at levels more rostral than the superior cervical ganglion. An accessory sympathetic ganglion frequently occurs on the internal carotid artery near the bifurcation of the common carotid both in man and lower mammals. Ganglion cells also occur scattered along the internal carotid artery in some instances. According to Chorobski and Penfield (1932), the intracranial vessels also have a parasympathetic innervation. The post-ganglionic fibers concerned are derived chiefly from ganglion cells located in proximity to the union of the greater superficial petrosal with the internal carotid nerve. The preganglionic fibers that make synaptic connections with these ganglion cells traverse the greater superficial petrosal nerve. Cranial nerve branches have been traced to the dural vessels particularly from the trigeminal, the glossopharyngeal, the vagus and the hypoglossal nerves. Slender rami from most of the cranial nerves also join the pial and the intracerebral vessels. They are made up predominantly of afferent fibers supplied to the vessel walls and the meninges.

In the cat, as reported by Christensen *et al.* (1952), the nerves associated with the vertebral arteries probably make no significant contribution to the efferent innervation of intracranial blood vessels. Most of the fibers of sympathetic origin in these nerves join the cervical spinal nerves. Following degeneration of the sympathetic fibers in the vertebral nerves, there remains a delicate perivertebral plexus that appears to be made up chiefly of dorsal root fibers derived from the cervical nerves. This plexus is continuous with the plexus on the basilar artery. The latter plexus is continuous with more delicate plexuses on the arteries that arise from the basilar artery. Like the one on the basilar artery, they also receive fibers, probably afferent, from cranial nerves.

On the basis of these findings, the arteries associated with the brain stem appear to be only meagerly supplied with vasomotor nerves. Certain physiological data also indicate that sympathetic stimulation elicits only slight vasomotor responses in the blood vessels of the hind-brain. The sensory nature of the plexus associated with these vessels in man is indicated by experimental and clinical data (Ray and Wolff, 1940).

The nerves associated with the more rostral intracranial blood vessels, including the meningeal and the intracerebral vessels, like those associated with the basilar and the rostral portions of the vertebral arteries, are derived predominantly from sources other than the sympathetic trunks. Interruption of the sympathetic nerves along the internal carotid artery does not result in extensive degeneration in the intracranial perivascular plexuses (Chorobski and Penfield, 1932). The intracranial blood vessels, consequently, appear to be only meagerly supplied with vasomotor nerves of sympathetic origin. Parasympathetic nerve fibers also enter the cranial cavity in only relatively small numbers. The available anatomical data warrant the conclusion that the nerves associated with the intracranial blood vessels are predominantly afferent. The available physiological data also support this conclusion.

The chief pressoreceptive and chemoreceptive vascular areas are abundantly supplied with afferent fibers most of which are components of the vagus and the glossopharyngeal nerves. These areas include the proximal portions of the aorta and the pulmonary artery, the terminal portions of the great veins and adjacent portions of the heart, the carotid sinuses and the carotid and aortic bodies. The carotid and the aortic bodies are not essential components of the vascular system, but they are intimately related to it both developmentally and functionally.

The aortic (depressor) branches of the vagi differ in their distribution on the two sides. On the right side the aortic nerve terminates in relation to the innominate artery at the base of the right subclavian. On the left side most of its fibers terminate in relation to the arch of the aorta and the pulmonary artery. Both aortic nerves supply fibers to the aortic bodies adjacent to them. The carotid sinus and the carotid body on either side receive their afferent innervation through the carotid sinus nerve (Fig. 40).

Distribution of Nerve Fibers in Vessel Walls.—The intrinsic nerves of arteries and veins are arranged in a more or less definite manner. An outer plexus in the adventitia, a deeper plexus at the border between the adventitia and the media, and a plexus in the media have been described. They have been designated respectively the "adventitial" plexus, the "border" plexus and the "muscular" plexus. Certain investigators have not recognized a border plexus. Some also question the advisability of regarding the complex of nerve fibers in the media as a plexus. All concede that the adventitia and the media are abundantly supplied with intrinsic nerve fibers, but there is no general agreement regarding the existence of nerve fibers in the intima.

In general, the nerve fibers run longitudinally in the adventitia, but there is no reason to assume that individual fiber bundles extend along the vessel except for short distances. The fibers are in part myelinated and in part unmyelinated. They enter the adventitia through slender rami that arise from the somatic nerves. These rami can usually be traced only a short distance, if at all, along the vessel until they are lost in the adventitial tissue. The fibers of any one ramus do not all take the same course in the adventitia. Most of them extend distad, but some extend in the opposite direction. The fiber bundles are usually arranged with reference to the vasa vasorum, but to what extent they are functionally related to these small vessels is not apparent from the histological picture. The vasa vasorum apparently afford convenient pathways for the nerve fiber bundles through the adventitial tissue. In most instances, a fiber bundle which joins one of these small vessels accompanies it for a short distance and then deviates from its course through the connective tissue and joins another of the vasa vasorum. Capillaries in the adventitia commonly are accompanied by one or more nerve fibers, but it is quite impossible, on the basis of histological observations, to decide whether these fibers are functionally related to the capillaries.

From the plexus in the adventitia (Fig. 43), bundles of nerve fibers, chiefly unmyelinated, approach the media and form a plexus on its surface. From this plexus small bundles and individual nerve fibers penetrate the superficial zone of the media. Discrete efferent fiber terminations are rarely observed in the media in silver impregnated preparations, and nerve fibers rarely appear in the inner zone of the media, but the plexus at the surface of the media is sufficiently abundant to account for innervation of the entire musculature. The neural complex in the media has been described as a real nerve net by Woollard (1928) and Burns (1935). According to Boeke (1932, 1933), the nerve fibers in the media form a dense, intricate plexus that covers the entire muscular coat and extends between the muscle fibers so that it is present throughout the entire layer.   The terminal elements of this plexus, according to Boeke, penetrate the muscle cells and become continuous with an extremely delicate network within the cytoplasm.   The findings of various other investigators do not support this

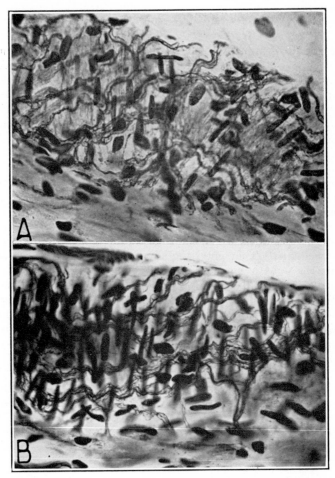

Fig. 43.—Photomicrographs showing nerve plexuses associated with arteries.   *A*, hepatic artery.   *B*, cystic artery.   (From sections prepared by Dr. W. F. *A*lexander.)

conclusion.   There is no general agreement regarding the morphological characteristics of the functional contacts of the nerves in the media with the muscle cells.   Jabonero (1951) reported histological data which he has interpreted as indicating that arteries and veins and smaller vessels, including arterioles, venules and capillaries, are surrounded by a syncytial neural structure that includes interstitial cells and is devoid of free nerve endings.   According to his concept, neuroeffector transmission is effected by the liberation of a chemical transmitter that diffuses in the interstitial tissue and produces simultaneous stimulation of the effector tissues in the affected area.

Following the sympathetic denervation of an extremity by extirpation of the corresponding segments of the sympathetic trunk, the nerves at the surface of the media undergo almost complete degeneration, but degeneration in the nerves located more superficially in the adventitia is hardly apparent. Following section of the dorsal nerve roots distal to the spinal ganglia, leaving the sympathetic nerves intact, the nerves in the adventitia undergo extensive degeneration, but those at the surface of the media show little degeneration (Polley, 1951). The nerves at the surface of the media obviously are predominantly sympathetic and those in the more superficial zone of the adventitia are predominantly afferent. The nerves associated with the subepidermal vascular plexus in the cat's hind foot pad were not appreciably altered following sympathectomy, in Polley's experiments, but section of the dorsal nerve roots resulted in almost complete degeneration of these nerves. The innervation of the subepidermal vascular plexus appears to be essentially afferent.

The intrinsic innervation of the veins has been studied less extensively than that of the arteries. The data available suggest that the general plan of distribution of the nerve components observed in the arteries also obtains in the veins, with such differences as may be correlated with the relative ratio of muscle to the other tissue elements in the vessels. The large lymph vessels appear to be abundantly innervated. Nerve fibers related to small lymph vessels have also been described (Röper, 1951).

Afferent Fiber Terminations and End Organs.—Fiber terminations and end organs of considerable variety have been described in the adventitia, particularly in the larger arteries and veins. Most of these probably are receptive organs that represent the terminal structures of myelinated afferent fibers. They fall roughly into two classes: (1) naked terminations consisting of terminal branches or terminal loops, and (2) encapsulated structures. Naked terminations may consist of simple terminal branches that end in bulb-like enlargements, tree-like or brush-like endings, and very delicate loop-like structures which are sometimes relatively simple, and sometimes highly complex. The tree-like and the brush-like endings occur very commonly in the adventitia of the vessels of the extremities and in the coronary arteries. Encapsulated end organs in the adventitia are abundant and widely distributed. They differ widely with respect to size and form, but exhibit the same general plan of architecture. In general, they are composed of layers of spindle-shaped cells that are separated from one another by interlamellar layers of non-cellular substance. In addition to the terminal loop of the nerve fiber, the interior of such a capsule contains a core of compact oval cells which, in silver preparations, usually appear darker than the surrounding tissue. Some of these end organs conform to the usual description of Pacinian corpuscles. Others resemble very closely the typical end bulbs of Krause. Still others exhibit a structure which may be regarded as intermediate between these two extremities. Woollard (1928) emphasized the possible relationship to the blood vessels of certain encapsulated fiber terminations situated in the adjacent fatty tissue. In some instances, according to his findings, a medullated nerve fiber, which terminates in the adventitia by means of one branch, also terminates in a sensory end organ lying in the fatty tissue adjacent to the vessel by means of another branch.

The pressoreceptive and chemoreceptive vascular areas exhibit relatively elaborate terminal structures. Sunder-Plassmann (1930) recognized afferent terminal structures of two general types in the adventitia of the carotid sinus in man and in animals. According to his account, those of Type I are characterized by arborizations of relatively coarse structure,

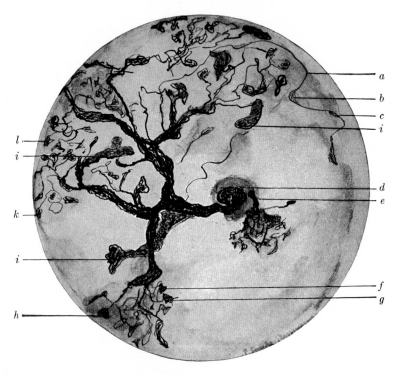

Fig. 44.—Terminations of fibers of the carotid sinus nerve in the wall of the carotid sinus. Type I, according to Sunder-Plassmann (1930). *a*, Fine nerve fiber with varicosities (*b*, *c*); *d*, coarse unmyelinated nerve fiber emerging from myelin sheath; *g*, *h*, *k*, *l*, terminal structures; *i*, terminal nests. (Ztschr. f. d. ges. Anat., courtesy of Julius Springer, Berlin.)

the branches of which end in coarse terminal nets (Fig. 44). Those of Type II are characterized by more diffuse arborizations, the branches of which are more slender and end in finer terminal nets (Fig. 45). Terminal structures of both these types, according to Sunder-Plassmann, are limited to the adventitia. According to Jabonero (1951), the receptors in the carotid sinus include cells of neuroglial origin. Receptive end organs similar to those in the carotid sinus have been described in the proximal portion of the aorta by various investigators. Less elaborate receptive structures have been described in the proximal portion of the pulmonary artery and in the carotid and the aortic bodies.

The existence of afferent nerve fiber terminations in the media of arteries and veins is suggested by the presence of some myelinated fibers in the inner zone of the adventitia. Data relative to the morphology of such terminations are meager. Woollard (1928) described fiber terminations in relation to certain large branching cells located in the media in both large and small vessels. The non-muscular nature of these cells appears to support the assumption that they may represent receptors.

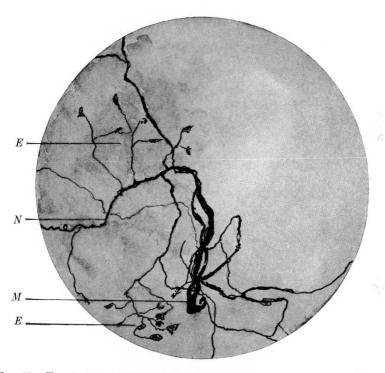

Fig. 45.—Terminations of fibers of the carotid sinus nerve in the wall of the carotid sinus. Type II, according to Sunder-Plassmann (1930). *E*, Fine branches with terminal plates; *M*, unmyelinated terminal portion of a myelinated nerve fiber; *N*, branch of *M*. (Ztschr. f. d. ges. Anat., courtesy of Julius Springer, Berlin.)

The assumption that nerve fibers extend into the intima of arteries and veins appears to be supported by certain reported observations. Such fibers probably would be afferent. Various investigators, however, have failed to find nerve fibers related to the intima.

Capillary Innervation.—Nerve fibers associated with capillaries have been described repeatedly but there is no general agreement regarding the exact anatomical and functional relationships of such fibers to the capillary wall. Nerve fibers in close proximity to capillaries have been described and illustrated by many investigators, but only a few have described structural

11

relationships which could be interpreted as mechanisms through which nerve impulses are transmitted to the capillary walls.

The nerve fibers in proximity to the capillaries lie in intimate contact with the capillary wall only for short distances. They commonly run a somewhat tortuous course, coming in contact with the capillary wall only at certain points. Frequently the nerve fiber is broad and flattened at these points and the neurofibrils are more loosely aggregated than at other points. Stoehr (1926) advanced the opinion that the nerve fibers are functionally related to the capillaries at these points of contact and that these contacts play a more significant rôle in the innervation of the capillaries than the specialized nerve fiber terminations.

The capillary wall contains no contractile tissue comparable with the musculature of the arteries and the veins. The Rouget cells, which are quite generally associated with the capillaries in the Amphibia, have been regarded as the contractile elements through which diminution in the caliber of the capillaries is brought about (Krogh, 1922). Similar cells have been observed in association with capillaries in mammals, but the data available at present do not warrant the conclusion that Rouget cells are associated with all the capillaries in mammals. Neither has it been demonstrated beyond question that they are the essential contractile elements through which capillary contraction is brought about even in the Amphibia. As observed by Clark and Clark (1925), capillary contraction may take place in the Amphibia quite independently of the Rouget cells. On the other hand, Bensley and Vimtrup (1928) observed actual contraction of the Rouget cells on the capillaries in the tongue of the living frog and in the surviving nictitating membrane. Beecher (1936) also reported spontaneous contractions of Rouget cells observed in a transparent chamber in the rabbit's ear. By means of supravital staining with Janus green B, Bensley and Vimtrup demonstrated myofibrils in the Rouget cells which react to the stain in the same manner and at the same time as those in the muscle cells in the walls of the arterioles. As observed by King (1939) in preparations of the rat's heart, some Rouget cells are supplied with nerve fibers, but most of them are not. These observations strongly suggest that the Rouget cells, when present, play a rôle in capillary contraction. Jones (1936), on the contrary, regarded them as components of the nervous system, but not as contractile elements.

The nerve fibers that are most intimately associated with the capillaries are of smaller caliber than those in the adventitia of arteries and veins, which generally are regarded as afferent. Most of them are unmyelinated. They also remain intact, in the corresponding area, after degeneration of the fibers of spinal origin following section of both dorsal and ventral nerve roots between the spinal ganglion and the communicating ramus; consequently, they must be regarded as fibers of sympathetic origin.

PHYSIOLOGICAL DATA

Nervous vs. Humoral Regulation.—The functional control of the blood vessels depends in part on nerve impulses and in part on the effects of hormones and other substances in the blood. The caliber of the blood vessels must play an important rôle in the functional state of the tissue or the organ supplied due to its effect on the rate of the interchange of substances between the blood and the tissue elements. This rate varies both with changes in the volume of blood in the tissue and changes in the rate at which the blood flows. The volume of blood supplied to an organ in a given unit of time must vary directly with the caliber of the vessels. In general the caliber of the vessels supplying an organ usually is increased while the organ is physiologically active and diminished while it is at rest. To what extent these changes depend on nerve impulses and to what extent they represent the direct effect on the blood vessels of products of metabolism that arise due to the activity of the organ is not known. The vascular dilatation observed in active organs usually involves the capillaries to a greater extent than the arteries and the veins. The changes in caliber which the capillaries undergo under normal physiological conditions are due in part to nerve impulses and in part to other influences. Direct responses of capillaries to nerve stimulation have been amply demonstrated.

The vasoconstrictor mechanism probably plays a dominant rôle in the neural control of the blood vessels. Inasmuch as the vasoconstrictor fibers are conveyed to the blood vessels in the same nerves which also convey other fibers, the effect of impulses conducted by the other fibers is not always apparent when the nerve trunk is stimulated. For example, stimulation of the fibers supplying a gland may inhibit secretion due to the constriction of its blood vessels elicited by stimulation of the vasoconstrictors, even though secretory impulses are reaching the gland cells. On the other hand, changes in the caliber of the blood vessels may follow stimulation of a nerve, though quite independently of vasomotor impulses. For example, stimulation of a nerve supplying skeletal muscle usually results in dilatation of the blood vessels in the muscle due to the effects of metabolic products arising as a result of muscle contraction. If the muscle is curarized so that the motor terminations are paralyzed, stimulation of the nerve is followed by little or no dilatation of the blood vessels. Dilatation of blood vessels that follows nerve stimulation is in many cases only indirectly dependent on nerve impulses; consequently, it does not in such cases demonstrate the existence of vasodilator fibers. Most arteries and veins probably are supplied with both vasoconstrictor and vasodilator fibers. Some of the large arteries are only meagerly innervated through vasomotor nerves. Studies on a limited number of patients failed to demonstrate any effective motor innervation of the proximal one-third of the femoral artery (Kinmonth and Simeone, 1952). In general, vasomotor nerve regulation of arteries is more important than that of veins, but that of veins is not unimportant. Data advanced by Peterson (1952) indicate that the volume flow of blood through the veins is determined in a large measure by their tonic state.

Vasomotor Nerves.—Vasoconstrictor activity is mediated chiefly through the sympathetic nerves. When the vasoconstrictor fibers that supply a given area are severed, the blood vessels in that area immediately dilate. This result probably is due to the removal of tonic impulses which normally are conducted to the vessels in a more or less constant stream and maintain their musculature in a state of tonus. After an interval that varies in different animals and at different times in the same animal, vessels deprived of their vasoconstrictor innervation regain tonus in some degree and may become actually smaller in caliber than the normally innervated vessels of the opposite side, even though regeneration of the vasoconstrictor fibers has not taken place. Since there are no ganglion cells along the walls of the peripheral arteries, it must be assumed that the musculature of the vessels develops a certain degree of tonus in the absence of nerve impulses, probably due to a reaction of the musculature of the vessels to vasoconstrictor substances in the blood. If only the preganglionic fibers are cut, leaving the sympathetic cells and fibers intact, the vessels regain tonus more promptly than if the postganglionic fibers are severed. Vasoconstrictor substances such as adrenin circulating in the blood undoubtedly play a rôle in the restoration of vascular tonus following section either of the preganglionic or the postganglionic vasomotor nerve fibers. Although tonus is restored more promptly following section of the preganglionic fibers, the tonic reaction of the vascular musculature to adrenin in the circulating blood is more marked following section of the postganglionic fibers.

Stimulation of a peripheral nerve which includes both vasoconstrictor and vasodilator fibers, under certain conditions, elicits not constriction but dilatation of the vessels affected. If, for example, the sciatic nerve is cut, stimulation of its peripheral end commonly elicits vasoconstriction throughout the portion of the limb affected. If, after several days, the peripheral end of the sciatic is again stimulated, the observed result may be vasodilatation and not vasoconstriction. It has been assumed that this result is due to the fact that the vasoconstrictor fibers undergo degeneration more rapidly than the vasodilator fibers. These results not only suggest a method of investigation by which the distribution of vasodilator fibers can be determined, but also indicate an inherent difference in the vasoconstrictor and the vasodilator fibers.

Central Vasoconstrictor Pathways.—Nerve impulses emanating from the central nervous system exert a constant tonic influence on the blood vessels. If the spinal cord is transected in the cervical region, the blood vessels at once lose tonus and become markedly dilated, particularly in the splanchnic and the cutaneous areas. The tonic impulses obviously are conducted caudad from the brain stem.

The vasoconstrictor center may be stimulated reflexly by afferent impulses conducted by sensory components of any spinal nerve and certain of the cranial nerves. Ranson (1916) pointed out that afferent impulses which initiate pressor reflexes are conducted by fibers which enter the dorsolateral funiculus of the spinal cord through the lateral divisions of the dorsal nerve roots, run a short distance in this funiculus and probably terminate in the substantia gelatinosa in the dorsal gray column. The pressor impulses probably are conducted rostrad in the cord through a series of short fibers which take origin in the substantia gelatinosa and run in the dorsolateral funiculus. They are conducted rostrad on both sides but somewhat better homolaterally than contralaterally. The corresponding efferent spinal vasomotor pathways are located either in the ventral or the lateral funiculi. They are not interrupted by section of the dorsal funiculi and the dorsal gray columns. Somatic afferent impulses that elicit reflex vasomotor responses are conducted rostrad in the spinothalamic tracts. The vasomotor reflex connections are made in the brain stem caudal to the thalamus. Vasoconstrictor reflexes are also carried out through reflex centers in the spinal cord.

The differential effects of reflex vasoconstrictor stimulation support the assumption that the neurons in different parts of the vasoconstrictor center are connected, by definite aggregates of fibers, with the vasoconstrictor neurons that supply various regions of the body. For example, some of the neurons control the activities of the vessels of the skin. Others are concerned with those of the vessels of the splanchnic area. The neurons in different parts of the center apparently may also be acted upon separately, at least under normal physiological conditions.

Vasodilator Nerves.—Stimulation of certain parasympathetic nerves under certain conditions results in vasodilatation, but a general distribution of vasodilator fibers throughout the parasympathetic system is not universally conceded. Early experimental data support the assumption that the parasympathetic innervation of the tongue includes vasodilator fibers. This has been confirmed in the cat by Erici and Uvnäs (1951). Cholinergic vasodilator fibers in the sympathetic nerves of the tongue have also been demonstrated (Erici *et al.*, 1951). Physiological data also indicate the existence of preganglionic vasodilator fibers in the glossopharyngeal and the sacral parasympathetic nerves. Various other parasympathetic nerves probably include no vasodilator fibers.

Certain experimental data have been interpreted as proof of the existence in the dorsal roots of the spinal nerves of fibers that conduct vasodilator impulses. Since efferent fibers in the dorsal nerve roots have not been demonstrated conclusively, such conduction must be regarded as antidromic. It probably plays no part in the maintenance of the normal tonus of blood vessels. There is no conclusive evidence that it is a normal physiological process. The reactions of the vessels to antidromic stimulation, furthermore, differ from their reactions to sympathetic stimulation in that they manifest a longer latent period as well as a delayed aftereffect. Second and third stimulations of the antidromic fibers usually are less effective than the first. These facts indicate that the muscle cells react to antidromic stimulation according to a different mode than to sympathetic stimulation. On the basis of the humoral theory of nerve conduction, this difference could be explained on the assumption that the substance liberated at the periphery by antidromic stimulation of dorsal root fibers differs from that liberated by stimulation of sympathetic fibers. Data reported by various investigators indicate that vasodilatation due to antidromic stimulation depends on the liberation of a histamine-like substance at the periphery. On the basis of all data available, Dale (1929) advanced the theory that the first substance liberated at the periphery as a result of antidromic stimulation or local injury is histamine, which directly causes dilatation of the minute blood vessels with which it comes in contact and acts as a persistent stimulus to the sensory endings. The impulses engendered in the sensory endings traverse collateral branches of the sensory fibers and act upon the arterioles, thus liberating acetylcholine as the effective vasodilator substance. The blood flowing through vessels that are under the influence of antidromic stimulation also acquires vasodilator properties.

The existence of vasodilator fibers in sympathetic nerves has been amply demonstrated in experimental animals and in man. In experiments on human subjects reported by Lewis and Pickering (1931), the subject was seated in a warming chamber arranged so that the head and the hands were unenclosed. By this means, the temperature to which the body is exposed may be raised to any desired degree while the hands are exposed to room temperature. If a large rise in the skin temperature of the hands is desired, it is essential to start with the hands cold, *i.e.*, the room temperature must not be above 14° to 16° C. Under these conditions warming of the body commonly resulted in warming of the hands. If the room temperature is 18° or over, the hands usually are warm, and further warming of the body does not result in a considerable rise in the skin temperature of the hands.

When the extremities of normal subjects are naturally cool, according to Pickering and Hess (1933), vasodilatation in response to warming the body becomes evident in the fingers earlier than in the toes. In some instances vasodilatation may fail in the feet. They have attributed the delayed response in the toes, as compared with the fingers, not to a difference in time, but to the difference in the intensity of the vasomotor relaxation in the upper and lower extremities. Warming of the body elicits complete relaxation of the vessels in the upper extremities but only incomplete relaxation of those in the lower extremities.

The rise in skin temperature of the hands in response to warming the body, according to Grant and Bland (1931), depends on the responsiveness of the arteriovenous anastomoses in the distal parts of the fingers to changes in body temperature. These anastomoses become constricted as the body is cooled and dilate as the body temperature rises. The curves of skin temperature of the normally innervated hand obtained in the experiments of Lewis and Pickering rise slowly at first, then more rapidly and gradually round off into a plateau. The vasodilatation involved in the warming of the hands, in these experiments, was effected through the sympathetic nerves. This is indicated by the fact that warming of the body did not elicit similar responses in hands deprived of their sympathetic innervation. That it is an active process and not the result of inhibition of vasoconstrictor impulses is also demonstrated by the results of experiments involving paralysis of certain peripheral nerves. For example, in patients with Raynaud's disease, the temperature of the fifth finger did not rise following narcotization of the ulnar nerve, although warming of the bodies of the same patients, the hands remaining exposed to cold, resulted in conspicuous vasodilatation in the hands and a marked rise in their skin temperature.

The action of the vasodilator nerves can be explained most satisfactorily on the assumption that vasoconstriction and vasodilation are mediated by different neurohormones. In general, the vasoconstrictor nerves are adrenergic. In the muscles of the dog the vasodilator fibers are cholinergic. The cholinergic nature of the vasodilator fibers in the muscles of the hind limb has been demonstrated in the cat (Folkow *et al.*, 1948) and in the dog (Folkow *et al.*, 1952). In the dog and the cat the cutaneous nerves, except in limited areas, probably include no vasodilator fibers (Folkow *et al.*, 1949). A general distribution of vasodilator fibers in the cutaneous nerves in man has not been demonstrated. Constricting the cutaneous blood vessels with adrenin, as reported by Barcroft *et al.* (1947), did not materially affect the increase in blood flow in the forearm caused by warming the body. The increased flow, therefore, must have taken place in the muscles. This response was abolished by sympathetic denervation of the extremity. It must, therefore, be mediated through vasodilator reflexes. Vasodilatation in the gastro-intestinal submucosa appears to be due to inhibition of contraction of the vascular musculature (Richins and Brizzee, 1949). The existence of venodilator fibers has not been demonstrated with certainty.

Pressoreceptive Reflex Mechanisms.—Very weak stimulation of afferent nerves, except perhaps the splanchnic, almost invariably elicits depressor reflexes, while strong stimulation of afferent nerves, except the so-called depressor nerve and the carotid sinus nerve, elicits pressor reflexes. These facts appear to support the assumption that there are two kinds of afferent vasomotor fibers which have been called pressor and depressor nerve fibers respectively.

The pressoreceptive mechanisms associated with the cardio-aortic zone and the carotid sinuses play a peculiarly significant rôle in the cardiovascular regulation. When the endovascular pressure rises in the left ventricle and the arch of the aorta, impulses conducted centrad in the depressor nerves elicit reflex slowing of the heart and peripheral vasodilatation. When the endovascular pressure falls the pressoreceptors in this area are no longer stimulated; consequently, the cardiac rate is accelerated, and peripheral vasoconstriction takes place. These reflex reactions tend to maintain normal blood pressure. Variations in pressure in the carotid sinus zone, likewise, result in immediate cardiovascular reactions. A rise in the endovascular pressure in this zone elicits reflex slowing of the heart and a fall in blood pressure in the general circulation. Conversely, reduction in the endovascular pressure in the carotid sinus results in cardiac acceleration and a general rise in blood pressure. The carotid sinus reflex mechanisms probably play no significant rôle in vasomotor regulation while the systemic blood pressure is very low. Under conditions of hypotension induced experimentally in dogs, as reported by Frumin *et al.* (1952), the rate of flow in the hind limb increased sometimes as much as 100 per cent in response to carotid sinus stimulation. This response did not occur following lumbar sympathectomy. Vasodilatation in the limb in response to carotid sinus stimulation, therefore, must have been mediated through sympathetic vasodilator fibers.

The pulmonary veins, the venæ cavæ and the right atrium constitute a pressoreceptive zone sensitive to changes in venous pressure. The assumption that reflexes initiated in this zone by changes in venous pressure play a rôle in the regulation of the cardiac rate and vascular tonus is supported by experimental data.

Stimulation of receptors in the pulmonary artery by increased pressure in the pulmonary arterial system results in reflex bradycardia and arterial vasodilatation. Lowering of pulmonary arterial pressure results in cardiac acceleration and increased arterial tonus. The vascular area comprising the celiac and the mesenteric arteries may also be regarded as a pressoreceptive zone.

Pressoreceptors probably are not present in all vascular areas. The general vascular tonus is regulated through reflexes initiated in pressoreceptors in certain well-localized areas: the carotid sinus and the cardioaortic, veno-atrial, pulmo-arterial and thoraco-splanchnic zones. The initiation of similar reflexes in other vascular areas has not been demonstrated. By the use of a balloon in the larger blood vessels, Knapp (1929) elicited reflex changes in blood pressure by changes in the internal pressure in the arch of the aorta and the carotid sinus but not in other parts of the large vessels. In experiments reported by Katz and Saphir (1933), stimulation of the aorta and the pulmonary artery, except in the region of the plexus in which the depressor nerve terminates, failed to elicit reflex changes either in blood pressure or in heart-rate. A decrease in blood pressure in other vascular areas may elicit local or regional vasomotor reactions which are not involved in the pressoreceptive regulation of the general blood pressure.

The control level of blood pressure following very rapid transfusion or hemorrhage, as observed by Guyton *et al.* (1951), appears to depend in a large measure on sympathetic nerve activity. It is relatively independent of the blood volume as long as the volume is sufficient. In normal animals the readjustment following transfusion at rates used clinically is rapid enough to prevent a significant rise in pressure. After rapid massive hemorrhage, a gradual rise in pressure takes place, but complete recovery is delayed because interstitial liquid enters the circulation slowly. The blood pressure differential appears to depend on the activity of pressoreceptor-vasomotor mechanisms. After complete pressoreceptor denervation the blood pressure differential is markedly increased. Other phenomena associated with abrupt changes in blood flow into and out of the circulatory system, such as the Traube-Hering waves, appear to be due to pressoreceptor-sympathetic activity.

Chemoreceptive Reflex Mechanisms.—The distribution of chemoreceptors and pressoreceptors overlaps in the cardio-aortic zone, but neither kind of receptor is equally abundant throughout the entire zone. Pressoreceptors predominate in the proximal portion of the aorta and the adjacent areas. Chemoreceptors are most abundant in the internal carotid arteries rostral to the carotid sinuses and in the carotid and the aortic bodies. The chemoreceptors connected with the carotid sinus nerve, consequently, exceed the pressoreceptors connected with this nerve, and the pressoreceptors connected with the vagi exceed the chemoreceptors. Chemical stimulation undoubtedly plays a more significant rôle in reflex vasomotor regulation through the carotid sinus nerves than through the vagi. Increased activity of the chemoreceptors results in increased activity of both the vasomotor and the respiratory centers. Decreased chemoreceptor activity produces opposite effects. The increased activity of the vasomotor and the respiratory centers is due to the positive stimulating effect of nerve impulses reaching them from the chemoreceptors through the corresponding afferent nerves. The usual stimuli for these end organs are a fall in pH, a rise in CO_2 tension and anoxemia. The stimulating effects of anoxemia on both circulation and respiration probably are due mainly to reflexes initiated in the chemoreceptors. Direct effects exerted on the vasomotor and the respiratory centers are not precluded, but the threshold of stimulation of the chemoreceptors by anoxemia is lower than that of the centers. Stimulation of the chemoreceptors by anoxemia also elicits more rapid and more vigorous responses than those resulting from central anoxemia. Excessive CO_2 tension, on the contrary, exerts its influence on blood pressure mainly through its stimulating effect on the vasomotor center. The reflex vasomotor response to chemoreceptor stimulation, therefore, is modified by the state of responsiveness of the vasomotor center.

Following severe hemorrhage in experimental animals, the blood pressure records frequently exhibit periodic waves that are independent of respiration and slower in periodicity (Mayer waves). These waves are abolished by inactivation of the chemoreceptors. The spontaneous appearance of Mayer waves in animals with enfeebled circulation appears to be due to the initial stimulation of chemoreceptor areas that results in a rise in blood pressure and improvement in the peripheral circulation. This in turn results in removal of the initial chemoreceptor stimulation and the production of pressoreceptor stimulation that causes a return of the blood pressure to its initial low level, which again results in chemoreceptor stimulation (Neil, 1951).

Reflex Regulation of Blood Pressure.—The blood is not distributed uniformly throughout the body, but its relative abundance in any given region is correlated with the requirements of the organs and tissues in question or the maintenance of constant body temperature at the moment. Under changing conditions, particularly of external temperature, considerable volumes of blood are displaced from the peripheral to the splanchnic area and *vice versa*. When the external temperature is low, the volume of blood circulating in the peripheral vessels is greatly reduced in order to prevent too great loss of heat, and that circulating in the splanchnic vessels is correspondingly increased. On the contrary, when the external temperature is high, the volume of blood in the peripheral vessels is increased and that in the splanchnic vessels is correspondingly decreased. The nutritive requirements of the tissues under changing conditions also necessitate changes in the distribution of the blood. For example, the volume of blood circulating through the skeletal muscles is markedly increased during muscular exercise.

A blood pressure raising reflex elicited by the stimulating effect of metabolites liberated in skeletal muscles during muscular exercise has been demonstrated in human subjects. It appears to be a physiological device to insure an increased blood supply to the active muscles. Exercise of a limited group of muscles may result in an appreciable rise in blood pressure. Vigorous exercise of the whole body results in a greater rise. If the accumulated metabolites are retained in the muscles, by arrest of the circulation, after the exercise of any group of large muscles, *e.g.*, the leg muscles, the cardiac acceleration and increased blood pressure are maintained above normal as long as the escape of the stimulating metabolites is prevented. The reflex rise in blood pressure does not depend wholly on the bulk of the active muscle. In the normal human subject, exercise of the hand or forearm usually causes a greater rise in pressure than exercise of both lower extremities. The local vasodilatation in active muscles is probably due to the direct stimulating effect of the accumulated metabolites. Sustained contraction of the muscles compresses the vessels, but it does not prevent their dilation and an increased flow of blood through the muscles. After exercise of any group of muscles the flow of blood is still further increased, and the degree of the resulting hyperemia and its duration is determined by the vigor of the exercise and the length of the interval during which it was maintained. The administration of adrenin in small doses, according to Grant and Pearson (1938), causes an increase in the flow of blood in the human forearm and leg and an increase in the limb volume due to vasodilatation in the voluntary muscles. The vasodilator effect of adrenin, in their experiments, was increased after sympathectomy.

The maintenance of constant blood pressure during the redistribution of the circulating blood and the loss of blood by hemorrhage involves marked vasoconstriction in extensive vascular areas and changes in the volume of certain organs, particularly the spleen and the liver. The spleen appears to play a significant rôle both in the redistribution of the circulating blood and in the maintenance of constant body temperature, particularly during severe hemorrhage. In experimental animals, the volume of blood that may be discharged from this organ may equal one-fifth of the volume of the circulating blood. The undulatory waves of blood pressure which ordinarily have a duration of about forty-five seconds, but which vary from 25 seconds upwards, appear to be due to the rhythmic contractions of the spleen (Barcroft and Nisimaru, 1932). Under certain conditions, the liver also releases blood into the general circulation. Due to the action of adrenin, it may release a volume of blood equal to one-half its normal size. By virtue of their capacity to undergo changes in size, the spleen and the liver may be regarded as reservoirs of blood that may be added to the circulating blood whenever the necessity arises. The reduction in the size of the spleen is brought about by contraction of its own musculature under the influence of nerve impulses. The reduction in the size of the liver appears to be conditioned by constriction of the splanchnic vessels, resulting in diminution of the volume of blood entering it through the portal vein. Splanchnic stimulation results in an increase in the outflow into the vena cava, but in a decrease in the flow of blood into the liver. Inasmuch as the outflow from the liver is not impeded, the volume of blood in the liver is diminished and the organ is reduced in size. Vasoconstriction accompanying the loss of blood does not take place equally throughout the body. It usually is more marked in the splanchnic than in the peripheral area. Vasoconstriction associated with diminished blood volume is most marked in the vascular fields in which the vessels are constricted already in the interest of temperature regulation. In fields in which the vessels are dilated in the interest of temperature regulation vasoconstriction takes place in a lesser degree. The responsiveness of the peripheral blood vessels is conditioned, in a large measure, by the external temperature. In general, measurable variations in blood pressure afford no index of the changes in the distribution or the volume of the circulating blood that may be taking place.

The hepatoportal system, including the liver, the spleen and the intestinal tract, constitutes the most extensive and significant blood reservoir in the body. It probably plays an important rôle in all circulatory adjustments. Even during ordinary activity constant and varying shifts occur in the various parts of this system the integration of which plays an important rôle in the coördination of the peripheral circulatory apparatus in response to the requirements of the moment. It constitutes a reservoir of large capacity that is delicately attuned particularly to the regulation of the circulating blood volume and the venous return to the heart. The liver alone may hold as much as 25 per cent of the total blood volume and the preportal bed, including the spleen and the intestinal tract, another 30 per cent. Circulation, therefore, is not necessarily controlled by the heart. Under a wide variety of circumstances the reactions of the hepatoportal system undoubtedly exert the major controlling influences.

In experiments reported by Rein (1943), occlusion of the hepatic artery in the dog resulted in immediate vasomotor throttling of the celiac and superior mesenteric arteries. This reaction was interpreted as a reflex response to stimulation of pressoreceptors in the hepatic artery which is carried out through spinal reflex centers and limited to the gastro-enteric vessels. It is independent of other pressoreceptive mechanisms but is augmented by simultaneous carotid sinus stimulation and oxygen deficiency and extinguished by pulmonary hyperventilation. It probably represents a protective reflex which tends to maintain an adequate arteriovenous pressure gradient within the liver. These experimental findings support the hypothesis that the vasomotor hepatic artery reflex results in a certain degree of antagonism between the blood flow through the hepatic artery and that through the arteries that supply the gastro-intestinal canal. The latter vessels, therefore, may be regarded as constituting a collateral vasoconstrictor zone for the arterial supply to the liver. The response of the gastro-intestinal vessels is elicited mainly by lowering of pressure in the hepatic artery, which may be caused or augmented by oxygen deficiency. This reflex, therefore, need not be regarded as a compensatory reaction which tends to maintain the general arterial pressure. It probably serves primarily to insure an adequate oxygen supply to the liver and aids in regulating the distribution of blood locally.

On the basis of experimental studies carried out on dogs, Chauchard et al. (1931) reported that hemorrhage results in modification of the excitability of the inhibitory mechanism of the heart and the vasomotor mechanisms. The chronaxie for all the reactions tested in their experiments was increased by loss of blood to an extent that was roughly proportional to the severity of the hemorrhage. Restoration of the blood lost, after defibrination, resulted in almost complete restoration of the excitability of the mechanisms in question to its former level. Temporary restoration of the excitability of these mechanisms could also be brought about by injection of a saline solution.

In dogs, as observed by Remington *et al.* (1950), the lethal blood volume was greatly reduced when vasoconstriction after hemorrhage was prevented by the use of dibenamine, but the animals could survive pressures and levels of flow that were fatal to the controls. Sustained vasoconstriction following carotid sinus extirpation and vagotomy or caused by the administration of adrenin resulted in shortening of the survival time at low pressure and blood flow levels and in reduction in the lethal bleeding volume. In dogs subjected to repeated small hemorrhages until death was inevitable three phases were apparent: (1) Cardiac output and arterial pressure were decreased, and resistance was slightly increased without significant alteration in heart-rate. (2) The heart-rate was accelerated, and the decline in blood pressure and blood flow was temporarily interrupted, but venous pressure was lowered and the cardiac volume was reduced. (3) Compensation gradually failed, and arterial pressure, blood flow and resistance were further decreased. Cardiac output and resistance appear to be reciprocally related during the early phases of hemorrhage but not during the late phases. The rise in blood pressure and in the vasomotor resistance of the body appear to be closely related to the onset and the intensity of the trauma. The survival rate after trauma of the limb was greatly increased by partial blocking of the reflex vasoconstriction by dibenamine in small doses. The sensitivity of the animals to reduction in blood volume appeared to be increased due to the vasoconstriction caused by the trauma. The displacement of fluid into the traumatized areas, where the vessels are dilated, consequently, constitutes lethal hemorrhage. On the basis of the regional distribution of blood flow after hemorrhage, Pickering (1950) has classified the vascular bed in two broad categories. In the one, which includes the vessels in the extremities, centrally imposed vasoconstriction is not negated by hypoxia. In the other, which includes the vascular bed in the viscera, the brain and presumably the heart, either hypoxia does not cause vasoconstriction or it is easily reversible. The difference in the vascular reactions in these two categories is less marked following the administration of dibenamine.

The rate at which the blood is propelled through the circulatory system depends in a large measure on the rate and force of the cardiac contractions and the caliber of the blood vessels, particularly the terminal arteries and arterioles. The fact that adrenin, following the administration of atropine, causes a reduced flow of blood in spite of a rapid heart, but results in a small central blood volume and hastens the velocity of the circulation indicates that the volume of flow is a function of the peripheral vasoconstriction and that the central active blood volume and, in part, the circulation times are functions of the cardiac rate. This, in turn, is the resultant of the functional balance between the accelerator and the inhibitory nerves of the heart prevailing at the moment. These nerves are activated by afferent impulses emanating from all parts of the body, but the inhibitory cardiac nerves are activated particularly by impulses arising in certain circumscribed vascular areas, particularly the cardio-aortic pressoreceptive zone and the carotid sinus. The caliber of the blood vessels is determined by the functional balance between the vasodilator and the vasoconstrictor nerves and the pressure exerted by the circulating blood. The vasodilator and, under certain conditions, the vasoconstrictor nerves also are activated by impulses arising in the cardio-aortic pressoreceptive zone and the carotid sinus.

Action currents in the so-called depressor nerve occur synchronously with the elevations in blood pressure in the aorta, due to the cardiac contractions and respiratory movements. In addition to the smaller oscillations, there are two larger paired waves with a definite pause between the succeeding pairs. The first of the larger waves coincides with the rapid rise in pressure following ventricular contractions. The second coincides with the first rebound following this contraction. The impulses arising in this manner are conducted by the depressor nerve to the vasomotor center in the medulla oblongata where they are transmitted to the cardiac inhibitory components of the vagus nerves.

The cardiac inhibitory reflexes that are elicited by stimulation in the carotid sinus area are mediated through the carotid sinus nerve and efferent components of the cardiac rami of the vagus nerves. Other reflexes arising in the carotid sinus area that play a rôle in the regulation of blood pressure are carried out both through the vagus and sympathetic nerves. Of the reflexes that arise in the carotid sinus area, those that affect the blood vessels directly play a greater rôle in the regulation of blood pressure than those that act upon the heart, but the fall in blood pressure due to the latter reflexes takes place more rapidly than that due to the former.

Under normal conditions, almost continuous conduction into the medulla oblongata through the carotid sinus nerve of impulses that arise in the carotid sinus area has been demonstrated. Every cardiac cycle is accompanied by a burst of impulses followed by an interval of comparative inactivity. The discharge is coincident with the rapid rise in arterial pressure during systole. Following this rapid discharge, there are scattered impulses throughout diastole. When the blood pressure is high, the discharge becomes continuous, a phenomenon which also accompanies asphyxia. The discharge in the carotid sinus nerve in general is similar to that in the depressor nerve. The activity of the receptive endings in the arch of the aorta and the carotid sinus appears to be a function both of the absolute level of pressure and the rate of pressure change.

In a study of afferent impulses from single end organs in the carotid sinus of the rabbit, Bronk and Stella (1932) demonstrated that with the beginning of the rapid rise in pressure during systole the end organ starts to discharge impulses at a rate of about 55 per second. The rate then decreases as the pressure falls. The duration of this discharge seems to be a function of the threshold of the end organ, the mean blood pressure and the form of the pulse curve. At low or medium pressure, the discharge sometimes ceases during diastole, although a second volley of impulses may occur, particularly when the pulse curve is dicrotic. In experiments carried out with the mean blood pressure ranging from about 40 mm. Hg to 150 mm. Hg, single end organs sometimes did not discharge at all or but a few times during systole. As the mean blood pressure increased, the impulses became more frequent during systole and the discharge of longer duration until, with high blood pressure, they became continuous with only slight variations in frequency corresponding to systole and diastole.

Starting with a subthreshold pressure at which no endings are stimulated, in preparations in which several nerve fibers are intact, they found that first one and then another end organ is stimulated during systole as their several thresholds are reached. It may be assumed, therefore, that more and more impulses reach the corresponding centers in the medulla oblongata from the carotid sinus, in the normal animal, as the blood pressure rises, due to an increasing number of end organs which become functionally active and a higher frequency and longer duration of discharge from the several end organs.

Heymans (1929) devised an experimental method by which the circulating blood of one dog could be passed through the blood vessels of the isolated head of another dog or through its isolated carotid sinuses; and the reflex effects on the heart-rate and blood pressure of the body of the latter dog, brought about through the intact vagus nerves, could be recorded. The body of the dog with the isolated head remained connected with the latter only by means of the intact vagus nerves, and it was kept alive during the experiment by means of artificial respiration. The results of the experiments in which the strange blood was passed through the vessels of the isolated head show clearly that hypertension in the cerebral vessels elicits cardiac inhibition, and hypotension in the cerebral vessels results in cardiac acceleration. The results of the experiments in which the strange blood was passed through the isolated carotid sinuses were essentially similar to those brought about by passing it through the entire cerebral circulation, but the same reflexes were not elicited when the strange blood was passed through the vessels of the isolated head following section of the carotid sinus nerves. On the basis of these results, the conclusion was drawn that the reflex effects of the cerebral circulation on the heart-rate are brought about through carotid sinus reflexes and that the receptors in the wall of the carotid sinus respond to chemical stimuli as well as to distention of the vessel. In another series of experiments in which the isolated carotid sinuses were perfused with the circulating blood of another animal, following section of the vagus nerves but with the animal otherwise intact, hypotension in the carotid sinuses resulted in a rise, and hypertension in a fall in blood pressure. The fall in blood pressure in this instance was not accompanied by cardiac inhibition.

The regulatory influence of the depressor and carotid sinus nerves on blood pressure is most apparent in the presence of a threatened rise in pressure, but these nerves also play an important rôle in protecting against a fall in blood pressure. In experiments reported by Kremer and Wright (1932), bilateral section of the splanchnic nerves in cats with the depressor and the carotid sinus nerves intact resulted in comparatively small falls in blood pressure, commonly 0 to 15 per cent and occasionally 25 per cent, although vasodilatation in the splanchnic area was evident. When the aortic and the carotid sinus nerves were inactivated, bilateral section of the splanchnic nerves resulted in falls in blood pressure which on the average amounted to 50 per cent. When either the aortic or the carotid sinus nerves were left intact the fall in blood pressure was greatly reduced. A lesser degree of protection was afforded by one intact carotid sinus nerve, but one intact depressor nerve alone was comparatively ineffective. These experimental data emphasize the rôle of compensatory vasoconstriction in parts of the body, including the skeletal muscles, in the regulation of blood pressure. The vasomotor control of the vessels of the skeletal muscles appears to be of greater functional significance than has been generally conceded.

Pressure on the carotid sinus in man, as has been demonstrated by means of electrocardiographic records, may reflexly arrest the heart completely. Atrio-ventricular conduction may also be impaired, and the heart block may be partial or complete. Paroxysmal tachycardia may also be arrested, but as a rule only for a short time. In certain individuals with hyperexcitable carotid sinus mechanisms reflex phenomena may be elicited with extraordinary ease. Hypersensitivity of the afferent nerve endings in the carotid sinus appears to be a factor in certain types of syncope and epileptiform convulsions.

The hypothesis that the depressor and the carotid sinus nerves constitute the afferent limbs of an autoregulatory reflex system which tends to check both high and low blood pressure is supported by experimental and clinical data. This system tends to maintain a functional balance between the cardiac accelerator and the vasoconstrictor nerves on the one hand and the cardiac inhibitory and the vasodilator nerves on the other. Any marked deviation from normal blood pressure, according to this hypothesis, must be regarded as the result of a functional disturbance of this autoregulatory mechanism.

According to Koch (1931), the carotid sinus nerves exercise solely a tonic inhibitory influence on the circulation. He regards acceleration of the heart and rise in blood pressure on occlusion of the carotid sinuses as due to a decrease or abolition of the inhibitory action due to a fall in pressure in the carotid sinuses below threshold value. This view is supported by the fact that section of the carotid sinus nerves or cocainization of the carotid sinuses produces similar pressor effects. Although the reflexes initiated in the carotid sinus are mainly depressor, the existence of pressor fibers in the carotid sinus nerves is not precluded.

Contrary to the view that the regulatory control of heart-rate and blood pressure is carried out solely through reflex mechanisms, certain data (Wright, 1930) seem to indicate that the regulation of blood pressure, at least under certain conditions, involves central mechanisms of a higher order. In Wright's experiments on cats, ergotamine in small doses prolonged the latent period of the depressor reflex, decreased the rate and the extent of the fall in blood pressure, and finally abolished the reflex completely. In larger doses, it also prolonged the latent period of the pressor reflex, decreased the rate and the extent of the rise in blood pressure, and finally abolished this reflex at a stage in which the vasomotor center still responded strikingly to acute anemia. These results, which indicate that the effect of ergotamine is exerted on the afferent side of the vasomotor center, militate against the assumption that the regulation of the heart-rate and blood pressure is mediated solely through direct reflex mechanisms. In a study of the effects of exercise on the heart-rate, blood pressure and respiration in dogs, Cromer and Ivy (1931) obtained results following section of the carotid sinus nerves which differed only slightly from the results obtained with the carotid sinus mechanisms intact. On the basis of these results, they concluded that "the physiological rôle of the carotid sinus as a reflexogenic center for controlling blood pressure, heart-rate and respiration is readily taken over by other mechanisms in the dogs." Certain other data also seem to indicate that the vasomotor center is stimulated directly by a decrease in the blood pressure in the cerebral vessels.

The discharge from the vasomotor center, according to Folkow (1951), rarely exceeds 6 to 8 impulses per second. One to 2 impulses per second are sufficient to maintain normal peripheral resistance. A slight increase in the rate of discharge exerts a marked effect on peripheral resistance. Within the physiological range, most of the adrenergic transmitter is destroyed at the site of liberation. In cats and dogs, as reported by Uvnäs (1951), stimulation in a limited region of the rostral portion of the hypothalamus elicits profound vasodilatation in the skeletal muscles, but not in the skin or the splanchnic region. The vasodilator response in the muscles is frequently associated with vasoconstriction in the skin and the enteric canal. According to Cicardo (1951), the hypothalamic vasomotor center is stimulated directly by impulses that arise due to respiratory activity.

Experimental data reported by Bouckaert and Heymans (1933) also fail to support the assumption that the low blood pressure and the reduction in the volume of blood flowing through the cerebral vessels brought about by occlusion of the common carotid arteries, their efferent branches, or the vertebral arteries directly stimulate the vasoconstrictor center. Low pressure in the carotid sinus, however, results in stimulation of the vasoconstrictor center through the carotid sinus nerve, although it also results in reflexly increasing the cerebral blood pressure and the volume of blood flowing through the cerebral vessels. Conversely, high pressure in the carotid sinus results in depression of the vasoconstrictor center through the carotid sinus nerve, although it also results in reflexly diminishing the cerebral blood pressure and blood supply. On the basis of these findings, they concluded that the vasoconstrictor center is not directly sensitive to changes in cerebral blood pressure and blood volume, unless the changes are very extreme. The tonus of the vasoconstrictor center is maintained chiefly by the arterial CO_2 tension, but normally it is inhibited by the effects of the normal blood pressure exerted through the aortic and the carotid sinus nerves; consequently, these nerves play a dominant rôle in the regulation of the blood pressure.

When tissues or organs are in a condition of high activity, their nutritional and respiratory requirements are increased and their blood vessels are dilated through local, direct and reflex effects of temperature and metabolites. Under these conditions they are temporarily irresponsive either to neural or hormonal vasoconstrictor influences exerted through the pressoreceptive reflex mechanisms involved in blood pressure regulation. The principal vasoconstrictor effect, frequently the only one, is exerted on the vessels of resting organs or tissues; consequently, blood is shifted readily from tissues whose respiratory and nutritional needs are slight for the time being to tissues whose needs are greater, although the general blood pressure is maintained at normal levels or regulated at levels above normal.

The cerebral vessels, according to Bouckaert and Heymans (1935), do not participate actively in the pressoreceptive regulation of the general blood pressure, but always behave like the vessels of an organ in which the nutritional requirements are elevated. Thus, whenever the necessity arises, blood may be shifted from other organs in a state of metabolic rest to the cerebral circulation. During periods of hypotension blood is diverted from the peripheral and the splanchnic areas toward the cerebral circulation, due to pressoreceptive reflex activity initiated particularly in the carotid sinuses. During periods of hypertension, some blood is diverted from the brain, due to the activity of the same reflex mechanisms. The peripheral cephalic tissues and the thyroid gland play a significant rôle in these reactions. As demonstrated by Rein et al. (1932), increased pressure in the carotid sinus elicits reflex thyroid vasodilatation, thus diverting a certain amount of blood from the carotid arteries through the thyroid gland. It also elicits vasodilatation in the peripheral cephalic tissues. Lowering of the pressure in the carotid sinus results in the opposite reactions. The extracranial circulation, consequently, plays a leading part in the regulation of cerebral circulation, particularly in emergencies (Heymans, 1938).

The significance of these findings regarding the behavior of the cerebral blood vessels is emphasized by the results of an extensive series of studies on the vasomotor control of the cerebral vessels summarized by Forbes and Cobb (1938). The results of these studies support the assumption that the cerebral vessels are supplied with both vasoconstrictor and vasodilator nerve fibers. Vasoconstrictor fibers are distributed unequally to the vessels in the various parts of the brain and probably do not reach the smallest arteries and arterioles. Direct stimulation of the vasoconstrictors elicits only slight constriction of the cerebral vessels, as compared with the vasoconstrictor response of comparable stimulation observed in other organs. The arterioles undergo no appreciable changes in caliber, and the flow of blood through the capillaries which, at least in the pia mater, appear to be always open is remarkably steady. The vasomotor mechanism obviously is more effective in some parts of the brain than in others and may aid in diverting blood from one region to another. It may help arteries to regain normal tonus after extreme dilatation and thus limit undesirable fluctuations, but experimental data do not support the assumption that it can cause the arteries to constrict sufficiently to bring about ischemia. Chemical agents, particularly CO_2, play a major rôle in cerebral vasomotor regulation. In an experimental study reported by Norcross (1938), CO_2 caused a marked increase in the flow of blood in the cerebral vessels. Inhalation of pure oxygen and hyperventilation with pure air caused a marked decrease. Administration of adrenin, ephedrin and posterior pituitary extract caused an increased flow in the brain as a secondary result of a rise in blood pressure.

The effects of the vasomotor reflexes initiated in the pressoreceptors in the mesenterico-intestinal zone usually are not markedly manifest but nonetheless important. These reflexes probably are concerned primarily in

12

local, segmental and regional distribution of blood in the splanchnic and the peripheral areas.

Upright posture in man frequently results in swelling of the legs and diminishing flow of blood through the lower half of the body. It may also result in a fall in blood pressure that can be accounted for in part by splanchnic vasodilatation. This probably is not a major factor, since section of the splanchnic nerves in man does not always materially alter the circulatory response to posture. Imperfect circulatory compensation in man in the upright position, therefore, may be due to stagnation of blood in the lower extremities rather than in the splanchnic area. In the cat Edholm (1942) found that the fall in blood pressure when the trunk is in the vertical position with the hind feet down is due to the collection of blood, not in the splanchnic area, but in the liver. The compensation following this fall is due in part to the reaction of the splanchnic vessels. The recovery of blood pressure on restoring the animal to the horizontal position is due to the return to the right atrium of blood accumulated in the liver.

Capillary Regulation.—Capillary contraction elicited by reflex and direct nerve stimulation has been reported by various investigators. In most instances, however, the latent period was so long that the capillary response could have been regarded as secondary to contraction of the arterioles. Many experimental data have been interpreted as supporting the theory that changes in the caliber of the capillaries in general are secondary to changes in the caliber of the arteries, especially their terminal branches, including the arterioles. On the other hand, certain investigators, including Bensley and Vimtrup (1928), have supported the theory that the capillary walls contain contractile elements that respond to nerve impulses. Krogh (1927) supported the theory that the capillaries, like the arteries, respond to reflex stimulation and that the efferent limbs of the reflex arcs in question are sympathetic. According to Hyndman and Wolkin (1941), the changes in the capillary beds include active capillary dilatation. They have advanced experimental data in support of the assumption that, in man, the cutaneous capillaries are supplied with sympathetic dilator fibers which constitute part of the general vasodilator mechanism. A third group of investigators has supported the hypothesis that chemical stimuli constitute a major factor in the causation of caliber changes in the capillaries.

The solution of the problems involved in caliber changes in capillaries is beset with inherent difficulties due to the marked hydrostatic effect on these vessels of any changes in the caliber of the arterioles. In most instances in which capillary contractions in response to nerve stimulation has been observed the latent period has been relatively long and the mechanism involved could not be clearly determined. Swelling of endothelial nuclei into the lumen, thus limiting or completely stopping the flow of blood, has been observed by Kahn and Pollack (1931) in the nictitating membrane, and by Beecher (1936) in the rabbit's ear. Beecher observed both swelling of endothelial cells and contraction of Rouget cells. Sanders *et al.* (1940) observed contraction of capillaries in the rabbit's ear in response to cervical sympathetic stimulation and a marked increase in the flow of blood through the capillaries following section of the cervical sympathetic trunk. The mechanism by which the capillary lumen is occluded in response to nerve stimulation involved swelling of an endothelial cell in the region of the nucleus sufficient to occlude the lumen. The outside diameter of the capillary was not sensibly diminished, and no changes were observed in the Rouget cells in the field of observation. The latent period from the beginning of stimulation was 15 to 20 seconds, and the capillary remained contracted up to 45 seconds after cessation of stimulation.

Vital dyes circulating in the blood pass through the normally innervated capillary walls more rapidly toward the venous than toward the arterial end. The capillaries, therefore, exhibit an increased gradient of permeability from the arterial toward the venous end (Rous *et al.*, 1931). This gradient disappears and the permeability of the capillary bed is increased following sympathetic denervation. The increase in the capillary permeability appears to be due to removal of the permeability gradient and does not depend entirely on capillary dilatation (Hesselman, 1932).

In experiments reported by Engel (1941), dye was perfused in the knee joints of cats, dogs and rabbits that had been sympathectomized on one side and the local blood flow measured thermo-electrically. In the majority of both acute and long term experiments excretion of the dye was apparently reduced on the sympathectomized side in spite of marked dilatation of the denervated capillaries. Engel has attempted to explain this result by postulating a permeability factor which is influenced by sympathetic nerve impulses. He has advanced the opinion that the effects of vasomotor changes might be counteracted or balanced by such a factor.

Other Vasomotor Reflexes.—Vasomotor responses in the viscera to localized thermal stimulation of the skin have long been recognized. Vasoconstriction in the corresponding portion of the gastro-intestinal tract in response to localized cooling of the skin and vasodilation in the same visceral area in response to localized warming of the skin have been demonstrated in experimental animals (Kuntz and Haselwood, 1940; Kuntz, 1945). These reflexes remain intact following transection of the spinal cord in the cervical region. Intense somatic pain producing stimulation elicits reflex vasoconstriction throughout the gastro-intestinal tract in both intact animals and in animals with cervical transection of the spinal cord. These reactions, therefore, involve neither suprasegmental mechanisms nor efferent parasympathetic pathways. Both the vasoconstrictor and the vasodilator fibers concerned are sympathetic. The former are adrenergic; the latter are cholinergic. In sections of the intestine prepared by the rapid freezing-drying method while the vascular bed is responding to localized thermal stimulation of the skin, the extent of the vasoconstriction or of the vasodilatation can be estimated quantitatively. In sections of the duodenum prepared by this method it is apparent that the responses are most marked in the larger arterioles in the submucosa (Richins and Brizzee, 1949).

Thermal stimulation, within a moderate temperature range, in a cutaneous area that has become hyperemic due to repeated warming and cooling, elicits no recognizable vasomotor reaction in the corresponding portion of the gastro-intestinal tract which, in the absence of disturbing stimuli, is also hyperemic. The receptors through which thermal sensations and those through which vasomotor reactions in the viscera, elicited by thermal stimulation of the skin, are mediated appear to be closely associated with the cutaneous blood vessels. Tissue deformations caused by tonic changes in the musculature of these vessels probably are an essential factor in the activation of the receptors in question and, consequently, in sensory adaptation.

Local heating of the forearms and the legs of human subjects in water at 43° to 44° C., results in a temporary feeling of warmth that is proportional to the general rise in skin temperature. Except in the parts immersed the rise in temperature is also temporary. Prolonged vasodilatation due to adequate local heating, therefore, appears to be mediated through central neural mechanisms (Martinez and Visscher, 1945). The effect of heating of the lower extremities by immersion in water at 38° to 44° C., as reported by Randall et al. (1948), is manifested immediately in the finger pads by an increase in the flow of blood. Increases in the blood flow and skin temperature on the forearm, the cheek and the forehead can be demonstrated only after a time lag. Immersion of the lower extremities and the lower trunk region in cold water results in a marked rapid decrease in the flow of blood in the fingers with little further change during the period of immersion. The flow of blood in the forearm also showed an immediate decrease and either remained low or returned to normal during the period of immersion (Smith et al., 1948).

In experiments reported by Kerslake and Cooper (1950), the time of onset of vasodilatation in the hand in response to heating of the trunk or the leg in a radiant heat cradle showed a latent period of 10 to 15 seconds irrespective of the rate of heating. Inflation of a thigh cuff to 200 mm. Hg when only the leg was heated did not alter the vasodilator response in the hand; consequently, it was interpreted as a reflex response elicited by afferent impulses that arose in the heated skin. Following complete sympathetic denervation of the upper extremity, or blocking of the sympathetic nerves, heating of the trunk failed to elicit vasodilatation in the hand (Löhr, 1950).

In patients with high transverse lesions of the spinal cord, as reported by Goetz and Ames (1949), immersion of the feet in warm water also resulted in vasodilatation in the upper extremities, but when the circulation through the immersed extremity was occluded this response was abolished. They concluded, therefore, that the vasodilatation in the upper extremity was dependent on the return of heated blood to the thermosensitive center in the hypothalamus. This conclusion appears to be directly opposite to that of Kerslake and Cooper. The assumption that the central vasomotor mechanisms are influenced by changes in the temperature of the circulating blood also appears to be supported by certain other data. In normal young human subjects, as observed by Glaser et al. (1950), the lungs and the liver contain more blood while the body is exposed to low ambient temperatures than when its environment is warm.

In dogs in which the central nervous system ischemia reflex was made very sensitive by elevation of the cerebrospinal fluid pressure, Guyton

(1952) described oscillating waves of blood pressure that may be explained as follows: Cerebrospinal fluid pressure causes ischemia of the central nervous system and consequent sympathetic excitation. As the blood pressure rises above the cerebrospinal fluid pressure, the ischemia subsides, and the sympathetic nerves become less active. As the blood pressure falls below the cerebrospinal fluid pressure, ischemia due to stimulation of the vasomotor center results, and a new cycle is initiated.

Vascular Reaction Patterns. — The peripheral blood flow, particularly in the extremities, fluctuates continually within relatively wide limits. Some of these fluctuations probably represent rhythmic changes in the vascular tonus. Others are due to various causes, including psychic factors.

Burton (1939) has adapted a simple plethysmographic method of recording the volume pulsations of the finger to measurement of instantaneous values of the blood flow of the finger in cc. per min. per 100 cc. of tissue. As indicated by such measurements, the blood flow in the fingers varies from 0.5 to 1 cc. to 80 to 90 cc. per min. per 100 cc. of tissue. These minimum and maximum values are subject to change upon slow adaptation to low or high environmental temperatures. The wide range of flow, made possible by the arteriovenous anastomoses, represents, not a metabolic requirement of the tissues, but a mechanism for the regulation of body temperature.

The magnitude of the volume pulse in the finger is closely correlated with volume flow of blood through the tissues; consequently, the method is useful in studying the fluctuations in the blood flow which occur from moment to moment. These fluctuations are rhythmic in nature and exhibit two main components, a respiratory wave of small amplitude and slower periodic constrictions of larger amplitude. These reactions occur simultaneously in the digits of all the extremities; consequently, they must be mediated through the vasomotor nerves and represent widespread responses through the peripheral sympathetic nerves. Constrictions elicited by pain, startle or emotional excitation may also be present and represent a third component in the vascular fluctuations. The amplitude of the volume pulse waves is greatest in the middle range of blood flow and of temperature. It is reduced somewhat during intervals of peripheral vasodilatation and more markedly during intervals of peripheral vasoconstriction. The rhythm also varies in frequency. In general the higher frequencies are associated with cooler conditions and consequent lower average values of the blood flow.

The reactions of the peripheral vessels in the digits and other cutaneous areas have been studied extensively by Hertzman and his collaborators with the aid of the photoelectric plethysmograph. According to their findings, spontaneous fluctuations may appear either as constrictions or as dilatations. They commonly appear as constrictions in the extremities, as dilatations in the skin of the head and of varied character in the ear and the nasal septum. They may or may not exhibit synchronism in the different vascular areas. Most of them seem to be related to vasomotor activity, but some probably represent activity of the vascular musculature that is independent of nerve impulses. Various means of stimulation, including auditory and psychic stimuli, cold applications, deep breath and breath-holding, elicit marked vasoconstrictor reactions in the digits, the skin of the hands and feet and the nasal septum, but variable reactions in the skin of the head and the ears (Hertzman and Dillon, 1939).

Large and small arteries do not react equally to vasomotor stimuli. The cutaneous arteries in the fingers, for example, may constrict strongly, as indicated by the volume pulse wave recorded in the pad of the distal segment, while the volume pulse wave record of the radial artery shows no appreciable change (Hertzman and Dillon, 1940). The dorsal metacarpal, digital and terminal cutaneous arteries of the hand usually do not participate in the spontaneous fluctuations or in the vasomotor reflexes elicited by loud noises, immersion of the contralateral hand in ice water or application of cold to the finger in the pad of which the volume pulse wave is being recorded. A high degree of selectivity in the vasomotor apparatus therefore is indicated (Hertzman, 1941).

The normal volume pulse wave of the finger pad is essentially similar in contour to the normal volume pulse wave of the radial artery (Dillon and Hertzman, 1941). In patients with arteriosclerosis or hypertension, the digital pulse is altered earlier and to a greater extent than the radial pulse, but, because of discrepancies in the alterations which take place in the waves, it is impossible to predict from the contour of the radial volume pulse wave what the contour of the digital volume pulse wave will be. It is impossible likewise, by study of the contours of the digital volume pulse waves, to differentiate arteriosclerotic changes in the digital vessel walls from those produced by hypertension, particularly if the hypertension is of long standing. The contour of the digital volume pulse wave, nevertheless, may afford significant information regarding early changes in the elasticity of the arterial system.

The elastic reservoir action of the arterial system has long been recognized. The data advanced by Dillon and Hertzman seem to support the suggestion of Greven and Federschmidt (1939) that there may be a central and a peripheral elastic reservoir, the latter, with respect to the hand, beginning somewhere peripheral to the radial artery. Other experimental data also support this hypothesis. Strict anatomical delimitation of the peripheral reservoir must await further study.

A quantitative correlation in the blood flow and the skin pulses in the same area has been expressed in the form of an equation (Hertzman *et al.*, 1946). Different areas of a given phalanx exhibit inequalities in the blood flow, but the rates of flow in adjacent fingers of a normal individual are approximately equal.

The blood flows are approximately uniform and equal in the skin of the trunk, the arm and the leg, but they are considerably higher in the skin of the face, the head and the plantar and palmar surfaces. The regional differences in the maximal rates of flow parallel the regional patterns for the basal rates. Photoelectric plethysmographic recordings of the skin volume pulses afford a basis for the estimation of the rates of cutaneous blood flow that is sufficiently accurate to be of value in the study of vascular patterns in the skin (Hertzman and Randall, 1948).

In an experimental study of vascular reactions to local cooling, Hertzman and Roth (1942) found that when a single finger is immersed in cold water the initial, immediate vasoconstriction is due to vasoconstrictor reflexes, as is indicated by the simultaneous vasoconstriction which occurs in the other fingers of the same hand and the opposite hand. The reactive vasodilatation which takes place in a chilled finger 3 to 8 minutes after the application of cold is independent of the vasomotor nerves. This is evidenced by the facts that the reactive vasodilatation may be limited to the chilled finger and that it may occur while the vasomotor tonus is high in the control fingers. In some instances vasoconstriction could be elicited in the chilled finger while the reactive vasodilatation was going on. The digital artery does not participate either in the vasoconstrictor reflexes elicited by local chilling or the reactive vasodilatation which follows. Its late constriction during continued chilling of the finger seems to be due to the direct effect of reduction in temperature on the artery. Certain cutaneous areas seem to be devoid of vasoconstrictor reflex mechanisms. Chilling of the skin of the forehead, for example, results in gradual vasoconstriction as the temperature falls, which is not followed by reactive vasodilatation. The vascular reaction to chilling in this area is comparable to that of a finger of a sympathectomized hand.

Chapter IX

INNERVATION OF THE RESPIRATORY SYSTEM

EXTRINSIC NERVES OF THE RESPIRATORY TRACT

THE respiratory tract, including the nasal mucosa, the larynx, the trachea, the bronchi and the lungs, is innervated through sympathetic and parasympathetic nerves. Associated with these nerves are afferent fibers of spinal ganglion origin and afferent components of the vagi. The afferent innervation of the nasal mucosa is derived chiefly from the trigeminal nerves and the nervi intermedii. The sympathetic innervation of the nasal mucosa is derived chiefly from the superior cervical ganglion through the internal carotid plexus. Its parasympathetic innervation is derived chiefly from the sphenopalatine ganglion. The voluntary musculature of the rostral portion of the respiratory tract is innervated through the facial, the glossopharyngeal and the vagus nerves. The parasympathetic and the vagus afferent innervation of the larynx and the trachea is derived chiefly through the laryngeal branches of the vagi. Their sympathetic supply is derived from the superior cervical sympathetic ganglia through the pharyngeal plexus and the sympathetic rami that join the vagi. The bronchi and the lungs are innervated chiefly through the pulmonary plexuses which are made up of vagus and sympathetic components plus the neurons in the pulmonary ganglia (Fig. 46).

The superior laryngeal nerve is a branch of the vagus that conveys efferent fibers from the accessory nerve. It passes caudad and mesad toward the thyroid cartilage and ends by dividing into a large internal and a small external laryngeal branch. It is joined by rami from the pharyngeal plexus and the sympathetic trunk. The internal laryngeal branch supplies the mucous membrane of the pharynx, extending rostrad to the epiglottis and the base of the tongue. It communicates, beneath the lamina of the thyroid cartilage, with the inferior laryngeal nerve. The external branch supplies the cricothyroid muscle. All the other muscles of the larynx derive their motor innervation from the inferior laryngeal, a terminal branch of the recurrent nerve. The recurrent nerve also gives off branches to the trachea and commonly is joined by a ramus from the middle cervical sympathetic ganglion. The nerves that approach the trachea and the bronchi give rise to a loose-meshed plexus in the connective tissue along the ventral and the lateral aspects of these organs that includes minute sparsely scattered ganglia, and another along their dorsal aspect that includes a large number of ganglia of various sizes and forms. These plexuses are continuous with the pulmonary plexuses.

As the vagus nerve on either side reaches the dorsal aspect of the root of the lung, it breaks up into numerous branches that become incorporated in the posterior pulmonary plexus. Some fibers from both vagi pass over the rostral border of the root of the lung and enter the much smaller anterior pulmonary plexus. The pulmonary plexuses are intimately connected with each other and with the cardiac plexuses.

The anterior pulmonary plexus lies in contact with the root of the lung ventrally. It is joined on both sides by a few fibers from the corresponding part of the deep cardiac plexus and on the left side also by fibers from the superficial cardiac plexus. It supplies structures in the ventral part of the root of the lung.

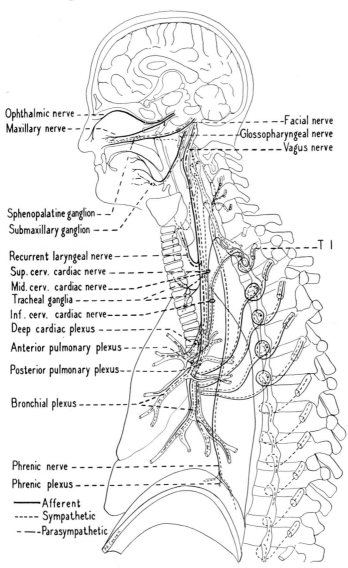

Fig. 46.—Diagrammatic illustration of the sympathetic, parasympathetic and afferent innervation of the respiratory tract.

The posterior pulmonary plexus lies dorsal to the root of the lung. It is made up chiefly of branches of the vagus nerve and slender rami from the second, the third and the fourth thoracic sympathetic trunk ganglia. It gives rise to numerous branches that form delicate plexuses on the bronchi and the blood vessels as they enter the substance of the lung.

INTRINSIC NERVES OF THE RESPIRATORY TRACT

The nerves in the walls of the respiratory tract include large and small myelinated and unmyelinated fibers and numerous ganglia. The ganglion cells are similar to those in the cardiac and the enteric plexuses. They are synaptically connected with preganglionic vagus nerve fibers. The occurrence of ganglion cells as far distad as the alveolar ducts has been reported. In general, the larger fiber bundles in the walls of the respiratory passages run longitudinally but branch and anastomose freely to form plexuses. In the larynx there is a subepithelial and a deep plexus. Here only the deep plexus includes ganglia. The epiglottis includes only a subepithelial plexus. Both the subepithelial and the deep plexuses are present in the walls of the trachea and the larger bronchi. In the walls of the smaller bronchi, the two plexuses blend into a single one that can be traced as far as the respiratory bronchioles, but nerve fibers running either singly or in small bundles continue still farther into the walls of the atria. Afferent fibers extend distad as far as the proximal ends of the alveolar ducts.

The plexuses in the bronchi are continuous with those in the trachea, but they are made up chiefly of fibers derived from the anterior and the posterior pulmonary plexuses. The nerves that enter the lungs from the latter plexuses are distributed to the bronchi, the blood vessels and the visceral pleuræ chiefly through the bronchial plexuses. The major portion of the subepithelial plexus is located between the cartilaginous plates and the bronchial musculature. The deep plexus is located between the cartilaginous plates and the parenchyma of the lung. The intrapulmonary ganglia are located chiefly in the latter plexus. They usually occur at the bifurcations of the bronchi and at the points of junction of the larger fiber bundles in the plexus.

The plexuses in the respiratory tract include both myelinated and unmyelinated fibers. Many of the larger myelinated fibers can be traced to sensory terminations in the epithelium and the subepithelial tissue as far distad as the bronchioles and the atria. These are general visceral afferent fibers, most of which are of vagus origin. Other myelinated fibers terminate in the intrinsic ganglia in pericellular networks. They are preganglionic fibers of vagus origin. Preganglionic fibers of spinal origin do not terminate in the ganglia in the walls of the respiratory tract. The smallest myelinated fibers and the unmyelinated ones are sympathetic postganglionic fibers and axons of the neurons in the intrinsic ganglia. They are distributed to blood vessels, the musculature and the glands of the respiratory tract. The mucous glands are innervated chiefly through the subepithelial plexus.

NERVE TERMINATIONS IN THE RESPIRATORY TRACT

Sensory.—The receptors in the larynx and the epiglottis are located in part in the subepithelial tissue and in part in the epithelium. They are connected with relatively large myelinated fibers.

Using the methylene blue technic on the rabbit's lungs, Larsell (1921) found sensory nerve endings in the epithelium of the primary bronchi at the points of origin of the bronchi of the various orders and in the walls of the atria. Those in the epithelium of the primary bronchi are highly com-

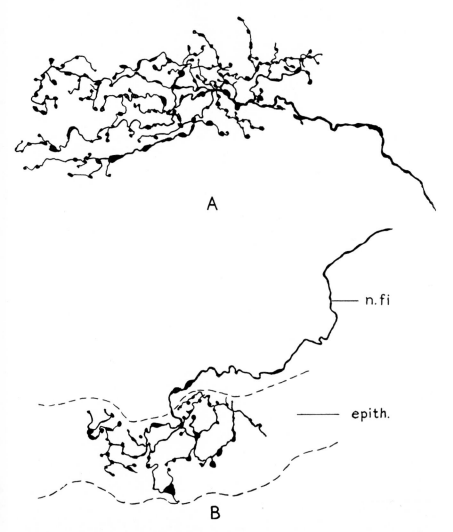

Fig. 47.—*A*, Sensory nerve termination in the epithelium of a primary bronchus within the lung in the rabbit. *B*, Sensory nerve termination at the point of division of one of the larger bronchi in the rabbit. (Larsell.)

plex. Relatively large myelinated fibers deviate from the fiber bundles in the plexiform meshworks around the bronchi and approach the bronchial epithelium either singly or in bundles of two or three fibers. Individual fibers penetrate the epithelium and terminate in elaborate ramifications among the epithelial cells. These ramifications show numerous varicosities,

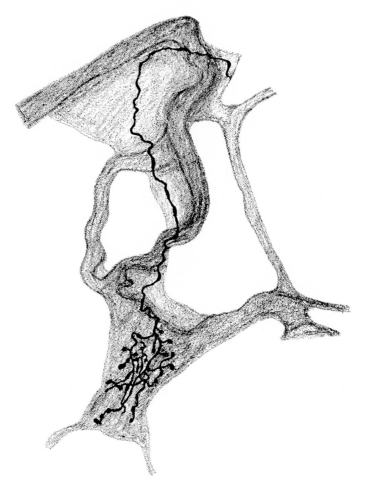

Fig. 48.—Sensory nerve termination at the division point of a small bronchus in the rabbit. (Larsell.)

and each terminal branch ends in a slight enlargement. Some of the terminal branches approach the surface of the epithelium, but most of them lie relatively deep between the columnar cells (Fig. 47). The ramifications of the larger terminations occupy an area approximately 150 microns in length and 125 microns in width. Larsell and Dow (1933) described nerve fiber terminations of the same kind in the bronchial epithelium in man.

The sensory nerve terminations in the epithelium of the successively smaller bronchi are essentially similar to those in the epithelium of the primary bronchi but less elaborate and smaller. The most characteristic position of these terminations is in the angle between two bronchi of successive orders, where masses of lymphoid tissue usually lie close to the epithelium (Fig. 48).

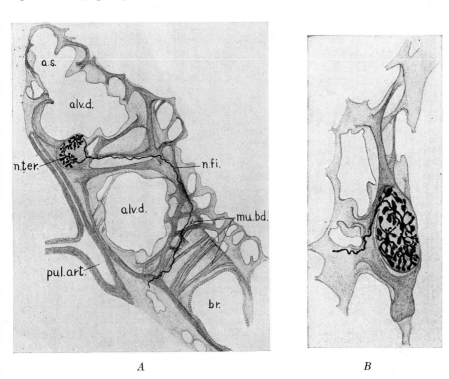

A   B

Fig. 49.—*A*, Nerve endings at point of division of respiratory bronchiolus into alveolar duct, child, aged eight months. Intra vitam methylene blue and borax carmine. *B*, Nerve endings in wall of atrium, child, aged eight months. Intra vitam methylene blue and aurantia. (Larsell and Dow.)

The sensory nerve terminations situated at the points of division of the bronchioles and the alveolar ducts differ somewhat from those in the larger bronchi. Not only are they smaller, but their terminal branches are curved and appear somewhat drawn together, in contrast with the extended and radiating terminal branches of those located in the larger bronchi (Fig. 49, *A*). Terminations similar to these but smaller are found in the human lung as far distad as the proximal ends of the respiratory bronchioles and at the bases of the alveolar ducts. Afferent terminations of a somewhat different type are also present in the walls of the atria (Fig. 49, *B*). In these terminations the entire mass of branching fibers forms a flattened end-organ that lies between the squamous epithelium on the one side and the frail framework of the elastic connective tissue and the capillary bed that surrounds the atrium on the other. Larsell and Dow (1933) have advanced the opinion that these end-organs are chemoreceptors which probably are stimulated by increase of carbon dioxide tension beyond a certain point. They also described smooth muscle spindles located at various points in the musculature of the bronchi in man (Fig. 50). Elftman (1943) described sensory end-organs in somewhat greater variety in the respiratory tract in the dog, including flattened receptors along the alveolar ducts, complex branching ones in nodules in the walls of the air sacs and more delicate ones with straight and coiled terminal branches in the alveolar walls.

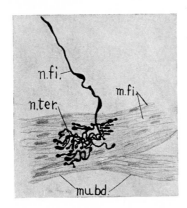 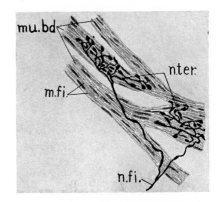

Fig. 50.—Smooth muscle spindles in bronchial musculature, child, aged eight months. Intra vitam methylene and borax carmine. (Larsell and Dow.)

Motor.—The musculature of the larynx, the trachea and the bronchi is abundantly innervated through efferent nerve fibers of small caliber that are either unmyelinated or invested with a very thin myelin sheath. Many of them can be traced directly from neurons in the intrinsic ganglia. Others merely traverse these ganglia on the way to their peripheral distribution. The latter are postganglionic fibers which have their origins in ganglia of the sympathetic trunk.

In the larger bronchi, the bundles of nerve fibers in general run parallel to the smooth muscle bands. At intervals, nerve fibers deviate from these bundles either singly or in small strands and penetrate the muscle. On reaching the muscle the individual nerve fibers give rise to numerous slender branches that run between the muscle fibers and at intervals give off short twigs that terminate near the nuclei of the smooth muscle cells. Nerve bundles, constantly diminishing in size, may be traced as far as the bronchioles and the alveolar ducts. From these bundles, fibers may be traced into the musculature of the bronchioles and the sphincter-like bands at the openings of the alveolar ducts into the atria. Efferent nerve fibers also terminate in relation to the bronchial glands.

INNERVATION OF THE PULMONARY VESSELS

The pulmonary artery and its branches are more abundantly innervated than current anatomical accounts and the results of physiological experimentation seem to indicate, but less abundantly than the bronchial arteries. In the rabbit, according to Larsell (1921), relatively large nerve trunks become associated, near the hilum of the lung, with the larger branches of the pulmonary artery. They wind about the blood vessels as they continue distad and, at irregular intervals, give off fibers which run roughly parallel to the artery for a short distance and then turn almost at right angles and divide into several main branches. One branch usually extends distad and another in the opposite direction along the artery (Fig. 51). In turn they give rise to smaller varicose branches which may undergo still further subdivision and finally terminate in relation to the smooth muscle

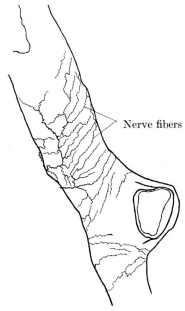

Nerve fibers

FIG. 51.—Distribution of nerve fibers in the musculature of the pulmonary artery in the rabbit. (Larsell.)

cells in the media. Larsell also observed sensory nerve terminations in the adventitia of the pulmonary arteries in the rabbit that are connected with relatively large myelinated fibers like those which may be traced to the sensory terminations in the bronchi.

The nerve fiber bundles along the branches of pulmonary arteries diminish in size with the arteries. The smaller arteries are accompanied by nerve fiber bundles of minute size. Slender filaments also follow the courses of the capillaries about the alveolar ducts and air sacs and at intervals give rise to twigs that probably terminate in relation to the capillary walls. The pulmonary veins have a relatively meager nerve supply, but the nerve fibers observed in relation to the media bear the same relation to the musculature as in the pulmonary arteries. Most of the available data, particularly those obtained in experimental studies carried out on mammals, support the view that the efferent innervation of the pulmonary vessels is chiefly sympathetic. Afferent nerve fiber terminations in the adventitia of the pulmonary arteries have also been described.

INNERVATION OF THE VISCERAL PLEURA

Afferent nerve endings in the visceral pleura have been described by various investigators. The nerves concerned emerge from the plexus on the pulmonary arteries near the hilum of the lung, enter the pleura and run for some distance as fairly compact bundles and then break up into smaller ones. The nerve fibers are distributed to the pleura chiefly near the margins of the pulmonary lobes, particularly on the inner surfaces. In the rabbit, the fiber terminations in the visceral pleura are small and of simple structure. In the dog they are larger and more complex. The results of degeneration experiments on rabbits reported by Larsell (1922), though not conclusive, strongly suggest that the nerve fibers distributed to the visceral pleura are mainly components of the dorsal roots of the upper thoracic nerves that reach the lung through the rostral thoracic and the inferior cervical sympathetic ganglia.

PULMONARY REFLEXES

Direct Bronchial Reflexes.—Direct reflexes involving the tracheal and bronchial musculature which are initiated by stimulation of afferent nerve fibers that supply the respiratory tract play an important rôle in the respiratory processes. Irritation of any part of the tracheal or the bronchial mucosa elicits reflexes that involve the musculature of the respiratory tract either in whole or in part. The receptors situated at the openings into the respiratory portion of the lung differ somewhat morphologically from those situated in the mucosa of the larger bronchi. It seems probable, as has been suggested by Larsell (1921), that those in the larger bronchi, are tactile receptors that are stimulated by masses of mucus or foreign particles within the bronchi. The reflex contraction of the bronchial musculature elicited by such stimulation would tend to prevent the displacement distad of matter in the respiratory passages. The receptors situated at the portals of the respiratory portion of the lungs might conceivably also serve the purpose of guarding against the entrance of foreign matter into the atria and the air sacs by eliciting reflex constriction of the muscle bands at the openings of the alveolar ducts into the atria, but, as Larsell suggested, they appear to be better adapted, due to their structure, to react to pressure stimuli than to touch. Although they may mediate impulses that elicit direct bronchial reflexes, they probably are stimulated by partial collapse of the lungs at every expiration and mediate impulses that are involved in the reflex control of respiratory rhythm. If the receptors located in the walls of the atria are stimulated by changes in the CO_2 tension of the air in the atria and air sacs, they also play a rôle in the reflex control of the respiratory rhythm.

The visceral pleura has quite generally been regarded as insensitive to stimulation. Larsell (1928) elicited respiratory reflexes in decerebrated dogs by inflating a small rubber balloon placed between the lobes of the lung. These reflexes involved inhibition of the inspiratory movement and initiation of expiration. The receptors in the visceral pleura on the interlobular surfaces of the lung, therefore, appear to be stimulated by mechanical contact. Larsell also expressed the opinion "that the nerve endings in the pleura are normally stimulated by the contact of adjoining interlobular surfaces during extreme inflation of the lung, although such stimulation probably occurs but rarely, if ever, in normal respiration with intact vagus nerves."

Bronchoconstrictor Fibers.—Due to the elasticity of the cartilage rings in the trachea and the larger bronchi, these tubes tend to assume a maximum diameter, but the tonus of the tracheal and the bronchial muscles normally imposes on the cartilage rings a certain degree of tension. This tonus, as indicated by the results of physiological experimentation, is mediated through the parasympathetic nerves. Section of the vagi results in dilatation of both the trachea and the bronchi. Stimulation of the peripheral end of the vagus nerve, if it is cut proximal to the origin of its recurrent branch, results in diminution in the caliber of both the trachea and the bronchi. When either vagus nerve is stimulated in this manner, diminution in the caliber of the bronchi is most marked on the homolateral side, but it is also apparent on the contralateral side. This result indicates that some vagus fibers normally cross over and enter the pulmonary plexus on the opposite side. The extent of the crossing varies within wide limits.

In experiments reported by Hebb (1940), the most frequent response of the bronchial musculature in the isolated perfused lung of the guinea-pig to sympathetic stimulation was marked contraction. Bronchodilatation occurred occasionally under special conditions. The bronchoconstrictor response was quantitatively comparable to that resulting from the injection of acetylcholine. The sympathetic innervation of the bronchial musculature obviously includes some cholinergic fibers, at least in some animals.

Bronchodilator Fibers.—The bronchodilator fibers are chiefly sympathetic and arise mainly in the inferior cervical and the rostral thoracic ganglia. The preganglionic fibers concerned are components of the rostral three thoracic nerves. Stimulation of the thoracic end of the cut cervical sympathetic trunk commonly results in bronchodilatation on one or both sides. The reaction is more marked, however, when the stimulus is applied to the rostral thoracic rami. The bronchodilator fibers also have a bilateral distribution. In some cases, according to Dixon and Ransom (1912), the sympathetic supply to the bronchioles is derived almost entirely from the opposite side. In others, the crossing of these fibers is less complete. The crossing of a certain percentage of the sympathetic fibers that are distributed to the bronchi seems to be the rule rather than the exception.

Vasomotor Control of the Pulmonary Vessels.—The pulmonary vessels, as stated above, are innervated both through the sympathetic and the parasympathetic nerves. The data bearing on the physiological actions of these nerves respectively in the regulation of the pulmonary circulation are not in complete agreement. They appear to warrant the conclusion that the sympathetic nerves to the pulmonary vessels include the vaso-

13

constrictor fibers and at least some vasodilator fibers, but vasodilator fibers are also included in the parasympathetic nerves. In general, the effect of the vasoconstrictors is more marked than that of the vasodilators. Either vasodilatation or vasoconstriction may take place independently of changes in the caliber of the bronchi; consequently, it may be assumed that the pulmonary circulation, under physiological conditions, is subject to regulation, at least in some degree, through vasomotor nerves. In view of the mechanical conditions that obtain it must be apparent that the regulation of the pulmonary circulation depends in a large measure on the regulatory control of the systemic circulation.

REGULATION OF RESPIRATORY MOVEMENTS

Respiratory Nerves.—Although respiration is a vegetative function, the respiratory movements in mammals involve extensive somatic neural mechanisms. The somatic nerves concerned are essentially voluntary, but the respiratory movements are carried out automatically and are subject to voluntary control only within well defined limits.

The phrenic nerves, which arise from the third, the fourth and the fifth cervical spinal nerves, supply the diaphragm. The spinal accessory nerves and branches of the cervical and the brachial plexuses innervate the neck and shoulder muscles that are concerned in respiration. The intercostal nerves innervate the muscles of the thorax and the abdomen. A branch of each facial nerve innervates the muscles of the nose, and branches of the vagi supply the muscles of the larynx. All these muscles belong to the somatic system, and their innervation is essentially somatic.

General Reflex Regulation.—The chief respiratory centers (see Chapter III) are located in the medulla oblongata approximately at the level of the rostral half of the inferior olivary nucleus. Functionally associated with these centers is the pneumotaxic center located in the rostral portion of the pons. The major coördinated activities of the extensive mechanisms involved in the respiratory movements are regulated through the respiratory centers. Reflexes involving respiratory movements of the mouth and ala nasi are mediated at the level of the nucleus of the facial nerve. Respiratory inhibition due to swallowing and vomiting reflexes is mediated at the level of the nucleus of the vagus and glossopharyngeal nerves. The coughing reflex is mediated at a somewhat lower level and the sneezing reflex near the level of the chief sensory nucleus of the trigeminal nerve. A vertical section of the medulla in the median plane does not interfere with normal respiration. Transverse section of the spinal cord above the origin of the phrenic nerves results in immediate cessation of all respiratory movements except those of the nose and the larynx. Section of the brain stem above the respiratory centers does not result in cessation of respiration.

The medullary respiratory center comprises separate neuron aggregates through which the inspiratory and the expiratory movements are mediated. The locations of the inspiratory and the expiratory centers do not coincide, but the internuncial neurons concerned with both centers are located in the nucleus of the tractus solitarius (Wyss, 1947). When cut off from impulses from all higher centers and from afferent impulses conducted by the vagi, these centers are no longer capable of rhythmic activity, but can only induce a sustained inspiration. Data advanced by Mansfield and Hamori (1938) seem to indicate that, under physiological conditions, the respiratory movements are regulated, not through the center in the medulla, but through the pneumotaxic center. They regard the medullary center as comparable to the primitive respiratory center of lower vertebrates which is inadequate for the requirements of warm blooded animals. Since the respiratory rhythm is not materially altered by transection of the pons while the vagi remain intact, it cannot be determined solely by the pneumotaxic center. It obviously involves periodic inhibition of the activity of the inspiratory center by nerve impulses generated by the inspiratory act, a function which can be carried out adequately either by efferent impulses from the pontile pneumotaxic center or by afferent impulses conducted by the vagi (Stella, 1939; Pitts et al., 1939). The chief function of the expiratory neurons seems to be inhibition of the activity of the inspiratory neurons. Nerve impulses that subserve this function act by primarily stimulating the expiratory center (Pitts et al., 1939).

Afferent impulses conducted by the vagus and the carotid sinus nerves undoubtedly play a major rôle in the reflex regulation of respiration through the respiratory centers, but stimulation of any other afferent nerve may result in changes in the rate or the amplitude of the respiratory movements. Emotional excitation may also elicit changes in respiration. Stimulation of certain portions of the cerebral cortex likewise results in alteration of respiration. It may be assumed, therefore, that afferent impulses conducted by any of the cranial or spinal nerves may reach the respiratory center and that this center is also influenced by impulses emanating from the cerebral cortex.

The central respiratory complex, according to Pitts (1942), may be functionally subdivided into four subsidiary systems: (a) the respiratory center-motor neuron system; (b) the vagal inhibitory system; (c) the brain stem inhibitory system, and (d) other excitatory and inhibitory systems. In studying these systems in isolation and in various combinations, he found that the respiratory center-motor neuron system regulates inspiration through its control of motor unit impulse frequency and the number of active units. In isolation the activity of this center is continuous and graded in relation to the CO_2 tension of the arterial blood. Normally its activities are inhibited periodically by the vagal and the brain stem inhibitory systems. Such periodic inhibition results in rhythmic respiration and affords the basis for variations in rate. Stimulation of afferent nerves affects the activity of the respiratory center in various ways. The respiratory rate may be changed together with an increase or a decrease in amplitude, the inspirations and expirations may be increased or decreased, or one phase may be modified to a greater degree than the other. Under experimental conditions, stimulation of an afferent nerve which includes cutaneous fibers usually results either in acceleration, manifested by quicker and stronger inspirations and active expirations, or inhibition, manifested by slower and more feeble respiratory movements or complete cessation of respiration. Stimulation of the splanchnic nerves, as by excessive, rapid distention of any part of the small intestine, elicits reflex respiratory changes of characteristic pattern accompanied by synchronous fluctuations in blood pressure. The vagi play no part in this reaction. Whether afferent impulses which augment and those which inhibit the respiratory movements are conducted by the same or different afferent fibers is not definitely known. The afferent fibers which mediate these impulses probably also subserve other functions, *e.g.*, the ascending fibers in the spinal cord and the brain stem which conduct cutaneous impulses to the thalamus, whence they are relayed to the cerebral cortex, may also make connections in the respiratory center through collaterals.

The afferent vagus nerve fibers, particularly those that are distributed along the respiratory tract, sustain a peculiarly intimate functional relationship to the respiratory center. The commonly observed physiological effect of afferent vagus stimulation is inspiratory inhibition. If both vagi are cooled until they cease to conduct, inspiration is both lengthened and deepened, probably due to the absence of inhibitory impulses, but expiration is not appreciably altered. A like result may be obtained by extirpation of the inferior colliculi. Bilateral vagotomy combined with this operation results in inspiratory spasm. The inferior colliculus apparently includes a center which exerts an inhibitory influence on the respiratory center and functions concurrently with vagus stimulation.

Section of both vagi in the neck immediately alters the character of the respiratory movements. The rate is retarded, the amplitude is increased, inspirations become longer and deeper and are followed by an appreciable pause. Section of only one vagus may result in an intermediate effect, *i.e.*, the respiratory rate is retarded somewhat and inspiration is slightly deepened. It may be assumed, therefore, that some influence which normally maintains the respiratory movements at a more rapid rate has been cut off. This influence consists in the tonic action on the respiratory center of impulses conducted by the afferent vagus fibers that are distributed to the lungs. It constitutes one of the major factors in the maintenance of normal respiratory rhythm. When these vagus fibers are severed the respiratory center drops into a slower, unregulated rhythm. Expansion of the alveoli during inspiration gives rise to vagus impulses that depress the respiratory center and result in inhibition of inspiration. In experiments designed to reveal the relations of impulses in the pulmonary branch of the vagus to the phases of respiration, Partridge (1933) obtained no evidence that either normal or artificial maximal deflation of the lungs stimulates the pulmonary vagal endings, but inflation of the lungs initiated afferent impulses. The frequency of these impulses increased during the period of expansion of the lungs. The increase was related to the volume of inspiration but was independent of the rate of expansion of the lungs. Obviously, inspiration requires no vagus stimulation, but is the natural function of the respiratory center. Cessation of the inhibitory influence of vagus stimulation probably is sufficient to release the inspiratory impulses that are held in abeyance during expiration. The increase in lung volume during inspiration initiates impulses that inhibit the inspiratory center, thus limiting the duration and the amplitude of inspiration. The decrease in lung volume during expiration tends to limit its duration and amplitude due to removal of the stimulus which initiates the inhibitory impulses.

Stimulation of the central end of the divided vagus affects the respiratory center in a variety of ways, depending on the strength of the stimulus and the condition of the center. Such stimulation usually inhibits the respiratory movements partially or completely, resulting either in smaller movements or complete cessation of respiration with the thorax in the condition of passive expiration. On the other hand, the rate of the respiratory movements may be increased until respiration ceases with the thorax in an inspiratory position and the inspiratory muscles in a state of tetanic contraction. These two main effects of stimulation of the central end of the vagus have been interpreted as indicating that the afferent vagus fibers that are distributed to the lungs are of two kinds, each of which has a specific effect: (a) inspiratory fibers, whose influence tends to increase the rate of respiration by increasing the rate of inspiratory discharge from the respiratory center, and (b) expiratory (or inspiratory inhibiting) fibers, whose influence tends to retard the rate of respiration by inhibiting the inspiratory discharges from the respiratory center either partially or comteplely.

The data on which the classification of vagal afferent fibers in inspiratory and expiratory categories is based appear to be inconclusive. Hammouda and Wilson (1935) supported the assumption that the vagus fibers that conduct impulses of intrapulmonary origin that excite the respiratory center are of smaller caliber than those which conduct impulses that inhibit this center. Their experimental data seemed to indicate that augmentor impulses are constantly reaching the respiratory center from the lungs, and that inhibitory impulses are not initiated at or below the level of normal expiratory expansion. Later experimental data advanced by Hammouda and Wilson (1943) appear to support the assumptions that both respiratory accelerator and respiratory inhibitory vagus afferents conduct impulses from receptors located within the tissues of the lungs and that all reflex changes in respiration that accompany inflation or deflation of the lungs are elicited by impulses that arise in these intrapulmonary receptors. They do not support the point of view that respiratory reflexes following inflation or deflation of the lungs are, at least in part, due to impulses arising in receptors in the thoracic wall or the diaphragm. In their experiments the inflation and the deflation reflexes were not affected by elimination of all afferent impulses from the thoracic walls, the diaphragm and the parietal pleura or by section of the cardiac branches of the vagi and extirpation of the carotid sinus. Circulatory changes within the lungs also have no direct effect on these reflexes. These findings do not militate against the theory that normal respiration may be carried out through the respiratory center independently of afferent vagus impulses.

Since afferent vagus stimulation commonly results in cessation of rhythmic inspiration, the vagi have been regarded as inspiratory inhibitory nerves. This interpretation does not take account of the expiratory activity frequently elicited by vagus stimulation and its reciprocal inhibitory action on the inspiratory portion of the respiratory center. Artificial inflation of the lungs, which presumably affords adequate and selective stimulation of the pulmonary stretch receptors may result in selective reinforcement of either the inspiratory or the expiratory act. Every stretch receptor, therefore, probably is synaptically connected with both inspiratory and expiratory neurons in the respiratory center. In experiments reported by Gesell and Hamilton (1941), faradic stimulation of the vagus nerves beginning during the expiratory phase resulted in intensification and prolongation of the period of expiratory activity, thus preventing the normally recurring inspiratory cycles. Similar stimulation begun during the inspiratory phase frequently resulted in intensifying the inspiratory act which immediately gave way to a sustained expiratory response. They, therefore, regarded the pulmonary vagus, in which proprioceptive fibers predominate, as chiefly expiratory. Faradic stimulation of the carotid sinus nerve, in which chemoreceptive fibers predominate, in their experiments, resulted in a rhythmic form of breathing, faster or slower than normal, in which the depth of both inspiration and expiration was increased. Since the inspiratory action was most pronounced, they regarded this nerve as predominantly inspiratory. Faradic stimulation of the saphenous nerve, in which nociceptive fibers predominate, resulted in a rapid rhythmic form of breathing in which both inspiration and expiration frequently were equally increased in intensity. They, therefore, regarded the action of sensory cutaneous nerves on the respiratory center as approximately midway between that of the vagus and that of the carotid sinus nerve.

Intermittent faradic stimulation of any one of these nerves, carried out to vary the incidence of stimulation with respect to the phase of the respiratory act, commonly resulted in selective excitation of either inspiratory or expiratory neurons in the respiratory center, depending on the phase of respiratory activity existing at the moment of stimulation. The sensitivity of the inspiratory and the expiratory neurons, therefore, appears to depend on the prevailing phase of activity. Such selective activation of normally discharging inspiratory and expiratory neurons illustrates the principle of precedence of stimulation which, according to Gesell and Hamilton, obtains also for more abnormal conditions of respiration. When respiratory rhythm was abolished and replaced by prolonged artificial expiratory contraction by vagus stimulation, in their experiments, stimulation of either the saphenous or the carotid sinus nerve resulted in intensification of that contraction without inspiratory complications. When sustained expiratory activity, due to intermittently interrupted vagus stimulation, was converted into a slowly developing inspiration by intravenous injection of sodium cyanide, the reflexogenic inspiration was reinforced by every vagal stimulation. These reactions illustrate the selective addition of the effects on the respiratory center of the diverse components of very unlike afferent nerves. This selective summation of impulses arising in receptors of diverse types indicates their common action in the respiratory center and emphasizes the primary importance of the principle of precedence of stimulation (Gesell and Hamilton, 1941).

Data advanced by Rice and Joy (1947) appear to support the assumption that every afferent vagal impulse constitutes a unitary contribution to the development of a central state that affects the respiratory center. In experiments on dogs they found that low frequency vagal stimulation tends to develop such a central state only in a slight degree and that prolonged high frequency stimulation results in its development in a marked degree. Its development in only a slight degree tends to augment respiratory movements, but its development in a marked degree tends to inhibit them. Specific augmentor and inhibitory afferent vagal fibers could not be recognized. The difference in the respiratory responses appears to be due to central selection of impulses conducted by fibers of the same functional category. Wyss (1947) found that in monkeys afferent vagal stimulation of low frequency and low intensity elicited weak inspiratory reactions and that further decreasing the frequency or the intensity of the stimulation resulted in strong inspiratory reactions.

In an analysis of the cyclic changes in the respiratory center as revealed by the effects on the electrical activity of the phrenic nerve of timed afferent impulses conducted through the superior laryngeal nerve, Larrabee and Hodes (1948) found that the threshold number of afferent impulses decreased with the progression of the inspiratory phase and that afferent volleys during the expiratory phase delayed the initiation of the next inspiration. These and other findings appear to support the assumption that normally occurring afferent impulses to the respiratory center are monitored by cyclic changes somewhere within it. Certain data appear to support the assumption that the phasic control of the phrenic nerves depends on afferent impulses conducted through fibers of one category and that modulation of the cycle is mediated through fibers of another category (Rijlant, 1948). According to Wyss and Rivkine (1950), the afferent vagal fibers concerned with respiratory reflexes fall into three categories with respect to conduction rates, but those in each category do not appear to be connected with functionally distinct receptors.

The carotid sinus nerve, like the visceral afferent vagal fibers, conducts into the nucleus of the tractus solitarius, through which connections are made with the respiratory and the vasomotor centers. In cats and dogs, as reported by Daly and Schwitzer (1951), electrical stimulation of the carotid sinus nerve may elicit either bronchoconstriction or bronchodilatation. The bronchodilator response is diminished, abolished or reversed following section of the sympathetic nerves to the respiratory tract. In dogs, according to Daly et al. (1952), lowering of the blood pressure results in bronchodilatation. Anemia of the medullary centers probably is not a factor in this response, and it is not altered by inactivation of the carotid and the aortic chemoreceptors. Normal bronchomotor tonus is maintained, at least in part, by reflex activity initiated in the carotid sinus and the aortic baroreceptors.

Normal quiet expiration may be regarded as a purely passive process. The inspiratory muscles are relaxed and the displaced masses return to a resting position due to the force of gravity and the normal elasticity of the tissues involved. The collaboration of the lungs themselves in this process is augmented by their almost ideal elasticity which becomes effective as soon as the intrathoracic pressure begins to rise following inspiration. On the other hand, under conditions of physical exertion or dyspnea, passive expiration no longer suffices and expiration, though still automatic, becomes an active process.

Pressoreceptive Regulation.—The pressoreceptive mechansims, so important in cardiovascular regulation (see Chapters VII and VIII), also play a significant rôle in the reflex regulation of respiration. Changes in intravascular pressure acting on the pressoreceptors in the cardio-aortic zone initiate impulses that influence the respiratory center as well as the vasomotor center. An increase in blood pressure in the cardio-aortic area elicits reflex inhibition of the respiratory center, or even apnea. Lowering of the cardio-aortic pressure results in the opposite respiratory response.

A decrease in the cephalic blood pressure and blood flow, due to occlusion of the common carotid arteries, produces hyperpnea, and an increase inhibits the activity of the respiratory center. These results have been interpreted by some as indicating that the activity of the respiratory center is regulated by changes in its blood supply, but the activity of the respiratory center is altered much more profoundly following occlusion of the carotids than following occlusion of the vertebral arteries, although the latter are more important for the blood supply of the brain stem. The effects on the respiratory center of changes in carotid blood pressure are due to nerve impulses conducted by the carotid sinus nerve. Blood pressure changes in the aortic arch likewise influence the activity of the respiratory center. A rise in intra-aortic pressure elicits reflex respiratory inhibition, even apnea. A fall in intra-aortic pressure results in reflex hyperpnea. Venous pressure may also influence respiration reflexly. An increase in pressure in the vena cava and the right atrium may elicit reflex augmentation of respiratory activity, even hyperpnea.

Experimental data support the assumption that respiratory acceleration produced by electrical stimulation of the vagi, as described by Mammouda and Wilson (1935), may be attributed to stimulation of afferent fibers connected with cardio-aortic pressoreceptors. The respiratory augmentation elicited while the lungs are distended appears to be due chiefly to the activity of the cardio-aortic and the carotid sinus depressor mechanisms.

The pressoreceptors are highly sensitive to intravascular pressure changes, whereas the respiratory center is relatively insensitive to changes in blood pressure and blood flow. The resistance of the respiratory center to central anemia or anoxemia, as demonstrated by Heymans *et al.* (1937), is so great that its activity can be revived even after complete arrest of the circulation for thirty minutes. It may be assumed, therefore, that the effects of intravascular pressure changes on the respiratory rhythm which are exerted through the pressoreceptive mechanisms are more significant than those due to the direct influence of changes in blood pressure or blood flow on the respiratory center. Heymans and Pannier (1948) also pointed out that the respiratory center is more sensitive to pressure stimuli in the carotid sinus than to the humoral effect of CO_2.

The respiratory movements and the ventilation of the lungs may be influenced reflexly by afferent impulses that arise in any part of the body. The significance of respiratory reflexes elicited by proprioceptive impulses arising in the limbs has been emphasized by various investigators. Reflexes elicited by such impulses probably are a major factor in the initial increase in pulmonary ventilation during exercise. Passive movements of the limbs also initiate reflexes that augment pulmonary ventilation. Continuous measurements of the alveolar O_2 and CO_2 tension in human subjects and calculation of the stimulus of movements of the limbs per se by means of Gray's multiple factor theory, as reported by Otis (1949), show that the stimulus from such movements is sufficient to produce a ventilation increment of 100 to 150 per cent of the resting ventilation.

Chemical Regulation.—The theory of the chemical control of respiration by the respiratory center has been dominant for many years, but during the past two decades the reflex factors have claimed increasing attention. The weight of experimental evidence now favors the assumption that chemical stimulation of the respiratory center is effected chiefly through chemoreceptors, particularly those in the carotid sinus and the carotid and aortic bodies. Direct chemical stimulation of the respiratory center is not precluded, but this center probably is less sensitive to some of the normal chemical stimulants than the peripheral chemoreceptors. The effectiveness of the latter has been amply demonstrated experimentally.

The chief chemical factors are O_2 deficiency and excessive CO_2 tension. Asphyxia of only the cardio-aortic circulation results in reflex stimulation of the respiratory center through the cardio-aortic nerves. The walls of the carotid sinuses include receptors that are stimulated by changes in pressure and receptors that are stimulated by chemical substances in the blood. Heymans *et al.* (1930) reported reflex modifications in the respiratory movements due to changes in the pH of the solution with which the isolated carotid sinuses were perfused and changes in the O_2 and CO_2 contents of the blood of another animal flowing through the isolated carotid sinuses. On the basis of their experimental findings, they concluded that the chemoreceptors in the carotid sinuses are more sensitive to chemical stimuli than the respiratory center. They advanced the opinion that the respiratory center is not stimulated directly by changes in the O_2 and CO_2 contents of the blood, but the action of such changes on this center is exerted by afferent impulses reaching it through the carotid sinus nerves. Direct chemical stimulation of the respiratory center, therefore, may be regarded as a secondary factor in the regulation of respiration.

These objective findings have been corroborated by the results of later experimental studies carried out by Heymans and his collaborators and by other investigators, but some have maintained that the data available do not warrant the conclusion that the respiratory center is not stimulated directly by changes in the O_2 and CO_2 contents of the blood. Bouckaert and Heymans (1933) also found that the respiratory center is sensitive to the CO_2 content of the arterial blood but not to anoxemia. Animals with both vagi and carotid sinus nerves depressed or interrupted show no appreciable hyperpnea during acute anoxemia (Heymans, 1938), whereas animals with these nerves intact exhibit respiratory augmentation. The hyperpnea due to O_2 deficiency, according to Gesell *et al.* (1940), is purely reflexogenic. Lack of oxygen in the circulating blood, therefore, obviously results in stimulation of the respiratory center mainly through the chemoreceptive mechanisms. The chemoreceptors connected with the vagi are less important in this reflex activity than those connected with the carotid sinus nerves.

Hyperpnea induced by acute oxygen deficiency appears to be brought about exclusively through the chemoreceptive reflex mechanisms, but acute oxygen lack also results in direct depression of the respiratory center. Hypoxic hyperventilation associated with blood alkalosis appears to be due solely to chemoreflex activity, at least in the initial stages of the oxygen deficiency (Hesser, 1949). The conclusion that hyperventilation during oxygen deficiency results from the direct stimulating effect of hypoxemia on the respiratory center, which formerly appeared to be supported by experimental data, therefore, is untenable. The initial effect of oxygen lack on respiration probably is due exclusively to the chemoreflex drive, while the effect of prolonged hypoxemia is due chiefly to direct central impulses. As the alkalinity of the blood gradually subsides due to hyperpnea, the chemoreflex drive becomes less active, and the central drive becomes increasingly important, so that finally it may control respiration almost entirely.

The point of view that the chemoreceptors exert no significant influence on respiration under normal conditions, but become active only under conditions typified by anoxemia is untenable, in view of the great volume of data that indicate chemoreflex activity also under normal conditions of respiration. The relative importance of the chemoreflex component and the direct central component in the regulation of breathing in different physiological and pathological conditions, however, requires further investigation. Under some conditions the chemoreflex component undoubtedly is the more important. Under other conditions the centrogenic component may predominate. For example, hyperpnea during acidosis appears to be chiefly centrogenic, since it persists following elimination of the chemoreflex component (Hesser, 1949).

The activity of the respiratory center appears to run parallel to the reaction of the blood. The oxygen lack probably is exerted solely through the chemoreceptive reflex mechanisms, whose activity depends on the H-ion concentration in the chemoreceptive cells. In hypoxemia respiratory regulation results in an increase in the alkalinity of the blood due to the induced hyperpnea. The change in the blood toward alkalinity is accompanied by a reduction in the oxygen tension of the blood for the same oxygen concentration and a consequent increase in the H-ion concentration in the chemoreceptive cells. Hyperpnea, consequently, is reinforced by the chemoreflex drive. The changes in respiration induced by CO_2 and by hypoxemia, therefore, may be explained by the sensitivity of the chemoreceptors and the respiratory center to variations in H-ion concentration, but the chemoreceptors respond more rapidly than the central chemoreceptive cells to changes in the H-ion concentration of the arterial blood. The possibility of a specific direct action of CO_2 on the chemoreceptors and on the respiratory center, independent of the action induced by the H-ion concentration, as yet remains open for further investigation (Heymans, 1951).

Modified Respiratory Rhythms. — Under normal physiological conditions vagal end organs are stimulated by distention of the lungs, thus bringing about reflex deflation, which is followed by the inspiratory act (Hering-Breuer reflex). Either inflation or deflation of the lungs results in changing the vagal impulses so that the opposite phase is encouraged. Afferent vagal impulses thus play a rôle in regulating the length of each phase and, consequently, exert an influence in the control of the respiratory system.

When inspiration is forced for a few minutes, the desire to breathe again may not be experienced for three-quarters of a minute or longer. A condition of apnea exists which is followed by frequent shallow breathing, but the normal rhythm is gradually restored. Vagal impulses arising in the lungs are not the major factors in this reaction, since overventilation produces apnea in animals in which the pulmonary branches of both vagi are interrupted. The apneic pause probably is due chiefly to excessive elimination of CO_2 from the blood, which affects both the respiratory center and the peripheral chemoreceptors.

Overventilation of the lungs by an increase in the volume of air inhaled (hyperpnea) may be brought about by impulses reaching the respiratory center from the cerebral cortex, the hypothalamus or the periphery. Conditions that increase the demand of the tissues for oxygen, *e.g.*, muscular exercise, are particularly effective. Since the respiratory center is relatively insensitive to lack of oxygen in the blood, hyperpnea induced by muscular exercise probably is essentially reflexogenic. Associated changes in the CO_2 content of the blood also exert a direct effect on the respiratory center.

Periodic breathing, *e.g.*, the Cheyne-Stokes type, is characterized by a period in which the individual respirations are shallow and slow at the beginning but gradually increase in depth and rate to a maximum and then subside until they finally cease for a short time. This involves an interval of activation of the respiratory center followed by an interval of depression. The oxygen lack is intensified by the shallow breathing during the depressed state of the respiratory center. This acts as a stimulus to the chemoreceptors and probably increases the sensitivity of the respiratory center to CO_2. The respiratory movements increase in vigor but subside as the CO_2 tension is reduced. Reduction of the CO_2 tension of the blood below the level at which the center is stimulated results in the temporary apnea, which in turn increases the oxygen lack and prevents the elimination of CO_2. Thus the center is stimulated and the respiratory movements are reëstablished, but cease again when sufficient O_2 has been absorbed and sufficient CO_2 eliminated to prevent further excitation of the center. Under normal physiologic conditions, any sudden decrease in the CO_2 tension of the blood supplying the respiratory center is prevented by the store of CO_2 which the body holds in the lungs and the tissue fluids. Any sharp increase in CO_2 tension is prevented due to the buffering of the excess CO_2 by the tissue fluids.

Respiratory Reflexes from the Upper Air Passages.—Stimulation of the sensory fibers that supply the nasal mucosa (trigeminal) by injurious or irritating gases elicits reflex inhibition of the sensory fibers that supply the pharynx (glossopharyngeal). Indeed, every act of swallowing elicits temporary inhibition of respiration through the glossopharyngeal nerve. Mild irritants and odorous substances also elicit reflex modification of the respiratory movements. Inhalation of such substances commonly causes either a lowered respiratory phase and an increase in the rate of the excursions or a deepened inspiratory phase and a decrease in the rate of the excursions. The reflex responses to disagreeable odors and mild irritants commonly are stronger than those to agreeable ones. Odorous substances which are not irritating elicit no reflex respiratory responses in anosmatic subjects. The respiratory response to odors is mediated through the olafactory reflex system. The reflex inhilition of respiration elicited by stimulation of the sensory fibers distributed along the upper air passages may be regarded as a reaction that automatically protects the lungs from injurious gases. The protective character of this reaction is evidenced by the fact that reflex closure of the larynx occurs simultaneously with the cessation of respiration. If the stimulation is strong enough, the bronchial musculature also contracts, so that the passage to the alveoli is made still more difficult. Although this reflex cessation of respiration is only temporary, it is automatic and affords at least a short interval before the inhibition is broken through by the increasing irritability of the respiratory center during which the individual may escape from a dangerous locality. In certain animals, *e.g.*, certain of the water birds, reflex inhibition of respiration may be maintained for relatively long intervals. This undoubtedly is a special adaptation of the reflex to meet the requirements of diving. The reflex coughing caused by irritating gases or foreign bodies which enter the larynx may be regarded as an automatic but purposeful attempt to expel the stimulating object. In the act of coughing, the rima glottis which shortly before was closed is forced open by a sudden explosive expiration. This involves not only reflex inhibition of the inspiratory movements, but also reflex excitation of expiratory movements of a peculiar type. The coughing reflex may be elicited by stimulation of the vagus fibers distributed to any part of the respiratory tract, but it is not elicited with equal facility from all the areas of vagus distribution in the respiratory tract. Stimulation of the deeper parts of the larynx is most effective. The facility with which this reflex is elicited gradually decreases as the sites of stimulation approach the smaller subdivisions of the bronchial tree. It is also rarely elicited by irritation of the pharynx and the base of the tongue. On the other hand, the coughing reflex may be elicited by stimulation of the afferent vagus fibers that supply various visceral organs, *e.g.*, the liver and the spleen. It has also been observed clinically that under certain conditions irritation of the parietal pleura elicits the coughing reflex.

Sneezing may also be regarded as a protective respiratory reflex. In this reaction the posterior nares just previously closed by contraction of the superior constrictor muscles of the pharynx is forced open by explosive expiration. This reflex is elicited most commonly by stimulation of the afferent fibers (trigeminal) that supply the nasal epithelium. It serves to remove mucus or other extraneous matter from the nasal mucosa. Spasmodic respiratory reactions such as coughing and sneezing appear to be mediated through a specific area in the medulla oblongata (Borison, 1948).

Other Special Respiratory Reflexes.—Yawning is in part a respiratory reaction which may be regarded as a type of indirect vascular reflex which

erves the purpose of improving the circulation (Regelsberger, 1924
Simultaneous stretching reflexes commonly aid in this process. Th
stretching and the yawning reflexes appear to be intimately associated in
their phylogenetic origin. Man, therefore, is able only by practice to
separate these two reflexes and to suppress the stretching reflex entirely.
The clinical observation that in patients with hemiplegia yawning is commonly accompanied by forced stretching movements in the paralyzed
limbs suggests the primitive origin of the reflexes and their incorporation
in the reflex pattern of the older parts of the brain. The frequent occurrence of yawning in cases of brain tumor and encephalitis also suggests the
primitive origin of this reflex. On the basis of observations made before
and after sympathectomy in patients with Berger's and Raynaud's diseases, Heusner (1946) pointed out that peripheral vasoconstriction becomes
apparent 4 to 4.5 seconds after initiation of the inspiratory phase of the
yawn, becomes maximal within 9 to 10 seconds, and gradually subsides
during the subsequent 45 seconds. The vasoconstrictor response is commonly accompanied by a simultaneous temporary increase in the heart
rate of 10 or more per minute. Since it is absent or hardly apparent in
sympathetically denervated digits, the vasoconstriction is reflex. The
magnitude of the vascular response varies in the same individual and is
roughly proportional to the depth and the duration of the inspiratory
movement.

Sobbing, laughing and weeping involve forced automatic movements,
particularly of the larynx and diaphragm, that affect respiration and are
coördinated with the movements of expression. These reflexes are elicited
by emotional states. Although, in most instances, they may be inhibited
voluntarily in greater or less degree, they are carried out through centers
which are essentially automatic.

Hiccup is a respiratory reflex which is purely automatic and, in most
instances, not subject to voluntary inhibition. The familiar phonation
accompanying this reflex is inspiratory. It is caused by suction of air past
the just closing vocal folds by spastic contraction of the diaphragm. The
diaphragmatic movement consists essentially of a short sudden beat. The
afferent impulses commonly are conducted by afferent fibers in the phrenic
nerve, but the stimuli which elicit this reflex are obscure. Hiccup may
arise without any apparent cause and persist for a short or a long interval.
Hiccup of short duration may be regarded as a harmless disturbance of
respiration, but when it persists for a relatively long time, as it frequently
does in certain pathological conditions, it becomes a matter of grave
clinical importance because of its effect on the general physical condition
of the patient.

Hiccup frequently is caused by irritation of the phrenic nerve. It
occurs commonly in cases of aortic aneurism, carcinoma in the region of
the root of the lung and in all affections of the diaphragm. It also occurs
frequently in cases of peritonitis and carcinoma of the stomach, liver,
kidney or adrenal gland. It has also been reported in operations for hernia.
It usually is a reflex phenomenon. Regelsberger (1924) has pointed out
that the stimuli which elicit this reflex may arise throughout the entire
area of distribution of the phrenic nerve.

In certain cases, hiccup arises not as a reflex phenomenon but as a result of stimuli arising in the blood, *e.g.*, in cases of uremia, acetonemia and venous stasis in the region of the medulla oblongata. In such cases, certain cells in the brain stem probably react to toxic substances in the blood. It may also arise as a result of psychic disturbances or of organic diseases of the central nervous system. Persistent epidemic and persistent postoperative hiccup may also arise as forms of mild myoclonic encephalitis due to an infective agent. The existence of a special center in the brain which mediates this peculiar respiratory phenomenon seems improbable. It probably is carried out through the general respiratory center.

Chapter X

INNERVATION OF THE DIGESTIVE TUBE

EXTRINSIC NERVES

Pharynx. — The pharynx is innervated through the glossopharyngeal, the vagus and sympathetic nerves. The glossopharyngeal supplies chiefly the oral portion. The pharyngeal branches of the vagus are distributed to the middle and the aboral portions. Where the branches of the glossopharyngeal and the vagus nerves meet they enter into a plexus formation which, together with some of the sympathetic rami that supply the pharynx, constitutes the pharyngeal plexus. The sympathetic nerves of the pharynx are derived chiefly from the superior cervical ganglion. Some of the sympathetic fibers enter the pharyngeal plexus through separate sympathetic rami. Others become incorporated in the pharyngeal branches of the vagus, before they reach the pharynx, and join the plexus with these nerves. Some extend directly to the pharyngeal musculature without taking part in the plexus formation. Most of the sympathetic fibers seem to be distributed to the aboral portion of the pharynx.

Esophagus. — The esophagus is innervated through the vagus and sympathetic nerves. The vagus supply to the cervical portion is derived from the recurrent nerve through parallel branches that enter the esophageal wall. In general, these branches neither cross the median plane nor enter into a plexus formation. In the thorax, both vagi lie close to the esophagus and give off branches to it. Two or three branches of the right vagus commonly join the left at this level. The distribution of branches of each vagus nerve to the thoracic portion of the esophagus is not limited to the same side, but each nerve also sends branches to the opposite side. Branches of the left vagus are distributed chiefly to the ventral surface, and branches of the right vagus are distributed chiefly to the dorsal surface of this portion of the esophagus.

Most of the sympathetic nerves of the esophagus arise from the inferior cervical, or stellate, ganglion. Some fibers that arise in the cervical sympathetic ganglia also reach the esophagus through communications of the sympathetic cardiac nerves with the recurrent branch of the vagus. One or more rami derived from the stellate ganglion join the recurrent nerve. Others either join the vagus trunk or pass directly to the esophagus. Some of the thoracic rami extend directly to the esophagus. Others join the aortic plexus from which some of their fibers extend to the esophagus. The distal portion of the esophagus also receives sympathetic fibers through the plexuses on the left gastric and the inferior phrenic arteries and through the greater splanchnic and occasionally the lesser splanchnic nerve. In the posterior mediastinum, the sympathetic nerves and the vagi with their

(207)

intercommunicating branches constitute a plexus around the esophagus (esophageal plexus) from which branches penetrate the esophageal wall.

Stomach.—The stomach, like the esophagus, is innervated through the vagus and sympathetic nerves. From the esophageal plexus, both vagi continue onto the stomach where each commonly breaks up into a left, a middle and a right division. The plexus around the esophagus and the gastric

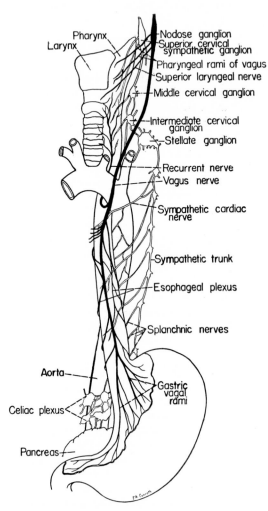

Pharynx
Larynx

Nodose ganglion
Superior cervical sympathetic ganglion
Pharyngeal rami of vagus
Superior laryngeal nerve
Middle cervical ganglion
Intermediate cervical ganglion
Stellate ganglion
Recurrent nerve
Vagus nerve
Sympathetic cardiac nerve
Sympathetic trunk
Esophageal plexus
Splanchnic nerves

Aorta
Celiac plexus
Pancreas

Gastric vagal rami

Fig. 52.—Diagrammatic illustration of the extrinsic nerves of the pharynx, esophagus and stomach.

rami of the vagus nerves are somewhat variable. On the basis of dissections of these nerves in 100 adult human cadavers, Bradley *et al.* (1947) described three major patterns. In a high percentage of the bodies these nerves fell into the dominant pattern in which the gastric nerves arise directly from the esophageal plexus. In an extensive series of human dissections, Jackson (1948, 1949) found that the major portion of the nerve trunk on the ventral aspect of the esophagus is derived from the left vagus nerve and the major portion of the one on the dorsal aspect of the esophagus is derived from the right vagus nerve, but generally the ventral trunk also receives some rami from the right vagus and the dorsal trunk receives some rami from the left vagus. In most bodies the ventral and the dorsal trunks

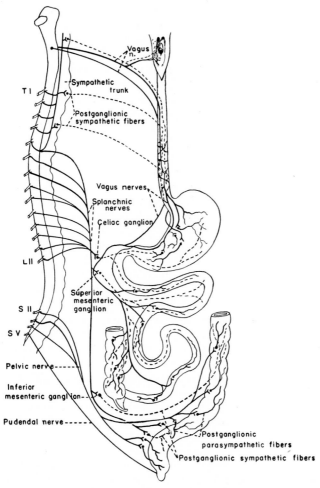

Fig. 53.—Diagram illustrating the distribution of the sympathetic and the parasympathetic nerves to the digestive tract and the pudendal nerve to the anal sphincter.

become well defined at a level somewhat rostral to the diaphragm. As the ventral vagus trunk extends caudad over the ventral surface of the stomach, its left division gives off branches to the fundus and approximately the rostral two-thirds of the corpus. Its middle division supplies the prepyloric region. Its right division extends to the liver. As the dorsal vagus trunk extends caudad over the dorsal surface of the stomach, its left

14

division supplies the cardia, the lesser curvature and a portion of the corpus. Its middle division supplies the prepyloric region. Its right division joins the right celiac ganglion. Frequently branches of both vagi anastomose and form a plexus at the right side of the cardia from which fibers are given off to the cardiac region. In the prepyloric region, branches of the middle division of both vagi enter the hepato-gastric ligament.

The major portion of the sympathetic innervation of the stomach is derived from the celiac plexus. Most of the fibers accompany the various gastric arteries. The proximal portion also receives sympathetic fibers from the left and occasionally the right phrenic plexus, the left gastric plexus and the hepatic plexus. A few rami that arise from the rostral lumbar segments of the sympathetic trunk also join the stomach. In the hepato-gastric ligament, sympathetic fibers derived from the celiac plexus mingle with vagus fibers as both approach the stomach. These fibers do not form an intricate plexus but, in general, bundles of vagus and of sympathetic fibers lie parallel to one another. The fibers derived from the hepatic plexus also traverse the hepatogastric ligament. Mitchell (1940) proposed that these fibers be designated the hepatogastric nerves.

Small Intestine.—The small intestine, like the stomach, is innervated through both vagus and sympathetic nerves. Most of the vagus fibers are derived through the division of the dorsal vagus trunk that joins the celiac plexus (Fig. 53). The sympathetic fibers are derived chiefly from the celiac and the superior mesenteric plexuses. Both sets of fibers enter the small intestine through the mesenteric nerves which, in general, accompany the mesenteric arteries. Vagus and sympathetic fibers can be distinguished from one another by differences in caliber and their distribution in the intestinal wall. After leaving the celiac plexus, the vagus fibers form bundles which either take independent courses in the mesentery or accompany the larger blood vessels and usually enter the intestinal wall with the latter. They penetrate the subserosa and the longitudinal muscle layer and enter the myenteric plexus. Some extend farther toward the mucosa and enter the submucous plexus. The sympathetic nerves, in general, are more intimately associated with the mesenteric vessels. They anastomose freely in the subserosa. Most of the fibers enter the intestinal wall in close association with the larger vessels, but some form a plexus in the sub-serous layer. The latter probably are general visceral afferent fibers.

Large Intestine.—The cecum, the vermiform appendix and the ascending and transverse portions of the colon are innervated through nerves that arise directly from the superior mesenteric plexus. These nerves include both vagus and sympathetic fibers. The descending colon and the proximal portion of the rectum are innervated through nerves that arise from the inferior mesenteric plexus. The portion of the large intestine that receives vagus fibers varies somewhat in different animals. The exact distribution of efferent vagus fibers in the large intestine in man is unknown. The parasympathetic innervation of the descending colon and the rectum is derived through the sacral outflow. The preganglionic fibers concerned traverse the visceral rami of the second and the third or the third and the fourth sacral nerves. The major portion of the parasympathetic innervation of the distal colon in man is independent of the hypogastric plexus. The fibers concerned constitute a small but definite trunk derived from the pelvic nerves on either side which, after traversing the pelvic plexuses, ascends on the left side of the hypogastric plexus. The distal portion of the rectum receives sympathetic fibers from the hypogastric plexus that accompany the superior and the middle hemorrhoidal arteries. The inferior hemorrhoidal branches of the pudendal nerve (third and fourth sacral) also supply fibers to the distal portion of the anal canal and the external sphincter.

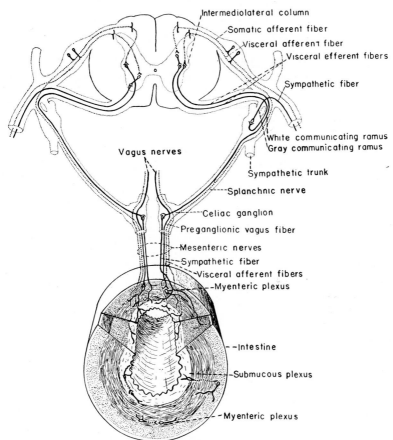

Fig. 54.—Diagram illustrating the sympathetic, parasympathetic and afferent conduction pathways to the small intestine.

INTRINSIC NERVES

General Morphology.—The intrinsic nerves of the enteric canal (enteric nervous system) include the myenteric plexus situated between the longitudinal and the circular muscle layers, and the submucous plexus situated in the submucosa. Various authors have also described a subserous plexus, particularly in the stomach.   Both the myenteric and the submucous plexuses include numerous ganglia that are intimately connected with one another through strands made up largely of nerve fibers that arise in the ganglia and to a lesser extent of fibers that enter the wall of the digestive tube through its extrinsic nerves.   The myenteric and the submucous plexuses are connected with each other by numerous strands that include both fibers that arise in their intrinsic ganglia and fibers that enter the digestive tube through its extrinsic nerves.   The efferent components of the vagus and the sacral nerves that enter the wall of the digestive tube are preganglionic neurons that make synaptic connections with neurons in the enteric ganglia.   The sympathetic components of the nerves that enter the wall of the digestive tube are postganglionic fibers.   They terminate directly in relation to the effector tissues.

Structure and Relationships of the Enteric Plexuses.—The enteric plexuses differ structurally somewhat in the several divisions of the digestive tube.   They probably are most perfectly developed in the small intestine.   Here the major portion of the myenteric plexus is situated in the interspaces between the longitudinal and the circular muscle layers, and the submucous plexus is situated in the submucosa.

The myenteric plexus consists of an abundant meshwork of nerve-fiber bundles and numerous ganglia most of which are located at the nodal points.   These ganglia vary greatly both in size and in the number of their constituent neurons and conform to the shape of the intermuscular spaces that they occupy.   Many of them are flattened or lens-shaped and, when viewed from the surface, usually appear somewhat angular in outline, depending on the number and the arrangement of the fiber bundles associated with them.   Fibers arising in the ganglia frequently may be traced for some distance in these fiber bundles.

According to the findings of certain investigators, the myenteric plexus includes three plexiform meshworks: a primary, a secondary and a tertiary plexus.   The primary plexus is a relatively coarse structure.   Its meshes vary within relatively wide limits in size and form, but exhibit a longitudinal arrangement.   The secondary plexus is intimately connected with the primary one, but it is made up of more slender bundles of nerve fibers.   The tertiary plexus is a very delicate meshwork of fibers directly connected with the secondary plexus.   It lies in intimate contact with the circular muscle.   From this plexus, nerve fibers extend into the muscle to terminate in relation to muscle cells.

In preparations taken in the region of the mesenteric attachment, branches of the extrinsic nerves may be traced into many of the myenteric ganglia.   Some of the fibers terminate in the first ganglion entered.   Others pass through this ganglion into rami that connect it with other ganglia in the myenteric plexus, or into rami that lead into the submucous plexus. The rami that extend from the myenteric plexus into the submucosa where they join the submucous plexus usually arise at a nodal point or directly from the ganglion in the myenteric plexus and run between the bundles of circular fibers into the submucous layer.   They include both fibers of extrinsic origin and fibers that arise in enteric ganglia.

The submucous plexus consists of a meshwork of relatively slender fiber bundles with small ganglia located at nodal points. It is not confined to a definitely delimited zone in the submucous layer, but some fiber bundles lie near the circular muscle layer and others lie close to the muscularis mucosæ. Mechanical separation of the mucosa and the submucosa from the outer musculature usually effectively removes the submucous plexus from the circular muscle layer.

Some of the ganglia in the submucous plexus are flattened but not to the same extent as the majority of the myenteric ganglia. Many of them are somewhat elongated and rounded or oval in cross-section. In many instances, a ramus that connects the submucous with the myenteric plexus may be traced into one of these ganglia where some of its fibers terminate. Others merely pass through to continue farther in the submucous plexus. Nerve fibers may also be traced, either singly or in small bundles, from the submucous plexus to the muscularis mucosæ. Many of these fibers penetrate the muscularis mucosæ and ramify among the mucous glands or continue into the intestinal villi. Some of the latter terminate in relation to the muscle fibers in the villi. Others approach the intestinal epithelium and end in terminal ramifications among the epithelial cells or in a subepithelial plexus.

No intrinsic nerve plexuses have been described in the wall of the pharynx except the pharyngeal plexus which, as stated above, is made up of glossopharyngeal, vagus and sympathetic fibers. Many of the fibers that are distributed to the pharyngeal mucosa and musculature traverse this plexus. Others extend directly to these tissues without entering the plexus.

In man the rostral limit of the myenteric plexus is 3 to 4 cm. below the caudal border of the larynx. Rostral to this level bundles of nerve fibers that do not form a plexus are present between the muscle layers, but no ganglia have been observed in the esophageal wall above the rostral limit of the myenteric plexus. The submucous plexus in the esophagus consists of a meshwork of very slender fiber bundles most of which lie close to the muscularis, but it is devoid of ganglia. It is intimately connected with the myenteric plexus by numerous fiber bundles and fibers extend from it into the mucosa where many of them terminate either in the epithelium or in subepithelial receptors. Most of the latter fibers are relatively large. They include visceral afferent components of the vagus and thoracic nerves. Afferent fibers also terminate in the esophageal musculature.

In the stomach, both the myenteric and the submucous plexuses exhibit the same general plan of structure as in the small intestine. Both the fiber bundles and the ganglia are small and relatively few in the cardiac region, but increase materially both in size and number toward the mid-gastric zone and more gradually from this zone toward the pylorus (Irwin, 1931). The submucous plexus is more abundantly developed in the stomach than in the esophagus, but it includes relatively few ganglia.

In the large intestine, the enteric plexuses exhibit the same general plan of structure as in the small intestine. In the guinea-pig, the ganglia of the myenteric plexus are aggregated beneath the longitudinal muscle bands (tænia coli) to some extent, leaving the intervening longitudinal zones with

relatively few ganglia (Irwin, 1931).   The rectal portion of the myenteric
plexus is particularly rich both in fibers and ganglia.   It terminates abruptly
at the level of the internal sphincter, to which it supplies efferent fibers.
The rectal columns are abundantly innervated through nerves in which
somatic fibers predominate.   The innervation of the internal and the external anal spincters involves a common plexiform structure that includes
many somatic fibers (Ottaviani, 1940).

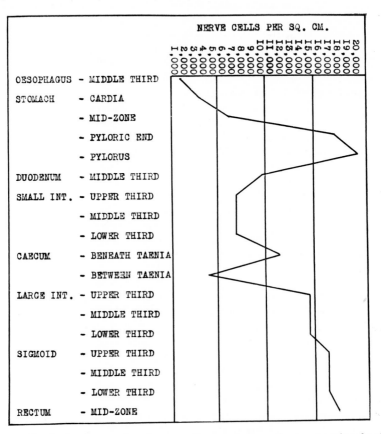

Fig. 55.—Graph showing number of nerve cells per square centimeter at various levels of
Auerbach's plexus.   (Irwin: Am. Jour. Anat., 1930.)

The enteric ganglia and their constituent neurons are not uniformly
abundant throughout the digestive tube, but vary within a relatively wide
range both in the myenteric and the submucous plexus.   The numbers of
ganglion cells per sq. cm. in the myenteric plexus at successive levels in
the digestive tube of the guinea-pig, as determined by Irwin (1931), show
a rapid rise from the middle third of the esophagus to the pylorus, then an
abrupt fall in the first one-third of the small intestine, another marked rise
in the proximal one-third of the colon and a more gradual rise from this
level to the anal sphincter (Fig. 55).

In patients with congenital megacolon the myenteric plexus has been found to be devoid of ganglia in a zone near the distal end of the large intestine. This developmental anomaly appears to be a major causative factor in the etiology of this disease.

Actual counts of the ganglion cells in the myenteric and in the submucous ganglia in representative sections of the intestines of five cats, as reported by Sauer and Rumble (1946), indicate over 5,000,000 nerve cells in the myenteric and two to three times that number in the submucous plexus

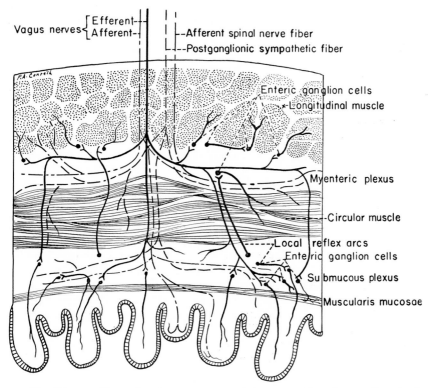

Fig. 56.—Diagram illustrating the arrangement of the nerve cells and nerve fibers in the intramural plexuses in the intestine.

in the small intestine. No evidence of gradients was observed, but the ganglion cells appear to be fairly uniformly distributed in both plexuses throughout the small intestine.

The Enteric Ganglion Cells. — Most of the enteric ganglion cells are multipolar, but bipolar and unipolar neurons have also been described in the enteric plexuses. On the basis of very careful histologic studies of Bielchowsky preparations of the intestine of man and other mammals, Müller (1911) concluded that the enteric ganglion cells differ sufficiently in their morphologic characters from the neurons in other parts of the autonomic system to warrant their classification in a distinct category that includes ganglion cells of at least two recognizable types. Those of the one type lie quite free in the intermuscular spaces. Those of the other type sustain a peculiarly intimate relationship to the muscle. In sections of a flattened piece of intestine taken in the plane of the myenteric plexus, the cell bodies of the first type usually appear rounded in outline and their dendrites, which are relatively broad at the base, taper distally and radiate in all directions, may be traced for some distance from the cell body. In some instances, dendrites of neurons of this type terminate in foot-like enlargements in contact with the adjacent musculature. Frequently a single process, probably the axon, may be traced into the muscle. The ganglion cells of the second type usually lie close to the musculature. The cell body commonly is elongated or pyriform and lies with its long axis parallel to the adjacent muscle. It usually gives rise to relatively large cone-shaped processes at the side toward the muscle, some of which give rise to terminal branches that terminate in small foot-like expansions in direct contact with muscle cells. Frequently one of these ganglion cells may be observed in a slight depression in the muscle at the periphery of the ganglion. Müller regarded the ganglion cells so situated as of peculiar interest due to their intimate relationships, through their short dendrites, to the musculature.

According to Hill (1927), the neurons in the myenteric ganglia in general conform to Dogiel's Types I and II. Those of Type I are characterized by short dendrites and those of Type II by longer dendrites. According to her observations, the neurons of Type I are easily recognizable in silver preparations due to their intense staining reactions and their superficial position in the ganglia. Their short dendrites commonly form brush-like arborizations on the neurons located deeper and more centrally in the ganglia. The longer dendrites of the neurons of Type I sometimes arborize around the cell bodies of the more centrally located neurons or mingle with the fibers in the intercellular plexus. The axons of these neurons can in some instances be traced for a relatively long distance through neighboring ganglia and fiber tracts, but they generally disappear among the fibers of the intercellular plexus. Hill failed to trace axons of neurons of Type I either into the musculature or outside the myenteric plexus; consequently, she did not regard these cells as motor in function but suggested that they may be associative.

The neurons of Type II, according to Hill, are larger and more variable than those of Type I. Their dendrites are relatively long and branch freely. They commonly extend into a fiber bundle and can frequently be traced for a relatively long distance. The axon eventually passes into the musculature where it terminates in relation to muscle cells. On the basis of these findings, she regarded the neurons of this type as motor in function.

Van Esveld (1928), Stöhr, Jr. (1930), Cavazzana and Borosetto (1948), Greving (1951), Jabonero (1951) and others also recognized ganglion cells of Dogiel's Types I and II in the myenteric ganglia. The associational character of the cells of Dogiel's Type I has also been suggested particularly by Jabonero. Ganglion cells that conform to both these morphological types have also been recognized in the submucous plexus.

In the submucous plexus in the intestine, the neurons are more compactly aggregated in the ganglia than in the myenteric plexus. They are also less angular in outline, except in instances in which they seem to be pressed together in the ganglionic mass. The dendrites of most of these neurons are relatively long and frequently may be traced beyond the borders of the ganglion. In most instances it is quite impossible to distinguish between the axon and the dendrites of these cells. The fact that many of the neurons in the submucous plexus send their dendrites far beyond the confines of the ganglion in which the cell body is located, as will be pointed out below, has an important bearing on the interpretation of their functional relationships.

Certain early investigators have regarded the enteric plexuses as syncytial structures characterized by actual continuity of the cytoplasm of every ganglion cell with that of adjacent ones. Bethe (1903) and R. Müller (1908) described the enteric plexuses in the frog as true nerve nets. Erik Müller (1920, 1921) described the enteric plexuses as exclusively syncytial in the Selachii and as in part syncytial in birds and mammals. Ganglion cells united in pairs by cytoplasmic bridges have been reported as occurring infrequently in the enteric plexuses in lower vertebrates and in mammals. The terminal autonomic structures in all parts of the body have also been interpreted as syncytial by many investigators following the lead of Boeke, Stöhr, Jr., and others.

The concept of protoplasmic continuity of the ganglion cells in the enteric plexus has been further elaborated by Greving (1952). On the basis of a review of the literature and the results of extensive studies of sections of the stomachs of animals and man prepared according to the Bielchowsky and the Gros methods, he has described interconnections of ganglion cells by means of (1) protoplasmic bridges of varying width and thickness, (2) anastomosis of dendrites, (3) fibrillar anastomosis of dendrites, (4) cellular nerve nets and (5) communications in which the neurofibrils of dendrites of one ganglion cell enter directly the intracellular neurofibrillar structures of adjacent ones. He has designated the structure formed by these means as an "intercellular fibrillar net." The possibility of continuity of preganglionic fibers with the intercellular fibrillar net is also suggested. This entire neural complex is enclosed in a plasmodial sheath. On the basis of this concept, as Greving has pointed out, the neurons in the enteric plexuses cannot be regarded as independent anatomical units, but he does not abandon the neuron theory, since the ganglion cells in an intercellular fibrillar net must still be regarded as biological units.

On the basis of extensive anatomical and physiological studies of the enteric plexuses in man, Jabonero et al. (1951) have advanced the conclusion that the preganglionic parasympathetic fibers make synaptic contacts only with ganglion cells of Dogiel's Type I. Through collaterals these cells make synaptic contacts with adjacent ganglion cells in the same category. Ganglion cells of Dogiel's Type I are also related to one another in groups through dendritic plexuses through which preganglionic axons may discharge into entire groups. The ganglion cells of Dogiel's Type II form a syncytium that is continuous with the syncytial structure formed by the interstitial cells of Cajal. Both axons of ganglion cells of Dogiel's Type I and postganglionic sympathetic fibers make functional connections with the syncytium formed by the ganglion cells of Dogiel's Type II. The terminal syncytial structure is distributed to the effector tissues, particularly the enteric musculature and the blood vessels.

The technical difficulties inherent in the methods employed in attempts to determine the exact anatomical relationships of the enteric ganglion cells to one another and the structure of the synaptic and the neuroeffector junctions in the enteric canal are indicated by the diversity of the findings that have been reported and the conclusions that have been derived from them. The ultimate solution of these problems awaits further investigation.

The interstitial cells of Cajal in the enteric canal have engaged the attention of many investigators. They have been variously interpreted as neural and as connective tissue elements. Most of those who have interpreted them as nerve cells have also discussed their relationships to the enteric plexuses and their probable rôle in the transmission of nerve impulses to the effector tissues. Additional data that seem to indicate the neural nature of these cells have been reported by Spoerri (1947). According to her account, processes of these cells make direct contacts with gastric epithelial cells of all types, including both the glandular and the surface epithelium. They may represent terminal elements of enteric nerves.

The length of the axons of the enteric neurons and their longitudinal distribution cannot be determined by direct histological observations. In an extensive physiological investigation, using the isolated intestine of the fowl, Nolf (1929) found that nicotinization of a segment 8 cm. or over in length abolishes longitudinal conduction in the myenteric plexus. On the basis of this and other experimental observations, he concluded that the myenteric neurons in the intestine of the fowl are approximately 8 cm. in length and that the myenteric plexus includes longitudinal conduction pathways made up of intrinsic neurons which sustain a synaptic relationship to one another. He also advanced certain evidence which he interpreted as indicating that the axons of some of the enteric neurons divide dichotomously, sending one division oralward and the other aboralward, the former being approximately 4.5 cm., the latter approximately 8 cm. in length. These findings have not been confirmed by later investigations.

According to the findings of most investigators, the enteric ganglion cells are not enclosed in pericellular capsules. In the stomach and intestine, according to Greving (1920), numerous cells with small rounded nuclei and no apparent processes lie scattered between the ganglion cells throughout the ganglia, but they do not form pericellular capsules. On the basis of more recent findings, they must be interpreted as cells of neuroglial origin. Cells of the same kind also occur in the fiber bundles connecting the myenteric ganglia.

On the basis of differential staining in preparations of the gastro-intestinal tract in the mouse, Honjin (1951) classified the enteric ganglion cells as argentophile and argentophobe. According to his account, preganglionic vagus nerve fibers make synaptic connections only with argentophile ganglion cells. The argentophobe ganglion cells are synaptically related to argentophile cells. Chemical differences in the nerve fibers in the enteric plexuses have also been pointed out (Coujard, 1951).

The Intercellular Plexus.—In the ganglia of both the myenteric and the submucous plexus there exists an intraganglionic fiber complex that is made up in part of the processes of the local neurons and in part of fibers of extrinsic origin. This fiber complex is more abundant in the myenteric than in the submucous ganglia. In the ganglia of either plexus most of the fibers of extrinsic origin are small unmyelinated ones that stain darkly in pyridine-silver preparations. Those of local origin include both large and small fibers. The large ones represent mainly the short dendrites and the proximal portions of the longer ones. The distal portions of the longer dendrites, like the fibers of extrinsic origin, are slender and stain darkly in pyridine-silver preparations. The large fibers usually run through the ganglion in various directions without showing much evidence of plexus formation. The smaller fibers commonly give rise to very fine intercellular plexuses.

The results of experimental studies seem to support the assumption that the most slender fibers in the pericellular plexuses in the myenteric ganglia, which are brought out so well in pyridine-silver preparations, represent chiefly the terminal portions of preganglionic vagus fibers. They also indicate that the postganglionic sympathetic fibers which enter the intestinal wall pass through the myenteric plexus but take no part in the formation of the intercellular plexuses. If, as seems highly probable, the synapses of preganglionic with enteric neurons are made through the intercellular plexuses, these findings conform fully to the current teaching that the efferent vagus fibers to the intestine are preganglionic and enter into synaptic relationship with neurons in the enteric ganglia, while the sympathetic fibers that enter the intestinal wall through the extrinsic nerves terminate in direct relationship to the musculature. Since the occurrence of local reflex arcs in the enteric plexuses has been demonstrated it need not be assumed that the pericellular plexuses in the ganglia are made up solely of the terminal branches of fibers of extrinsic origin. These plexuses must include the terminal arborizations of the axons of many enteric ganglion cells.

According to the above interpretation, vagus and sympathetic fibers sustain the same relationships to the enteric plexuses as to certain other peripheral plexuses, *e.g.*, the pulmonary and the cardiac plexuses. It does not follow that all the neurons in the enteric plexuses are components of vagus efferent chains. The great abundance of these neurons has been emphasized by various investigators, and it has seemed to some quite impossible that the preganglionic vagus fibers could make synaptic connections with all of them. This apparent difficulty has been resolved by the demonstration of enteric reflex arcs. Many of the ganglion cells concerned in these local reflex mechanisms undoubtedly are synaptically related only to other enteric ganglion cells. The possibility that some of them are also synaptically related to efferent vagus nerve fibers is not precluded.

Anatomic Evidence for the Occurrence of Enteric Reflex Arcs.—The existence of local reflex mechanisms in the enteric nervous system is clearly indicated by abundant physiological data, but the anatomic evidence in support of the assumption that some enteric ganglion cells make synaptic contacts with others in the same or adjacent ganglia as yet is meager.

In methylene-blue preparations of the intestine of the cat, as reported by Kuntz (1922), an intensely stained process of one ganglion cell could in some instances be traced without interruption to its termination in a

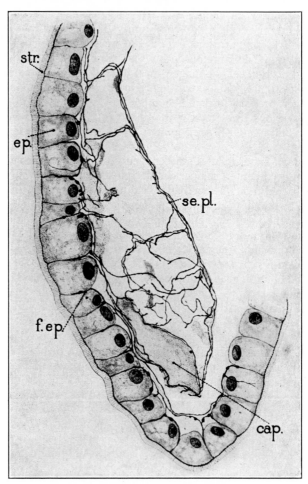

Fig. 57.—Subepithelial plexus and nerve terminations between the epithelial cells of a villus in the small intestine of a new-born rabbit (silver method of de Castro). (Catherine J. Hill.) *cap.*, Capillary; *ep.*, epithelial cell; *f.ep.*, terminal branch of a nerve fiber between epithelial cells; *se. pl.*, subepithelial plexus.

pericellular network on the lightly stained cell body of another ganglion cell in the same ganglion or an adjacent one. Although these pericellular networks resemble very closely those which have been described in other autonomic ganglia and interpreted as synapses, they might still be regarded as pericellular terminations of dendrites. In certain instances fibers that enter the myenteric ganglia from the submucous plexus could be traced to their terminations in similar pericellular networks on the bodies of lightly stained ganglion cells. The possibility that these fibers represent dendrites is not precluded, but it appears more probable that they are the axons of ganglion cells in the submucous plexus. If they are axons, the terminations in question must be regarded as synapses. Since the fibers extend from the submucous into the myenteric plexus they cannot reasonably be interpreted as preganglionic fibers of vagus or spinal origin, but must be regarded as fibers of enteric origin. In both the myenteric and the submucous plexus, fibers could be traced from one ganglion without interruption to pericellular terminations of the same type in neighboring

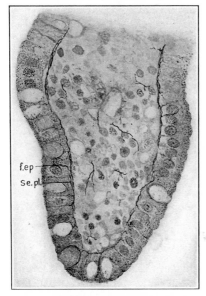

Fig. 58.—Subepithelial plexus and nerve terminations between the epithelial cells of a villus in the small intestine of the dog (pyridine silver). (Waddell.) *f.ep.*, Terminal branch of a nerve fiber between epithelial cells; *Se.pl.*, subepithelial plexus.

ganglia. Some of these formations, particularly in the myenteric plexus, might possibly be interpreted as synapses of preganglionic vagus fibers with enteric ganglion cells. The intercellular plexuses that undergo degeneration following vagus section, however, are grosser structures and sustain a less intimate relationship to the cell bodies of the enteric ganglion cells than the pericellular terminations in question. It seems highly probable, therefore, that the latter represent synapses involving two enteric neurons.

Relationships of two enteric ganglion cells to each other comparable to those described above have also been described by Waddell (1929) in the intestine of the dog after degeneration of the preganglionic fibers following section of the vagus nerves. He also pointed out that the intercellular plexuses do not undergo complete degeneration following vagus section and that the portion that remains intact is made up of fibers of smaller caliber than the portion that undergoes degeneration.

According to the current teaching, two enteric neurons which sustain a synaptic relationship to one another cannot be regarded as terminal links of a vagus efferent chain. They must be interpreted as components of a local reflex arc, even though the dendrites of the one cannot actually be traced to terminations of a recognized sensory type, or the existence of association neurons in the enteric plexuses must be conceded. Of these two possibilities the former appears the more probable on anatomic grounds. It is also supported by abundant physiological data which will be considered below. Some of the probable relationships of enteric reflex arcs are illustrated diagrammatically in figure 56.

Nerve fibers of enteric origin, some of which presumably represent dendrites, have been traced to the gastro-intestinal epithelium, particularly in lower vertebrates (Dogiel, 1896; Sakusseff, 1897). In methylene-blue preparations of the intestine of the cat, Kuntz (1922) traced fibers from the submucous plexus through the muscularis mucosæ into the intestinal villi where some of them were distributed to the muscle fibers which extend into the villi, and others appeared to terminate in relation to the intestinal epithelium. A subepithelial plexus, presumably made up of afferent fibers, has been described by Hill (1927) and Waddell (1929). This plexus, as has been pointed out by Waddell, does not undergo extensive degeneration following section of the extrinsic nerves of the intestine. It must, therefore, consist in part of fibers derived from enteric ganglia. These fibers probably conduct impulses that arise within the epithelium or close to it.

Afferent Nerve Fiber Terminations.—Afferent nerve fibers terminate in all the layers of the enteric wall. Relatively complex receptors have been described in the musculature and in the mucosa and the submucosa in the esophagus in various mammals. Nonidez (1946), also described receptors within the connective tissue capsules of myenteric ganglia in the esophagus in young mammals, including a rhesus monkey, that consist of end arborizations of large myelinated vagus nerve fibers. Receptors in the forms of terminal skeins and nets consisting of fine varicose fibers have been described in the stomach and the intestine by Carpenter (1918) who pointed out that their relationships to the musculature are such that they could be stimulated directly by contraction or distention of the organ. Complicated skein-like receptors have also been observed in the rectal mucosa (Otaviani, 1940). Smooth muscle spindles have been observed particularly in the esophagus.

The subepithelial plexus in the gastro-intestinal mucosa is a relatively delicate structure that appears to be made up in part of the terminal branches of afferent vagus and spinal nerve fibers. Since it does not undergo complete degeneration following section of the extrinsic nerves (Waddell, 1929), it probably also includes receptive fibers that arise in enteric ganglia.

PHYSIOLOGIC DATA

Esophagus.—The esophagus differs structurally from the other divisions of the digestive tube in that its musculature is made up of both striated and smooth muscle fibers. In the dog, the cat and the ape it consists mainly of striated muscle, but includes some smooth muscle in the distal portion. In man the transition from striated to smooth muscle takes place in the upper thoracic portion of the esophagus, beginning somewhat more rostral in the ventral than in the dorsal wall.

The chief function of the esophagus is illustrated by the swallowing reaction, which may be initiated as a voluntary act, but becomes reflex during its execution. Voluntary initiation of the act of swallowing requires the presence of liquid or solid matter in the pharynx. In the absence of food or other foreign matter, a little saliva is passed backward by the tongue. This serves as a mechanical stimulus for the initiation of the reflex reaction. Voluntary deglutition is impossible when the mouth is entirely free of saliva. The swallowing reaction may also be elicited as a pure reflex by stimulation of certain areas of the mucosa of the mouth and pharynx. These areas vary somewhat in different animals, but the afferent impulses concerned are conducted by fibers of the trigeminal, the glosso-pharyngeal or the vagus nerves. Such afferent conduction probably takes place most commonly through the superior laryngeal branch of the vagus nerve. The glossopharyngeal nerve also conducts impulses which inhibit the swallowing reflex. The efferent impulses concerned in the swallowing reaction are conducted chiefly through the glossopharyngeal and branches of the vagus nerves. Fibers of the hypoglossal nerve and the mandibular division of the trigeminal also play a part. The motor innervation of the esophagus involves the recurrent and certain thoracic branches of the vagus, the sympathetic nerves and the intramural plexuses. The sympathetic nerves probably play no significant part in the swallowing reflex. The effective motor innervation of the esophagus in the dog appears to be purely vagal. This probably is correlated with the extensive distribution of striated muscle in the esophagus of this animal. Knight (1934) reported reduction in tonus of the musculature in the distal portion of the esophagus due to sympathetic stimulation, but no change in the tonus of the musculature in the proximal portion. Contraction of the striated musculature of the esophagus elicited by vagus stimulation, according to Knight, is augmented by simultaneous sympathetic stimulation. The data available do not indicate a dominant rôle of the sympathetic nerves in esophageal functions.

Efferent stimulation of a single vagus branch to the esophagus elicits a purely segmental contraction. A peristaltic wave that is propagated along the esophagus cannot be initiated by efferent stimulation of the esophagus at any given point. The esophagus differs in this respect from the more aboral divisions of the digestive tube. Stimulation of the central end of one divided vagus, while the other is intact, results in contraction along the entire esophagus. This in turn stimulates the afferent vagus endings throughout the esophagus, from which impulses that activate the efferent neurons of the intact vagus are conducted into the brain stem and result in still further contraction of the entire esophageal musculature.

Shortening of the esophagus in the dog sufficient to draw the stomach into the hiatus in the diaphragm elicited by electrical vagal stimulation has been reported by Dey et al. (1945). They also reported reflex shortening of the esophagus elicited by impulses arising in the rostral portion of the abdomen due to manipulation of the liver, pressure on the gall bladder or its distention.

Peristalsis in the esophagus, like the swallowing reflex, is mediated through extrinsic nerves. Transection of the esophagus or even resection of entire segments does not prevent peristalsis if the nerve supply to the several pieces remains intact. Meltzer (1906) also observed the propagation of peristaltic waves along the esophagus in the rabbit following its transection at several levels. He noted, however, that when the animal was under deep anesthesia, a peristaltic wave initiated in one segment stopped at the lower border of that segment and did not pass on to the next. A foreign body introduced into the esophagus results in a peristaltic wave beginning above the point of stimulation; consequently, if the primary reflex initiated at the beginning of the swallowing act succeeds only in forcing a bolus of food into the upper part of the esophagus, the bolus itself causes a series of reflex contractions, by local stimulation of the sensory fibers, which tend to move it caudad. This does not occur following section of the vagi, which also indicates that the peristaltic reflex is mediated through extrinsic nerves.

The orderly sequence of the movements involved in the swallowing reflex and esophageal peristalsis is dependent on a center in the medulla oblongata (deglutition center), located lateral to the ala cinera and just above it, which probably involves portions of the tractus solitarius and the nucleus ambiguus. Whether it consists of a definite group of cells which send their axons directly to the motor nuclei of the several efferent nerves concerned is not definitely known. The close coördination of the swallowing reflex and respiratory movements suggests that the deglutition center is intimately associated with the respiratory center. Respiration is always inhibited during deglutition.

The swallowing reaction and esophageal peristalsis are also influenced by psychic stimulation. Strong emotional disturbances, e.g., joy, anger or fright, commonly are accompanied by spasm of the pharynx and the esophagus that may temporarily render the swallowing reaction impossible. Hysterical individuals frequently complain of sensory disturbances in the esophagus which undoubtedly are associated with disturbances in its motor activity.

An essential rôle of the intrinsic neurons in the swallowing reflex or esophageal peristalsis has not been demonstrated. Rhythmic contractions of isolated pieces of the esophagus have been observed, but this does not prove independent functional activity on the part of the intrinsic nerves. Section of the vagus fibers that supply the distal portion of the esophagus and the cardia results in spastic contraction of the cardiac sphincter. Bilateral vagotomy at a more rostral level results in dilatation of the distal portion of the esophagus and contraction of the cardia (Knight, 1934).

This condition subsides after a few days, and the parts involved resume functional activity which continues in an apparently normal manner. This suggests that tonus and single contractions, at least in the distal portion of the esophagus, are influenced by the intrinsic neural mechanism, although it has not been demonstrated that any single reaction involving the esophageal musculature is mediated solely through its intrinsic nerves. In the dog, as observed by Hwang *et al.* (1947), bilateral vagotomy may result in retention of secretions in the esophagus which may be displaced distad or regurgitated apparently by diffuse tonic contractions of the entire esophagus.

Cardiac Sphincter. —The circular muscle is somewhat thickened at the cardiac orifice of the stomach and acts as a sphincter. Its innervation includes both vagus and sympathetic fibers and the intrinsic neural mechanism, particularly the myenteric plexus. The sympathetic fibers concerned are derived chiefly from the celiac plexus. The corresponding preganglionic fibers are components of the greater splanchnic nerve.

The results of experiments involving stimulation of the vagus and sympathetic fibers to the cardiac sphincter are not all in full accord, due in part to differences in the innervation of this muscle in the various experimental animals and other variable factors. The interpretation of the pertinent data is beset by still further difficulties due to the fact that the fibers that supply the sphincter cannot be stimulated without at the same time stimulating vasomotor and secretory fibers and perhaps the adrenals. The stage of anesthesia, furthermore, plays an important rôle. In barbitalized dogs, as reported by Lehman (1945), cervical vagal stimulation resulted in relaxation of the cardia followed by contraction. The inhibitory mechanism appears to be located in the distal portion of the esophagus. Bilateral vagotomy in the cervical region was followed by cardiospasm presumably due to preponderance of the sympathetic innervation of the cardia.

The vagus, like the sympathetic nerves to the cardiac sphincter, exert both motor and inhibitory effects. If the muscle is relaxed or in a state of low tonus, vagus stimulation results in contraction. If the sphincter is closed, it results in relaxation, thus opening the cardiac orifice (Carlson *et al.*, 1922). In Carlson's experiments, splanchnic stimulation resulted only in motor action of the cardiac sphincter in the dog, only in inhibitory action in the rabbit, and in both motor and inhibitory action in the cat. Knight (1934) reported only contraction of the sphincter in the cat in response to stimulation of fibers from the celiac ganglia and its relaxation following bilateral sympathectomy. In experiments reported by Ferguson (1936), bilateral vagotomy in the monkey resulted in persistent cardiospasm. Brücke and Stern (1938) also reported cardiospasm due to bilateral vagotomy which was abolished by atropine and adrenin but exaggerated by eserine, acetylcholine and pilocarpine. That relaxation of the cardiac sphincter is not the result of mechanical pressure due to contraction of the esophagus that tends to force the esophageal content into the stomach is indicated by the fact that following vagus stimulation liquids flow from the esophagus into the stomach under pressure conditions that are inadequate to bring about mechanical opening of the cardiac orifice. The

15

peristaltic wave passing along the esophagus is preceded, at least in the distal portion, by a wave of inhibition or relaxation which also affects the cardiac sphincter and the adjacent gastric musculature. In this manner, the way is opened so that the peristaltic contraction may force a bolus through the cardiac orifice without much resistance. By the use of the esophagoscope it may be observed that the cardiac sphincter remains closed until the tube of the instrument approaches to within a few centimeters of the cardia and that as the tube approaches the sphincter more closely it gradually opens. This reflex inhibition apparently is elicited by stimulation of receptors in the mucosa of the distal portion of the esophagus. The reflexes concerned in this reaction are mediated through afferent and efferent components of the vagus nerves.

Following the passage of a bolus of food into the stomach, the cardiac sphincter again closes until another peristaltic wave in the esophagus approaches. The tonic contraction of the cardiac sphincter, which develops when the stomach contains food, appears to be maintained through reflex activity of intramural neural mechanisms initiated by the stimulating effect of the acid in the gastric secretion. The tonus of the cardiac sphincter is relatively high while gastric digestion is in progress. According to Carlson (1922), "this hypertonus persists after removing the food from the stomach, washing the stomach cavity with water at body temperature, or rendering the stomach content alkaline; 0.4 per cent HCl in the stomach does not increase the tonus of the cardia parallel to that found in the digesting stomach." He also observed that the tonus of the cardiac sphincter is diminished under light, but increased under deep anesthesia.

Stomach.—Although the musculature of the stomach is composed exclusively of smooth muscle fibers, it is more complex than that of the other divisions of the digestive tube. Its motor activities also are correspondingly complex. Under the influence of the enteric neural mechanisms, the gastric musculature possesses the capacity to undergo reflex adjustment to the changing volume of the gastric contents without exhibiting appreciable changes in tonus. The pressure within the stomach is not necessarily increased by an increase in the volume of the stomach content, nor does an increase in the volume of the stomach increase the intra-abdominal pressure. The abdominal muscles undergo reflex adjustment to changes in the gastric content. The latter reaction is a reflex phenomenon mediated through reflex arcs whose afferent limbs are components of the splanchnic nerves and whose efferent limbs are components of the spinal nerves through which the abdominal muscles are innervated.

The neural regulation of the vascular bed in the stomach appears to be exerted through the sympathetic nerves. In dogs, as reported by Friesen and Hemingway (1952), prolonged sympathetic stimulation resulted in reduction in the flow of blood through the gastric wall, and vagus stimulation resulted in no appreciable alteration in the blood flow.

Gastric motility is not interrupted following bilateral section of vagus and splanchnic nerves. Under proper conditions, activity may still be observed in the excised stomach. With respect to its motor activities, therefore, the stomach may be regarded as an automatic organ. Its automatic activities are elicited by stimuli that arise within itself and appear to be carried out through its intrinsic neural mechanisms. These activities normally are regulated and controlled through the vagus and the splanchnic nerves.

In general, vagus stimulation augments gastric motility, but, under certain conditions, it inhibits it. The gastric rami of the vagus nerves, consequently, include some inhibitory fibers. The specific effect of vagus stimulation on the gastric musculature appears to be conditioned by the tonic state of the muscle. If it is in a state of low tonus, vagus stimulation may initiate motility; or if movements are present, it may augment and accelerate them. If the gastric musculature is in a state of high tonus, motility may be inhibited and the muscle relaxed. In view of all the data available, the initial tonic state of the gastric musculature seems to play a more decisive rôle than the frequency or the strength of the stimulus in determining the effect on the stomach of vagus stimulation.

The left vagus nerve exerts a greater influence than the right on gastric motility. Bilateral vagotomy in experimental animals results in decreased tonus and motility of the gastric musculature and delayed gastric emptying. In rabbits, as reported by Postlethwait et al. (1948), complete vagotomy was followed by cessation of gastric motility for 12 to 48 hours. The hypermotility that follows the arrest of gastric motility due to insulin hypoglycemia was also abolished. It could be effectively restored by the administration of pilocarpine or choline derivatives. Reduced tonus and motility of the gastric musculature and delayed gastric emptying have become recognized as common results of bilateral vagotomy in man.

Splanchnic stimulation commonly results in inhibition of gastric motility and relaxation of the gastric musculature. An opposite effect has also been observed. McCrea and McSwiney (1928) reported that stimulation of the distal portion of either splanchnic nerve after section results in an increase in the tonus of the gastric musculature if its initial state is one of low tonus, but in inhibition of motility and relaxation of the gastric musculature if its initial state is one of high tonus. Brown et al. (1930), working with spinal and decerebrate cats and dogs with the stomach divided at the incisura, found that the effect of splanchnic stimulation on the stomach is determined at least in part by the type of stimulation employed. In their experiments, stimulation with a frequency of 1 per second brought about contraction, while stimulation with a tetanizing current resulted in relaxation of the gastric musculature. The antrum did not respond in the same manner, but was always inhibited in the cat and usually in the dog by splanchnic stimulation regardless of the type employed. Brown and McSwiney (1932) reported reversal of the effect of splanchnic stimulation on the stomach following anesthesia with luminal or injection of this substance into a spinal animal. They advanced the opinion that the reversed effect of splanchnic stimulation on the stomach, following the administration of luminal, is due to the depressing effect of this substance on the rate of production or the action of the hormonal substance liberated at the periphery as a result of sympathetic stimulation.

The stomach also responds reflexly to stimulation of somatic afferent nerves. Impulses that arise in any somatic area may exert an influence on the stomach through reflex mechanisms involving efferent components of both the vagus and the splanchnic nerves. The nature of the response is determined by the preëxisting state of tonicity of the gastric neuromuscular mechanism.

In view of all the data available, it must be conceded that the initial state of tonicity of the gastric musculature is an important factor in determining the effect either of direct or reflex stimulation of the stomach through either the vagus or the splanchnic nerves. The concentration of adrenin and other humoral substances in the circulating blood and the substances liberated as a result of nerve stimulation constitute additional factors. Under certain conditions, the type of stimulation employed also seems to play a rôle in determining the nature of the response.

Splanchnic resection results in marked acceleration of gastric motility and reduced emptying time. In human subjects, Barron (1937) observed short periods of motility alternating with short periods of quiescence eight to ten days after unilateral splanchnic resection. Subsequently the periods of gastric activity became greatly lengthened and the amplitude of the contractions increased. The effects of bilateral splanchnic resection were essentially similar to those of unilateral resection.

In fasting rabbits under urethane anesthesia, as reported by Takeda and Ito (1951), stimulation of the ventromedial hypothalamic nucleus resulted in a rise in intracardiac and intrapyloric pressure and a subsequent increase in peristalsis. Stimulation of the lateral hypothalamic nucleus resulted in a slight fall in intracardiac pressure and complete abolition of motility. The effects on the corpus of the stomach were the opposite of those on the cardia and the pylorus.

Pyloric Sphincter.—According to most observers, the pyloric sphincter responds both to vagus and to splanchnic stimulation in essentially the same manner as the gastric musculature. Thomas and Wheelon (1922) have pointed out that the effect of stimulation of the extrinsic nerves is the same on the motility of the pyloric sphincter as on that of the pyloric antrum. This finding supports the theory that the pyloric sphincter is not a separate functional entity, but that the pyloric antrum and the sphincter constitute a functional unit and have a common nerve supply. Both the vagus and the splanchnic nerve fibers distributed to the pyloric sphincter are predominantly motor, but both nerves also include some inhibitory fibers. Inhibitory fibers to the pyloric sphincter are more abundant in the splanchnic than in the vagus nerves. The initial tonic state of the pyloric sphincter also is a factor in determining its response to both vagus and splanchnic stimulation.

The effects of artificial stimulation of the extrinsic nerves in question indicate the functional character of their efferent fibers, but afford no adequate concept of the normal functioning of the pylorus. When food is taken into the stomach, contractions are initiated about the middle of the organ and advance toward the pylorus. As digestion progresses, these contractions become stronger, and at certain irregular intervals, but not with each contraction wave, the pylorus opens as a wave of contraction approaches. Relaxation of the pyloric sphincter follows a peristaltic contraction that carries a mass of the stomach contents into the pyloric region. When a considerable mass has passed into the duodenum and still remains there, the pylorus does not open at the approach of a peristaltic wave that carries an adequate volume of the stomach contents before it regardless of the strength of the peristaltic contraction. The normal functioning of the pyloric sphincter appears to be controlled by closely coördinated reflex mechanisms which involve both the stomach and the duodenum. In the dog, as observed by Quigley and Loukes (1952), the pyloric sphincter characteristically contracts rhythmically, especially after feeding. The pattern for individual animals is quite constant, with an average cycle of 11 seconds. Noxious stimuli or emotional disturbances may suppress 1 to 4 cycles. The cycles are also lengthened somewhat by ingestion of food.

Retention of the gastric content in the stomach until it has reached a satisfactory state of digestion depends on impulses that arise within the stomach. The rate of discharge from the stomach is adapted to the functional capacity of the intestine by reflex activity initiated within the intestine. The reflex activity involved in gastric evacuation is mediated chiefly through the myenteric plexus and the vagus nerves. The myenteric reflexes are concerned chiefly with regulation of the tonus of the pyloric sphincter. Reflexes through the vagi exert an inhibitory influence on the pyloric portion of the stomach which tends to decrease the motility of the pyloric antrum, including the sphincter. The threshold of stimulation of the vagus reflex mechanism is lower than that of the myenteric; consequently, the former usually dominate the latter, particularly in the chemical regulation of the discharge of the gastric contents of the intestine.

Among the intra-intestinal stimuli that affect gastric motility are mechanical distention, chemical irritation, acid, hypotonic and hypertonic solutions, fat and the products of protein and carbohydrate digestion. The regulation of gastric evacuation, as outlined by Thomas (1938), may be explained as follows. The material discharged from the stomach into the duodenum, after gastric digestion has been going on for some time, normally includes HCl, proteoses and peptones, fat and the products of carbohydrate digestion. One or more of these substances soon accumulates in the intestine in sufficient concentration to stimulate the appropriate receptors for enterogastric reflex activity or initiate the liberation of enterogastrone. The tonus of the gastric musculature and the intragastric pressure, consequently, are diminished, and peristalsis grows weaker, so that the discharge of gastric contents into the duodenum proceeds at a slower rate. As soon as the gastric discharge fails to keep pace with intestinal digestion and absorption, gastric motor activity may be expected to increase. As soon as the stimulating materials are again present in the intestine in adequate concentration gastric motility is again reflexly inhibited. When once the rate of emptying is adjusted so that the concentration of the gastro-inhibitory substances in the intestine is maintained at the threshold level or a little above it, gastric activity probably continues with little further change. The initial discharge of stomach contents into the intestine following the ingestion of food undoubtedly can be explained most satisfactorily as due to the gastric "motor drive" which is constantly present during digestion. The regulation of gastric evacuation, therefore, tends to prevent overloading of the intestine, which is accomplished mainly through gastro-inhibitory reflexes and humoral influences initiated within the intestine by the presence of food materials and the products of their digestion. Since the changes in the tonus of the pyloric sphincter correspond to those of the pyloric antrum, it constantly tends to resist the discharge of the gastric contents into the duodenum and blocks the passage of solid particles. It also tends to limit regurgitation by contracting when the duodenum contracts.

Hunger Contractions.—In man the empty stomach exhibits movements of two types: (*a*) rhythmic tonus changes of the fundus and the corpus, and (*b*) hunger contractions. The former usually are not very marked. The latter are powerful waves that arise at the cardia and traverse the entire stomach. Hunger contractions are initiated about three hours after a meal, *i.e.*, when the stomach is nearly empty. They are superimposed on the tonus rhythm and occur in series (hunger periods) separated by intervals in which the stomach exhibits no motility except the tonus rhythm. Hunger periods usually last from thirty to forty-five minutes, but they may be as brief as six minutes or as long as one and one-half hours. The intervals of quiescence commonly last from one-half to two and one-half hours. Hunger contractions commonly give rise to a sensation of hunger with which may be associated actual discomfort or pain (hunger pang). During extended periods of fasting the hunger contractions are not diminished, but the hunger pangs and the general sensation of hunger become less intense after the third day. Hunger contractions may also be inhibited reflexly by various means, *e.g.*, strenuous muscular exercise, taking a quantity of water into the stomach, application of cold to the surface of the body, compression of the abdomen, *etc.* (Carlson, 1916).

Dextrose solutions introduced into the stomach have a marked inhibitory effect on hunger contractions. Gastric motility induced by pilocarpine and insulin is also inhibited by this means. In patients with anorexia nervosa treatment with amphetamine was found to improve the appetite for food, possibly by stimulating cerebral activity to the point at which hunger contractions reach the sensory level (Meyer *et al.*, 1945). Unpleasant odors that abolished appetite in human subjects, as reported by Ginsberg *et al.* (1948), occasionally inhibited gastric hunger contractions in dogs, but not in the human subjects. In the dog, as observed by Janowitz and Grossman (1949), the food intake is regulated both by food in the mouth and by distention of the stomach. Sham feeding in dogs may induce or inhibit gastric motility depending on the basal state of gastric activity (Lorber *et al.*, 1949). Kennedy (1950) has advanced certain data in support of the hypothesis that hyperphagia is normally inhibited by a hypothalamic satiety mechanism that is sensitive to changes in the blood brought about by the ingestion of food.

THE NERVOUS MECHANISM OF VOMITING

Vomiting is a reflex reaction that borders on the pathological and frequently serves the useful purpose of ridding the stomach of harmful substances. The rôle of the stomach in this reaction consists in tonic contraction of the pylorus and the pyloric antrum, inhibition of fundic peristalsis, and relaxation of the cardia and the cardiac sphincter. The gastric content is expelled through the esophagus by the sudden and simultaneous contraction of the diaphragm and the abdominal muscles. Vomiting commonly is caused by abnormal stimulation of receptors in the stomach that are connected with vagus nerve fibers. It may also be elicited by artificial stimulation of afferent vagus fibers and other sensory nerves. Frequently it is caused by disturbances of the urogenital apparatus, the liver and other visceral organs. It may also be caused by disagreeable emotions and disturbances of equilibrium. The afferent impulses concerned reach the medulla regardless of whether they are conducted by the vagus or other afferent nerves. The efferent impulses, through which contraction of the pyloric sphincter and the antrum is brought about, are conducted by the vagus nerves. Those which bring about relaxation of the fundus and the cardia are conducted through the splanchnic nerves. The contraction of the diaphragm and the abdominal muscles is brought about by impulses conducted by the phrenic and the lower thoracic nerves. The coördinated impulses which are sent out to the various muscles involved arise in the medulla. A medullary area in the vicinity of the motor nucleus of the vagus and close to the respiratory center, but distinct from the latter, probably includes a vomiting center, since vomiting cannot be carried out following destruction of this area. In the dog, as reported by Gregory (1946), the first signs of nausea and vomiting induced by subcutaneous injections of morphine are accompanied by rapid inhibition of intestinal tonus and motility that is followed by an equally rapid increase in tonus which is maintained for several seconds before retching occurs. This response appears to be a reflex carried out through the vomiting center.

Vomiting frequently is a symptom of disease or injury of the brain (meningitis, brain tumor, etc.) which brings about an increase in intracranial pressure. In this condition, the direct cause of vomiting probably is the increased hydrostatic pressure in the fourth ventricle which stimulates the vagus nuclei directly. Localized injuries of the brain and the spinal cord are not commonly accompanied by vomiting.

NERVOUS REGULATION OF GASTRIC SECRETION

Gastric secretory activity is regulated in part through neural mechanisms and in part through hormonal agencies. The neural regulation is mediated chiefly through the vagus nerves and the enteric plexuses. In experimental animals section of the sympathetic nerves of the stomach is followed by a marked increase, and section of the vagus nerves is followed by a marked decrease in gastric secretion. According to Jabonero et al. (1951), the neural influence on the enteric glands is fundamentally indirect, and is mediated through the blood supply.

Under normal physiological conditions, the secretory activity of the fundic glands ceases while the stomach is empty. The pyloric glands remain active, producing in small quantities an enzyme-containing secretion in which the pepsin must remain inactive due to the lack of hydrochloric acid, unless hydrochloric acid is secreted in small quantities by the parietal cells. When food is taken into the mouth the stimulation of the sense organs concerned and the accompanying psychophysiological processes initiate strong reflex parasympathetic excitation in the presence of which the central inhibitory influences acting on the fundic glands gradually subside, and these glands are thrown into secretory activity. As the food enters the stomach, it stimulates the gastric mucosa directly, first in the fundus, then in the pyloric region, and somewhat later in the duodenum, giving rise to afferent impulses that are conducted by general visceral afferent nerve fibers to the appropriate centers in the central nervous system. Both secretory and inhibitory impulses emanating from these centers are conducted back to the glands through visceral efferent conduction chains. As the process of digestion progresses, the secretin produced by the active mucosa and the secretin-like substances contained in the food reach the intestine and, being absorbed, are added to the secretin already present in the blood. This in turn exerts an influence on the secretory activity of the gastric glands.

As the food passes into the intestine and the stomach once more becomes empty, both the reflex and the humoral excitation of the gastric glands subsides, and the central inhibitory impulses again gain the ascendency. The fundic glands become quiescent, and the pyloric glands, in the absence of reflex inhibition, continue their normal secretory activity.

The chemical phase of gastric secretion, according to Babkin (1938), is regulated through (1) a hormonal substance, probably gastrin, which acts directly on the gastric glands, (2) certain food substances, or products liberated by them, which stimulate the gastric glands after being absorbed in the intestine, and (3) certain absorbed products of digestion, as well as a hypoglycemic state of the blood, which exert a direct influence on the vagal centers.

The assumption that the acidity of the gastric secretion is regulated chiefly by duodenal regurgitation and acid inhibition is supported by abundant experimental data, particularly those advanced by Wilhelmj and his collaborators. As summarized by Wilhelmj and Sachs (1939), the acidity of the gastric contents (cc. of acid secretion per 100 cc. of gastric contents) is controlled primarily by acid inhibition, the acidity of the total secretions entering the stomach primarily by duodenal regurgitation. The latter process may or may not influence the acidity of the gastric contents. These two mechanisms probably vary in relative importance in different normal subjects. Failure of one or the other in disease is theoretically possible. If, during normal acid inhibition, duodenal regurgitation did not occur, the secretory curve would show a high and maintained value for the acidity of the total secretions entering the stomach, but a normal acidity value for the gastric contents. If, in the presence of normal duodenal regurgitation, acid inhibition should fail, the secretory curve would show normal acidity of the total secretions entering the stomach but a high value for the acidity of the gastric contents.

Gastric secretory activity may be modified by the administration of various pharmacologic agents. Ephedrine, a sympathomimetic substance, causes a distinct reduction in the total acidity and the free HCl in the gastric juice. Acetyl-beta-methylcholine chloride and acetylcholine, parasympathomimetic substances, stimulate the production of free acid.

Ergotamine tartrate in large doses diminishes the acid secretory response to histamine. Dextrose introduced into the stomach tends to inhibit the gastric secretory activity caused by histamine, pilocarpine or insulin. Centrally acting emetics, *e.g.*, apomorphine, emetine and quinine, in sub-emetic doses decrease the total acid output, but a decrease in the titratable acidity requires emetic doses. Olive oil in the duodenum causes inhibition of gastric secretory activity which is followed by stimulation. Histamine causes an increase in the production of pepsin as well as in that of hydro-chloric acid. The excessive secretion of gastric juice associated with in-flammation or ulceration in the intestine appears to be due to the stim-ulating effect of the histamine liberated at the site of the lesion. In experi-mental animals, as reported by Ivy and Bachrach (1940), atropine de-pressed the gastric secretion after a meal to only about the same extent as it did the secretory response to histamine.

Studies of the effects of vagotomy in the treatment of patients with peptic ulcers and associated animal experimentation, carried out by numerous investigators during the past decade, have yielded significant data relative to gastric secretory activity. A neural, a gastric and an in-testinal phase of gastric secretion are generally recognized. The neural phase, also referred to as the cephalic phase, of gastric secretion depends on efferent conduction through the vagus nerves. These impulses may be elicited reflexly by sight, odor or taste of food, and by food in the stomach or the intestine. In normal dogs, as reported by Dragstedt *et al.* (1950), the neural phase of secretory activity accounts for approximately 45 per cent of the gastric juice secreted in a 24-hour period. The gastric phase accounts for approximately 45 per cent, and the intestinal phase for about 10 per cent. There appears to be no precise interrelationship between the neural and the gastric phases of secretory activity, since elimination of the neural phase by complete bilateral vagotomy also results in a material reduction in the gastric phase. The gastric phase of secretory activity appears to depend entirely on the antral mucosa which, in contact with food or when the antrum is moderately distended, functions as an endocrine organ in the production of gastrin, which is a gastric secretory stimulant. Elimination of the gastric phase by resection of the antrum also reduces the neural phase. Elimination of both the neural and the gastric phases by complete vagotomy and resection of the antrum results in marked reduc-tion of the secretory activity in the fundus and the body of the stomach. The intestinal phase of gastric secretion, therefore, appears to be relatively unimportant.

Certain data support the assumption that the neural phase of gastric secretion involves a neurohumoral mechanism. The peptic cells appear to be activated by vagus nerve impulses. Gastrin probably exerts its effect by the release of histamine (Linde, 1951). Vagus stimulation exerts no marked influence or none in the production of gastrin (Janowitz and Hol-lander, 1951). In man the secretion of mucoprotein is completely sup-pressed and the concentration of mucoproteose is increased following bilateral vagotomy (Glass *et al.*, 1951).

On the basis of all the data available, excessive gastric secretory activity appears to be neurogenic. Emotional stimulation undoubtedly is a significant factor in gastric hypersecretory activity. In patients with gastric fistulae, Wolf and Wolff (1948) observed that the patterns of gastric disturbances are characterized by either hypo- or hyperfunctioning of the stomach. Either pattern may be exhibited by the same person under different circumstances. The pattern of response in a given person, furthermore, may be determined due to conditioning by a previous experience that resulted in that particular pattern. In general, agreeable emotional experiences promote gastric hyperfunction. In distressing situations, the stomach usually is hypoactive. As observed by Crider and Walker (1948) in a young adult female patient with a gastric fistula, gastric secretory activity and the HCl content of the secretion were diminished during periods of anger, resentment, fear and anxiety. In patients with peptic ulcer, as observed by Szasz *et al.* (1947), the effect of anger on gastric secretory activity is abolished following bilateral vagotomy.

INTESTINE

In general, vagus stimulation results in excitation of the intestinal musculature as far as it is innervated through the vagus nerves, and stimulation of the splanchnic or the hypogastric nerves results in inhibition of the intestinal musculature. In some instances stimulation either of the vagus or the sympathetic nerves produces the reverse effect. Section of the vagus nerves in general results in decreased intestinal motility. Section of the sympathetic nerves results in increased motility. Stimulation of the sacral parasympathetic nerves commonly elicits contraction of the musculature of the colon, the rectum and the anal canal. The ileocolic sphincter apparently is innervated chiefly through sympathetic fibers. It commonly contracts in response to splanchnic stimulation and is not affected by stimulation either of the vagus or the sacral parasympathetic nerves.

The reversed action of vagus and splanchnic stimulation on the intestinal musculature has been explained on the assumption that the vagus nerves include some inhibitory fibers and the sympathetic nerves include some motor fibers to the intestine. Certain data strongly suggest that the specific effect of either vagus or sympathetic stimulation on the intestine is determined at least in part by the initial tonic state of its musculature. According to Carlson (1930), stimulation of the peripheral ends of the hypogastric nerves, all the efferent fibers of which probably are sympathetic, elicits contraction of both muscle layers of the large intestine if the musculature is relatively atonic, and inhibition of both layers if the muscles are active and in a fair degree of tonus.

In Carlson's (1930) experiments, stimulation of the sacral parasympathetic nerves produced only a motor effect on both muscle layers in the large intestine. According to Learmonth and Markowitz (1930), the lumbar colonic nerves exert a constant inhibitory influence on the distal parts of the colon. Section of these nerves, in their experiments, resulted in an immediate increase in intracolonic pressure and sometimes in an increase in the amplitude of the colonic contractions. In experiments reported by Wells *et al.* (1943), electrical stimulation of the pelvic nerves elicited contraction of both the longitudinal and the circular muscles of the descending colon. Impulses conducted by these nerves also influenced the musculature of the proximal portion of the colon through enteric conduction pathways. Electrical stimulation of the vagi elicited no response in the colon of the dog, but sometimes elicited weak and inconstant contractions in part of the cecum in the pig and the monkey. Electrical stimulation of the preganglionic fibers to the inferior mesenteric plexus elicited inconstant circular contraction of the colonic musculature limited to the descending colon. Stimulation of the hypogastric nerves elicited inconstant circular contraction limited to the distal portion of the descending colon.

Distention of the jejunum in dogs, as reported by Youmans *et al.* (1938), results in inhibition of motility of all types and diminution of the tonus of its undistended parts in both directions from the site of the distention. The degree of inhibition is determined by the rapidity of the distention and the final pressure attained. A weaker inhibitory response is elicited by distention following section of the extrinsic nerves, but destruction of the enteric connections while the extrinsic nerves are intact does not alter the response. The inhibition caused by distention of the jejunum, therefore, seems to be mediated primarily through extrinsic nerves. The degree of motility observed at the site of a distention depends in part on the balance between the reflex inhibitory and the direct stimulatory effects (Youmans, 1940). Stimulation of a loop of the small intestine by pressure, heat, mechanical injury or electrical stimulation of its afferent nerves, as reported by Pei and Fong (1942), elicits inhibition of the entire intestine. The reflexes involved are mediated through spinal cord centers in the eighth thoracic to the first lumbar segments inclusive.

In dogs, as reported by Raiford and Mulinos (1936), the jejunum is more irritable and responds more quickly to stimulation than other parts of the small intestine. Its minor rhythmic contractions at a definite oscillatory frequency also persist longer, and the contractions of the circular muscle are predominant. These facts are significant in relation to the function of the jejunum in the propulsion of the intestinal contents. The ileum is not only less irritable, but its contractions exhibit no rhythmic oscillations, and the amplitudes of the contractions of both the longitudinal and circular muscles are smaller. The colon exhibits the most powerful contractions, and those of either muscle layer may predominate, depending on the direction of the stimulus. This activity, according to these investigators, is mediated mainly through myenteric reflex mechanisms.

In studies carried out on exteriorized loops of intestine, in continuity and covered with a tube of skin, Douglas and Mann (1939, 1940) confirmed the current concepts of the gradient theory and the constancy of the rate of contraction in any given segment. They observed increased motility in the small intestine following ingestion of food which occurred earlier in the jejunum than in the ileum. This response was not abolished by bilateral vagotomy. It failed to occur following transection of the intestine, although the extrinsic nerves remained intact, but it did occur distal to the section following re-anastomosis of the intestine in such a way as to prevent immediate union of the muscular coats and the enteric plexuses. This response to food was also observed in the distal portion of the colon but not in its proximal portion. The response in the small intestine was as constant when the animal was fed through a fistula as when food was taken by mouth. Welch (1937) described reflex activity of the colon in man in response to feeding by mouth which did not occur when food was given through a gastric fistula. He therefore regarded the reaction as an appetite or taste reflex and not a gastrocolic reflex. He also described responses of the colonic musculature to psychic stimulation and to impulses arising in adjacent viscera.

Reflex inhibition of motility in the small intestine may be elicited by stimulation of any afferent nerve. Nociceptive stimulation may result in marked retardation of the propulsion of the intestinal contents. The inhibitory action of adrenin on intestinal motility is augmented by muscular exertion. Afferent stimulation of the vagus or somatic nerves commonly exerts a motor influence on the large intestine, and afferent stimulation of the splanchnic, the hypogastric or the pelvic nerves commonly exerts an inhibitory influence on this division of the enteric canal.

In dogs in which the sympathetic nerves were blocked by spinal anesthesia, Whitrock et al. (1948) demonstrated inhibition of intestinal motility at all levels elicited by distention of the jejunum or the ileum. The reflexes concerned were mediated through extrinsic nerves, but not through centers in the central nervous system. These findings corroborate the earlier demonstration of inhibition of motility in more proximal portions of the intestine elicited by distention of the ileum or direct faradic stimulation of mesenteric nerves following decentralization of the celiac plexus (Kuntz and Van Buskirk, 1941) and of inhibition of motility in the proximal segment of the transected colon elicited by distention of the distal segment or direct faradic stimulation of its nerves following decentralization of the inferior mesenteric plexus (Kuntz and Saccomanno, 1944). The reflex connections concerned obviously were made in prevertebral ganglia.

In vagotomized animals, as reported by Faik et al. (1950), the burst of intestinal activity which in normal animals usually is induced by the odor or the sight of food was abolished. The peristaltic waves appeared to be fewer and of shorter duration, and the periods of rhythmic segmentation were increased, but the gradient phenomenon was unaltered.

Peristalsis in the proximal portion of the colon is accompanied by rhythmic pulsations and shortening of the distal segments of the large intestine. The shortenings stand in the same reciprocal relationship to the rhythmic pulsations of these segments as does the proximal peristalsis. The reciprocal relationship between the longitudinal and the circular muscle activity of the distal segments of the large intestine is most marked in the region of the anal sphincters, i.e., the region in which circular activity is greatest. Whenever peristalsis is present in the proximal portions of the colon, longitudinal activity of the distal segments of the large intestine runs parallel with it, but there is no corresponding relationship between longitudinal activity of the distal segments and other types of activity in the proximal colon. The reciprocal relationship between the activity of the proximal and distal portions, observed in the intact large intestine, is preserved after transection in the region of the splenic flexure.

The anal canal is guarded by an internal and an external sphincter muscle. The external sphincter ani is composed of striated muscle and is subject to voluntary control within certain limits. It is innervated through the inferior hemorrhoidal branch of the pudendal nerve. The internal sphincter ani is composed of smooth muscle. Like the rest of the smooth musculature of the anal canal, it is innervated through sympathetic and parasympathetic nerves. Its sympathetic innervation includes both motor and inhibitory fibers. Both the internal and the external sphincters normally are in tonus, but the force of the tonic contraction of the external sphincter normally is greater than that of the internal sphincter. A certain degree of reflex interdependence of the internal and external sphincters has also been recognized. The effects on the internal sphincter ani of artificial stimulation of its sympathetic and its parasympathetic innervation seem to vary in different animals. Mechanical irritation or electrical stimulation of the anal sphincter area results in increased tonus and activity in this area and possibly in the adjacent segments and depression of the tonus and activity of the proximal portion of the colon. Electrical stimulation of other areas of the distal colon is less effective both locally and on the proximal colon. Moderate distention of either the proximal or the distal colon has no appreciable effect except for a slight local augmentation of activity without increase in tonus. By the use of simultaneous records of the exact intramural pressure in the proximal and the distal portions of the colon in unanesthetized dogs, Hoekstra *et al.* (1945) found that the tonus of the colon remained unaltered regardless of the volume of the gas present. Changes in pressure due to contraction of any part of the colon occurred simultaneously and usually were of the same magnitude in both the proximal and the distal portions.

Normal defecation is in part a voluntary and in part an involuntary act. Certain experimental data strongly suggest the existence of a defecation center in the medulla oblongata and of a center in the mesencephalon through which a tonic influence is exerted on the rectal musculature. Under certain conditions defecation may be carried out as a pure reflex. The defecation reflex involves peristaltic contractions of the rectum or the entire colon and inhibition of the anal sphincters. This reflex normally is excited by the entrance of feces into the rectum. Defecation may be inhibited voluntarily by contraction of the muscles of the pelvic floor. Contraction of these muscles gives rise to afferent impulses which bring about reflex inhibition of the movements of the colon and the rectum.

Defecation normally is mediated through reflex centers in the rostral lumbar and the sacral segments of the spinal cord. Destruction of these centers results in a temporary diarrhea lasting for several days. This may be followed by normal evacuation of the large intestine at the usual intervals. The results of destruction of the spinal cord vary somewhat in different animals, but, when free from both motor and inhibitory control through the spinal cord, the local neural mechanism seems to have the capacity to regulate and control the defecation reflex. The pelvic nerves undoubtedly play a major rôle in normal defecation. Stimulation of these nerves usually results in immediate shortening of the colon and drawing it distad. This reaction is followed after an interval by contraction of the circular muscle beginning in the upper part of the distal colon and spreading distad, driving feces before it. This wave of contraction is sometimes followed by other waves of like nature. When the pelvic nerves are divided peristaltic action of the colon is released and its storage function is temporarily abolished.

Following destructive lesions of the sacral innervation of the rectum and the anal canal in man, contraction of the rectum is accompanied by reciprocal relaxation of the anal sphincter. This reciprocal reaction is mediated through intrinsic reflex mechanisms that are activated by tension on the rectal wall. These mechanisms may be depressed by spinal shock for a brief interval during which passive distention of the rectum elicits only slight relaxation of the anal sphincter. Postural tonus of the rectum and the anal sphincter is a reaction to passive tension of the muscle involved. Rapidly increased tension of this musculature causes tonic contraction to give way to phasic contractions. Tension, therefore, is also the stimulus for phasic movement. If delivery of fecal material from the colon is adequate, the mechanism of defecation depends primarily on the reaction of the rectum to distention. The inefficiency of defecation following transverse spinal cord lesions is due to the relatively small force of rectal contraction even after recovery of the automatic reflex function.

PHYSIOLOGICAL RELATIONSHIPS OF THE ENTERIC PLEXUSES

Section of extrinsic nerves, as pointed out above, neither interrupts gastro-intestinal motility nor profoundly modifies the gastro-intestinal movements. There is a strong tendency on the part of the system, furthermore, to restore normal functional activity in a relatively short time following the disturbances that arise as the result of such operative interference. For example, bilateral vagus section at the level of the diaphragm results in diminution of tonus of the gastro-intestinal musculature and retardation of peristalsis, but both tonus and peristaltic activity are soon restored in a large measure. Bilateral section of the splanchnic nerves results in increased tonus and augmented peristaltic activity. This also subsides in a relatively short time and, in some instances, is followed by a hypotonic condition. Section of both vagus and splanchnic nerves results in marked hypotonicity of the stomach and retardation of peristalsis. This condition is of longer duration following bilateral than following unilateral section of these nerves. Section of the sympathetic nerves of the large intestine commonly results in mild diarrhea which gradually subsides. In experimental animals (cats and dogs), frequent discharge of soft feces may be observed, in many instances, for some time following removal of the inferior mesenteric ganglia or extirpation of the lumbar sympathetic trunks. Relief of chronic constipation in man has been reported following lumbar sympathectomy.

The nervous phenomena concerned with the normal functioning of the digestive tract obviously cannot be adequately explained on the basis of motor and inhibitory control mediated through the sympathetic and parasympathetic outflows from the central nervous system. Many reactions involve only the enteric nervous system. Gastro-intestinal motility of all known types has been observed following section of the extrinsic nerves that supply the part of the digestive tract in question. This motility, though normally subject to central nervous influences through the extrinsic nerves, originates in the neuromuscular mechanism in the wall of the gastro-intestinal canal. Gastro-intestinal motility of certain types probably is myogenic, but many of the reactions which commonly are recognized as reflexes are initiated in the enteric nervous system and carried out through it. The reciprocal inhibition involved in the coördinated activity of the two muscle layers also requires the functioning of the enteric mechanisms.

According to Jabonero *et al.* (1951), no effective responses of the enteric muscles or glands take place without the intervention of neural influences. The transmission of these influences to the effector tissues requires a chemical mediator which is the same regardless of whether sympathetic or parasympathetic nerves are stimulated. Sympathetic stimulation results in the liberation of adrenin in sufficient quantity to produce muscle contraction in the enteric vascular bed. This results in a progressive decrease in secretory activity that is secondary to the vasoconstriction. Parasympathetic stimulation results in more intense and more prolonged liberation of the same chemical mediator in the terminal syncytial structure. The initial contraction of the blood vessels is followed by prolonged vasodilatation or by an indifferent response. Secretory activity is facilitated due to the maintenance of an adequate or an increased blood supply. Following the elimination of impulses of central nervous origin, the enteric nerves continue to function independently according to the same basic pattern.

Enteric Conduction.—Since conduction within the walls of the enteric canal continues following section of the extrinsic nerves, it appears to be a function of the enteric nervous system. As observed by Alvarez (1929), in the rabbit, the rate at which the waves of a peristaltic rush advance along the intestine is not appreciably altered following section of the vagus nerves. The gradient of sensitivity from the duodenum distad also remains constant. The rate at which the peristaltic rushes travel also remains unaltered following section of the splanchnic nerves. The latent periods are shortened in all parts of the intestine except the duodenum, but their normal gradient remains unchanged. In rabbits that survived bilateral vagus and splanchnic nerve section three weeks or longer, peristaltic rushes advanced along the intestine at the normal rate, but the latent periods were shortened as in those that had been subjected only to bilateral splanchnic nerve section. Following section of all the layers of the intestinal wall except the mucosa, conduction is stopped at the scar, but peristaltic rushes are not interrupted because intestinal contents are pushed beyond the scar, causing mechanical distention of the segment just distal to it. The conduction of waves of contraction produced by local electrical stimulation of the intestine is not altered following degeneration of the vagus nerves, but it is altered somewhat following degeneration of the splanchnic nerves (Alvarez, 1930). In the dog peristaltic waves of contraction in the large intestine were also halted at the scar following transection of the colon in the region of the splenic flexure (Lawson and Templeton, 1932).

Enteric Reflexes.—Reflex activity in the gastro-intestinal tract following bilateral section and degeneration of the vagus and the splanchnic nerves has been amply demonstrated. With the stomach and the small intestine deprived of impulses emanating from the central nervous system, the differences in the rate of discharge of different kinds of food from the stomach persist. Mechanical and chemical stimulation of the mucosa in the proximal portion of the intestine elicits gastric tonus and hunger contractions, but they are less marked than while the extrinsic nerves are intact. It may be assumed, therefore, that these and similar responses elicited by stimulation of the gastric mucosa normally involve local as well as cerebrospinal reflex mechanisms. Mechanical irritation of the duodenal mucosa through a duodenal fistula elicits tonic contraction of the pyloric sphincter. This reaction could not be elicited when conduction through the local neuromuscular mechanism was arrested by compression of the wall of the proximal portion of the duodenum between a ligature on the outside and a solid cylindrical body in the lumen (Thomas and Kuntz, 1926). It may, therefore, be carried out as a reflex through the local neuromuscular mechanism, at least in the absence of intact extrinsic nerves. Retraction of the villi and ridging and pitting of the mucosa in response to mechanical and chemical stimuli applied to the intestinal epithelium also take place with the same intensity as in animals with the vagus and the splanchnic nerves intact. These phenomena must, therefore, be interpreted as local reflexes mediated through the neuromuscular mechanism (King and Arnold, 1922). In the dog, Lim *et al.* (1952) found no constant relationship between gastric motility and the secretion of gastrin. The enteric reflexes appeared to be concerned primarily with gastric motility, and the secretion of gastrin appeared to be mediated through adenteric reflexes. Peristalsis in the large intestine also involves local reflex mechanisms. In animals in which the spinal cord has been destroyed antiperistalsis in the large intestine ceases when food material enters it from the ileum. This also involves reflex activity of the enteric nervous system. As pointed out above, the defecation reflex also may be restored following destruction of the spinal center through which it normally is carried out.

Mild mechanical localized stimulation of the mucosa in exteriorized pieces of the dog's colon, as reported by Raiford and Mulinos (1934), elicited reflex muscular responses both before and after section of the extrinsic nerves. In unanesthetized dogs localized stimulation of the colonic mucosa was followed by contraction of the longitudinal muscle at the site of the stimulation and distal to it and by contraction of the circular muscle, three to five seconds later, at the site of the stimulation and proximal to it.

Rhythmic Gastro-intestinal Contractions.—The hypothesis that the purely rhythmic contractions of the gastro-intestinal musculature are myogenic seems to be amply supported. As observed by Bayliss and Starling (1899), the rhythmic contractions of the small intestine persist following the administration of drugs in doses which they regarded as sufficient to paralyze the myenteric plexus. Under these conditions, waves of contraction which, unlike peristaltic contractions, are not preceded by inhibition, advance indifferently in either direction along the small intestine. Antiperistalsis in the large intestine also persists following the administration of nicotine in doses sufficient to abolish peristalsis in the small intestine. Gastric peristalsis persists following the administration of nicotine in large doses or multiple incisions through the muscular layers of the stomach deep enough to interrupt the continuity of the myenteric plexus. Cannon (1912) also reported rhythmic contractions in the small intestine following multiple incisions through the muscular layers.

Bayliss and Starling (1899) advanced the theory that the rhythmic contractions of the intestine, *i.e.*, those that persist after the coördinated movements which they regarded as reflex are abolished, are myogenic. This conclusion may be essentially correct, but it cannot be regarded as fully substantiated by the results of their experimental work with nicotine. The inference that the enteric plexuses are no longer functional following abolition of the myenteric reflex is untenable. As observed by King and Arnold (1922), responses of the intestinal villi to chemical and mechanical stimulation of the intestinal epithelium are not abolished by nicotine until it is present in sufficient concentration to paralyze the muscularis mucosæ. They interpreted these reactions as reflexes mediated through the submucous plexus. They seemed to be of the opinion that this plexus is not affected by nicotine in the same manner as, according to current concepts, this drug affects other autonomic ganglia. They were not convinced that nicotine paralyzes the myenteric plexus. Thomas and Kuntz (1926) have shown that the influence of the vagus nerves on the small intestine, as judged by the motor effects of vagus stimulation, is not abolished by doses of nicotine many times as large as the dosage which, in the experiments of Bayliss and Starling, abolished the peristaltic reflex. The dosage employed by Bayliss and Starling (2 to 3 cc. of a 1 per cent solution for a small dog), if not increased, holds the manifestation of the typical effects of vagus stimulation in abeyance. When nicotine is administered in greatly increased doses, vagus stimulation again becomes effective and remains so until the drug is present in a concentration representing 2 to 3 grams of the undiluted alkaloid per kilogram of body weight (Thomas and Kuntz, 1926). This finding has been confirmed by Mulinos (1927) and Alvarez (1931). The small dosage of nicotine employed by Bayliss and Starling obviously does not paralyze the vago-enteric mechanism, but holds certain of its functions in abeyance, probably by a process of inhibition. The results of the experiments of Bayliss and Starling, consequently, do not demonstrate the myogenic nature of the rhythmic contractions that persist following abolition of the myenteric reflex by small doses of nicotine.

The inherent capacity of gastro-intestinal muscle for rhythmic contraction has been demonstrated in experiments with isolated strips of muscle freed as completely as possible of neural elements and studied in appropriate solutions. This does not prove, however, that in the intact animal the rhythmic contractions of the gastro-intestinal musculature are independent of neural regulation. In an experimental study involving the use of nicotine in massive doses, Thomas and Kuntz (1926) have shown that rhythmic gastric and intestinal contractions, both in the intact animal and in excised pieces of the stomach and intestine, persist following complete

16

paralysis of the enteric nervous system, but the kymographic records of these contractions differ characteristically from the records of rhythmic contractions obtained while the enteric nervous system remains functional. In so far as the results of these experiments indicate that the gastro-intestinal musculature possesses the inherent capacity to contract rhythmically, they corroborate the findings of those investigators who regard the rhythmic contractions of the stomach and intestine as myogenic, but they neither indicate that these rhythmic contractions are normally carried out without neural regulation nor that the gastro-intestinal musculature could adequately perform even its simpler motor functions in the absence of neural regulation. The rhythmic gastro-intestinal contractions that persist after the enteric nervous system is paralyzed differ widely from those carried out in the unpoisoned organs. The records of even the simplest forms of rhythmic activity in an unpoisoned segment of the intestine, in which functional activity of the enteric nervous system may still be assumed, are characterized by frequent changes in tonus and amplitude which show a high degree of variation and complexity. None of these irregularities appear in the records obtained following denervation with nicotine. The movements which persist consist of mechanically regular contractions and relaxations. While the records obtained before administration of nicotine cannot be regarded as representing strictly normal functional activity, the difference between the extremely variable activity of the unpoisoned viscus and the mechanical regularity exhibited by the denervated preparation probably represents in some measure the functional control normally exercised through the enteric nervous system. The frequent changes and irregularities observed in the records of the activity of the unpoisoned viscus under experimental conditions probably represent the functional activity of a neural mechanism that is capable of bringing about similar changes in an orderly and purposeful sequence under the influence of the stimuli of its natural environment.

As the dosage of nicotine was increased, in both the experiments carried out on excised pieces of the intestine and those carried out with the stomach and intestine *in situ*, the amplitude of the rhythmic contractions increased progressively until the concentration of nicotine became relatively high and then gradually decreased. Assuming that the influence of nicotine in moderate doses is exerted chiefly on the neural mechanism, this fact suggests a functional relationship of the enteric nervous system to the amplitude of the rhythmic contractions. Since all activity ceased in very high concentrations of nicotine, it seems highly probable that the gradual reduction in the amplitude of the rhythmic contractions, after the maximum amplitude was reached, was due to the depressing effect of nicotine in high concentration on the muscle directly. The cause of the progressive increase in amplitude which preceded this depression is less apparent. It may be the primary stimulating effect of nicotine on the muscle preceding the depression.

The rate of the contractions is not increased in proportion to the increase in amplitude as the dosage of nicotine is increased. Nerve stimulation, furthermore, does not exert a constant effect on the rate of contraction. On the other hand, the depressing effect of nicotine in high concentration affects both the amplitude and the rate of the contractions. These facts suggest that the effect of removal of inhibition may be quantitatively greater than the effect of direct stimulation of the muscle in increasing the amplitude of contraction. They also suggest that the inhibition, which is generally regarded as responsible for the quiescence of the gastro-intestinal musculature, so commonly observed following operative procedures or manipulation of these organs, is not the result of reflexes involving the extrinsic nerves alone, but is due in part to inhibitory influences exerted through the enteric nervous system.

The relative constancy of the rate of the rhythmic contractions as compared with the great variability in tonus and amplitude, under the influence of drug action and nerve stimulation by means of the galvanic current, throughout these experiments suggests that the rate may be quite independent of the neural influences that bring about changes in tonus and amplitude. The rate of the rhythmic contractions probably depends on properties that are inherent in the gastro-intestinal musculature. It would, therefore, be subject to neural regulation in a lesser degree than tonus and amplitude.

Inasmuch as the effect of vagus stimulation is held in abeyance and certain of the gastro-intestinal movements are abolished by the effect of nicotine in moderate dosage, it has been assumed by some that any functional activity manifested by the enteric nervous system following the administration of moderate doses of nicotine must be mediated by asynaptic neural mechanisms. In the light of the experimental results here cited, this assumption is unnecessary. As we have seen, when the dosage of nicotine is progressively increased, vagus stimulation, the effect of which was held in abeyance by the smaller doses of nicotine, again becomes effective and remains so until nicotine is present in sufficient concentration to paralyze the enteric neural mechanism; consequently, there must be synapses in the vagus efferent chains which are as resistant to nicotine paralysis as the neuromuscular junctions themselves. If, as indicated by some of the anatomical data set forth above, some enteric neurons actually make synaptic connections with others, these synapses probably are equally resistant to nicotine paralysis. It seems highly probable, therefore, that whatever functional activity persists in the enteric nervous system following the administration of nicotine in moderate dosage is true reflex activity. This view obviates the necessity both of denying the regulatory neural control of rhythmic gastro-intestinal contractions under physiological conditions and of postulating the existence of syncytial nerve nets in the enteric nervous system.

In view of the fact that the coördinated reflex activities of the gastro-intestinal musculature may be carried out apparently according to their normal physiological mode in the absence of impulses that emanate from the central nervous system, the enteric nervous system must be regarded as more complex both in its anatomical structure and its physiological functions than other peripheral plexuses, *e.g.*, the cardiac and the pulmonary plexuses. It seems most reasonable to regard it as a reflex system capable of independent coördinated reflex activity, but subject to reflex motor and inhibitory influences through the central nervous system.

NEURAL REGULATION OF INTESTINAL SECRETION

Under normal conditions, the secretory activity of the intestinal glands depends in a large measure on the intestinal contents. The glands in the small intestine normally secrete very little or not at all while the intestine is at rest. Mechanical stimulation of the mucosa calls forth an immediate flow of secretion from these glands. The quality of this secretion also depends on the character of the mechanical stimulus employed. In general, glandular activity elicited by direct mechanical stimulation of the intestinal mucosa involves only a localized area of the intestine. This fact strongly suggests that the reflex mechanisms employed involve only neurons in the enteric plexuses.

A secretory influence of the vagus nerves on the intestinal glands has been demonstrated. In experiments on spinal cats, as reported by Sawitsch and Soshestvensky (1917, 1921), vagus stimulation resulted in an increase in both the liquid and enzyme contents of the intestinal secretion. Within certain limits, the enzyme content of the intestinal secretion increased with increasing strength of stimulation regardless of the quantity of liquid secreted. Administration of atropine in moderate doses resulted in diminution of the secretory effect of vagus stimulation and, in large doses, abolished it. Abolition of the secretory effect of vagus stimulation on the intestinal glands required larger doses of atropine than abolition of the vagus effect on intestinal motility. This finding was regarded as supporting the theory that secretory activity of the intestinal glands and intestinal motility are independent of each other.

Section of the extrinsic nerves supplying a given portion of the intestine is followed by continuous secretory activity of the glands in that portion. This has been called paralytic intestinal secretion. Possibly the vasodilatation which follows section of the extrinsic nerves is a factor in the output of intestinal secretion under these conditions. Certain experimental data indicate quite clearly that the abundant and continuous secretory activity of the intestinal glands, following section of the extrinsic nerves of the intestine, is due chiefly to the elimination of normal inhibitory nerve impulses. These data, like those bearing on the effects of vagus stimulation, suggest that the secretory activity of the intestinal glands normally is subject to a measure of regulatory neural control.

In experiments reported by Wright et al. (1940), vagus stimulation, in decerebrate and decapitate cats, elicited secretory activity of Brunner's glands in the duodenum, but none in the jejunum or the ileum. Section of the greater splanchnic nerves in the thorax also resulted in secretory activity in the duodenum only, but section of all the preganglionic sympathetic nerves to the intestine resulted in secretory activity throughout the small intestine. These findings, like those of various other investigators, support the point of view that the intestinal glands are activated by hormonal agents and the neural influences in intestinal secretion are chiefly inhibitory.

Chapter XI

INNERVATION OF THE BILIARY SYSTEM

EXTRINSIC NERVES

THE innervation of the biliary system is derived mainly from the celiac plexus and the vagi. The phrenic plexus probably contributes to the biliary nerves in some instances. The nerves of the liver, the gall bladder and the bile ducts form a plexiform structure which may be subdivided into an anterior and a posterior hepatic plexus. The anterior hepatic plexus is located in relation to the hepatic artery, around which it forms a dense meshwork. It is derived chiefly from the left portion of the celiac plexus and the right abdominal branch of the left vagus which approaches the hepatic portal through the hepatogastric ligament. Some of its branches join the celiac plexus. The anterior hepatic plexus includes the internal nerve to the cystic duct and the gall bladder and the nervus pancreaticocholedochus. The posterior hepatic plexus is located in relation to the portal vein and the bile duct. Most of its fibers are derived from the right portion of the celiac plexus and branches of the right vagus that traverse this plexus. It includes three or four main trunks which take a transverse course dorsal to the portal vein and reach the dorsal surfaces of the bile ducts. The right lateral trunk assumes a position along the dorsal surface of the common bile duct to which most of its fibers are distributed. It gives rise to the lateral nerve of the gall bladder and some anastomotic rami to the ventral hepatic plexus.

The major ganglion in the right portion of the celiac plexus usually is larger than the one in the left portion and probably contributes most of the sympathetic fibers in the biliary nerves (Alexander, 1940). Rami arising from both the right and the left portions of the celiac plexus contribute to the plexiform structure of the hepatic artery and mingle to some extent in the ventral and dorsal hepatic plexuses. The plexiform structure in the hepatic portal includes numerous small ganglia.

In those cases in which the phrenic nerve contributes to the innervation of the liver, phrenic branches join sympathetic rami that enter the liver either through the hepatic portal or near the posterior hepatic border. In some instances branches of the phrenic nerve join hepatic rami of the left vagus.

The innervation of the choledochoduodenal junction appears to be particularly abundant. In the cat, according to Schulze and Boyden (1943), this region is supplied through two independent pathways, the gastroduodenal nerve and the gastroduodenal plexus. The gastroduodenal nerve arises by confluence of branches of the hepatic plexus, which include fibers derived from both right and left celiac ganglia, and branches of the celiac division of the right vagus (Fig. 60). One of its two main branches

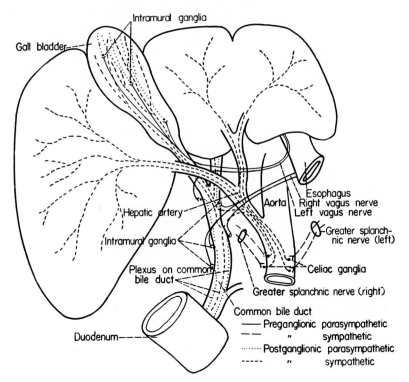

FIG. 59.—Diagrammatic illustration of the innervation of the biliary system.

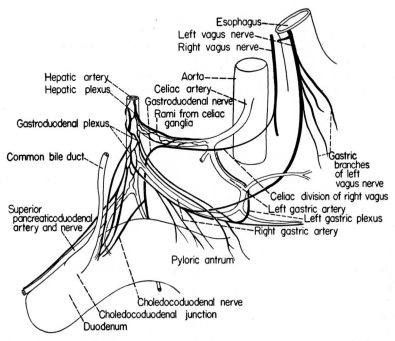

FIG. 60.—Diagrammatic illustration of the extrinsic innervation of the choledochoduodenal junction in the cat. (Redrawn from Schulze and Boyden, 1943.)

(246)

terminates at the junction of the bile duct and the intestine. The gastro-duodenal plexus, associated with the gastroduodenal artery, is made up of fibers derived from the hepatic plexus and a few recurrent fibers of the coronary nerve. Both pathways contribute fibers to the paracholedochal plexus. At the choledochoduodenal junction those derived from the gastro-duodenal plexus tend to follow the superior pancreaticoduodenal artery and its branch, the common duodenal artery. Those derived from the gastro-duodenal nerve terminate both in the intramural plexus of the bile duct and adjacent portions of the myenteric plexus. With the exception of two vagus branches, according to Royster *et al.* (1949), the sympathetic and the para-sympathetic nerves of the biliary tract and the duodenum traverse common pathways. Those from the right and the left sides inosculate freely. The nerves of the biliary tract and those of the proximal portion of the duo-denum, consequently, include both sympathetic and vagus fibers.

INTRINSIC NERVES

As the hepatic artery and the portal vein enter the liver, they are ac-companied by nerves of which most of the fibers are unmyelinated. These nerves give rise to branches which continue along the branches of the blood vessels and the bile ducts. The intrahepatic nerves include a limited num-ber of myelinated fibers. They probably are visceral afferents. In general the intrahepatic nerves are closely associated with the blood vessels and the bile ducts to which they are functionally related. Alexander could trace no nerve fibers into the parenchyma of the liver lobules.

The intramural nerves of the bile ducts and the gall bladder form irreg-ular plexuses in the adventitia, the muscularis and the submucosa. The adventitial and the intramuscular plexuses include small ganglia at their nodal points. These plexuses are intimately connected with one another and with the submucous plexus which probably includes no ganglia. Alexander (1940) reported individual ganglion cells in this plexus in the gall bladder. Fibers of the submucous plexus approach the epithelium, but probably do not penetrate it.

At the choledochoduodenal junction, according to Schulze and Boyden (1943), the more delicate choledochal plexus and the heavier myenteric plexus are connected by strands of nerve fibers, but there is no direct continuity of the one plexus with the other. In the sphincter of Oddi, as demonstrated by Boyden and Van Buskirk (1943) in the cat, the intrinsic plexus includes numerous small ganglia. This plexus undergoes no marked change due to degeneration of the fibers of extrinsic origin.

In experiments reported by Alexander (1940), bilateral degeneration of the vagus nerves did not appreciably alter the abundance and the distribu-tion of nerve fibers in preparations of the biliary system, except in the hepatic portal where the myelinated fibers were reduced in numbers in some of the nerves accompanying blood vessels and bile ducts. Extirpation of the celiac ganglia cannot be carried out without also interrupting part of the vagus branches to the biliary system. This operation resulted in al-most complete degeneration of the intrahepatic nerves, except for some fibers in the nerves associated with the bile ducts. It probably completely eliminated the vascular innervation and materially reduced the numbers of intramural fibers in the bile ducts and the gall bladder. Bilateral vagus section and extirpation of the celiac ganglia resulted in degeneration of nearly all the fibers in the extrinsic biliary nerves, complete degeneration of the nerve supply to the blood vessels throughout the biliary system and degeneration of all the fibers in the walls of the bile ducts and the gall bladder except those that arise in the intramural ganglia and ganglia in the hepatic portal. These results support the assumptions that the afferent innervation of the hepatic blood vessels is solely sympathetic and that the musculature of the bile ducts and the gall bladder is innervated through both sympathetic and parasympathetic nerves.

The neural structure in the walls of the gall bladder and the common bile duct includes small ganglia and isolated ganglion cells. Hermann (1952) described a nerve plexus including ganglia at the outer surface of the musculature and an abundant plexus of nerve fibers in the adventitia of the gall bladder in man. According to his account, ganglion cells also occur associated with the nerves in the connective tissue between the musculature and the mucous epithelium and in the neural structure between the muscle-fiber bundles.

NERVOUS REGULATION OF LIVER FUNCTIONS

Intrahepatic Vasomotor Regulation.—Functional sympathetic innervation of the intrahepatic vessels has been amply demonstrated, but the data bearing on the possible influence of parasympathetic nerves on these vessels are not in complete agreement. Stimulation of the splanchnic nerves or the hepatic plexus uniformly elicits constriction of the hepatic arterioles and the terminal branches of the hepatic portal vein, causing a rise in portal pressure. The inflow of blood, consequently, is reduced. The same stimulus results in an increased outflow from the liver, consequently, liver volume is reduced. Under certain conditions, the liver, like the spleen, plays a rôle in the regulation of the systemic blood pressure. (See Chapter VIII.) Changes in intrahepatic circulation also play a rôle in the metabolic and secretory functions of the liver. Data relative to the possible influence of parasympathetic nerve impulses in the regulation of intrahepatic circulation are inconclusive. The neural regulation of the hepatic vascular bed appears to be mediated solely through the sympathetic nerves.

Bile Secretion.—The secretion of bile continues uninterruptedly, but the rate of secretion varies from hour to hour and under varying conditions of nutrition. During periods of fasting it is very low and is increased but little after a meal of carbohydrates. It is increased appreciably after a meal of fat and still more markedly after a meal of proteins. Corresponding changes in the output of bile after meals of carbohydrate, fat and protein respectively have been observed in dogs following complete denervation of the liver.

Although the secretion of bile is not directly influenced by nerve impulses, it is definitely altered by changes in intrahepatic blood pressure. Stimulation of the sympathetic nerves of the liver results in diminished bile production due to its vasoconstricting effect. In dogs, stimulation of the right splanchnic nerves also inhibits the musculature of the biliary tract. Stimulation of the left splanchnic nerves exerts no influence on the biliary musculature (Mallet-Guy *et al.*, 1952). In general, reduction in the blood volume flow through the liver results in a decrease in the output of bile, and an increase in the blood flow results in an increase in the bile output except when the increase in the blood flow is associated with increased intrahepatic blood pressure.

Certain data reported by Tanturi and Ivy (1938) seem to indicate a direct effect of vagus impulses on the production of bile in the dog and the monkey, but not in the cat or the rabbit. They reported an excitatory-secretory effect in the dog and the monkey produced by stimulating the peripheral end of the vagus in the neck five days after section of this nerve. They also reported augmentation of bile secretion in the dog elicited by stimulating the central end of the divided vagus while the other vagus remained intact. Section of the second vagus abolished this effect. When both vagi were divided, stimulation of the central end of one of them resulted in diminishing bile secretion. These results seem to indicate both direct and reflex effects of vagus stimulation on bile secretion. In view of the functional capacity of the liver following section of all its extrinsic nerves and the absence of conclusive evidence of nerve fibers within the liver lobules, they probably can be explained without the necessity of postulating direct contact of nerve fibers with the liver cells.

Carbohydrate Metabolism.—Stimulation of the center for carbohydrate metabolism in the floor of the fourth ventricle commonly results in hyperglycemia and glycosuria. Claude Bernard (1887) observed that puncture of this center is not followed by glycosuria or hyperglycemia in animals whose supply of glycogen has been depleted by continued fasting. He also observed that section of the spinal cord in the caudal thoracic region does not prevent glycosuria following stimulation by puncture of the so-called sugar center, but that such stimulation has no influence on the conversion of glycogen into sugar following section of the spinal cord in the rostral thoracic region. This led him to conclude that puncture of the medullary center in question stimulates sugar production only in the liver and that the efferent impulses that bring about this result reach the liver through the splanchnic nerves. The results of more recent experiments indicate that these impulses are conducted from the spinal cord via the fifth and the sixth thoracic nerve roots. That the liver is the seat of the increased sugar production following puncture of the sugar center is also indicated by the fact that glycosuria does not follow this operation when the hepatic vessels are ligated.

The carbohydrate center in the medulla oblongata probably receives a constant influx of afferent impulses, particularly through the vagi, which play an important rôle in the regulation of the normal production of sugar in the liver. Pflüger (1903) advanced the theory that the body, by virtue of this reflex mechanism, is enabled to draw upon the food supply represented by the glycogen in the liver whenever an increased expenditure of energy is required. For example, when a particular group of muscles, through prolonged activity, has exhausted its local nutrient supply, afferent impulses conducted to the medulla activate the carbohydrate center and thus bring about the release of energy-producing food material for immediate use.

Certain diencephalic centers also play a part in the regulatory control of carbohydrate metabolism, but they do not appear to be essential for the mobilization of carbohydrate as manifested in reflex rises in blood sugar. Reflex rises in blood sugar equal to those produced in animals with intact central nervous systems have been produced after section of the brain stem below the mid-brain.

The regulatory control of carbohydrate metabolism in the liver is brought about in part through vasomotor regulation of the hepatic blood vessels and in part through the effect on the secretory activity of the appropriate endocrine glands of nerve impulses emanating from the centers concerned. Stimulation of the carbohydrate center commonly results in an increased output of adrenin which in turn causes a rise in blood sugar. Variations in the concentration of sugar in the blood constitute the chief physiological stimuli for the carbohydrate center. Injury to this center results only in temporary glycosuria. Frank diabetes mellitus probably results only from disease of a peripheral organ involved in carbohydrate metabolism, particularly the pancreas. Experimental data seem to indicate that the production of hyperglycemia by the intravenous injection of pituitrin is not influenced by autonomic nerve impulses.

The essential rôle of hormonal agents in carbohydrate metabolism is indicated by experimental observations on totally sympathectomized animals. With or without removal of the adrenal medulla, blood sugar balance can be maintained within the normal range during exercise and following it, after ingestion of glucose and after injection of adrenin after adequate time has been allowed for recovery from the operation (Brouha *et al.* 1939).

Hypoglycemia is commonly accompanied by alterations in blood pressure, accelerated pulse rate, perspiration, etc., due to sympathetic stimulation, and increased gastric motility and secretion due to parasympathetic stimulation. These symptoms may be attributed to diencephalic stimulation. They subside following the administration of sugar since restoration of the blood sugar level removes the cause of the central stimulation (Fortuyn, 1941).

Protein Metabolism.—Data that seem to indicate that protein metabolism in the liver is influenced by nerve impulses are not wanting. On the other hand, the inherent capacity of the liver cells to break up proteins is not impaired by complete denervation of the liver. The influence of nerve impulses in protein metabolism in the liver probably is exerted through circulatory regulation.

NERVOUS REGULATION OF GALL BLADDER AND BILE DUCTS

The bile ducts and the gall bladder are provided with a muscular tunic The opening of the common duct into the duodenum is also guarded by a sphincteric mechanism, the so-called sphincter of Oddi. This system is innervated through both visceral afferent and autonomic nerves. Afferent nerve fibers reach the biliary tract through both the splanchnic and the vagus nerves. Distention of the gall bladder and the bile ducts elicits pain which is abolished by section of the splanchnic nerves, particularly the right, nausea and vomiting which are abolished by vagus section, and respiratory disturbances which are diminished by section of either the splanchnic or the vagus nerves. These findings have been corroborated by experimental data and by the use of spinal anesthesia in operations involving the gall bladder and the bile ducts in man. In a clinical study reported by Bergh and Layne (1940), the intense pain caused by suddenly distending the common bile duct could be correlated only with spasm of the sphincter of Oddi.

Both the vagi and the splanchnic nerves convey both motor and inhibitory fibers to the gall bladder but the vagi are predominantly motor and the splanchnic nerves are predominantly inhibitory. In experiments on guinea-pigs reported by Westphal (1923), vagus stimulation elicited contraction of the gall bladder and relaxation of the sphincter, resulting in the discharge of bile into the duodenum, and splanchnic stimulation inhibited the rhythmic contractions of the gall bladder and peristalsis of the bile ducts and caused contraction of the sphincter. The effects on the gall bladder and the bile ducts of vagus and of splanchnic nerve stimulation are exerted predominantly through the nerves on the right side (Poilleux *et al.*, 1952). Certain experimental data support the assumption that the resistance to the flow of bile into the intestine is due to the tonicity of the duodenum rather than to contraction of the sphincter of Oddi, but contraction of the sphincter may be a factor in the filling of the gall bladder.

Lueth (1931) confirmed the claim of Oddi (1894) that the sphincter has an independent nervous control, but pointed out that, although it may act independently, it is functionally coördinated with the mechanisms concerned with duodenal peristalsis and tonus. Changes in the tonicity of the sphincter of Oddi in human subjects that seem to be entirely independent of changes in the activity or the tonicity of the duodenal musculature have been demonstrated. In many instances contraction of the sphincter is accompanied by contractions of the duodenum, but the latter frequently do not affect the patency of the sphincter, *i.e.*, sphincter and duodenal tonus frequently are independent of one another. Independent activity of the sphincter of Oddi and the duodenum has also been observed during contractions of the duodenum produced by various drugs. In human subjects sphincter resistance is increased by coughing, nausea and defecation. In cats and dogs spasm of the sphincter of Oddi is abolished following vagotomy and celiac ganglionectomy, but not following thoracolumbar sympathetic trunk extirpation and splanchnicectomy (Singleton *et al.*, 1952).

In a series of experiments reported by Birch and Boyden (1930), faradic stimulation of the pyloric portion of the stomach elicited contraction of the relaxed gall bladder. Faradic stimulation of the stomach, the pylorus, the small intestine or the cecum, while the gall bladder was emptying after a meal of egg yolk, temporarily inhibited the discharge of bile. They also observed rhythmic contractions of the gall bladder which took place synchronously with the hunger contractions of the stomach. Such contractions of the gall bladder coördinated with the hunger contractions of the stomach probably account for the periodic emptying of the gall bladder during fasting. The results of these experiments demonstrate the existence of reflex pathways between the gastro-intestinal tract and the gall bladder. They also support the theory that dysfunction of the gall bladder or biliary stasis, at least in some instances, may be due to inhibitory reflexes from chronically diseased portions of the digestive tube. Du Bois and Kistler (1933) reported marked contractions of the gall bladder in response to faradic stimulation of the viscus itself, the duodenal portion (ampulla) of the common bile duct and either vagus nerve in its cervical portion. When the common bile duct was severed stimulation of its duodenal portion no longer elicited contraction of the gall bladder, but contraction of the latter organ was elicited by stimulation of the hepatic end of the severed bile duct. These findings have been interpreted as evidence of the existence of a direct reflex pathway from the ampulla to the gall bladder along the wall of the bile duct, but not as indicating that all reflex responses of the gall bladder to stimulation at the duodenal end of the bile duct are mediated through this pathway. Responses of the gall bladder to stimulation in this area, like those to stimulation in other parts of the gastro-intestinal tract, may be mediated through less direct reflex mechanisms.

In experiments on cats reported by Johnson and Boyden (1943), interruption of the nerve fibers which reach the choledochoduodenal junction via the gastroduodenal plexus did not alter the rate of emptying of the bile passages following ingestion of food or abolish the inhibitory reflex from the cecum to the gall bladder. The efferent fibers in this plexus presumably are mainly vasomotor. Interruption of the gastroduodenal nerve resulted in marked retardation of the bile flow. Section of the right vagus resulted in even greater retardation of flow. This observation supports the assumption that the right vagus not only sends inhibitory fibers to the sphincter of Oddi through the gastroduodenal nerve but also motor fibers to the gall bladder through the hepatic plexus. Interruption of the left vagus, which plays no part in the innervation of the sphincter of Oddi, resulted in retardation of emptying of the gall bladder but in a lesser degree. Section of the splanchnic roots of the celiac ganglia abolished the inhibitory reflex from the cecum to the gall bladder and resulted in acceleration of emptying of the gall bladder in some degree.

On the basis of their experimental results, Johnson and Boyden advanced the opinion that the gastroduodenal nerve conveys no sympathetic fibers involved in maintaining the tonus of the sphincter of Oddi and suggested that the biliary outlet may be kept closed during fasting by the activity of the intrinsic neural mechanisms and that after meals the tonic contraction of the sphincter may be overcome by the inhibitory influence of the right vagus and by hormones produced in the intestinal mucosa. They also pointed out that the reciprocal relationship between gall bladder and sphincter is not obligatory, since each responds to appropriate stimulation when the nerve to the other is interrupted.

Influences emanating from the central nervous system, under certain conditions, profoundly affect the biliary system. Strong emotional disturbances, *e.g.*, rage or fright, may give rise to temporary icterus, probably due in part to biliary stasis caused by closure of the common bile duct either by increased tonicity of the duodenum or contraction of the sphincter of Oddi or both. Under these conditions bile is absorbed into the blood with resulting icterus. The efferent pathways concerned in this reaction are chiefly vagus. Conversely, disturbances of the biliary system, especially gall bladder disease, may give rise to afferent impulses that result in reflex vomiting, tachycardia, regional pruritus, perspiration, dyspnea, salivation or inhibition of salivary secretion, and pupillary disturbances. Such disturbances also result in changes in the content of choline and choline-like substances in the blood that profoundly affect the functional balance of the autonomic nervous system.

The data cited above support the assumptions that the biliary tract is subject to direct and reflex regulation through its nerve supply and that evacuation of the gall bladder is accomplished, under physiological conditions, by contraction of its intrinsic musculature. Data which apparently do not support these assumptions are not wanting, but their consideration in this connection could serve no useful purpose. The assumption that the fatty constituents of the food play a major rôle in the reflex regulation of the flow of bile from the gall bladder is also amply supported by both experimental and clinical data.

In unanesthetized dogs, Snape (1948) recognized two phases of contraction of the gall bladder both before and after section of the vagus nerves. The first phase is neurogenic. The second phase is humoral. The effect of cholecystokinin administered intravenously appears to be independent of the parasympathetic nerves. In the presence of cream in the duodenum the latent period tends to be prolonged following section of the nerves to the gall bladder.

Boyden (1925) reported experiments in which cats fed a diet of egg yolk and heavy cream immediately exhibited a functional periodicity of the gall bladder in relation to meals, and cats fed a pure protein and carbohydrate diet showed no marked volume changes in the gall bladder. Boyden also demonstrated the effectiveness of fatty food, particularly egg yolk and cream, in evacuating the gall bladder in man. One hour and forty minutes after the beginning of a meal consisting of the yolks of four eggs and a pint of cream, cholecystograms showed that the gall bladder had undergone a reduction in volume from the fully distended condition, due to going without food for eighteen hours, to a condition in which it was nearly empty. One hour later evacuation was apparently complete. By means of roentgen-ray examination of patients, Boyden (1928) found that the time required for complete evacuation of the gall bladder after the ingestion of egg yolk or cream varies from sixteen minutes to four and one-half hours. The first phase of the contraction usually discharged three-quarters of the contents within thirty-two minutes after the meal. In patients who had undergone surgical removal of the gall bladder, as reported by Bergh (1942), a meal consisting of egg yolk and cream produced relaxation of the sphincter of Oddi, but fresh olive oil produced no appreciable effect. Relaxation of the sphincter was observed occasionally following a protein meal.

Carbohydrate meals produced no significant effects on the sphincter resistance.

As reported by Boyden and Birch (1930), the yolk of one egg injected into the duodenum in man elicited a single phase of contraction of the gall bladder which evacuated three-quarters of its contents. Bile could be aspirated from the duodenum seven to fifteen minutes after the injection of the yolk. Injection of a strong solution of $MgSO_4$, $MgCl_2$ or Na_2SO_4 elicited evacuation of two-thirds of the contents of the gall bladder and the bile could be aspirated from the duodenum in the same time as following the injection of egg yolk. When given by mouth, these salts are nearly as effective as when injected into the duodenum through a Rehfuss tube. Solutions of $NaCl$, Na_2CO_3 or Na_2PO_4 introduced into the duodenum elicit temporary relaxation and filling of the gall bladder. Alternating changes in the hydrogen-ion concentration of the duodenal content seem to have no appreciable effect on the tonus of the gall bladder. Injection of liquid petrolatum into the duodenum causes initial inhibition of the gall bladder and retards its response to food injected subsequently. The latter effect probably is due to the local action of the petrolatum in closing the sphincter.

In man, as observed by Boyden *et al.* (1943), the gall gladder and the sphincter of Oddi react to egg yolk and to $MgSO_4$ introduced into the duodenum in the same manner and for the same length of time, but not in the same degree. Egg yolk is more effective than $MgSO_4$, probably due to its more rapid rate of absorption and its stronger chemical action. They have suggested that both these substances stimulate the production of hormones which act directly on both the gall bladder and the sphincter of Oddi and that these end organs react differently to a given stimulus. The initial response to either egg yolk or $MgSO_4$ usually is contraction of the sphincter, which in turn may interrupt the contraction of gall bladder that was initiated somewhat later, thus producing a pause. After four or five minutes, a phase of progressive relaxation of the sphincter is initiated which continues for an average period of seventeen minutes. During this interval, the main contraction phase of the gall bladder is initiated which continues for an average period of thirty minutes. On the basis of evidence obtained in animal experiments, they have advanced the opinion that the hormone acts upon the sphincter for a shorter time than upon the gall bladder because during fasting the tonus of the sphincter is maintained by the local neural mechanism which has a threshold of stimulation higher than that of the gall bladder.

In a study of 115 individuals ranging from 6 to 78 years of age, Boyden and Grantham (1936) found that the gall bladder evacuation occurs more rapidly in children than in young adults. Before puberty it occurs more rapidly in males than in females. After puberty it occurs more rapidly in females than in males. If the biliary tract escapes pathological alterations the rate of evacuation of the gall bladder is not retarded in advanced age. It is slightly increased in patients with carcinoma of the stomach (Ritchie and Boyden, 1937) and markedly increased in patients with peptic ulcer (Boyden and Berman, 1937).

Chapter XII

INNERVATION OF THE PANCREAS, SPLEEN, THYROID, ADRENALS AND BONE MARROW

THE PANCREAS

Extrinsic Nerves.—The innervation of the pancreas is derived from the celiac plexus chiefly through the hepatic, the superior mesenteric and the splenic plexuses. Rami that arise from these plexuses give rise to plexuses on the splenic and the pancreatico-duodenal artery (Fig. 61). Most of the innervation of the pancreas is derived through the pancreatico-duodenal plexus. Isolated rami from the celiac plexus enter the pancreas directly without traversing the plexuses on the blood vessels. According to Mallet-Guy *et al.* (1952), only the left splanchnic nerves convey preganglionic sympathetic fibers concerned in the innervation of the pancreas.

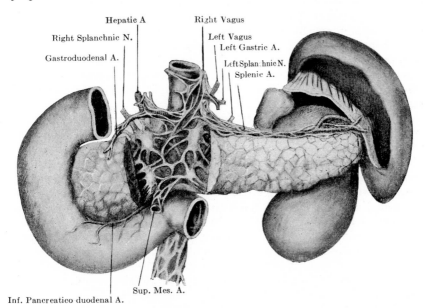

Hepatic A
Right Vagus
Right Splanchnic N.
Left Vagus
Left Gastric A.
Gastroduodenal A.
Left Splanchnic N.
Splenic A.
Inf. Pancreatico duodenal A.
Sup. Mes. A.

FIG. 61.—Diagrammatic illustration of the innervation of the pancreas and the spleen. (Modified from Greving.)

The nerves of the pancreas include sympathetic, parasympathetic and afferent fibers. In the cat, as reported by Richins (1945), the nerves along the pancreatico-duodenal artery are made up of myelinated and unmyelinated fibers in the ratio of approximately 1 to 19. The myelinated ones

(255)

include preganglionic parasympathetic and afferent fibers. Most of the unmyelinated ones are sympathetic. Most of the ganglia concerned in the parasympathetic pathways are located within the gland. On the basis of an analysis of the nerves of the pancreas by means of degenerative section of the splanchnic and the vagus nerves and extirpation of the celiac ganglia, Richins advanced the conclusions that the afferent innervation of the gland is derived solely through the splanchnic nerves and that the preganglionic fibers that extend beyond the celiac plexus are chiefly of vagus origin.

Intrinsic Nerves.—Most of the nerve fibers within the pancreas are unmyelinated. As the nerves enter the gland they are closely associated with the blood vessels. The efferent vagus nerve fibers terminate in minute ganglia most of which are located in the interlobular septa. The fibers that arise in these ganglia, which are parasympathetic, are distributed to the acinar and the islet cells and to the duct system. The sympathetic fibers are distributed to the blood vessels and probably to the distal portions of the ducts. On the basis of a study of preparations in which the nerves were intact and preparations in which the sympathetic and the afferent nerve fibers had undergone degeneration, Richins concluded that the acinar and the islet cells are innervated directly only through parasympathetic nerves and that the efferent innervation of the blood vessels of the pancreas is solely sympathetic.

Receptors of several morphological types occur in the pancreas. Pacinian corpuscles are particularly abundant in this organ in the cat. They also occur commonly in the pancreas in man. Most of them are located in relation to the blood vessels and the serosa, but some also occur in the parenchymatous tissue. Receptors of other types, particularly unencapsulated fiber terminations, have also been observed in the pancreas in man and in animals.

Regulation of Pancreatic Secretion.—The secretory activity of the pancreas is regulated in part through the nerves and in part through hormonal mechanisms. Effects of vagus nerve stimulation on the secretory activity of the pancreas have been amply demonstrated. The vagus nerve influence is apparent both in the rate of secretion and in the percentage of the solid contents of the pancreatic juice (Babkin and Sawitsch, 1908). Some of the pertinent data seem to support the hypothesis that vagus stimulation augments the action of other stimuli such as secretin. The vagus influence in pancreatic secretion, however, has been demonstrated in the absence of the secretin mechanism. The usual effect of parasympathetic stimulation is activation of both the exocrine and the endocrine secretory cells, but inhibitory effects on the exocrine secretory activity have been demonstrated. The parasympathetic fibers that mediate inhibition of secretion probably are adrenergic.

Certain experimental data have been interpreted as supporting the hypothesis that splanchnic nerve stimulation exerts a direct effect on the secretory activity of the acinar cells. In the absence of conclusive evidence of direct sympathetic innervation of these cells, the alterations in their secretory activity due to sympathetic nerve stimulation must be explained on the basis of alterations in the flow of blood through the gland. Section of the splanchnic nerves alone results in no appreciable alteration in pancreatic function. In general, reduction in the flow of blood through the pancreas is accompanied by a decrease in the flow of pancreatic juice, and an increase in the flow of blood is accompanied by an increase in the pancreatic output.

By the use of the rapid freezing-drying technic to demonstrate the condition of the vascular bed in the pancreas of the cat produced by direct stimulation of the celiac plexus after section of the splanchnic nerves, Richins (1950) found that when the adrenergic conduction pathways were blocked the arterioles were dilated and the capillary bed contained a large amount of blood, and when the cholinergic pathways were blocked the arterioles were constricted and the capillary bed contained a relatively small amount of blood, but the arteriovenous shunts located primarily in the interlobular septa were open. Most of the blood apparently passed through these channels during adrenergic stimulation. Distention of a segment of the small intestine elicited complete reflex ischemia of the capillary bed in the pancreas. Since the splanchnic nerves were interrupted, the reflexes concerned must have been carried out through local reflex mechanisms, probably with synapses in the celiac ganglia. The existence of reflex pathways from the intestine to the pancreas that do not traverse the central nervous system has been demonstrated (Kuntz and Richins, 1949). The observed alterations in pancreatic function caused by sympathetic nerve stimulation probably can be explained satisfactorily by effects on the secretory cells of variations in the blood supply.

The possible rôle of local reflex mechanisms in the regulation of the pancreatic secretory activity has been suggested particularly by Popielski (1901) and more recently by Crider and Thomas (1944). As indicated above, reflex pathways from the intestine to the vascular bed in the pancreas that include synaptic connections in the celiac ganglia have been demonstrated. Local reflex mechanisms directly concerned in the regulation of pancreatic secretory activity would involve neurons in the enteric plexuses and neurons in the intrinsic ganglia of the pancreas. Such reflex arcs have not been actually demonstrated, but their existence is strongly suggested. If they exist, the extrinsic nerves, as has been pointed out by Thomas (1948), could be considered not only as pathways for reflexes carried out through centers in the central nervous system but also as association pathways to facilitate or inhibit local reflexes. The cephalic phase of pancreatic secretion undoubtedly is mediated in part through long reflex arcs. The intestinal phase probably is facilitated through local reflex activity that is influenced through the vagus nerves.

THE SPLEEN

Extrinsic Nerves.—The major portion of the innervation of the spleen is derived from the celiac plexus. The left phrenic nerve may contribute in some degree. In man the extrinsic nerves approach the spleen mainly through the plexus on the splenic artery (Fig. 61). In some mammals, *e.g.*, the cat, they accompany the several splenic arteries. The preganglionic splanchnic fibers are components of the sixth to the eighth thoracic nerves. The results of degeneration studies of the splenic nerves carried out on the cat, as reported by Utterback (1944), afford no evidence that parasympathetic nerves play a part in the innervation of the spleen. Section of the vagi, in his experiments, resulted in no change in the numbers of myelinated or unmyelinated fibers in the splenic nerves. Extirpation of the celiac and the superior mesenteric ganglia resulted in complete degeneration of all the nerves that enter the spleen. Most of the afferent fibers in the splenic nerves are splanchnic nerve components. Counts of the splenic nerve fibers in the cat, made by Utterback, indicate an average of approximately 2000 unmyelinated ones and an average of approximately 110 myelinated ones, a ratio of approximately 20 to 1. Thus, the spleen is supplied with relatively few afferent nerve fibers.

Intrinsic Nerves.—In man the nerves enter the spleen mainly through the hilus. Most of the rami continue into the organ along the arteries. A few ramify in the capsule and give rise to a relatively meager subserous plexus. Within the spleen, every nerve, like the vessel which it accompanies, supplies a circumscribed portion of the gland, but there is some overlapping of the terminal branches of adjacent nerves. The spleen is divided into a number of zones that correspond to the ultimate branches of the splenic nerves. These zones represent neural and arterial units. The venomotor nerves are also distributed to localized parts of the splenic veins. The intrinsic splenic nerves are composed chiefly of unmyelinated sympathetic fibers, but they include visceral afferents most of which are myelinated. The efferent fibers are distributed to the splenic blood vessels and the smooth muscle in the splenic capsule and the trabeculæ. As the nerves advance into the trabeculæ, they break up into very delicate strands which in general run parallel to the bundles of smooth muscle fibers. The muscle in the smallest trabeculæ seems to be supplied most abundantly.

As the arterial branches enter the pulp they are accompanied by slender bundles of nerve fibers that branch according to the branching of the arteries and continue along the smaller arteries, including the arterioles. Some nerve fibers also accompany the tributaries of the trabecular veins. Strands of just a few fibers and in some instances individual fibers may be observed adjacent to the inlets and the outlets of the sinusoidal spaces in the red pulp where they terminate in relation to contractile cells in the walls of these vessels (Utterback, 1944). These fibers undoubtedly innervate the sphincter mechanisms associated with the sinuses.

Regulation of Splenic Volume Changes and Blood Flow.—Contraction of the spleen in response to sympathetic stimulation is a common phenomenon. The initial phase of this contraction is accompanied by blanching of the organ. This is followed by the appearance of lobulation and rounding off of the angles at the margins. Stimulation of the peripheral portion of the divided vagus nerve elicits no apparent reaction in the spleen, but stimulation of the proximal portion results in reflex splenic contraction. The vagus nerves apparently exert no direct influence on the spleen. Physiological dilatation of the spleen probably is brought about by impulses conducted through the venomotor fibers. In the experiments of Cleland and Tait (1927), electrical stimulation of these fibers resulted in engorgement of the spleen corresponding in degree and in duration to the contraction of the splenic vein. Section of these fibers abolished reflex dilatation, and the spleen remained in a state of partial contraction following their degeneration.

Spontaneous rhythmic contractions of the spleen have been observed repeatedly. In the cat, according to Barcroft *et al.* (1932), the periodicity of these contractions varies between 25 and 83 seconds, but it usually falls between 25 and 50 seconds. These rhythmic contractions are accompanied by undulatory waves of blood pressure with a corresponding rhythmicity that are related both to the amplitude and the frequency of the splenic contractions, but they also vary with the general blood pressure. Under given conditions, the blood pressure changes are proportional not only to the splenic volume changes but also to the volume changes in the circulating blood.

A sudden rise in the general blood pressure produces an initial passive dilatation of the spleen that is followed by rhythmic splenic contractions, but a sudden fall in the general blood pressure produces only a passive contraction of the spleen. Nerve impulses obviously play no essential part in these reactions, since the same results are obtained both before and after denervation of the spleen and removal of the adrenals.

The volume of the blood circulating through the spleen is not related to the size of this organ but to the state of the blood vascular system as a whole. The rhythmic changes in splenic volume are not brought about by rhythmic contractions and relaxations of the splenic musculature, but by rhythmic variations in the blood flow. The waves of arterial blood flow and splenic volume correspond in period and are synchronous. The waves of venous flow correspond in period but lag about five seconds behind those of arterial flow and splenic volume. The blood flow and splenic volume manifestations of splenic rhythm are not abolished or disturbed by denervation of the spleen. The cause of the rhythmic waves of blood flow through the spleen, therefore, appears to be independent of the splenic musculature (Grindlay *et al.*, 1939).

Restoration of the splenic circulation after its temporary stoppage also initiates rhythmic contractions of the spleen with or without an intact nerve supply. Various other means may also be employed to produce rhythmic splenic contractions. For example, the injection of curare causes an initial fall in blood pressure and an increase in splenic volume followed by rhythmic splenic contractions. The injection of histamine causes an initial fall in blood pressure and a decrease in splenic volume followed by rhythmic splenic contractions. The injection of a hemoglobin solution causes a remarkable splenic rhythm that is characterized by a gradual increase in the amplitude of the contractions.

Barcroft (1932) reported the results of certain experiments in which necrosis of the skin, caused either by friction or high temperature, was accompanied by contraction of the spleen both in intact animals and in animals in which the spleen had been denervated. He also reported that estrus, pregnancy and lactation are accompanied by contractions of the spleen. The splenic contractions associated with estrus and pregnancy are abolished by denervation of the spleen. Those associated with lactation are not abolished by splenic denervation. These phenomena, according to Barcroft, indicate a large humoral element in the causation of the contractions in the former conditions, whereas in the latter conditions the splenic contractions are elicited by nerve impulses.

In an experimental study of the behavior of the spleen in the dog in hemorrhagic hypotension and shock, Lewis *et al.* (1943) obtained data which support the assumption that splenic contraction does not contribute to the elevation and maintenance of arterial blood pressure by increasing the resistance in the splenic shunt, but by its augmenting effect on venous return and cardiac output. They advanced the opinion that the spleen does not withold blood from active circulation in conditions of shock due to hemorrhage; consequently, if this organ is found large and congested at autopsy, other factors must have been operative.

THE THYROID GLAND

Extrinsic nerves.—Nerves of both sympathetic and parasympathetic origin extend into the thyroid gland (Fig. 62). In man most of the sympathetic nerves in question arise from the middle cervical ganglion or the middle cervical portion of the sympathetic trunk. Some fibers arise in other cervical sympathetic ganglia, particularly the superior cervical. Most of the fibers of vagus origin that enter the thyroid gland traverse the superior laryngeal nerve. Others are incorporated in the inferior laryngeal nerve. Some rami enter the thyroid directly from the sympathetic trunks, the common carotid, the subclavian and the tracheal plexuses, the glossopharyngeal nerve and the ansa hypoglossi. Some of the sympathetic rami and the nerves of vagus origin that reach the thyroid also include afferent fibers. As the extrinsic nerves approach the thyroid gland most of the rami accompany the superior thyroid artery without becoming intimately incorporated in a plexus.

Intrinsic Nerves.—Within the thyroid gland the nerves in general accompany the branches of the thyroid arteries. Some rami run independently among the thyroid follicles. Most of the nerve fibers are unmyelinated, but the larger rami include both large and medium-sized myelinated fibers. Aggregates of autonomic ganglion cells in the superior laryngeal nerve and within the thyroid gland have been reported. Nonidez (1931) also reported the occurrence of scattered neurons in the thyroid of the dog which he regarded as sensory ganglion cells that became displaced from the nodose ganglion of the vagus along the superior laryngeal nerve. He also recognized terminal arborizations in the arterial walls which he regarded as sensory, since they do not lie in contact with the smooth muscle of the media.

Most of the more recent investigators who have studied the distribution of the nerves within the thyroid gland have supported the theory that nerve fibers terminate both in the walls of the blood vessels and in relation to the thyroid follicles. Nonidez (1935) described an interfollicular plexus and nerve fibers ending freely among the follicles but failed to observe nerve fiber terminations in contact with follicular cells. In his preparations, most of the follicles were not in contact with fibers of the interfollicular plexus. His data do not indicate a direct innervation of the thyroid gland cells. The interfollicular fiber terminations are regarded as receptive. The innervation of the blood vessels in the thyroid is particularly abundant.

Regulation of Thyroid Function.—If the anatomical concept that the efferent nerves within the thyroid gland are distributed solely to the blood vessels be correct, direct influences of nerve impulses on thyroid secretory activity are precluded. Experimental data that have been interpreted as supporting the hypothesis that the thyroid cells are influenced directly

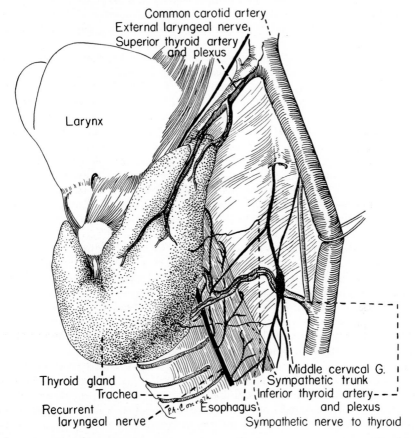

Common carotid artery
External laryngeal nerve,
Superior thyroid artery
and plexus

Larynx

Thyroid gland
Trachea
Recurrent
laryngeal nerve

Esophagus

Middle cervical G.
Sympathetic trunk
Inferior thyroid artery
and plexus
Sympathetic nerve to thyroid

Fig. 62.—Diagrammatic illustration of the extrinsic nerves related to the thyroid gland.

through secretory nerve fibers are not wanting, but they are not unequivocal. More convincing experimental data support the assumption that thyroid secretory activity is influenced through the neural regulation of the flow of blood through the gland. It is also influenced through hormonal mechanisms.

The vasoconstrictor action of the sympathetic nerves of the thyroid gland has been amply demonstrated. These nerves probably include vasodilator fibers. Reflex effects on the flow of blood through the thyroid of afferent vagus and of carotid sinus nerve stimulation have been demonstrated. These effects probably are related to changes in the systemic blood pressure. The threshold of stimulation by adrenin of the vasoconstrictor nerves in the thyroid appears to be definitely lower than that of those in the submandibular gland. This undoubtedly is significant in view of the synergistic action of adrenin and thyroxin.

The results of experiments carried out to determine whether the secretory thyroid cells undergo cytological changes due to nerve stimulation lack uniformity. Experimental studies carried out to determine the possible effect of nerve stimulation of the thyroglobulin content of the thyroid gland have yielded no significant data relative to the regulation of thyroid secretory activity.

The effect on thyroid function of the thyrotropic hormone produced in the anterior hypophyseal lobe is well known. Data reported by various investigators support the assumption that the effects on thyroid secretory activity caused by sympathetic nerve stimulation are exerted through the thyrotropic hormone which acts directly on the thyroid gland cells.

In experiments carried out on rabbits and guinea-pigs, Krayer (1933) observed the same effects of preparations of the anterior hypophyseal lobe on thyroid activity in normal animals and in animals which had been subjected to bilateral cervical sympathectomy. On the basis of the results obtained in experiments involving removal of the hypophysis and partial destruction of the tuber cinereum in puppies, Houssay et al. (1932) advanced the opinion that the hypophysis exerts a constant regulating action on the thyroid by which its normal functional condition is maintained. After hypophysectomy, according to their findings, the thyroid gland enters a transient phase of activity during which the iodine content of the blood is increased and that of the thyroid gland is diminished. This phase of thyroid activity also has been observed in dogs following lesions of the tuber cinereum. A permanent phase of hypothyroidism sets in later during which the iodine content of the thyroid increases and that of the blood diminishes and the basal metabolism is low. According to these investigators, hypothyroidism is etiologically related to hypophyseal insufficiency. The observations of Eitel et al. (1933) that the hypophyseal thyrotropic hormone induces hypertrophy and hyperplasia of thyroid tissue in blood serum cultures and the finding of Marine and Rosen (1934) that this hormone induces characteristic histological changes in autotransplanted bits of thyroid tissue are in complete accord with this point of view.

In experiments on guinea-pigs reported by Friedgood et al. (1940), the effect of the anterior hypophyseal hormone was significantly enhanced by combining either adrenin or pilocarpine with it in daily administrations. Their data seem to support the assumptions that the pilocarpine acts through the adrenal medulla and that adrenin increases the sensitivity of the thyroid cells to the thyrotropic hormone. They also concluded, on the basis of experimental data, that the administration of thyroid substance results in reduction of the functional activity of the animal's own thyroid via the mechanism through which the secretion of the thyroid hormone is normally regulated.

In view of all the data bearing on the regulatory control of the secretory activity of the thyroid gland, it is apparent that hormonal agents, particularly the anterior hypophyseal thyrotropic hormone, play a major rôle. Direct secretory effects of nerve impulses have not been demonstrated beyond question, but changes in the blood flow through the gland brought about through the vasomotor nerves and the neural regulation of the production of the hypophyseal thyrotropic hormone are not unimportant. The innervation of the thyroid obviously is not essential for continued thyroid secretory activity under ordinary conditions, but certain data emphasize the importance of the sympathetic nerves in the responses of the thyroid to certain situations.

THE PARATHYROID GLANDS

The nerves related to the parathyroid glands are derived from those associated with the vascular bed in the thyroid. The arteries that enter the parathyroids are invested with delicate nerve plexuses that are continuous with those on the arteries of which they are branches. These plexuses include both myelinated and unmyelinated fibers most of which probably are functionally related to the blood vessels. Some unmyelinated fibers deviate from the courses of the blood vessels and appear to terminate in relation to secretory cells. After degeneration of the sympathetic nerves, only a few myelinated fibers, probably afferent, remain intact in the parathyroid glands (Raybuck, 1952).

THE ADRENAL GLANDS

Extrinsic Nerves.—The innervation of the adrenal gland is derived chiefly from the celiac plexus through the adrenal plexus (Fig. 63). The latter plexus is continuous with the inferior phrenic plexus rostrally and with the renal plexus caudally. Its constituent fibers include components of the splanchnic, the vagus and the phrenic nerves and postganglionic axons arising in the celiac ganglia and lesser ganglia located in the adrenal plexus. Some splanchnic nerve fibers join the adrenal plexus or enter the gland directly without passing through the celiac plexus. Most of the preganglionic neurons concerned are located in the 8th to the 11th thoracic segments of the spinal cord. The available data indicate a wider range of distribution of these cells in the spinal cord in some mammalian species than in others. In the cat, as reported by Hollingshead (1936) and Swinyard (1937), some of the preganglionic fibers in question are derived from the rostral lumbar spinal cord segments. In the rat, as reported by Young (1939), preganglionic fibers concerned in the innervation of the adrenals emerge from the spinal cord from the 6th thoracic to the 2nd or the 3rd lumbar segments. Those concerned in the innervation of the adrenal medulla in the rat, according to Hillarp (1947), are derived almost exclusively from the 8th to the 11th thoracic segments, but most of them emerge in the 9th thoracic nerve. In the dog and the cat, according to Kiss (1951), the preganglionic fibers to the adrenal medulla traverse the ventral roots of the 7th, the 8th and the 9th thoracic nerves. The preganglionic and the afferent fibers concerned in the innervation of the adrenal cortex traverse the 9th, the 10th and the 11th thoracic nerves.

Intrinsic Nerves.—As the adrenal nerves approach the gland many fiber bundles enter the medulla through the hilum. Others traverse the adrenal capsule. Many of the fibers in the latter nerves sweep around the glomerular arches in the outer cortical zone and extend inward in the interfascicular septa. Some of them terminate in relation to blood vessels in the cortex. Others extend into the medulla without making terminal connections in the cortex. Since preganglionic fibers extend into the adrenal

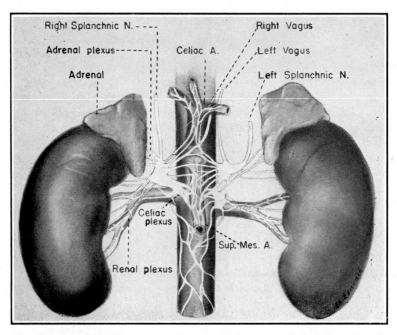

Fig. 63.—Diagrammatic illustration of the extrinsic innervation of the adrenals and the kidneys.

medulla, a high percentage of the nerve fibers within the gland are myelinated. The chromaffine tissue in the medulla is innervated directly through preganglionic fibers. The postganglionic fibers that enter the medulla are distributed to the vascular bed.

In experiments on rats reported by Young (1939), section of only some of the nerve roots through which preganglionic fibers reach the adrenal medulla resulted in localized nerve fiber degeneration in the medullary tissue. Section of the greater splanchnic nerve resulted in denervation of the rostral half of the medulla. As reported by MacFarland and Davenport (1941), section of this nerve at the diaphragm, in the rat, resulted in degeneration of 75 to 90 per cent of all the preganglionic fibers concerned in the innervation of the adrenal gland. Hillarp (1947) also failed to observe strictly localized nerve fiber degeneration in the adrenal medulla following section of the greater splanchnic nerve. In agreement with certain earlier investigators, he also observed ganglion cells in large numbers interspersed in the medulla, but he concluded that they probably are of no essential importance in the innervation of the gland.

Plexiform arrangements of nerve fibers in the several zones of the adrenal cortex have been described. Certain findings have also been interpreted as supporting the assumption that the cortical tissue is directly innervated. The results of most of the more recent investigations fail to support this point of view, but seem to warrant the conclusion that the cortical secretory cells are not directly innervated.

In view of the high percentages of nerve fiber degeneration in the adrenal glands caused by incomplete splanchnic nerve section, although the vasomotor fibers are postganglionic, the vagus or parasympathetic nerves can play no important part in adrenal innervation. Although vagus components apparently are present in the intrinsic nerves, the available anatomical data do not support the assumption that the intrinsic adrenal nerves include parasympathetic components.

Innervation of Paraganglia.—Irregular aggregates of chromaffine tissue, not incorporated in the adrenal glands, frequently occur in relation to the abdominal aorta and the segmental arteries arising from it. This tissue is innervated according to the same mode as the chromaffine tissue in the adrenal medulla. In the cat, the dog and the rabbit the abdominal aortic paraganglion is connected through strands of nerve fibers with the celiac, the adrenal and the inferior mesenteric plexuses. These nerves, like the slender rami connected with the minor paraganglia, are made up mainly of myelinated fibers most of which are preganglionic components of the splanchnic nerves that terminate in direct relation to the chromaffine cells (Hollingshead, 1940). The remaining fibers probably are afferent.

Regulation of Adrenal Functions.—The secretory cells of the adrenal cortex, as stated above, probably are not directly innervated. The cortical tissue is known to be capable of secretory activity following complete denervation of the gland. Its regulatory control probably is essentially hormonal.

The secretory activity of the medullary tissue is controlled in a large measure through its sympathetic innervation. Increased secretory activity of the adrenal medulla in response to splanchnic stimulation has been amply demonstrated. This response, furthermore, may be independent of changes in the flow of blood through the gland. According to Gley and Quinquad (1921), the discharge of adrenin due to splanchnic stimulation is responsible for the second phase in the blood pressure changes produced. The first phase is characterized by an immediate rise in blood pressure due to the direct vasomotor effect of the splanchnic impulses. The second is initiated a little later by the effect of an increased discharge of adrenin into the blood. This finding corroborated the results of certain experiments reported by Tournade and Chabrol (1919) in which an anastomosis was effected between the adrenal vein of a large dog and the jugular vein of a smaller one. Thus the adrenin produced by the gland of the large dog was introduced into the blood of the smaller one. On stimulation of the peripheral end of the splanchnic nerve of the large dog, blood pressure rose immediately in this animal and a little later in the smaller one. Inasmuch as the increased output of adrenin due to splanchnic stimulation could not change the adrenin content of the blood of the first animal, this result proves conclusively that the rise in blood pressure in this animal was due to the direct vasomotor effect of splanchnic stimulation. The rise in blood pressure which followed in the second animal was due to the increased adrenin content of the blood flowing into its jugular vein from the adrenal vein of the first, brought about by splanchnic stimulation. This represents the second phase in the effect of splanchnic stimulation on blood pressure and proves conclusively that the output of adrenin is increased on sympathetic stimulation of the adrenal gland.

Sympathetic stimulation through the splanchnic nerves commonly results in adrenal hyperemia and an increased outflow of blood from the gland. It may be assumed, therefore, that the sympathetic nerves of the adrenals include vasodilator fibers. Although splanchnic stimulation does not elicit vasoconstriction in the adrenals, it has been assumed by certain physiologists that the sympathetic innervation of this gland includes vasoconstrictor fibers, since the administration of adrenin results in vasoconstriction in the adrenals.

The secretion of adrenin may be influenced reflexly by stimulation of afferent nerves from various parts of the body. Somatic afferent stimulation commonly elicits increased medulliadrenal secretion. Afferent impulses conducted by either vagus nerve from the regions of the heart and the lungs inhibit this secretion, but afferent vagus impulses from the splanchnic area do not (Freeman and Phillips, 1931). The medulliadrenal mechanism is also influenced by impulses emanating from the central nervous system. Experimental data reported by Rogoff et al. (1946) indicate the existence of a central inhibitory mechanism, located approximately at the level of the optic chiasm, that influences medulliadrenal secretory activity. Removal of this influence, according to their findings, results in the output of adrenin at a rate that corresponds to the maximal rate of spontaneous medulliadrenal secretory activity than can be sustained through the physiological activity of the spinal cord center. Following mechanical destruction of this center by compression of the brain, afferent nerve stimulation failed to elicit augmentation of the output of adrenin.

Psychic disturbances or direct injury to the brain, like afferent nerve stimulation, may exhaust the adrenin supply. Section of the splanchnic nerves prevents this result. Certain experimental data also support the assumption that the medulliadrenal mechanism may be either stimulated or inhibited reflexly through a center located in the floor of the fourth ventricle. Puncture in this area which brings about hyperglycemia also affects adrenal secretion. Indeed, the changes in the sugar content of the blood are in part referable to the effect of modified medulliadrenal activity. Takahashi (1931) also reported activation of the medulliadrenal mechanism in the dog by injection of peptone, venesection or afferent nerve stimulation following transection of the spinal cord in the lower cervical region. The chemical mediator liberated in the adrenal glands by sympathetic stimulation, according to Feldberg et al. (1933), exhibits the properties of acetylcholine. According to their view, the secretion of adrenin is brought about by the direct action of this chemical mediator on the chromaffine cells.

THE BONE MARROW

Nerves that include both myelinated and unmyelinated fibers enter the marrow cavities with the nutrient vessels. Most of the unmyelinated fibers are distributed to the blood vessels. The myelinated ones undoubtedly are afferent. Within the marrow cavity, as observed by Kuntz and Richins (1945) in the humerus and the femur of the cat and the dog, most of the nerve fibers remain closely associated with the blood vessels. Some, chiefly myelinated ones, deviate from the perivascular plexuses and pursue courses, apparently independent of the blood vessels. Many of these fibers appear to be connected with delicate arborizing structures that probably represent receptors. The afferent nature of the myelinated fibers is indicated by their persistence after degeneration of the unmyelinated ones following sympathetic denervation of the limb. The sympathetic fibers appear to be distributed solely to the blood vessels. Most of the afferent fibers probably are functionally related to the blood vessels. Some appear to be connected with receptors that are imbedded in the parenchymatous tissue. Some probably are connected with receptors in the endosteum. Both afferent and sympathetic nerve fibers probably are concerned in the reflex vasomotor responses in the bone marrow.

The functional relationships of the vasomotor nerves in the bone marrow undoubtedly are comparable to those of other vasomotor nerves. Vasomotor regulation also exerts a regulatory influence on the hemopoietic and other activities of the bone marrow. Certain data also suggest a more direct functional relationship of the hemopoietic tissue to the autonomic nerves.

The assumption that the phagocytic activity of reticulo-endothelial cells in the bone marrow, like that of the corresponding cells in other organs, may be increased due to sympathetic stimulation is supported by experimental and clinical data. The hemopoietic activity of the bone marrow also appears to be subject to modification through sympathetic nerve stimulation. In experiments reported by Somogyi (1938), long continued administration of ergotamine in cats (0.2 mg. per kilo of body weight daily) inhibited blood regeneration following blood loss. Extirpation of the cervical portions of the sympathetic trunks without or including the stellate ganglia resulted in marked decreases in the numbers of erythrocytes and the percentage of hemoglobin and an increase in the number of leukocytes. Faradic stimulation of the cervical sympathetic trunks resulted in increases of 27 per cent in the number of erythrocytes and 23 per cent in the amount of hemoglobin. These responses could not be obtained in animals previously subjected to extirpation of the thyroid gland. In experiments on human subjects reported by Scheer (1940), smoking to the point of signs of intoxication was followed by an increase in the number of reticulocytes in the peripheral blood in most cases. Increased production of these cells was not indicated. The stimulus of nicotine apparently caused their discharge from the bone marrow in increased numbers. An increase in the number of leukocytes in the peripheral blood and of megakaryocytes in the bone marrow due to sympathetic paralysis has been reported by Kwerch and Leibetseder (1951). A significant influence of the autonomic nerves in hemopoiesis and in the regulation of the leukocyte count is also indicated by recent experimental and clinical data (Wachholder and Neuberg, 1950; Thalhammer and Janicek, 1951).

Chapter XIII

INNERVATION OF THE URINARY ORGANS

THE KIDNEY

Extrinsic Nerves.—The innervation of the kidney is derived chiefly through the renal plexus which extends from the celiac and the aortic plexuses to the hilum of the kidney along the renal artery and the renal vein. It is less intimately related to the renal vein than to the renal artery. Some of the nerve fiber bundles are imbedded in the adventitial layers of these vessels. Most of the fibers are derived directly from the celiac ganglia and the aortic plexus. It is also joined by the least splanchnic nerve and by communicating branches from the adrenal plexus. In some instances, at least one branch of the lesser splanchnic nerve also joins the renal plexus directly. It also receives fibers through one or more slender rami from the lumbar portion of the sympathetic trunk and from the inter-mesenteric nerves. Direct vagus branches join the renal plexus in many cases. Such branches occur more commonly on the right side than on the left. Most of the vagus fibers in the renal supply traverse the celiac plexus. Preganglionic fibers concerned with the innervation of the kidney are present in all the splanchnic nerves. The afferent fibers are mainly components of the tenth, the eleventh and the twelfth thoracic nerves (Fig. 64). Mitchell (1950) traced some fibers from the superior hypogastric plexus into the renal plexus. They probably are distributed to the renal pelvis and the rostral portion of the ureter.

The renal plexus shows a wide range of variation in the configuration of its nerve fiber bundles. It includes a variable number of ganglia some of which can only be detected microscopically. The aortico-renal ganglion commonly is located near the origin of the renal artery. It usually is connected with the celiac ganglion through one or more slender rami, and with the superior mesenteric ganglion. The dorsal renal ganglion, located dorsal to the renal artery, appears to be the most constant one in the renal plexus in man (Mitchell, 1950). It usually is connected with the celiac ganglion and receives a ramus from the lesser splanchnic nerve. In some instances it also receives rami from the least splanchnic nerve and from the rostral lumbar sympathetic trunk ganglia. A ganglion located ventral to the renal artery, the ventral renal ganglion, is present in some instances. Minute ganglia located at nodal points and groups of ganglion cells imbedded in bundles of nerve fibers may occur in any part of the renal plexus.

The occurrence of ganglia in the renal plexus is consistent with the conclusion that it includes both preganglionic and postganglionic fibers. The postganglionic fibers are derived in part from the celiac and the aortico-renal ganglia and in part from ganglia in the plexus. Nerve fibers of vagus origin have been traced into the renal plexus by various investigators. The preganglionic vagal fibers probably are concerned with the parasympathetic innervation of the smooth muscle in the renal pelvis and the ureter. Parasympathetic nerve fibers probably do not extend into the renal parenchyma. The preganglionic sympathetic fibers traverse the splanchnic nerves. Some of them pass through the celiac plexus. Others join the renal plexus directly. Afferent fibers both of spinal and of the vagus nerves traverse the renal plexus.

Intrinsic Nerves.—The nerves that enter the kidney from the renal plexus accompany the renal artery and its branches around which they form plexuses. The intrinsic nerve plexuses commonly divide at the bifurcations of the arteries and continue along even the smaller arterial branches. In favorable microscopic preparations, nerve fibers may be observed in relation to arterioles and capillaries. Afferent nerve fiber terminations have also been described in the kidney, particularly in the musculature of the renal pelvis, the adventitia of the renal vessels and the renal capsule.

Most of the nerve fibers in the parenchyma are unmyelinated and of small caliber. Some small myelinated nerve fibers occur in the renal parenchyma. Myelinated fibers are more abundant in the region of the renal calyces and in the renal pelvis. The renal calyces are also richly supplied with unmyelinated nerve fibers that terminate in relation to the musculature, including the smooth muscle fibers in the renal calyces above the sphincter papillæ. The early investigators quite generally supported the assumption that the renal tubules are directly innervated, even though unmistakable nerve fiber terminations in contact with parenchymal cells had not been demonstrated. Certain data reported by Szabo (1948), Knoche (1950) and Mitchell (1951) have also been interpreted as supporting this assumption. The opposite point of view has been supported by Christensen *et al.* (1951).

As observed by Christensen *et al.*, the nerves that enter the parenchyma of the kidney are distributed solely in relation to the blood vessels. From the slender rami associated with the interlobular arteries, strands of nerve fibers extend along the afferent arterioles to the juxtaglomerular bodies. In some instances nerve fibers can be traced from a strand associated with an afferent arteriole or its juxtaglomerular body along the surface of the glomerular capsule to the efferent arteriole. Some of the nerve fibers that enter a juxtaglomerular body apparently do not emerge from it. They probably are functionally related to endocrine cells. Nerve fiber terminations in the perivascular spaces adjacent to glomerular capsules, as described by Harman and Davis (1948), were not observed.

The nerves associated with the intrarenal blood vessels include some myelinated fibers which undoubtedly are afferent. The efferent fibers probably are solely sympathetic. Any parasympathetic fibers incorporated in the renal nerves probably terminate in relation to the smooth muscle in the renal pelvis and the ureter.

Regulation of Renal Functions.—**Function of the Renal Nerves.**—The assumption that the efferent components of the intrarenal nerves are essentially vasomotor is supported by ample physiological and experimental data. Splanchnic nerve stimulation results in constriction of the renal blood vessels with consequent diminution of the volume of blood flowing through the kidney and diminution in the output of urine. Section of the splanchnic nerves results in dilatation of the renal blood vessels with increased output of urine. It seems unnecessary, therefore, to assume the existence of renal secretory fibers in the splanchnic nerves.

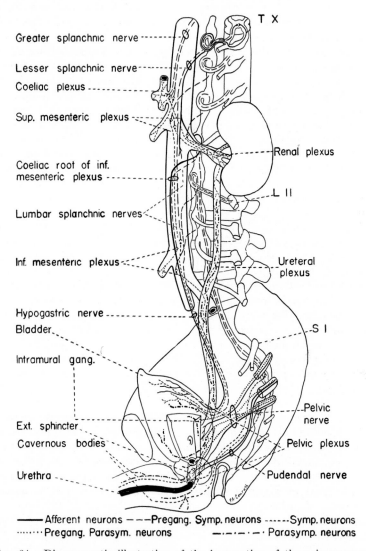

Greater splanchnic nerve

Lesser splanchnic nerve

Coeliac plexus

Sup. mesenteric plexus

Coeliac root of inf. mesenteric plexus

Lumbar splanchnic nerves

Inf. mesenteric plexus

Hypogastric nerve

Bladder

Intramural gang.

Ext. sphincter

Cavernous bodies

Urethra

T X

Renal plexus

L II

Ureteral plexus

S I

Pelvic nerve

Pelvic plexus

Pudendal nerve

——— Afferent neurons — — — Pregang. Symp. neurons - - - - - - Symp. neurons
········· Pregang. Parasym. neurons   —·—·—·—· Parasymp. neurons

Fig. 64.—Diagrammatic illustration of the innervation of the urinary organs.

Denervation of the kidneys is not incompatible with renal function. Excretion of urine may continue many months, perhaps indefinitely, after all connections of the kidney with the central nervous system have been divided. Kidneys removed from their normal positions and connected with another artery and another vein, and kidneys transplanted from one animal into another of the same species have continued to function. In experiments reported by Lobenhoffer (1913) the pedicle was severed and the kidney was transposed to the splenic vessels. On the basis of his results, he concluded that a kidney transposed in this manner is able to meet the ordinary demands of life. Zaaijer (1914) reported the case of a dog that lived six years following transposition of its single kidney to the iliac vessels. Carrel and Guthrie (1906) transplanted the kidneys of one dog into another. The dog with the transplanted kidneys lived many days after removal of its own kidneys. Dederer (1918) transposed the left kidney of a dog to the vessels of the neck and two weeks later removed the right kidney. The dog remained alive and well for more than four months after removal of the right kidney. Phenolsulphonphthalein was excreted rapidly by the transposed kidney and its output of urine was markedly increased following removal of the other kidney. In another experiment, Dederer (1920) homotransplanted a kidney and an ovary from one dog to another of the same litter. The dog with the transplanted kidney died of distemper twenty-six days later. Examination of the transplanted kidney showed that it reacted to the severe constitutional infection, distemper, in a manner similar to that of the animal's own organs. In this case, the transplanted kidney could have had no nerve connections, yet, although the animal had two kidneys of its own, phenolsulphonphthalein appeared in the urine of the transplanted kidney two minutes and forty seconds after its intravenous injection.

In an extensive series of experiments carried out on dogs, as reported by Quinby (1916), the kidney on one side was removed and then reimplanted by anastomosing the severed vessels and the ureter. In one series of animals the ureters were brought out through the flanks two days to three weeks after the primary operation, and the urines were collected and compared. In this series, the output of both liquid and salt by the reimplanted kidney was increased, and this increase persisted ten to fourteen days. On the normal side, the flow of urine was temporarily inhibited by handling the ureter. Such temporary inhibition was not apparent on the opposite side, but urine flowed from the denervated kidney as soon as the ureter was opened. In another series of animals, the normal kidney was removed five days to two weeks after the primary operation. The capacity of the single denervated kidney to eliminate following intravenous injection of normal salt solution, lactose solution and phenolsulphonphthalein was compared with that of a normal dog that had been subjected to unilateral nephrectomy. In a third series of animals (Quinby, 1915) the response of the denervated kidney to intravenous injection of hypertonic solutions of sodium chloride, urea and caffein was practically identical to that of the normal kidney.

Marshall and Kolls (1919–1920) found that the increased excretion of urine by the denervated kidney persisted for months after the operation, whereas Quinby had reported that it persisted for only ten days to two weeks. On the basis of their experimental results, they concluded that the changes noted in the secretory activity of the denervated kidney were due solely to vasodilatation with the consequent increased flow of blood through the organ. When the renal artery was constricted by artificial means, after denervation of the kidney, the output of urine was correspondingly reduced. They also found that when the denervated kidney was secreting much more urine than the normal kidney the normal ratio could be reëstablished by paralyzing the splanchnic nerves on the normal side. Additional evidence that denervation of both kidneys, as far as this is possible by cutting all the visible fibers of the renal plexus, produces no untoward results and that the animal may continue to live in good health for an indefinite period has been advanced by various investigators.

In experiments reported by Grabfield and Swanson (1939), in which sodium chloride was added to the diet of dogs that had been subjected to denervation of one kidney, the excretion of the salt by both kidneys occurred more promptly than in normal dogs. They interpreted this result as indicating a coördinating mechanism of humoral nature affecting both kidneys which probably is associated with the renal nerves.

In a study of renal circulation and secretion in dogs, with special reference to the effect of extracts of the posterior hypophyseal lobe, Handovsky and Samaan (1937) found that the renal blood flow is constant within narrow limits in the resting animal and is diminished for a brief period when the animal is disturbed. Diuresis produced by administration of water was preceded by an increase in renal circulation which was independent of nerve impulses and unrelated to changes in systemic blood pressure. Unilateral section of the splanchnic nerves resulted in increased renal circulation and secretion in the affected kidney. Administration of adrenin caused a decrease in renal circulation and secretion, depending on the dosage, but the output of urine returned to the normal level in 10 to 20 minutes. The effect of adrenin was more pronounced after ingestion of water. In conscious dogs with water diuresis the administration of posterior hypophyseal extract resulted in a decrease in the output of urine although the renal blood flow remained almost constant. Large doses produced a marked antidiuretic effect in unanesthetized animals. In anesthetized animals large doses produced a diuretic effect. In both instances renal circulation showed an initial reduction followed by a prolonged increase.

Experimental data that have been interpreted as demonstrating an ininfluence in renal function of impulses conducted by the vagus nerves are not wanting, but they are not unequivocal. In view of the inconclusive nature of these data, and the lack of evidence that the intrarenal nerves include parasympathetic fibers, no attempt will be made to evaluate them in this connection.

In experiments reported by Kusakari (1930), in which the rate at which phenolsulphonphthalein previously injected was excreted by the kidneys was determined, it was found that both water and the drug were excreted in equal quantities by both kidneys while the nerves were intact. Following section of one splanchnic nerve, the output or urine by the kidney on the corresponding side was increased, but the rate at which the drug was excreted remained practically unaltered. This result was interpreted as indicating an influence of splanchnic impulses on the resorptive activity of the renal tubules. The effect of caffein on the renal functions, in Kusakari's experiments, was not appreciably influenced by section of either the

18

vagus or the splanchnic nerves. This drug apparently inhibits resorption by its direct action on the cells of the renal tubules.

In experiments reported by Müller *et al.* (1930) the normally innervated kidneys of the dog gave no evidence of damage for about thirty minutes following heavy injections of Bacillus coli, but, with the onset of a chill, albumin, red blood cells and bacteria appeared in the urine very promptly. In animals with one kidney previously denervated, this kidney continued to excrete normal urine after the injection of the bacteria in spite of the chill, but, with the onset of the chill, the urine from the normally innervated kidney promptly showed the presence of albumin, red blood cells and bacteria in large quantities.

Water-diuresis of a rapid type, dependent on the integrity of the sympathetic innervation of the kidneys and the adrenals, and an inhibitory effect of increased sympathetic activity during emotional stress on the release of antidiuretic substance from the posterior pituitary lobe have been recognized by O'Connor and Verney (1945). In their experiments, faradic stimulation of the splanchnic nerves for 30 to 60 seconds during water-diuresis in normal dogs revealed rapid inhibition of the flow of urine, that was abolished by section of the splanchnic nerves and denervation of the kidneys and the adrenals, and slow inhibition due to the release of antidiuretic substance from the posterior pituitary lobe. The slow inhibition was effectively prevented by the injection of adrenin just before the faradic stimulation was applied. The inhibition produced by the injection of the extract on the posterior lobe of the pituitary was not abolished by the injection of adrenin. The results reported support the assumption that the absence of slow inhibition of water-diuresis during emotional stress following the injection of adrenin, in animals with denervated kidneys and adrenals, is due to failure of the release of antidiuretic substance and not to failure of the released hormone to act on the kidneys. The irregular occurrence of slow inhibition of the flow of urine during emotional stress in normal dogs appears to be due to failure of the release of antidiuretic substance caused by increased sympathetic activity.

Closing of nephrons and constriction of renal blood vessels sufficient to cause temporary cessation of blood flow in the dog's kidney due to direct stimulation of the renal nerves has been reported by Houck (1951). Block *et al.* (1952) reported complete cessation of the flow of blood through the kidney for a few minutes due to direct electrical stimulation of the renal nerves. The vasoconstriction was limited to the cortex, including the juxtamedullary zone, but significant shunting of blood from the cortex to the medulla was not observed. Prolonged anuria or oliguria does not appear to be due to vasoconstriction mediated by the renal nerves. Cortical ischemia of the cat's kidney elicited by electrical stimulation of foci in the anterior sigmoid gyrus of the brain has been reported by Hoff *et al.* (1951). This reaction was abolished by denervation of the kidney. The ability of the dog's kidney to excrete sodium and chloride during loading with mannitol in the hydropenic state, according to Kaplan *et al.* (1951), depends on the functional integrity of the sympathetic nerves.

Certain of the experimental data reported above suggest that renal secretory activity is influenced to some extent by nerve impulses acting directly on the cells of the renal tubules. A direct influence of the renal nerves on the resorptive capacity of the renal tubules is suggested by certain data advanced by Sartorius and Burlington (1952). In their experiments acute renal denervation of anesthetized dogs resulted in increased excretion of water and salt with no significant alteration in glomerular filtration or renal plasma flow, but, with the establishment of diuresis in unanesthetized dogs, acute renal denervation resulted in a decreased flow of urine with no significant alteration in hemodynamics. The output of both water and the solid constituents of the urine is determined by the volume of blood flowing through the kidney. In view of the fact that denervation of both kidneys, in experimental animals, is not necessarily followed by untoward results, and in view of the volume of experimental data which seems to indicate that the renal output is determined solely by the volume and the content of the blood flowing through the kidney, the hypothesis that the kidney is supplied with true secretory fibers appears to be untenable.

Reflex Regulation of Renal Function.—Local cooling of the skin in the lumbar region results in inhibition, and local warming of the skin in this region results in augmentation of renal secretion. These functional changes are due to reflex vasomotor changes in the kidney. Cold applications to the skin of an experimental animal result in an appreciable decrease in the size of the kidney and diminution of pressure in the renal vein. In experiments on dogs and rabbits, Nedzel (1952) found that chilling of the animal's body results in vasoconstriction in the kidney that is most marked in the cortical zone. The flow of urine becomes irregular and may be arrested temporarily. Reduction in the size of the kidney may also be brought about by afferent stimulation of a peripheral nerve, *e.g.*, the sciatic or an intercostal nerve. Reflex inhibition of renal function elicited by impulses arising in some other part of the urinary system is not uncommon. Renal colic frequently is accompanied by anuria which may persist for hours or even days due to reflex spasm of the renal arteries. The same result may be brought about by kinking or compression of the ureter. Inhibition of renal secretion may be elicited by increasing pressure in the urinary bladder (vesico-renal reflex). Ureteral stasis also inhibits the output of urine (uretero-renal reflex). Stimulation of the lower third of the ureter also elicits reflex volume changes in the kidneys on the opposite side. Direct warming or cooling of one kidney usually elicits no reaction in the other, but strong thermal stimulation of the one usually calls forth a reflex response in the other. Clinical cases have been reported in which marked diminution of the urinary output of an apparently normal kidney was associated with a lesion of the other kidney. The output of the normal kidney in such cases appears to be limited by reflex vasoconstriction elicited by the stimulating effect of the lesion in the contralateral organ.

Central Regulation of Renal Function.—Claude Bernard observed polyuria following a lesion in the floor of the fourth ventricle between the vagus and vestibular nuclei. Jungmann and Meyer (1913) produced a lesion in the floor of the fourth ventricle which resulted in an increase in the output of urine but in a proportionately greater increase in the sodium chloride output which did not affect the salt content of the blood even though the animal had previously been rendered salt-poor. This result of the lesion was not observed following section of the splanchnic nerves. According to Jungmann (1922), puncture of the center for carbohydrate metabolism in the medulla results in diuresis with increased elimination of sodium chloride independently of its effect on the sugar content of the blood. Certain data have been interpreted as indicating that the effects on renal secretion of lesions in the medulla are not the results of injuries to fiber tracts but to medullary centers. A region medial to the spinal tract of the trigeminal nerve, ventromedial to the restiform body and dorsal to the nucleus of the facial nerve has been localized that has been regarded as the center that regulates both the elimination of water and sodium chloride.

Polyuria frequently occurs as an accompaniment of epileptic seizures and violent attacks of migraine. It also accompanies certain psychic states, *e.g.*, expectancy or fright. These effects undoubtedly are mediated through hypothalamic autonomic centers and the efferent pathways that lead from these centers to the cells of origin of the splanchnic nerves. The rôle of hypothalamic centers in water metabolism is discussed more specifically in Chapter IV.

Although nerve impulses play an important rôle in renal secretion, this rôle must be regarded as only regulatory and dependent on the vasomotor control of the renal blood vessels exerted through the sympathetic nerves. Renal function is determined by the inherent capacity of the renal elements, the hydrostatic relationship of the blood to the kidney and the stimuli to the renal secretory elements afforded by substances in the circulating blood.

THE URETER

Nerve Supply.—The innervation of the ureter is derived from the renal, the spermatic (or ovarian) and the hypogastric plexuses (Fig. 64). A subordinate plexus derived from the vesical plexus also surrounds its lower portion. The afferent fibers related to the ureter are chiefly components of the eleventh and the twelfth thoracic and the first lumbar nerves. Its vagus supply probably also includes afferent components.

The arrangement of the nerves in the wall of the ureter seems to be relatively simple. Most of the fiber bundles run longitudinally, but branch freely and intercommunicate with one another. In man and certain other mammals, particularly dogs and cats, groups of ganglion cells are associated with the intrinsic nerves in the caudal third of the ureter. Ganglion cells have not been observed in its rostral two-thirds. The sympathetic and the parasympathetic components of the nerves of the ureter cannot be differentiated anatomically, but it is highly probable that the ganglion cells in the caudal third are incorporated in parasympathetic efferent chains. Most of the intrinsic nerve fibers are unmyelinated and of small caliber.

Control of the Ureteral Musculature.—The musculature of the ureter, like other smooth muscle, possesses the inherent capacity to undergo rhythmic contractions. Rhythmic peristalsis plays an important part in propelling the renal secretion toward the bladder. Such contractions of the ureter persist, in the intact animal, following section of all its extrinsic nerves. Under proper conditions, they can be elicited in excised pieces of the ureter. Ureteral activity, under normal conditions, probably is subject to neural regulation. If, in an experimental animal, the kidney is actively secreting, peristaltic waves of contraction may be observed that are propagated along the ureter from the kidney to the urinary bladder in regular sequence. Direct stimulation of the ureter at any point gives rise to a contraction wave that is propagated in both directions from the point stimulated, thus peristalsis and antiperistalsis may be observed at the same time. The opinion that the musculature of the ureter is stimulated automatically to undergo periodic contractions and that its functional regulation requires neither intrinsic ganglion cells nor extrinsic nerves has been prevalent. The abundant innervation of the ureter, however, cannot be regarded as devoid of functional significance.

The data obtained in experiments involving direct stimulation of the nerves to the ureters are not unequivocal. On the basis of an extensive review of the literature, including the reports of studies of the effects of various drugs on the ureteral musculature, Gruber (1933) concluded that, although the results of many of the reported studies are inconclusive, the data available support the assumption that the sympathetic innervation of the ureter includes both excitatory and inhibitory fibers, and the parasympathetic innervation includes only excitatory fibers. In experiments on dogs reported by Durand and Descotes (1952) stimulation or section of the vagus nerve exerted no effect on pyelo-ureteral motility, but stimulation of either the splanchnic or the hypogastric nerve resulted in increased motility.

The lower end of the ureter is not provided with a special sphincter muscle. Its opening and closing appear to be regulated by the activity of the bladder musculature and the internal vesical pressure. According to the current teaching, contraction of the bladder tends to close the ureter so that urine cannot be forced back into it while the bladder is expelling its contents. Contraction of the bladder probably also results in reflex contractions of the lower portion of the ureter. This also would tend to prevent the back flow of urine into the pelvis of the kidney. Maintenance of the tonus of the ureteral musculature and reflex coördination of the activities of the ureter to contractions of the bladder probably represent the most important functions of the nerves of the ureter.

THE URINARY BLADDER

Extrinsic Nerves.—The urinary bladder is innervated through the vesical plexuses which are complex meshworks of nerve-fiber bundles and flattened ganglia extending from the region of the trigone along the lateral aspects of the bladder. Each vesical plexus may be regarded as a subdivision of the corresponding pelvic plexus. It receives preganglionic and visceral afferent fibers through both the hypogastric and the pelvic nerves. The preganglionic parasympathetic fibers concerned in the innervation of the bladder are derived chiefly through the second and the third sacral nerves (Kuhn, 1949). The pudendal nerve, through which the external vesical sphincter is supplied, also conveys afferent fibers to the internal vesical sphincter and adjacent parts of the bladder (Fig. 64).

Most of the sympathetic preganglionic fibers concerned in the innervation of the bladder terminate in the ganglia in the vesical plexus. Some probably terminate in the lumbar ganglia of the sympathetic trunk. The ganglia in the vesical plexus are neither exclusively sympathetic nor exclusively parasympathetic, but preganglionic fibers of both the thoracolumbar sympathetic and the sacral parasympathetic outflows make synaptic connections in them.

Intrinsic Nerves.—The nerves that penetrate the bladder wall from the vesical plexus join the intramural plexus which includes numerous ganglia. The intramural ganglia are most abundant in the trigone and gradually become less abundant as the distance from the trigone increases. The fundic area probably is devoid of ganglia. The larger intramural ganglia and some of the smaller ones are situated just beneath the serosa. Other small ganglia are located between muscle bundles, but relatively few lie deeply imbedded in the muscle. The intramural ganglia, like those of the vesical plexus, receive preganglionic fibers through both the hypogastric and the pelvic nerves. In experiments carried out on cats, Moseley (1936) found that approximately 40 per cent of the intramural ganglia receive preganglionic fibers exclusively through the hypogastric nerves (sympathetic outflow), approximately 40 per cent exclusively through the pelvic nerves (parasympathetic outflow) and approximately 20 per cent through both the hypogastric and the pelvic nerves. Although the number of ganglia which, according to their preganglionic connections, must be classified as sympathetic is approximately equal to the number which, by the same criterion, must be classified as parasympathetic, there is a preponderance of parasympathetic ganglion cells in the bladder wall, since most of the larger ganglia are parasympathetic. Most of the ganglia that receive preganglionic fibers through both the hypogastric and the pelvic nerves also are relatively small.

Most of the nerve fibers in the bladder wall are unmyelinated and of small caliber. Myelinated fibers also occur. Of the latter, those that penetrate deeply into the wall undoubtedly are afferent. Nerve fiber terminations in the mucous membrane which presumably are afferent have been described by various investigators. According to Langworthy and Murphy (1939), receptors are widely distributed in the mucosa and the submucosa, but most of those in the trigone and adjacent areas are connected with afferent fibers that traverse the hypogastric nerves and most of those farther removed from the base of the bladder are connected with afferent components of the pelvic nerves. Kleyntjens and Langworthy (1937) demonstrated complex terminal arborizations of relatively large afferent fibers in the musculature of the bladder which they interpreted as stretch receptors since, in their experiments, the bladder did not respond normally to stretch following section of the dorsal sacral nerve roots. On the basis of their findings relative to the distribution of the sympathetic and the parasympathetic motor endings in the bladder musculature, Langworthy and Murphy (1939) advanced the opinion that the efferent innervation of the detrusor muscle is effected solely through parasympathetic fibers and that the sympathetic fibers in the bladder wall are distributed to the blood vessels, Bell's muscle and the crista of the urethra. In sections of the urinary bladder and adjacent tissue in newborn kittens prepared by the silver technic used by Nonidez (1939) to differentially impregnate sympathetic and parasympathetic fibers in young animals, Kuntz and Saccomanno (1944) obtained evidence of the innervation of the detrusor muscle by both parasympathetic and sympathetic fibers. In these preparations, the heavily impregnated fibers, presumably parasympathetic, appeared to be distributed solely to the muscle tissue. The less heavily impregnated ones, presumably sympathetic, appeared to be distributed to the blood vessels and the muscle throughout the bladder wall.

INNERVATION OF THE URETHRA

The male urethra is innervated through the prostatic and the cavernous plexuses, both of which are parts of the pelvic plexus. They include both parasympathetic and sympathetic fibers. The prostatic plexus is continuous with the vesical plexus and lies in intimate contact with the prostate gland. It supplies fibers to the neck of the bladder, the prostate and the prostatic urethra. The cavernous plexus may be regarded as the extension of the prostatic plexus along the urethra. Nerves that arise from it are distributed to the corpora cavernosa penis and, communicating with branches of the pudendal nerves, give off rami to the corpus cavernosum urethræ and the penile portion of the urethra.

The female urethra is innervated through the vaginal plexus which is composed chiefly of parasympathetic fibers derived from the pelvic plexus, but includes some sympathetic fibers derived from the pelvic plexus and in part directly from the sacral segments of the sympathetic trunk. The external vesical sphincter and the compressor urethræ muscles are innervated through the pudendal nerves.

REGULATION OF VESICAL FUNCTION

Specific Actions of Sympathetic and Parasympathetic Nerves.—The urinary bladder is a muscular organ whose functions are storage of the renal secretion and its periodic discharge. Its musculature consists of three layers the components of which are so intimately interwoven that they constitute a functional unit, the detrusor muscle. Its outlet is provided with an internal sphincter composed of smooth muscle and an external sphincter composed of striated muscle. The smooth muscle, including the internal sphincter, is innervated through both sympathetic and parasympathetic nerves. The external sphincter is innervated through somatic nerves.

In general stimulation of the parasympathetic innervation of the bladder results in functional activity and stimulation of the sympathetic nerves results in inhibition of function. Under certain conditions, these common responses to parasympathetic and sympathetic stimulation may be reversed. In experiments on cats reported by Langworthy et al. (1940) sympathetic stimulation caused an initial rise in intravesical pressure followed by a fall below the normal resting level, when the volume was held constant, and an initial decrease in the vesical volume followed by an increase, when the intravesical pressure was held constant. Stimulation of the hypogastric nerves also resulted in closure of the ureteral orifices and their displacement toward the mid-line. The base of the bladder also was drawn caudad by the contraction of Bell's muscle. Following sympathetic denervation of the bladder it accommodated a smaller volume of liquid before micturition occurred. They advanced the opinion that the detrusor muscle is devoid of functional sympathetic innervation.

In experiments on cats and dogs reported by Kuntz and Saccomanno (1944), in which the responses of the musculature near the apex of the bladder to sympathetic stimulation were recorded under conditions calculated to eliminate any effects on the records of responses of the musculature at the base of the viscus, faradic stimulation of the hypogastric nerves elicited an initial contraction followed by prolonged inhibition. Functional sympathetic innervation of the detrusor muscle, consequently, is

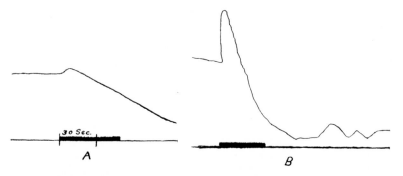

30 Sec.

A

B

FIG. 65.—Kymographic records showing initial contraction of the detrusor muscle followed by prolonged inhibition in response to moderate (*A*) and strong (*B*) stimulation (Kuntz and Saccomanno, 1944).

demonstrated. In these experiments, the initial contraction elicited by moderate sympathetic stimulation was of short duration and small amplitude. The following relaxation was prolonged but usually not very marked (Fig. 65). The results of experiments carried out on male human subjects, under spinal anesthesia, which, with respect to the sympathetic innervation of the bladder, are comparable to those cited above, have been reported by Learmonth (1931). In general, his findings corroborate those cited above. Stimulation of the entire sympathetic supply to the bladder results in powerful contraction of the ureteric orifices, increased tonus in the trigone and contraction of the internal vesical sphincter, but no observable effect on the detrusor muscle, although this muscle is inhibited. Stimulation of either hypogastric nerve results in contraction of the ureteric orifice on the same side, increased tonus in the trigone and contraction of the internal sphincter. No reflex responses in the bladder could be elicited by stimulation of the proximal portion of one hypogastric nerve after its section alone or after section of the entire sympathetic supply. The immediate results of section of the sympathetic supply are relaxation of the ureteric orifices, the entire trigone and the internal sphincter, but no observable change in the detrusor muscle. After an interval of about 21 days, the ureteric orifices close in the intervals between jets of urine, the trigone appears less relaxed but still abnormal, and the internal sphincter may close completely, although it offers less resistance than the normally innervated sphincter to the advancing beak of the cystoscope. Intravenous injection of adrenin in appropriate dosage, in Learmonth's experiments, resulted in an immediate active dilatation of the bladder which remained at its increased capacity for approximately five minutes. This result definitely indicates the existence of inhibitory fibers in the sympathetic supply to the detrusor muscle in man.

In an experimental analysis of the responses of the detrusor muscle elicited by electrical stimulation of the hypogastric nerves in the cat, Hegre and Ingersoll (1949) found that all parts of the muscle participate in a diphasic response to sympathetic stimulation. The magnitude of each phase of the response is conditioned by the physiological state of the bladder at the time of stimulation. The responses elicited in various regions of the bladder under given experimental conditions also show characteristic differences. In the anesthetized cat various portions of the detrusor muscle rarely begin to contract simultaneously in spontaneous movements. The coordinated activity observed during the late filling stage and during micturition usually exhibits peristaltic waves that begin near the urethral orifice and progress toward the distal region of the bladder. Such activity is regarded as characteristic of parasympathetic responses (Ingersoll *et al.*, 1951).

On the basis of experimental studies carried out on dogs, Henderson and Roepke (1934) advanced the hypothesis that the functional activity of the bladder involves both a tonic and a contractile mechanism. Tonic stimulation in their experiments, resulted in liberation of an acetylcholine-like substance. The tonic mechanism, furthermore, was depressed by atropine. Contractile stimulation did not result in liberation of an acetylcholine-like substance and the contractile mechanism was not depressed by atropine.

In experiments on cats reported by Mellanby and Pratt (1940), instantaneous change from constant intravesical pressure to constant volume conditions caused either an isometric contraction or a state of quiescence at zero pressure, according to the phase of isotonic rhythm at which the change was made. The isometric contraction was followed by a state of quiescence at zero pressure for an indefinite period or by a series of similar rhythmic contractions. Division of the pelvic nerve abolished the isometric contractions. Stimulation of its peripheral portion elicited maximal isometric contractions. Acetylcholine elicited prompt responses similar to isometric contractions. Adrenin elicited similar responses after a long latent period. Atropine abolished the isometric contractions more readily than it destroyed the isotonic rhythm.

Unilateral stimulation of the pelvic nerve elicits contraction of the corresponding lateral half of the detrusor muscle without appreciably affecting the other half. If one pelvic nerve has been cut several weeks previously stimulation of the intact pelvic nerve results in contraction of the entire bladder musculature. Bilateral section of the pelvic nerves results in marked atony of the detrusor muscle and closure of the sphincter. The liquid content is held at higher pressure than in the normally innervated bladder and for the first few days the vesical capacity is increased, but it drops somewhat below the normal level when automatic micturition begins. The emptying reflex is then initiated earlier in response to filling than in the normally innervated bladder.

Micturition.—Normal micturition is in part reflex and in part a voluntary act. The nervous mechanism through which the voluntary control of this function is exercised has engaged the attention of many investigators. According to some, the cortical impulses involved in voluntary micturition are not conducted to the bladder musculature directly but to the external sphincter which is a voluntary muscle. The peripheral fibers through which these impulses are conducted are components of the pudendal nerve. Their direct effect is relaxation of the external sphincter. This reaction gives rise to stimuli that are conducted back to the spinal cord through afferent pudendal nerve fibers that make reflex connections with efferent components of the pelvic nerves, *i.e.*, the micturition reflex is initiated by voluntary inhibition of a striated muscle and is then carried out as a spinal reflex through the appropriate visceral efferent chains, like the spinal reflexes concerned in the functional control of other visceral organs.

On the basis of experimental studies carried out on cats, Barrington (1914, 1921, 1931) described a series of six micturition reflexes: (1) A hind-brain reflex through which contraction of the detrusor muscle is elicited by distending the bladder. Both the afferent and the efferent pathways involved in this reflex traverse the pelvic nerves. (2) A hind-brain reflex through which contraction of the detrusor muscle is elicited by running water through the urethra. The afferent pathway of this reflex traverses the pudendal, and the efferent pathway traverses the pelvic nerve. (3) A spinal reflex through which a slight transitory contraction of the bladder is elicited by distending the proximal urethra. Both afferent and efferent limbs of the reflex arcs employed traverse the hypogastric nerves. (4) A spinal reflex through which relaxation of the urethra is elicited by running water through it. Both afferent and efferent limbs of the reflex arcs employed traverse the pudendal nerves. (5) A spinal reflex through which relaxation of the urethra is elicited by distending the bladder. The afferent limbs of the reflex arcs employed traverse the pelvic, and the efferent limbs the pudendal nerves. (6) A spinal reflex through which relaxation of the smooth muscle, particularly of the proximal third of the urethra, is elicited by distending the bladder. Both the afferent and the efferent limbs of the reflex arcs employed traverse the pelvic nerves. In decerebrate animals, according to Barrington, distention of the bladder through filling elicits reflex contraction of the detrusor muscle. This in turn elicits reflex relaxation of the urethra, which elicits further contraction of the detrusor muscle, resulting in complete emptying of the bladder. The reflexes are carried out in part through centers in the spinal cord and in part through centers in the brain stem. On the basis of all the pertinent data, Barrington (1942) concluded that urethral stimulation by liquid passing through it may elicit contraction of the detrusor muscle through a hind-brain reflex carried out through afferent components of the pudendal and efferent components of the pelvic nerves or through a spinal reflex carried out through afferent and efferent components of the pelvic nerves. The former reflex is elicited more easily than the latter and results in the greater contraction.

In experiments on dogs reported by Denning (1924) the mere flowing of liquid through the distal part of the urethra did not elicit contraction of the bladder. He, therefore, concluded that opening of the external sphincter constitutes the adequate stimulus for the micturition reflex. He also demonstrated experimentally that voluntary micturition can be carried out following section of the pudendal nerves. Although closure of the sphincter mechanism is less perfect following bilateral section of the pudendal nerve than before, dogs that had previously been trained to micturate at a designated place persisted in this habit, after section of the pudendal nerves, and discharged urine voluntarily whenever they were brought to the place in question. Since no other somatic efferent fibers reach the bladder or the urethra and the direct stimulating effect on the bladder of increased intra-abdominal pressure due to contraction of the abdominal muscles was ruled out due to the ease with which the flow of urine was brought about, Denning concluded that voluntary impulses affect the bladder directly through the autonomic nerves. Further experimentation also proved that the autonomic nerves concerned are parasympathetic. Following section of the pudendal nerves, section of the hypogastric nerves had no apparent effect on voluntary micturition. It could not be carried out voluntarily following section of the pelvic nerves, leaving only the hypogastric nerves intact, until the bladder became adjusted so that it would contract in response to increased intra-abdominal pressure due to contraction of the abdominal muscles.

Denning's experimental results also shed some light on the specific functional defects of the bladder due to elimination of any one of the several components of its nerve supply. Section of the pudendal nerves results in imperfect closure of the sphincter and loss of urethral sensibility, but it does not otherwise materially disturb the normal functioning of the bladder. Section of the hypogastric nerves either alone or in addition to the pudendal nerves results in no marked changes in bladder function. Section of the pelvic nerves brings about profound functional and trophic disturbances of the bladder. Section of all the nerves of the bladder is followed by a more or less constant flow of urine in small quantities, but also periodic discharges of larger quantities brought about by mechanical stimuli to which the bladder is now hypersensitive. Incomplete emptying and cystitis are common under these conditions.

Inasmuch as voluntary micturition can be carried out following section of the pudendal nerves, certain investigators have maintained that the autonomic mechanisms employed in micturition are subject to direct voluntary influences. Evidence that contraction of the detrusor muscle can be initiated or continued by direct voluntary effort is wanting. Micturition cannot be adequately explained, however, on the assumption that the proximal portion of the urethra and the external sphincter constitute the only "trigger zone" for starting the act. On the basis of all the data available, including clinical and experimental observations on man, Learmonth (1931) advanced the opinion that the bladder musculature and the internal sphincter also constitute a "trigger zone" for the initiation of the act of micturition. When the bladder is adequately distended the opening of the internal sphincter takes place automatically. This, according to Learmonth, "is the mechanism of micturition on desire to urinate." On the other hand, voluntary relaxation of the internal sphincter is accompanied by automatic contraction of the detrusor muscle. This, according to Learmonth, "is the mechanism of voluntary micturition."

Powerful contractions of the detrusor muscle that have a very short latent period and do not differ in form and rhythm from the spontaneous contractions of this muscle can be called forth by voluntary effort. They appear to be inseparably associated with relaxation of the musculature of the perineum. Voluntary restraint of micturition exerts an inhibiting effect on the contractions of the detrusor muscle and is accompanied by contraction of the perineal musculature and closure of the external sphincter. Since micturition may be initiated by voluntary effort and is subject to voluntary interruption at any point in the cycle, it can hardly be regarded as purely reflex. Voluntary closure of the external vesical sphincter presents a barrier to the outflow of urine. This, however, is not an adequate explanation of the sudden interruption of the flow of urine particularly in the female, since in the female the external sphincter is only feebly developed. The available data favor the assumption that contraction of the detrusor muscle ceases simultaneously with the closure of the internal sphincter and at once becomes tonically adjusted to the vesical content. Clinical observations also indicate that the flow of urine may be voluntarily interrupted without discomfort following surgical destruction of the internal sphincter. In view of these facts, it must be assumed that the change in the behavior of the detrusor muscle is brought about reflexly by afferent impulses that arise either in the internal or the external sphincter, or that the impulses which interrupt the process of micturition are integrated at higher levels and both the detrusor muscle and the sphincters receive impulses simultaneously from these levels. The latter hypothesis obviously is the more attractive. On the basis of either hypothesis, the concept of micturition as a purely reflex reaction must be limited to infancy. Voluntary control of micturition undoubtedly is facilitated by a normal functional balance of the autonomic nerves. True enuresis probably is associated with hyperirritability of the parasympathetic innervation of the bladder.

Reflex micturition is mediated through centers located in the sacral segments of the spinal cord. The reflex centers for inhibition of the detrusor muscle and contraction of the internal vesical sphincter are located in the first and the second lumbar segments of the spinal cord. These centers receive impulses through afferent nerves from other parts of the body as well as from the urinary bladder and its outlet, including the sphincter mechanisms; consequently, micturition may be facilitated or inhibited by stimuli effective in widely separated areas. Reflex responses of the bladder are elicited with greater facility by stimulation in certain areas than in others. Automatic emptying of the bladder in patients with extensive spinal lesions has been regarded as part of a "mass reflex" that can be evoked by stimulation of the lower extremities or other parts below the level of the lesion. Holmes (1933) has taken exception to this interpretation and has pointed out that the involuntary micturition that frequently is associated with spasms of the lower extremities, in patients with spinal cord lesions, is not the direct result of stimulation of the extremities, but due to the associated spasm of the abdominal wall, which, by increasing the intra-abdominal pressure, suddenly increases the tension on the bladder musculature. In patients with transverse lesions of the spinal cord the contractions of the bladder do not occur simultaneously with the spasm of the abdominal wall but after an interval. This suggests that the overflow of impulses into the micturition center does not take place immediately. The more vigorous contraction that expels the contents of the bladder usually is preceded by a short series of oscillations of pressure. In patients with a spinal cord lesion so low that the reflex excited in the lower extremities does not spread to the abdominal muscles spasm of the extremities is not accompanied by evacuation of the bladder. Schlesinger (1933) emphasized the importance of stimulating the anterior abdominal wall by percussion or rubbing in order to elicit reflex contraction of the detrusor muscle in patients without spinal cord lesions in whom complete evacuation of the bladder is difficult. If the first reflex response does not result in completely emptying the bladder the reflex may be elicited a second and a third time after short intervening intervals.

A frank lesion of the brain or spinal cord may result in complete vesical paralysis. Retention of urine, in such cases, usually is accompanied by overflow incontinence. If the lesion is located above the lumbar segments of the spinal cord, cutaneous stimulation, particularly in the ventral abdominal area, may elicit reflex micturition. If the paralysis is associated with a complete transverse lesion of the spinal cord periodic emptying of the bladder may gradually become automatic after several weeks, unless complications, such as cystitis or pyelitis, have set in.

In cases in which a spinal cord lesion causes acute paralysis of the bladder but leaves the sympathetic pathways intact and does not completely destroy the parasympathetic pathways a condition may develop, following the acute phase, that is known as "cord bladder." Urinary retention is not complete in this condition and is not accompanied by incontinence. Section of the hypogastric nerves, in such cases, may be followed by increased tonus of the detrusor muscle and reduction in the residual urine. Parasympathetic stimulation may also be beneficial.

The "atonic bladder" of childhood, which commonly is associated with malformation of the sacral portion of the spinal cord, usually exhibits an atonic detrusor muscle without dilatation of the sphincter, due to defective parasympathetic innervation, which renders establishment of a proper functional balance between the sympathetic and the parasympathetic nerves impossible. Bucy *et al.* (1937) reported such a case in which section of the hypogastric nerves was followed by marked improvement in bladder function that had been maintained for three years. Relaxation of the sphincter was regarded as the important factor in the improvement in bladder function in this case.

Bladder Sensibility.—Although the internal sphincter is composed of smooth muscle, it probably receives its afferent innervation at least in part through the pudendal nerves. Experimental and clinical evidence suggests that both contraction of the detrusor muscle and relaxation of the internal sphincter play a part in the urge to voluntary micturition. The sensations experienced are not all of the same quality. Indefinite sensations that are referred to the region of the bladder but are not definitely localized probably result from impulses that arise in the bladder musculature. The more acute sensations that can be more or less definitely localized at the neck of the bladder are due to afferent impulses that arise in that region. Because of the physiological character of the parasympathetic fibers distributed to the internal sphincter muscle, contraction of the detrusor muscle also tends to bring about reflex relaxation of the internal sphincter. Under these conditions, emptying of the bladder can only be prevented by voluntary contraction of the external sphincter. If the external sphincter holds, a short period of rest usually ensues during which the detrusor muscle relaxes somewhat and relieves the intravesical pressure. If the bladder is not voluntarily emptied, stronger contractions of the detrusor muscle set in and, if they succeed in pressing a few drops of urine into the urethra, the impulse to micturate becomes irresistible and reflex micturition takes place. If the external sphincter mechanism withstands the pressure produced by repeated contractions of the detrusor muscle this muscle may become inactive, so that soon after the urge to micturate reaches its maximum strength spontaneous micturition becomes impossible.

Voluntary micturition is preceded by a sudden increase in intravesical pressure. This has been regarded as the cause of the emptying reflex, but increased intravesical pressure alone probably does not give rise to a flow of urine, under physiological conditions. According to Müller (1924), the primary cause of micturition is distention of the bladder wall. Contraction of the musculature in response to distention of the bladder is an adaptive process that does not intrude upon consciousness until the intravesical pressure reaches a certain level and the active vesical contractions reach a threshold intensity beyond which they give rise to sensations (Denny-Brown and Robertson, 1933). Passive distention of the organ also gives rise to sensation. It is apparent, therefore, that sensation is only indirectly related to intravesical pressure, since even slight enlargement of the organ may lower the threshold at which added spontaneous active contractions give rise to impulses that reach the sensory level.

Electrical stimulation of the fundus of the bladder gives rise to afferent impulses mediated through the pelvic nerves that result in painful sensations. Similar stimulation in the region of the sphincter gives rise to afferent impulses mediated through the pudendal nerve which also result in painful sensations. These results afford definite information regarding the afferent pathways of impulses that arise in circumscribed areas of the bladder, but afford no unmistakable clues regarding the pathways of afferent impulses that result in the desire to micturate.

In experiments reported by Denning (1924), marked distention of the bladder by filling it through a catheter resulted in uneasiness on the part of the animal. If the distention elicited reflex contraction of the bladder musculature, the animal exhibited increased uneasiness until the liquid began to escape along the catheter and the internal pressure was reduced. Section of the pudendal nerves had no apparent effect on the uneasiness manifested by the animal due to artificial distention of the bladder. When both hypogastric and pelvic nerves were cut, leaving the pudendal nerves intact, the uneasiness manifested by the animal was much less marked. Following section of all the nerves to the bladder the animal no longer manifested uneasiness regardless of the extent to which the bladder was artificially distended; therefore, it may be assumed that either the pelvic or the hypogastric nerves play the major rôle in the conduction of afferent impulses that result in the urge to voluntary micturition. This function probably is subserved chiefly by the pelvic nerves, but clinical observations indicate that the hypogastric nerves also play a part in afferent conduction. The impulses that give rise to the sensation of emptying of the bladder probably are mediated through the pudendal nerve. The bladder, like other visceral organs, is highly insensitive to the ordinary artificial stimuli, but parts of the mucous membrane are sensitive to tactile as well as to painful stimuli.

Certain experimental data support the assumption that some of the receptors in the bladder wall are stimulated by rapid changes in the volume of the contents of the bladder and contraction of the detrusor muscle and others are stimulated by a rise in intravesical pressure. The former adapt rapidly. The latter adapt slowly and vary greatly in the threshold of excitation. Receptors located outside the bladder wall are stimulated by changes in the position of the organ. Impulses that arise in the receptors within and impulses that arise outside the bladder wall are conducted centrad through both the hypogastric and the pelvic nerves. Most of those conducted through the hypogastric nerves are impulses of pain due to distention of the bladder. The receptors concerned adapt very slowly.

Central Nervous Centers Concerned in Bladder Function. — The sympathetic preganglionic neurons concerned in the innervation of the bladder are located in the rostral lumbar segments of the spinal cord. The parasympathetic preganglionic neurons are located in the second, third and fourth sacral segments. Reflex responses of the bladder to diverse afferent stimuli are carried out through these centers. Descending impulses from centers in the brain stem, including the hypothalamus, also reach the bladder through both of them.

Certain experimental data seem to support the hypothesis that the tonus of the bladder musculature is regulated through centers located near the rostral border of the hind-brain and that these centers are subject to influences from cortical areas in both cerebral hemispheres. Impulses emanating from autonomic centers in the diencephalon also influence bladder function. In the cat, as reported by Uvnas (1947), stimulation at certain points in the hypothalamus may elicit either excitation or inhibition of the bladder musculature. Contraction of the detrusor muscle was elicited only by stimulation in the rostral portion of the hypothalamus. Low frequency stimulation usually resulted in contraction of the bladder. The response in the bladder to stimulation in appropriate hypothalamic areas frequently could be reversed by changing the frequency of the stimulation.

Psychic influences on the bladder probably are also mediated through hypothalamic centers. Strong emotional disturbances, *e.g.*, anxiety or fright, commonly give rise to an urge to micturate and, under certain conditions, actually result in involuntary micturition. The suggestion offered by the sound of running water or even the thought of voiding the bladder may also give rise to an almost irresistible urge to micturate. Bladder reactions to psychic influences are mediated through the autonomic centers in the hypothalamus. The ascending and descending conduction pathways concerned in the control of bladder function, according to Barrington (1933), are located in the lateral funiculus of the spinal cord and undergo extensive crossing in the caudal portions of their courses. He detected no crossing at higher levels in the spinal cord. According to Wang and Ranson (1939), the pathways which conduct impulses of hypothalamic origin to the bladder undergo partial decussation in the brain stem and descend in the ventral portion of the lateral funiculus in the spinal cord. On the basis of clinical data, Nathan and Smith (1951) have advanced the hypothesis that impulses that give rise to sensations of fullness of the bladder, impulses that give rise to the urge to micturate and nociceptive impulses from the bladder, the urethra, and the distal portions of the ureters are conducted cephalad through central pathways that are included in the lateral spino-thalamic tracts, and that the conduction pathways for impulses of touch, pressure and tension in the urethra are located in the dorsal funiculi in the spinal cord.

The assumption that bladder function is influenced by impulses emanating from the cerebral cortex is supported by both experimental and clinical data. Bilateral lesions in the motor and the premotor areas, particularly on the medial surfaces of the cerebral hemispheres, may result in loss of voluntary control of micturition and urinary incontinence. Hypotonicity of the bladder musculature in some cases and hyperexcitability in others associated with brain tumors and cortical lesions have been reported. Attempts to elicit purely sympathetic and purely parasympathetic responses in the bladder by electrical stimulation of selected cortical areas in the forebrain of the cat yielded only negative results (Ingersoll *et al.*, 1951). Cortical influences on the bladder probably are exerted through extrapyramidal projections to subcortical centers.

Regulation of the Urethra.—The smooth muscle in the wall of the urethra, like the internal vesical sphincter, relaxes during active contraction of the detrusor muscle. It likewise undergoes tonic contraction simultaneously with the internal sphincter. Contraction of the smooth musculature of the urethra, like that of the internal sphincter, is brought about by stimulation of its sympathetic innervation and relaxation of this musculature is brought about by stimulation of its parasympathetic innervation. The effect of the sympathetic and the parasympathetic nerves respectively on the urethra is the opposite to their effects on the detrusor muscle. This may be regarded as a functional adaptation to facilitate the flow of urine during micturition and to support the sphincter mechanism during relaxation of the detrusor muscle and filling of the bladder. As in the case of the internal sphincter, voluntary contraction and relaxation of the external sphincter and the compressor urethræ muscles also play a rôle in the reflex nervous regulation of the smooth musculature of the urethra.

Chapter XIV

INNERVATION OF THE SEX ORGANS

THE MALE SEX ORGANS

Anatomical Data

Extrinsic Nerves.—The testis and the spermatic cord are innervated through the spermatic, the hypogastric and the vesical plexuses. The spermatic plexus is derived chiefly from the aortic plexus, but it also receives fibers from the renal and the hypogastric plexuses. It invests the spermatic artery throughout its course and includes chiefly sympathetic postganglionic and afferent fibers. According to Mitchell's (1935) account, based on detailed dissections of still born human fetuses, the spermatic nerves consist of a rostral, an intermediate and a caudal group. Those in the rostral group are derived from the aortic and the renal plexuses. They extend along the spermatic artery and terminate in the testis. The intermediate spermatic nerve arises from the proximal portion of the hypogastric plexus and extends caudad and laterad to the internal inguinal ring where it enters the spermatic cord. Its terminal branches are distributed to the epididymis and the proximal portion of the vas deferens. Those in the caudal group are derived in part from a neural complex that forms a loop around the distal portion of the ureter and in part directly from the vesical plexus. One or more of them may be traced along the vas deferens to the epididymis to which some of their branches are distributed. The vas deferens and the seminal vesicle are innervated through the caudal spermatic nerves and rami that arise directly from the vesical plexus. The same general arrangement of the spermatic nerves has also been recognized in other mammals, particularly the cat and the rat (Kuntz and Morris, 1946).

Most of the preganglionic sympathetic and the afferent fibers concerned with the innervation of the testis in man are components of the tenth and more rostral thoracic nerves. Some of the afferent fibers, according to Mitchell (1938), enter the spinal cord as high as the sixth thoracic segment. Most of the afferent fibers that supply the epididymis reach the spinal cord through the eleventh and the twelfth thoracic and the first lumbar nerves.

The prostatic plexus is a relatively large plexiform structure, located lateral to the prostate gland, that includes both sympathetic and parasympathetic components. It supplies fibers to the prostate and the prostatic urethra and gives rise to the cavernous plexus of the penis. The latter plexus gives off rami to the corpora cavernosa penis and, communicating with branches of the pudendal nerves, sends rami to the corpus cavernosum urethræ and the penile portion of the urethra. The retractor muscle

19   (289)

of the penis, present in many mammals, derives its nerve supply from the same sources as does the smooth muscle of the urethra.

The glans and the skin of the penis are innervated exclusively through branches of the dorsal nerve of the penis which arises from the pudendal nerve and consists of fibers derived from the third and the fourth sacral nerves. The compressor urethræ, the ischiocavernous and the bulbo-cavernosus muscles, *i.e.*, the voluntary muscles employed in the act of ejaculation, also are innervated through branches of the pudendal nerve. Vasoconstrictor fibers derived from the hypogastric plexus join the pudendal nerve to be distributed through its branches to the blood vessels of the penis.

Intrinsic Nerves.—The spermatic plexus is made up chiefly of unmyelinated nerve fibers, but it includes some myelinated ones. In the spermatic cord it is made up of numerous slender fiber bundles that are more or less closely associated with the blood vessels. Slender filaments derived from the spermatic plexus become associated with the vas deferens and join the plexus on this duct. Farther distad nerve fibers become associated with the ductus epididymidis to innervate the thin layer of smooth muscle in its wall. Slender rami also occur among the ductuli efferentes. Most of them are closely associated with blood vessels, but they also supply fibers to the very thin layer of smooth muscle in the walls of these ducts.

In the human testis, as pointed out by Gray (1947), most of the nerve fibers penetrate the tunica albuginea obliquely, pass toward the inferior pole between the tunica albuginea and the tunica vasculosa and then along the ventral border of the gland toward the superior pole. Within the testis most of the nerve fibers are closely associated with blood vessels. Their distribution appears to be determined in a large measure by the distribution of the blood vessels. Most of the efferent fibers probably are functionally related to the vascular bed. Some investigators have supported the assumption that the seminiferous epithelium is directly innervated. Others have failed to trace nerve fibers through the membrana propria of the seminiferous tubules. Certain investigators, particularly Okkels and Sand (1941), have described an abundant innervation of the interstitial secretory tissue in the human testis through fibers that make direct contacts with the secretory cells. Various other investigators have failed to corroborate this finding. The data available do not warrant the conclusion that either the seminal epithelium or the interstitial secretory tissue is directly innervated.

The tunica albuginea and the tunica vasculosa are abundantly innervated. Numerous nerve fiber bundles are intimately associated with the blood vessels. Others are not apparently related to the vascular bed. Many of the fibers in these bundles undoubtedly are afferent.

The nerves of the epididymis form a plexus around the duct that appears to be related to both the epithelium and the muscle. Slender bundles of nerve fibers are also associated with the vascular bed in the connective tissue stroma. Most of the fibers concerned with the innervation of the epididymis are derived through the caudal spermatic nerves. Some are derived through nerves of the vas deferens that arise directly from the vesical plexus. Most of the efferent fibers in the caudal spermatic nerves are sympathetic, but they also include some parasympathetic fibers derived from the vesical plexus, since in animals not all the unmyelinated fibers undergo degeneration following extirpation of the inferior mesenteric ganglia (Kuntz and Morris, 1946). The efferent nerves that extend from the vesical plexus along the vas deferens are predominantly para-

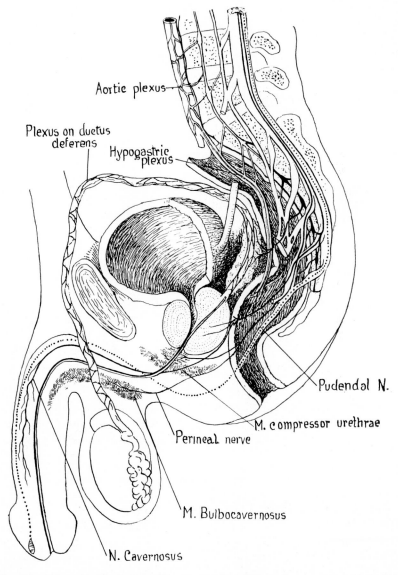

FIG. 66.—Schematic illustration of the innervation of the male sex organs. Dotted line indicates afferent cerebrospinal fibers; double lines indicate sympathetic nerves; heavy black lines indicate parasympathetic nerves.

sympathetic, although they may include some fibers derived from the inferior mesenteric ganglia and some derived from sympathetic ganglion cells located in the pelvic plexus. The innervation of the epididymis, therefore, includes both sympathetic and parasympathetic fibers. The vascular bed in the epididymis, like the vascular bed in the testis that is innervated solely through the spermatic nerves in the rostral group, probably is devoid of parasympathetic innervation. The nerves of the epididymis also include afferent fibers.

The vas deferens is innervated through the spermatic nerves in the caudal group and rami derived directly from the vesical plexus. The efferent fibers of the caudal spermatic nerves are predominantly sympathetic. Those derived from the vesical plexus are predominantly parasympathetic. Extirpation of the inferior mesenteric ganglia, from which most of the sympathetic fibers in the caudal spermatic nerves are derived, results in degeneration of only a minor portion of the innervation of the musculature of the vas deferens. The innervation of this muscle, therefore, is predominantly parasympathetic. The subepithelial plexus in the lamina propria of the vas deferens is essentially afferent. It is made up of fibers derived via the inferior mesenteric plexus and fibers of the pelvic nerves.

The prostatic plexus, the plexus on the seminal vesicle and the cavernous plexus of the penis include sympathetic, parasympathetic and afferent fibers. From these plexuses fibers extend into the prostate gland and the seminal vesicle.

The nerves that arise from the cavernous plexus of the penis contain relatively few myelinated fibers. In addition to supplying the membranous and the penile portion of the urethra they also supply the blood vessels and smooth muscle of the corpora cavernosa penis, the corpus cavernosum urethræ and the skin of the penis.

Sense organs in the glans penis have been described by numerous investigators. They occur in considerable abundance in both the superficial and the deeper layers of the chorium. They have been variously regarded as similar to Pacinian corpuscles, end-bulbs of Krause, and sense organs that are characteristic for the external genital organs. They exhibit a wide range of variation in various mammals, but they probably do not differ in any essential respects from the cutaneous sense organs found in other parts of the body. They are connected with the terminal branches of afferent fibers that are incorporated in the dorsal nerve of the penis and reach the spinal cord through the pudendal nerve.

Physiological Data

Effects of Sympathetic and Parasympathetic Stimulation.—Our knowledge of the rôle of nerve impulses in the regulatory control of the functions of the male sex organs is based mainly on the findings of early physiologists. Recent investigations have added much to our knowledge of the general physiology of the male reproductive system, but little that bears directly on the rôle of neural regulation in the functioning of this system.

Electrical stimulation of the communicating rami of the third and the fourth lumbar nerves in the rabbit elicits contractions of the ductus deferens which are propagated from the testis toward the seminal vesicle. Stimulation of the inferior mesenteric ganglia or the hypogastric nerves elicits the same reaction of the ductus deferens, but stimulation of the aortic plexus above the inferior mesenteric ganglion calls forth no reaction of the ductus deferens. These findings established the important fact that the spinal center through which motor activities of the ductus deferens and the seminal vesicle are mediated is located in the lumbar segments of the spinal cord. In man it is located in the rostral two or three lumbar segments.

Eckhardt (1863) found that electrical stimulation of the visceral rami of the sacral nerves in the dog elicits erection of the penis. He, therefore, designated these rami the "nervi erigentes." He could elicit no reaction of the penis by electrical stimulation of the pudendal nerve but observed that mechanical stimulation of the glans no longer results in erection of the penis following section of the pudendal nerve. He also failed to bring about erection by painful stimulation of the central end of the severed pudendal nerve. These findings established the important rôle of the pelvic nerves in the process of erection and suggested the rôle of the afferent pudendal fibers in erection elicited by stimulation of the glans. Section of the nervi erigentes is followed by contraction of the blood vessels in the penis. Electrical stimulation of the distal portions of the divided nerves elicits dilatation of the blood vessels and filling of the sinuses in the erectile tissue. The fibers that join the pudendal nerve from the hypogastric plexus exert a constrictor effect on the blood vessels of the penis. The hypogastric nerves also exert a true secretory influence on the prostate gland. Certain experimental data indicate that the prostate receives both secretory and inhibitory fibers. In man stimulation of the sympathetic nerves in the pelvis results in the expulsion of semen from the ejaculatory ducts, due to contraction of the musculature of the seminal vesicles, and expulsion of secretion from the prostatic ducts, due to the contraction of the smooth muscle which permeates the prostate gland.

In experiments reported by Farrell and Lyman (1937) stimulation of the hypogastric nerves in the dog resulted in increased secretory activity of the prostate gland and wave-like contractions of its capsule. Stimulation of the pelvic nerves resulted in marked contraction of the musculature in the stroma of the prostate, but caused no increase in the secretory activity of the gland. Administration of adrenin, pilocarpine, nicotine or acetylcholine resulted in increased prostatic secretory activity. On the basis of these findings, they concluded that the secretory fibers to the prostate are cholinergic components of the sympathetic nerves. On the basis of animal experimentation, Langley and Anderson (1895) concluded that the preganglionic fibers concerned with vasoconstriction in the external genitalia traverse the rostral lumbar nerves. Following section of the lumbar nerves or extirpation of the caudal lumbar portion of the sympathetic trunks mild erection may come about due to the removal of the vasoconstrictor influence of the hypogastric nerves. Under normal conditions stimulation of the lumbar nerves elicits contraction of the entire musculature of the ducti deferentia and the seminal vesicles.

Spina (1897) observed erection and ejaculation in the absence of stimulation of the genitalia in a guinea-pig following transection of the spinal cord in the caudal thoracic region. He also observed that if the spinal cord is destroyed, in a guinea-pig, by passing a slender rod caudad through the vertebral canal ejaculation without erection is elicited when the end of the rod reaches the lumbar region.

Müller (1901) reported the results of experiments in which dogs that had been subjected to extirpation of the caudal lumbar and sacral portions of the spinal cord, in spite of the paralysis of the posterior portions of the body, exhibited erection in response to appropriate stimulation. Pressure on the abdomen which resulted in emptying of the bladder, in these dogs, also resulted in reflex erection of the penis. Reflex erection could also be elicited by direct stimulation of the glans or the shaft of the penis, but none of these stimuli elicited ejaculation. Root and Bard (1947) also reported erection in male cats in which the spinal origin of the nervi erigentes had been destroyed. Deafferentation of the genitalia did not abolish the reaction.

Although the genital organs normally are subject to regulatory influences through the autonomic nerves, sympathetic denervation of these organs has no marked effect on their functional activity. Failure of semen to be discharged through the urethra following lumbar sympathectomy in man has led to the conclusion that ejaculation is abolished by sympathetic denervation of the ejaculatory duct. As reported by Retief (1950), who studied male patients after bilateral extirpation of the sympathetic trunk from the 9th thoracic to the 3rd lumbar segments, ejaculation took place, but the semen was discharged into the urinary bladder instead of distad in the urethra because the internal vesical sphincter was not closed at the time of ejaculation, due to the absence of impulses conducted through its sympathetic nerves. Contraction of the ejaculatory duct appears to be elicited by impulses conducted through parasympathetic nerves.

According to Bacq and Brouha (1932), sympathetic denervation of the genital organs in male rats, guinea-pigs and rabbits has no influence on puberty or the internal and external secretory activity of the testes. These organs also remain sensitive to the anterior pituitary hormone. The changes that take place in the genital tract, particularly the seminal vesicles, according to Bacq and Brouha, are more marked following extirpation of the hypogastric plexus than following extirpation of the abdominal sympathetic trunks.

Reflex Regulation Through Centers in the Spinal Cord.—The pertinent data cited above clearly indicate that reflex erection is mediated through centers in the lumbar and the sacral segments of the spinal cord. Contraction of the ejaculatory duct can be elicited through the sacral reflex center, but normal ejaculation probably requires the functional integrity of both the sacral and the lumbar spinal cord centers. There is no conclusive evidence that either the erection or the ejaculation reflex can be carried out through the plexuses associated with the genital organs alone either in the intact animal or following destruction of the centers in question. Erection may be brought about by psychic stimulation following destruction of the sacral spinal cord but not following destruction of the lumbar cord. It must be assumed, therefore, that the efferent impulses concerned in bringing about erection due to psychic stimulation, in the absence of the sacral center, are mediated through the lumbar center and the vasomotor nerves to the cavernous bodies.

Erection.—The act of erection involves engorgement of the cavernous bodies in the penis, particularly the corpora cavernosa. In mammals which do not possess a long os penis, according to Deysach (1939), the venæ profundæ in the cavernous bodies possess thick muscular walls similar to those of arteries. Most of the numerous side branches of these veins have very thin walls which extend through all the layers of the thick wall of the vein (small sluice channels). The others exhibit the typical histological structure of veins in other tissues (large sluice channels). When the arteries which supply the erectile tissue dilate, thus permitting more blood to flow into the cavernous bodies, a mild state of erection is produced which may be called "arterial erection." Compression of the veins which drain the cavernous bodies also results in a mild state of erection which may be called "venous erection." Erection of either of these types may be adequate for copulation in mammals that possess a long os penis. Erection which is adequate for copulation in mammals devoid of a long os penis requires closure of the sluice valves which consist of the thick walls of the venæ profundæ and the small sluice channels. The reactions of these vessels are determined in part by nerve impulses and in part by mechanical factors.

Erection may be brought about as a purely reflex reaction or as a result of psychic stimulation. It is mediated mainly through the parasympathetic nerves. The normal innervation of the cavernous tissue, particularly that of the vascular musculature, includes sympathetic nerve fibers. The latter are not essential for engorgement of the cavernous bodies since erection may take place following sympathetic denervation of the penis. Sympathetic stimulation generally tends to inhibit erection due to limitation of the volume of blood which may flow into the cavernous bodies by constriction of the arterioles. Dilatation of the arterioles coincides with inhibition of the smooth muscle in the walls of the venous sinuses and partial closure of their outlets through the small sluice channels. This partial closure undoubtedly involves mechanical factors brought into play by the rapid rise in pressure within the cavernous bodies. Erection does not require compression of the efferent veins by the action of skeletal muscles, but the ischiocavernosus and bulbocavernosus muscles undoubtedly play a rôle in this reaction. Removal of the ischiocavernosus and bulbocavernosus muscles in dogs, in experiments reported by Lowsley and Bray (1936), resulted in inability to perform effective copulation. Shortening of these muscles by plication, on the contrary, resulted in increased sexual activity. Excessive shortening resulted in priapism. They also reported relief of impotence in man, in certain cases, following plication of these muscles.

Under normal conditions, engorgement of the cavernous tissue subsides as soon as the stimulation which caused it ceases. If ejaculation takes place, erection commonly subsides promptly since the stimulus which elicits contraction of the seminal vesicles and the ejaculatory ducts also elicits constriction of the arterioles in the cavernous tissue, thus relieving the turgor. Since all the smooth muscle in the penis reacts in the same manner, the organ may be reduced temporarily to less than its normal size. In animals in which the penis is provided with a retractor muscle, the reflex reactions associated with ejaculation include contraction of this muscle, resulting in retraction of the organ.

Contraction of all the smooth muscle in the penis may be associated with psychic states which counteract sexual desire, *e.g.*, disgust or fear, or by cold applications to the skin of the organ or adjacent areas, including the proximal portions of the thighs. Temporary contraction of the penis commonly occurs during a cold bath. Mild engorgement of the erectile tissue may be elicited by warm applications or by a warm bath.

The duration of erection associated with sexual excitation is determined in part by the reactivity of the reflex mechanisms employed and in part by psychogenic factors. Prolonged, continuous erection (priapism) must be regarded as pathological. This condition commonly is associated with local irritation, injury to the cavernous tissue, leukemia or a lesion of the spinal cord. In certain cases it is psychogenic.

In the absence of anatomical barriers that prevent the normal outflow of the blood from the cavernous bodies, maintained engorgement may be due to excessive parasympathetic stimulation. The clinical observation that extensive bilateral lumbosacral sympathectomy fails to relieve persistent priapism seems to support this assumption. Resection of the cavernous plexus undoubtedly would relieve priapism of neurogenic origin, but it would also result in impotence. Therapeutic measures designed to depress the parasympathetic reflex mechanisms and appropriate psychotherapy obviously are indicated in treatment for the relief of priapism.

Impotence of neurogenic origin may be psychogenic or due to sympathetic hyperreactivity or hyporeactivity of the reflex mechanisms employed in the act of erection. In cases which fall within the first category appropriate psychotherapy is indicated. The inhibitory effect of sympathetic stimulation on erection is evidenced by the fact that emotional states characterized by strong sympathetic excitation and the administration of adrenin tend to inhibit this reaction. In cases of functional virile impotence bilateral lumbar sympathectomy may result in marked improvement in erections, although the ability to discharge semen through the urethra is lost. In cases of impotence due to hyporeactivity of the reflex mechanisms employed in erection parasympathetic stimulation is indicated.

Ejaculation.—Ejaculation is not a necessary accompaniment of erection. In normal healthy individuals in the waking state, the discharge of seminal fluid normally is elicited only by stimulation of the glans. This reaction, in a large measure, depends on the quality of the stimulus. Simple contact, electrical or thermal stimulation or pain usually do not elicit ejaculation. The adequate stimulus seems to be gentle friction, particularly of the moist glans. The necessary duration of such stimulation depends on conditions affecting the individual, such as his general physical condition, age, psychic excitability and the secretory content of the sex glands.

Inasmuch as stimulation of the glans, under normal conditions, must be continued at least for a short interval in order to elicit ejaculation, this reaction must involve the summation of impulses, which probably occurs in the ejaculatory center in the spinal cord. When such summation has reached the threshold level, a sudden discharge of efferent impulses takes place which calls forth sudden contraction of the smooth musculature of the entire internal sexual apparatus, resulting in the propulsion of seminal fluid into the urethra. This in turn elicits reflex contraction of the striated constrictor urethræ, bulbocavernosus and ischiocavernosus muscles which brings about the expulsion of the seminal fluid from the urethra. The ejaculatory act, consequently, is completed by the reflex contraction of voluntary muscles. Premature ejaculation is commonly associated with hyperirritability of the reflex mechanisms employed. Delayed ejaculation, is commonly associated with hypoirritability of these mechanisms. In certain cases either premature or delayed ejaculation may be psychogenic.

The discharge of seminal fluid may take place during sleep (nocturnal emission) in the absence of specific stimulation of the glans. The adequate stimulus involved in nocturnal emission is unknown. It has been generally assumed that erotic dreams constitute an important factor in this reaction. Similar psychic manifestations during the waking state, at least in healthy individuals, do not call forth the discharge of seminal fluid. It may be assumed that certain inhibitory influences that prevent this reaction to psychic stimulation during the waking state are not effective during sleep. On the other hand, erotic dreams in some instances probably are a consequence rather than the cause of nocturnal emissions. That the discharge of seminal fluid during sleep, as well as during the waking state, gives rise to afferent impulses which result in psychic manifestations is certain. Possibly, erotic dreams associated with nocturnal emissions are to be regarded only as the outcome of such psychic manifestations. It seems highly probable that the discharge of seminal fluid may be called forth reflexly during sleep by the stimulus afforded by internal pressure, particularly in the seminal vesicles and the prostate gland, due to the accumulation of seminal and prostatic secretion. The data available at present do not afford an adequate basis for the complete understanding of this sexual phenomenon.

The Sexual Orgasm.—The sensations immediately associated with ejaculation constitute the sexual orgasm. They arise simultaneously with the initiation of the peristaltic contraction of the ducti deferentia. The beginning of the orgasm, consequently, precedes the expulsion of the seminal fluid from the urethra by a short interval.

How and where the sensations which constitute the sexual orgasm arise is not definitely known. It has been assumed that the afferent impulses involved arise in the genital organs as a result of the contraction of the smooth musculature concerned in the ejaculation reflex. Learmonth (1931), however, has reported that male patients, following section of the sympathetic nerves to the pelvic organs, are still able to perform the sexual act and experience a psychic orgasm that is indistinguishable from the normal. The afferent impulses concerned probably are conducted into the spinal cord chiefly through visceral afferent fibers and reach the appropriate integrating centers via the same ascending pathways which also conduct other visceral impulses that give rise to sensations. Impulses that arise in the striated muscles concerned in the reaction are conducted into the spinal cord through somatic afferent fibers. Inasmuch as sexual sensations are essentially of a primitive type, it need not be assumed that all the afferent impulses that play a part in sexual feeling or awareness reach the cerebral cortex. Many of them undoubtedly are integrated in the diencephalon.

The impulses that give rise to the sexual orgasm also call forth reactions in other visceral organs. The excitation apparently spreads throughout the entire autonomic nervous system. Both the rate and the force of the cardiac contractions are augmented, respiration is stimulated and perspiration may be called forth. In addition to the contractions of the compressor urethræ, the ischiocavernosus and the bulbocavernosus muscles which play a part in the expulsion of the seminal fluid, spastic contractions of the extensor muscles of the lower extremities commonly occur simultaneously with the orgasm.

Cortical Influences.—Sexual excitation is a complex phenomenon which, in a large measure, depends on the functional state of the internal secretory tissue in the sex glands. It cannot be brought about during childhood until the sex glands, particularly the internal secretory tissue, have become functional. If the sex glands are removed early, the development of the seminal vesicles and prostate gland is arrested and sexual excitation never can be achieved. On the other hand, overactivity of the internal secretory function of the sex glands results in a state of sexual hyperexcitability. The functional balance between the sex glands and other endocrine organs plays an important rôle; consequently, it may be assumed that the psychic functions of the cerebral cortex are influenced by the internal secretions of the sex glands and other endocrine glands and that sexual excitability, in a large measure, is determined by cortical reactions to these influences. Sexual excitability and sexual desire, furthermore, vary with the physiological condition of the sex glands. This is apparent particularly in those species which have a limited mating season. In man, voluntary inhibition also plays an important rôle in sexual excitability and, under normal conditions, is the controlling factor in sexual behavior.

THE FEMALE SEX ORGANS

Anatomical Data

Extrinsic Nerves.—The ovary is innervated through the ovarian plexus. The major portion of this plexus is derived from the aortic plexus, but it also includes fibers derived from the renal plexus. Many of the fiber bundles that enter the ovarian plexus may be traced directly from the ovarian ganglion located near the origin of the ovarian artery and from ganglia that are incorporated in the celiac and the renal plexuses. The preganglionic sympathetic fibers concerned and the afferent fibers that traverse the ovarian plexus are components of the splanchnic nerves. The ovarian plexus invests the ovarian artery and the ovarian vein. It supplies fibers to the ovary, the Fallopian tube and the broad ligament. It communicates, in the broad ligament, with the uterine plexus through which it also supplies fibers to the uterus. Most of the afferent fibers that are distributed to the ovary enter the spinal cord through the 10th thoracic nerve.

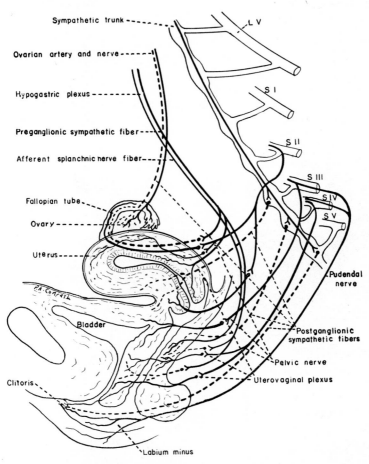

Fig. 67.—Diagram illustrating the innervation of the female genital organs.

The major portion of the innervation of the Fallopian tube is derived through the uterine plexus. This viscus also receives nerve fibers from the ovarian plexus and the hypogastric plexus and through mesenteric nerves. Most of the efferent fibers derived from the uterine plexus are parasympathetic. Those derived from the other sources are sympathetic. The afferent fibers that accompany the sympathetic nerves to the Fallopian tube enter the spinal cord through the 12th thoracic and the rostral lumbar nerves.

The uterus receives most of its innervation through the uterine portion of the utero-vaginal plexus. This plexus corresponds to the prostatic plexus in the male. It receives preganglionic sympathetic and visceral afferent fibers through the hypogastric plexus and preganglionic parasympathetic and visceral afferent fibers through the pelvic nerves. It also receives some sympathetic fibers directly from the lumbar and the sacral segments of the sympathetic trunk. It includes a variable number of ganglia, one of which, the cervical ganglion, situated about the level of the cervix uteri, usually is considerably larger than the rest and, in some instances, includes

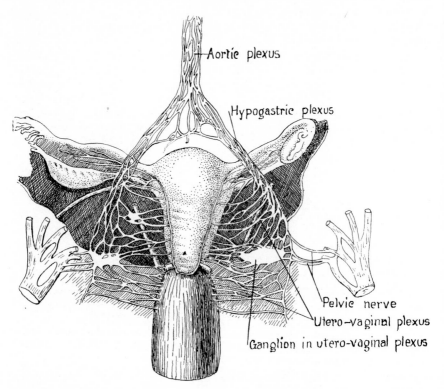

Fig. 68.—Diagrammatic illustration of the extrinsic nerves of the uterus and vagina. (After Dahl.)

most of the ganglion cells in the plexus. As demonstrated by the use of paravertebral anesthesia, afferent nerve fibers reach the uterus via the roots of the eleventh and the twelfth thoracic nerves in the human species and via the first and the second lumbar nerves in the dog (Cleland, 1933).

The vaginal plexus consists predominantly of parasympathetic components derived from the sacral parasympathetic outflow, but it also includes sympathetic components derived in part from the hypogastric plexus and in part directly from the sacral sympathetic trunk. It supplies fibers to the wall and the mucous membrane of the vagina and the urethra and gives rise to a cavernous plexus for the clitoris. The latter structure is also supplied by the dorsal nerve of the clitoris which is a branch of the pudendal nerve.

The labia are innervated through both cerebrospinal and autonomic nerves. The cerebrospinal innervation of the ventral part of each labium is derived from branches of the ileo-inguinal, and that of the dorsal part from branches of the pudendal nerve and the perineal branch of the posterior cutaneous nerve of the thigh. The autonomic supply is derived from the vesical and the vaginal plexuses.

Intrinsic Nerves of the Ovary.—Nearly all the nerve fibers that enter the ovary from the ovarian plexus are unmyelinated and of small caliber. They accompany the ovarian vessels into the stroma, where the larger bundles give rise to branches that accompany the branches of the ovarian vessels. Accounts of the distribution of the nerve fibers of the ovary have been prepared by many investigators. They agree in general that the vascular bed is abundantly innervated. According to some accounts, nerve fibers occur among the interstitial secretory cells, in the membrana granulosa of the follicles and in the corpora lutea. Certain investigators have interpreted their findings as supporting the assumption that the follicles and the secretory tissue, including the corpora lutea, are directly innervated. Others who observed nerve fibers in proximity to follicles and interstitial secretory cells did not conclude that these tissues are directly innervated. The efferent nerve fibers in the ovary probably are solely sympathetic. They probably are distributed only to the blood vessels and other structures that contain smooth muscle. Myelinated fibers occur in the ovary in relatively small numbers. They probably are afferent. Ganglion cells have been observed within the ovary in isolated instances. The presence of ganglion cells in this organ probably is accidental.

Intrinsic Nerves of the Fallopian Tube.—The Fallopian tube is innervated through both unmyelinated and myelinated fibers derived from the ovarian and the uterine plexuses. As the nerves penetrate the wall of the tube they give rise to branches that are distributed to all the layers except possibly the mucous epithelium. A definite plexiform arrangement of these fiber bundles is not apparent. The hypothesis that nerve fibers penetrate the mucous epithelium and terminate in relation to the epithelial cells has been supported. Dahl (1916) described nerve fibers in all the layers of the Fallopian tube except the mucous epithelium. He observed very fine branching fibers that approach the epithelium very closely, but could not determine that they actually terminate in relation to the epithelial cells. Harting (1929) described the nerve supply in the wall of the tube as abundant and pointed out that the fibers in the mucosa decrease and those in the musculature increase in number toward the uterine end of the tube. He also reported the existence of bodies similar to tactile corpuscles in the mucosa in the rostral third of the tube.

The Utero-vaginal Plexus.—This includes both myelinated and unmyelinated nerve fibers. The cervical ganglion varies greatly in size and compactness. If this ganglion is large and its component ganglion cells are compactly aggregated, there are relatively few small ganglia scattered about in the plexus. If the cervical ganglion is relatively small or comprises relatively few ganglion cells arranged in loosely aggregated groups, there is a relatively large number of small ganglia scattered in the plexus. Blote-vogel (1927) proposed the following classification of the ganglia cervicale uteri in the human and various animal species: (1) Forma compacta. This is a large compact ganglion which is traversed by all the nerves that join the uterus. Cervical ganglia of this type occur in the mouse, the rat, the hyena and sometimes in the human species. (2) Forma disseminata. The ganglion complex does not exhibit a single large ganglion, but a small ganglion occurs near the uterus in the course of every nerve joining this organ. This arrangement is observed in the cat, the kangaroo and, in some instances, in the human species. (3) Forma compacta-disseminata. Cervical ganglia of this type consist of a large ganglionic mass made up of numerous groups of ganglion cells that are loosely associated with one another. This arrangement occurs in the cat, the ape and, in some instances, in the human species. In all cases in which a large cervical ganglion exists, it is situated on the dorsolateral aspect of the uterus and close to the upper end of the vagina. As observed by Gasparini (1952), the ganglion cells related to the uterus become larger and more complex during pregnancy. The degree of hypertrophy of the ganglion cells appears to be related to the increase in the volume of the tissue to be innervated.

Intrinsic Nerves of the Uterus.—Most of the fibers that enter the wall of the uterus from the utero-vaginal plexus lie along the blood vessels. The larger trunks lie deep within the myometrium and approximately parallel to the long axis of the organ. As observed by Brown and Hirsch (1941) in the immature human uterus, branches that extend into the endometrium form an intricate plexus in the lamina propria which is more abundant in the cervical canal than in the body of the uterus. The nerves that supply the fundic area traverse the broad ligament or the superficial layer of the myometrium. Within the myometrium the smaller nerve fiber bundles, in general, run parallel to adjacent bundles of muscle fibers to which they give off branches the fibers of which terminate in relation to muscle cells. The nerve supply appears to be fairly uniform throughout the uterine wall, except in the areas adjacent to the Fallopian tubes where it is particularly abundant.

Nearly all the investigators who studied the intrinsic nerves of the uterus emphasized the abundance of nerve fibers in the musculature and along the blood vessels. Certain of them traced nerve fibers into the uterine mucosa and claimed to have observed nerve fiber terminations in relation to the epithelium. Others observed no nerve fibers which actually reach the mucous epithelium. In view of the profound degenerative and regenerative changes that take place in the uterine mucosa, the existence of nerve fiber terminations in the epithelium must be regarded as extremely doubtful. In preparations of the adult human uterus, State and Hirsch (1941) observed nerves throughout the basal third of the endometrium most of which are related to the arteries, but some fibers end freely in the stroma. Their data afford no evidence of fiber terminations in relation to the epithelium. Koppen's (1950) account is in general agreement with that of State and Hirsch. He described an abundant innervation of the myometrium, the blood vessels and the glands in the human uterus, but observed no nerve fibers in the superficial portions of the endometrium.

Certain investigators described elements in the wall of the uterus in the human and animal species which they interpreted as ganglion cells. Others found no ganglion cells within the uterine wall. On the basis of a review of the pertinent literature and an intensive study of preparations of the human uterus, Koppen (1950) concurred in the conclusion that ganglion cells do not occur regularly in the uterine wall.

Intrinsic Nerves of the Vagina.—Most of the nerves that join the vagina from the utero-vaginal plexus enter its rostral and middle parts. No nerves of macroscopic size can be traced from this plexus to the caudal part of the vagina. The intrinsic nerves of the vagina form a plexiform meshwork that includes numerous small ganglia. Some early investigators described end organs similar to Pacinian corpuscles in the vaginal mucosa. Dahl (1916) found no ganglion cells either in the caudal portion of the vagina or in the inner layers of the muscularis and the connective tissue between the muscularis and the vaginal epithelium and no receptive end organs in the vaginal mucosa.

Nerves of the External Genitalia.—Sensory end organs in the female external genitalia were observed by many early anatomists. On the basis of their accounts and the results of his own studies, Dahl (1916) advanced the opinion that the various morphological types of sensory end organs in the female external genitalia possess certain common characteristics. Although they vary in form and structure, the arrangement of the terminal portions of the nerve fibers with which they are connected is quite uniform. He, therefore, proposed that they be regarded collectively as genital sense organs. He found these organs present in abundance in the clitoris and the labia minora, but absent in the labia majora. He also pointed out that they are less abundant but situated more superficially in the labia minora than in the clitoris. In general, the genital sense organs are separated from the surrounding tissue by connective-tissue capsules. The afferent nerve fibers with which they are connected are myelinated components of the nerve of the clitoris that reach the spinal cord through the pudendal nerve.

In addition to the myelinated fibers that terminate in the genital sense organs, the external genitalia are supplied with unmyelinated nerve fibers. Some of the latter lie close to the epidermis, but most of them obviously are related to the blood vessels. Most of the unmyelinated nerve fibers in the clitoris and the labia minora are derived from the cavernous plexus of the clitoris.

PHYSIOLOGICAL DATA

The early literature bearing on the rôle of the nervous system in the regulatory control of the female sex organs is exceedingly abundant and replete with conflicting data and conclusions which, in the light of present knowledge, obviously are erroneous. A comprehensive review of this literature in this connection could serve no useful purpose; therefore, an attempt will be made to state the main facts regarding the rôle of nervous influences in the functional control of the female sex organs with only such references to the literature as may be necessary to indicate the experimental background of the current physiological concepts of the functional innervation of the female reproductive system.

Functional Regulation of the Ovary.—Although the ovary is abundantly supplied with nerve fibers, the distribution of these fibers seems to be limited to the blood vessels and the fibromuscular tissue in the stroma. There is no conclusive evidence for the direct functional innervation either of the ovarian follicles or the interstitial secretory tissue; therefore, it cannot be assumed that the ovarian functions are subject to direct neural regulation. They are influenced by vasomotor changes in the ovary that are mediated through the ovarian plexus and the nerves arising from it which innervate the ovarian blood vessels. Willig (1952) reported the development of new ovarian follicles in some senile animals following the administration of parasympathetocomimetic substances. The same treatment produced no similar reaction in infantile animals. Spontaneous ovulation has been reported in animals in which the ovaries were devoid of efferent nerves.

Functional Regulation of Fallopian Tubes, Uterus and Vagina.—The smooth musculature of the female genital tract has the capacity to undergo rhythmic contractions in the absence of nerve impulses. The activity of this musculature is regulated in part through hormonal agents and in part through its innervation. The importance of the non-neural factors is emphasized by the records of spontaneous activity and the reported instances of parturition following partial or complete denervation of the genital organs. According to Sauter (1948), labor contractions represent an automatic function of the uterus.

Spontaneous contractions of the musculature of the Fallopian tubes, the uterus and the vagina have been recorded by many investigators. These records indicate that the musculature of the entire genital tract is capable of automatic activity in a high degree.

Spontaneous parturition following experimental denervation of the genital tract or following lesions of the spinal cord which result in paralysis of the caudal half of the body commonly proceeds with abnormal rapidity. The contractions of the uterus seem to be more powerful than under normal innervation. Impulses normally emanating from the central nervous system undoubtedly exert an inhibitory influence in uterine activity. The fact that tonus-stimulating drugs produce more marked effects on the uterine musculature following section of the extrinsic uterine nerves than under conditions of normal innervation also supports this assumption.

The experimental data bearing on the responses of the female genital organs to direct sympathetic and parasympathetic stimulations are not unequivocal. The muscular reactions vary in different animal species and under different physiological conditions in the same species. The reactions of the pregnant uterus also differ from those of the non-pregnant uterus.

Cushny (1906) advanced the hypothesis that the sympathetic nerves exert a diphasic effect on the uterus. In virgin, pregnant and multiparous rabbits he observed powerful contractions of the whole uterus in response to sympathetic stimulation, followed by marked dilatation and inhibition of the spontaneous movements. In virgin cats he observed only relaxation and in pregnant cats only contraction of the uterus in response to sympathetic stimulation. On the basis of these findings, he expressed the opinion that the hypogastric nerves include both sympathetic inhibitory and sympathetic excitatory fibers to the uterus. Following paralysis of the sympathetic motor mechanisms, he observed either short contractions followed by marked relaxation and inhibition of the spontaneous uterine movements or pure relaxation and temporary cessation of uterine activity in response to stimulation of the hypogastric nerves in non-pregnant rabbits and pregnant cats. Dale (1906) observed similar responses to stimulation of the hypogastric nerves before and after the administration of ergotoxine. Cushny also expressed the opinion that the hypogastric nerves normally exert no tonic influence on the uterine musculature since section of these nerves causes no change except a quick contraction followed by a return to the resting condition.

The experimental data bearing on the effects of parasympathetic stimulation on the Fallopian tubes and the uterus afford no adequate basis for a positive conclusion. In experiments reported by Langley and Anderson (1895, 1896) and Dale and Laidlaw (1912), stimulation of the pelvic nerves in cats, guinea-pigs and rabbits elicited no recognizable responses in either the Fallopian tubes or the uterus. Similar experiments have been carried out by other investigators with similar negative results. Sauter (1948) reported augmentation of the tonus of the uterine musculature due to sympathetic stimulation and inhibition of tonus due to parasympathetic stimulation. Contraction of the uterus in response to parasympathetic stimulation has also been reported. In view of all the data available it seems most probable that if the parasympathetic nerves exert an influence on the motility of the Fallopian tubes and the uterus it is generally inhibitory. Lundberg (1925) advanced the opinion that the effect of the parasympathetic nerves on the uterine musculature is excitatory, but this effect is usually concealed by the stronger effect of the sympathetic nerves.

The response of the smooth musculature of the vagina to sympathetic stimulation commonly differs from that of the uterine musculature particularly in non-pregnant animals. In the cat, the guinea-pig, and the rat, according to Gunn and Franklin (1922), the vagina contracts in response to sympathetic nerve stimulation during coitus. In experiments involving nerve stimulation they observed only contraction of the vagina, in response to sympathetic stimulation, accompanied by relaxation of the uterus in some cases and contraction of the uterus in others. The motor response to sympathetic stimulation or to adrenin, in their experiments, involved both the longitudinal and circular smooth muscle of the vagina and was most marked in the half of the vagina nearest the vulva. In experiments on cats reported by Van Dyke (1926), in which he studied the effect of ergotoxine on the response of the vagina to sympathetic stimulation, the normal responses obtained confirmed the findings of Gunn and his collaborators. Following the administration of ergotoxine stimulation of the hypogastric nerve no longer elicited contraction of the vaginal musculature but either relaxation followed by contraction or complete relaxation. He interpreted these findings as supporting the assumption that the hypogastric nerves include inhibitory as well as motor fibers to the vagina.

20

Certain experimental data seem to support the assumption that pelvic nerve stimulation elicits inhibition of the smooth muscle of the vagina, but the inhibitory response is not marked. Certain investigators recognized no effect of pelvic nerve stimulation on the vagina.

The sympathetic nerves to the female genital organs include both vasoconstrictor and vasodilator fibers. Vasodilatation, particularly in the erectile tissue in the clitoris, may be elicited by parasympathetic stimulation. The data available do not support the assumption that the blood vessels throughout the genital organs are supplied with parasympathetic vasodilator fibers. Both the hypogastric and the pelvic nerves include visceral afferent components that are connected with receptors in various parts of the genital organs.

Genital Reflexes.—The spinal centers concerned in the reflex control of the sex organs in the female, as in the male, are located in the sacral and the rostral lumbar segments of the spinal cord. The anatomical relationships of these centers and the afferent and efferent nerves concerned are essentially identical in both sexes. The physiological relationships are also comparable. Stimuli arising within the uterus, the Fallopian tubes or Bartholin's glands may elicit reflex contraction of the smooth musculature of the genital tract through the lumbar center. Stimulation of the sensory end organs in the clitoris elicits reflexes through the sacral center which bring about vasodilatation and turgor of the erectile tissue in the clitoris. This reaction is comparable to erection in the male. Summation of the sensory impulses arising in the external genitalia also results in a discharge of efferent impulses from the spinal cord that brings about expulsion of the accumulated secretion of Bartholin's glands, a reaction which is comparable to the expulsion of seminal fluid in the male. In like manner the summation of impulses arising in the external genitalia may result in the discharge of efferent impulses from the lumbar center through the hypogastric and the uterine plexuses that result in peristaltic contractions of the uterine musculature and expulsion of mucus from the cavity of the uterus.

Reflex uterine contractions elicited by stimulation of the mammary glands were not unknown to Hippocrates. Such reflex contractions may give rise to painful sensations. Uterine responses to stimulation of the breasts become more pronounced near the termination of pregnancy. In an analysis of the reflex responses of the uterus to stimulation of the nipple at the termination of pregnancy, the beginning of parturition and during the postparturition period Lóránd and Asbót (1952) found that some of the uterine reactions are temporary and some endure for some time. The strong uterine contractions elicited by stimulation of the nipple after parturition are an important factor in the involution of the uterus. If the uterus is highly sensitive, strong stimulation of the nipple during pregnancy may cause abortion. Stimulation of the nipples also elicits reflex reactions in other parts of the genital system. In the rat and the mouse suckling of the young results in long periods of diestrus which are interrupted by an estrus cycle only once in two or three weeks. If the young are removed during a diestrus period the estrus cycle immediately returns to normal. This disturbance of the sexual cyclicity during lactation seems to be independent of the secretory activity of the mammary glands and is due to stimulation of the nipples. It differs from copulation pseudopregnancy, which is caused by a single nerve stimulus, in that its maintenance requires continuous stimulation of the nipples.

A functional relationship between the erectile tissue in the genital organs and the cavernous tissue in the nasal mucosa has long been recognized. The genital and the nasal cavernous tissues frequently react synchronously, *i.e.*, when either the genital or the nasal cavernous tissue becomes engorged the other also becomes engorged and when either one empties the other likewise empties. Under certain conditions either the genital or the nasal cavernous tissue may react independently of the other. The assumption that afferent impulses that arise in the nasal mucosa elicit reflex reactions in the anterior hypophyseal lobe which in turn exert an influence on the genital organs probably through a hormonal mechanism is supported by both experimental and anatomical data.

Reflex responses in the female genital organs may be elicited by impulses that arise in adjacent viscera or by afferent stimulation of somatic nerves. Some of these reflexes are mediated through the genital centers in the lumbar and the sacral segments of the spinal cord. Others involve centers in the brain stem, including the autonomic centers in the hypothalamus. The assumption that impulses emanating from the hypothalamus influence diverse genital functions, including menstruation, ovulation, gestation and parturition is supported by abundant experimental data.

The Sexual Orgasm.—The reactions concerned in the sexual orgasm in the female are less definitely known than those concerned in the corresponding phenomenon in the male. The sexual orgasm involves comparable reactions in both sexes. The afferent impulses that give rise to the sensations associated with this phenomenon arise in the female, as in the male, in consequence of the contractions of the smooth musculature of the genital tract. Peristaltic contractions are normally initiated in the Fallopian tubes when sexual excitation is at its height. These contractions are propagated to the uterus and the vagina and are followed by rhythmic contractions of the striated sphincter vaginæ muscles. The afferent impulses in question probably traverse the same nerves and central conduction pathways in the female as in the male.

Chapter XV

INNERVATION OF THE SKIN AND ITS APPENDAGES

ANATOMICAL DATA

Cutaneous Nerves.—The skin includes the sense organs through which most of the stimulating factors in the external environment influence the body; consequently, it is abundantly innervated through afferent nerves. The cutaneous vessels, other cutaneous muscular structures and the cutaneous glands also are innervated through autonomic nerve fibers which in general are associated with the afferent cutaneous nerves.

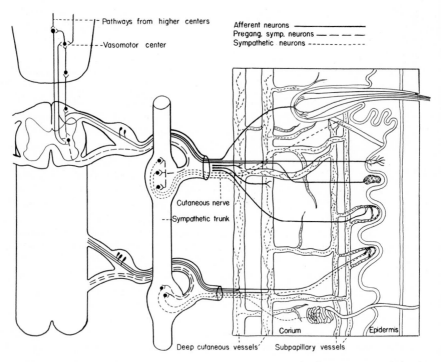

Fig. 69.—Diagrammatic illustration of sympathetic and afferent innervation of cutaneous structures.

As the cutaneous nerves approach the skin they form a coarse plexiform structure in the subcutaneous stratum. From this level smaller nerves penetrate the corium and form a plexiform meshwork at the border of the reticular and the papillary strata. Rami that arise from the plexus approach the epidermis and form a subepithelial plexus from which terminal branches of afferent fibers penetrate the deeper layers of the epidermis. The cutaneous nerves include both myelinated and unmyelinated afferent fibers. The terminal branches of most of the myelinated fibers also are unmyelinated. Most of the autonomic fibers in the skin are unmyelinated and of small caliber. Except in the cephalic area, they are derived exclusively from the ganglia of the sympathetic trunks (Fig. 69). The autonomic innervation of the skin in the cephalic area is also predominantly sympathetic. Parasympathetic fibers probably reach the skin in the cephalic area, but their cutaneous distribution is not fully known.

Regeneration of sympathetic nerve fibers in the skin following lesions of cutaneous nerves or section of the nerves in the preparation of pedicle flaps takes place slowly. The earliest return of sympathetic function in pedicle flaps, according to Kredel and Phemister (1939), becomes apparent only after sensory function has become reëstablished. Early and adequate sensory recovery, in their experience, was usually, but not invariably, followed by sympathetic recovery.

The afferent fibers terminate in relation to the specialized cutaneous sense organs and the hair follicles and in naked arborizations both in the corium and the deep layers of the epidermis. Most of the autonomic fibers terminate in relation to the cutaneous vessels, including capillaries, the erector pili muscles and the cutaneous glands.

Sympathetic nerve fibers are conveyed to the skin in cutaneous branches of the cerebrospinal nerves. Those that traverse the spinal nerves join them through the corresponding sympathetic roots. Those that reach the skin in the cephalic area join the corresponding cranial nerves mainly through the plexuses on the internal and the external carotid arteries. Since the preganglionic fibers that supply the cervical sympathetic ganglia are components of the rostral thoracic nerves, the spinal centers for the sympathetic innervation of the skin of the entire head, the neck, the upper extremity and the rostral portion of the thorax are located in the rostral thoracic segments of the spinal cord. Since those that supply the sympathetic trunk ganglia in the lumbar and the sacral segments are components of the caudal thoracic and the rostral lumbar nerves, the spinal centers for the sympathetic innervation of the skin of the lower extremities and the caudal portions of the trunk are located in the caudal thoracic and the rostral lumbar segments of the spinal cord. In general the sympathetic innervation of the skin of the trunk is segmental, but preganglionic fibers that arise in a given segment of the spinal cord may make synaptic connections with sympathetic ganglion cells whose axons are distributed to the skin in several segments. For example, stimulation of the ventral root of the fifth thoracic nerve activates sweat glands from the fourth to the tenth thoracic segments.

The simplest reflex arc concerned in the reflex activity of cutaneous effectors may be conceived as follows: The afferent limb consists of an afferent spinal nerve component that terminates peripherally in a cutaneous receptor. The efferent limb consists of a preganglionic neuron located in the intermediolateral cell column and a sympathetic ganglion cell located in the sympathetic trunk (Fig. 69). If both afferent and efferent limbs are components of the same or adjacent nerves it may be assumed that the central connections are made within the segments in question. If, as in the case of effectors in the cephalic area, the afferent and the efferent limbs of the reflex arcs are connected with the central nervous system through widely separated nerve roots the central reflex connections must be regarded as relatively complex. Reflexes of a higher order carried out through afferent and efferent components of the same or adjacent spinal nerves also involve centers in the brain stem.

Hair Follicles. — The hair follicles are abundantly supplied with nerve fibers that form relatively dense plexuses around them. These plexuses include both myelinated and unmyelinated fibers. Most of the latter are the unmyelinated terminal branches of myelinated fibers. Many nerve fiber terminations undoubtedly occur in the connective tissue layers of follicles. Terminal branches also penetrate into the epithelial layers. The innervation of the hair follicles is essentially sensory, but some fibers of sympathetic origin are included in the perifollicular plexuses. Unmyelinated fibers, probably of sympathetic origin, and myelinated ones also terminate in the connective tissue papillæ. The sympathetic fibers probably terminate in relation to the nutritive vessels in the papillæ. Nerve fibers in close relation to the sebaceous glands have been described, but the data available do not warrant the conclusion that sympathetic fibers actually make functional contacts with sebaceous gland cells. Terminations of sympathetic nerve fibers in the erector pili muscles have been abundantly demonstrated.

Sweat Glands. — The sweat glands are simple tubular structures the ducts of which are provided with smooth muscle fibers that probably play a rôle in expelling the secretion. These tubules are surrounded by delicate networks of unmyelinated fibers that lie close to the basement membrane. Terminal branches of these fibers end in relation to the muscular elements and probably in relation to the secretory gland cells.

In man sweat glands are distributed over the entire surface of the body, but they are more abundant and larger in certain areas than in others. They are particularly abundant in the head, the face, the palms, the soles and the genital region. Perspiration usually is most profuse in these areas. In many of the hairy mammals sweat glands occur only in restricted areas of the skin. Cats have functional sweat glands only in the paw pads. Young dogs have functional sweat glands in their paw pads. These probably become nonfunctional as the animals grow older. Pigs have functional sweat glands in the snout. Rabbits, rats and mice probably have no sweat glands. Certain other hairy mammals, e.g., the horse, have functional sweat glands over the entire surface of the body.

Mammary Glands. — In the human species the mammary glands are innervated through the lateral cutaneous rami of the second to the sixth intercostal nerves. The nipple and the areola are abundantly supplied with afferent fibers that terminate in cutaneous receptors and sympathetic fibers that terminate in relation to the smooth muscle in the nipple and the adjacent superficial area. The body of the gland is sparsely supplied with nerve fibers most of which are sympathetic and reach the gland through the fourth, the fifth and the sixth intercostal nerves. The lateral cutaneous rami of these nerves give off mammary rami through which sympathetic fibers are distributed throughout the gland. Sympathetic nerve fibers also reach the mammary gland along the course of the long thoracic artery and the anterior perforating branches of the intercostal arteries that supply the gland. Within the mammary gland the sympathetic fibers terminate mainly in relation to the blood vessels and the smooth muscle which is sparsely distributed throughout the gland. Certain physiological data seem to indicate the existence of secretory fibers in the mammary gland, but nerve fiber terminations in relation to mammary gland cells have not been demonstrated anatomically. In the sheep, according to Peeters *et al.* (1952), the sympathetic innervation of the udder is derived from the lumbar segments of the sympathetic trunk. Extirpation of the lumbar sympathetic trunk resulted in vasodilatation of the half of the udder on the same side, which subsided after three days. The secretion and the ejection of milk remained unaffected.

PHYSIOLOGICAL DATA

Hair Growth in Relation to Sympathetic Nerves. — Excessive growth of hair in a circumscribed area associated with a lesion of the nerves through which it is innervated has been reported frequently. This phenomenon probably can be explained most satisfactorily on the assumption that the papillary blood supply has been increased due to partial or complete functional interruption of the sympathetic innervation of the vessels in question. Loss of hair in a circumscribed area and failure of its restoration also is common. This phenomenon undoubtedly involves reduction of the papillary blood supply due to peripheral vasoconstriction in the area in question.

In areas of alopecia areata the patent capillaries are reduced in number. Those that remain patent are reduced in caliber and there is evidence of spastic contraction of the arterioles. Localized vasoconstrictor hypertonicity probably is also a factor in the etiology of alopecia areata. The frequent occurrence of bald spots in patients with diseases in which the sympathetic nerves are known to be involved, such as exophthalmic goiter, scleroderma and vitiligo, also supports the assumption that sympathetic hypertonicity is a significant factor in spontaneous failure of hair growth. Measures that result in overcoming peripheral vasoconstriction, *e.g.*, mild local stimulation by mechanical, chemical, actinic or thermal agencies, frequently result in augmentation of hair growth probably due to increased circulation through the papillary vessels.

Regulation of Erector Pili Activity. — The erector pili muscles contract in response to sympathetic stimulation. Generalized pilo-erection is a common phenomenon associated with emotional excitation, due to the discharge of impulses from hypothalamic sympathetic centers. Contraction of the erector pili muscles is also elicited reflexly by appropriate cutaneous stimulation, particularly exposure to cold. Localized pilo-erection in an area of referred hyperalgesia associated with visceral disease is a common phenomenon. It undoubtedly represents a reflex response to the stimulation of visceral afferent fibers, in the area of the lesion, that gives rise to the referred sensory phenomena.

Intracutaneous administration of acetylcholine and other drugs with nicotine-like action elicits strong fleeting pilo-erector activity in the vicinity of the injection. This reaction is abolished by sympathetic nerve degeneration, but it can be elicited in areas anesthetized by nerve block and in excised pieces of skin. These results have been interpreted as supporting the conclusion that the localized pilo-erector activity elicited by the drugs in question represents an axon reflex response mediated through the terminal branches of the sympathetic fibers that innervate the erector pili muscles.

Pilo-erection is essentially an involuntary response. Individual cases have been reported in which the hairs could be erected voluntarily. Lindsley and Sassman (1938) reported a case in which voluntary erection of the hairs was accompanied by an increase in the cardiac rhythm, an increase in the rate and depth of respiration, dilatation of the pupils, a decrease in the galvanic skin resistance in areas rich in sweat glands, and a slight increase in blood pressure. These phenomena indicate a generalized sympathetic discharge. Involvement of impulses that emanate from the cerebral cortex is indicated by characteristic changes in the brain potentials in the premotor area that preceded the peripheral autonomic changes and appeared to be associated with them.

Regulation of Sweat Secretion.—Unlike various other organs with sympathetic innervation, the sweat glands react only to a limited number of direct stimulating agents. Normally they are activated only by nerve impulses. Sympathetic denervation of a cutaneous area, except in certain portions of the head and the face, results in complete and permanent cessation of perspiration except in the presence of stimulating agents that act upon the glands directly.

Localized lesions of the sympathetic trunks or their rami result in the cessation of thermoregulatory sweating in circumscribed areas. Such areas frequently are bounded by a zone of increased perspiration. Sympathetic denervation of extensive areas of the skin results in a marked increase in the sudomotor activity of the remaining areas, which may be regarded as a compensatory thermoregulatory response. Denervated sweat glands undergo no appreciable histological alterations, but retain the capacity to respond to excessive heat and to certain pharmacological agents. Prolonged continuous stimulation at low voltage of the sciatic nerve in the rat, as reported by Ring and Randall (1946), resulted in profound degranulation of the secretory cells in the sweat glands in the hind paw pad and diminution in their height by as much as 75 per cent. After maximal secretory activity was attained the rate of secretion gradually diminished until it reached the zero level in approximately 4.5 hours. Fatigue of sweat glands due to secretory activity within physiological limits has also been reported (Thaysen *et al.*, 1952).

The secretory output of the sweat glands is determined in some measure by the cutaneous blood supply, but these glands may exhibit secretory activity even in the absence of cutaneous circulation. Such activity is demonstrated by the finding that nerve stimulation elicits sweat secretion in a newly amputated limb. On the other hand, the administration of adrenin results in diminished sweat production due to the vasoconstrictor action of this hormone. This is in full accord with the common observation that the production of sweat is diminished by chilling of the skin which brings about constriction of the peripheral blood vessels. Burn (1925) demonstrated that pilocarpine, a potent sweat-producing stimulant, is ineffective if the capillary dilatation brought about by the drug is prevented by section of the spinal nerve roots. In the absence of capillary tonus, pilocarpine is without effect on the cutaneous blood supply. Although the postganglionic fibers that innervate the sweat glands remain intact, the drug has no effect on their secretory activity. Profuse sweating in man often accompanies a pallid skin, as in nausea or terror. On the other hand, the flushed skin of fever is characterized by the absence of perspiration. These facts indicate that the sweat glands are activated by impulses conducted by true secretory nerve fibers and that their activity may under certain conditions be quite independent of the functional state of the cutaneous blood vessels.

Concentration of the blood by extraction of water through the digestive system does not suppress perspiration completely. Profuse sweating sometimes occurs in cases of violent diarrhea and exhaustion even when a deficiency of water in the blood and the tissues is indicated by profound thirst. Abundance of water in the blood and the tissues exerts no marked influence on the output of perspiration. The drinking of cold water in large quantities does not appreciably affect the secretory activity of the sweat glands. On the other hand, the drinking of hot liquids, *e.g.*, hot tea, frequently calls forth sudden profuse perspiration.

Under physiological conditions the most common causes of profuse sweating are high external temperature and muscular activity. In either case it may be regarded as thermoregulatory. Such sweating is centrally induced and is generalized. The appropriate autonomic centers in the brain stem are stimulated by the increased temperature of the circulating blood. As has been pointed out by Adolph (1946), secretory activity of the sweat glands in man does not attain its maximal rate until the heat content of the body as a whole has been appreciably increased. When warm air impinges on the surface the skin temperature begins to rise at once, but maximal sweating is delayed 5 to 15 minutes, which is too long to represent reflex reaction time. The spinal centers concerned in the innervation of the sweat glands also react to increased blood temperature, as is demonstrated by the finding that, following transection of the spinal cord, perfusion of a portion of the cord caudal to the section with blood heated to 45° C. brings about profuse perspiration in the skin areas innervated from the portion of the spinal cord perfused.

Perspiration in response to external temperature which is limited to the area exposed to the high temperature may be regarded as reflex. The afferent impulses that arise at the periphery are conducted centrad through sensory cutaneous fibers, probably the heat fibers, and the sweat glands are activated through their sympathetic nerves (Fig. 69). Such reflex activity may play a rôle in thermoregulatory sweating particularly in response to external temperatures not sufficiently high to cause an appreciable increase in blood temperature.

Localized reflex sweating is a common phenomenon in visceral disease. The segmental perspiration in patients with pulmonary tuberculosis can be explained most satisfactorily on the assumption that impulses conducted from the site of a pulmonary lesion by visceral afferent spinal nerve components elicit reflex responses through preganglionic and sympathetic neurons concerned with the innervation of the sweat glands in the corresponding cutaneous segment. Reflex sudomotor activity in localized areas of referred hyperalgesia associated with various visceral lesions may be explained on the same basis.

In many persons, particularly among the frail and the obese, profuse perspiration over the entire body may be elicited by exposure of a limited area, e.g., an arm or a leg, to a high external temperature. In such cases warming of a limited part of the body surface undoubtedly results in an increase in the temperature of the circulating blood sufficient to stimulate the appropriate centers in the brain stem. The occurrence of normal sweating in other parts of the body in response to exposure of an anesthetized cutaneous area to high temperature supports this assumption.

The central sweat centers also react to changes in the acid-base balance of the blood. According to Hasama (1930), perfusion of the fourth ventricle with Ringer's solution or injection of this solution into the carotid artery results in profuse perspiration and a rise in body temperature. If the Ringer's solution is alcoholic it results in inhibition of perspiration and a rise in body temperature. These reactions probably are mediated through centers in the medulla oblongata since they may be obtained after transection of the mesencephalon.

Perspiration may be elicited reflexly by various external stimuli other than temperature. In experimental animals unilateral faradic stimulation of the brachial plexus elicits secretory activity of the sweat glands in both forelimbs. Localized painful stimulation, if sufficiently intense, may result in sudden profuse perspiration over the entire surface of the body. This reaction may be reflex in part, but emotional excitation undoubtedly constitutes a major factor. Purely reflex sweating probably is always localized. As observed by Randall (1946), when radiant heat is applied locally to one arm sweating may be limited to the area heated. If the heating is intense the response is bilateral, but the number of sweat glands activated is greater on the heated arm than on the contralateral one. Unilateral or bilateral activation of sweat glands by the application of radiant heat to one arm does not necessarily depend on elevation of the temperature of the blood flowing through the central nervous system or in direct heating of the sweat glands since the reflex sweating persists relatively unaltered for 5 to 15 minutes after occlusion of the blood flow from the heated arm (Randall et al., 1948).

Following immersion of the lower extremities and the lower portion of the trunk of male subjects in warm water (38 to 44° C.), as reported by Randall et al. (1948), the cutaneous blood flow and the skin temperature of the finger pads promptly increased. Simultaneous sweating responses on the finger pad were either unaltered or showed a slight increase. On the forearm, the cheek and the forehead an increase in the blood flow, the temperature and sweating could be detected only after a latent period. In general the increase in blood flow and in sweating occurred approximately simultaneously, but in some experiments the sweating response preceded vasodilation.

Several different combinations of vasoconstriction and sweating in the finger pads and the skin of the forearm have been observed by Franke *et al.* (1947). Some patterns occur more frequently than others. Noises, deep inspiration, mental arithmetic, etc., regularly induce vasoconstriction and sweating in the finger pads. Simultaneous vasoconstriction and sweating may take place in the skin of the forearm, but the magnitude of the responses is less than in the finger pads. Vasomotor and sudomotor responses in the finger pads may occur simultaneously in the absence of detectable corresponding responses in the forearm. The converse was not observed.

When subjected to appropriate ambient temperature, as reported by Randall *et al.* (1951), sweating in nude subjects usually is limited to the more distal portions of the lower extremities. As the environmental temperature is increased, sudomotor activity extends upward to involve the entire limb and the trunk and finally the arms and the face in fairly regular sequence. The sweating is characteristically cyclic. The peaks of sweating become successively higher as the ambient temperature is increased. Marked differences in the recruitment of sweat glands frequently may be observed in adjacent dermatomes. While the ambient temperature is rising cyclic sweating may increase progressively on the dorsal surfaces of the hands and the feet while it decreases on the palmar and the plantar surfaces. Elimination of water through the skin in the absence of detectable perspiration appears to be correlated with the local blood supply (Peiss *et al.*, 1951).

As observed by Bazett (1951), the superficial heat receptors are concerned with vascular readjustments. The deeper ones are concerned with sweating. The deep receptors are readily stimulated by heat produced in working muscles. The apparent relationship of sweating to skin temperature is due to a temperature gradient between the arterial and the venous blood. The responses of the body to external heat utilize vasomotor adjustments until the surface temperature exceeds 34° C., when sweating supervenes. Heat of internal origin maintains the existing surface temperature and utilizes sweating proportionately. Since sensations of heat do not necessarily parallel sweating caused by local heating, Issikutz *et al.* (1950) concluded that sensations of heat are not mediated through the afferent fibers concerned in reflex sweating. Interruption of the efferent pathways from the central reflex centers concerned, according to Pollock *et al.* (1951), results in defective regulation of sweating, but interruption of the pathways for inhibitory impulses from suprasegmental centers results in excessive reflex sweating.

Localized sweating may be elicited by direct stimulation of cutaneous nerves. The local sweat response to faradic stimulation, according to Wilkins *et al.* (1938), represents an axon reflex mediated through postganglionic sympathetic fibers. It may be inhibited by the administration of atropine or augmented by the administration of prostigmine or blocked by the intradermal injection of novocain. It is independent of ganglionic connections since it may be elicited following section of the cutaneous nerves. Local spread of the response also indicates that a given gland may be stimulated from different points, which supports the assumption that the terminal branches of the sympathetic fibers in question form a peripheral plexus. On the basis of these findings, Wilkins *et al.* have advanced the opinion that the sympathetic fibers that innervate sweat glands divide near their terminations into numerous fine branches that radiate through the skin in all directions. Every axon with its terminal branches, therefore, may be regarded as an axon system. Since these systems overlap, stimulation at any given point may activate nearly all the glands in the immediate vicinity. A very small novocain wheal, therefore, does not entirely block the spread of impulses in any given direction from the point of stimulation, but a larger one does. Unique patterns of localized sweating following intradermal and subcutaneous injections of mecholyl that suggest spread of the drug from the site of injection through lymph channels have been reported by Randall *et al.* (1947). They were characterized by narrow zones of sweating radiating outward from the wheal, the most prominent of which extended centrad.

The electrical resistance of the skin is closely coördinated with sweat gland activity. Richter and Levine (1937) reported a marked increase in electrical resistance in the skin of the palms and less in the skin on the volar surface of the hand in ten patients following cervical sympathectomy. They recommend the use of readings of the electrical resistance of the skin in the study of sympathetic disturbances in man since it requires little time, as compared with other methods, and may be repeated at frequent intervals with little inconvenience to the patient. Convenient and efficient technics for recording electrical skin resistance, therefore, are desirable.

Richter and Whelan (1949) described a skin galvanometer that gives a graphic record of the sympathetic nerve activity indirectly through the alterations in the electrical resistance of the skin. Thomas and Korr (1951) have described a procedure for the photographic recording of electrical skin resistance patterns on the human trunk. These technics facilitate the localization of cutaneous areas in which sympathetic nerve activity is either increased or decreased. The term, "sympathetic dermatome," has been proposed by Mentha (1949) to designate the cutaneous area of distribution of the sympathetic nerves derived from a given segment. Sympathetic dermatomes do not necessarily coincide with the corresponding sensory dermatomes. Randall *et al.* (1952) have called attention to some disparity of the areas in which sudomotor and pilomotor responses are elicited by the same segmental stimulation.

By the use of the electrical skin resistance method following thoracolumbar sympathectomies, Richter and Otenasek (1946) found that the outlines of the sympathetically denervated areas are in many instances irregular and unsymmetrical. In some patients the areas devoid of sympathetic innervation did not completely encircle the body, but there remained a gap near the midline either dorsally or ventrally that varied from 1 to 4 inches.

In patients with visceral disease Korr (1949) observed areas of low resistance in the dermatomes corresponding to the segmental innervation of the diseased viscus. Sympathetic hyperactivity, as indicated by decreased skin resistance, in the corresponding cutaneous areas may also be induced and maintained by myofascial and postural disturbances. The areas of reduced skin resistance coincide with the areas of referred pain. According to Morrison and Spiegel (1945), an increase of 10 millivolts or more in the skin potential in the dermatome corresponding to a painful viscus is indicative of organic disease.

On the basis of an extensive electrodermatographic study of autonomic reflex phenomena, Regelsberger (1952) has emphasized the conditioned reflex character of many visceral reactions and the reflex relationships between dermatomes and visceral organs. Electrodermatography affords a means of evaluating the functional status of the autonomic nerves. It also possesses diagnostic and prognostic value.

In certain individuals pungent odors and the ingestion of spicy foods elicit sweating in the face which has been called gustatory sweating. Faint sweating of this kind occurs in many apparently normal persons. Gustatory hyperhydrosis has been reported, particularly by List and Peet (1938), associated with auriculotemporal lesions and lesions in other cephalic areas following cervical sympathectomy. They have regarded such exaggerated gustatory sweating as probably due to locally increased irritability of the cholinergic fibers. Wilson (1936) advanced the opinion that excessive gustatory sweating may be related to a hyperactive condition of the sweat glands, as indicated by their response to pilocarpine.

Haxton (1948) reported gustatory sweating in patients following sympathetic denervation of the upper extremities. He observed it in approximately 35% of the patients studied. Some of them had been subjected to sympathetic trunk extirpation and others to preganglionic sympathectomy. Gustatory sweating was not observed immediately after sympathectomy, but after a latent period of a few weeks to several years.

By the use of technics by which the number of active sweat glands per unit area of skin can be determined and a qualitative measure of the amount of sweat secreted from each functional sweat pore can be obtained, Randall (1946) found that maximal sweating is brought about through increased numbers of participating sweat glands and increased output per gland. The patterns of distribution of sweat glands under conditions of maximal or nearly maximal sweating indicate marked numerical variation in sweat glands in different cutaneous areas and in different individuals. The output per gland also varies in different areas and under different conditions.

As reported by Randall and McClure (1949), quantitative calculations of the output of sweat glands on the arm and the leg show greater average values than calculations of the output on the dorsal surfaces of the hand and the foot. Mild muscular exercise results in an increase in the number of active sweat glands, but in no appreciable increase in the output per gland. Under more intense stimulation, the total output may be supplemented by an increase in the output per gland.

With ambient temperatures of 20 to 35° C. sweat glands on the dorsal surface of the forearm are phasically active. Larger and smaller numbers of glands are active during alternating periods, but the periodicity and the numbers of glands participating in every cycle are irregular. The cycles are influenced by alterations in the ambient temperature, peripheral and visceral stimulation and emotional excitation. In the undisturbed resting subject sweating is characterized by the sudden activation of a number of glands for a few seconds followed by a period during which the output of these glands approximates the zero level. Although the periods of activity of individual glands are short, activity may alternate between many glands in a given area and thus prolong the duration of a given cycle. When subjected to prolonged strong stimulation the sweat mechanism responds first with activity of an increased number of sweat glands and then with a marked increase in the output per gland. The simultaneous peaks and depressions in the numbers of active sweat glands on both fore-arms suggests that the phasic activity of the sweat glands is regulated through a central neural mechanism (Randall, 1946).

Psychic Stimulation of Sweat Secretion.—Strong emotions, particularly anxiety and expectancy, frequently are accompanied by profuse perspiration even in persons in good health, but more often in "nervous" individuals. This need not be regarded as essentially pathological. Perspiration during emotional disturbances, however, may assume a pathological aspect. Patients in whom such is the case usually also complain of other nervous disorders, e.g., tachycardia, gastric pains and headache. Many individuals experience localized perspiration, especially in the palms of the hands and sometimes also on the soles of the feet, during even minor emotional disturbances such as embarrassment and perplexity. Sweating on the forehead in response to emotional stimuli has been studied by Mc-Gregor (1952). According to his findings, this area represents only the most conspicuous portion of a wider area of the face, variable in extent in different individuals, that responds to emotional stimuli. Outbreaks of profuse perspiration without any apparent cause also have been observed in hysterical patients. Emotional sweating is essentially of central origin, but differs from thermoregulatory sweating in that it may occur during peripheral vasoconstriction, whereas thermoregulatory sweating is accompanied by peripheral vasodilatation (Ebbecke, 1951).

Response of Sweat Glands to Cerebral Stimulation.—Cortical stimulation, under certain conditions, results in excitation of the sweat glands. This fact and the fact that perspiration is a common accompaniment of certain emotional states led certain of the earlier investigators to assume the existence of a cortical sweat center. Disturbances in the regulatory control of perspiration on the paralyzed side in cases of hemiplegia due to cerebral lesions have been observed frequently. Such disturbances prob-ably are not directly referable to the cerebral lesions in question. Certain data obtained from patients with cerebral lesions indicate that sudomotor activity may be influenced by impulses that emanate from widely separated cortical areas. Guttmann (1931) reported perspiration on the contra-lateral side in man in response to electrical stimulation of the cortex both in the precentral and the postcentral gyri. The onset of perspiration fol-lowed the beginning of stimulation after a latent period, and the secretory activity of the sweat glands continued for some time after stimulation of the cortex ceased. Extirpation of the premotor cortex may be followed by excessive palmar sweating probably due to impulses emanating from centers in the hypothalamus that are released from cortical control. As observed by Buck *et al.* (1951), temperature regulation is more nearly normal in schizophrenic patients following prefrontal lobotomy than it was before the operation. In persons capable of voluntary pilo-erection this act usually is accompanied by secretory activity of the sweat glands. These observations unmistakably prove that impulses emanating from the cerebral cortex exert an influence on the secretory activity of the sweat glands which is exerted through subcortical centers, particularly the autonomic centers in the hypothalamus, but none of the data available indicate the existence of a cortical sweat center.

Direct Influence of Spinal Centers on Sweat Secretion.—Recorded observations on the effect of organic lesions of the spinal cord on the functional activity of the sweat glands are somewhat contradictory. Normal perspiration as well as a decrease in sweat secretion or even its cessation in the paralyzed portion of the body has been reported following transverse lesions of the spinal cord. In a careful study of twelve paraplegic patients, Böwing (1924) never observed complete absence of perspiration in the affected areas, but usually found that the secretory activity of the sweat glands in these areas was somewhat diminished. Neither did he find a sharp line of demarcation between the areas of normal and diminished perspiration at the level of the spinal cord lesion in cases in which the lesion was located in the thoracic or the lumbar region. This may be explained on the basis of the peripheral distribution of the preganglionic fibers concerned in the innervation of the sweat glands. Most of them, as previously stated, terminate in more than one ganglion of the sympathetic trunk.

Unilateral lesions of the spinal cord frequently are followed by diminished perspiration in the affected region on the side of the lesion. Diseases that involve localized degeneration of spinal cord tissue, *e.g.*, syringomyelia and poliomyelitis, are also accompanied by functional disturbances of the sweat glands in the affected area. Whether such disturbances involve a diminished or an increased output of perspiration depends on the exact site of the lesion and the character of the degenerative process. Destruction of cells in the intermediolateral cell column commonly results in localized anhydrosis.

Effect of Drugs on Sweat Secretion.—Since the innervation of the sweat glands is essentially cholinergic, pharmacological agents in this category generally exert a stimulating effect on the sudomotor mechanisms. In general they exert their influence through the nerve fibers that supply the sweat glands. Certain pharmacological agents, *e.g.*, pilocarpine, probably exert a direct stimulating effect on the glands. When administered subcutaneously in customary doses, pilocarpine usually exerts no detectable direct action on the sweat glands, but stimulates the endings of the cholinergic nerve fibers. Sweating elicited in this manner may be inhibited by the administration of atropine. Following preganglionic sympathectomy the sudomotor effect of pilocarpine is more marked than under normal conditions. Antipyretic drugs, *e.g.*, the salicylates, probably cause perspiration due to their action on hypothalamic centers. Certain other drugs, *e.g.*, strychnine and camphor, exert their sudomotor effects on the spinal sweat centers. Muscarine and physostigmine bring about perspiration by their stimulating effect on the terminations of the nerve fibers that supply the sweat glands. Atropine paralyzes these nerve fiber terminations and, therefore, brings about cessation of perspiration.

Adrenin commonly exerts an inhibitory influence on spontaneous perspiration particularly in neurotic patients. It also counteracts the sudomotor effect of pilocarpine. A sudomotor effect of adrenin in man has been reported (Wada, 1950; Haimovici, 1950). This has been interpreted as indicating that the innervation of the sweat glands, at least in some human subjects, includes some adrenergic fibers.

Nervous Influences in Mammary Function.—The results obtained in the experimental studies carried out by the earlier investigators to determine the possible rôle of nerve impulses in the secretory activity of the mammary glands afford no basis for definite positive conclusions. The results of all the experimental studies in which partial or complete denervation of the mammary glands was carried out indicate quite clearly that the secretory function of these glands, in a large measure, is independent of neural regulation. Certain experimental data strongly suggest that the mammary secretion may be influenced, at least qualitatively, through the nerves that innervate the mammary gland. Certain data seem to indicate that sympathetic denervation of lactating mammary glands results in qualitative alterations in the milk produced. Other available data fail to support this assumption.

The development and growth of the mammary glands preceding puberty, their enlargement during gestation, the initiation of secretory activity, and the beginning of milk production following parturition are correlated with changes in the genital organs and are brought about largely through the stimulating influence of hormonal substances produced by the internal sex organs. Chemical stimuli and nutritive conditions also play a major rôle in milk production throughout the period of lactation. Neural regulation, nevertheless, plays an important rôle in the flow of milk or the facilitation of its extraction from the mammary gland. The stimulus afforded by the sucking of the young, in mammals including the human species, is an important factor in increasing the output of milk at the beginning of lactation following parturition and in facilitating the extraction of milk throughout the lactating period. This stimulation of the nipple and the areola elicits definite reflex reactions in the mammary glands that facilitate the movement of milk toward the outlet. These reactions in turn give rise to afferent impulses that result in more or less definite sensations.

The fact that unilateral stimulation of the nipple elicits reflex responses in both breasts indicates that the reflexes concerned traverse the central nervous system. The afferent impulses are conducted to the spinal cord through the afferent fibers that are distributed to the nipple and the areola. The efferent impulses reach the glands through their sympathetic nerves. The reflex reactions in question involve the smooth muscles in the nipple and the areolar area and that which occurs in small quantity throughout the gland. The existence of secretory fibers in the mammary glands has not been demonstrated.

Stimulation of the hypothalamus in the vicinity of the supraoptic nuclei in lactating sheep and goats (Anderson, 1951) and stimulation of the supraopticohypophyseal tract in rabbits (Cross and Harris, 1952) resulted in the ejection of milk. This reaction appears to be mediated through hormonal mechanisms since it persists unaltered following sympathetic denervation of the mammary glands. It is abolished by section of the supraopticohypophyseal tract. Ejection of milk can also be elicited by afferent vagus stimulation and by the administration of pitoxin or pitressin.

Trophic Regulation of the Skin.—The nutritive and the functional states of the skin are constantly influenced through the sympathetic nerves and may be modified locally by sympathectomy. Regulation of the caliber of the cutaneous blood vessels and tissue spaces and capillary permeability undoubtedly is a major factor in trophic regulation.

In experiments reported by Asher (1937) the reaction of sympathectomized skin to intracutaneous injections of histamine was compared with that of the normally innervated skin. In appropriate concentration, histamine produced a large bleb in the sympathectomized skin, but had no appreciable effect on the normally innervated skin. When the concentration of the drug was increased it also produced a bleb in the normally innervated skin that subsided much more rapidly than the one produced by the same concentration of histamine in the sympathectomized skin. Deprived of its sympathetic innervation, the skin obviously becomes less resistant to the effect of histamine possibly due to decreased permeability of the cutaneous capillaries. The dry, scaly condition of the human skin following sympathectomy obviously is due chiefly to cessation of the secretory activity of the sweat glands. Localized atrophy of the subcutaneous tissue and the connective tissue layer of the skin associated with chronic pulmonary tuberculosis (Pottinger, 1929) undoubtedly is a result of reflex vasoconstriction in the areas in question elicited by afferent stimulation at the sites of the pulmonary lesions. Such areas of cutaneous and subcutaneous atrophy are localized with respect to the lesions in question in conformity to Head's principle of localization of referred sensory phenomena. Their diagnostic significance has been emphasized particularly by Pottinger. The diagnostic value of localized trophic alterations in the skin and the subcutaneous tissue that are associated with focal infections has also been emphasized by Wunche (1949).

Chapter XVI

INNERVATION OF CEPHALIC
AUTONOMIC EFFECTORS

The extension of the sympathetic division of the autonomic nervous system into the head, the distribution of the sympathetic plexuses and nerves in the cephalic region and the anatomical relationships of the cephalic parasympathetic ganglia and nerves are described in Chapter I. In the present chapter the anatomical relationships of the cephalic autonomic nerves will be treated only in relation to the autonomic effectors innervated through them.

INNERVATION OF THE EYE

Extrinsic Nerves.—The eye is innervated through sympathetic, parasympathetic and sensory nerve fibers that reach it through the ciliary nerves. The short ciliary nerves arise from the ciliary ganglion. The long ciliary nerves arise from the nasociliary branch of the ophthalmic nerve. The smooth muscle of the eyelids (tarsal muscles) is innervated through sympathetic fibers that traverse the voluntary nerves to these organs. The sympathetic fibers in question are derived from the superior cervical sympathetic ganglion through the internal carotid and the cavernous plexuses. The parasympathetic fibers arise in the ciliary ganglion. The afferent fibers that supply the sensory innervation of the eye are components of the nasociliary branch of the ophthalmic nerve.

The preganglionic fibers to the ciliary ganglion arise in the mid-brain in a special group of visceral efferent neurons, the Edinger-Westphal nucleus, that is associated with the motor nucleus of the oculomotor nerve. They traverse the oculomotor nerve, the inferior division of which gives rise to the short motor root through which they reach the ciliary ganglion. The sympathetic fibers that traverse the ciliary ganglion are derived directly from the cavernous plexus on the internal carotid artery through a slender ramus that either reaches the ganglion as an independent sympathetic root or becomes incorporated in the long root that connects the ciliary ganglion with the nasociliary branch of the ophthalmic nerve and conveys the sensory fibers that traverse the ciliary ganglion to be distributed through the short ciliary nerves. The preganglionic fibers concerned with the sympathetic innervation of the eye arise in the rostral thoracic segments of the spinal cord. Those concerned with the innervation of the dilator pupillæ muscles leave the spinal cord in the first three thoracic nerves. Most of them are components of the second thoracic nerve. Most of those concerned with the innervation of the nictitating membrane are components of the third thoracic nerve. The postganglionic sympathetic fibers that innervate the dilator pupillæ muscle do not follow the course of the internal carotid artery all the way to the cavernous plexus. From their site of origin in the superior cervical sympathetic ganglion they follow the internal carotid artery for a short distance and then deviate into the middle ear with the carotico-tympanic fibers. Leaving the middle ear, they pass through the base of the cranium lateral to the nerve in the

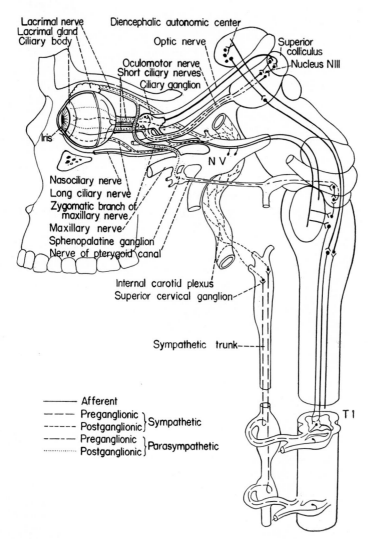

Fig. 70.—Diagrammatic illustration of pupillary and accommodation reflex mechanisms.

pterygoid canal and become associated with the cavernous plexus. Most of the sympathetic fibers to the eye do not actually pass through the ciliary ganglion. Some of them reach the eye through the long ciliary nerves. Others traverse the sympathetic root of the ciliary ganglion and become incorporated in the short ciliary nerves just distal to the ganglion. The long ciliary nerves do not communicate with the ciliary ganglion but pass directly to the eyeball. In general these nerves comprise fibers that traverse the nasociliary nerve. They include afferent fibers for the sensory innervation of the eye and fibers derived directly from the plexus on the ophthalmic artery. Those that innervate the dilator pupillæ muscles belong to the latter group.

Intrinsic Nerves.—The short ciliary nerves, fifteen or more in number, extend from the ciliary ganglion to the eyeball. They convey parasympathetic fibers that arise in the ciliary ganglion and sympathetic and sensory fibers that join this ganglion through its sympathetic and sensory roots. The short ciliary nerves penetrate the sclera and the choroid to be distributed to the various parts of the eye. Nerve fibers ramify in the sclera, but their exact distribution and mode of termination are unknown. The cornea is richly supplied with sensory fibers that form an annular plexus at its periphery. From this plexus, fibers pass into the cornea and ramify in the substantia propria, forming the fundamental or stroma plexus, from which fibers penetrate the elastic lamina and form a subepithelial plexus which gives off delicate fibers that ramify between the epithelial cells. Some of these fibers extend into the superficial layers. Fibers that arise from the annular and the stroma plexuses extend into the substantia propria and come into close relation to the corneal cells. The choroid and the iris are supplied by fibers derived from both the long and the short ciliary nerves. These fibers traverse the perichoroidal lymph spaces where they form a plexus from which fibers are given off to the choroidal blood vessels. A second plexus is located in front of the ciliary muscle. From it fibers are given off to the ciliary muscle and the iris. Ganglion cells have been described in both these plexuses. On the basis of the results of the more recent anatomical studies the existence of ganglion cells in the ciliary body and the iris in mammals seems highly improbable, but unmistakable ganglion cells have been demonstrated in the plexuses associated with the intraocular muscles in birds. The nerve fibers that innervate the iris extend as far as the pupillary margin and supply both the muscles of the iris and its blood vessels.

The muscles of the iris and the ciliary body are abundantly innervated. The efferent nerves of the radial muscles of the iris are solely sympathetic. Those of the circular muscle are solely parasympathetic. The efferent innervation of the ciliary muscles probably is solely parasympathetic.

Contrary to these anatomical findings, certain experimental data have been interpreted as indicating that the circular muscle of the iris and the ciliary muscles are innervated through both sympathetic and parasympathetic nerves. In cats, following unilateral cervical sympathectomy, Boros and Takats (1952) found that the circular muscle of the iris became sensitized to adrenin on the sympathectomized side, but not on the contralateral side. They interpreted this as indicative of sympathetic innervation of the circular muscle. Meesman (1952) observed no reaction of the ciliary muscle to parasympathetic stimulation, but concluded, on the basis of the reactions of this muscle to acetylcholine and other parasympathomimetic drugs, that it is innervated through both sympathetic and parasympathetic nerves. Piper (1952) observed that a change from near to distant vision is accompanied by a shift in the autonomic balance toward parasympathetic predominance. He regarded this as indicating double innervation of the ciliary muscle. These phenomena probably can be explained satisfactorily on the basis of the demonstration in the parasympathetic innervation of the intrinsic muscles of the eye of some adrenergic fibers (Kuntz and Richins, 1946).

The intrinsic muscles of the eye probably are devoid of afferent innervation (Stotler, 1937; Clark, 1937; Hirano, 1941). The sclera and the cornea are abundantly supplied with afferent nerve fibers. The nictitating membrane and the smooth muscle in the eyelids are innervated through sympathetic nerves, but probably are devoid of parasympathetic innervation.

SYMPATHETIC REGULATION OF OCULAR FUNCTIONS

Stimulation of the cervical sympathetic trunk or the superior cervical sympathetic ganglion elicits dilatation of the pupil and retraction of the nictitating membrane. According to Bishop and Heinbecker (1932), these reactions are mediated through the largest preganglionic fibers in the cervical sympathetic trunk, *i.e.*, those whose threshold of stimulation is lowest; consequently, they respond to stimuli that are too weak to excite the fibers of higher threshold that subserve other physiological functions. Dilatation of the pupil in response to sympathetic nerve stimulation is independent of vascular changes in the eye. In experiments on dogs reported by Berteau and Jones (1950) the pupil dilated in response to stimulation of the cervical sympathetic trunk 45 to 60 minutes after elimination of the blood supply to the eye.

Section of the cervical sympathetic trunk or extirpation of the superior cervical sympathetic ganglion results in certain definite ocular changes. They include slight recession of the eye, narrowing of the rima oculi, constriction of the pupil, extension of the nictitating membrane and dilatation of the vessels of the conjunctiva. These ocular changes are familiar clinical phenomena following cervical sympathectomy in man. The sunken position of the eye is more apparent than real because of the reduction in the width of the palpebral fissure caused by drooping of the upper eyelid and slight elevation of the lower one due to relaxation of the smooth muscle in the eyelids. The intraocular pressure increases somewhat following cervical sympathectomy due to the hyperemia resulting from section of the vasoconstrictor fibers, but later it gradually returns toward the preoperative level as the blood vessels regain their inherent tonus.

In experiments on rabbits reported by Chervet (1936) the cornea of an eye deprived of its sympathetic innervation was less resistant to the effect of quartz light than the cornea of the normally innervated eye. The corneal injury produced by quartz light also healed less promptly in the sympathectomized eye than in the normal one. These results seem to indicate a trophic influence of the sympathetic nerves on tissue that is devoid of circulating blood.

The aggregate of preganglionic sympathetic neurons in the rostral thoracic segments of the spinal cord that is concerned with the innervation of the eye has been called the ciliospinal center. The diencephalon also includes centers from which impulses reach the dilator pupillæ muscles through the sympathetic nerves. Dilatation of the pupil may also be elicited by stimulation of various other parts of the brain stem. This does not prove that the pupillary response, in every instance, is called forth by impulses that emanate from neurons located at the point stimulated, since the stimulus may affect descending visceral fibers that are widely scattered in the tegmental portion of the brain stem. The impulses in question reach the cervical sympathetic trunk through neurons in the ciliospinal center. In experimental animals activity in the ocular structures that are innervated through sympathetic fibers can be elicited by physiological stimuli following transection of the brain stem at the middle level of the mesencephalon. This result shows that the sympathetic tonus of the eyes due to physiological stimuli is not wholly dependent on the functional integrity of centers above the middle level of the mesencephalon, but it neither adds to nor detracts from the evidence that has given rise to the theory that the tonic sympathetic control of the eye is mediated through autonomic centers in the diencephalon.

Dilatation of the pupil, separation of the eyelids, and retraction of the nictitating membrane may be brought about, in experimental animals, by stimulation of the cerebral cortex. This does not prove that the smooth musculature of the eye and other orbital structures are directly represented in delimited cortical areas. Cortical influences on sympathetically innervated ocular structures probably are mediated through autonomic centers in the hypothalamus. The impulses in question are conducted through the same pathways in the spinal cord as impulses that arise from direct stimulation of the hypothalamic centers. Destruction of the hypothalamus on one side abolishes the effect on the cervical sympathetic of stimulation of the frontal cortex on the same side, but not of stimulation of frontal cortex on the opposite side.

PARASYMPATHETIC REGULATION OF OCULAR FUNCTIONS

Stimulation of the oculomotor nerve brings about constriction of the pupil by active contraction of the constrictor pupillæ muscle. Section of the oculomotor nerve is followed by dilatation of the pupil due to the absence of tonus in the sphincter in the presence of normal tonus in the dilator pupillæ muscle. Sympathetic stimulation, following section of the oculomotor nerve, brings about still further pupillary dilatation due to active contraction of the dilator pupillæ muscle. Constriction of the pupil may also be elicited reflexly by stimulation of the optic chiasm, the optic tract or the superior quadrigeminal brachium. Ranson and Magoun (1933) also reported pupillary constriction in response to stimulation of the pretectal region, the posterior commissure and the fibers emerging from the posterior commissure that arch around the ventral aspect of the central gray matter at the upper end of the cerebral aqueduct. Stimulation of the superior colliculus, in their experiments, did not elicit pupillary constriction.

Dilatation of the pupil elicited by peripheral stimulation, particularly nociceptive stimulation, has been regarded as a reflex reaction mediated through the sympathetic innervation of the iris. Data now available afford conclusive evidence that the parasympathetic nerves play the major rôle in dilatation of the pupil in response to peripheral pain producing stimulation and other emotional stimuli. These data have been interpreted by some investigators as supporting the assumption that pupillary dilatation elicited by nociceptive stimulation is brought about through inhibition of the mesencephalic parasympathetic center, *i.e.*, the Edinger-Westphal nucleus. In an experimental study of this phenomenon, Kuntz and Richins (1946) found that the moderate reflex dilatation of the pupil that is regularly elicited by peripheral nociceptive stimulation is not altered by sympathetic denervation of the eye, but it is abolished by section of the oculomotor nerve or extirpation of the ciliary ganglion. It must, therefore, be mediated through the parasympathetic nerves. When the pupil is dilated due to depression of the cholinergic innervation of the iris, moderate stimulation of the oculomotor nerve elicits further pupillary dilatation. Incomplete depression of the adrenergic nerves by the administration of ergotoxine results in marked reduction of the reflex pupillary response to peripheral stimulation. These findings support the assumption that the pupillodilator reaction mediated through the mesencephalic parasympathetic center is actively integrated and controlled. The circular muscle of the iris is inhibited, not by inhibition of the Edinger-Westphal nucleus, but by activation of this nucleus that results in the discharge of efferent impulses through adrenergic fibers that arise in the ciliary ganglion.

The light reflex is mediated through the parasympathetic innervation of the muscles of the iris. It is elicited by stimulation of retinal receptors. The pupil dilates in darkness or dim light and contracts to a pin-point when the retina is strongly illuminated. The functional value of these reactions is obvious. Enlargement of the pupil in dim light increases the total illumination of the retina, thereby increasing visual power. Constriction of the pupil in strong light facilitates vision by decreasing the illumination of the retina and diminishing spherical aberration. The effective stimulus that brings about this reflex is the light falling on the retina. The afferent fibers concerned traverse the optic nerve. Inasmuch as part of the optic nerve fibers cross in the optic chiasm, the light reflex involves both eyes. The efferent fibers concerned are preganglionic components of the oculomotor nerve and postganglionic fibers that arise in the ciliary ganglion. The central connections probably are made chiefly in the pretectal region. In the monkey and the cat, according to Magoun *et al.* (1936), the afferent fibers concerned in the light reflex do not enter the superior colliculus but deviate from the superior quadrigeminal brachium into the pretectal region where they make connections with neurons whose axons enter the Edinger-Westphal nuclei. Some of these fibers cross the median plane in the posterior commissure and ventral to the cerebral aqueduct in the immediate vicinity of the oculomotor nuclei. Injury to either the afferent or the efferent path diminishes or destroys the reflex. It is also lost in some cases in which neither of these paths appears to be injured. For example, in tabes dorsalis and general paresis the pupil is constricted and does not react to light (Argyll-Robertson pupil), but the accommodation reflex remains intact. This phenomenon suggests that the central connections for the light reflex differ from those for the accommodation reflex. The reflex reaction of the sphincter pupillæ to light probably is greatest when the retina is stimulated at or near the fovea and varies directly with the intensity of the light and the area illuminated.

After sympathetic denervation of one eye, as reported by Berteau and Jones (1950), the response of the circular muscle of the iris to stimulation of the oculomotor nerve may be more marked in the sympathectomized eye than in the normally innervated one, due to disinhibition of the parasympathetic nerves. The extent of the dilatation of the pupil in an experimental animal, according to Lowenstein and Lowenfeld (1950), is determined by the stimulus, the emotional state of the animal and the level of illumination. The dynamic pattern of the light reflex is determined by the strength, the duration and the timing of coincident parasympathetic and sympathetic impulses.

The accommodation reflexes are mediated through the parasympathetic innervation of both the ciliary muscles and the circular muscle of the iris. Contraction of the ciliary muscles in the act of accommodation is accompanied by simultaneous contraction of the sphincter pupillæ. Thus, when the eye is accommodated for near vision, the pupil is constricted. The reaction of the constrictor pupillæ in this instance in reality represents an associated movement in which the act of accommodation carries with it the constriction of the pupil, probably due to activation of neurons in the mid-brain that control the sphincter pupillæ by the stimulus which activates the neurons that control the ciliary muscles. The accommodation reflex is also accompanied by associated activity of the extrinsic muscles of the eye. Under normal conditions every act of accommodation for near vision is accompanied by convergence of the eyes due to contraction of both medial rectus muscles. The sympathetic innervation of the eyes probably plays no direct part in accommodation for near vision.

Accommodation for distant vision has quite generally been regarded as a passive process, but certain investigators, particularly Morgan *et al.* (1940) and Olmstead and Morgan (1941), have advanced the conclusion that sympathetic nerves play an active rôle in accommodation for distant vision. In experiments on rabbits, cats, dogs and monkeys, as reported by Olmstead (1944), stimulation of the sympathetic nerves of the eye resulted in flattening of the lens in some degree. In some of these experiments reflex inhibition of the parasympathetic nerves was ruled out by section of the oculomotor nerve and the roots of the rostral thoracic spinal nerves or by extirpation of the ciliary ganglion. The flattening of the lens in these experiments was regarded as the result of tension on the lens capsule caused by contraction of the radial ciliary muscles elicited by sympathetic stimulation. Momentary responses of the same order have been induced in animals and in human subjects by startle. The reduction in the curvature of the anterior surface of the lens that accompanied sympathetic stimulation, as Olmstead pointed out, was relatively small as compared with the increase in curvature induced by parasympathetic stimulation.

Experimental data reported by Kuntz *et al.* (1946) support the assumptions that the efferent innervation of the ciliary muscles is exclusively parasympathetic and that the sympathetic nerves in the ciliary body are functionally related only to the blood vessels. In cats under nembutal anesthesia faradic stimulation of the skin of the snout or of peripheral nerves elicited a dioptric change in the direction of hypermetropia both before and after sympathetic denervation of the eye. Depression of the cholinergic fibers by complete atropinization of the eye did not abolish this response. It was abolished by depression of the adrenergic nerves by means of intravenous injection of ergotoxine phosphate and by intracranial section of the oculomotor nerve. Stimulation of the oculomotor nerve intracranially while the cholinergic nerves were depressed due to atropinization of the eye resulted in a dioptric change toward hypermetropia. While the adrenergic nerves were depressed due to the administration of ergotoxine the same stimulation resulted in a dioptric change toward myopia. In human subjects mild faradic stimulation of the skin of the forearm or of the finger tips elicited dioptric changes of small magnitude in the direction of hypermetropia both in untreated eyes and during cyclopegia produced by instillation of homatropine into the conjunctival sac with resultant depression of the cholinergic nerves.

These results are consistent with the point of view that dioptric changes in the direction of hypermetropia elicited by startling stimuli, like those elicited by peripheral nerve stimulation, are mediated through the parasympathetic nerves of the eye. The normal reflex responses of the ciliary muscles, including those of accommodation, can, therefore, be explained satisfactorily without assuming the existence of fibers of sympathetic origin in its innervation. Reflex inhibition of the ciliary muscles appears to be an actively integrated and controlled reaction mediated through the parasympathetic innervation of the eye that involves the conduction of impulses from the ciliary ganglion to these muscles through adrenergic fibers in the short ciliary nerves.

Data that seem to support the assumption that parasympathetically innervated ocular structures may be influenced by impulses emanating from the cerebral cortex are not wanting, but they do not indicate representation of these structures in delimited cortical areas. Parasympathetic ocular responses have been observed due to cortical stimulation in widely separated areas. Such responses probably are mediated through parasympathetic centers in the hypothalamus. Stimulation in some cortical areas results in the discharge of impulses through both the parasympathetic and the sympathetic nerves of the eye.

SYNERGIC ACTION OF SPHINCTER AND DILATOR PUPILLÆ

Under normal conditions the sphincter and the dilator muscles of the iris are maintained in a state of tonic activity by impulses received through their respective motor fibers. They constitute a synergic mechanism that responds promptly and smoothly to stimulation of either set of nerves. The synergic action of these muscles, at least in a measure, is comparable to that of the flexor and the extensor muscles around a joint. The explanation of specific pupillary reactions is complicated by the fact that dilatation of the pupil may be brought about either by contraction of the dilator muscle or relaxation (inhibition) of the sphincter, while constriction of the pupil may be brought about either by contraction of the sphincter or relaxation of the dilator muscle. On the other hand, the contraction of one of these muscles may always be accompanied by inhibition of the other, as is assumed to be the case with the flexor and extensor muscles of the limbs. Certain experimental data strongly suggest that dilatation of the pupil may normally be brought about by a double action of this sort, *i.e.*, contraction of the dilator muscle followed by inhibition of the sphincter. Alterations in the size of the pupil occur not only in response to the effect of light on the retina and in the accommodation reaction but also under a variety of other conditions both normal and pathological. In sleep the pupils are constricted and the eyes rotate upward and outward. Pupillary constriction, in this case, may be due to inhibition of the tonus of the dilator muscle or increased tonicity of the sphincter. The assumption that the tonicity of the sphincter pupillæ is increased during sleep is supported by certain experimental data which indicate that, during the waking state, the mid-brain center that controls the sphincter pupillæ is kept in a state of inhibition by a constant influx of sensory impulses. Most of these inhibitory impulses are cut off during sleep; consequently, the sphincter tonus is increased. Emotional states also are accompanied by changes in the size of the pupil that aid in producing the facial expressions characteristic of the emotional state existing at the moment. For example, deep emotions of pleasure and fear are commonly accompanied by pupillary dilatation. This reaction may be explained either as the result of stimulation of the dilator muscle or of tonic inhibition of the sphincter. In favor of the former explanation is the fact that strong emotional states are accompanied by general sympathetic stimulation. Psychic or emotional mydriasis is closely allied to the typical reflex contraction of the dilator pupillæ muscle ordinarily elicited by cutaneous stimulation. Like many other effectors that are innervated through autonomic nerves, this muscle responds to all manner of psychic stimuli as well as to a great variety of sensory stimuli. It is conceivable that the same efferent impulses that give rise to the emotional state also inhibit the pupillary center in the mid-brain.

In the cat, according to Greaves and Perkins (1952), stimulation of the cervical sympathetic trunk elicited an initial, temporary rise in intraocular pressure probably due to contraction of smooth muscles in the orbit. Section of the cervical sympathetic trunk had no effect on intraocular pressure. In the rabbit stimulation of the cervical sympathetic trunk caused an apparent increase in drainage of aqueous liquid from the anterior chamber. It also elicited some constriction of the choriocapillaris vessels but no marked changes in the larger choroidal vessels.

RELATIVE IMPORTANCE OF SPHINCTER AND DILATOR MECHANISMS

Although the sphincter and the dilator pupillæ muscles sustain the relation of synergists to each other, the former must be regarded as of much greater functional importance than the latter. The dilator pupillæ muscle is closely related functionally to other visceral structures that are innervated through the thoracolumbar autonomic outflow. The sphincter mechanism is more highly specialized than the dilator mechanism both structurally and functionally and is strictly a part of the visual organ. The dilator mechanism is not essential for vision, although it may play a minor rôle in the visual functions of the eye. Unlike the sphincter, it is extremely responsive, at least in the higher vertebrates, to stimuli that elicit general sympathetic reactions. Whatever influence it has on the accommodation and the light reflexes is exerted chiefly by virtue of the tonus which is constantly maintained in it through its sympathetic innervation.

Both these muscles are of epithelial origin. The sphincter muscle is stronger than the dilator and contracts more rapidly. In the lower vertebrates, *e.g.*, fishes and Amphibia, the sphincter pupillæ is pigmented and itself reacts to light. In the higher vertebrates, as pointed out above, the light reflex is mediated by a relatively complex reflex mechanism. In man it is present at or before birth, while the accommodation reflex does not appear until the fifth month of postnatal life. The pupil exhibits considerable variation in size under the same conditions of illumination. Very early and also late in life, it is relatively small probably due to the relatively weak antagonism of the dilator muscle during these periods. Albino and blue eyes normally exhibit smaller pupils than dark eyes. This may be regarded as a normal ocular reaction to light. Under ordinary conditions the ciliary and the sphincter muscles usually react together, but the pupil may react independently to the amount of light entering it; consequently, there may be myosis in distant vision under conditions of strong illumination and mydriasis in near vision under conditions of weak illumination. The dilator pupillæ plays only a secondary rôle in these reactions which are mainly expressions of tonus changes in the sphincter muscle.

ACTION OF DRUGS ON IRIS AND CILIARY BODY

The dilator pupillæ, like other smooth muscles with sympathetic innervation, contract in the presence of adrenin. Atropine, homatropine and cocaine exert a mydriatic effect. In animals in which morphine causes excitement, *e.g.*, the cat, it also causes dilatation of the pupil. Physostigmine and pilocarpine are well known myotics. Regarding the site of the action of these drugs, it may be stated that adrenin stimulates the sympathetic fiber terminations in the dilator muscle and atropine paralyzes the parasympathetic fiber terminations in the constrictor muscle. Physostigmine and pilocarpine probably cause myosis by stimulating the endings of the same parasympathetic fibers. Cocaine probably first stimulates the endings of the sympathetic fibers in the dilator muscles and in stronger doses paralyzes the endings of the parasympathetic fibers in the sphincter muscle. The stronger mydriatics paralyze the ciliary muscle as well as the sphincter pupillæ, thus destroying the power of accommodation. In the mydriasis of cocaine and the myosis of physostigmine the light reflex is not abolished. The stronger myotics stimulate the ciliary muscle; consequently, the eye exhibits a condition of forced accommodation during the period of their activity.

Parasympathetic denervation of the eye results in a marked increase in the sensitivity of the sphincter pupillæ to acetylcholine and certain other parasympathomimetic substances, *e.g.*, acetyl-beta-methylcholine chloride and carbaminoylcholine. In experiments reported by Keil and Root (1941, 1942), sensitization of the iris sphincter in the cat to acetylcholine reached its maximum about five days after parasympathectomy and continued at approximately the same level until the eighteenth day and then gradually subsided, reaching a minimum low level about the thirty-fifth day following parasympathectomy. Their data support the assumption that the decrease in acetylcholine sensitivity following a period of maximum sensitization is associated with increased cholineesterase activity.

REGULATION OF NICTITATING MEMBRANE

Protrusion of the nictitating membrane following cervical sympathectomy in experimental animals is a common phenomenon. Slight protrusion of this membrane also occurs in man following cervical sympathectomy. Certain data seem to indicate that this membrane includes two groups of muscles, one of which brings about its retraction and the other its protrusion. According to Rosenblueth and Bard (1932), the smooth muscle which retracts the nictitating membrane in the cat is innervated by sympathetic fibers, and protrusion of this membrane is brought about by contraction of the outer fibers of the external rectus muscle that insert in its inferior horn. According to their observations, protrusion of the nictitating membrane may be accomplished by the contraction of these fibers independently of outward rotation or retraction of the eyeball. Cervical sympathectomy combined either with section of the abducens nerve or deep anesthesia completely paralyzes the nictitating membrane in the cat.

The nictitating membrane, the iris and the ocular blood vessels in the cat, as observed by Burn and Robinson (1952), contain amine oxidase. Sympathetic denervation of the eye results in a decrease of this substance in the denervated tissues and a decrease in the sensitivity of the nictitating membrane to adrenin and nor-adrenin 8 to 10 days after operation. After 10 days the amine oxidase again increases in the sympathetically denervated tissues and reaches the normal level about the 33rd day. This substance appears to play a rôle in the nictitating membrane, the iris and the ocular blood vessels comparable to that of cholinesterase at cholinergic neuroeffector junctions.

Reflex responses of the nictitating membrane may be elicited by afferent impulses from various parts of the body. In cats its contraction elicited by afferent stimulation of the sciatic nerve was increased following section of the vagi and denervation of the carotid arteries. The effects of simultaneous stimulation of two afferent nerves also were summated in the reflex response of the nictitating membrane (Rosenblueth and Schwartz, 1935). Liu (1935) reported summation of the effects of sympathetic nerve impulses, sympathin from other sources and adrenin applied simultaneously in the responses of the nictitating membrane in cocainized cats. A subliminal application of either of these stimulating agents is capable of increasing the response of the nictitating membrane to either of the others or to both in combination. In cats under urethane anesthesia distention of the urinary bladder or the rectum elicited reflex responses of the nictitating membrane (Watkins, 1938). In some instances the membrane contracted in response to distention of the bladder, but usually it relaxed and showed a positive rebound when the bladder was emptied. Dilatation of the rectum usually elicited relaxation of the nictitating membrane. Dilatation of the anal sphincter elicited contraction. The afferent impulses in question were conducted centrad through both the hypogastric and the pelvic nerves.

INNERVATION OF THE LACRIMAL GLAND

The parasympathetic innervation of the lacrimal gland is derived from the sphenopalatine ganglion. The postganglionic fibers traverse the maxillary nerve, its zygomatic ramus, the zygomatico-temporal branch of this ramus and the lacrimal nerve which is joined by the zygomatico-temporal. A sympathetic innervation of the lacrimal gland has not been demonstrated.

LACRIMAL SECRETORY REGULATION

The regulatory influence of the parasympathetic innervation of the lacrimal gland in its secretory activity has been demonstrated both experimentally and clinically. Section of the lacrimal nerve distal to the point at which the zygomatico-temporal nerve joins it or section of the greater superficial petrosal nerve abolishes reflex lacrimation. Functional disturbance of the lacrimal gland has also been observed immediately after paralysis of the facial nerve due to a lesion proximal to the geniculate ganglion. The paroxysmal lacrimation that is associated with facial palsy, according to Ford (1933), can be explained most satisfactorily on the assumption that some of the preganglionic secretory fibers that formerly made synaptic connections with ganglion cells whose axons innervate salivary glands on regeneration make connections with ganglion cells whose axons innervate the lacrimal gland. Section or paralysis of its sympathetic nerves has no marked effect on the secretory activity of the lacrimal gland.

INNERVATION OF THE NASAL AND ORAL MUCOUS MEMBRANES

The mucous membranes of the nares, including the paranasal sinuses, and the oral and pharyngeal cavities are innervated through both sympathetic and parasympathetic nerves and afferent components of both cranial and spinal nerves. Most of the sympathetic fibers are derived from the superior cervical sympathetic ganglia through the plexuses on the internal and the external carotid arteries and their branches. The parasympathetic fibers are derived chiefly from the sphenopalatine, the otic and the submandibular ganglia through peripheral rami some of which reach the mucous membranes directly and others of which join peripheral branches of the corresponding cranial nerves (see p. 40). Most of the afferent fibers are components of the trigeminal nerves. Afferent fibers of the glossopharyn-geal and the vagus nerves reach the mucous membranes particularly of the tongue and the pharynx. Some afferent vagus fibers also join the plexuses on the internal and the external carotid arteries to be distributed to various cephalic areas (Kuntz, 1934). Some afferent components of the rostral thoracic spinal nerves traverse the inferior cervical sympathetic ganglion, join the plexus on the common carotid artery and extend cephalad in it. Most of them continue cephalad in the internal and the external carotid plexuses and probably reach their terminal distribution in association with the sympathetic fibers that traverse these plexuses (Kuntz, 1934). The presence of myelin degeneration in Marchi preparations of nasal and nasociliary nerves following section of the roots of the rostral four thoracic nerves, as observed by Christensen (1934), indicate that some of the afferent components of the thoracic nerves that extend into the cephalic region actually reach the mucous membranes of the nose and the paranasal sinuses. The assumption that afferent spinal nerve fibers reach the nasal and the oral mucous membranes in man through the plexuses on the carotid arteries is also supported by clinical data.

FUNCTIONAL REGULATION OF NASAL AND ORAL MUCOUS MEMBRANES

The mucous and serous glands in the nasal, the oral and the pharyngeal mucous membranes, like the parotid and the submandibular glands, do not secrete continuously, but are activated reflexly by a wide variety of un-conditioned and conditioned stimuli. The oral and the pharyngeal glands respond more readily to mechanical stimulation of the oral mucosa than the larger salivary glands. Their thresholds for weak food and taste stimuli, with the exception of acid, are lower than those of the parotid and the submandibular glands, but the latter react more intensely than the former to strong food and taste stimuli. During periods of water deprivation the glands in the mucous membranes maintain their normal secretory rate longer than the parotid and the submandibular glands. Their reflex activation probably is mediated solely through the parasympathetic nerves. The vasomotor reactions in the mucous membranes are mediated through the sympathetic nerves.

Observations on the effects of nerve stimulation on ciliary activity in the upper respiratory tract, including the nares, particularly in the frog, have been reported by various investigators. According to Lucas (1935), sympathetic stimulation has no effect on the movement of the cilia on the frog's palate, but parasympathetic stimulation elicits acceleration of ciliary movement in this area.

The sympathetic nerves exert a calorogenic influence on the mucous membranes. By means of differential and absolute thermoelectric measure-ments in animals which had been subjected to unilateral cervical sym-pathectomy, Burkart (1936) found the mucous membranes generally warmer on the sympathectomized than on the normally innervated side. During sympathetic stimulation the mucous membranes became warmer on the normally innervated than on the sympathectomized side.

Although the blood vessels in the cavernous, or erectile, tissue in the nasal mucosa are innervated by the same nerves as those in the adjacent mucous membrane, this tissue does not always conform to the vascular state of the adjacent mucosa. The cavernous tissue frequently becomes engorged while the mucous membrane is relatively ischemic and frequently contracts while the mucous membrane is markedly hyperemic. Application to the nasal mucosa of certain pharmacological agents which regularly cause hyperemia of the mucous membrane results in contraction of the cavernous tissue; consequently, it has been assumed that the vessels of the cavernous tissue react to nerve stimulation according to a mode which differs from that of the vessels in the adjacent mucous membrane. This assumption is unwarranted, due to the anatomical relationships of the vessels in question.

According to Zuckerkandl's (1893) account, the capillary bed in the cavernous tissue is interposed between veins, whereas the capillary bed in other parts of the nasal mucosa is interposed between arteries and veins. The blood enters the cavernous bodies from the subepithelial capillary plexus and the more superficial portions of the periglandular plexus. In view of this arrangement, it seems probable that reflex stimulation that elicits vasoconstriction in the nasal mucosa might prevent emptying of the capillary bed in the cavernous tissue by contraction of the veins that drain it. Reflex stimulation that elicits vasodilatation in the nasal mucosa, on the contrary, probably results in contraction of the cavernous tissue due to facilitation of the outflow of the blood by the dilatation of the efferent veins.

Data reported by Higbee (1949) indicate that the threshold of stimulation of the parasympathetic nerves of the nasal mucosa is relatively low and that the dominant effect on this membrane of sympathetic stimulation is vasoconstriction. Clinical data also suggest that adjustments to atmospheric conditions and constitutional states are continually being made, through the secretory and the vasomotor nerves, that tend to maintain the nasal mucosa in a normal functional state.

INNERVATION OF THE SALIVARY GLANDS

The major salivary glands, the parotid, the submandibular and the sublingual, the ducts of which lead into the oral cavity, are innervated through both parasympathetic and sympathetic nerves. Their parasympathetic innervation is derived from the otic and the submandibular ganglia. Their sympathetic innervation is derived from the superior cervical sympathetic ganglia through the plexuses on the internal and the external carotid arteries (Fig. 71).

Parasympathetic fibers reach the parotid gland from the otic ganglion through the auriculo-temporal nerve. The parasympathetic innervation of the submandibular and the sublingual glands is derived from the submandibular ganglion and ganglion cells located within the hilum of the submandibular gland. The nerve fibers reach the glands through direct rami and through the lingual nerve. Sympathetic fibers reach the parotid gland through the internal carotid plexus. Those that reach the sub-

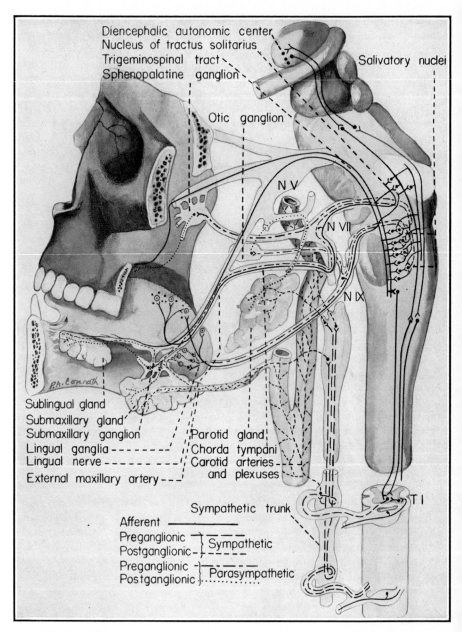

Fɪɢ. 71.—Diagrammatic illustration of the innervation of the salivary glands.

mandibular and the sublingual glands traverse the external carotid plexus and the plexus on the external maxillary artery.

Innervation of the salivary glands through both parasympathetic and sympathetic nerves is generally conceded. In most of the anatomical investigations, no attempts have been made to determine the relative abundance and the specific distribution within the glands of the parasympathetic and the sympathetic fibers. As the nerves enter the glands they are closely associated with the blood vessels and the ducts. Within the glands most of the nerve fiber bundles lie in proximity to the interlobar and the interlobular ducts and the arteries. Perialveolar plexuses are also apparent. Most of the fibers are unmyelinated and of small caliber. With relatively few exceptions, the unmyelinated fibers are postganglionic. Myelinated fibers, probably afferent, occur within the glands in relatively small numbers.

In an experimental investigation carried out on cats, Kuntz and Richins (1946) found that the nerve fibers associated with the blood vessels in both the parotid and the submandibular glands were greatly reduced in numbers after degeneration of the sympathetic fibers following extirpation of the superior cervical sympathetic ganglia, but the plexuses around the ducts and the alveoli were not appreciably altered. Degeneration of the parasympathetic and the afferent fibers interrupted by section of the auriculo-temporal nerve resulted in complete elimination of the plexuses around the ducts and the alveoli in the parotid gland. Degeneration of all the postganglionic parasympathetic fibers in the submandibular gland could not be obtained because many parasympathetic ganglion cells are located within the gland.

The data obtained in this investigation support the assumptions that both the parotid and the submandibular glands are more abundantly innervated through parasympathetic than through sympathetic nerves, that the parasympathetic nerves are distributed predominantly, perhaps exclusively, to the ducts and the alveolar tissue and that the sympathetic nerves are distributed chiefly to the blood vessels. The possibility that some sympathetic nerve fibers may be functionally related to secretory cells is not precluded, but the findings do not support the assumption that the mucous and the serous cells are innervated selectively through parasympathetic and sympathetic nerves. The serous cells are more abundantly innervated than the mucous cells. The myoepithelial cells probably are innervated exclusively through the parasympathetic nerves.

FUNCTIONAL REGULATION OF THE SALIVARY GLANDS

The parotid, the submandibular and the sublingual glands exhibit secretory activity chiefly while food is being eaten and in response to reflex and psychic stimulation. In the ruminants the parotid gland exhibits some secretory activity even in the absence of food in the mouth and while the animal is at rest. In the sheep, according to Scheunert and Trautman (1921), the parotid gland produces a continuous flow of saliva, but the submandibular gland exhibits secretory activity only while the animal is feeding. They observed no secretory output from the submandibular gland in this animal during the intervals between feeding, even while cud chewing was in progress. Scheunert *et al.* (1930) found no evidence of psychic stimulation of the parotid gland in the sheep and the cow, but movements of the lips, tongue and jaws by the hungry animals in the presence of food elicit reflex secretory activity of this gland. Cud chewing also acts as a strong stimulus to parotid activity on the chewing side, whereas the parotid on the opposite side is not appreciably stimulated by this process. Eating of hay commonly elicits parotid activity on the chewing side, whereas eating of oats or turnips elicits parotid activity on both sides. This stimulation is essentially mechanical. Chemical stimulation of salivary secretion probably is unimportant in the ruminants. The continuous secretion of the parotid in these animals probably is correlated with the functional activity of the ruminant stomach.

Specific Effects of Nerve Stimulation.—According to current physiological concepts, based on abundant experimental data, secretory activity of the salivary glands may be elicited by stimulation of either the parasympathetic or the sympathetic nerves. This seems to imply the direct innervation of salivary gland cells through both parasympathetic and sympathetic nerve fibers. The hypothesis that the mucous cells are innervated through parasympathetic fibers and that the serous cells are innervated through sympathetic fibers has been supported by various investigators. Certain data have also been advanced in support of the hypothesis that the same gland cells are innervated through both parasympathetic and sympathetic nerve fibers.

Double innervation of individual secretory cells in the submandibular gland of the cat has been denied by Babkin (1944) on the basis of extensive experimental studies. He concluded, however, that the mucous cells are innervated through fibers of the one division and the serous cells are innervated through fibers of the other division of the autonomic nervous system. On the basis of his own experimental studies carried out on rats, and other reported data, Hillarp (1949) could neither prove nor disprove the double innervation of salivary gland cells. According to his findings the efferent innervation of the ducts of the submandibular and the sublingual glands is solely parasympathetic, except that special cells in the striated portions of the ducts are innervated through sympathetic fibers. The mucous cells in the sublingual gland responded to parasympathetic, but not to sympathetic stimulation. He could not determine whether the serous cells are innervated through sympathetic or parasympathetic fibers since these cells underwent no apparent cytological alterations due to stimulation or elimination of either the sympathetic or the parasympathetic nerves. The data obtained seemed to indicate that the submandibular gland cells are influenced through both parasympathetic and sympathetic nerves.

In general parasympathetic stimulation of the salivary glands results in an abundant output of watery saliva. During sympathetic stimulation the output is less abundant and the saliva is less liquid. Both the rate of secretion and the fluidity of the saliva produced appear to be related to the volume flow of blood through the glands. During parasympathetic stimulation, without simultaneous sympathetic stimulation, the vascular bed in the salivary glands is dilated and the glands are abundantly supplied with blood. During sympathetic stimulation the blood vessels in the parotid gland probably are constricted and the blood flow through the gland is reduced. In the cat, according to Babkin (1944), either parasympathetic or sympathetic nerve stimulation results in vasodilatation in the submandibular gland. The observed effects of parasympathetic stimulation on salivary secretion can be explained satisfactorily on the basis of the anatomical demonstration of direct parasympathetic innervation of the secretory tissue and relaxation of the vascular bed in the absence of sympathetic vasoconstrictor stimulation. In view of the anatomical data that indicate a distribution of sympathetic nerve fibers only to the blood vessels in the salivary glands, the reported effects of sympathetic stimulation on salivary secretion are less readily explainable, but they probably can be explained satisfactorily without assuming the direct sympathetic innervation of the gland cells in question.

In a quantitative study of the protein content of the saliva secreted by the submandibular gland due to varied stimulation of the chorda tympani, Langstroth *et al.* (1938) found that the secretion of protein involves a chemical reaction which transforms granular material within the gland cells to a state in which it is readily carried out by the flow of water. They also found that the secretion of protein, the secretion of water and the regulation of cell membrane permeability are dependent on the rate at which some activating substance is liberated within the gland due to the stimulation. In a spectroscopic study of the composition of the secretion of the submandibular gland in the cat due to stimulation of the chorda tympani, sympathetic stimulation and the administration of adrenin they found that the saliva secreted during stimulation of the chorda tympani differs widely from that secreted during sympathetic stimulation. That secreted due to the administration of adrenin is similar to that secreted during sympathetic stimulation but not identical with it. The saliva secreted during stimulation of the chorda tympani following the administration of adrenin also differs from that secreted during chorda tympani stimulation before the administration of adrenin. Komarov and Stavraky (1940) also demonstrated that the protein in the saliva during parasympathetic stimulation differs from that present during sympathetic stimulation. After the administration of adrenin even in very small doses, but not after sympathetic stimulation, as demonstrated by Hebb and Stavraky (1936), glucose can be detected in the secretion of the submandibular gland following parasympathetic stimulation. This probably can be explained on the assumption that sympathin released on stimulation of the vasomotor nerves acts locally on certain groups of gland cells, whereas injected adrenin exerts an influence on all the gland cells. In view of the possibility that sympathin released due to vasomotor stimulation may influence the secretory activity of salivary gland cells, all the demonstrated secretory effects of sympathetic stimulation in the salivary glands probably can be explained on this basis.

In a series of experiments on cats under nembutal anesthesia, Richins and Kuntz (1952) found that the secretory effect of parasympathetic stimulation persists for some time following cessation of circulation through the gland, but that of sympathetic stimulation is promptly abolished following circulatory occlusion. Following depression of the adrenergic nerves by intravenous administration of ergotoxine ethanesulphonate, both direct and reflex parasympathetic stimulation resulted in copious secretory activity of the parotid gland, but direct sympathetic stimulation elicited no parotid secretory activity. Following depression of the cholinergic nerves by intravenous administration of atropine sulphate, reflex parasympathetic stimulation resulted in no secretory activity of the parotid gland, but direct sympathetic stimulation elicited slight secretory activity of this gland which was abolished by occlusion of the external carotid artery near its origin. The secretory activity of the parotid gland elicited by parasympathetic stimulation while the adrenergic nerves were depressed was not abolished by external carotid occlusion. During depression of the adrenergic nerves with ergotoxine ethanesulphonate, parasympathetic stimulation elicited copious secretory activity of the submandibular gland both with intact circulation and during occlusion of the external carotid artery, but sympathetic stimulation elicited no secretory activity of this gland. During depression of the cholinergic nerves with atropine sulphate, parasympathetic stimulation elicited no secretory activity of the submandibular gland, but sympathetic stimulation elicited copious secretory activity which was almost completely abolished by occlusion of the external carotid artery.

In these experiments, when neither the adrenergic nor the cholinergic nerves were depressed, sympathetic stimulation elicited marked secretory activity of the submandibular gland, but parasympathetic stimulation elicited only slight secretory activity of this gland. This is in marked contrast to the copious submandibular secretion elicited by reflex parasympathetic stimulation during depression of the adrenergic nerves. The secretory effect on this gland of stimulation of its parasympathetic nerves, which are cholinergic, therefore, appears to be increased during depression of the adrenergic sympathetic nerves. The mechanism through which the apparent inhibitory effect of the sympathetic adrenergic nerves on the cholinergic secretory nerves in question is exerted requires further investigation.

The results of these experiments afford no conclusive evidence of direct sympathetic innervation of salivary gland cells. The secretory activity of the parotid gland appears to be controlled predominantly through parasympathetic cholinergic fibers. It is undoubtedly influenced in some measure through adrenergic fibers of sympathetic origin, but the observation that the secretory effect of sympathetic stimulation is abolished by occlusion of the external carotid artery supports the assumption that the sympathetic influence is exerted through vasomotor nerves. The observation that direct sympathetic stimulation results in secretory activity of the submandibular gland following depression of the cholinergic nerves might be interpreted as indicative of direct sympathetic innervation of its secretory cells, but the observation that this effect is almost completely abolished by occlusion of the external carotid artery is incompatible with this point of view. Since sympathetic stimulation results in vasodilation in the submandibular gland (Babkin, 1944), the secretory effect of sympathetic stimulation on this gland while the blood is flowing through it probably can be accounted for by the spread of the adrenergic mediator from the capillary bed to the gland cells. When the external carotid artery is occluded and the flow of blood through the capillary bed in the gland is interrupted, the chemical mediator liberated due to vasomotor stimulation probably does not reach the gland cells. The observation that reflex parasympathetic stimulation resulted in secretory activity of the parotid gland and of the submandibular gland during depression of the adrenergic nerves, both with intact circulation and following occlusion of the external carotid artery, indicates that stimulation of nerve fibers that terminate in direct relation to the gland cells may elicit secretory activity at least for a limited time interval following cessation of circulation through the gland and that the secretory effect of those that terminate in relation to the blood vessels depends on the diffusion of the chemical mediator from the capillary bed to the gland cells, which does not take place following circulatory occlusion.

Henderson and Roepke (1933) reported certain data which they interpreted as indicating the presence of acetylcholine in the saliva secreted by the submandibular gland during stimulation of the chorda tympani. Secker (1934–1936) and Feldberg and Guimarais (1935) reported experimental data that indicate the presence of a depressor substance in the secretion of the submandibular gland in the cat during sympathetic stimulation that is not identical with acetylcholine.

Reflex Salivary Secretion.—The salivary glands react reflexly both to stimulation of the oral mucosa and strong stimulation of afferent nerves from other parts of the body, particularly the eyes, the ears, and the nasal mucosa. In general the mere presence of water at ordinary temperatures or inert substances, *e.g.*, pebbles, in the mouth does not call forth a flow of saliva, but the salivary glands react more or less specifically to mechanical, chemical and thermal stimulation of the oral mucosa. The oral mucosa includes receptors that are highly specific. Those that possess a high degree of specificity are not uniformly distributed. The reflex response of the salivary glands, therefore, varies with the kind of stimulation and the area of the oral mucosa concerned. This probably is an important factor in determining the quantitative and the qualitative variations in the salivary secretion while different kinds of food are being eaten.

Strong afferent stimulation of a somatic nerve, *e.g.*, the sciatic, results not only in an increased output of saliva but also in an increase in its organic constituents. Section of the cervical sympathetic trunk does not abolish reflex salivary secretion but results in qualitative changes in the saliva produced on the side of the operation, probably due to alteration in the blood flow through the glands. Section of the chorda tympani abolishes reflex activity of the submandibular gland. This observation favors the point of view that the salivary gland cells are innervated directly only through parasympathetic nerves.

The flow of saliva induced by the odor or the sight of food has commonly been designated as psychic salivation. The facility with which conditioned salivary responses may be established in animals strongly suggests that the salivary responses in man that are elicited by olfactory and visual stimuli pertaining to food also represent conditioned responses. Secretory responses of the salivary glands in man undoubtedly are elicited by conditioned stimuli of a wide variety.

Paralytic Salivary Secretion.—The secretion of saliva by the submandibular gland following section of the chorda tympani, *i.e.*, following preganglionic section of its parasympathetic nerves, is a physiological phenomenon the occurrence of which has long been known. It has been called paralytic salivary secretion. It does not occur immediately after section of the chorda but is initiated after a latent period of variable duration. Secretory activity begins slowly, reaches its maximum usually within two weeks and may remain at this level or near it for a considerable period, but the rate of flow has been observed to decrease in dogs after the third week. It is not appreciably modified by section of the sympathetic nerves to the gland, and section of these nerves alone does not call forth paralytic secretion.

Early attempts to explain this phenomenon have led to no satisfactory solution. Data now available support the hypothesis that sensitization of the gland cells to chemical agents, particularly adrenin, following section of their parasympathetic innervation is a major causative factor. Immediately after section of the chorda tympani the gland exhibits no secretory activity, and its cells show no evidence of sensitization. As Emmelin (1952) has pointed out, paralytic secretory activity and sensitization of the gland cells are initiated at about the same time. They are not marked at the beginning but develop rapidly. Both are usually well marked after about a week and reach their maximum levels in about two weeks. The rate of paralytic salivary secretion appears to be influenced by many factors. It also varies in different animals of the same species, even though the experimental conditions are kept as nearly uniform as possible. The degree of sensitization of the salivary gland cells in different animals under controlled experimental conditions also varies within a correspondingly wide range. In general a high rate of paralytic secretory activity coincides with a high degree of sensitization of the gland cells. Measures that increase the hypersensitivity of the gland cells also result in increased paralytic secretory activity. Measures that decrease the sensitivity of the gland cells to chemical stimuli likewise result in decreased paralytic secretion. Paralytic salivary secretion, consequently, can be explained most satisfactorily as a manifestation of sensitization of the denervated gland cells to chemical stimuli. The stimulating substance of major importance appears to be adrenin. After section of the chorda tympani the submandibular gland cells become hypersensitive both to sympathetic stimulation and to adrenin in the blood. Their sensitization following extirpation of the superior cervical sympathetic ganglion has also been reported. They also become hypersensitive to acetylcholine following section of the chorda tympani. In small doses this substance stimulates and in large doses it inhibits salivary secretion.

INNERVATION OF THE TEETH

The teeth are abundantly innervated through afferent nerve fibers most of which are components of the alveolar rami of the trigeminal nerves. The distribution of the afferent fibers in the dental pulp has been described by various investigators. These fibers form an abundant plexiform structure in relation to the odontoblasts, and, according to some of the accounts, some nerve fibers terminate in relation to the distal processes of odontoblasts that traverse the dentinal canals. If the odontoblasts may be regarded as receptive cells, this arrangement would readily explain the sensitivity of the dentine. Afferent nerve fibers also supply the peridental membrane.

The occurrence of sympathetic nerve fibers in the dental pulp and the peridental membrane has been amply demonstrated. According to Christensen's (1940) account, sympathetic nerve fibers join the alveolar nerves through the plexus on the external carotid artery and its branches. As determined by degeneration experiments, relatively few sympathetic fibers actually enter the dental pulp. Within the pulp most of them remain closely associated with the blood vessels. Sympathetic fibers also enter the peridental membrane along the blood vessels. Most of these fibers are distributed to the vascular musculature.

INNERVATION OF THE HYPOPHYSIS

The hypophysis is innervated through nerve fibers that are abundantly distributed throughout the posterior lobe and less abundantly throughout the anterior lobe. The numbers of fibers in the posterior lobe bear no direct relationship to the degree of its vascularity. Most of these fibers are derived directly from the supraoptic and the paraventricular hypothalamic nuclei, the floor of the third ventricle and the lateral regions of the tuber cinereum. Sympathetic fibers derived from the carotid plexuses may be traced into the capsule of the hypophysis particularly on the upper surface of the anterior lobe. Many of them enter the gland along blood vessels, and some apparently terminate in relation to gland cells. Fibers arising from cephalic parasympathetic ganglia probably play no part in the innervation of the hypophysis.

In an intensive study based on preparations of human material, Rasmussen (1938) found that not fewer than 50,000 unmyelinated nerve fibers of small caliber extend from the hypothalamus into the infundibulum. Most of them appear to be distributed to the posterior lobe, and relatively few enter the anterior lobe through the pars intermedia. The number of those which penetrate into the anterior lobe is regarded by Rasmussen as negligible.

As the sympathetic fibers derived from the cavernous plexus approach the hypophysis, according to Rasmussen, they form a bundle along either lateral aspect of the infundibular stalk. Many of them penetrate deeply into the anterior lobe where some become associated with blood vessels and some ramify among the gland cells. Strands of fibers that deviate from the bundles along the infundibulum extend downward and forward in the capsule. From these strands fibers enter the substance of the anterior lobe in small numbers at many points. Some of these fibers also ramify among gland cells, but relatively large portions of the anterior lobe appear to be devoid of nerve fibers.

REGULATION OF HYPOPHYSEAL FUNCTIONS

Much of the secretory activity of the hypophysis is regulated through hormonal agents and probably is independent of nerve impulses. Data bearing directly on the influence of nerve impulses in hypophyseal functions are meager, but certain data indicate clearly that some hypophyseal functions are subject to regulatory influences exerted through hypothalamico-hypophyseal fibers and some through the sympathetic innervation of the gland.

The influence on the production of the antidiuretic hormone in the posterior hypophyseal lobe of nerve impulses emanating from the hypothalamus through the hypothalamico-hypophyseal tract and the effect of interruption of this tract on water and fat metabolism are discussed in Chapter IV. The release of gonadotropic hormone from the anterior hypophyseal lobe in response to electrical stimulation of the hypothalamus has been amply demonstrated. Section of the infundibulum results in immediate disturbance of various anterior lobe functions in some degree. Fisher *et al.* (1938) reported that female cats with small hypothalamic lesions which interrupted the hypothalamico-hypophyseal tract, thus causing diabetes insipidus, were never observed to come into heat and did not breed in the laboratory. Disturbances of the reproductive functions associated with damage to the hypothalamico-hypophyseal tract, particularly in female guinea-pigs, have been reported in greater detail by Dey *et al.* (1940).

As reported by Brooks (1938), ovulation in rabbits, which normally occurs only after coitus, was abolished by transection of the infundibulum. In experiments on guinea-pigs, in which ovulation occurs spontaneously, as reported by Dempsey (1939), this function was not disturbed by transection of the infundibulum. Ovulation, mating, pregnancy, parturition and lactation in rats with the infundibular stalk interrupted have also been reported (Uotila, 1939).

In view of these and other experimental data, it may be assumed that the integrity of the hypothalamico-hypophyseal tract is not essential for the normal functioning of the anterior hypophyseal lobe in animals living under ordinary conditions. The gonadotropic, thyrotropic, adrenocorticotropic, growth and probably lactotropic hormones apparently may be secreted in sufficient quantity, in the absence of nerve impulses that emanate from the hypothalamus, to supply the normal requirements of the respective end-organs. The functional rhythm of the anterior lobe, however, may be modified in certain environmental situations by nerve impulses that reach the hypophysis through the hypothalamico-hypophyseal tract.

The accumulated data relative to the seasonal reproductive activities of various species of birds and mammals seem to support the assumption that the resumption of gonadal activity in the spring in these species is associated with the increasing daily illumination. Light obviously is a stimulating factor in the production of the gonadotropic anterior hypophyseal hormone. According to Scharrer (1937), light impulses that reach the hypothalamus may affect the entire autonomic system and thus play a rôle in the day-night rhythm. Through the hypothalamico-hypophyseal tract they exert a stimulating influence on various hypophyseal functions, particularly the production of the gonadotropic hormone, thus effecting increased gonadal activity.

The effect of hypothalamic impulses in the regulation of body temperature seems to be exerted in part through the hypothalamico-hypophyseal tract. In experiments on dogs reported by Hemingway *et al.* (1940), transection of the infundibulum resulted in a persistent hyperthermia, the body temperature being elevated 0.5 to 1.0 degree above the normal level. The operated animals reacted normally to cold, but, due to their continuous elevated temperatures, the threshold temperatures for shivering and peripheral vasoconstriction were elevated to the same degree as body temperature. They were somewhat hypersensitive to heat, as indicated by the measured diathermy heat required to cause panting and peripheral vasodilatation and the casual observation that they panted more frequently than normal dogs.

The sympathetic nerves probably exert no direct influence on hypophyseal functions except in the anterior lobe. In experiments on rabbits reported by Friedgood and Pincus (1935), the rate of production of the gonadotropic hormone was increased by faradic stimulation of the sympathetic nerves to the hypophysis. This observation supports the assumption that the sympathetic nerves may be responsible at least in part for the stimulation of the anterior hypophyseal lobe during coitus, which in the female rabbit results in the release of its gonadotropic hormone in increased amounts.

INNERVATION OF THE PINEAL BODY

Nerve fibers in the pineal body have been demonstrated in various mammals including man. They are derived from the sympathetic plexuses associated with the pineal arteries and from the habenular and the posterior commissures. Most of the earlier accounts of these nerves support the assumption that the sympathetic fibers are distributed exclusively to the blood vessels, but they are not in agreement relative to the distribution of the fibers that are derived from the commissures. Herring (1927) found no connections of nerve fibers with pineal gland cells. Pines (1927) regarded the intrapineal nerve fibers derived from the commissures in the dog as secretory. Clark (1940) regarded the fibers of commissural origin in the pineal body in the monkey and in man as aberrant and of no functional significance.

In the hooded rat Gardner (1952) described abundant nerve fibers in the pineal body that terminate in relation to parenchymal cells. After degeneration of the fibers interrupted by section of the nerves derived from the habenular and the posterior commissures no fiber terminations on parenchymal cells could be observed. Degeneration of the fibers interrupted by bilateral extirpation of the superior cervical sympathetic ganglia resulted in no apparent reduction in the abundance of the fibers that terminate in the pineal parenchyma. These findings support the point of view that the sympathetic fibers in the pineal body are functionally related to the vascular bed, and the fibers derived from the commissures are functionally related to gland cells.

Chapter XVII

SYMPATHETIC NERVES IN RELATION TO SKELETAL MUSCLES

ANATOMICAL DATA

The cerebrospinal nerves through which the skeletal muscles are innervated are traversed by numerous sympathetic nerve fibers which innervate blood vessels and other peripheral tissues. Many sympathetic
nerve fibers, consequently, lie in proximity to skeletal muscle fibers. Certain recorded observations also support the assumption that sympathetic
nerve fibers actually make functional connections with skeletal muscle
fibers. The most significant anatomical data in support of the view that
the skeletal muscles are innervated through sympathetic fibers have been
advanced by Boeke and his associates. As early as 1909 Boeke recognized
the existence in skeletal muscles of a system of fine unmyelinated nerve
fibers. In a series of later papers (1911–1913), he discussed this "accessory" system more fully and advanced the opinion that the fibers in question belong to the autonomic nervous system.

In order to determine the origin of these fibers more accurately, he
attacked the problem by experimental methods. In one series of experiments (1916, 1917) one or another of the nerves supplying the extrinsic
muscles of the eye was resected close to its origin from the brain. Three to
five days were allowed for the degeneration of the divided fibers. The
animal was then killed, and the ocular muscles were prepared for study according to the Bielchowsky method. A careful study of these preparations
showed that the myelinated nerve fibers and their terminal structures were
undergoing degeneration, but the unmyelinated "accessory" fibers with
their hypolemmal endings on the muscle fibers remained intact. Sections
of the extrinsic ocular muscles prepared after degeneration of the sympathetic fibers following extirpation of the superior cervical sympathetic
ganglion also showed intact unmyelinated fibers, but in reduced numbers.
Boeke, therefore, concluded that the unmyelinated nerve fibers observed
in preparations of the extrinsic eye muscles are autonomic.

In a further experimental study, carried out by Boeke and Dusser de
Barenne (1919), both ventral and dorsal roots of the sixth to the ninth
thoracic nerves inclusive were resected and the corresponding spinal
ganglia extirpated. The animals (cats) were killed one month after operation. In order to avoid confusion due to overlapping of the areas of distribution of the intercostal nerves, muscle tissue to be prepared for study
was taken from the seventh intercostal space. Preparations of this tissue
showed neither intact myelinated nerve fibers nor the motor end-plates
associated with them, but fine unmyelinated nerve fibers terminating
on muscle fibers by means of delicate end-rings, end-loops or end-nets were
present. In view of the conditions of the experiments, the conclusion that

the unmyelinated fibers in question are sympathetic in origin could hardly be avoided.

In a similar experimental investigation, Agduhr (1919) examined preparations of certain of the small muscles of the extremities, particularly the interossei, in the cat following degeneration of the spinal nerve fibers. His findings in general corroborated the earlier findings of Boeke. Kuntz and Kerper (1924) and Kuntz (1927) also recorded data obtained in experimental studies similar to those of Boeke and Agduhr which they interpreted as indicating the existence of fibers of sympathetic origin with terminal structures on muscle fibers in the intercostal muscles, the muscles of mastication and the muscles of the extremities in the dog.

On the basis of a review of his earlier work and further experimental data, including the results of investigations carried out by others, particularly those involving degeneration of the cerebrospinal nerve fibers, Boeke (1927) concluded that the morphological data available show unmistakably that skeletal muscles are innervated through sympathetic as well as through sensory and motor cerebrospinal nerve fibers. Nakanishi (1932) also reported the existence of unmyelinated fibers of sympathetic origin in the muscles of the posterior extremities of the frog after degeneration of the spinal nerve fibers.

The results of certain other histological studies, particularly those of Kulschitsky (1924), Hunter and Latham (1925), Kuré *et al.* (1925), Garven (1925) and Stefanelli (1929), also support the theory that skeletal muscles are supplied with fibers of sympathetic origin, but inasmuch as they are based on preparations of normally innervated muscles they are less convincing than the results of the experimental anatomical studies cited above.

In spite of the volume of anatomical and physiological data which seem to support the hypothesis that sympathetic nerve fibers make functional connections with skeletal muscles, this concept has not been universally accepted. Langworthy (1924) found no intact nerve fibers except those associated with the blood vessels in preparations of the muscles of the cat's tongue following bilateral section of the hypoglossal nerve. Hinsey (1927) attempted to show that most of the recorded observations which have been interpreted as supporting the theory of the sympathetic innervation of skeletal muscles could be interpreted quite as well in some other way. He suggested that the fine unmyelinated nerve fibers observed in preparations of skeletal muscles following degenerative section of the cerebrospinal nerve fibers may be either unmyelinated branches of sensory or motor fibers which have not undergone degeneration or regenerating somatic motor fibers. Hines and Tower (1928) found no evidence of the existence of nerve fibers of sympathetic origin that terminate in relation to skeletal muscle fibers. In a more comprehensive study of the innervation of limb muscles in cats, dogs and goats in normal material, sympathetically denervated material and material in which each of the three components of the innervation, *viz.*, the sensory, the motor and the sympathetic nerve fibers, had been isolated by degenerative section of the other two, using the methylene-blue, Bielschowsky's silver and Ranvier's gold-chloride technics, Tower (1931) again found no evidence of sympathetic nerve fiber termina-

tions on skeletal muscle fibers and advanced certain data which she interpreted as indicating that the nerve fibers that supply the blood vessels
and those that supply the striated muscle fibers are derived from the
intramuscular nerve trunks separately and do not communicate at any
point in their peripheral distribution.

Wilkinson (1929) reported that he had critically examined some of the
original preparations of Boeke and Agduhr, *i.e.*, some of the preparations
which represent the principal available histological evidence of the sympathetic innervation of skeletal muscles, and found them unconvincing. With
regard to Boeke's findings in preparations of the eye muscles following
section of their somatic nerve supply, he maintained that there were certain
sources of error which Boeke failed to avoid, particularly the short period
allowed for the degeneration of the somatic nerve fibers, the possible
existence of ganglion cells along the nerve trunks distal to the point of
section, and the existence of fine epilemmal endings of proprioceptive nerve
fibers. He interpreted the nerve endings in the eye muscles, which Boeke
described as the terminations of sympathetic or parasympathetic fibers, as
terminations in the arborizations of proprioceptive sensory fibers. The
findings of Boeke and Dusser de Barenne in preparations of intercostal
muscles in which the spinal nerve fibers had undergone disintegration, he
asserted, cannot be accepted. With regard to Agduhr's preparations,
which were taken from kittens after allowing five to six days for the degeneration of the somatic nerve fibers, he stated that the endings which this
investigator regarded as those of fibers of sympathetic origin are normal
endings of myelinated somatic motor fibers. In another study (1930) in
which he avowedly attempted "to repeat the work of Boeke and Agduhr,
if possible, in a more comprehensive manner," he again failed to corroborate the findings of these investigators. In another paper (Wilkinson, 1934), which embodies the results of further experimental studies, he
again reported only negative findings regarding the existence of a sympathetic innervation of skeletal muscles.

Coates and Tiegs (1931) found no sympathetic fibers, except those that
innervate the blood vessels, in preparations of muscles of the hind limb of a
dog eight and a half days after section of both roots of the lumbar and the
sacral nerves, leaving the communicating rami intact. In preparations of
muscles of the fore limb of a dog taken 38 days after extirpation of the
inferior cervical sympathetic ganglion, they found no nerve supply to
the blood vessels but recognized certain terminal structures which they
regarded as identical with those of the accessory fibers of Agduhr and
others. These they interpreted as the terminations of branches of somatic
fibers.

The negative findings recorded above regarding the existence of a
sympathetic nerve supply to skeletal muscles cannot be disregarded, but
they neither prove the non-existence of such a nerve supply nor disprove
the positive findings of Boeke and others. That the Dutch investigators
should have fallen into the particular errors attributed to them by Wilkinson seems improbable. Boeke (1930) also called attention to the dissim-
ilarity between certain of his published drawings and those of Wilkinson
which presumably were made from the same preparations, and pointed

out that Wilkinson's drawings do not illustrate correctly the structures in question and in some instances are misleading. In view of Boeke's extensive experience with histological technic and in the interpretation of histological preparations, his criticism of Wilkinson's work does not inspire confidence in the latter's findings.

In Boeke's (1933, 1937) later investigations of the innervation of skeletal muscles he described in minute detail a plexiform structure made up of

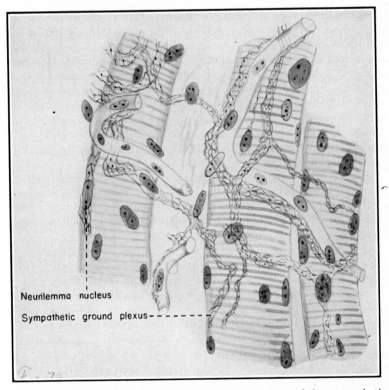

Neurilemma nucleus

Sympathetic ground plexus - - - - - - - -

Fig. 72.—Redrawn from Boeke (1933) to illustrate his concept of the sympathetic terminal structure in relation to skeletal muscle and its capillary vessels.

anastomosing bands of extremely delicate neurofibrillar strands which encircle and envelope the muscle fibers and are so closely applied to them that they appear to be nearly imbedded in the sarcolemma. At some points these strands actually lie in the same planes as the striations of the muscle fibers (Fig. 72). This plexiform structure, as Boeke has pointed out, obviously has not been observed in the preparations studied by any of the investigators who failed to find evidence of the existence of sympathetic fibers that terminate in relation to skeletal muscle fibers. He also failed to observe it in his own earlier studies. After he had become familiar with its structural characters and staining reactions in material prepared according to improved technical methods, he recognized it at least in some areas in his older preparations. He, therefore, expressed the opinion that failure on the part of some investigators to observe fibers of sympathetic origin that terminate in relation to skeletal muscle fibers has been due at least in part to faulty technic; consequently, their negative findings can have little weight as compared with the positive findings reported by himself and others.

PHYSIOLOGICAL DATA

Sympathetic Nerves and Muscle Tonus.—General Experimental Data.— The earlier investigators who undertook to study the effects of sympathetic nerve impulses on skeletal muscles by the use of physiological and experimental methods quite naturally surmised that any influence exerted on skeletal muscles through the sympathetic nerves must affect muscle tonus. On the basis of experimental studies carried out on frogs, de Boer (1915) advanced the theory that the tonus of skeletal muscles is mediated solely through the sympathetic nerves. Although this theory obviously is erroneous the experimental findings reported by de Boer focussed attention on the sympathetic nerves as a possible factor in the regulation of muscle tonus.

Langelaan (1915) advanced the theory that muscle tonus comprises a "contractile" component concerned with movement and the assumption of posture, and a "plastic" component concerned with the maintenance of assumed posture, the former being mediated through the cerebrospinal and the latter through the sympathetic nerves. On the basis of an extensive series of experiments carried out on frogs he (1922) concluded that muscles deprived of their sympathetic innervation lose much of their plasticity, the effect of which is most apparent in the attitudes of the animal. In a later paper (Langelaan, 1931) he reported permanent hypotonus of the muscles of the corresponding hind limb of a cat two years after unilateral extirpation of the lumbar segments of the sympathetic trunk, which he regarded as due to the loss of the plastic component. Experimental data reported by Dusser de Barenne (1916), Salek and Weitbrecht (1920) and Maumary (1922) also support the assumption that sympathetic denervation results in diminution of tonus in the skeletal muscle in the area affected. The concept of contractile and plastic tonus as distinct components mediated through separate systems of nerve fibers, although not supported by the results of later investigations, has exerted a significant influence in many of the subsequent discussions of muscle tonus as related to the sympathetic nerves.

In contrast to the observations cited above, many investigators, including Cobb (1918), Newton (1924), Coman (1926), Tower (1926), Tower and Hines (1929), Bisgard (1931) and others, using various mammals as the experimental animals, have failed, by direct methods of observation, to detect even a temporary diminution in the tonus of the corresponding limb muscles following sympathetic denervation. On the other hand, Fulton (1928) reported well marked diminution of tonus in the muscles of the lower extremity in a patient following lumbar sympathectomy. McCullagh et al. (1930) also reported appreciable diminution of tonus in the corresponding quadriceps femoris muscle in the dog following unilateral lumbar sympathectomy.

In experimental studies on cats and dogs, Kuntz and Kerper (1926) failed, except possibly in a few cases, following sympathetic denervation of a limb, to detect a diminution of tonus in the muscles of that limb by direct observation or palpation of the muscles while the animal was in the waking state. When the animal was subjected to surgical anesthesia the muscles of the limb deprived of its sympathetic innervation became more flaccid than those of the other limbs. When the animal, under deep anesthesia, rested on its back in a symmetrical position, so that the force of gravity acted equally on the limbs on both sides and postural reflexes due to an asymmetrical position of the head and the neck were obviated, the limb deprived of its sympathetic innervation almost invariably dropped to a lower position than the one on the opposite side. In the case of either the fore or the hind limbs the difference in the posture of the limb deprived of its sympathetic innervation and the one on the opposite side was sufficiently well marked, under these conditions, to be easily observed. This phenomenon could be demonstrated in all but a few animals in a relatively large series. Coates and Tiegs (1928) failed to corroborate these findings in a series of five dogs.

On the basis of a series of experiments carried out on birds (fowls and sea gulls), Hunter (1924) reported that the adducted position characteristic of the wing at rest is no longer fully maintained following section of the sympathetic trunk immediately caudal to the roots of the nerves that make up the brachial plexus. He interpreted this result as indicating that the plastic tonus of the wing muscles is mediated through their sympathetic innervation. Following section of the dorsal roots of the lower four cervical nerves, he found that the wing exhibited a tendency to remain in any position in which it was passively placed. This he regarded as due to the plastic component of tonus mediated through the sympathetic nerves. Following section of the sympathetic trunk just caudal to the brachial plexus and the dorsal roots of the caudal four cervical nerves, he found that the wing tended to hang dependent. This he regarded as due to the loss of plastic tonus. Hunter interpreted these findings as proving conclusively that the plastic tonus of the wing muscles is mediated through their sympathetic innervation.

In a series of experiments carried out on fowls and pigeons, Kuntz and Kerper (1926) corroborated most of the observations of Hunter cited above. Section of the sympathetic trunk just below the brachial plexus did not result in appreciable drooping of the wing in all cases, particularly if the operation was carried out with minimum traumatic injury to the nerves of the brachial plexus. Coates and Tiegs (1928) also reported that section of the sympathetic trunk caudal to the brachial plexus, in their experiments, did not result in appreciable drooping of the wing when the proper operative precautions were observed. Tiegs (1931) reported that division of the preganglionic fibers concerned with the sympathetic innervation of the wing of the pigeon did not result in drooping of the wing even when the possibility of reflex compensation by somatic nerves was eliminated by section of the dorsal roots of the nerves of the brachial plexus. According to Van Dijk (1930), section of the sympathetic trunk or the dorsal root of the first thoracic nerve, in the pigeon, results in abduction of the wing and lowering of its tip, particularly after exercise. He (1932) also reported a marked difference in the tonic state of the muscles of the bird's wing following section of only its afferent nerve supply and following sympathetic denervation in addition to section of the afferent nerve fibers. In the former condition the wing, when supported in a folded and high position, according to his account, remains in that position when the support is withdrawn. In the latter condition it assumes a more dependent posture when the support is withdrawn.

We do not now regard the tendency of the wing to remain in whatever position it is passively placed, following section of the dorsal roots of the nerves of the brachial plexus, as due to a component of tonus which is mediated through the sympathetic nerves, but rather as the result of the loss of the sense of position of the wing due to interruption of the proprioceptive fibers in the dorsal nerve roots. The muscles of the deafferented wing are not atonic. If the wing is drawn down to the fully dependent position and somewhat away from the bird's body, it does not remain in that position when released, but recoils to the bird's side. It is also subject to voluntary control and may at any time be replaced voluntarily into its normal position.

Popa and Popa (1931) advanced anatomical evidence of the existence of preganglionic fibers in the cervical nerves in the pigeon and corresponding ganglion cell groups in the cervical sympathetic trunk. In the light of these findings they cut the communicating rami of the caudal four cervical and the first thoracic nerves in order to deprive the wing completely of its sympathetic innervation. When this operation was carried out on one side, with minimum traumatic injury to the nerves of the brachial plexus, and the same operation, without section of the communicating rami, was carried out on the opposite side, the wing on the sympathectomized side drooped, whereas the other maintained its normal position. The drooping of the sympathectomized wing remained constant for 35 months in one bird and at least 12 months in another.

The apparent reduction in the tonus of the resting wing muscles in these instances cannot be explained as the result of injury to the nerves of the brachial plexus since care was taken to avoid injury to these nerves, and the corresponding nerves on the opposite side were treated in the same manner except that their communicating rami were not divided. Any slight injury which might have been suffered by these nerves, furthermore, would have been fully repaired long before the close of the long periods reported during which the resting wings maintained the drooping positions.

The discovery by Popa and Popa of preganglionic fibers in the cervical nerves in the pigeon must be regarded as highly significant since it affords an anatomical basis for the explanation of the discrepancies in the results of the experiments referred to above in which attempts were made to deprive the bird's wing of its sympathetic innervation. In the light of this discovery, it is evident that the wing was not wholly deprived of its sympathetic innervation in most of the experiments in question. The results of the experiments in which sympathetic denervation of the wing was incomplete, in as far as they have any bearing on the problem of muscle tonus, can have but little value.

Ducceschi (1922) and Ducceschi and Canpanari (1925) reported marked diminution of the postural tonus of the external ear in rabbits following extirpation of the superior cervical sympathetic ganglion, but pointed out that a difference in the posture of the two external ears, following unilateral extirpation of the superior cervical sympathetic ganglion, usually cannot be observed unless the animal is at rest or feeding in an undisturbed condition. Ducceschi also observed that the external auditory meatus has a somewhat greater diameter on the side of the operation than on the opposite side while the animal is at rest. Hintze and Seager (1929) observed temporary drooping of the rabbit's ear following cervical sympathectomy but concluded that the sympathetic nerves normally play no part in the tonus of the external ear muscles.

Fridman (1931) reported the results of a large series of experiments in which sympathetic stimulation resulted in increasing muscle tonus in most cases. In experiments reported by Spychala (1932), sympathetic stimulation resulted in strengthening the quadriceps reflex in dogs with the spinal cord transected at the tenth thoracic level. Pressure on the carotid sinus in intact animals, in his experiments, resulted in weakening the quadriceps reflex. In experiments reported by Mies (1933), stimulation of the aortic and the carotid sinus nerves in rabbits resulted in diminution of muscle tonus and section of these nerves resulted in increasing muscle tonus. The former effect was regarded as the result of lowering of the sympathetic tonus due to stimulation of the aortic and the carotid sinus nerves. The latter was regarded as the result of increased sympathetic tonus due to the absence of impulses from the aorta and the carotid sinuses. Similar results were not obtained when the animals were anesthetized with urethane.

Experiments Involving Decerebrate Rigidity.—The characteristic posture of the limbs of mammals in a state of decerebrate rigidity is well known. It has been assumed by some that if muscle tonus is mediated solely or in part through the sympathetic nerves, sympathetic denervation of a limb either would prevent the onset of decerebrate rigidity in that limb or bring about a diminution in the degree of rigidity exhibited by the extensor muscles. Many experimental studies have been undertaken to determine the possible effect of sympathetic denervation on decerebrate rigidity. Most of them have yielded only negative results. Positive results have also been reported. Royle (1924) observed diminished extensor tonus during decerebrate rigidity in the affected limbs of goats following unilateral lumbar sympathectomy. Van Dijk (1933) reported that, following unilateral extirpation of the stellate ganglion and deafferentation of the fore limb, in decerebrate cats, the muscles of that limb are definitely less spastic than those of the opposite limb, as indicated by positions and movements passively imposed on both fore limbs or during periods of heightened rigidity.

In order to repeat Royle's experiments as nearly as possible, Mortensen et al. (1928) carried out decerebration experiments in a series of goats, following unilateral lumbar sympathectomy. Like the majority of the investigators who used other mammals, they could demonstrate no con-

23

stant effect of sympathectomy on the extensor tonus in the corresponding limb during decerebrate rigidity. Occasionally, they observed differences in the extensor tonus of the two hind limbs while the animal
was in a certain position, but found that by changing the position the
difference in tonus disappeared. In a series of experiments carried out
on decerebrate cats following unilateral extirpation of the lumbar sympathetic trunk, Phillips (1931) observed certain differences in postural tonus
and reflexes in the two hind limbs. According to his account, the posterior
part of the body could be supported at the normal standing height by the
limb on the unoperated side but not by the one on the side of the operation.
Passive flexing force which was sufficient to elicit lengthening reaction
on the sympathectomized side produced a myotatic contracture on the
opposite side due to the stretch reflex. The lengthening reaction could be
elicited on the unoperated side only by increasing the passive flexing force.
The crossed extension reflex could be elicited on the unoperated side by a
weaker stimulus (less stretch) than on the sympathectomized side. The
amplitude of the crossed extension reflex response also was greater on the
normal than on the sympathectomized side. The myotatic contraction
following the knee-jerk also appeared earlier during relaxation on the
sympathectomized than on the opposite side. These results, according to
Phillips, could be explained on the assumption that the excitability of the
receptor ending in the muscles is increased following sympathectomy or on
the basis of changes in the circulation.

The results of the decerebration experiments cited above show clearly
that the exaggerated extensor tonus of decerebrate rigidity is not mediated
through the sympathetic nerves, but they do not disprove the theory that
the sympathetic nerves play a rôle in the maintenance of normal muscle
tonus. They afford no positive evidence of real value bearing on the
possible functional significance of the sympathetic nerves in relation to
skeletal muscles. As is well known, decerebrate rigidity follows destruction
or impairment of the rubrospinal system. The exaggerated extensor tonus
characteristic of this condition depends predominantly on efferent impulses
that reach the extensor muscles through somatic efferent fibers. The
component of tonus mediated through these fibers is greatly exaggerated.
Unless the influence of the sympathetic fibers on muscle tonus were equally
exaggerated (which is not the case), the absence of the sympathetic influence on the tonus of the muscles of a limb deprived of its sympathetic
innervation might easily escape detection, during decerebrate rigidity, except by very accurate quantitative methods. In view of the central neural
mechanisms concerned and the important rôle of the somatic efferent fibers
in the exaggerated extensor tonus in the extremities of decerebrate preparations, it must be apparent that experiments involving decerebrate
rigidity are not well adapted to reveal the influence of the sympathetic
nerves on the tonus of skeletal muscles.

Tonus Measurements.—Although muscle tonus has been the subject of
many investigations, few investigators have employed quantitative methods in the study of this problem. Spiegel (1923) described a method for
the study of tonus in the extensor muscles of the knee in which the results
of actual measurements of the resistance of the resting muscles to passive

extension are expressed in the form of a tonus curve. He showed, by the use of this method, that the tonus curve of the normally innervated quadriceps femoris, both in man and other mammals, rises very slowly at the beginning of passive extension and then more rapidly as the length of the muscle is increased. Evidently a mechanism exists which tends to hold the muscle in its normal resting posture (brake phenomenon of Rieger). Spiegel also showed that this mechanism is still effective in animals following section of the tendons of the flexor muscles of the knee, *i.e.*, the tonus curve of the extensor muscles obtained following section of its antagonists is identical with that obtained while the antagonists are intact. He also showed that the brake phenomenon persists following elimination of the voluntary innervation by light anesthesia and that it disappears following degeneration of the posterior funiculi in the spinal cord in tabetic patients. He regarded this as the result of interruption of the proprioceptive reflex arcs. The brake phenomenon, according to Spiegel, depends on sustained reflex stimulation which tends to hold the muscle at whatever length is imposed on it by reflex contractions. The efferent neurons involved in this reflex mechanism are independent of the pyramidal system since the brake phenomenon persists and may even become exaggerated following pyramidal lesions. It usually is not demonstrable in cases of flaccid paralysis, although the rapid components of the tendon reflex mechanisms may still be intact. This dissociation of the tendon reflex and the brake phenomenon, according to Spiegel, shows clearly that the central mechanisms of the static and the kinetic innervation of the extensor muscles in a large measure are independent of each other.

Spiegel's method may also be adapted for measuring the resistance to passive extension of the triceps brachii and extensor muscles of the manus in animals. Kuntz and Kerper (1924, 1926) reported the results of several series of experiments in which the difference in the tonus curves of the quadriceps femoris and triceps brachii in cats and dogs, obtained by the use of Spiegel's method, before and after sympathetic denervation was taken as the criterion of the influence of the sympathetic nerves on the tonus of an extensor muscle. In most of these experiments the measurements were carried out while the animal was under light ether anesthesia. In order still further to insure the validity of the measurements, many of our experiments were carried out in animals in which the brain stem was transected at the caudal level of the thalamus. This operation, if successfully carried out, neither affects the normal distribution of muscle tonus nor results in diminution of tonus while the muscle is in a resting condition. In these experiments, tonus measurements carried out on an extensor muscle in the same animal both before and after section of the brain stem at this level, but under otherwise similar conditions, were essentially identical. Since animals with transected brain stem require no anesthesia and exhibit no voluntary movements, they lend themselves advantageously to experiments involving tonus measurements carried out according to the method in question. Extirpation of the lumbar sympathetic trunk almost invariably resulted in diminution of the resistance offered by the quadriceps femoris muscle to passive extension in the absence of voluntary contraction. As indicated by the normal tonus curves (Fig. 73, *A, R*), this muscle, under normal innervation, offers considerable resistance at the beginning of passive extension, but the resistance gradually decreases as the degree of passive extension increases, *i.e.*, the brake phenomenon is exhibited in a well-marked degree. Following sympathetic denervation of the limb, the tonus of this muscle, as manifested by its measurable resistance to passive extension, is materially diminished (Fig. 73, *A*, *L* and

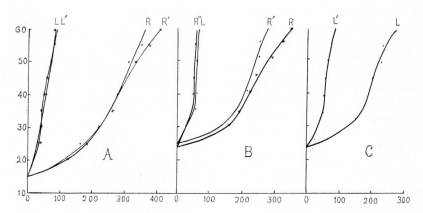

Fig. 73.—Tonus curves of extensor muscles with and without sympathetic innervation, (*A*) *R* and *L*, Tonus curves of right and left quadriceps respectively of a cat following extirpation of left lumbar sympathetic trunk, animal under light ether anesthesia; *R'* and *L'*, Tonus curves of right and left quadriceps respectively in the same animal three hours after section of the brain stem at the caudal level of the thalamus. (*B*) *R* and *L*, Tonus curves of right and left triceps respectively of a dog following extirpation of the left inferior cervical sympathetic ganglion. The measurements were carried out four hours after section of the brain stem at the caudal level of the thalamus. *R'* and *R''*, Tonus curves of the right triceps of a cat four hours after section of the brain stem at the caudal level of the thalamus, before and after extirpation of the left inferior cervical sympathetic ganglion respectively. (*C*) Tonus curves of the left extensor muscles of the manus of a dog before (*L*) and after (*L'*) extirpation of the left inferior cervical sympathetic ganglion, animal under light ether anesthesia.

L'). Curves *R* and *L*, Figure 73, *A*, are the tonus curves of the right and the left quadriceps respectively obtained, following extirpation of the left lumbar sympathetic trunk, while the animal (cat) was under light ether anesthesia. Curves *R'* and *L'* are the corresponding tonus curves obtained from the same animal three hours after transection of the brain stem at the caudal level of the thalamus. While the corresponding curves taken before and after section of the brain stem do not coincide perfectly, they are nearly equal and show clearly that the results of the experiments are not vitiated by carrying out the measurements while the animal is under light ether anesthesia.

Experiments involving measurement of the resistance of extensor muscles of the fore limbs to passive extension before and after sympathetic extirpation were carried out on a large series of animals (cats and dogs). Sometimes the measurements were taken on the same side before and after extirpation of the stellate ganglion on that side. Sometimes they were taken on the same muscle of both fore limbs following unilateral sympathetic denervation. In numerous experiments the measurements were carried out in animals with the brain stem transected after unilateral extirpation of the stellate ganglion. In some instances the measurements were first carried out while the animal was under light ether anesthesia and again several hours after transection of the brain stem. In most of these experiments the corresponding tonus curves derived from the measurements obtained before and after transection of the brain stem were essentially similar and almost coincident.

The tonus curves of both the triceps brachii and the extensor muscles of the manus derived from measurements carried out before sympathetic denervation of the limb (Fig. 73, *B* and *C*), like those of the quadriceps femoris, rise very slowly at the beginning and then more rapidly as the length of the muscle is increased by passive extension until flexion of the limb reaches a relatively high degree. The tonus curves derived from measurements carried out on these muscles following sympathetic denervation of the limb (Fig. 73, *B* and *C*), like the corresponding curves of the quadriceps femoris, rise more rapidly from the beginning. These curves indicate that the triceps brachii and the extensor muscles of the manus, like the quadriceps femoris, exhibit diminution of tonus, while at rest, following elimination of the sympathetic innervation of the limb.

The experimental data set forth above demonstrate the influence of the sympathetic nerves on the tonus of a resting muscle only as it is manifested by diminution of the resistance offered by the muscle to passive extension. In order to obtain tonus curves which actually represent a component of tonus which is mediated through the sympathetic innervation and at the same time obviate any possible effect of changes in circulation due to interference with the innervation of the blood vessels supplying the limb, tonus measurements were carried out on the triceps brachii muscle following section of both roots of the sixth, the seventh and the eighth cervical nerves within the spinal canal. This operation completely eliminates the somatic innervation of the triceps, but, since the preganglionic neurons concerned with the sympathetic innervation of the limb are components of thoracic nerves, it leaves the sympathetic innervation of the limb intact; consequently, the efferent innervation of blood vessels is not interfered with by the operative procedure. Tonus curves based on measurements carried out on the triceps brachii following section of both roots of the sixth to the eighth cervical nerves, compared with the normal tonus curves of this muscle (Fig. 74), show diminution of tonus, but, as indicated by the slow rise in the first part of the curve, the muscle still exhibits the brake phenomenon. This is well illustrated by curves *R'* and *L'*, Figure 74, *B*, which are the tonus curves of the right and the left triceps muscles respectively of the same animal (dog) following section of the roots of the sixth to the eighth cervical nerves on the right and extirpation of the inferior cervical sympathetic ganglion on the left side. Since the entire spinal nerve supply to the triceps is derived from the sixth, the seventh and the eighth cervical nerves, and most of the preganglionic fibers concerned with the sympathetic innervation of the fore limb emerge caudal to the first thoracic segment, section of the roots of the first thoracic nerve has no influence on the tonus

measurements carried out on the triceps.   The curves obtained following
section of the roots of the first thoracic, in addition to those of the sixth,
the seventh and the eighth cervical nerves, are essentially identical with
those obtained following section of the roots of only the cervical nerves.
In order to be of value, these measurements must be carried out within a
few days after the operation since the muscles undergo atrophy following
section of their somatic nerves and the extensors gradually lose the component of tonus that was still measurable immediately after section of the
spinal nerve roots.

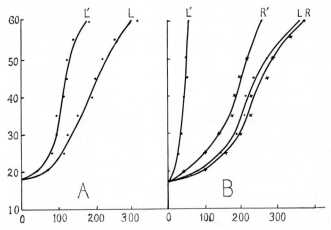

Fig. 74.—(A) Tonus curves of the left triceps of a cat before (L) and after (L') section
of both roots of the sixth, seventh and eighth cervical nerves, leaving the sympathetic
innervation of the fore limb intact. (B) R and L, Normal tonus curves of the right and
left triceps respectively of a dog. R', Tonus curve of the right triceps following section
of both roots of the sixth, seventh and eighth cervical nerves on the right side. L',
Tonus curve of the left triceps following extirpation of the left inferior cervical sympathetic ganglion.

In criticizing the results of our earlier experiments, Fulton (1926) raised
the following objections: (1) "Experimental analysis of tonic reactions in
the intact animals, in which various extraneous reflex factors cannot be
excluded, are unreliable." (2) "The 'active' muscle not being isolated by
complete denervation of the surrounding muscular and cutaneous structures, especially of the antagonistic muscles, renders difficult and uncertain
the interpretation of their responses." (3) Possibly the differences in the
resistance of the muscle to passive extension are due to secondary circulatory changes. (4) The brake phenomenon "can be little other than a
manifestation of the stretch reflex, since it was elicited by extension of an
antigravity muscle." He suggested that the diminution in the resistance
of the muscle to passive extension indicated by the difference in the curves
obtained before and after sympathectomy may be due to modified responses
of the proprioceptive endings in the muscle brought about by alterations
in the blood supply.

The difficulties attending the analysis of tonic reactions in the intact animal are fully recognized. We do not regard the results of our experiments as affording the data necessary for an analysis of tonic reactions but only as indicating that the sympathetic nerves exert an influence in the normal tonus of skeletal muscles in the absence of active contraction. An influence of the intact flexor muscles is not precluded, but the fact that Spiegel obtained tonus curves of the quadriceps femoris, following section of the tendons of its antagonists, which are essentially identical with the curves obtained while the flexor tendons were intact, strongly suggests that curves obtained, under the conditions of our experiments, are not materially modified by the intact antagonists. An influence of circulatory changes due to sympathetic denervation is not precluded in the results of our experiments, but there are no data available which clearly indicate that the changes in circulation following sympathectomy exert either a direct or an indirect effect on muscle tonus.

The effect of sympathetic denervation on the so-called brake phenomenon was overemphasized in our earlier reports. We do not regard this phenomenon as dependent on the sympathetic innervation alone, although the curves obtained, following sympathectomy, in many of our experiments rise almost as rapidly at the beginning as throughout the latter part of their course. Many of the curves obtained following sympathectomy show clearly that the brake phenomenon still persists. Any appreciable diminution of the resistance of the muscle to passive extension obviously must also affect the brake phenomenon, as manifested in the curves obtained by the method employed in these experiments.

The experimental data set forth above show quite clearly that the resistance of an extensor muscle to passive extension is diminished following sympathetic denervation of the limb and that an extensor muscle deprived of its spinal nerve supply, but with the sympathetic innervation of the limb intact, still offers greater resistance to passive extension than the completely denervated muscle until the muscle has undergone atrophy in some degree. The loss of the influence of the sympathetic innervation of a limb on the tonus of its muscles, at least in the animals studied by us, is so completely compensated by the cerebrospinal nervous mechanisms, under normal physiological conditions, that the deficiency usually cannot be detected by palpation of the muscles or by direct observation. Delicate quantitative methods are of primary importance in detecting the influence of the sympathetic innervation in the tonus of skeletal muscles. Since the influence of the voluntary innervation is constantly changing during muscular activity, quantitative methods designed to reveal the influence of the sympathetic nerves in skeletal muscle tonus can be successfully applied only while the muscle is at rest, i.e., while it does not exhibit active contraction.

The results of our experiments are not expressed in definite units of measurement, but they are quantitative. The method used also is sufficiently delicate to reveal changes in tonus which are quantitatively minute. That which actually is measured is the resistance offered by the muscle to passive extension. It may be objected that this is not tonus. The tonic state of the muscle, however, must be regarded as an important factor in determining the resistance offered to passive extension. Since, under the conditions of the experiments, the curve of resistance of the atonic muscle is regarded as a vertical line, the curve of resistance of the muscle under complete or partial innervation may properly be regarded as the tonus curve.

The tonus exhibited by an extensor muscle in the absence of active contraction, as manifested by the resistance offered by the muscle to passive extension, is quantitatively small. Any deficiency in tonus due to elimination of the sympathetic nerves, furthermore, is quite completely compensated, in the normal postures and activities of the animal, by the cerebrospinal innervation. It is not surprising, therefore, that so many investigators have failed, in the absence of quantitative methods, to detect any diminution of tonus in the affected muscles following sympathectomy.

In view of the data available, there is no advantage in postulating a sympathetic component of tonus that differs in quality from the tonus that is mediated through the cerebrospinal nerves. The concepts of contractile and plastic tonus may be useful, but the theory that plastic tonus is subserved by the sympathetic nerves alone is untenable.

Clinical Data.—Clinical data bearing on the rôle of the sympathetic nerves in the production and the maintenance of muscle tonus are not un-equivocal. The beneficial effects of sympathetic ganglionectomy and rami-section in the treatment of spastic paralysis, as reported in certain cases, strongly suggest that the exaggerated tonus exhibited by the spastic muscles is due at least in part to impulses conducted through the sympa-thetic nerves. Some surgeons observed no change in the tonus of spastic muscles following sympathectomy. Mark (1951) advanced certain clinical data in support of the assumption that in patients with frank autonomic dystonia fibrillation of skeletal muscles may be mediated through autonomic nerves.

Sympathetic Nerves and Muscle Fatigue.—Certain experimental data seem to indicate quite clearly that the sympathetic nerves play an im-portant rôle in sustained muscular activity. Certain other data, on the contrary, fail to support this theory.

Hunter (1925) reported that birds with one wing deprived of its sym-pathetic innervation showed the effect of this deficiency in increasing degree during prolonged flight. In contrast to these observations, Tower (1926) concluded, on the basis of experiments carried out on dogs, that "the capacity for prolonged muscular work and the onset and severity of fatigue were in no way affected by sympathectomy."

Coates and Tiegs (1928) reported the results of experiments that seem to indicate a marked effect of the sympathetic nerves on the resistance of an isolated muscle to fatigue. In animals (several goats and a dog) that had been subjected to extirpation of the left lumbar sympathetic trunk three to four months earlier, the gastrocnemius or the tibialis anterior muscle on both sides was isolated, the branches of the sciatic nerves sup-plying other muscles were severed and the proximal ends of the sciatic nerves were crushed in order to abolish reflex control of the muscle. The tendon of the muscle on either side was attached to a lever that recorded on a slowly rotating drum the contractions produced by short tetanic shocks at the rate of 2 to 3 per second. The nerves on both the right and the left sides were stimulated simultaneously from the same induction coil. In some instances the femoral arteries were ligated while the nerves were being stimulated. In all but one of their experiments the muscle on the normally innervated side resisted fatigue longer than the one on the sympathetically denervated side.

Büttner and Heimbrecht (1928) reported that in frogs that had been subjected to unilateral sympathetic denervation of the hind limb, the gastrocnemius muscle on the side of the operation remained shortened, after strong contractions, 95% longer than the one on the unoperated side. They also reported that when both gastrocnemius muscles were thrown into complete tetanus the curve of contraction of the muscle of the limb deprived of its sympathetic innervation dropped more rapidly than that of the one in the normally innervated limb in three-fourths of the cases. Schneider (1929, 1930) failed to corroborate these findings. Ginetzinsky (1924) reported experiments in which the isolated gastrocnemius of the frog was stimulated through its motor nerves by short tetani 5 seconds in duration at intervals of 55 seconds and isometric records obtained. The plateau tension developed in each successive response diminished progressively under these circumstances, but when the sympathetic trunk was stimulated during the 55 second intervals the diminution in the plateau tension did not occur during the first five or six tetanic responses. In another series of experiments, Ginetzinsky (1926) brought about fatigue of the gastrocnemius of the frog in an atmosphere of hydrogen by stimulation of the motor nerves. In most of these experiments (75%) stimulation of the sympathetic trunk following the onset of fatigue also resulted in increasing the strength of the contractions and the resistance of the muscle to fatigue. This result was interpreted as showing that the effect of sympathetic stimulation on muscular activity is not due solely to increased oxidation of the products of metabolism. It strongly suggests that sympathetic stimulation actually retards the onset of fatigue.

In experiments carried out by Orbeli (1924, 1925) the isolated gastrocnemius of the frog was made to contract at repeated short intervals (30 to 300 per minute) by stimulation of the ventral roots of the seventh, the eighth and the ninth nerves. When the onset of fatigue became apparent in the diminution of the amplitude of the successive contractions, the sympathetic trunk was stimulated for 20 to 60 seconds. After a latent period of 10 to 30 seconds the amplitude of the successive contractions again increased. The maximum effect occurred some time after the sympathetic stimulation had ceased. This reaction, known as the Orbeli phenomenon, also suggests that sympathetic stimulation tends to increase the resistance of skeletal muscles to fatigue.

In contrast to the results reported by Ginetzinsky and Orbeli, Wastl (1925) failed to demonstrate a direct effect of sympathetic stimulation on the activity of a muscle, following the onset of fatigue, in either the frog or the cat. Jaschwili (1928) also failed to corroborate Orbeli's findings. He reported that sympathetic stimulation resulted in augmentation of the contractions of the muscles even in the absence of fatigue when the stimulation was submaximal but not when it was supermaximal.

Maibach (1928) reported the results of experiments which may be regarded as a repetition of experiments reported by Orbeli. They were carried out with more refined technic and under more rigidly controlled conditions. Using bloodless preparations of the frog, the isolated gastrocnemius or gracilis muscle was made to contract at uniform short intervals by stimulation of the ventral roots of the eighth and the ninth spinal nerves. The sympathetic trunk was stimulated by means of a current just above the threshold of sympathetic stimulation at various intervals during the activity of the muscle. Like Orbeli, Maibach found that when the sympathetic trunk was stimulated following the onset of fatigue of the muscle, as indicated by the gradual diminution of the amplitude of the contractions, the amplitude gradually increased after a latent period of several seconds, reached a maximum, and then gradually decreased. The effect of sympathetic stimulation always continued for a short time after stimulation of the sympathetic trunk ceased. The results obtained with the muscle in air, but kept moist by frequent applications of physiological salt solution, and with the muscle immersed in a bath designed to compensate as nearly as possible for the lack of circulation and respiration were comparable although the muscle became fatigued more rapidly under the former than under the latter conditions. Stimulation of the sympathetic trunk before the onset of fatigue of the muscle had no effect on the amplitude of the contractions. Maibach, therefore, concluded that muscular contraction is augmented by sympathetic stimulation only after the muscle has become somewhat fatigued.

The results reported by Maibach fully corroborate those of Orbeli. Like the latter, he concluded that sympathetic stimulation during muscular activity increases the capacity of the muscle to resist fatigue. Since the preparations used were bloodless, and comparable results were obtained both with the muscle in air and in a bath designed to restore physiological conditions as nearly as possible, the increased capacity of the muscle to resist fatigue cannot be regarded as the result of changes brought about through the vasomotor mechanism in response to sympathetic stimulation, but must be regarded as the effect of impulses conducted through sympathetic fibers. In view of the experimental technic employed and the results reported by Maibach, it seems highly probable that the reported failures to corroborate Orbeli's findings were due to faulty technic.

Labhart (1929) confirmed the findings of Maibach and advanced additional experimental evidence of the augmenting effect of sympathetic stimulation on the activity of fatigued muscle in the frog. When the muscle became fatigued by stimulation of the ventral nerve roots, in his experiments, single induction shocks applied to the sympathetic trunk at one second intervals increased the amplitude of the contractions. The restoration of the muscle brought about in this manner lasts longer, according to Labhart, than that which is brought about by tetanic stimulation of the sympathetic trunk. He also reported that if the fatigued muscle is allowed to recover by decreasing the frequency of stimulation of the ventral nerve roots and at the same time single induction shocks are applied to the sympathetic trunk the effects are summated. Nakanischi (1927, 1928, 1930) and Gersuni and Chudoroseva (1930) also reported the results of experiments in which the effects of sympathetic stimulation on the fatigued gastrocnemius muscle of the frog were observed which in general corroborate Orbeli's findings. Sinizin (1937) studied the effect of sympathetic stimulation on the curve of fatigue of the frog's gastrocnemius under the following conditions: direct stimulation, successive direct and indirect stimulation, during infusion with a solution of curare and following degen-

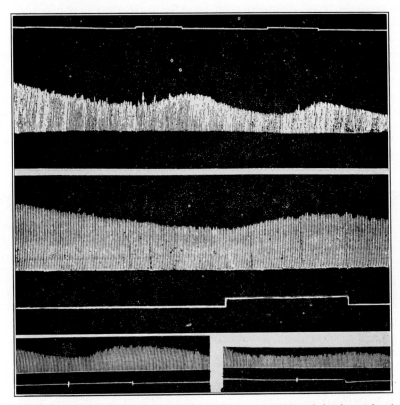

FIG. 75.—The effect of sympathetic stimulation on an active skeletal muscle of the frog. Successive contractions of the gastrocnemius or gracilis muscle were elicited by stimulation of the ventral root of the eighth and ninth spinal nerves. After the onset of fatigue the sympathetic trunk was stimulated at intervals indicated by the time signal. It will be seen that the amplitude of the contractions gradually increased after a latent period. (*A* from Orbeli: Pavlov Jubilee volume, 1924; *B* and *C* from Maibach: Ztschr. f. Biol., 1928, vol. 88, No. 3, München, Germany, J. T. Lehmann's Press.)

eration of the somatic nerves. Under all these conditions, according to his account, sympathetic stimulation resulted in delaying the onset of fatigue.

Van Dijk (1930) reported that when the triceps muscle of the decerebrated pigeon was fatigued by stimulation of the motor nerves for several hours stimulation of the sympathetic trunk usually increased the amplitude of the contractions but sometimes decreased it. Baetjer (1930) likewise reported that when the tibialis anticus of the cat, in his experiments, was undergoing rhythmic contractions elicited by single induction shocks applied to the ventral nerve roots, superadded stimulation of the sympathetic trunk sometimes resulted in increasing and sometimes in decreasing the amplitude of the contractions. He regarded augmentation of the contractions, under these conditions, as the direct result of impulses that reach the muscle through the sympathetic nerve fibers and diminution of the contractions as an indirect result of vasoconstriction. Chudoroseva (1932) reported an augmenting effect of sympathetic stimulation on the contractions of fatigued muscles and pointed out that this effect is more marked three or four days after section of the motor fibers than while the motor fibers are intact. These results may also be regarded as in agreement with Orbeli's findings.

Charlet (1930) employed a method by which the effect of sympathetic stimulation on the isometric contractions of fatigued muscle in the frog was recorded photographically. According to his records, sympathetic stimulation results in a steeper rise in the curve of isometric contraction of the fatigued muscle. The height of the curve is also increased, but the duration of the entire contraction is unaltered (Fig. 76).

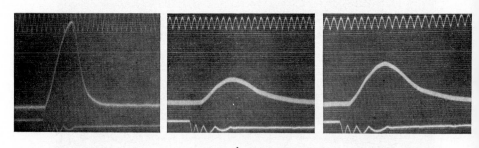

a   *b*   *c*

Fig. 76.—Isometric contraction curves of the frog's muscle. *a*, Normal muscle; *b*, fatigued muscle; *c*, same as *b*, but with sympathetic stimulation. (Charlet: Ztschr. f. Biol., 1930, vol. 90, No. 4, München, Germany, J. T. Lehmann's Press.)

Michol (1930) reported the results of a series of experiments in which the effect of sympathetic stimulation of muscles of the frog fatigued by direct stimulation was recorded. In these experiments the nerve to the muscle was curarized so that electric stimulation of the nerve trunk did not produce contraction. The muscle was then fatigued by direct rhythmic stimulation. When fatigue had set in, stimulation of the nerve trunk resulted in increasing the amplitude of the contractions called forth by direct stimulation. This result was interpreted as indicating restitution of the muscle brought about by stimulation of the sympathetic fibers in the nerve trunk. When the motor end-plates were rendered ineffective due to the lack of calcium, in Michol's experiments, sympathetic stimulation was without effect on the contractions called forth by direct stimulation.

Schnyder (1936) reported the results of experiments carried out on rabbits which are comparable to those reported by Michol. When, in his experiments, the mixed nerve supplying a muscle was stimulated by means of a stimulus above the threshold for the sympathetic fibers the onset of fatigue occurred appreciably later than when the motor fibers alone were stimulated.

Voser (1931) reported the results of experiments in which the effects of sympathetic stimulation on the normal reflex responses of fatigued muscles in the frog were studied. In his animals, either the cerebrum alone or the entire brain was destroyed, but the circulation was left intact. The sympathetic rami joining the nerves of one hind limb were divided and the skin or an appropriate afferent nerve on that side was stimulated to elicit reflex contraction of limb muscles on both sides. Records of the simultaneous reflex contractions of the muscles of both hind limbs elicited by repeated stimulation of the skin or an afferent nerve on the sympathectomized side at short intervals show that the amplitude of the successive contractions decreases more rapidly on the sympathectomized than on the normal side (Fig. 77, A and B). On the basis of these experiments Voser

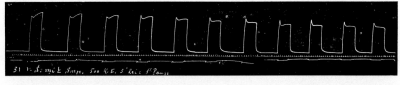

A

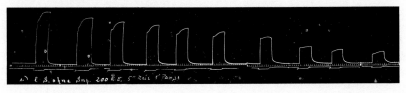

B

Fig. 77.—Records of simultaneous contractions of corresponding muscles of the frog's hind limb with the sympathetic supply intact on one side (A) and removed on the other (B). (Voser: Ztschr. f. Biol., 1931, vol. 91, No. 2, München, Germany, J. T. Lehmann's Press.)

concluded that the muscles normally receive impulses through their sympathetic innervation and that deprivation of these impulses reduces their capacity for work. He also regarded his findings as corroborating those of Maibach, Labhart, Charlet and Michol and advanced the opinion that the results obtained can be explained only on the assumption that sympathetic fibers actually terminate in relation to the skeletal muscles, since, under the conditions of his experiments, the changes in the blood supply to the limb muscles resulting from the operative procedure favors the muscles on the sympathectomized side.

By means of an oscillograph of high frequency, Haller (1932) recorded the action currents produced by reflex contractions, elicited by equal stimuli, of corresponding muscles of both hind limbs of decerebrated frogs with the abdominal portion of the sympathetic trunk on one side removed.

The action currents produced on the sympathectomized side always were weaker, of shorter duration and of lower frequency than those produced on the normally innervated side. Notter (1936) recorded action currents by means of the cathode ray oscillograph in the gastrocnemius muscle of the frog due to reflex stimulation following section of the corresponding motor nerve roots. Such action currents could not be recorded following section of both the motor nerve roots and the sympathetic rami. Both Haller and Notter concluded, on the basis of their experimental findings, that nerve impulses conducted through the sympathetic fibers normally exert an influence on the activity of skeletal muscles.

According to Lapicque and Lapicque (1930) and Lapicque (1931), fatigue in skeletal muscles is accompanied by an increase in the chronaxie of the muscles, while the chronaxie of the nerves remains unchanged; consequently, the synchronism between the chronaxies of the muscles and the nerves is disturbed. They advanced certain experimental data which seem to indicate that sympathetic stimulation following the onset of muscle fatigue decreases the chronaxie of the muscle, tending to restore the synchronism between the chronaxie of the nerves and that of the muscles. This they regard as the explanation of the restitution of fatigued muscle brought about by sympathetic stimulation. Volochor and Gersuni (1933) also reported shortening of the chronaxie in fatigued nerve-muscle preparations of the frog due to sympathetic stimulation.

By the use of the finger ergograph, Döring (1949) demonstrated an appreciable reduction in the capacity of the muscles of the index finger for work following blocking of the stellate ganglion with novocaine and following cervicothoracic sympathectomy. By means of ergographic records, Bochnik and Magun (1950) demonstrated an average reduction in the capacity for work of the index finger muscles, due to blocking of the stellate ganglion with novocaine, of 45 per cent after exercise for 20 minutes. Increased fatigueability of the finger muscles due to blocking of the stellate ganglion was also demonstrated while the blood flow through the finger was reduced by partial arterial occlusion. They concluded, on the basis of their findings, that the augmenting influence of sympathetic stimulation of fatiguing skeletal muscle depends on the conduction of impulses through the sympathetic nerves directly to the muscle fibers.

The results obtained by all the investigators cited above, who observed restitution of fatigued muscle brought about by sympathetic stimulation, seem to be in accord with most of the data available relative to the effect of adrenin on fatigued muscle. Although certain investigators have failed to observe a direct effect of sympathetic stimulation on the capacity of skeletal muscles to resist fatigue, we do not regard such negative findings as constituting an adequate reason to question the corroborative evidence afforded by the positive findings reviewed above. The latter have an important bearing on the functional relationship of the sympathetic nerves to skeletal muscles since any mechanism through which the capacity of skeletal muscles to resist fatigue is augmented must be of fundamental importance to the organism.

Site of Action of Sympathetic Nerves on Skeletal Muscles.—The results of much of the earlier experimental work bearing on the influence of sympathetic nerve impulses on skeletal muscles seemed to support the assumption that such impulses are transmitted directly to the muscle fibers. Many data available at present do not support this assumption. Orbeli advanced the hypothesis, on the basis of his findings, that the sympathetic nerves exert their influence on skeletal muscles through the peripheral apparatus of the motor nerves. Certain observations of Weiss (1930) also seem to support this hypothesis.

In a series of experiments, the results of which have not been published elsewhere, Kuntz and Kerper obtained certain evidence that seems to support the theory that the sympathetic nerves exert an influence on the irritability of the muscle fibers in some manner. These experiments were designed to show the effect of sympathetic denervation of a limb on the facility with which viscero-somatic reflexes are elicited by stimulation of the visceral organs or mesenteric nerves. The experimental animals (cats) were subjected to unilateral extirpation of the lumbar and the rostral sacral portions of the sympathetic trunk. The spinal cord was transected at the level of the foramen magnum. After the initial shock of the latter operation had subsided, the visceral organs or the mesenteric nerves were stimulated either mechanically or by means of an electric current. In all the animals in which the experiment was successful reflex responses to both mechanical stimulation of visceral organs (pressure on the spleen, duodenum or pancreas, inflation of the stomach, etc.) and electrical stimulation of mesenteric nerves were observed in the hind limb on the side on which the sympathetic trunk was left intact, but rarely in the hind limb deprived of its sympathetic innervation. Viscero-somatic reflexes involving the muscles of the hind limb on the sympathectomized side could only be elicited by much stronger visceral stimulation than that required to elicit fairly vigorous reflex responses in the normally innervated limb. In some animals no reflex muscular reactions in response to visceral stimulation were observed in the hind limb deprived of its sympathetic innervation, although the stimulation employed was sufficiently strong to elicit vigorous reflex responses in the normally innervated hind limb. Under the conditions of these experiments, the viscero-motor reflex arcs on the side of the sympathectomy were not impaired. It seems not improbable, therefore, that the difference in the degree of reactivity of the muscles of the two hind limbs to visceral stimulation was due to the presence in the one limb of the intact sympathetic nerves and their absence in the other.

The results of the experiments of Maibach, Labhart, Charlet, Michol, Voser, Haller and Notter cited above, all of which were carried out in Asher's laboratory, seem to support the hypothesis that the effect of impulses that reach the skeletal muscles through sympathetic nerve fibers is exerted on some mechanisms within the muscle fibers and not on the motor end-plates. On the basis of these experiments, in which the effects of sympathetic stimulation on the skeletal muscles were observed only after the onset of fatigue, Asher (1931) advanced the theory that the substratum on which the sympathetic nerves act is lacking in the unfatigued muscles but arises with the onset of fatigue. He (1932) also reported the results of other experiments carried out in his laboratory which indicate that sympathetic stimulation results in an increase in the phosphoric acid content of the muscle, which probably plays an important rôle in its restitution following the onset of fatigue.

In view of all the data which support the theory that sympathetic nerve impulses are mediated through humoral substances, the assumption that sympathetic stimulation influences skeletal muscles only after the onset of fatigue seems to be unwarranted. On the contrary, the humoral mediators liberated as a result of sympathetic nerve stimulation undoubtedly influence unfatigued as well as fatigued muscle.

The experimental data cited in the preceding pages are compatible with the hypothesis that the influence of the sympathetic nerves on skeletal muscles is mediated through humoral substances. This hypothesis is further supported by the results of experimental studies bearing directly on the problem of humoral mediators. Corkill and Tiegs (1933) advanced experimental evidence in support of the assumption that the increase in the strength of contraction of a fatiguing muscle brought about by sympathetic stimulation (Orbeli phenomenon) is effected through a humoral agent. They also pointed out that this phenomenon can be reproduced by appropriate treatment with adrenin. Tiegs (1934) reported further that stimulation of the sympathetic nerves to the skinned hind limbs of the frog results in the liberation of a substance which has the capacity to increase the strength of contraction of an isolated heart or another muscle into which it is perfused. Data reported by Schmid (1936), Brack (1936) and Meis (1937) also support the assumption that the increased heat production in skeletal muscle that results from sympathetic stimulation is brought about through humoral agents.

The exact sites of the liberation of the hormonal substances in question as yet are unknown. Those who do not admit the existence of sympathetic nerve-fiber terminations on skeletal muscle fibers cannot assume that these substances are liberated in immediate contact with the muscle fibers or within them. In view of the properties of the humoral mediators, it is not inconceivable that all the observed effects of sympathetic stimulation on skeletal muscles could be brought about through such mediators liberated in the walls of the blood vessels or in immediate proximity to them.

Sympathetic Nerves and Muscle Metabolism.—Certain investigators have maintained that the ratio of the creatinin to the creatin content of skeletal muscle is determined at least in part by influences exerted through the sympathetic nerves. Creatin metabolism, however, is increased during muscular activity; consequently, it cannot be dependent on sympathetic influences alone. The data bearing on this point indicate that creatin metabolism is influenced to a far greater extent by the somatic than by the sympathetic nerves.

According to Büttner (1926, 1929) the glycogen content of muscles is increased following sympathetic denervation. The results of certain of his experiments also indicate an increase in the lactic acid content of the muscles. In animals which had been starved before section of the sciatic nerve and then fed abundantly, as reported by Hoffmann and Wertheimer (1927, 1928), the glycogen content of the denervated muscles was not appreciably increased. In animals that had been subjected to unilateral sympathectomy more glycogen was found on the operated side than on the other side following the administration of strychnine or adrenin. Britton (1930) reported marked diminution in the glycogen content of the limb muscles of the cat during many weeks following sympathetic denervation. This result, he believes, is not referable to circulatory changes. Herrin and Meek (1931) reported reductions of 12 to 20 per cent in the glycogen content of the tonic muscles in dogs and rabbits 20 to 86 days after sympathectomy. In animals with hyperthyroidism the reductions in the glycogen content of the muscles following sympathetic denervation were even greater. Wenger (1933), who measured the heat generated in the same muscles on both sides following reduction of body temperature by cooling and in the presence of chemically induced fever, in animals that had been subjected to unilateral sympathectomy, always found the generation of heat greatest on the normally innervated side. In experiments reported by Schmid (1936), the muscles of the fore limb and the masseter muscle on the normally innervated side, in rabbits that had been subjected to unilateral cervical sympathectomy, became warmer while working than those on the sympathectomized side, whereas the latter were warmer than the former while at rest. Barron (1934) and Scheinfinkel (1938) also reported that cooling of the body of a unilaterally sympathectomized animal resulted in greater heat production, as determined by thermoelectrical measurements, in the muscles on the normally innervated side than in the affected muscles on the sympathectomized side. These findings strongly suggest that glycogen metabolism in skeletal muscles is subject to regulation in some measure through the sympathetic nerves.

The influence of the sympathetic nerves on the processes of oxidation and reduction in skeletal muscles is well illustrated by the effects of sympathectomy and sympathetic stimulation on the reaction of the muscles to vital dyes. When a vital dye, e.g., methylene blue, is injected into the lymph hearts of a frog, the muscles of the extremities become lightly stained. Magnus-Alsleben and Hoffman (1922) observed that if the nerves of one of the hind limbs are cut following the injection of methylene blue into the posterior lymph hearts, the muscles of that limb assume a more intense color than those of the other hind limb. In a further investigation of this phenomenon, they found that neither section of the dorsal nerve roots nor paralysis of the motor components alone exert an influence on the staining reaction of the muscles. When the communicating rami of the seventh, the eighth and the ninth nerves were divided, leaving the dorsal and ventral nerve roots intact, the muscles of the hind limb on this side assumed a more intense color than when the entire nerve supply to the limb was cut. This seemed to prove that the observed difference in the staining reaction of the muscles of the two hind limbs was due to section of the sympathetic fibers. They also demonstrated that the more intense staining reaction of the muscles deprived of their sympathetic innervation was not due to an excessive amount of the dye taken up by the muscle fibers but to retardation of the processes of reduction. When the lightly stained muscles of the normally innervated limb were treated with oxidizing agents they also became intensely blue.

On the basis of results obtained in experiments designed to demonstrate the effect of sympathetic stimulation on the reaction of the skeletal muscles

24

to methylene blue, Krestownikoff (1927), working in Orbeli's laboratory, reported that the oxidative processes in skeletal muscle are augmented by sympathetic stimulation. By the use of the mikrorespirometer, Orbeli also demonstrated a relative increase in O_2 consumption in skeletal muscles during sympathetic stimulation. This relative increase in the oxidative processes was manifested chiefly in the retardation of the continuous decrease in O_2 consumption during muscular excitation and in the fact that the oxygen intake remained constant during sympathetic stimulation and for some time after its cessation.

Sympathetic denervation is followed by dilatation of the capillaries in skeletal muscles. The permeability of the capillaries is also increased, which is an important factor in the metabolic changes observed in skeletal muscles deprived of their sympathetic innervation. It need not be assumed, however, that all the metabolic changes referable to sympathetic denervation are due to vascular changes. On the basis of the results of experiments involving ligation of the blood vessels and the injection of caffein in doses sufficient to produce maximal vasoconstriction and irreversible rigidity, Büttner (1926) concluded that the metabolic changes observed in skeletal muscles following sympathectomy are brought about, at least in part, by the direct effects of elimination of the influence of sympathetic nerve impulses on the muscles. In this connection it is not without interest to recall that Claude Bernard (1871) discussed the possibility of a sympathetic influence in muscle metabolism which is independent of vasomotor control.

Chapter XVIII

HISTOPATHOLOGY

INTEREST in the autonomic nervous system in relation to disease has increased with increasing knowledge of the physiological relationships of the autonomic nerves, but the advances in our knowledge of the histopathological alterations in the autonomic ganglia and nerves and the central autonomic centers have not kept pace with the advances in the various aspects of the physiology of the autonomic nerves. Most of the studies bearing on the rôle of the autonomic nerves in disease deal chiefly with the clinical and the pharmacological aspects of the problem. Varied and extensive pathological changes in the autonomic ganglia and ganglion cells have been described, but the data bearing on the specific relationships of these changes to particular diseases are relatively meager. A comprehensive review of the literature relative to the pathology of the autonomic ganglia has been prepared by Herzog (1950).

Histopathological studies have been carried out on preparations of material obtained at autopsy following deaths due to a wide variety of causes and preparations of ganglia removed surgically in the treatment of patients representing a limited group of diseases. In most instances it was quite impossible to establish a direct relationship between the neural lesion in question and a given disease process, due to the variety of pathological conditions present which frequently included senile degeneration in some degree. In spite of these difficulties, the available data strongly suggest a direct relationship of recognizable lesions of the autonomic nervous system and the disease process in many acute and chronic clinical conditions. In studies reported by Hermann (1952) ganglia obtained from persons in good health showed degenerative alterations in 12 per cent of the ganglion cells. Those obtained from patients with various diseases exhibited degenerative alterations in 45 to 90 per cent of the ganglion cells. In certain patients with endocarditis 70 per cent of the cardiac ganglion cells were regarded as pathological. The conditions of the ganglion cells in different patients with similar diseases vary within a wide range. The state of the circulation through the ganglia undoubtedly is a significant factor in the pathology of the ganglion cells. More exact knowledge of the nature and the causes of lesions of the autonomic nervous system and of their relation to disease must await further clinical and experimental investigation.

GANGLIA AND GANGLION CELLS

Chromidial Substance and Nucleus-plasma Ratio.—Most investigators who have reported the results of histopathological studies of autonomic ganglion cells have described alterations in the chromidial substance that include changes in its abundance and in its distribution in the cytoplasm and alterations in the chromatin in the nucleus. In many instances attempts have been made to correlate the observed changes in the ganglion cells with a particular disease process, but in relatively few instances have attempts been made to interpret the changes in the ganglion cells in terms of modified function.

In an extensive series of studies of the cytological changes brought about in nerve cells by physiological stimulation and depression, under experimental conditions, Dolley obtained data that support the hypothesis that alterations in the quantity and the distribution of the chromidial substance and variations in the nucleus-plasma ratio are natural consequences of functional activity and depression of these cells. According to his account (Dolley, 1911) of the sequence of the alterations in the Purkinje cells in the cerebellum in experimental animals subjected to prolonged continuous stimulation, the initial response is expressed in increased production of chromidial substance. The cell then becomes progressively hyperchromatic and increases in size. Following the stage of hyperchromatism, the cell undergoes a decrease in size and hyperchromatism recedes until the chromidial content of the cytoplasm has become reduced to the average normal level, but the nucleus exhibits edema. The nucleus-plasma ratio, consequently, is shifted in favor of the nucleus. The chromidial substance in the cytoplasm undergoes further reduction until secondary restoration of the chromidial substance sets in. The newly formed chromidial substance is at first concentrated close to the nuclear membrane and gradually becomes displaced toward the periphery. Secondary diminution of the chromidial substance then sets in and continues until the supply is depleted and the cell appears pale and exhausted. During the final phase of exhaustive activity the nucleus-plasma ratio is shifted in favor of the cytoplasm. This succession of changes in the nerve cells suggests that the chromidial substance is consumed during cellular activity and that it is continually being replaced. If activity is continued long enough, the production of chromidial substance becomes less rapid than its consumption, and the supply undergoes progressive diminution until no chromidial substance remains in the cytoplasm.

Functional depression of a nerve cell may intervene during any phase of functional activity. The immediate result of functional depression, according to Dolley (1913), is cessation of production of chromidial substance. The supply is gradually consumed, a deficiency of cytoplasmic chromidial substance becomes apparent and the nucleus-plasma ratio is shifted in favor of the nucleus. If long-continued, depression becomes a degenerative condition, shrinkage and dissolution of the nucleus take place and the cell may become reduced to a shrunken, anucleated, homogeneous hyaline mass.

Studies of the effects of stimulation and depression on autonomic ganglion cells that are comparable to those of Dolley on the effects of stimulation and depression on the Purkinje cells are not available. On the basis of a study of the effects of stimulation of the abdominal viscera on the celiac ganglion cells in the albino rat, Ingersoll (1934) reported a sequence of changes in the chromidial substance and the nucleus-plasma ratio which, in the main, parallels the sequence of alterations in the Purkinje cells due to stimulation as described by Dolley. The ganglion cells were classified in 9 types according to the quantity and the distribution of the chromidial substance in the cytoplasm and the nucleus-plasma ratio. The cells of the first 3 types, which may be regarded as Group I, make up the great majority of the ganglion cells present. They possess abundant chromidial substance which is distributed more or less uniformly throughout the cytoplasm. Those of the second 3 types, which may be regarded as Group II, usually are present in relatively small numbers. On the average, they are somewhat smaller than the cells of Group I and possess less chromidial substance most of which usually is distributed in the perinuclear or the peripheral zone. Those of the last 3 types, which may be regarded as Group III, also are present in small numbers. On the average these cells are somewhat smaller than those of Group II and possess still less chromidial substance. Some of them are almost devoid of this material and have but little chromatin in the nucleus. By differential counting of the cells in the several groups in preparations of the celiac ganglia from normal resting animals and from animals that had been subjected to manipulation of the abdominal viscera, under anesthesia, for periods of varying duration, Ingersoll demonstrated a progressive decrease in the percentage of the ganglion cells in Group I and an increase in the percentage of those in Group III as the length of the period of stimulation was increased. The number of cells in Group II changed relatively little with stimulation. Prolonged administration of nicotine resulted in comparable changes in the celiac ganglion cells in rabbits (Ingersoll, 1936). Herzog and Schüler (1941) reported an initial increase followed by a gradual decrease to complete depletion of the chromidial substance in the autonomic ganglion cells of the bullfrog during fatigue of the animal by forced continuous muscular activity.

The initial response of the celiac ganglion cells to stimulation, like that of the Purkinje cells in Dolley's experiments, appears to be increased production of chromidial substance, resulting in hyperchromatism, slight enlargement of the cells and a slight shift in the nucleus-plasma ratio. Following this stage the chromidial substance is reduced until it approaches the normal level, and the cell undergoes some reduction in size with a shifting of the nucleus-plasma ratio in favor of the nucleus. Secondary restoration of the chromidial substance is less apparent than in the Purkinje cells, but probably is evidenced by the perinuclear distribution of this substance in many of the cells of Group II. Following this stage the chromidial substance becomes further reduced, if stimulation is continued, until the cytoplasm is practically devoid of this substance. The nucleus, having given up most of its chromatin, also appears pale and vesicular and usually is located eccentrically. Following the initiation of stimulation, the production of chromidial substances exceeds its consumption, giving rise to hyperchromatism. Later, the requirements of the cell exceed its capacity to produce chromidial substance, and its supply gradually becomes depleted.

In preparations of human sympathetic ganglia removed by operation in a variety of diseases, including chronic polyarthritis, Raynaud's disease, and other peripheral vascular disorders, and sympathetic ganglia removed

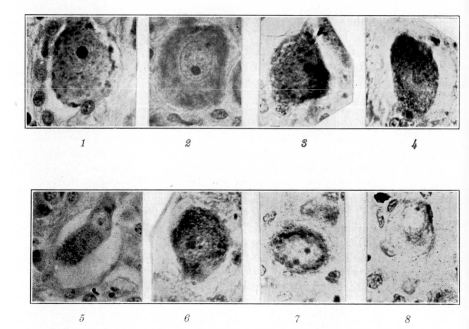

Fig. 78.—Autonomic ganglion cells (human), illustrating the progressive changes in the quantity and distribution of the chromidal substance and the nucleus-plasma ratio due to cellular activity. *1*, Resting cell; *2*, early hyperchromatism; *3*, advanced hyperchromatism; *4*, early shrinkage of the cell and receding hyperchromatism; *5*, advanced shrinkage of the cell and further recession of hyperchromatism; *6*, reduction of cytoplasmic chromidial substance to normal level with edema of both nucleus and cytoplasm, resulting in rounding out of the cell; *7*, further reduction of the cytoplasmic chromidial substance; *8*, almost complete depletion of the cytoplasmic chromidial substance and extrusion of the nuclear chromatin into the cytoplasm.

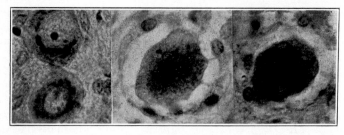

Fig. 79.—Autonomic ganglion cells (human), illustrating successive stages in functional depression.

at autopsy in a variety of pathological conditions, Kuntz (1934) recognized variations in the quantity and the distribution of the chromidial substance which conform very closely to the cell types described by Ingersoll in the celiac ganglia in the albino rat and the series of changes described by Dolley in the Purkinje cells, particularly in the dog, during excitation and depression. Some of these variations are illustrated in Figures 78 and 79.

In preparations of ganglia removed surgically in cases of essential hypertension and thrombo-angiitis obliterans most of the ganglion cells exhibit marked reduction in the quantity of the chromidial substance in

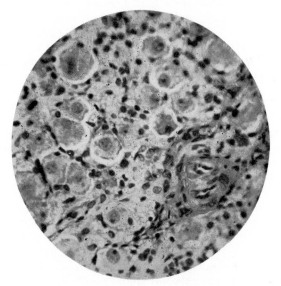

Fig. 80.—Photomicrograph from a section of a celiac ganglion removed surgically from a patient with hypertension. The ganglion cells appear almost devoid of chromidial substance, probably due to limitation of the blood supply caused by partial occlusion of arterioles.

the cytoplasm and some reduction in the chromatin in the nucleus (Fig. 80). In these conditions the reduction in the chromidial substance appears to be due in part to limitation of the blood supply to the ganglion and the consequent reduction of the nutrition of the ganglion cells. The chromidial substance that remains is finely granular and quite uniformly distributed in the cytoplasm, and the ganglion cells exhibit no apparent restorative reaction.

Certain pathological conditions result in more profound changes in the chromidial content of the autonomic ganglion cells than others, probably due to their stronger stimulating or depressing effect. For example, in arsenic poisoning and in poliomyelitis the chromidial bodies in the autonomic ganglion cells break up and the chromidial substance apparently goes into solution. In many cases the chromatolysis involves most of the autonomic ganglion cells and, in some instances, terminates in complete disintegration of many of them. The alterations observed in the autonomic ganglion cells in cases of arsenic poisoning correspond to those that have been described in the neurons in the central nervous system in similar cases. In addition to chromatolysis, they involve homogeneous swelling of the protoplasm and displacement of the nucleus toward the periphery. The occurrence of chromatolysis in the autonomic ganglion cells in patients with poliomyelitis shows clearly that this disease may involve the autonomic ganglia as well as the gray substance in the spinal cord.

Rapid disintegration of the chromidial bodies in the autonomic ganglion cells in patients with acute infectious diseases such as pneumonia, septicemia, diphtheria, tetanus and miliary tuberculosis, has been reported (Mogilnizcky, 1923). Following death due to burns many autonomic ganglion cells exhibit fragmentation of the chromidial bodies, clumping of the chromidial substance and chromatolysis (Spiegel and Adolph, 1922). During senility and cachectic states most of the ganglion cells exhibit only a meager supply of chromidial substance. The abundance of the chromidial substance in the ganglion cells appears to be closely related to the nutritive condition of the body.

Pigmentation.—The occurrence of pigmentation in autonomic ganglion cells is of peculiar interest in relation to intracellular metabolism. Although pigment is observed only rarely in the autonomic ganglion cells in animals (cat, dog, rabbit), except under experimental conditions and during senility, a moderate degree of pigmentation of these cells is a common phenomenon in man after middle age, and sometimes occurs even in the young. While moderate pigmentation of the autonomic ganglion cells does not necessarily indicate morbidity, exaggerated pigmentation of these cells probably is always pathological. Certain pathological conditions, e.g., arsenic poisoning, carcinoma, etc., probably are always accompanied by exaggerated pigmentation of the autonomic ganglion cells.

The distribution of pigment within the ganglion cells varies within a wide range (Fig. 81). In many of the cells dark pigment occurs only in a narrow peripheral zone. In others it is aggregated in a restricted portion of the cell body at the base of a dendrite or the axon. In occasional cells it appears as a cap-shaped mass at the periphery of the nucleus. In certain cells masses of pigment granules also occur occasionally in the cytoplasmic processes. Extracellular pigment granules occur, particularly in ganglia in which most of the ganglion cells are heavily pigmented. Under certain conditions, e.g., in patients with carcinoma, pigment may be distributed quite uniformly throughout the cytoplasm and become so dense that the nucleus is obscured.

Preparations of human autonomic ganglia in which many of the ganglion cells contain a moderate amount of pigment frequently exhibit no other evidence of pathological alteration. This may be regarded as evidence of a previous pathological condition, involving functional depression of the cells in question, from which they have quite fully recovered. In other instances even moderate pigmentation of the ganglion cells is accompanied by alterations in the structure and the distribution of the chromidial substance, probably indicating an existing pathological state of these cells. Heavy pigmentation probably is always accompanied by other degenerative changes in the autonomic ganglion cells. Many undoubtedly become functionless as the normal cytoplasmic constituents are replaced by pigment granules. In pyridine-silver preparations of heavily pigmented ganglia, many of the ganglion cells have the appearance of a compact mass of pigment granules from which no cytoplasmic processes can be traced (Fig. 82). Such excessive pigmentation results in necrosis of the ganglion cells. In the advanced stages of certain chronic diseases, *e.g.*, carcinoma, most of the ganglion cells in the sympathetic trunk ganglia show exceedingly heavy pigmentation and necrosis.

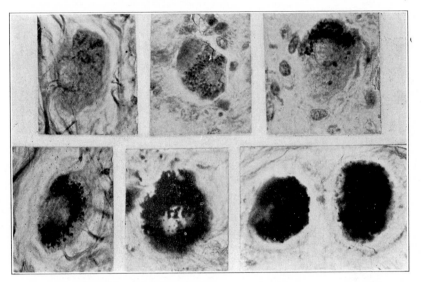

Fig. 81.—Autonomic ganglion cells (human), illustrating successive stages in pigmentation.

In a study based on preparations of ganglia of the sympathetic trunks and the celiac plexus obtained in an extensive series of autopsies following death due to a wide variety of causes, at ages ranging from 5 weeks to 78 years, and preparations of sympathetic ganglia removed in the surgical treatment of approximately 50 patients with peripheral vascular disease, arthritis, etc., Kuntz (1938) found pigment in some of the ganglion cells in nearly all individuals 30 years of age or older and in some in the younger age groups. Some of the ganglia that fall within the age limits of 18 to 25 years showed moderate pigmentation in some cells, but none below the age of 35 years showed marked pigmentation. The most heavily pigmented ganglia in this series are those obtained following death from carcinoma. In general the ganglia from the younger individuals are less heavily pigmented than those from the older, but the difference is not marked except in the most extreme cases. The excessive pigmentation of the autonomic ganglion cells in this group of patients undoubtedly is associated with the

malignant disease.   Corroborative data relative to pigmentation of ganglion cells, obtained in a study of preparations of a more extensive series
of human ganglia, have been reported by Sulkin and Kuntz (1952).

The occurrence of pigment in autonomic ganglion cells in human fetuses
during the fifth and later months of intrauterine life and in newborn infants has been reported.   The occurrence of pigment, except in very small
amounts, in ganglion cells before puberty probably is always pathological.

The genesis of pigment in autonomic ganglion cells as yet is not fully
understood.   Certain data reported by Gatenby and Moussa (1951) have
been interpreted by them as indicating that it is derived from broken-down
parts of the Golgi apparatus.   In autonomic ganglia of the mouse, Moussa

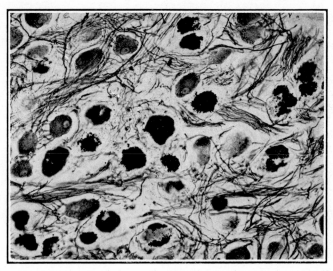

Fig. 82.—Photomicrograph from a section of a sympathetic trunk ganglion obtained
at autopsy following death due to carcinoma, showing heavy pigmentation of ganglion cells.

(1952) demonstrated the simultaneous existence of the Golgi apparatus and
granules stainable with neutral red and Sudan black.   Sudanophile granules were not observed in very young animals.   In the ganglion cells of old
mice the pigment granules are strongly sudanophile.   They also stain with
neutral red and are resistant to fat solvents.   Both lipid and pigment
granules appear first in contact with the Golgi apparatus and later become
scattered throughout the cytoplasm.   Finally they become aggregated
near the base of the axon.   The sudanophile bodies, both lipid and pigment,
are regarded by Moussa as secretion products of the Golgi apparatus.

In an experimental study carried out on dogs and rabbits, Dolley (1917)
always found pigmentation of the Purkinje cells associated with chronic
depression.   Stimulation ranging from normal activity to functional senility failed to produce pigmentation in these cells.   Chronic depression alone
resulted in pigmentation of the Purkinje cells.   In another series of ex-

periments, carried out on fowls, lipoid pigment was observed in the Purkinje cells following acute depression. It should be recalled in this connection that lipoid pigment does not occur in the dog and the rabbit since their fat is always lipochrome-free. In still another series of experiments carried out on dogs and rabbits, in which pigmentation of nerve cells was induced by chronic functional depression, Dolley and Guthrie (1918) observed pigment in the nerve cells in various parts of the nervous system including the superior cervical sympathetic ganglion. They advanced the opinion that pigmentation of the nerve cells in the dog and the rabbit is induced solely by functional depression.

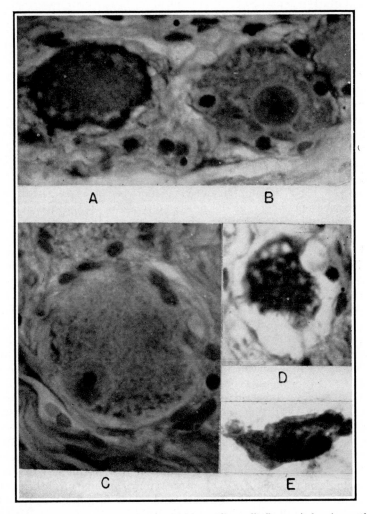

Fig. 83.—Photomicrographs of sympathetic ganglion cells (human) showing pathological alterations. *A*, vacuolization; early neuronophagia; *C*, hydropic enlargement; *D*, shrinkage with vacuolization; *E*, shrinkage with partial chromatolysis.

In preparations of autonomic ganglia obtained from an extensive series of dogs 30 days to 9 years of age Sulkin and Kuntz (1952) observed no pigment in ganglion cells. In preparations of ganglia obtained from dogs 12 to 16.5 years of age pigment was observed in some ganglion cells in every case. Most of these dogs showed evidence of senility. In the dog pigmentation of the autonomic ganglion cells appears to be associated with ageing.

Vacuolization.—The occurrence of vacuoles in occasional ganglion cells in sections of autonomic ganglia prepared by the usual methods need not be regarded as abnormal (Fig. 83, *A*). Vacuolization of ganglion cells in large numbers usually is associated with other degenerative changes in the cells and must be regarded as pathological. In some instances small vacuoles occur which are separated from one another only by thin protoplasmic septa. In some instances large vacuoles are formed through confluence of smaller ones. A single giant vacuole may occupy the major portion of the cell body, crowding the nucleus toward one pole. Some vacuolated ganglion cells are characterized by enormous swelling of the cell body, causing distention of the cell capsule. Ganglion cells in this condition usually show evidence of neurofibrillar degeneration.

Neuronolysis.—Partial or complete dissolution of ganglion cells by cells that become free in the ganglion cell capsules and invade the ganglion cell bodies has been called neuronophagia. Since the invading cells do not ingest cytoplasmic particles or tissue debris, but the cytoplasm of the ganglion cells appears to be consumed by a cytolytic process, the term, neuronolysis, has been adopted since it is more accurately descriptive than the term, neuronophagia, of the process of dissolution that actually takes place. The cells responsible for the cytolytic process are not phagocytes in the ordinary sense. In preparations of ganglia obtained from cats that have been given intravenous injections of 2 cc. of a 50 per cent solution of India ink every other day for a period of 8 days no carbon granules could be detected in any of the neuroglial cells, including the free cells in the ganglion cell capsules, whereas certain other cells particularly in proximity to blood vessels had ingested carbon granules (Kuntz and Sulkin, 1947).

In preparations of ganglia in which neuronolysis is taking place, proliferation of neuroglia including capsule cells is apparent. As capsule cells undergo division, some of the new cells remain flat. Others exhibit thickening of the cytoplasmic body and reduction in the number of processes (Fig. 84 *C*). Still others become spheroid and appear to be devoid of processes (Fig. 84 *E*). Spheroid cells frequently are so intimately associated with the ganglion cell that they lie in part within concavities in its cytoplasm (Fig. 84, *D* and *E*). Most of the spheroid cells that are associated with ganglion cells in this manner appear to be detached from the capsular wall. They gradually sink more deeply into the cytoplasm of the ganglion cell. The concavities in which they lie appear to be formed by dissolution of the cytoplasm (Fig. 84 *F*). This process may continue until the ganglion cell is completely destroyed. In ganglia obtained from human subjects in advanced age or following chronic pathological states, capsules that contain no ganglion cells occur frequently. Most of the ganglia in our series that have been removed surgically in the treatment of patients with peripheral vascular disease and other disorders in which vasomotor hyper-activity is a factor exhibit neuronolysis in some degree.

Hyaline Degeneration.—Under certain conditions hyaline degeneration in autonomic ganglion cells is a common phenomenon. Herzog (1926) reported eosinophile cells in cases of paralysis agitans and chronic morphinism. Onuma (1929) reported similar bodies in autonomic ganglion cells in

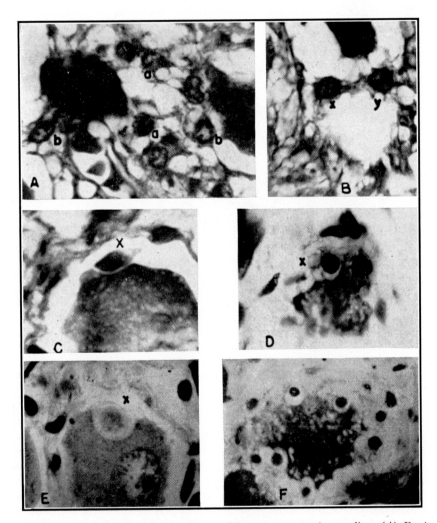

FIG. 84.—Photomicrographs of sections of human autonomic ganglia: (A) Ferric gallate preparation showing interstitial cells (a) and capsule cells (b); (B) ferric gallate preparation showing capsule cells (y and x); (C) ferric gallate preparation showing cell (x) detached from capsular wall in early phase of change to spheroid form; (D) toluidine blue preparation showing cell detached from capsular wall in late phase of change to spheroid form; (E) preparation showing spheroid cell devoid of processes (x) in concavity in ganglion cell; (F) toluidine blue preparation showing spheroid cells invading cytoplasm of ganglion cell. (Kuntz and Sulkin, 1947, courtesy of Jour. Comp. Neurol.)

cases of poisoning with sulphuric acid. Grünberg (1930) reported hyaline changes in autonomic ganglion cells in experimental animals subjected to chronic lead poisoning. In his preparations the major portion of the cytoplasm appears uniformly pale and agranular in many of the cells. The cell body is somewhat swollen and the nucleus is displaced toward the periphery. In some instances it actually protrudes at the surface. Occasional ganglion cells that exhibit hyaline degeneration occur in many of the ganglia in our series that have been removed surgically.

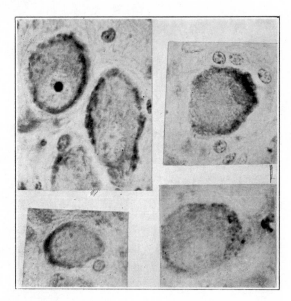

Fig. 85.—Autonomic ganglion cells (human), showing hyaline degeneration.

Hydropic Alteration.—Hydropic alteration of autonomic ganglion cells, as described by de Castro (1932), is characterized by marked enlargement of the cell body, acquisition of globular form and degenerative changes in the neurofibrillar structure that suggest pathological coagulation of the neurofibrillar substance rather than hypertrophy of the neurofibrils (Fig. 83, *C*) The central portion of the cell body is made up of polyhedral alveoli which appear to be filled with amorphous matter which may include argentophile concretions. The entire cell body appears pale due to diminution of the chromidial substance. The nucleus is large and vesicular The dendrites usually show hypertrophy of the neurofibrils, particularly at the surface, and a clear crystal core. They may also show vacuoles and argentophile concretions. Hydropic alterations may be observed in some ganglion cells in a wide variety of pathological conditions including chronic alcoholism (de Castro, 1932), chronic polyarthritis and advanced carcinoma.

Shrinkage.—Shrinkage of autonomic ganglion cells is a common phenomenon associated with various pathological states particularly senility and cachexia. The shrunken cells usually also exhibit other pathological changes, *e.g.*, chromatolysis and pigmentation. The most heavily pigmented cells commonly are shrunken to a relatively small mass. Shrunken ganglion cells that contain no pigment frequently also exhibit displacement of the nucleus toward the periphery and other nuclear changes. In some instances the nucleus actually is extruded from the cell.

Preparations of apparently normal ganglia frequently exhibit some shrunken ganglion cells that stain intensely, particularly after formalin fixation (Fig. 83, *E*). Both the cytoplasm and the nucleus appear hyper-

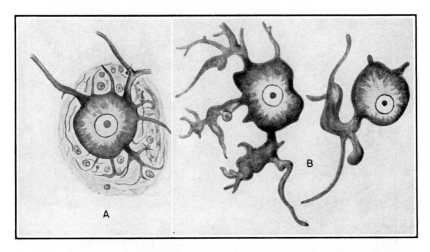

Fig. 86.—Ganglion cells drawn from silver preparations of sympathetic ganglia (human, age seventy-eight years) showing (*A*) development of short accessory dendrites and (*B*) irregular hypertrophy of dendrites.

chromatic, but the chromidial substance in the cytoplasm does not exhibit discrete granules. Herzog and Schüler (1941) reported extreme shrinkage of both the cytoplasm and the nucleus of the autonomic ganglion cells of the bullfrog associated with fatigue of the animal caused by forced continuous movements.

Neurofibrillar Changes.—Most of the histopathological alterations in autonomic ganglion cells described above involve changes in the neurofibrillar structure in some degree. The retrogressive changes following injury to the axon or its complete interruption sometimes involve hypertrophy of the neurofibrillar structure particularly in the perinuclear zone and hyalinization of the peripheral cytoplasm with or without neurofibrillar hypertrophy. Hypertrophy and coalescence of the neurofibrils in some of the ganglion cells has been reported in certain diseases, particularly hydrophobia and tabes. The interpretation of observed neurofibrillar changes is particularly difficult because the appearance of the neurofibrillar structure in sections is determined largely by the fixation and the staining technic employed. Frequently modifications in the neurofibrillar network represent artifacts.

Dendritic Modifications.—Budding and hypertrophy of the dendrites of some ganglion cells occurs frequently particularly in advanced age. Short dendrites frequently present a tuberose or beaded appearance and terminate in club-shaped enlargements. Longer dendrites frequently exhibit irregular local thickenings by virtue of which they appear highly distorted (Fig. 86, B). In some instances dendrites give rise to new processes of variable length and caliber which form one or more complex brushes or

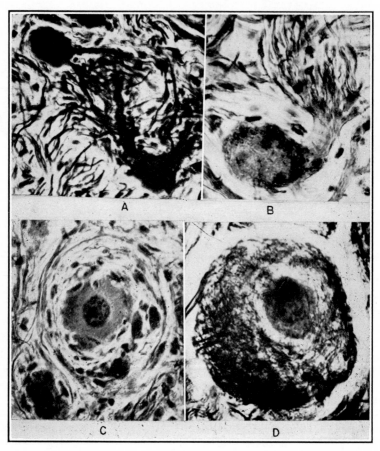

FIG. 87.—Photomicrographs of ganglion cells (human, age seventy-eight years) showing (A) hypertrophy of dendrites, (B) dendritic brush, and (C and D) pericellular dendritic nests.

tracts (Fig. 87, A and B). Structures of this kind have been reported by de Castro (1932) particularly in cases of tabes, alcoholism, and multiple sclerosis and by Kuntz (1938) in cases of advanced carcinoma and senility.

New dendritic processes may arise relatively late. Some investigators, particularly de Castro (1923), have supported the assumption that autonomic ganglion cells may undergo continuous differentiation throughout life. More or less elaborate pericellular dendritic nests are not uncommon particularly after the age of 40 years. They may include terminal branches of dendrites of adjacent ganglion cells or only dendrites of the same cells that have grown relatively long and, branching profusely, form a dense fibrous structure around the cell body (Fig. 87, C and D). In the more elaborate dendritic nests the terminal branches of the dendrites resemble the terminal branches of axons. In the simpler ones formed by the terminal branches of dendrites of adjacent ganglion cells, the processes involved retain their typical dendritic appearance. In some instances numerous short dendrites which do not penetrate the ganglion cell capsule undergo anastomosis, thus giving rise to simple or complex fenestrations.

Changes in the Interstitial Tissue.—The interstitial tissue in the autonomic ganglia is essentially neuroglial (see Chapter II). Preparations of autonomic ganglia taken from newborn or young children contain relatively little interstitial tissue; consequently, the ganglion cells are closely aggregated. In many instances adjacent ganglion cell capsules lie in intimate contact with one another. Some are separated somewhat by bundles of nerve fibers. Preparations of autonomic ganglia taken from persons of middle age and older, in the absence of marked pathological changes, show a progressive increase in the amount of interstitial tissue, but, in most cases, it does not become excessive. In the presence of pathological conditions that are accompanied by marked alterations in the autonomic ganglion cells the interstitial tissue usually also shows a marked increase. For example, in cases of senility with cachexia the interstitial tissue becomes so excessive that most of the ganglion cell capsules are separated widely from one another. In cases of arteriosclerosis the autonomic ganglia exhibit excessive development of the interstitial tissue and marked thickening of the adventitia of the arteries and the veins. The findings in preparations of autonomic ganglia taken at autopsy in a wide variety of cases strongly suggest that all chronic pathological conditions that involve marked alterations in the autonomic ganglion cells are accompanied by an abnormal increase in the interstitial tissue. Chronic infections and other conditions that result in inflammation of the autonomic ganglia also result in hyperplasia of the interstitial tissue. In a study of 100 cases following infectious diseases, Laignel-Lavastine (1905) observed hyperplasia of the interstitial tissue in all in which the infection had run a chronic course. Stämmler (1923) reported pathological alterations in the interstitial tissue in approximately 50 cases in which death resulted from infectious disease.

Most of the human ganglia in our series that have been removed surgically in the treatment of patients with hypertension and peripheral vascular disease and many of those obtained at autopsy following various pathological processes give evidence of hyperplasia of the interstitial tissue including the ganglion cell capsules. Amitotic nuclear division of both capsular cells and extracapsular interstitial cells has been observed frequently. Amitotic cell division has also been observed in bundles of nerve fibers that traverse a ganglion or emerge from it and in neurofibromatous nodules. The proliferating cells in these locations obviously are neurilemma cells. In the sections of many of the ganglia in our series nuclei in the process of division occur in sufficient abundance to suggest rapid hyperplasia.

25

In experiments carried out on cats and dogs (Kuntz and Sulkin, 1947) hyperplasia of the neuroglial tissue in autonomic ganglia was induced by stimulation of the ganglia by various means including faradic stimulation of the preganglionic fibers, subcutaneous administration of diphtheria toxin and direct application of alcohol to sympathetic trunk ganglia. The hyperplasia induced was well marked in most instances. The histological preparations of ganglia removed after prolonged stimulation showed a marked increase in the numbers of interstitial cells and many capsular

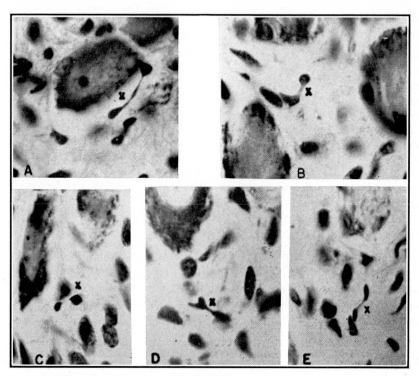

Fig. 88.—Photomicrographs from sections of autonomic ganglia (cat) showing cells in the process of amitotic division: (*A*) capsule cell (*x*); (*B*, *C* and *D*) interstitial cells (*x*); (*E*) neurilemma cell (*x*). (Kuntz and Sulkin, 1947, courtesy of Jour. Comp. Neurol.)

(Fig. 88, *A*) and extracapsular cells (Fig. 88, *B*, *C*, *D*) in the process of amitosis. Mitotic division of neuroglial cells was not observed.

It is significant that within the duration of these experiments some of the cells derived by the division of capsule cells have become detached from the capsular wall, assumed a spheroid form and encroached upon the ganglion cell. In many instances the process of neuronolysis was already initiated.

The data obtained in these experiments strongly suggest that the neuroglial proliferation induced by artificial stimulation of autonomic ganglia is comparable to that which takes place in human autonomic ganglia in the presence of a disease in which exaggerated reflex vasomotor activity is a factor or in which the autonomic ganglia become irritated or inflamed. Since the preparations of most of the ganglia that had been subjected to stimulation in this experimental series exhibit invasion of ganglion cells by cells derived from their capsules, and in some instances extensive dissolution of ganglion cells, it is evident that hyperplasia of capsule cells may be a significant factor in degenerative alterations in ganglion cells and, consequently, in autonomic dysfunction.

In the presence of certain infectious diseases, as Stämmler (1923) has pointed out, marked hyperplasia of the interstitial tissue in the autonomic ganglia does not occur and the ganglion cells undergo no marked alterations, but the ganglia become hyperemic. Such hyperemia, according to Stämmler, is commonly accompanied by abundant diapedesis of white cells that become aggregated in the perivascular lymph vessels and gradually invade the interstitial tissue throughout the ganglion. Under these conditions, the invading cells are mainly lymphocytes and mononuclear leukocytes. Such cells do not commonly invade the ganglion cell capsules. Spiegel and Adolf (1922) have advanced certain evidence which indicates that wandering phagocytic cells in autonomic ganglia may take part in the transportation of waste metabolites toward the blood vessels, thus facilitating their elimination through the blood stream. In acute infectious diseases according to Stämmler (1923), the infecting organisms usually are not found in the autonomic ganglia. If degenerative alterations occur in ganglion cells they represent reactions to toxic substances that may call forth secondary inflammatory reactions in the ganglia. In rats, as reported by Dempsher et al. (1952), inoculation of one eye with pseudorabies virus resulted in inflammation of the superior cervical sympathetic ganglion on the same side, but not on the opposite side. Potential records showed a spontaneous discharge of impulses from the inflamed ganglion, but not from the contralateral one. Later histological examination of the ganglion on the side of the inoculation revealed chromatolysis and other degenerative changes including severe nuclear changes with inclusion bodies in most of the ganglion cells and complete destruction of some of them. In the contralateral ganglion, the ganglion cells were essentially normal. The capacity of non-infective toxic substances to produce inflammation in autonomic ganglion cells has also been demonstrated experimentally (Fischer and Kaiserling, 1939).

Changes in Nerve Fibers.—In contrast to the pathological alterations observed in autonomic ganglion cells, no well-marked pathological alterations in autonomic nerve fibers have been described. Preparations of autonomic ganglia exhibit a wide range of variation in the abundance of nerve fibers, but this does not afford an adequate basis for conclusions relative to pathological alterations in the ganglion cells or their processes. Silver preparations show clearly that the processes of many ganglion cells that contain a relatively large amount of pigment and exhibit other degenerative changes, including thickening of the neurofibrils, remain intact. In many instances, an intact fiber may be traced from a ganglion cell which obviously is swollen and vacuolated and in which the nucleus has been displaced toward the periphery. On the other hand, the most heavily pigmented and shrunken ones in preparations in which the processes of most of the ganglion cells are well impregnated appear to be devoid of processes. Silver impregnation methods are not well adapted to reveal initial pathological changes in nerve fibers. Other methods have not been used extensively in investigations bearing on this problem. Most of the early reports relative to pathological alterations in autonomic nerve fibers are relatively insignificant. Certain investigators have called attention to lesions of the nerve fibers in the areas of chronic peptic ulcers and adjacent to them. According to Katsurashima (1932), the nerve fibers in the area of the ulcer first become hyperplastic and later undergo regressive changes. Stöhr (1934), on the contrary, has emphasized the pathological changes observed in the ganglion cells, in cases of chronic peptic ulcers, not only in the ulcerated areas and adjacent to them but also in areas remote from the sites of the ulcers, and the rarity of significant degenerative changes in the nerve fibers even in advanced cases. Some thickening of postganglionic fibers associated with tubercular lesions in the larynx, the lung, and the intestine has been reported. Abnormalities of the nerve fiber bundles in the aganglionic zone of the distal portion of the colon in patients with congenital megacolon have also been pointed out. Alterations in the terminal branches of preganglionic fibers under certain conditions have been described by Herzog (1948). Jabonero (1951) described alterations in preganglionic vagus nerve fibers and intramural ganglion cells in the esophagus in patients with pulmonary tuberculosis.

Capacity for Restoration.—Experimental data regarding the capacity of damaged autonomic ganglion cells for recovery as yet are very meager. The consensus seems to be that these cells possess the capacity for regeneration of any part of the cell body in only a limited degree, but their capacity for regeneration greatly exceeds that of the more highly specialized neurons in the central nervous system. Vitamin C deficiency results in alterations in autonomic ganglion cells that can be demonstrated by cytological and histochemical methods. In scorbutic guinea-pigs, as observed by Weatherford and Sulkin (1952), most of the ganglion cells showed alterations in the concentration and the distribution of ribonucleoproteins, shrinkage, vacuolization, alterations in the Golgi apparatus and in the alkaline and the acid phosphatase activity, accumulation of lipids and deposition of mucopolysaccharides in the cytoplasm and pyknosis of the nucleus. When vitamin C was administered intraperitoneally and orally most of the scorbutic animals recovered. Preparations of ganglia removed after recovery revealed that some ganglion cells had undergone complete degeneration, but most of them had reverted to the normal condition, as indicated by the cytological and the histochemical methods employed. Improvement in the pentose nucleic acid content, of the ganglion cells in young rats by parenteral administration of vitamin B_{12} has been demonstrated (Alexander and Backlar, 1951).

Interrupted preganglionic axons exhibit the capacity for regeneration in approximately the same degree as somatic nerve fibers of corresponding caliber. The capacity of postganglionic axons for regeneration is limited. According to de Castro's (1931) account, regenerating postganglionic axons, while advancing through scar tissue, frequently exhibit thickenings at the growing tips which resemble the growth cones of embryonic nerve fibers. Several slender branches commonly may be traced from a single enlargement. Collateral branches may also arise from the axon proximal to the point of damage and grow distad parallel to it, unless prevented by scar tissue. Relatively compact scar tissue may prevent the growth of the axon or collaterals distad and cause the formation of minute masses of tortuous fibers. If the scar tissue is not too extensive or too compact and the distal segment of the interrupted nerve has not been too far displaced, the growing axons gradually extend into it and continue to grow. Collateral branches that succeed in entering the nerve sheath grow distad in it, thus the number of fibers growing distad commonly exceeds the number of original regenerated axons. The collaterals that arise from regenerated postganglionic axons, however, are usually fewer than those that arise from regenerating preganglionic axons. Under favorable conditions, according to de Castro (1931), damaged or interrupted postganglionic nerves may be completely repaired after 15 to 50 days, depending on the nature of the lesion and the degree of displacement of the distal segment of the nerve. Experimental findings of certain other investigators do not support this point of view, but fail to indicate appreciable regeneration of interrupted postganglionic fibers. Kirgis and Ohler (1944) reported regrowth of postganglionic sympathetic fibers in cats following their interruption but failed, by physiological tests, to demonstrate reëstablishment of functional connections within a postoperative period of 300 days. In cats in which the influence of adrenin was eliminated by bilateral adrenalectomy, and the animals were kept alive by transplants of adrenal cortex, Kirgis and Pearce (1950) could demonstrate no sympathetic nerve function in the eye 10 months after preganglionic sympathectomy, but fright and anger were accompanied by dilatation of the pupil 14 months after inferior cervical sympathectomy. In experiments on young dogs, Kubicek *et al.* (1952) demonstrated that, with careful placement of shielded silver electrodes on the sympathetic trunk, sympathetic nerve fibers and ganglion cells can survive at least 6 weeks of chronic electrical stimulation.

Variations in Autonomic Ganglia Related to Age and Variations Related to Disease.—On the basis of a study of preparations of ganglia obtained in an extensive series of autopsies following death at ages ranging from 5 weeks to 90 years and ganglia removed in the surgical treatment of disease in approximately 50 patients ranging in age from 6 to 71 years, it may be stated that preparations of ganglia within any given age group exhibit certain variations common to all the ganglia in that group, but the ganglia of certain individuals in every age group exhibit a wider range of variation than others. Certain variations appear in some cases which are not common to all in the same age group, and certain of the common variations appear in exaggerated form. The ganglia in every age group that exhibit only those variations which are common to all ganglia within this group undoubtedly may be regarded as most nearly normal. These common variations, consequently, are related to age. Variations that appear in some of the ganglia in a given age group and not in others obviously depend on factors other than age. Some of these variations undoubtedly are pathological in some degree. The appearance in exaggerated form of variations common to all the ganglia in the same age group probably is causally related to pathological lesions in the body which at least result in modifications of metabolic functions.

According to these criteria, variations in autonomic ganglia that may be regarded as related to age include (1) growth and differentiation of the ganglion cells to maturity, (2) development of secondary dendrites and other dendritic modifications in some of the ganglion cells during adult life, (3) deposition of pigment in moderate amounts in some of the ganglion cells, particularly after the age of 30 to 35 years, (4) degenerative changes in occasional ganglion cells particularly in advanced age, including hydropic enlargement, vacuolization, neuronolysis in moderate degree and necrosis. Variations that may be regarded as pathological include (1) elaborate development of dendritic nests, dendritic brushes, etc., and excessive budding and hypertrophy of dendrites, (2) marked changes in the chromidial structure in large numbers of ganglion cells, including hypochromatism in some cells and hyperchromatism in others, (3) excessive pigmentation of ganglion cells, (4) marked degenerative changes in relatively large numbers of ganglion cells, particularly in the less advanced age groups, including hydropic enlargement, vacuolization, hyalinization, neuronolysis and necrosis, (5) hyperplasia of the interstitial tissue and (6) marked thickening of ganglion cell capsules with proliferation of capsule cells. On the basis of these criteria, the establishment of a norm for human ganglia must be regarded as hazardous because of the effects of pathological conditions either preceding or associated with the cause of death, in the case of ganglia obtained at autopsy, or preceding the condition because of which ganglia are removed surgically, which may have exerted an influence on the ganglia and the ganglion cells.

In animals, particularly cats and dogs, the autonomic ganglia and the ganglion cells are more uniform in their cytological structure than in man. A norm for the ganglion cells in any given age group can, therefore, be established within relatively narrow limits. Many of the variations observed in human ganglia and ganglion cells have also been induced in experimental animals by preganglionic nerve section, stimulation and controlled diets. Norms established in animals, therefore, afford useful criteria for the study of human ganglia and ganglion cells.

In a cytological and histochemical study of ganglia obtained from a series of dogs ranging in age from 20 days to 16.5 years, as reported by Sulkin and Kuntz (1952), hyperplasia of the interstitial tissue was observed only rarely except in the ganglia of senile animals. Pigmentation of ganglion cells was not observed in animals less than 10 years of age. In general the ganglia of all the dogs except those in the advanced age group showed but few of the alterations in the ganglion cells and the interstitial tissue that are commonly observed in human ganglia.

In the ganglia of dogs 20 to 40 days of age the ganglion cells remain relatively small and, as compared with those of adult animals, the nucleus-plasma ratio favors the nucleus. The dendritic processes give evidence of continuing growth. The chromidial substance of the cytoplasm is relatively meager.

In the ganglia of young adult dogs the interstitial tissue is somewhat more abundant than in those of the very young animals. The ganglion cells vary somewhat in size and show a normal complement of dendrites. Most of them exhibit a fairly abundant supply of chromidial substance that is usually distributed throughout the cytoplasm. The Golgi apparatus appears in the form of a typical Golgi network. Ascorbic acid is demonstrable in all the ganglion cells. Most of them also contain glycogen in appreciable quantities. Shrinkage, vacuolization and other alterations in ganglion cells that might be regarded as pathological were observed only rarely.

In preparations of ganglia of dogs over 12 years of age, particularly those that showed evidence of senility, the chromidial substance in most of the ganglion cells is depleted, the Golgi apparatus no longer exists in the form of a Golgi net, but the remaining Golgi substance appears in granules and many ganglion cells are almost devoid of osmophilic substance. Many are pigmented in some degree. The alkaline phosphatase activity in the ganglion cells is not appreciably altered, but that in the interstitial tissue is materially reduced. Neuroglial proliferation is also reduced. The ascorbic acid content of the ganglion cells is reduced. Mucoprotein deposition could be demonstrated in the ganglion cells in all animals over 10 years of age. Neuronolysis is apparent, but not excessive. Shrinkage, vacuolization and other degenerative alterations in ganglion cells also are more frequent than in the ganglia in the younger age groups.

The demonstration that some of the alterations commonly observed in human ganglia, such as hyperplasia of the interstitial tissue, neuronolysis, and alterations in the chromidial substance, the ascorbic acid content and phosphatase activity, can be induced experimentally in animals strongly suggests that these variations are not primarily related to ageing but to nutritive and pathological states. Most of the alterations observed in preparations of human ganglia undoubtedly are more fundamentally related to nutritive and pathological states than to the process of ageing.

General Effect of Autonomic Lesions on the Course of the Associated Disease. — Histopathological changes in the autonomic ganglia and ganglion cells that are associated with disease may be induced by the cause of the disease or they may arise as a result of the disease process. The pathological changes that arise in the autonomic ganglia and ganglion cells during the course of an infectious disease obviously must be regarded as a result of the disease process. They are referable to the direct effect of intoxication and metabolic disturbances, including inflammatory reactions in the ganglia. In many cases they play an important rôle in the course and the termination of the disease due to their stimulating or depressing effect on the nerves through which the regulatory neural control of the visceral functions is mediated. For example, continued stimulation of the sympathetic or depression of the parasympathetic innervation of the gastro-intestinal tract results in chronic constipation. On the contrary, depression of the sympathetic or stimulation of the parasympathetic innervation of the stomach and the intestine results in hypermotility of the gastro-intestinal musculature.

Many investigators have called attention to the clinical importance of the effect on the vasomotor apparatus of changes in the sympathetic ganglion cells brought about during the course of infectious diseases.

Those in which the symptoms referable to depression of the vasomotor apparatus are most marked are also accompanied by the most marked degenerative changes in the autonomic ganglion cells. On the other hand, certain infectious diseases usually are not accompanied by marked vasomotor disturbances even though many of the autonomic ganglion cells undergo pathological changes.

Chronic infections as well as repeated acute infections and other forms of intoxication invariably result in necrosis of many autonomic ganglion cells and less extensive damage to others, resulting in impairment of function of the autonomic nerves in a greater or lesser degree. Although it must be assumed that the autonomic ganglion cells possess the capacity for recuperation within relatively wide limits, it is conceivable that even moderate pathological changes in these cells may result in changes in their reactivity of relatively long duration. Many visceral neuroses undoubtedly have their origin in functional impairment of the autonomic nerves. The occurrence of chronic parenchymatous and interstitial inflammation of the enteric ganglia in cases of gastritis is in full accord with this assumption. The opinion that many gastro-intestinal neuroses have their histopathological substratum in impairment of autonomic functions is supported by ample clinical data. A significant rôle of lesions of the autonomic nervous system in the genesis of arteriosclerosis also is indicated. Degenerative alterations in cardiac ganglion cells in cases of coronary sclerosis have been described by Hermann (1949). Although no positive conclusions could be drawn relative to the relationship of the observed alterations to coronary disease, they were regarded as etiologically significant. The common occurrence in sympathetic ganglia removed surgically in the treatment of chronic polyarthritis, Raynaud's disease and other peripheral vascular diseases of histological alterations indicative of hyperactivity of the ganglion cells supports the assumption that, irrespective of its cause, peripheral vasomotor hyperactivity is a significant factor in the progress of diseases characterized by vascular hypertonus particularly in the extremities.

NEOPLASMS

True nerve tumors, *i.e.*, neoplasms that consist of cells of neural origin, occur relatively infrequently, but they are more common in the autonomic than in the central nervous system. They also are more common in the sympathetic than in the parasympathetic division of the autonomic nervous system. Neoplasms of the autonomic system include both benign and malignant tumors, but their clinical manifestations are not well known. In most of the cases reported, the neoplasm was not recognized clinically, but was discovered at autopsy and usually regarded as a purely secondary finding. Malignant neoplasms of the autonomic nervous system occur almost exclusively in infants and young children. The symptoms most commonly associated with them are pain in the lower extremities, swelling of the abdomen and periodic fever. Benign tumors of the autonomic system may occur at any age. The fact that they usually are not recognized clinically suggests that they exist without giving rise to marked symptoms. In most cases, neither the patient nor the physician is aware of their presence. Symptoms referable to a benign tumor of the autonomic system are due primarily to the mechanical effects of the tumor mass. In some cases they may warrant surgical interference.

Neoplasms of the autonomic nervous system may be classified as (1) neurocytomata, (2) neuroblastomata, (3) sympathoblastomata, (4) ganglioneuromata, (5) paragangliomata, and (6) neurofibromata, all of which are closely related ontogenetically. All the cellular types not only merge almost imperceptibly into one another but cells in all stages of development may also occur in the same tumor. Neurofibromatosis may be combined with any of the other types of tumor formation.

Neurocytoma.—The neurocytoma consists chiefly of undifferentiated cells of neural origin. The cells in neoplasms of this type are neurocytes in the undifferentiated stage. In some instances, the ground substance reveals delicate fibrils that react to Mallory's stain neither like neuroglia, collagenous fibers nor fibroglia, but resemble the fibrils that occur in the primordia of the autonomic nervous system. Both the cells and the fibrils in the tumor exhibit the same morphological characters and arrangement as the cells and the fibrils in the autonomic primordia and the adrenal medulla. The fibrils tend to run in parallel bundles with which characteristic aggregates of cells are associated. Preparations of these tumors exhibit ball-like structures composed of two or three concentric rows of nuclei surrounding a central meshwork of delicate fibrils. They conform to the rosettes described by Kuster (1905) in preparations of neuroblastomata, but they are not morphologically identical with the rosettes which are characteristic of the glioma. Inasmuch as undifferentiated cells of neural origin (indifferent cells) migrate from all parts of the central nervous system, neurocytomata may occur in any part of the body. They probably occur more frequently than is indicated by the number of reported cases.

Neuroblastoma.—The neuroblastoma is a malignant neoplasm that may involve any part of the nervous system. It occurs most frequently at the site of a sympathetic ganglion, in the adrenal medulla or elsewhere behind the peritoneum, whence it commonly metastasizes to the liver, the skeletal system and lymph nodes. The primary tumor frequently is located in the adrenal medulla or an adjacent sympathetic ganglion. It is composed chiefly of neuroblasts that tend to become arranged in solid masses (Kuster's rosettes). Fibrils usually are present in the ground substance, although some tumors of this type exhibit very little fibrillar differentiation. The fibrils represent only a degree of differentiation of the cells. If the cells remain in the early phases of neuroblast differentiation, fibrils are scarcely apparent and the tumors may present a histological picture similar to that of a lymphosarcoma, but if cell differentiation has advanced beyond the earliest neuroblast stages the fibrils are more numerous. In general, the degree of differentiation of the cells in these tumors is correlated with age. Most of the neuroblastomata reported have occurred in infants or young children. A few neoplasms probably of this type in adults have also been reported. The younger the patient the less differentiated are the cells and the more malignant is the neoplasm. If the host survives, tissue differentiation increases with age, but malignancy decreases and the tumor assumes the appearance of a malformation. Most of the neuroblastomata of the differentiated type include cells in various stages of differentiation, but either those of the undifferentiated or those of the more differentiated type predominate. Foci of indifferent cells may also be present. Differentiated cells occur, but less frequently, in the undifferentiated neuroblastomata. Neoplasms of this type may exhibit any combination of differentiated and undifferentiated cells.

The primary diagnosis of a neuroblastoma has rarely been made without a biopsy. During the early stages of the disease symptoms may be absent. Frequently, the first evidence of the disease is due to metastases in the head, resulting in intracranial pressure with protrusion of one or both eyes, discoloration of the eyelids, profound anemia and swellings about the bones of the skull. Drowsiness, optic neuritis and blindness may follow. A peculiar type of periosteal reaction and calcification is associated with metastasis in the bones. This osseous lesion yields a characteristic roentgenogram that may be regarded as pathognomonic of the neoplasm.

Sympathoblastoma.—The sympathoblastoma represents a somewhat later stage in the differentiation of sympathetic nerve cells than the neuroblastoma. It is a malignant neoplasm, occupying a position midway between the undifferentiated neuroblastoma and the ganglioneuroma, and is composed chiefly of cells that have become differentiated beyond the neuroblast stage. Tumors of this type are relatively rare, but may occur in various locations and give rise to a multiplicity of symptoms. In general those in the younger patients are less differentiated and more malignant than in those in the older ones.

Ganglioneuroma.—The ganglioneuroma represents a later stage in the differentiation of nerve cells. It consists chiefly of ganglion cells and fibers. The ganglion cells exhibit a wide range of variation both in size and general morphology. Many of them are relatively small round cells which, in their general appearance, have little in common with normal ganglion cells. Their neural origin is indicated by the vesicular character and meager chromatin content of the nucleus and the character and arrangement of the chromidial bodies in the cytoplasm. The larger cells show all the characters of ganglion cells. Many of them are binuclear or polymorphonuclear. Degenerative changes in the cytoplasm and pigmentation occur frequently. Many of the ganglion cells show multiple processes in which, as well as in the cell body, neurofibrils can be demonstrated, particularly by silver impregnation methods. Pericellular meshworks of fibers have also been observed. The fibrous components of the tumor include both myelinated and unmyelinated nerve fibers, but the latter usually predominate. The myelinated fibers frequently show evidence of degeneration. The myelin sheaths may be fragmented or they may show varicose swelling. Neurilemma cells may be numerous. As a rule, these tumors are solitary and benign. In certain cases they are multiple and malignant. The solitary tumors usually are definitely delimited and do not infiltrate or metastasize. Malignancy probably depends on the inclusion of groups of immature or undifferentiated cells. In such cases, infiltration and metastasis may take place. The growth of these tumors usually is slow, but they may attain relatively large size. Most of the reported malignant ganglioneuromata have occurred in young persons. The younger the patient, the more undifferentiated are the cells and the more apt is the tumor to become malignant. Tumors of this type occur more frequently in females than in males. They may occur at any age but are most common in children and young adults and are rarely found after the age of 40 years. They have been reported in still born fetuses and newborn children.

Paraganglioma.—The paraganglioma represents the most common tumor of the autonomic system. It exhibits many variations and usually is benign, but becomes malignant in some cases. Being composed predominantly of chromaffine tissue, it may occur wherever such tissue exists, but is found most commonly in the carotid body, the appendix and the small intestine. Paragangliomata in the adrenal medulla are relatively rare. Since the chromaffin tissue arises from cells that become displaced from the central nervous system with the cells that give rise to the sympathetic primordia, the paraganglioma is genetically related to the other neoplasms of the autonomic system. These tumors are relatively small and, as a rule, are discovered in middle aged and elderly persons, being found sometimes accidentally at autopsy. Frequently they are associated with neurofibromatosis. Inasmuch as the cells composing the paraganglioma represent fairly mature chromaffine cells, this tumor corresponds to the ganglioneuroma.

Tumors made up solely of immature chromaffine cells are unknown, but most paragangliomata exhibit a wide range in the degree of differentiation of the chromaffine cells. Most of the cells are large epithelioid elements some of which contain adrenin and glycogen. Many of them assume a characteristic brown color after fixation with chrome salts. Those which do not react to chrome salts in this manner probably are not fully differentiated. Although these tumors are made up chiefly of chromaffine cells that appear as polymorphous or polyhedral elements with finely granular vacuolated cytoplasm, transitional forms, multinucleated giant cells, ganglion cells and cystic or hemorrhagic areas are often observed. Myelinated or unmyelinated nerve fibers are also encountered occasionally.

Neurofibromatosis.—Neurofibromatosis usually involves peripheral nerves. It is frequently characterized by the appearance of multiple tumors in the subcutaneous tissue, areas of pigmentation, and less often by a condition resembling elephantiasis (elephantiasis neuromatosa). According to von Recklinghausen's original concept, these tumors are derived exclusively from the perineurium and the endoneurium. Later investigators have shown that in many cases neurofibromatous growths exhibit very little connective tissue, but are made up mainly of nerve fibers. Some consist predominantly of neurilemma cells.

In isolated cases neurofibromatosis has been observed in the autonomic nervous system. Askanazy (1907) described tumors between the longitudinal and circular muscles in the gastro-intestinal tract in which he found ganglion cells and nerve fibers. These tumors obviously involved the myenteric plexus. In rare instances, fibromatosis of the nerves supplying the bladder and the seminal vesicles has also been reported. Roux (1926) described neurofibromatosis involving the sympathetic fibers ac-

companying the arteries in the pelvic region in certain cases of sclerous
and cystic degeneration of the ovaries accompanied by dysmenorrhea and
other pelvic disorders.   Brocher (1927) reported three cases of neurofibromatosis in the autonomic nervous system.   In one of these, the
growth involved the myenteric plexus near the cardiac end of the stomach.
In another, it involved the entire left sympathetic trunk from the rostral
end of the common carotid artery to the promontory of the sacrum.   In
the third case, only the thoracic portion of the left sympathetic trunk was
involved.   In all three cases, the neurofibromata were discovered as purely
secondary findings at autopsy.   Kass (1932) reported a rare case of neurofibromatosis involving the bladder and the skin in a boy 7 years of age.
In a patient with neurofibromatosis, a woman past middle age, brought to
our attention by the late Dr. Joseph Grindon, the disease was characterized
by cutaneous and subcutaneous tumors throughout the area of distribution
of the sympathetic nerves derived from the left superior cervical sympathetic ganglion and complete paralysis of the sympathetic nerves in this
area.   Examination of sections of the tumors showed that they were made
up almost exclusively of hyperplastic neurilemma cells that multiplied by
amitotic division.   The sympathetic fibers had undergone almost complete
degeneration.

Various investigators have called attention to alterations in the nerves
adjoining gastric ulcers which are not always destructive but exhibit a
marked tendency toward proliferative, degenerative activity.   According
to Okkels (1927), who carried out a detailed study of the changes in the
nerves in the vicinity of gastric ulcers in an extensive series of cases, the
proliferative alterations of the nerve tissue constitute a central cicatrix
neuroma which may originate in the enteric plexuses or in periarterial
nerves.   These alterations are not specific for gastric ulcer; consequently,
they may be regarded as secondary.

CENTRAL AUTONOMIC LESIONS

Intermediolateral Cell Column. — Degenerative changes in preganglionic
neurons in the intermediolateral cell column in the corresponding segments
of the spinal cord have been reported following section of communicating
rami or splanchnic nerves, carcinoma involving the brachial plexus and
section of the cervical sympathetic trunks.   Chromatolysis and other
changes in preganglionic neurons in the sacral spinal cord segments also have
been reported following resection of the rectum and suppuration and gangrene in the pelvis.

Disease of the spinal cord, e.g., tumors, cavities and inflammatory
processes, may give rise to disturbances of visceral functions due to its
effect on the neurons in the intermediolateral column.   In some patients
with poliomyelitis, muscular paralysis is accompanied by segmental vasomotor and sweat secretory disturbances.   In this disease, the inflammatory
process in the spinal cord may involve the intermediolateral cell column
directly, but frequently pathological cahnges also occur in the corresponding ganglia of the sympathetic trunk.   In some instances, syringomyelia is

accompanied by scleroderma and pupillary disturbances, probably due to encroachment of the spinal cord lesion on the intermediolateral cell column.

Visceral disturbances resulting from localized lesions of the spinal cord, in most instances, probably are due to the effect of the lesion on the preganglionic neurons. In some instances the effect may be excessive stimulation of these neurons. In others it may be depression or complete cessation of function. Excessive preganglionic stimulation undoubtedly plays a rôle in the causation of peptic ulcers in certain cases. Burdenko (1933) reported the occurrence of peptic ulcer in three patients with spinal cord lesions which involved the intermediolateral cell column. In one of these the ulcers healed promptly following surgical removal of an intramedullary tumor extending from the fourth to the seventh thoracic segments inclusive. He also reported a case in which chronic peptic ulcer associated with chronic irritation of the celiac plexus healed following removal of a fragment of shrapnel from the celiac plexus.

Autonomic Centers in the Medulla Oblongata.—Pathological changes in certain of the visceral nuclei in the medulla oblongata have been reported. In postmortem examination of the brain stem, Vonderahe (1939) found diffuse hemorrhage in the dorsal motor nuclei of the vagus nerves in 7 of 14 cases of peptic ulcer. A causal relationship of this lesion to the production of peptic ulcer is not apparent, in these cases, since it was associated with other lesions in the brain stem. It probably represents a secondary effect of afferent impulses arising at the site of the gastrointestinal lesion. Neurogenic factors in the causation of peptic ulcer are not precluded, but, in all instances, as pointed out by Vonderahe, such irritative lesions in the stomach or duodenum give rise to more or less constant afferent stimulation resulting in reflex vasodilatation in the brain stem which, in conjunction with other factors acting diffusely, may reach the stage of hemorrhage. Certain associated disturbances undoubtedly are caused by the lesions in the vagus nuclei. For example, the marked increase in the pulse rate in certain peptic ulcer patients may result from loss of the inhibitory influence of the vagus nerves due to destruction of the cardiac neurons by the hemorrhagic lesions. Autonomic imbalance with respect to other viscera may, in certain cases, be explained on the same basis.

Autonomic Centers in the Mesencephalon.—Certain diseases which involve the mid-brain (encephalitis, hemorrhage, tumors) are known to give rise to pupillary disturbances. These disturbances are brought about by the effect of the mid-brain lesion on the preganglionic components of the oculomotor nerves, but little is known regarding pathological changes in these neurons or their relationship to specific mid-brain lesions.

Autonomic Centers in the Diencephalon.—The chief diencephalic autonomic centers are located in the hypothalamus. Their influence in the regulation of visceral functions is exerted in part through descending pathways that conduct impulses to the visceral efferent nuclei and in part through the hypophysis and other endocrine glands. Certain visceral disorders are obviously related to hypophyseal lesions, but in many instances the hypophyseal lesions are causally related to lesions of the hypothalamus. The effect of hypophyseal lesions, therefore, cannot be properly evaluated apart from those of the hypothalamic lesions with which they are associated. An account of the effects of experimental hypothalamic and hypophyseal lesions on various visceral functions is included in Chapter IV. In the present connection attention will be given particularly to clinical and pathological data.

Although it is located superficially and in relation to the walls of the third ventricle, clinical evidence of damage to the hypothalamus in cases of severe head injury is observed relatively infrequently. Even in fatal injuries pathological changes in the hypothalamus are not commonly observed except in conjunction with more extensive and severe damage in other parts of the brain (Vonderahe, 1940).

Wounds that involve localized areas of the hypothalamus in man result in metabolic disturbances comparable to those caused by experimental lesions in the corresponding areas in animals, Any injury, therefore, that damages or interrupts the hypothalamico-hypophyseal tract may result in profound disturbances particularly in water, carbohydrate and fat metabolism. Tumors of the hypothalamus may cause even more diverse disturbances, including somnolence and hypo- and hyperthermia. Tumors adjacent to the hypothalamus which cause direct pressure upon it or occlude the interventricular foramina or the cerebral aqueduct, resulting in the accumulation of cerebrospinal fluid in the third ventricle, may produce similar disturbances.

Diabetes insipidus may be caused by a lesion of the hypothalamus involving damage to the supraoptic nuclei or the hypothalamico-hypophyseal tract, but it probably always involves changes in the posterior hypophyseal lobe (Fisher *et al.*, 1938). Diabetes mellitus frequently is associated with a hypothalamic lesion, but the available evidence does not justify the conclusion that this disease is invariably caused by a central nervous lesion. The assumptions that the paraventricular nucleus in the hypothalamus is stimulated by the presence of sugar in the blood and that such stimulation elicits increased insulin secretion in the pancreatic islets are supported by clinical and pathological data (Vonderahe, 1937). The hypothalamus, therefore, plays an important rôle in the cycle of events which constitute the phenomena of this disease. In cases in which diabetes was associated with internal hydrocephalus, according to Niemer and Vonderahe ((1940), the intensity of the disease appeared to vary with the intensity of the hydrocephalic pressure on diencephalic structures. Cell counts of hypothalamic nuclei carried out in their study, like those previously reported by Morgan *et al.* (1937) in cases of diabetes, indicate an appreciable reduction in the number of neurons.

Postmortem examination of the brain stem in cases of heat stroke, as observed by Morgan and Vonderahe (1939) and Vonderahe (1940), frequently reveals evidence of previous injury in the hypothalamus in the form of glial scars and reduced nerve cell counts particularly in the paraventricular nucleus, the lateral nucleus of the tuber cinereum and the tubero-mammillary nucleus. The losses of nerve cells in the supraoptic nuclei and the gray matter in the walls of the third ventricle in these cases were not sufficiently constant to be regarded as significant. On the basis of these findings, Morgan and Vonderahe advanced the hypothesis that the larger neurons in the more rostrally located paraventricular nucleus and the neurons in the lateral nucleus of the tuber cinereum are primarily concerned with heat elimination, while the tubero-mammillary nucleus and the smaller neurons in the paraventricular nucleus are primarily concerned with heat production and heat conservation. In heat stroke, acceleration of heat elimination fails, probably due to previous injury to the neurons aggregates which normally regulate this process, while the heat producing mechanisms are hyperactive. This is suggested by the alterations observed in the tubero-mammillary nucleus and the smaller neurons in the paraventricular nucleus.

Histopathological changes in the hypothalamus and other parts of the brain stem frequently are associated with lesions of the abdominal viscera. In a study of 28 cases with lesions in the hypothalamus or the mesencephalon or both, reported by Fried (1936), 18 gave evidence of direct involvement of the autonomic nerves, and 6 exhibited pathological changes in the gastro-intestinal tract. Conversely, Vonderahe (1939) reported postmortem findings, in a series of peptic ulcer cases, which included multiple hemorrhage in the rostral portion of the hypothalamus, particularly the paraventricular nucleus and the gray matter in the wall of the third ventricle and in some cases the supraoptic nucleus. The neurons in these areas showed varying degrees of retrograde change. These lesions probably are to be regarded as secondary to the gastro-intestinal lesions, due to the reflex effects of afferent impulses arising in the latter. They may nonetheless play a rôle in the progress and the sequelæ of the visceral disease.

The infectious agents of certain diseases frequently reach the hypothalamus through the blood stream, the olfactory and the optic pathways and the meninges. Viruses which extend along the nerve pathways connected with the hypothalamus tend to localize in it and produce local necrosis. The virus of poliomyelitis frequently invades the hypothalamus along these routes. The hypothalamic lesion caused by this virus frequently results in disturbances of visceral functions including tachycardia, periodic sweating, urinary retention, constipation, etc. (Schönholzer, 1937). Hypothalamic syndromes associated with epidemic encephalitis occur frequently. According to various investigators, including von Economo (1931), the hypothalamus is invariably involved in this disease and more extensively than any other part of the brain except the substantia nigra. Inflammatory changes in the walls and floor of the third ventricle in the St. Louis type of encephalitis have been reported particularly by Löwenburg and Zbinden (1936). In cases of measles complicated with encephalitis Malamud (1937) found perivascular demyelinization, glial proliferation, congestion and hemorrhage in the hypothalamus as well as alterations elsewhere in the brain. The occurrence of diabetes insipidus, obesity and other hypothalamic syndromes as sequellæ of encephalitis associated with scarlet fever, pertussis, diphtheria, mumps, typhoid fever, etc., emphasizes the damaging effect of the virus of this disease on the hypothalamus. In a case of lymphocytic meningo-encephalitis cellular alterations also occurred throughout the brain, but were most severe in the nuclei of the tuber cinereum and the medula.

Data relative to fatigue and the recovery of autonomic regulation advanced by Lowenstein and Lowenfeld (1952) support the assumption that in general nervous fatigue is central in origin. It is manifested earlier in cortical than in subcortical centers, and earlier in subcortical sympathetic than in parasympathetic centers. Subcortical centers defatigue earlier than cortical ones, and the parasympathetic earlier than the sympathetic centers.

Chapter XIX

VISCERAL SENSITIVITY AND REFERRED PAIN

Sensations that result from stimuli applied at the external surface of the animal organism and impulses that are received through its distance receptors play a major rôle in the reactions of the organism to environmental factors and in its adjustment to the external environment as a whole. Sensations that result from stimuli arising within the body likewise play a significant rôle in the adjustment of the organism to its internal environment. The visceral organs normally are not subjected to the stimuli that constantly play upon the surface receptors. They are relatively insensitive to these forms of stimulation. Most afferent impulses that arise in the viscera do not reach the sensory level, although they play a significant rôle in reflex functional regulation and the general feeling tone. Certain visceral stimuli give rise to sensations which in some instances are more or less definitely localizable and in others instances diffuse. True visceral pain probably is always deep-seated and poorly localized (Schutz, 1946).

In general, the visceral organs, including the central nervous system, are insensitive to mechanical, chemical, thermal and electrical stimulation in the ordinary sense, *i.e.*, the application of these stimuli to the visceral organs, with certain exceptions, does not give rise to sensations. On the basis of experimental and clinical observations, certain investigators have denied the possibility of painful sensations referable to any of the internal organs that are innervated solely through visceral nerves unless the stimulation is of such a nature that it spreads beyond the area innervated solely by the visceral nerves and affects afferent components of the somatic rami of the spinal nerves. Lennander (1906) advanced the hypothesis that all the internal organs that are innervated solely through the sympathetic nerves and the vagi, distal to the origin of the recurrent laryngeal nerves, are devoid of pain. This point of view obviously is untenable. Adequate physiological stimuli, *e.g.*, hunger contractions of the stomach, give rise to afferent impulses that result in sensations which in general are referable to the stomach. Adequate stimulation of various other viscera likewise gives rise to sensations referable to the organs in question.

The production of sensations is conditioned by the character of the stimulus and the tissue on which it acts. The absence of sensations due to manipulation, pinching, cutting or tearing of the visceral organs has been abundantly observed during operative procedures. In the application of any mechanical stimulus it may be observed that on passing from the skin into any of the orifices, *e.g.*, the mouth, there is a gradual diminution in sensitiveness as the area stimulated becomes farther removed from the external surface. In the oral portion of the enteric canal, sensitivity is lost at some level of the esophagus. Extending from the perianal skin into the rectum, mechanical stimulation elicits no sensory response beyond the line that separates the skin from the mucous membrane.   In investigations bearing on the problem of visceral pain it has almost invariably been found that when pain was produced by mechanical stimulation the stimulus affected tissues that are innervated through sensory cerebrospinal nerve fibers that are not incorporated in the autonomic nerves.   This may be illustrated by the effects of stimulation of the serous membranes.   The parietal layers of the pleura and the peritoneum are sensitive due to the receptors connected with somatic afferent spinal nerve fibers.   The visceral layers of these membranes and the serous surface of the parietal layers are insensitive.

The vital processes that produce visceral pain usually involve contraction or stretching of smooth muscle.   The normal functioning of all the hollow viscera involves the contraction of smooth muscle, but, under physiological conditions, this does not generally give rise to sensations.   When stimulated to contract in a particular way, as when the contractions become violent or spastic, or under circumstances in which the blood supply to the muscle is greatly diminished, the contraction of smooth muscle gives rise to pain.   Contraction of smooth muscle therefore may be regarded as a major factor in the production of visceral pain.   Although the production of pain in other visceral tissues in which the contraction of smooth muscle can be definitely ruled out as a contributing factor has not been clearly demonstrated, it seems probable that visceral processes other than the contraction of smooth muscle may under certain conditions produce pain.   The viscera, like other deep structures such as the skeletal muscles, require massive stimulation because they are relatively meagerly supplied with sensory nerve fibers.

VISCERAL AFFERENT CONDUCTION

Visceral impulses that give rise to pain localized in the viscus in which they arise are conducted into the spinal cord through afferent components of the thoracic and the rostral lumbar spinal nerves.   Visceral impulses conducted through afferent vagus nerve fibers probably do not reach the sensory level.   In experiments involving direct electrical stimulation of visceral nerves in unanesthetized cats, B. Cannon (1933) found the abdominal portions of the vagi and the caudal lumbar segments of the sympathetic trunks entirely insensitive.   As reported by Moore (1938), extirpation of the sympathetic trunks and their splanchnic branches in the cat rendered the abdominal viscera anesthetic, although the vagus and the phrenic nerves remained intact.   The conclusion that afferent nerve fibers that conduct impulses of pain from the viscera, except the pelvic organs, the esophagus and the respiratory tract, traverse the sympathetic trunk and enter the spinal cord through dorsal nerve roots is amply supported.   In the dorsal nerve roots they intermingle with somatic afferent nerve fibers.

Conduction of impulses of pain from the lungs through the vagus nerves appears to be demonstrated.   Morton et al. (1951) have reported relief of pain due to carcinoma of the lungs following section of the vagus nerves distal to the origins of their recurrent laryngeal branches.   Following unilateral vagus section, electrical stimulation of the bronchial walls no longer elicited pain on the side of the operation. Distention of the distal portion of the esophagus with a balloon, according to Jones and Chapman (1942), was distinctly felt by patients after extensive thoracic sympathectomy and ventrolateral cordotomy causing analgesia to the rostral thoracic level. The vagus afferent fibers concerned apparently extend rostrad for some distance to the wall of the esophagus, since distention of the distal portion of the esophagus still causes discomfort in patients following bilateral vagus section distal to the origins of the recurrent laryngeal nerves (Moore et al., 1946).

Conduction of impulses of pain and other sensations from the urinary bladder through the lateral spinothalamic tract has been demonstrated in clinical patients (Nathan and Smith, 1951). The conduction of impulses from the uterus through the hypogastric nerves has been amply demonstrated, but pain due to impulses that arise in the cervix of the uterus is mediated through the pelvic nerves. Impulses of pain that arise in the prostate, the bladder and the rectum are also conducted into the spinal cord through the pelvic nerves. Following resection of the hypogastric plexus, stimulation of the cervix or distention of the bladder or the rectum still gives rise to characteristic discomfort that is abolished by blocking of the sacral nerves (White et al., 1952).

Clearly delimited central conduction pathways for visceral pain have not been demonstrated. In most mammals abolition of true visceral pain by cordotomy requires more extensive section than abolition of somatic pain. It usually requires bilateral cordotomy deep enough to include the fasciculus proprius in the ventral portion of the lateral funiculus and part of the ventral gray column. The fibers concerned probably lie somewhat scattered in the fasciculus proprius system, particularly in the ventral portion of the lateral funiculus in the spinal cord and in the reticular formation in the brain stem. The integration of visceral pain probably takes place in the diencephalon.

The visceral afferent spinal nerve fibers, like the somatic afferent fibers that conduct impulses of pain, probably enter the spinal cord through the lateral divisions of the dorsal spinal nerve roots. Their connections within the spinal cord are not fully known, but in experimental animals conduction of visceral impulses rostrad in the fasciculus proprius system has been amply demonstrated. Pressor impulses of visceral origin are conducted rostrad in the postero-lateral funiculi on both sides. Depressor impulses are conducted in the ventral part of the lateral funiculus on both sides, but conduction of both pressor and depressor impulses is more efficient on the ipsilateral than on the contralateral side.

In experiments on cats reported by Spiegel (1923), the afferent conduction of impulses of pain caused by injecting barium chloride into the femoral arteries was not altered by transection of the dorsal funiculus of the spinal cord, but the pain reactions elicited by the injection of this irritating substance into either femoral artery were diminished following unilateral section of the ventral part of the lateral funiculus in the caudal thoracic segments. They were diminished still further, but not abolished, by an additional hemisection of the spinal cord on the opposite side in the cervical region. Experimental data reported by Spiegel and Bermis (1925) and Davis *et al.* (1929) support the conclusion that impulses of pain that arise in the abdominal viscera, like those that arise in peripheral blood vessels, are conducted rostrad in the spinal cord bilaterally in the ventral portion of the lateral funiculus through pathways made up of short neurons some of which cross to the contralateral side. Visceral pain impulses, therefore, are conducted bilaterally in the spinal cord and the brain stem, but with greater facility on the ipsilateral than on the contralateral side.

The data relative to the conduction pathways that mediate visceral pain in the mammals commonly used in experimental studies obviously do not apply strictly to the human species. Certain clinical data support the assumption that impulses of visceral origin that give rise to pain are conducted rostrad in the spinal cord in the pathways that mediate pain of somatic origin. White (1952) has demonstrated that such painful stimuli as distention of the renal pelvis and chronic irritation following cholecystectomy no longer give rise to pain following interruption of the appropriate lateral spinothalamic tract. Distention of a balloon in the proximal portion of the small intestine can also be felt only on the side ipsilateral to the cordotomy. Impulses of visceral pain, consequently, do not cross the median plane in the spinal cord in man rostral to the level of the original crossing of the lateral spinothalamic tract fibers concerned.

SENSITIVITY OF VISCERAL ORGANS

Respiratory Organs.—Irritation of any part of the respiratory epithelium may elicit reflex reactions that affect consciousness. The sensations in question are not essentially visceral. Clinical observations amply support the assumption that the lungs are insensitive to injurious or destructive stimuli. Lacerating wounds or disease processes that involve destruction of the lung tissue do not give rise to pain that is localizable within the organ. Inflammatory processes in the lungs give rise to no localized pain unless they involve the parietal pleura. Inflammation of the parietal pleura gives rise to acute pain. The nerve fibers that conduct the impulses in question obviously are the sensory cerebrospinal fibers that terminate in the deeper layers of the parietal pleura or in the subpleural connective tissue. This acute pain usually subsides after a few days, even though involvement of the parietal pleura still is indicated by the physical findings. It is also significant that the acute pain accompanying pleuritic inflammation subsides rapidly with the accumulation of an exudate.

The serous surface of the parietal pleura is relatively insensitive. Slight friction on this surface usually gives rise to no sensations. Pricking of the parietal pleura and moderate pressure on its serous surface usually were felt as such. Irritation of the central area of the diaphragmatic pleura frequently results in pain in the shoulder region. According to Capps (1932), the pain induced by irritation of the parietal pleura is definitely localizable and is never referred. The pain induced by irritation of the diaphragmatic pleura, on the contrary, always is referred to a superficial area. In his experiments, irritation of the area of the diaphragm that is innervated through the phrenic nerves induced pain localized in the region of the shoulder and the neck within the area innervated through the third and the fourth cervical nerves. Irritation of the peripheral rim of the diaphragmatic pleura, which is innervated through intercostal nerves, induced pain in the caudal thoracic and the rostral lumbar segments or in the abdomen. All the data available regarding the effects of stimulation of the visceral pleura seem to warrant the conclusion that no impulses that arise in this membrane reach the threshold of consciousness.

Circulatory Organs.—*The Heart.*—The normal activities of the heart give rise to no sensations, although in many instances the impact of the apex against the thoracic wall may be distinctly perceived by the palpating hand. It may be assumed that the portion of the thoracic wall in question has become so accustomed to the normal impact of the heart that it no longer gives rise to impulses that reach the threshold of consciousness. Whenever the action of the heart becomes exaggerated, as by physical exercise or emotional excitation, the beating of the heart becomes clearly perceptible. In some instances the sensations are referable to the thoracic wall. In others they appear to be referable to the heart. The latter condition obtains particularly in cases of paroxysmal tachycardia in which patients commonly interpret their sensations as due to the contraction of the heart musculature. Such patients may also experience a feeling of inadequate heart action and "heart flutter." Sensations due to exaggerated heart action that are clearly referable to the thoracic wall probably result from impulses that arise due to the unusual impact of the apex beat. In chronic cardiac conditions, exaggerated or irregular heart action frequently gives rise to no sensations. Many patients with chronic cardiac diseases are quite unable to form accurate judgments regarding their own cardiac activity.

Injuries to the heart and inflammation of the cardiac muscle probably give rise to no sensations that are referable to the heart itself. Stretching of the ventricular walls or the aortic ring, likewise, gives rise to no pain reaction. The endocardium also is insensitive to stimulation. Inflammation or even ulceration of the endocardium gives rise to no sensations. Frequent failures to recognize even ulcerative forms of endocarditis attest to the fact that such conditions may exist without giving rise to symptoms directly referable to the heart. On the other hand, endocarditis sometimes gives rise to discomfort, such as a feeling of pressure in the cardiac region, palpation of the heart and dyspnea. These sensations are not due to impulses of endocardial origin, but to impulses that arise as a result of impaired circulation.

Regarding the visceral pericardium, it may be stated that the data available do not indicate that impulses arising in this tissue ever reach the threshold of consciousness. Pericarditis may exist in the absence of symptoms referable to the heart. In severe cases of pericarditis, disturbances occur which give rise to sensations of pressure in the cardiac region and frequently to shortness of breath and a feeling of anxiety. These sensations are not the result of impulses arising at the seat of the inflammatory process, but are manifestations of impaired heart action or pressure phenomena. According to Capps (1932), pain associated with pericarditis is due chiefly to three complications: (1) Effusion exerting extreme tension on the pericardial sac, which gives rise to a dull ache or feeling of oppression over the heart; (2) myocardial involvement due to embarrassment of the coronary circulation, which gives rise to anginal pain; (3) pleuropericarditis, the pain of which may be localized over the heart or referred to the neck or abdomen. The pain associated with pneumonic and rheumatic pericarditis, according to Capps, is due to pleuropericarditis which is a frequent complication in these infections. As reported by Simenauer (1927), direct stimulation of the pericardium by contact at the apex of the heart resulted in a feeling of pressure on the inner side of the left arm. Moderate pressure on the pericardium of the right ventricle was not felt, but heavier pressure resulted in an unpleasant feeling along the fourth rib. Paracentesis of the pericardium at the level of the fifth or the sixth interspace lateral to the mammary line may elicit pain in the neck at a point along the trapezius ridge (Capps, 1932).

Limitation of the blood supply to the cardiac muscle, such as may be brought about by arteriosclerosis or spasm of the coronary arteries, frequently is accompanied by pain that is directly referable to the heart and pain that is referred to the thoracic wall and along the medial aspect of one or both arms. Pain caused by reduction of the flow of blood through the myocardium has also been demonstrated experimentally. The ischemic condition of the contracting cardiac muscle probably is a major factor in the production of the afferent impulses concerned. They are conducted centrad through visceral afferent fibers that traverse the sympathetic cardiac nerves, but the irradiation in the thoracic wall and upper extremities involves somatic components of the spinal nerves through which the preganglionic and the visceral afferent fibers concerned in the innervation of the heart join the sympathetic trunks.

The Blood Vessels. — Pain of vascular origin is a recognized clinical phenomenon, but the blood vessels vary in sensitivity within relatively wide limits. The adequate stimuli for pain referable to the blood vessels are not fully known. Strong peripheral vasoconstriction frequently is accompanied by pain. Certain data seem to support the theory that the pain is caused by the contraction of the vascular musculature. Other data seem to indicate that the ischemia produced in the tissues by the contraction of the blood vessels may be a contributing factor in the causation of pain. Under experimental conditions, pain may be produced by the injection of irritating substances into the arteries without spasm or stretching of the arterial muscle and without ischemia. The irritating substances apparently stimulate afferent nerve endings located in proximity to the smaller arterial branches. Chemical stimulation may also play a part in the causation of pain in blood vessels. Experimental and clinical data seem to support the assumption that accumulated metabolites in ischemic tissues may stimulate receptors closely associated with the smaller blood vessels.

In experiments reported by Frölich and Meyer (1922) the contraction of the vascular musculature elicited by the intravenous injection of adrenin produced no pain reaction, whereas the intra-arterial injection of barium chloride gave rise to intense pain. As observed by Odermatt (1922), distention of arteries, regardless of their caliber, may give rise to pain due to its effect on the periarterial nerve plexus. Ligation of certain arteries, *e.g.*, the common carotid, the iliac and certain of the mesenteric arteries, commonly gives rise to pain, whereas ligation of certain other arteries, *e.g.*, the inferior thyroid, and veins rarely causes pain. Pain caused by ligation, like that caused by distention of arteries, probably is due to stimulation of the periarterial nerves. The findings of Spiegel and Wasserman (1926) that distention of a portion of the aorta, isolated by a ligature at either end, by introducing a physiological saline solution under pressure or the application of a stimulating substance to its outer surface gives rise to pain, support this point of view. The intima of the larger vessels probably is insensitive to irritating substances.

In experiments reported by Burget and Livingston (1931), the injection of a 5 per cent solution of lactic acid into the brachial artery of the dog elicited pain reactions similar to those elicited by the intra-arterial injection of barium chloride. In cats, as reported by Moore and Moore (1932), pain reactions were elicited by the injection of a concentrated solution of sodium iodide into the femoral artery. When the injected solution was confined to the arterial trunk by ligation of its branches, no pain reaction occurred. When the femoral arterioles were blocked with lycopodium spores, the pain reaction was delayed. This delay suggested that the receptors stimulated by the injected solution are not located in the arterial wall but either in relation to the arterioles or the capillaries or in the adjacent tissues.

An isotonic or a normal sodium chloride solution (0.9 per cent) may be injected intra-arterially in any quantity or at any rate without causing painful stimulation even though the artery may be visibly distended. If the sodium chloride concentration is gradually increased, pain is elicited when it reaches 3.0 per cent or half-molar strength. Other salt solutions also elicit pain reactions when the total salt concentration approximates half-molar strength (Moore and Singleton, 1933).

When sodium chloride solutions of progressively diminishing concentration were injected intra-arterially, painful stimulation occurred when the salt content had fallen to 0.3 per cent or one-third isotonic. Other markedly hypotonic solutions and distilled water likewise elicited pain reactions. Normal or isotonic salt solutions also became irritating when they were rendered acid or alkaline. On the acid side, the solutions became irritating when the acidity reached a pH of 6.3; on the basic side, when the alkalinity reached a pH of 9.3. The pain receptors obviously are more sensitive to acid than to base.

The pain produced by arterial puncture can readily be differentiated from pain due to other causes. As observed by Bazett and McGlone (1928), a dull aching sensation is felt when the needle reaches the arterial wall, which is less acute than the pain caused by simple puncture of the dermis but much less bearable. It is diffuse, often referred to a more distal position and frequently accompanied by uncontrollable reflex reactions. The subject may experience a sudden sensation of warmth, sweat profusely and then feel cold, faint or actually lose consciousness. The pain accompanying puncture of different arteries is not of equal intensity. Puncture of small arteries beneath the deep fascia usually was accompanied by a dull aching pain which was not easily bearable and by reflex reactions of the fainting type. In general, puncture of the smaller arteries, except those in the dermis, was accompanied by more intense pain and more profound reflex reactions than puncture of the larger ones.

The sensations accompanying venipuncture, according to Bazett and McGlone, are similar to those caused by dermal puncture alone unless, as occasionally happens, a small nerve is affected. In the latter event, the sensations experienced are similar to those of arterial puncture but less severe.

Pain resulting from manipulation of the arteries appears to be due to trauma of the accompanying nerves. Moore and Moore (1933) advanced the opinion that much of the pain that attends surgical procedures is caused by trauma to nerve fibers rather than by stimulation of sensory receptors and that arterial distention and arterial spasm are only of secondary importance in the causation of pain. In cases in which vascular spasm is accompanied by pain, a secondary factor probably is the real cause of the painful stimulation.

Pain caused by the injection of irritating substances into peripheral arteries is not abolished by sympathetic denervation of the area in question. Obviously, most of the fibers concerned with the conduction of afferent impulses from the peripheral arteries reach the spinal cord without traversing the sympathetic trunk. Those concerned with the conduction of afferent impulses from splanchnic blood vessels traverse the splanchnic nerves. Afferent fibers that are stimulated by irritants injected into the hepatic, the splenic and the inferior mesenteric arteries enter the spinal cord in the thoracic region, whereas the fibers of similar function related to the renal artery enter the spinal cord in the lumbar region.

Alimentary Canal.—Esophagus.—The esophageal mucosa is sensitive in some degree, particularly to thermal stimulation. The presence of food in the esophagus usually is not perceived unless it causes marked distention of the esophageal musculature. In the experiments of Payne and Poulton (1927), carried out on themselves, pain caused by stretching a portion of the esophagus was relieved by peristaltic contractions that overcame the stretch, or by postural adaptation of the viscus that increased its capacity. Peristaltic contractions which failed to overcome the stretch resulted in more intense pain. Continuous stretching of the esophagus gave rise to burning pain (heartburn). As reported by Polland and Bloomfield (1931), inflation of small balloons in the esophagus gave rise to sensations akin to pain which usually could not be accurately described by the subject and frequently were identical with spontaneous "digestive" discomforts. These sensations were localized most frequently at the xiphoid or in the suprasternal notch, sometimes over the anterior chest wall or in the back and rarely in the neck or the face.

In experiments reported by Jones (1938), in which the esophagus was distended or blocked at different levels by means of an inflated balloon, most of the subjects felt only a sensation of uncomfortable fullness when the balloon was inflated in the proximal portion. Less than 20 per cent noted a burning sensation. As the stimulus was applied at more distal levels the sensation of fullness or pressure diminished and that of heat or burning increased. When the balloon was inflated in the distal portion of the esophagus most of the subjects experienced definite "heartburn."

This sensation probably is associated with reversed peristaltic contractions of the esophageal musculature. Fluoroscopic examination of patients experiencing heartburn showed definite reversed peristaltic activity in the distal portion of the esophagus. When this activity subsided the sensation of heartburn almost completely disappeared, only to reappear with increased intensity when the antiperistaltic contractions recurred. In most instances the sensations were localized near the midsternal line and approximately at the level of the stimulus.

Stomach.—The stomach appears to be insensitive to mechanical, chemical, thermal and electrical stimuli. It may be cut, torn or otherwise injured during operative procedures, carried out under local anesthesia of the abdominal wall, without giving rise to pain. Certain forms of gastric stimulation give rise to painful sensations. For example, strong chemical stimulation of the gastric mucosa always gives rise to pain. In certain types of gastritis, substances normal for the stomach, *e.g.*, water or gastric juice, may cause pain. Strong tonic contractions of the stomach also give rise to pain. Such reactions may also be a factor in the pain resulting from the destructive action of chemical substances on the mucosa of the normal stomach or from normal stimulation of the hypersensitive mucosa. According to Carlson (1916), gastric pain probably is essentially muscular, but the injured mucosa must be regarded as a causative factor. Hyperdistention of the stomach causes pain that is localized in this organ, but the nerves in the mucosa probably play no part in such pain. All pains due to impulses that arise in the gastric mucosa probably should be regarded as indications of pathological processes. They are due either to normal stimuli acting on the hypersensitive mucosa or to destructive stimuli acting on the normal mucosa.

The mucosa of the stomach, like that of the esophagus, is provided with receptors for heat and cold, but they are either less abundant or their threshold of stimulation is higher than that of those in the esophagus. Chemical substances like pepper, mustard, strong alcohol, acid (5 to 20 per cent HCl), etc., introduced into the stomcah through a tube in sufficient quantity give rise to varying degrees of pain accompanied at first by a sensation of warmth in the stomach (Carlson, 1916). All chemicals taken into the stomach in sufficient concentration to cause pain probably injure the mucosa and the receptors in it, as is indicated by the development of gastritis. When chemical substances are taken into the stomach in dilutions that do not cause pain or discomfort, their contact with the mucosa may still give rise to sensations that are not akin to pain but related to appetite. In Carlson's experiments, the sensations produced by beer, wine, weak acid (0.5 to 2 per cent HCl), weak alcohol or carbonated drinks, introduced into the stomach through a tube, were rather transitory, but characteristic, and could not always be distinguished from appetite. The fact that these sensations arise immediately when the appropriate substances are introduced, even though the stomach is quiescent and greatly relaxed, indicates that they are due to stimulation of receptors in the gastric mucosa and do not depend on gastric motility. They also differ qualitatively from the sensation of relief following relaxation of the stomach at the end of a period of hunger contractions in that they possess the positive character that directs attention to food and eating. When the gastric mucosa is stimulated in this manner during a period of hunger contractions, it is quite impossible to differentiate the sensation caused by the chemical stimulus from the sensation of relief from hunger. It is evident, therefore, that chemical stimulation of the gastric mucosa plays an important rôle in appetite and the desire for food.

The sensation of fullness probably requires a degree of tension of the gastric musculature. It usually is independent of stretching of the body wall. The sensation of satiety following a palatable meal probably arises independently of impulses emanating from the gastric mucosa. In order to insure this sensation, eating must be preceded by some degree of hunger and appetite, the food must be palatable and it must be eaten in sufficient quantity to produce moderate distention of the stomach, but not the sensation of fullness. The sensation of satiety, according to Carlson, "involves the element of contrast between the uncomfortable tension of hunger and the sensation of fullness, together with the lingering memories of the taste and smell of the food."

Nausea is a very complex sensation that is referable only in part to the stomach. It may be initiated by stimulation of the gastric mucosa, but it usually involves other factors, and frequently arises entirely independently of gastric disorder. It probably always involves a characteristic feeling of distress referable to the stomach. Under certain conditions, nausea seems to be allied to hunger. Both nausea and hunger involve sensations of uncomfortable tension and pain and cause salivation. In some persons, both these states also involve bodily weakness, headaches, dizziness, etc., but the gastric distress that is most characteristic of nausea is lacking in normal persons in any stage of hunger. The central effects of nausea, in normal persons, also are unlike those produced by hunger. Nausea is incompatible with appetite. Hunger commonly intensifies the desire for food. Since hunger, though normally caused by stimulation of the kinesthetic nerves of the stomach, like nausea, may be caused by stimulation of the nerves of the gastric mucosa, it may, under certain conditions, be accompanied by nausea or become apparently identical with it.

The gastric factor in appetite depends in a large measure on moderate chemical stimulation of the nerves of the gastric mucosa, while the sensation of hunger arises from stimulation of nerves in the submucosa or the muscularis by a certain type of contraction of the empty or nearly empty stomach that has been called the hunger contraction (Carlson, 1916). In a series of experiments carried out on a man, in which a graphic record of the gastric contractions was obtained by means of a rubber balloon that had been swallowed into the stomach, Cannon and Washburn (1912) showed that the periods of contractions of the empty stomach coincide with the periods of hunger sensations and that each contraction synchronizes with a hunger pang. They also obtained evidence that contractions occur in the aboral third of the esophagus that are synchronous with the gastric contractions, and concluded that esophageal contractions play a part in hunger. They also noted that the sensation of hunger tends to lag behind the gastric contraction both at its beginning and its termination. They advanced the opinion that these contractions of the stomach and the distal third of the esophagus cause the sensation of hunger through stimulation of the appropriate receptors.

Although the assumption of Cannon and Washburn was essentially correct, it remained for Carlson and his students (1912) to demonstrate, in man and experimental animals, that the sensation of hunger is caused by contractions of the empty or nearly empty stomach of a certain type and that the sensory nerve fibers concerned are not those that innervate the gastric mucosa, but those that are connected with receptors in the submucosa or the muscularis. Carlson (1914) also obtained certain experimental data which he interpreted as indicating that the hunger contractions are initiated in the stomach itself and, in a large measure, are independent of efferent impulses emanating from the central nervous system. In his experiments, moderate exercise had little stimulating effect on gastric tonus and hunger contractions. Moderate stimulation of the receptors for cold had no effect but intense stimulation of these receptors inhibited hunger contractions and, as an after-effect, elicited an increase in gastric tonus and hunger contractions. Intellectual processes seemed to have no effect except as they caused inhibition of gastric tonus and hunger contractions through the splanchnic nerves. On the basis of these experimental findings, he concluded that "in normal individuals the vagogastric tonus apparatus, at least so far as it concerns the empty stomach, is physiologically isolated from the exteroceptors and from many, if not all, central processes." He admitted, however, that this mechanism is affected by the nutrient content of the blood when he advanced the opinion that "the biological significance of this exceptional and unique isolation of the tonus apparatus of the hunger mechanism probably lies in the importance of the hunger mechanism being regulated on its positive side primarily by the state of nutrition, that is, through the blood rather than by the fleeting changes in the nervous system."

Emptiness of the stomach alone does not cause hunger. The sensation of hunger, furthermore, subsides temporarily following the subcutaneous injection of a nutrient solution, *e.g.*, glucose, even though the stomach remains empty. It has also been observed clinically that the stomach, under certain pathological conditions, may remain empty for days without giving rise to hunger sensations. On the other hand, a patient with pyloric stenosis may experience intense hunger although the stomach is filled with food. Certain data also support the assumption that a central mechanism closely related to the temperature regulating center reacts to the lack of nutrient material in the blood by sending out efferent impulses that bring about reactions which in turn initiate afferent impulses that result in the sensation of hunger.

The chief causes of gastric pain undoubtedly are hyperdistention of the stomach wall and spastic contractions of the gastric musculature. Moderate inflation of the stomach gives rise to sensations that may be described as feelings of fullness, tightness or pressure with a superadded element of pain. They cannot always be accurately localized, but in most instances they can be recognized as arising within the abdomen near the median plane. In experiments reported by Boyden and Rigler (1934), faradic stimulation of the gastric mucosa by means of a Rehfuss tube the metal end of which had been converted into an electrode and swallowed to the desired depth caused a ring of contraction of the gastric musculature accompanied by sensations ranging from barely perceptible feelings of pressure to severe colicky pains localized deep in the body wall in the upper abdominal quadrants. Balchum and Weaver (1943) elicited pain reactions in dogs by inflating the stomach with an air-filled balloon until the intragastric pressure was elevated to 50 to 60 mm. of mercury. The threshold for painful stimulation was fairly constant in every animal and did not change significantly after repeated inflations of the stomach over periods as long as seven months. The impulses of pain were conducted centrad only through afferent components of the splanchnic nerves and did not give rise to recognizable referred phenomena. Infiltration of the skin over the back and the abdomen with procaine or bilateral section of the intercostal nerves caudal to the sixth and the ventral roots of the thoracic and the lumbar spinal nerves neither abolished the pain elicited by inflation of the stomach nor appreciably elevated the threshold of painful stimulation.

Gastric ulcer that involves only the gastric mucosa may be the underlying cause of gastric pain, but gastric ulceration may go on to the point of perforation, in some cases, without giving rise to pain. The onset of this pain commonly bears a definite relationship to the time of eating. It does not occur immediately following the ingestion of food but after the food has become thoroughly mixed with gastric juice and is ready to be discharged into the duodenum. As has been shown by fluoroscopic examination of patients with gastric ulcer, the pain, in many instances, coincides with a period of peristaltic contractions that sweep over the pyloric portion of the stomach against the contracted pylorus. These contractions probably constitute the major factor in the genesis of gastric pain, although they may be no stronger than the normal peristaltic contractions of the filled stomach or the hunger contractions of the empty stomach. A condition of hyperexcitability of the gastric pain nerves, therefore, is indicated in ulcer patients who experience the typical ulcer pains.

Certain patients with gastric ulcer also experience pain while the stomach is empty. It has been assumed by certain investigators that the contractions that give rise to the pain in such cases are caused by gastric hyperacidity. The motility of the stomach, however, is in a large measure independent of the chemical reaction of the gastric contents. Ulcer pains may also occur when the acidity of the stomach contents is normal. Strauss (1928), who had previously maintained that free hydrochloric acid in the stomach and a zone of inflammation around the eroded area are important factors in the production of ulcer pains, was convinced by the results of his later studies that an excessive amount of normal gastric juice may stimulate the nerves through which the pain of gastric ulcer is mediated. He also conceded that gastric peristalsis may play a contributing rôle. According to Palmer and Heinz (1934), the pain of gastric or duodenal ulcer has its origin at the site of the lesion. The usual stimulus is free hydrochloric acid acting upon an irritable mechanism located within the lesion or adjacent to it. This mechanism may also be stimulated by peristaltic contractions or local spasm.

On the basis of extensive clinical and experimental studies, Balint (1928) advanced the conclusion that the pain of gastric ulcer is not caused by gastric hyperacidity but by two factors acting simultaneously: contraction of the gastric musculature and a shift in the hydrogen-ion concentration of the blood toward the acid side. He called attention to the fact, recorded by various investigators, that the introduction of acid in relatively high concentration into the stomach of a gastric ulcer patient does not elicit pain. In his own clinical experiments, the gastric ulcer pains subsided following the contemplation and mastication of palatable food by the patient, although none of it was swallowed. The effect on the ulcer pain of such sham feeding was similar to that of the introduction of food into the stomach, although the acidity of the gastric contents was appreciably increased by reason of the increased activity of the gastric glands due to the stimulus afforded by the sham feeding. Balint also maintained that the alleviation of ulcer pain by alkali therapy does not depend on neutralization of the acid in the stomach, since such therapy frequently results in the alleviation of ulcer pains in cases which exhibit anacidity as well as in cases which still exhibit gastric hyperacidity following alkali treatment. He also pointed out that the intravenous injection of alkali produces the same result. This supports the conclusion that the therapeutic effect of alkali, in cases of gastric ulcer, depends in some measure on its effect on the hydrogen-ion concentration of the blood. This conclusion is also supported by the fact that ulcer pains are alleviated by hyperventilation of the lungs, which has the same effect on the acid-base balance of the blood as alkali therapy. Changes in the acid-base balance of the blood toward the acid side may also play a rôle in the causation of ulcer pains. This is suggested by the fact that other therapeutic agents which tend to shift the acid-base balance toward the basic side, *e.g.*, atropine, roentgen radiation, etc., also tend to alleviate these pains, whereas measures that tend to shift the acid-base balance of the blood toward the acid side, *e.g.*, physical exertion, aggravate the ulcer pains. Inasmuch as gastric ulcer pains commonly accompany gastric motility, which must be regarded as a factor in their causation, it may be assumed that the influence of changes in the acid-base reaction of the blood in the causation of ulcer pains is due at least in part to the effect of these changes on the functional balance between the sympathetic and the parasympathetic components of the autonomic system, which in turn is reflected in the gastric motility.

The pain experienced during acute gastritis is also due to impulses that arise in the deeper layers of the stomach wall. It arises only when the stomach becomes distended due to faulty emptying or generation of gas and probably is caused by hyperdistention of the stomach wall or contraction of the gastric musculature. The normal stomach may react in essentially the same manner when overfilled with food of low digestibility. Under these conditions the subject may experience discomfort due to pressure, or even acute pain.

Intestine.—Like the stomach, the intestine is insensitive to the ordinary stimuli, but appropriate intestinal stimulation results in pain of varying degrees of intensity. Moderate inflation of a small balloon in various parts of the small and the large intestine gives rise to sensations which the subject usually recognizes as similar to spontaneous discomforts previously experienced and not unlike sensations of overeating, indigestion, etc. Strong contractions of the intestine frequently give rise to pain which is more or less definitely localizable in the abdomen. Limitation of the blood supply to the intestine, such as occurs in cases of advanced arteriosclerosis of the aorta that constricts the portals of the mesenteric arteries, also gives rise to intense intestinal pain, particularly while digestive activity is at its height. The powerful contractions of the intestinal musculature which occur in cases of partial or complete intestinal occlusion, resulting from carcinoma or other causes, also give rise to pain of varying degrees of intensity.

In the experiments of Boyden and Rigler (1934) the results of faradic stimulation of the duodenal mucosa were comparable to those of stimulation of the gastric mucosa. The sphincteric contraction of the musculature initiated at the level of the stimulation was followed by increased peristalsis distal to that level. The accompanying sensations were localized in the upper abdominal quadrant. As the electrode was drawn through successive portions of the duodenum and the stomach, the sites of the pain progressively indicated the positions of these organs, but with marked aberrancy in many instances. The visceral nature of this pain was indicated by its persistence when the overlying cutaneous area was anesthetized. Pain caused by inflation of a balloon in the intestine is felt most commonly in the midline or near it. With the balloon in the proximal portion of the duodenum the usual site of the pain is in the epigastrium. As the more distal portions of the duodenum become distended, the pain of discomfort tends to descend toward the umbilicus. Pain or discomfort due to distention of any portion of the jejunum and the ileum, except the most distal portion, is felt most commonly near the umbilical level. Distention of the terminal portion of the ileum frequently is felt in the umbilical area and sometimes lower. Frequently the sensation is localized some distance from the midline. Pain caused by distention of the large intestine is less acute and less definitely localizable than that arising in the small intestine. It is commonly felt below the umbilicus, and there is no constant relationship between the actual position of the part distended and the point in the lower abdomen at which the sensation is localized. The pain usually is felt near the midline or to the left. Pain caused by distention of the cecum just distal to the ileocecal valve is commonly localized at the usual site of appendiceal pain, *i.e.*, in the region of McBurney's point.

The terminal portion of the large intestine, viz., the pelvic colon and rectum, are sensitive in a certain degree to stimuli other than those that give rise to pain. This is in keeping with the functional requirements of the lower portion of the digestive tube and illustrates the general principle that receptors for various types of stimuli exist in all parts of the body in which they are demanded by the vital interests of the organism.

Liver and Biliary System.—The parenchyma of the liver may be regarded as insensitive to the ordinary stimuli. It may be cut, torn or otherwise injured without giving rise to sensations. Inflammatory processes and ulceration in the liver give rise to no impulses that reach the threshold of consciousness. The serous covering of the liver is also insensitive. Inflammatory processes that involve the parietal peritoneum give rise to painful sensations, but they are not directly referable to the liver. Rapid enlargement of the liver, such as occurs in cases of cardiac decompensation, frequently gives rise to pain and sensations of pressure in the epigastric region probably due to distention of the hepatic capsule and the weight of the enlarged organ pulling on its attachment to the diaphragm.

The pain experienced in attacks of biliary colic and other disturbances of the biliary system, like pain arising in other visceral organs containing smooth muscle, probably is due to impulses that arise from hyperdistention or spastic contraction of the musculature of the bile ducts. Pain reactions may be elicited in animals by distending parts of the biliary system. Experimental data support the assumption that both spasm and stretching of the biliary musculature may give rise to pain. Moderate distention of the bile ducts alone may give rise to slight pain, but spastic contraction of the biliary musculature probably constitutes the major factor in the genesis of biliary pain. The dull pain associated with biliary stasis probably is due to distention of the bile ducts. The acute pain of biliary colic is due to spastic contraction of this musculature. This pain commonly is localized in the region of the gall bladder. Frequently it cannot be clearly dissociated from the accompanying gastric pain. The true visceral nature of gall bladder pain is indicated by the observations that distention of the gall bladder in animals elicits pain reactions after desensitization of the appropriate area of the body wall by section of the intercostal nerves distal to the communicating rami and after complete section of the ventral portion of the lateral funiculus in the spinal cord and even bilateral hemisection of the cord at separate levels (Davis *et al.*, 1929). The impulses that result in pain of biliary origin are conducted into the spinal cord through the splanchnic nerves on the right side.

Pancreas.—The pancreas may be regarded as insensitive to the ordinary stimuli, yet certain pancreatic lesions are known to give rise to excruciating pain. The clinical manifestations, in these cases, are relatively complex. Pain may also be elicited by direct faradic stimulation of the pancreas. The receptors concerned probably are associated with the blood vessels. As reported by Bliss *et al.* (1950), threshold stimulation of the head of the pancreas in man gives rise to pain that is localized in the 6th to the 11th dermatomes, and is most intense at the right of the ventral midline. Threshold stimulation of the body of the pancreas gives rise to pain that is localized in the same dermatomes and is most intense along the ventral midline. Threshold stimulation of the tail of the pancreas gives rise to pain that is localized in the 6th thoracic to the 1st lumbar dermatomes and is most intense at the right of the ventral midline. Afferent pain impulses are conducted from the head of the pancreas through the right splanchnic nerves, from the body of the pancreas through both the right and the left splanchnic nerves, and from the tail of the pancreas through the left splanchnic nerves.

Spleen.—The spleen may be regarded as insensitive to the ordinary stimuli. Impulses arising in this organ probably do not reach the threshold of consciousness. Inflammation of the serosa of the spleen may give rise to pain, probably due to involvement of the parietal peritoneum. The pain associated with enlargement of the spleen probably is due to traction on the splenic attachments.

Kidney.—The kidneys are relatively insensitive to ordinary stimuli, but the renal pelvis seems to be sensitive under certain conditions. In most cases of renal pain, the afferent impulses involved probably arise in the renal pelvis. Traction on the kidney also gives rise to pain, undoubtedly due to the pull on the renal blood vessels and the parietal peritoneum. Renal pain probably can be explained most satisfactorily on the basis of stimulation of receptors in the prerenal peritoneum, particularly at the level of the root of the kidney. It is commonly localized in the back just below the costal margin and frequently radiates to the ovary or the testis and along the ureter to the bladder. In some cases, it also radiates into the thigh.

Pathological conditions of the kidney commonly are accompanied by pain. In some cases the pain is due at least in part to traction caused by shifting of the position of the organ. In cases of renal enlargement, the sensory nerves in the adjacent parietal peritoneum may be stimulated by pressure. This may be regarded as one of the major factors in renal pain. Distention of the renal capsule has also been regarded as a factor in the causation of pain. A shrunken kidney may also give rise to pain although its capsule is not under tension. Under certain conditions pain of renal origin may involve conduction through somatic afferent fibers that supply the adjacent parietal peritoneum, but in general impulses that give rise to renal pain are mediated through visceral afferent fibers that traverse the renal plexus.

Ureter.—Spastic contraction and excessive distention of the ureter give rise to pain that may be localized in the organ, but usually is referred. In clinical experiments reported by Okerblad and Carlson (1937), direct faradic stimulation of the ureter by means of a catheter electrode in the lumen elicited pain which in most instances was referred. With the electrode in the distal portion of the ureter the pain usually was felt in the suprapubic area near the midline and in some instances on the medial and lateral sides of the thigh and the medial side of the leg. Stimulation of the proximal portion of the ureter elicited pain particularly over the ventral portion of the iliac crest and the iliac spine. Since the position of the ureter is retroperitoneal, it seems not improbable that the stimulus employed in these experiments may have affected somatic receptors, thus facilitating the radiation of pain to the somatic areas indicated.

Urinary Bladder.—Sensitivity of the urinary bladder to certain types of stimulation is generally conceded. Under normal conditions, the urge to micturate depends on afferent impulses that arise in the bladder; consequently, sensations that have their origin in the urinary bladder play an important rôle in the functional regulation of this viscus. Overdistention of the bladder not only results in a strong desire to micturate but also gives rise to acute pain.

The mucosa of the bladder, like that of the gastro-intestinal canal, is insensitive to most of the ordinary stimuli, but parts of it are sensitive to tactile as well as painful stimulation. Irrigation of the bladder with hot or cold water gives rise to no temperature sensations. The pain caused by electrical stimulation of the bladder mucosa probably is due to contraction of the bladder musculature. The pain resulting from cystitis and ulceration of the bladder mucosa, likewise, probably is not due to the direct effect of the lesion of the mucosa alone but in part to reflex muscle spasm.

Impulses that arise in the bladder are conducted through both the hypogastric and pelvic nerves. Those that give rise to the ordinary vesical sensations are mediated mainly through the pelvic nerves. According to Frölich and Meyer (1922), the sensitivity of the bladder is not affected by section of the hypogastric nerves. On the other hand, Pieri (1928) reported incomplete relief of pain due to disease of the bladder following hypogastric nerve section. According to Learmonth (1932), section of the hypogastric nerves leaves the ordinary sensibility of the bladder unaltered, but renders it definitely less sensitive to uncoördinated and spasmodic contractions; consequently, certain pains of vesical origin may be abolished by this operative procedure. Impulses that arise in the sphincters of the bladder reach the central nervous system through the pudendal nerve.

Female Genitalia.—The vaginal mucosa, like the mucosa of the other hollow viscera, may be regarded as insensitive to the ordinary stimuli. When applied to the uterus, the Fallopian tubes or the ovaries these stimuli give rise to no sensations unless they cause traction on the parietal peritoneum or the attachments of the organs in question to the body wall. Pains arising in the uterus usually are due to contractions of the uterine musculature. Pains resulting from displacement of the uterus are not directly referable to this organ. They probably are due to the effects of its displacement on adjacent structures.

Sensory Conduction from Cephalic Areas Through Spinal Nerve Components.—On the basis of experimental and clinical data, certain investigators have assumed that the nerves extending cephalad from the superior cervical ganglion include afferent fibers that traverse the cervical sympathetic trunk and enter the spinal cord through the dorsal roots of the rostral thoracic nerves. Anatomical proof of the existence of such fibers is not forthcoming. Clinical observations following total and subtotal resection of the sensory root of the trigeminal nerve for the relief of trigeminal neuralgia led Fraser to suspect that fibers extending from the cervical sympathetic into the head play a rôle in certain sensory phenomena in the area of distribution of the trigeminal nerve, particularly following sensory trigeminal paralysis. The findings reported by Helson (1932), who carried out an intensive study of the different forms of sensibility detectible in the area of distribution of the trigeminal nerve following section of its sensory root in certain of Fraser's patients, tended to confirm this view. According to his findings, sensibility to light touch and ordinary painful stimuli is lost permanently. Sensibility to deep pressure and the ability to localize touch are greatly reduced immediately after the operation but later are gradually restored to an appreciable degree. Temperature stimuli between 15° and 45° C. evoke no sensations, but hot stimuli (60° to 75° C.) usually give rise to stinging or prickling sensations. Following cervical sympathectomy in addition to trigeminal root section, hot stimuli applied in any part of the area of distribution of the trigeminal nerve elicited no response.

The sensory phenomena in this area following resection of the sensory root of the trigeminal nerve, therefore, cannot be explained on the assumption that they are mediated solely through the facial nerve. According to Helson, "the absolute zero of cutaneous sensitivity cannot be reached through section of the peripheral nerve supply (trigeminal and intermedius) but requires deletion of the sympathetic supply as well." In a study of patients with trigeminal neuralgia who had been treated by alcoholic injections of the Gasserian ganglion, patients with facial palsy due to lesions at various levels of the nerve, and patients who had been subjected to injury or extirpation of the cervical sympathetic trunk on one or both sides, Carmichael and Woollard (1933) obtained no evidence that impulses that subserve pain in the face or the orbit are conducted centrad by nerve fibers other than components of the trigeminal nerve. Although these negative data fail to confirm Helson's findings, they do not prove them erroneous.

On the basis of an analysis of the clinical results of various surgical procedures carried out in the treatment of atypical facial neuralgia, Fay (1932) advanced the opinion that afferent components both of the rostral thoracic and the vagus nerves extend into the cephalic region along the carotid arteries. This opinion has been confirmed by the results of experimental anatomical studies carried out on cats (Kuntz, 1934). After degeneration of the divided nerve fibers had taken place following extirpation of the superior cervical sympathetic and the nodose ganglia, sections through the common, the internal and the external carotid arteries and the nerves closely associated with them still revealed intact nerve fibers. Marchi preparations of the common and the internal carotid arteries, following section of the roots of the rostral four thoracic nerves just distal to the spinal ganglia, revealed degenerated myelinated fibers in considerable numbers. On the basis of these findings it is evident that afferent thoracic nerve components traverse the plexus on the common carotid artery and extend cephalad along the internal and probably also along the external carotid artery. The presence of myelin degeneration in Marchi preparations of the nasal and the nasociliary nerves following section of the roots of the rostral four thoracic nerves (Christensen, 1934) indicates that some of the afferent components of the thoracic nerves that extend into the cephalic region reach the orbit and the nasal mucosa. The relationships of these fibers to the plexuses on the carotid arteries and their distribution in the cephalic area are illustrated diagrammatically in Figure 89. After degeneration of the divided fibers following extirpation of the entire cervical sympathetic trunk, including the superior cervical ganglion, but leaving the vagus nerve intact, sections of the internal and the external carotid arteries and the nerves associated with them reveal numerous intact fibers obviously of vagus origin. They probably are afferent vagus nerve fibers with their cells of origin in the nodose ganglion.

The afferent spinal nerve components that extend into the cephalic region probably are not primarily pain-conducting fibers. Most of those that underwent myelin degeneration in the plexuses on the common and internal carotid arteries following section of the nerve roots, as observed in the Marchi preparations, are fibers of larger caliber than the spinal nerve fibers which are known to mediate pain. Mild electrical stimulation of the plexus on the common carotid artery, in our experiments, did not elicit pain reactions but resulted in reflex responses in the caudal cervical and the rostral thoracic segments and particularly in the forelimb.   The vagus components that join the plexuses on the internal and the external carotid arteries are predominantly fibers of small caliber many of which are either unmyelinated or only thinly meylinated.   Many of them probably are fibers that normally mediate pain.

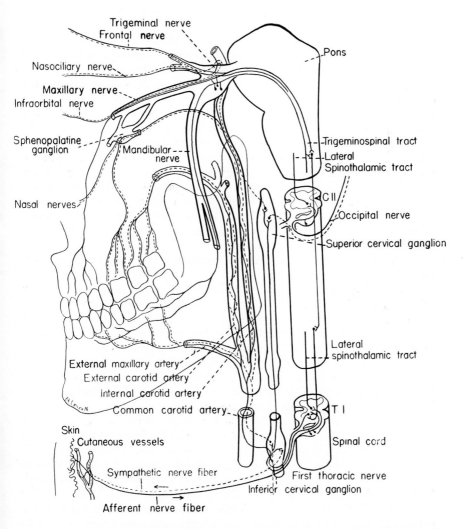

Fig. 89.—Diagrammatic illustration of the distribution of sympathetic nerve fibers and afferent components of the upper thoracic spinal nerves in the cephalic region via the plexuses on the common, internal and external carotid arteries and the probable conduction pathways involved in sensory and autonomic phenomena referred from cephalic lesions to the neck, upper thorax and upper extremities.

REFERRED PAIN

Nature and Localization of Referred Sensations.—Under certain conditions, pain is localized, not at the site of its cause, but in another area which is innervated through nerves that are connected with the same segments of the central nervous system as those through which the area in which the cause of the pain is located is innervated. Such pain is known as referred pain. Both the site of the cause and the area of reference may be either visceral or somatic, but usually the referred pain associated with a visceral lesion is localized in a somatic area. Visceral lesions frequently give rise, not to sensations that are definitely painful, but to hyperalgesia or tenderness in the corresponding somatic area. The referred pain or hyperalgesia may accompany pain in the viscus which is the site of its origin or it may exist in the absence of true visceral pain. The area in which a referred pain is localized, as determined by Head, always falls within the range of distribution of the segmental nerves through which afferent fibers reach the site of the causative lesion. Such localization is not apparent in all cases, particularly if the causative lesion is located in deep somatic tissue. A deep somatic lesion, such as injury to muscle, tendon or periosteum, may give rise to pain that radiates along the pathway corresponding approximately to the segmental innervation of the deep somatic tissues. In contrast to the areas of cutaneous innervation known as the dermatomes, the segmental areas of skeletal innervation have been designated the scleratomes. In certain parts of the body, particularly the extremities and the dorsal cervical region, the scleratomes do not coincide in spacial relationships with the corresponding dermatomes.

Nature of Visceral Lesions that Are Commonly Accompanied by Referred Pain.—Non-inflammatory visceral lesions rarely give rise to referred pain or somatic hyperalgesia unless they fall into the group of severe visceral crises. The differentiation of true visceral pain from referred pain frequently is difficult. Statements of patients relative to their own subjective symptoms cannot always be relied upon, but certain gestures are significant. As a rule, they do not apply to the somatic segment but to the area occupied by the visceral organs in question. In case of anginal pain, the patient commonly places the clenched hand on the sternum as though to indicate that the pain has its origin in the aorta. The clenching of the hand undoubtedly implies the gripping character of the pain. Cardiac pain commonly is indicated by the flat hand in the left submammary area. The location of the pain of gastric ulcer frequently is indicated by placing two or three fingers in the mid-epigastric region a little to the left of the ventral midline. The pain of duodenal ulcer usually is localized at the right of the midline. In the case of renal colic, the patient grasps the back with the fingers toward the spine in the region of the kidney, indicating deep pain in the position of this organ. The pain associated with appendicitis and gall bladder disease usually is localized with remarkable accuracy unless inflammation or other gastro-intestinal lesions are associated with it. The position of a calculus in the ureter, likewise, can be localized quite accurately unless there is associated renal pain. Intestinal pain usually is localized less accurately, probably due to the changing positions of the painful contractions. Pain arising in the small intestine frequently is localized in the region around the umbilicus. Pain arising in the large intestine usually is localized between the umbilicus and the symphysis pubis but beneath the parietal peritoneum. Obstruction of the intestine at a fixed point, *e.g.*, the hepatic flexure, usually is localized with remarkable precision.

Referred pain is best demonstrated (1) in cases in which it is associated with severe visceral pain, (2) in cases in which it is associated with inflammatory visceral disease and (3) in cases in which it is associated with a somatic lesion such as an inflamed joint or a focus of irritation in muscle, tendon or fascia. The pain that radiates into the arm in patients with angina pectoris, the subscapular pain of cholelithiasis and the testicular pain of ureteral colic are classical examples of the first group. Cutaneous hyperalgesia and muscular rigidity in the corresponding areas of the abdominal wall in patients with chronic gastric and duodenal ulcers are classical examples of the second group. These phenomena are commonly associated with diseases which involve organic changes in the viscera in question but rarely accompany functional diseases. For example, cutaneous hyperalgesia and muscular guarding rarely are associated with gastric pain due to extragastric causes. The subscapular pain of cholelithiasis may be due to cholecystitis as well as to the presence of gall stones. In the presence of gall stones inflammation of the gall bladder can hardly be ruled out as a contributing factor in the referred pain. Testicular pain probably does not occur in ureteral colic unless the ureteral mucosa is inflamed or ulcerated. It may also occur in association with ureteral lesions in the absence of ureteral colic. On the basis of extensive clinical observations, Ryle (1926) concluded that "visceral pain expresses a perturbation of visceral function (which may or may not be due to local organic disease) while the somatic phenomena generally express a structural lesion of the wall of the viscus."

The somatic manifestations of visceral disease are not always coincident with the visceral pain and may persist for some time after the visceral pain has subsided. Gastric ulcer frequently is accompanied by tenderness, less frequently by superficial and deep hyperalgesia in the epigastric region, rigidity of one or the other rectus muscles and exaggerated abdominal reflexes on one side. These signs are most apt to be present if the patient has had a recent attack or is in pain at the time of the examination, but, in many cases, they persist for days after the visceral pain has subsided in response to appropriate treatment. They cannot be directly attributed to the gastric contractions, although they may be reinforced by them, but probably are due to a more or less constant flow of impulses from the site of the gastric lesion. The somatic manifestations of gastric ulcer are more constant when the ulcer invades the muscle layers than when it involves only the mucosa. On the other hand, gastric carcinoma is rarely accompanied by somatic hyperalgesia or referred pain. This discrepancy probably is due to the fact that simple ulcer erodes the tissue and directly affects the sensory nerve endings in the muscles, while carcinoma invades the muscle by growing between the muscle fibers.

Certain investigators, particularly Morley (1931, 1937), have advanced experimental and clinical data which support the assumption that the sensory phenomena in the abdominal wall and the reflex muscular rigidity associated with appendicitis and various other lesions of the abdominal viscera do not depend on afferent impulses that arise in the diseased viscus, but are elicited by stimulation of somatic receptors in the parietal peritoneum overlying the diseased organ, to which the inflammation has extended. Morley regards the superficial pain or hyperalgesia as due to peritoneo-cutaneous radiation; the muscular rigidity to peritoneo-muscular reflexes. In general every nerve that conveys sensory fibers to the parietal peritoneum also conveys sensory fibers to the corresponding cutaneous area and sensory and motor fibers to the underlying muscles. When the parietal peritoneum is irritated, according to Morley's hypothesis, the pain radiates to the more superficial structures in the corresponding segments of the abdominal wall. Its localization, consequently, conforms to Head's principle of the localization of referred pains. This sensory radiation may be compared to the radiation of pain from a carious tooth to adjacent teeth or the skin of the face. Irradiation within the central nervous system, known to be a phenomenon associated with spinal reflex activity, may be a factor in this process. According to this point of view, the somatic pain or tenderness associated with appendicitis is not a referred sensory phenomenon in the ordinary sense. Pain localized in a somatic area due to other visceral lesions from which the inflammatory process extends to the parietal peritoneum or the parietal pleura obviously falls into the same category unless the sensory phenomena in the somatic area can be demonstrated in the absence of parietal involvement in the inflammatory process.

Morley regards the pain in the area of distribution of the descending branches of the third and fourth cervical nerves, caused by stimulation of the abdominal surface of the central area of the diaphragm as comparable to the superficial pain caused by irritation of any other area of the parietal peritoneum. Since most of the afferent components of the phrenic nerves are essentially somatic, the shoulder pain caused by phrenic stimulation does not involve viscero-somatic sensory radiation. This phenomenon nevertheless conforms to the current concept of referred pain. It differs from the phenomenon of referred pain associated with certain cardiac lesions only in that the afferent conductors from the diaphragm may be classified as somatic afferent nerve components, whereas those from the heart or the coronary vessels are essentially visceral. In some instances afferent phrenic nerve fibers are connected with receptors in the region of the gall bladder. Shoulder pain associated with gall bladder disease in such instances could be regarded as referred from the visceral lesion.

True cardiac pain is a relatively rare symptom of cardiac disease. It is localized in the submammary area and is sometimes accompanied by cutaneous hyperalgesia in the precordial region. The deep pain of angina pectoris commonly is localized in the sternal region. The referred pain may be localized in the upper left thoracic area, along the inner side of the left arm to the elbow or the wrist or even to the fingers and more rarely in the right arm, the neck and the jaw. The segments particularly involved are innervated through the caudal cervical and the rostral two or three thoracic nerves. Myocardial infarction frequently is followed by persistent pain in one or both shoulders, which varies in severity from the clinical picture of periarthritis with intense pain and marked limitation of motion to one of mild aching pain with a sensation of weakness but no limitation of motion. These symptoms, which occur more commonly in the left shoulder than in the right, may persist for several weeks or months.

The testis is exquisitely sensitive to painful stimulation. When both the posterior scrotal and genitofemoral nerves are blocked, as observed by Woollard and Carmichael (1933), pain is no longer localized in the testis but is felt in the tenth thoracic segment on the same side. This finding is peculiarly significant since it indicates that reference of pain which has its site of origin in the testis may be obtained when the only pathway for the conduction of afferent impulses from the viscus consists of the nerve fibers associated with the spermatic artery, *i.e.*, the reference is independent of a somatic nerve supply to the viscus.

In patients who have not emptied the urinary bladder for 4 hours, Adams-Ray (1952) observed cutaneous hyperalgesia in the ventral portions of the 11th and the 12th thoracic dermatomes. Distention of the bladder elicited a pallor reflex in the same area. These phenomena were abolished following bilateral extirpation of the caudal 2 or 3 thoracic segments of the sympathetic trunk; consequently, they cannot be explained on the basis of impulses that arise in the parietal peritoneum due to pressure caused by the distended bladder. They can be explained most satisfactorily as phenomena referred directly from the urinary bladder.

Dental lesions and lesions of the nasal and the paranasal mucous membranes frequently give rise to pain in areas other than the site of the lesion, but within the area of distribution of the trigeminal nerve. These phenomena may be regarded as comparable to the association of superficial pain with irritation or inflammation of the parietal peritoneum or the parietal pleura. Lesions in the same locations sometimes give rise to pain localized outside the area of distribution of the trigeminal nerve. Pains referred to the ear from various lesions, including temporomandibular arthritis, inflammation of the paranasal sinuses, tonsillitis, carcinoma of the tongue, the pharynx or the larynx, meningitis, etc., are not uncommon. Dental lesions also give rise to sensory disturbances referred to the ear and other areas outside the limits of trigeminal nerve distribution. Main (1938) reported chronic otalgia and other symptoms referable to the ear, such as tick-like noises, sensations of pressure in the suboccipital region, numbness associated with ischemia and pain in the arm and the hand, etc. In many of his patients the particular syndrome observed, which frequently included headache and other sensory trigeminal disturbances, had been of long standing. In most of them extraction of the offending tooth resulted in permanent relief of the symptoms. Headache in the occipital or the parietal region is a frequent symptom associated with lesions of the third molar. Some of the pains associated with dental lesions obviously are referred. They conform to Head's theory of the localization of referred pains in all essential details. Others exhibit characteristic features of referred phenomena, but conformation to Head's theory of localization is less obvious (Kuntz and Main, 1940).

Lesions in the orbit, the mucous membranes of the nose and the paranasal sinuses and in the mastoid area frequently give rise to referred pains in the neck, shoulder, arm, forearm and hand. This condition, first described by Sluder, has become quite generally recognized as a clinical syndrome. In some instances, the pain is accompanied by other referred phenomena. For example, Terracol (1932) cited a case in which operation for the relief of nasal obstruction was followed by eruption on the chest and another in which dressings of the wound following a mastoid operation caused violent pains in the arm and eruptions on the chest. The afferent fibers through which the impulses that elicit the referred phenomenona in such instances are conducted from the causative lesions undoubtedly are components of thoracic nerves that traverse the inferior cervical sympathetic ganglion and ascend along the common and the internal carotid arteries. These fibers, due to their anatomical relationships, may be classified with the visceral afferent components of the spinal nerves (Fig. 89). Phenomena other than those which are essentially sensory that are referred to thoracic segments from cephalic lesions, such as the eruption on the chest cited by Terracol, undoubtedly involve reflex sympathetic excitation elicited by impulses that arise at the site of the lesion and are conducted into the spinal cord through afferent fibers in question.

Referred Pain Associated With Somatic Lesions.—Reference of pain from a somatic lesion may be conveniently illustrated by the familiar pain in the region of the knee that is associated with a lesion of the hip, and the pain in the hip region that is associated with a lesion of the knee. Since the site of the lesion and the area of reference receive afferent fibers through the same segmental nerves, these referred phenomena conform strictly to the segmental localization of referred pain.

Reference of pain from foci of irritation in skeletal muscles has been amply demonstrated. The localization of the area of reference, which may be superficial or deep, in general conforms to the segmental pattern of the spinal nerves concerned, but it does not always correspond to the dermatomal pattern. Sometimes it involves several segments or portions of segments. On the basis of data, obtained from approximately 1000 patients with pain syndromes related to myofascial trigger areas, Travell and Rinzler (1952) have localized a large number of so-called trigger spots and outlined the superficial areas to which pain caused by stimulation of these spots is referred. According to their findings, referred pain can be elicited by pressure, needling, or extreme heat or cold in the trigger area or stretching of the structure in which it is located. Intense stimulation of a trigger spot also elicits reflex vasoconstriction and other autonomic reflex effects in the area of reference. The referred pain elicited by stimulation of a particular trigger spot in different persons is always localized in the same area of reference. A known reference pattern, therefore, may be helpful in locating the myofacial source of an unfamiliar pain.

In patients with intermittent claudication infiltration with procaine of trigger areas in the calf muscles, located by their reference pattern, as reported by Travell et al. (1952), resulted in the relief of pain. The inferences were drawn that the trigger areas in the calf may interfere with the local blood flow by causing reflex vasospasm and that the myofascial component may be a major factor in continuing the pain cycle even in the presence of occlusive disease.

Myofascial trigger mechanisms may be initiated by trauma of a muscle or a joint, chronic muscular strain, acute myositis, arthritis, visceral ischemia, etc. The rôle of hypermyotonia induced by stimulation of somatic reflex arcs in the etiology of various bodily aches and pains has been emphasized particularly by Skillern (1947).

Irritation of deep somatic structures near the midline of the back by the injection of irritant liquid, as reported by Kellgren (1939), gave rise to referred pain, cutaneous hyperalgesia and deep tenderness in areas remote from the site of injection. These areas were usually within the limits of the distribution of the spinal nerve corresponding to the level at which the injection was made, but certain exceptions were noted. Data advanced by Lewis and Kellgren (1939) and Sinclair *et al.* (1948) support the assumption that some afferent spinal nerve fibers are connected with receptors in both deep somatic and visceral structures. Sinclair *et al.* also reported data that seem to support the assumption that some efferent nerve fibers are connected with receptors in both skeletal muscles and skin, and some are connected with receptors in muscles that are somewhat remote from one another. Afferent nerve fibers with multiple peripheral branches may be a significant factor in referred sensory phenomena the localization of which does not seem to conform strictly to Head's principle.

In human subjects in whom cephalic pain was produced by irritation of deep strictures in the cervical and the basi-occipital segments, particularly the periosteum and the periarticular tissues, Campbell and Parsons (1944) found that this pain resembled the symptomatic head pain characteristic of certain post-traumatic clinical states. Irritation in the occipito-atlantal condylar region and the first cervical interspace dorsally constantly resulted in pain localized in the cephalic region, predominantly in the occipital area, but with considerable reference to the forehead. Irritation of the cervical interspinous ligaments from the second to the fifth interspace resulted in pain predominantly in the occipital and the rostral cervical regions with only occasional reference to the frontal area. These pains were accompanied by autonomic disturbances such as pallor, sweating, pulsus alternans, nausea, etc., which varied in intensity, extent and duration with the amount of stimulation and the degree of preëxperimental pathology. The resemblances both of the subjective experiences and the objective signs to those of certain non-traumatic "neuralgias" and "myalgias" of the occipito-cervical-facial regions were striking.

The radiation of pain into the occipital area from lesions in deep structures in the dorsal cervical region may be explained on the basis of the morphology and the functions of the sacrospinalis muscles and their innervation. Irritation in any segment, but particularly in the cervical ones, may result in traction on the occipital attachments of these muscles, giving rise to pain in that area. Cephalic pain and its concomitants associated with thoracic and even lumbosacral lesions may be explained on the same basis. The muscles involved in balancing the cranium upon the vertebral column, including the trapezius, the sternocleidomastoid and a deep suboccipital group comprising the anterior, the lateral and the posterior recti and the superior and inferior obliques, like some of the external muscles of the cranium, are derived from cervical, occipital and branchial myotomes. Their motor innervation, consequently, is derived from cervical segments of the spinal cord and from the brain stem. Sensory impulses arising in these muscles, their associated sclerotomal tissues and the overlying integument predominantly reach the two rostral cervical spinal cord segments through the trigeminospinal tract. The sensory innervation of these structures, therefore, is related segmentally to that of the upper cervical myotomes; consequently, reference of pain into the cephalic region from deep cervical lesions is compatible with Head's theory of localization.

Theories Regarding the Mechanism of Referred Pain.—Among the early investigations carried out in attempts to explain the mechanism of referred pain, those of Lange (1871–1876), Ross (1888), Head (1898) and Faber (1899) deserve special mention. The theory which has commanded the most universal attention is that of Mackenzie (1910) which is essentially an elaboration of the theories of Lange and Ross. Like the earlier investigators named above, Mackenzie regarded the sensory manifestations of visceral disease which are localized in somatic areas as reflex phenomena and designated them "viscero-sensory" reflexes. He explained them on the basis of hyperirritability in the corresponding segments of the spinal cord due to exaggerated visceral stimulation. According to his view, irritation of a visceral organ sets up an exaggerated flow of nerve impulses that enter the corresponding segments of the spinal cord and give rise to an "irritable focus" in which the threshold of stimulation is reduced to such an extent that the normal impulses arising in the skin, the muscles and other peripheral structures give rise to painful sensations that are referred to the periphery in the somatic segments in question. He assumed that when any portion of the spinal cord has become hyperirritable due to excessive stimulation caused by visceral disease, it may remain so for some time, during which the threshold for stimulation for all the nerves connected with this portion of the cord is lowered. Both the somatic pain or hyperalgesia and the muscular rigidity associated with visceral disease, according to Mackenzie's theory, are expressions of the hyperirritability in the spinal cord. The pain or hyperalgesia is produced by exaggerated viscerosensory reflexes, and the muscular rigidity, by exaggerated viscero-motor reflexes. In the light of present physiological knowledge, the expression "viscero-sensory reflex," as employed by Mackenzie, must be regarded as unfortunate, since the hypothetical phenomenon in question is not of the nature of a reflex. His concept of "irritable foci" in the central gray matter undoubtedly expresses the phenomenon of irradiation now well known to physiologists and regarded as one of the properties of reflex arcs.

Szemzo (1927) advocated the theory of Mackenzie in a slightly modified form. He assumed that the visceral afferent fibers, at least in part, terminate in the dorsal gray column in the spinal cord in relation to neurons that are related to the spinothalamic system and that the hyperirritability of these cells, due to excessive visceral stimulation, is a major factor in the phenomenon of somatic hyperalgesia in visceral disease. As long as the threshold of stimulation of these cells for peripheral impulses remains sufficiently low, the slightest stimulation of the peripheral pain-conducting fibers in the somatic segments in question may elicit painful sensations the intensity of which is disproportionate to the intensity of the peripheral stimulus. Under certain conditions, pain may be felt in the corresponding somatic segments even in the absence of appreciable somatic stimulation. On this basis, somatic hyperalgesia associated with visceral disease, in the absence of visceral pain, must be regarded as due to hyper-excitation of the spinal cord cells in question through a flow of visceral impulses the intensity of which is below the threshold for visceral pain (Goldscheider, 1923). The lingering somatic hyperalgesia that frequently remains after the visceral pain has subsided, in cases of visceral disease, could be explained on the same basis.

The data advanced by Morley (1931), already referred to, seem to be incompatible with any theory based on the assumption that the referred phenomena associated with visceral disease are referred directly from the diseased viscus. According to his interpretation, they seem to support the assumption that the afferent impulses involved in the production of the somatic pain and other somatic phenomena associated with lesions of the abdominal viscera arise, not in the diseased viscus, but in the parietal peritoneum; consequently, they are conducted centrad through somatic afferent nerve fibers. He regards the phenomena of deep and superficial pain or tenderness and muscular rigidity of the abdominal wall associated with inflammatory disorders in the abdomen as brought about through two closely related mechanisms, "peritoneo-cutaneous radiation" and the "peritoneo-muscular reflex." These mechanisms presuppose irritation or inflammation of the parietal peritoneum. According to this theory, the pain produced by stimulation of the parietal peritoneum radiates to the superficial structures and is not felt as arising in the parietal peritoneum. The muscular rigidity is a purely somatic reflex response to stimulation of the parietal peritoneum.

The phenomena described by Morley undoubtedly occurr in cases in which visceral inflammation extends to the parietal peritoneum. The reflex muscular guarding or rigidity which accompanies somatic hyperalgesia or pain in many cases of visceral disease, e.g., acute appendicitis, can be explained most satisfactorily on this basis. The muscular response, furthermore, may be regarded as a contributing factor in the production of the associated hyperalgesia, muscle tenderness and pain. Since painful stimuli are the most provocative causes of reflexes, acutely tender muscles tend to remain permanently contracted. This tendency undoubtedly is an important factor in the maintenance of muscular rigidity, in many cases, after the visceral inflammation has subsided. As long as the muscle remains in a sufficiently high state of tonus it also remains hypersensitive.

The referred phenomena, including pain, associated with carious teeth and certain other lesions in the region of the mouth and the pharynx, like the muscular rigidity and tenderness caused by irritation of the parietal peritoneum, involve no visceral afferent fibers. Referred pains in certain other instances, e.g., pain referred to the knee due to a lesion in the region of the hip joint and pain referred from a skeletal muscle to other muscles or to a cutaneous area, involve afferent conduction only through somatic fibers.

The data available regarding the referred phenomena associated with purely visceral lesions do not warrant the conclusion that these phenomena can be explained on the assumption that the afferent impulses concerned in their production are conducted centrad through somatic nerve fibers in all cases of visceral disease. For example, stimulation of the testis, as has been pointed out by Woollard and Carmichael (1933), may give rise to pain which is referred to the appropriate somatic area in the absence of functional somatic afferent fibers to this viscus or adjacent tissues. The referred phenomena associated with angina pectoris likewise cannot be explained on the assumption that the afferent impulses concerned are conducted centrad through somatic fibers. These impulses undoubtedly arise in the walls of the heart or the coronary arteries and are conducted into the spinal cord through visceral afferent fibers.

The assumption that muscle spasm or rigidity associated with visceral disease is due in all cases to stimulation of somatic afferent fibers by irritation or inflammation of a serous membrane excludes consideration of the easily demonstrable fact that irritation of a visceral organ may elicit reflex contraction of skeletal muscles (viscero-skeletal reflex). This reaction may be demonstrated following high transection of the spinal cord which eliminates the higher reflex mechanisms and intentional contraction. Whenever muscular rigidity or hypertonus arises in association with visceral disease it may be a factor in the development and the maintenance of the associated pain or hyperalgesia.

Sinclair *et al.* (1948) have advanced a theory based on the assumption that pain and other sensory phenomena are referred through branching afferent nerve fibers. Physiological and experimental data that seem to indicate the existence of afferent fibers that are connected through one branch with visceral receptors and through another branch with somatic receptors are not wanting, but such relationships have not been demonstrated anatomically. If afferent fibers branch in this manner, it may be assumed that some have more than two peripheral branches. Multiple branches of afferent axons are known to exist in the skin. They probably also exist in skeletal muscles (Feindel, *et al.*, 1948). Through such mechanisms impulses that arise in a visceral lesion could be referred to skeletal muscle or to skin. Through axons with multiple branches they could be referred to both muscle and skin. Impulses that arise in somatic receptors could also be referred to other somatic areas. Mechanisms of this kind could be conceived of as working in two ways: (1) No ciceptive impulses that arise at the site of a lesion might be interpreted in the central nervous system as coming from the site of termination of one or more other branches of the axons in question. (2) Liberation of metabolites at the terminals of the branches in the region in which the referred pain is experienced might give rise to secondary pain impulses that actually arise in that region, thus increasing the flow of impulses to the sensory level. Both mechanisms could be concerned in any given case. The first would be initially more important than the second, but the second would increase in importance and becomes predominant in the later phases. Reference in stages could also take place. For example, impulses from a viscus might result in the liberation of metabolites in a muscle in which branches of the afferent nerve fibers in question terminate. The chemical stimulation by such metabolites of receptors in this area might result in reference through branching afferent fibers to another muscle or to a cutaneous area. The reference of sensory phenomena from either visceral or somatic lesions could be explained with equal facility by this theory. On the basis of further study of remote reference of pain elicited by stimulation in delimited cutaneous areas that may be regarded as "trigger points," Sinclair (1949) concluded that, in the light of current knowledge, this theory appears to afford the best available explanation of the mechanism of referred pain, although its anatomical basis has not been demonstrated.

Sympathetic Reflex Phenomena Associated With Referred Pain.—The theories outlined above afford plausible explanations of the mechanism of referred pain but they do not adequately take into consideration the viscero-cutaneous and the viscero-motor reflex phenomena which probably are invariably associated with somatic hyperalgesia, such as vasoconstriction, perspiration and pilo-erection. These phenomena are particularly marked in certain cases.

Wernoe's (1920–1925) clinical and experimental studies have contributed much to our knowledge of reflex viscero-cutaneous and viscero-motor reactions to visceral stimulation in relation to the sensory phenomena involved in referred somatic hyperalgesia. He observed clinically that cutaneous hyperalgesia commonly is accompanied by cutaneous ischemia, due to peripheral vasoconstriction, and that the area of cutaneous ischemia, in general, coincides exactly with the area of cutaneous hyperalgesia. In certain cases, he also observed localized cutis anserina in the hyperalgesic area. In his experience, cutaneous ischemia was so constantly present in areas of hyperalgesia associated with visceral disease that he was able to use it as a diagnostic character, being able, in many cases, to recognize the hyperalgesic area by virtue of the cutaneous ischemia when it would have been difficult or impossible to demonstrate hypersensitivity by the more usual methods. On the basis of these findings, Wernoe concluded that cutaneous hyperalgesia probably does not depend on the effect of visceral stimulation of neurons in the spinal cord but has its origin in changes brought about in the skin through viscero-cutaneous reflexes. In support of this conclusion from the clincial side, he pointed out that under certain conditions sympathetic stimulation alone gives rise to pain. For example, if the fingers are subjected to cold they gradually become ischemic and painful until, with complete anemia, the anesthetic stage is reached. If the hand is then warmed, the fingers again become painful until circulation is restored to normal. As the fingers are subjected to cold, vasoconstriction is brought about through reflex stimulation of the vasomotor fibers. The consequent pain is the result of the stimulation of pain receptors caused by the ischemic condition of the surrounding tissues and the hypertonic state of the smooth muscle in the vessel walls. In like manner, he assumed that the cutaneous pain receptors may be stimulated as a result of the ischemia brought about in the skin through viscero-cutaneous reflexes.

The vasoconstriction due to hypertonus or spastic contractions of the smooth muscle in the vessel walls or the consequent ischemia of the adjacent tissue undoubtedly is a major factor in the production of pain referable to the blood vessels. Peripheral vasoconstriction elicited reflexly through the sympathetic innervation of the blood vessels in a somatic area by impulses arising in a diseased viscus, therefore, may be regarded as a contributing factor in the production of hyperalgesia in the same area. Reflex contractions of the erector pili muscles, elicited in the same manner, likewise may well be regarded as a contributing factor in the hypersensitivity of the area in question, particularly to light touch and even air currents playing on the skin.

Davis and Pollock (1932, 1935, 1936) have supported a similar point of view. On the basis of experimental and clinical data that seem to support the assumption that stimulation of the sympathetic nerves of a peripheral area results in changes in that area that exert a direct stimulating effect on the pain receptors, they advanced the opinion that sympathetic stimulation may be a causative factor in the production of pain. They have, furthermore, regarded the abolition of referred pain by anesthesia of the area in which it is localized as indicating that the pain felt in that area due to a visceral lesion or stimulation of the appropriate afferent nerves is caused by stimulation of the peripheral pain receptors. In view of these considerations and the evidence of reflex activity mediated through the sympathetic nerves in the somatic area in which the referred pain associated with a visceral lesion is localized, they have supported the assumptions that this reflex activity represents the major factor in the causation of the pain in the somatic area and that the impulses generated at the periphery are conducted centrad through the somatic pain conducting pathways.

Some data which have been interpreted as supporting this point of view seem to be unequivocal. In 25 patients with well marked pains definitely localized in somatic areas, but due to visceral diseases, including angina pectoris, pleuritis, carcinoma of the esophagus, gastric ulcer, cholecystitis, nephrolithiasis, acute appendicitis, salpingitis and pyelitis, reported by Weiss and Davis (1928), the pain either was abolished or greatly alleviated by infiltration of the painful cutaneous areas with a 2 per cent solution of novocaine. They also reported the abolition, by the same means, of referred pains induced experimentally in two normal subjects by distention of a segment of the duodenum or the distal portion of the esophagus by inflation of a rubber balloon. In patients in whom a phrenic exeresis was being carried out, as reported by Davis and Pollock (1936), faradic stimulation of the phrenic nerve in the neck resulted in pain that was always referred to the trapezius ridge or the supraclavicular region. When this cutaneous area was anesthetized the same stimulations no longer resulted in pain.

The cutaneous area in which the referred pain is localized does not include the entire area supplied with afferent fibers that enter the spinal cord segments from which the viscus in question is innervated. As reported by Boyden and Rigler (1934), anesthesia of the circumscribed area in which a referred pain was localized abolished the pain in that area, but it was felt in an adjacent one. If the referred pain associated with a visceral lesion is felt only near the midline and this area is anesthetized, the pain moves laterad in the same segments due to the fact that pain is felt only in the area in which it is most intense.

The data outlined above are compatible with the theory that impulses may be generated in peripheral pain receptors as a result of sympathetic reflex activity elicited by visceral afferent stimulation. Reflex responses at the periphery which are elicited through either sympathetic or somatic efferent pathways by afferent stimulation at the site of a visceral lesion undoubtedly play a rôle in the referred pain or hyperalgesia associated with the visceral disease, particularly when the referred phenomena develop slowly and persist after the visceral stimulation has subsided. These factors obviously play no significant rôle in the production of the referred pain in certain instances. For example, the pain referred to the tip of the shoulder due to stimulation of the diaphragm usually arises almost instantaneously. In some instances, furthermore, it is not abolished by anesthetizing the cutaneous area in which it is localized. In order to test the hypothesis that shoulder pain elicited by phrenic nerve stimulation may be abolished by anesthetizing the cutaneous area in which the pain is localized, Livingston (1938) subjected it to clinical experimentation. In a patient with a subphrenic abscess, shoulder pain was elicited by touching the dome of the diaphragm with the tip of a uterine probe inserted through the incision made for the purpose of draining the abscess. The shoulder area was then infiltrated widely with a 1 per cent solution of novocaine and the stimulation of the diaphragm was repeated. In every trial the patient complained of pain in the shoulder the instant the diaphragm was stimulated and localized it within the novocainized area to which the pain had been originally referred. These results seem to preclude stimulation of pain receptors in the skin, due to the effects of reflex activity mediated through either sympathetic or somatic nerves, as a causative factor in the production of the referred pain.

The finding that impulses of visceral origin that give rise to sensations of pain and nociceptive impulses of somatic origin are conducted in the same central pathways has a significant bearing on the problem of referred pain. Since both visceral and somatic pain conducting fibers discharge into the neuron pool in the spinal cord from which the lateral spinothalamic tract fibers arise, these tract neurons may be facilitated by subthreshold impulses of either visceral or somatic origin or they may be activated by summation of impulses derived from both visceral and somatic receptors. The demonstration that in some instances referred pain is abolished by infiltration of the cutaneous area of reference with an anesthetic agent, and in other instances it persists following analgesia of the area of reference supports the assumption that subthreshold somatic afferent impulses that flow into the spinal cord segment into which impulses from a visceral lesion are being discharged may be necessary to produce awareness of mild degrees of visceral stimulation, but when the stimulation at the site of the visceral lesion becomes sufficiently intense the impulses break through to the level of consciousness even though conduction from the somatic area of reference is blocked. Due to the relatively meager supply of pain receptors in the viscera and other deep structures and the lack of experience of sensations arising in consciousness due to stimulation in these areas, the source of such impulses may be misinterpreted.

Convergence of impulses upon the lateral spinothalamic tract neurons may also be a significant factor in central interpretation. The number of pain conducting fibers in the dorsal nerve roots greatly exceeds the number of tract neurons in the corresponding neuron pools in the spinal cord; consequently, both visceral and somatic pain conducting fibers discharge into the same tract neurons. These neurons are activated much more frequently by impulses conducted from cutaneous and other superficial receptors than by impulses of visceral origin; consequently, a sensory pattern becomes established that favors cutaneous localization of sensations of pain. When impulses of visceral origin reach the sensory level they are interpreted according to the sensory pattern that has been built up through experience. Thus, pain of visceral or other deep origin may be localized in a cutaneous area.

The assumption that the neuron pools in the spinal cord into which the impulses that arise at the site of the causative lesion are conducted play a major rôle in the production of the referred phenomena, as is implied in the original Lange-Ross theory and its elaboration by Mackenzie, still affords a most helpful point of view for the understanding of the mechanism of referred pain. The concept of irradiation in the spinal gray matter undoubtedly can be substituted for Mackenzie's concept of irritable foci. The physiological concepts of convergence, summation, facilitation and inhibition also are applicable, since afferent impulses emanating from the site of a lesion giving rise to referred pain impinge upon a central neuron pool which also receives impulses from the peripheral area in which the referred phenomena are localized. Facilitation and inhibition undoubtedly play a rôle in the reflex phenomena associated with referred pain. The summation of visceral and somatic afferent impulses probably is essential for the production of referred pain in certain instances, as suggested by the abolition of the pain in the somatic area by cutaneous anesthesia. In other instances, particularly those in which the referred pain is not abolished by cutaneous anesthesia, summation seems to be unessential.

Chapter XX

AUTONOMIC IMBALANCE

THE CONCEPT

Genesis and Definition.—The visceral organs, with certain exceptions, are innervated through both the sympathetic and the parasympathetic divisions of the autonomic nervous system which are synergistic in function; consequently, any disturbance of the functional balance of the sympathetic and the parasympathetic nerves must result in visceral dysfunction in some degree. Von Noorden recognized this as early as 1892 and called attention to various clinical conditions associated with increased vagus irritability which he designated vagus neuroses. The clinical concepts of vagotonia and sympatheticotonia were first formulated by Eppinger and Hess in 1909 and further elaborated by them in a series of later papers. In many individuals in whom adrenin produced strong sympathetic stimulation, according to their findings, pilocarpine failed to stimulate the parasympathetic nerves and atropine did not paralyze them. In other individuals in whom pilocarpine or atropine produced a strong parasympathetic reaction, they found that the injection of adrenin resulted in no apparent effect on the sympathetic nerves. On the basis of extensive observations on the effects of these drugs in man, they concluded that all persons who react strongly to pilocarpine and atropine are relatively insensitive to adrenin, and all persons who react strongly to adrenin are relatively insensitive to atropine and pilocarpine. They classified clinical cases exhibiting a functional imbalance between the sympathetic and the parasympathetic nerves as vagotonic or sympatheticotonic, depending on the relative reactivity of the parasympathetic and the sympathetic nerves. They recognized more or less definite symptom-complexes which usually are associated with exaggerated reactivity of the parasympathetic and the sympathetic nerves respectively. According to their original theory, absolute vagotonia is characterized by actual hyperreactivity or exaggerated tonus of the parasympathetic nerves, and absolute sympatheticotonia is characterized by hyperreactivity or exaggerated tonus of the sympathetic nerves. They conceded that relative vagotonia may exist in the absence of exaggerated parasympathetic tonus if the reactivity of the sympathetic nerves is subnormal or there is a deficiency in the chromaffine system, and that relative sympatheticotonia may exist in the absence of exaggerated sympathetic tonus if the reactivity of the parasympathetic nerves is subnormal. In either case, vagotonia and sympatheticotonia involve an increase in functional activity in the respective division of the autonomic nervous system that may affect the entire division or only a portion of it.

According to the original theory of Eppinger and Hess, the entire sympathetic and parasympathetic divisions of the autonomic nervous system are tonically stimulated and sustain a physiological balance which may be shifted in favor of one or the other division by abnormal functional conditions. Exaggerated tonus of either system does not necessarily imply hyperirritability of the nerve centers concerned, but may be brought about by an excess of stimulating substances in the blood. In general, they regarded vagotonia as characterized by hyperreactivity to parasympathetic stimulation and sympatheticotonia as characterized by hyperreactivity to sympathetic stimulation of all the organs innervated through the autonomic nerves, although they recognized the possibility of localized vagotonia.

Critique.—On the basis of an extensive study of the effects of adrenin, pilocarpine and atropine in clinical conditions, Petren and Thorling (1911) pointed out that, in certain diseases in which exaggerated parasympathetic tonus usually is apparent, *e.g.*, gastric and duodenal ulcer, bronchial asthma, etc., some patients, as judged by their reactions to these drugs, exhibit exaggerated sympathetic tonus, and some react strongly to adrenin and also to pilocarpine and atropine, thus proving that the same individual may exhibit heightened reactivity of both divisions of the autonomic nervous system. They, therefore, suggested that the observed reactions to parasympathomimetic and sympathomimetic drugs can be explained most satisfactorily, in certain cases, on the assumption of heightened irritability of both the parasympathetic and the sympathetic nerves, but they agreed with Eppinger and Hess regarding the existence of vagotonia and sympathetioctonia as recognizable functional states which represent deviations from the normal functional balance between the parasympathetic and the sympathetic nerves.

These findings of Petren and Thorling have been amply confirmed by later investigators. It has also been amply demonstrated that the symptom-complexes commonly associated with certain diseases which, according to the theory of Eppinger and Hess, are related to vagotonia also include symptoms that suggest exaggerated reactivity of the sympathetic nerves. Symptom-complexes associated with diseases which, according to this theory, are related to sympatheticotonia, likewise, also include symptoms that suggest hyperreactivity of the parasympathetic nerves. For example, the dominant symptoms of pulmonary tuberculosis, particularly during the second and the third stages of the disease, usually indicate vagotonia, but the gastro-intestinal symptoms sometimes suggest exaggerated sympathetic tonus. The dominant symptoms of hyperthyroidism, such as tachycardia, increased metabolism, fever, etc., likewise, suggest sympatheticotonia, but gastro-intestinal hypermotility, so common in this disease, indicates exaggerated parasympathetic reactivity. Usually strong reactions to either parasympathomimetic or to sympathomimetic drugs or to both also have been reported repeatedly in certain individuals apparently in good health who exhibited no objective evidence of a functional autonomic imbalance.

The symptom-complex commonly associated with hyperthyroidism frequently has been cited as incompatible with the theory of vagotonia and sympatheticotonia. According to Eppinger and Hess, patients with exophthalmic goiter may be classified as vagotonic or sympatheticotonic on the basis of gastro-intestinal hypermotility and tachycardia respectively.

Many patients with exophthalmic goiter exhibit both gastro-intestinal hypermotility and tachycardia at the same time; consequently, it cannot be assumed, on the basis of these symptoms, that either vagotonia or sympatheticotonia exists in these cases. In many cases of this disease, the dominant symptom-complex, including persistent diarrhea, gastric hyperacidity, vomiting, vasodilatation, and circumscribed edema, strongly suggest parasympathetic hyperirritability, but absolute vagotonia or sympatheticotonia, in the sense of Eppinger and Hess, probably never is observed in patients with exophthalmic goiter.

One of the most striking symptom-complexes indicative of general parasympatheticotonia is that associated with spastic constipation which has been regarded by most investigators in this field as a purely parasympatheticotonic disease. In a study of patients with frank spastic constipation, in which the pupillary reaction was used as an index, Bernhold and Hauptstein (1928) observed the expected parasympathetic response to pilocarpine and atropine in every case.

Kraus and Zondek (1922, 1924) have forcibly called attention to the influence of electrolytes on the autonomic nerves and emphasized the importance of the acid-base balance in all diseases in which the autonomic system is directly concerned. According to their point of view, cellular activity results in diminution of the calcium concentration of the cell membrane. This diminution of calcium is accompanied by an increase in intracellular potassium, an increase in the permeability of the cell and hydration of its protoplasm. Cellular inactivity, on the other hand, results in a relative increase in the calcium concentration of the cell membrane, a decrease in the permeability of the cell and dehydration of its protoplasm. Potassium and calcium concentrations respectively, therefore, are indicative of cellular activity and cellular rest. Since these cellular changes may be initiated by nerve impulses, the concentration of either potassium or calcium in the serum may be an index of cellular change, but the serum levels do not necessarily change the reactions of the cells. Changes in the ionic concentration, however, frequently bring about changes in the autonomic balance.

Since the assumption that sympathetic and parasympathetic nerve tonus is associated with ionic concentration is based chiefly on the reactions to the injection of adrenin, observed in clinical cases, it is important to inquire into the validity of this criterion. A constant correlation between the reaction to adrenin and the K/Ca ratio in the blood cannot be demonstrated in all cases. In experiments reported by Petersen and Levinson (1930), carried out on normal men and clinical patients, individuals who, on the basis of their reactions to adrenin, were classified as frankly sympatheticotonic exhibited a lower K/Ca ratio than individuals who, on the same basis, were classified as frankly vagotonic, but they also found exceptions to this rule.

The lack of constancy in these experimental results does not minimize the importance of the ionic balance in relation to the functional balance between the sympathetic and the parasympathetic nerves since the K/Ca ratio in the body fluids is not a true index of the ionic concentration of the cell membranes on which the reactions of the cells depend. Petersen and

Levinson have demonstrated experimentally that the cell protoplasm liberates calcium and takes up potassium during cellular stimulation corresponding to the time of vasodilatation in the organ and, therefore, to a presumptive vagotonic status of the tissues. If the term vagotonia were used to denote a condition of tissue activity with capillary dilatation and increased permeability, the calcium in the blood should be increased and the potassium diminished, *i.e.*, the vagotonic person should have a low K/Ca ratio, the physiological effects being modified by differences in ionization. The vagotonic person, as clinically defined, does not exhibit increased metabolism with capillaries dilated and permeable but, on the contrary, exhibits decreased metabolism and reduced capillary permeability.

Inasmuch as the terms vagotonic and sympatheticotonic, as clinically defined, do not necessarily represent the functional states of the tissues, Petersen and Levinson have suggested that this classification be discarded. They have introduced and defined the terms "parasympathetic status" and "sympathetic status." The former, according to their definition, denotes capillary dilatation, tissue activity, calcium dissimilation and hydration. The latter denotes tissue rest with vasoconstriction, calcium accumulation and dehydration. They also pointed out that contraction of smooth muscle (which may represent the response either to sympathetic or parasympathetic stimulation) commonly has been regarded as tissue activity, but during the muscular contraction the capillaries are contracted, capillary permeability is diminished, metabolic processes are retarded and less energy is liberated. With relaxation, on the other hand, the vascular bed becomes dilated, capillary permeability is increased and metabolism is accelerated. The relaxation of smooth muscle, therefore, represents the parasympathetic status as defined above.

Inasmuch as the parasympathetic status and the sympathetic status represent states of tissue activity and tissue rest respectively, the same status obviously cannot obtain throughout the entire body at any given moment. This is well illustrated by the adaptive compensatory reactions between the peripheral and the splanchnic blood vessels.

The stimuli that elicit widespread vasoconstriction at the periphery also elicit vasodilatation in the splanchnic area and *vice versa*. These changes are accompanied by corresponding changes in the permeability of the blood vessels and the distribution of leukocytes. The area in which the sympathetic status obtains exhibits leukopenia. That in which the parasympathetic status obtains exhibits leukocytosis. Leukopenia and leukocytosis, consequently, parallel compensatory vasoconstriction and vasodilatation and may be regarded as indices of the functional autonomic status in the respective areas.

The peripheral and the splanchnic areas are so intimately interconnected through the autonomic regulatory mechanism that, when extensive areas are involved, the slightest change in the autonomic status at the periphery gives rise to a corresponding change in the opposite direction in the splanchnic area, and *vice versa*, under both physiological and pathological conditions. Disease processes may result either in chronic fixation of an abnormal autonomic status or in increased instability of the autonomic nervous system, either of which conditions may result in inadequate compensatory reactions or overcompensation and give rise to abnormal conditions of blood pressure.

In the light of our present knowledge of the innervation of the blood vessels (see Chapter VIII), the compensatory vascular reactions in the peripheral and the splanchnic areas obviously cannot be explained on the basis of changes in sympathetic-parasympathetic balance as commonly understood, but they can be explained on the basis of changes in the autonomic status of these areas respectively. As previously stated, the peripheral blood vessels are devoid of parasympathetic nerves. Most of the splanchnic blood vessels also appear to be devoid of parasympathetic innervation. The sympathetic nerves to the peripheral blood vessels, furthermore, include vasodilator fibers (see Chapter VIII). The peripheral vasomotor control, therefore, concerns only the sympathetic nerves; consequently, an autonomic imbalance in the ordinary sense in this area is inconceivable. The control of the peripheral temperature-regulating mechanism, likewise, is mediated chiefly through the sympathetic nerves. Certain synergic reactions of organs that are innervated through both the sympathetic and parasympathetic divisions of the autonomic system, *e.g.*, coördinated reactions of the sphincter and the detrusor muscles of the urinary bladder, may also be carried out in the absence of nerve impulses. Many visceral phenomena that have been regarded as manifestations of functional antagonism between the sympathetic and the parasympathetic nerves, therefore, must be explained on some other basis. In so far as they involve the functional activity of both sympathetic and parasympathetic nerves, these nerves are not mutually antagonistic, but synergistic.

In view of the data outlined above and our present knowledge of the humoral transmission of nerve impulses and the distribution of cholinergic and adrenergic fibers in both divisions of the autonomic nervous system, the concept of a clear functional difference between the parasympathetic and the sympathetic nerves is untenable. On the basis of this knowledge and the results of a study involving measurements, over an extended period, of 20 physiological variables of which at least 12 are mediated at least in part through the autonomic nerves, in 62 children 6 to 11 years of age, and a factor analysis of these data, Wenger (1941) has proposed the following restatement of the theory of Eppinger and Hess:

(*a*) "The differential chemical reactivity and the physiological antagonism of the adrenergic and cholinergic branches of the autonomic nervous system permit of a situation in which the action of one branch may predominate over that of the other. This predominance, or autonomic imbalance, may be phasic or chronic, and may obtain for either the adrenergic or the cholinergic system. (*b*) Autonomic imbalance, when measured in an unselected population, will be distributed continuously about a central tendency which shall be defined as autonomic balance."

Babkin (1947) advanced certain data in support of the assumption that the complex balance of excitation and inhibition exhibited by the autonomic nerves in mammals represents a recent evolutionary development. In Elasmobranch fishes, according to his findings, the autonomic nerves subserve only excitatory functions. In most of their functional relationships in the higher vertebrates, the sympathetic and the parasympathetic nerves are in no sense antagonistic, but essentially synergic. The existence of mutual antagonism within the autonomic nervous system, according to Babkin, cannot be denied, but it is not conclusively demonstrated. Under conditions of autonomic imbalance, as observed by Kehler (1949), parasympathetic hypertonus is suppressed more easily by sympathetic stimulation than sympathetic hypertonus is suppressed by parasympathetic stimulation.

FACTORS INFLUENCING THE AUTONOMIC BALANCE

The Acid-base Balance.—Experimental and clinical data afford ample proof that the acid-base balance can be shifted in the direction of acidity by the administration of calcium and that an increase in the potassium-ion concentration results in a shift in the acid-base balance in the direction of alkalinity. Alterations in the functional balance between the adrenergic and the cholinergic autonomic nerves due to changes in the acid-base balance have been amply demonstrated. The results of experiments involving the stimulating effect of adrenin on the sympathetic nerves prove conclusively that the effect of adrenin is influenced by the chemical reaction of the fluids circulating through the organs in question. Certain experimental data also indicate a greater rise in blood pressure in response to a given dose of adrenin when the reaction of the blood is alkaline than when the acid-base balance is shifted toward the acid side. In some instances, when the reaction of the blood tends toward the acid side, the administration of adrenin elicits no rise in blood pressure.

Weiss and Benkovics (1925) found that the effect of adrenin on blood pressure was reduced following the administration of calcium chloride which, as stated above, shifts the acid-base balance of the blood toward the acid side. This result is in full accord with actual clinical findings. Patients with hyperthyroidism commonly exhibit a shift in the acid-base balance toward the alkaline side. They also exhibit increased sympathetic reactivity to adrenin. In general, the degree of change toward the acid side corresponds to the degree of improvement. The decrease in the reactivity of the sympathetic nerves to adrenin also corresponds to the reduction in the alkalinity of the blood. Patients suffering with diseases that are commonly associated with hyperacidity, *e.g.*, bronchial asthma, diabetes insipidus, etc., likewise, rarely, if ever, exhibit increased sympathetic reactivity to adrenin. In many cases, the reactivity of the sympathetic nerves to adrenin is actually subnormal (Balint, 1927). Patients with diabetes mellitus exhibit a wide range of variation in the reactivity of the sympathetic system to adrenin. In a study involving comparison of sympathetic reactivity and the acid-base reaction of the blood in diabetic patients, Csepai *et al.* (1925) found that sympathetic reactivity to adrenin was subnormal in those exhibiting hyperacidity, but increased in those who had been subjected to massive sodium bicarbonate treatment. In certain cases in which they found subnormal sympathetic reactivity before treatment, adrenin elicited a normal or exaggerated response after alkaline therapy. These results strongly support the theory that sympathetic tonus is increased by a change in the acid-base balance in the blood toward the alkaline side, and parasympathetic tonus is increased by a change in the acid-base balance toward the acid side.

On the basis of data outlined above, we should expect to find evidence of hyperacidity in all cases in which vagotonia, as indicated by pharmacological criteria, exists. The data bearing on this point cannot be regarded as conclusive, but they are strongly suggestive. Chronic gastric and duodenal ulcer almost invariably is associated with parasympathetic hyperirritability and hyperacidity. In certain cases of cholelithiasis, the dominant symptoms resemble very closely those of gastric ulcer. This is true particularly of the reflex reactions of the stomach, including hypermotility and changes in gastric secretory activity which are manifestations of vagotonia. Although vagotonia usually is demonstrable in cases of cholelithiasis, the H-ion concentration of the blood falls within the normal range in many cases. In a clinical study of 14 patients with cholelithiasis, involving determination of the H-ion concentration of the blood and the elimination of alkali through the kidneys, Balint (1927) found that, although the H-ion concentration of the blood did not deviate beyond the normal limits in any of the 13 cases in which it was determined, the urine did not become alkaline or only slightly so following the injection of sodium bicarbonate in 9 cases, showed a neutral reaction in 1, and an alkaline reaction in the other 4. The majority of these cases (9 out of 14) exhibited alkali retention which, according to Balint, is associated with an acid condition of the tissues. It must be admitted, therefore, that the tissues were more acid than normal in these cases, although hyperacidity was not demonstrable in the blood. The results obtained in a limited number of cases of bronchial asthma, in general, corroborate the above findings in cases of cholelithiasis. On the basis of these findings, Balint concluded that some degree of hyperacidity is a common accompaniment of vagotonia, although the H-ion concentration of the blood may not deviate beyond the normal limits.

The Vasosensory Mechanisms.—Specific mechanisms of autonomic regulation, such as the carotid sinus and the cardio-aortic and abdominal vasosensory mechanisms described in Chapter VIII, play a significant rôle in the physiological processes involved in the maintenance of the functional balance throughout the body. These mechanisms are involved particularly in the reflex control of circulatory and respiratory equilibrium which they exercise by maintaining and varying the tonic inhibition of the organs concerned in these essential life-maintaining functions and through the influence that they exert in the more general functions particularly of the sympathetic nerves.

In general the carotid sinus mechanism is activated by optimal conditions of oxygenation and blood pressure which favor bodily activity. In turn it tends to lower blood pressure to the level that is commensurate with the maintenance of its own activity. Conditions of low blood pressure, low oxygen tension or excess of carbon dioxide in the carotid sinus, on the other hand, tend to inactivate the carotid sinus mechanism, or reduce its inhibitory action, and release the restrained sympathetic mechanisms from tonic inhibition. At the same time impulses emanating from the carotid sinus that elicit parasympathetic reflex activity are reduced. Like carotid sinus denervation, such conditions tend to produce hypertension and, in certain cases, hyperpnea. Under conditions of extremely low blood pressure "paradoxical" reactions may result in no rise in blood pressure and respiratory failure.

The vasoreceptive mechanisms that normally exercise a regulatory inhibitory control over sympathetic activity, actually reducing the magnitude of vasomotor and other sympathetic reflex reactions to afferent nerve stimulation, also exercise a positive control through the parasympathetic nerves, including increased intestinal tonus and motility.

Adrenin in the circulating blood tends to sensitize the carotid sinus mechanism and thus increase its inhibitory effects both on blood pressure and respiration. It also increases the sensitivity of the carotid sinus mechanisms to the existing blood pressure; consequently, a depressor reaction may be produced independently of the peripheral depressor effects of adrenin. By increasing the inhibitory control of the carotid sinus mechanism over sympathetic reactions adrenin also exercises an inhibitory control over medulliadrenal secretion and thereby provides homeostatic limitation on its own account. It may also limit other sympathetic responses.

The action of acetylcholine in the carotid sinus, according to Heymans *et al.* (1935), may result in hypertension by decreasing sympathetic inhibition. This undoubtedly is due to cholinergic inactivation of the carotid sinus mechanism, since the effects are similar in kind to those of carotid sinus denervation. The physostigmine-like action of ergotamine in the carotid sinus which, according to Bacq *et al.* (1932), may result in hypertension also indicates failure of sympathetic inhibition due to depression of the carotid sinus reflexes. The increased blood pressure in human subjects following the administration of ergotamine probably can be explained most satisfactorily on the same basis.

Carotid sinus dysfunction is commonly manifested in syncopal attacks proably due to hyperirritability of the carotid sinus mechanisms. Ferris *et al.* (1935) have classified such attacks as (1) cerebral, (2) cardiac and (3) vasomotor, depending upon which of the carotid sinus mechanisms are most involved. In the cerebral attacks the reflexes initiated in the carotid sinus affect primarily the brain or cerebral circulation. In the other types, the embarrassment of the general circulation secondarily results in syncope. Convulsions may occur in these cases, not as a direct effect of carotid sinus hyperirritability but in consequence of the syncopal attack (Freedberg and Sloan, 1937). In idiopathic epilepsy, as observed by Weiss and Baker (1933), carotid sinus pressure does not cause seizures. As reported by Marinesco and Kreindler (1931), epilepsy may actually be associated with carotid sinus hyposensitivity, in which case seizures may result from failure of the carotid sinus mechanism to protect the brain from mechanical shocks transmitted through the circulation. Darrow (1943) admitted this possibility, but, on the basis of electroencephalographic evidence, he advanced the opinion that lack of hydrodynamic control is less important in the etiology of epilepsy than inadequate buffering of the autonomic discharges to the brain.

Hypersensitivity and overregulation by the carotid sinus mechanisms are indicated in certain cases of schizophrenia by the depression of sympathetic functions. The blood pressure tends to be low and the pulse slow. Emotional hypoglycemia is the rule probably due to increased vago-insulin secretory activity. The observation that schizophrenic symptoms are aggrevated by the subcutaneous injection of adrenin supports the assumption that in resistant, uncoöperative patients the carotid sinus may become sensitized by increased production of adrenin. The effectiveness as a therapeutic agent in schizophrenia of ergotamine, a drug which desensitizes the carotid sinus, also supports this point of view.

TESTS OF AUTONOMIC FUNCTIONAL BALANCE

A test of autonomic function can be significant only if it circumvents the mutually antagonistic actions of the sympathetic and the parasympathetic nerves so that it may indicate clearly whether an observed reaction is due to increased activity in one division of the autonomic system or to decreased activity in the other. Tests that merely indicate a functional imbalance are of little value and may even be misleading, since they do not define the reactions in question in the neural and neurohumoral systems. Autonomic reactions, furthermore, may bear one relationship to the initiating processes in the nervous system under certain conditions and another relationship under other conditions.

Circumvention of the difficulties in interpreting observed autonomic reactions in terms of neurohumoral processes have been attempted in various ways: (1) by recording the reactions of mechanisms that are innervated through only one division of the autonomic system, e.g., the nictitating membranes; (2) by elimination of either the sympathetic or the parasympathetic innervation of the organ in question; (3) by assaying in vivo or in vitro the neurohumoral mediator liberated; (4) by analyis of the reactions to appropriate pharmacological agents; (5) by recording the action potentials of the respective autonomic nerves. All of these methods have been found useful, but the interpretation of the results obtained is beset with difficulties due to homeostasis, since autonomic reactions tend not only to bring about adaptive changes but also to maintain the constancy of the internal milieu. The criteria by which the sympathetic or the parasympathetic character of a given mechanism may be determined, furthermore, are varied and not always consistent with one another.

Tests Based on Singly Innervated Structures.—The nictitating membrane receives its efferent innervation solely through adrenergic sympathetic fibers; consequently, it provides an ideal sympathetic indicator. It provides an index not only of sympathetic excitation but also of inhibition of sympathetic tonus. Its reaction to adrenin may be enhanced by eserin and decreased by atropine. It may react to large doses of acetylcholine in animals in which it has become sensitized following denervation (Morrison and Acheson, 1938). These properties do not seriously detract from its usefulness as a sympathetic indicator under normal conditions.

The secretory activity of these glands has been utilized extensively as an index of sympathetic activity. Sweating and the concomitant changes in the electrical resistance of the skin, particularly in the palms of the hands, are extremely sensitive to changes in the level of activity of the sympathetic nerves. Excessive spontaneous sweating probably always indicates exaggerated sympathetic reactivity.

The adrenal medulla derives its efferent innervation solely through sympathetic preganglionic fibers. Since the secretory product of this gland is a sympathomimetic hormone, the production of which depends on sympathetic excitation, it may be utilized as a sympathetic indicator. The response to adrenin, as indicated particularly by the magnitude of the rise in blood pressure produced by a given dosage, provides a fairly reliable index of the level of sympathetic reactivity.

Tests Based on Sympathetic or Parasympathetic Denervation.—This method has been widely utilized in the delimitation of responses of mechanisms innervated through both divisions of the autonomic system. It should be limited to acute experiments since the denervated tissues may become sensitized to the humoral agent whose neural counterpart has undergone degeneration.

The pupil provides a convenient mechanism for the application of this method since the sympathetic nerves to one eye may be severed without affecting the innervation of the other eye, which affords a convenient experimental control. The difference between the reactions of the sympathetically denervated pupil and the normally innervated one on the opposite side provides an index of the concomitant sympathetic activity. Section of the oculomotor nerve, likewise, results in parasympathetic denervation of the pupil, leaving its sympathetic innervation intact. Sympathetic excitation undoubtedly contributes to the pupillary response to emotional stimulation and probably also when the inhibitory effects of adrenin have been eliminated. Dilatation of the pupil in response to peripheral nociceptive stimulation is mediated through the mesencephalic parasympathetic center. This reflex, as demonstrated by Kuntz and Richins (1946), represents an actively integrated and controlled reaction that involves the conduction of efferent impulses from the ciliary ganglion to the circular muscle of the iris through adrenergic components of the short ciliary nerves. The demonstration of active inhibition of the sphincter pupillæ through adrenergic parasympathetic fibers suggests the desirability of a reëxamination of the evidence on the basis of which some reactions of other mechanisms with dual autonomic innervation have been interpreted.

The salivary glands, particularly the parotid, provide a useful indicator particularly for parasympathetic reactivity. Data reported by Lourie (1943) support the assumption that the rate of parotid gland secretion is not influenced by sympathetic nerve impulses; consequently, elimination of its sympathetic innervation is unnecessary. Lourie has described a convenient technic for recovery of the parotid secretory output in children and determination of the rate of secretion. His findings support the assumption that children are essentially parasympatheticotonic with respect to the parotid gland and become less so as they approach puberty.

Blood pressure provides a useful indication of autonomic activity only when it is interpreted critically. A rise in blood pressure frequently indicates increased sympathetic activity, but an equal rise may actually be due to a decrease in parasympathetic tonus. A fall in blood pressure, likewise, may be due to inhibition of sympathetic tonus. The prevailing lack of correspondence between changes in blood pressure and changes in valid sympathetic indicators such as the nictitating membrane has been emphasized by the results of various studies. Vasomotor inhibition particularly by impulses emanating from the carotid sinus is an important factor in blood pressure, as indicated by the hypertension following carotid sinus denervation which may be prevented by prior complete sympathectomy.

Vasomotor tonus may be utilized as an indicator of autonomic function in a wide variety of conditions, but identification of vasoconstriction with sympathetic activity is not a rational procedure since the sympathetic innervation of most of the blood vessels includes both vasoconstrictor and vasodilator fibers. Sympathetic vasodilatation has long been recognized in the skeletal musculature where obviously it may serve an emergency function. This is particularly marked in "animals of the chase" such as the dog and the hare. In most mammals, including man, the cutaneous and the splanchnic vessels are supplied with adrenergic vasoconstrictor and cholinergic vasodilator fibers.

Tests for the reactivity of the adrenergic and the cholinergic systems are helpful particularly in the diagnosis and treatment of peripheral vascular diseases and other neurocirculatory disorders. Among those which have been used particularly to determine the capacity of the patient for vasodilatation may be mentioned induced fever, spinal and general anesthesia, warming of the extremities and the administration of cholinergic drugs. Tests of sympathetic reactivity which may be used in the diagnosis of hypertension include the cold pressor test, skin temperature determinations, plethysmographic blood volume and blood flow determinations and photoelectric plethysmographic technics.

Assay of the Output of Humoral Mediators.—The assay of the humoral mediators may be accomplished in vivo in the same animal or a second one by registration of their effects on denervated sensitized organs, or in vitro either by their effects on strips of excised, sensitized tissue or by chemical tests. The nictitating membrane sensitized by denervation is a relatively pure adrenergically excitable structure; consequently, it provides a sensitive indicator of the excitatory effect of sympathin. The musculature of the gastro-intestinal tract, particularly that of the large intestine, has proved useful as an indicator of the inhibitory action of sympathin and adrenin. Since gastro-intestinal motility and tonus are maintained through cholinergic parasympathetic nerves, this musculature may also be used as an indicator of cholinergic activity. The observation that the inhibitory effects of nerve stimulation on the gastro-intestinal musculature may be abolished by splanchnicotomy and restored by adrenin supports the assumption that they are mediated through the sympathetic nerves. Youmans *et al.* (1938) employed both innervated and denervated Thierry fistulæ in the same dog for simultaneously testing the effects of nerve stimulation and those of humoral agents.

The rate of the denervated heart provides a useful indicator for the effects of humoral agents and has been utilized extensively. It is sensitive to both adrenergic and cholinergic mediators but the cholinergic effects may be regarded as negligible except in the presence of eserine or similar drugs. In any case, the excitatory and the inhibitory actions of sympathin or adrenin are synergistic.

Tests Involving Reactions to Pharmacological Agents.—On the basis of actual experience, various investigators have maintained that the existence of an autonomic imbalance and its character can be determined by pharmacodynamic methods. Others have denied this possibility on the basis of data which indicate that certain individuals react strongly to both sympathetic and parasympathetic stimulants and the conflicting results obtained in many pharmacodynamic studies. In general, individuals with exaggerated sympathetic tonus react more strongly to sympathomimetic agents than those with normal autonomic balance. Individuals with exaggerated parasympathetic tonus, likewise, react more strongly to parasympathomimetic agents than those with normal balance. The effect of a given dose of a drug like ergotamine, which tends to block the adrenergic nerves, or atropine, which tends to block the cholinergic nerves, therefore, varies according to the functional balance of the autonomic system. In the presence of exaggerated sympathetic tonus a larger dose of ergotamine is required to block adrenergic function than in the presence of normal autonomic balance. Likewise, in the presence of exaggerated parasympathetic tonus a larger dose of atropine is required to block cholinergic function than in the presence of normal autonomic balance.

The assumption that ergotamine merely tends to block adrenergic conduction is misleading. Its primary action on smooth muscle, particularly that which is cholinergically activated, like the gastro-intestinal muscle, is to cause contraction. In the intact animal it increases intestinal motility, causes extreme miosis, lowers blood sugar and decreases blood pressure. In certain cases, the administration of this drug may be followed by increased blood pressure probably due to the contraction of muscular organs. Desensitization of the carotid sinus by ergotamine may be a contributing factor in the rise in blood pressure in these cases. Ergotamine blocks the inhibitory effect of adrenin or sympathetic stimulation on cholinergically activated mechanisms. The inability of adrenin or sympathetic stimulation to block the spontaneous activity or to relax the tonus of intestinal muscle in the presence of ergotamine can be explained most satisfactorily on this basis (Darrow, 1943). In the human placenta, which is devoid of nerves but rich in choline, constriction of the blood vessels by adrenin is blocked by ergotoxine. Cholinergic vasodilation probably is normally inhibited by adrenergic sympathetic stimulation or by adrenin, resulting in constriction which is synergic with adrenergic constrictor activity. This inhibition of the vasodilators does not take place following the administration of ergotoxine; consequently, the rise is less marked or there may be an actual fall in blood pressure. A similar vasomotor reversal after eserine, which is abolished by atropine, has been demonstrated. This also suggests that the inhibitory effects of adrenergic stimulation may be blocked in the presence of sufficient acetylcholine. The depressor effects of acetylcholine may be potentiated by ergotamine, and this action may be reversed by atropine. The chief value of ergotamine as an indicator of autonomic function undoubtedly lies in its effectiveness in testing for the presence of sympathetic inhibitory and adrenin inhibitory effects on cholinergic functions.

The use of atropine to determine the rôle of cholinergic mechanisms in a given response has become almost routine in physiological experiments. The measurements sought by its use have been predominantly of two types: (1) an index of the normal cholinergic activity as indicated by the changes induced when that activity is blocked, and (2) an index of sympathetic function as indicated by the total residual activity following blocking of the cholinergic mechanisms. The possible effects of the drug on cholinergic transmission of nerve impulses in the sympathetic ganglia, the adrenal medulla and the central nervous system and the possible compensatory action of the carotid sinus and other moderator nerves may vitiate both these effects to some extent. Atropine has nevertheless been found useful in the study of autonomic functions particularly in psychopathic patients and synergic and antagonistic pharmacologic responses in normal and diseased human subjects.

Autonomic Action Potentials.—Electric recording of the activity of autonomic effectors has been utilized widely in studies of autonomic activity. The literature bearing on the use of action potential records in investigations of various aspects of the physiology of the autonomic nerves is too extensive to be reviewed in this connection. Analytical studies of the electrical responses in smooth muscles in various organs such as the nictitating membranes, the pilo-erectors, the intestine, the uterus, the urinary bladder and the ureters and their autonomic nerves carried out by various investigators indicate that the action potential records obtained in inhibitory responses differ from those obtained in excitatory responses. The electrocardiogram also affords a reliable indication of the autonomic functional balance.

Adrenin, atropine and certain other pharmacological agents, as indicated by action potential records (Marrazzi, 1939), exert a damping influence on cholinergic transmission in autonomic ganglia, whereas such transmission is facilitated by parasympathomimetic drugs. Action potential records have been employed in investigations concerned with problems of autonomic control and in studies carried out to determine the specific functional relationship of the carotid sinus nerves to sympathetic regulation. Electrical recording technics undoubtedly can be employed still more widely in studies involving the synergic and the antagonistic actions of adrenergic and cholinergic autonomic mechanisms.

Chapter XXI

THE AUTONOMIC NERVOUS SYSTEM IN DISEASE

CLINICAL SIGNIFICANCE OF AUTONOMIC DYSFUNCTION

THE data outlined in Chapter XVIII show clearly that disease processes commonly are accompanied by histopathological lesions of autonomic ganglia and ganglion cells or of central autonomic centers. Such lesions usually are non-specific. In some instances they are obviously related to a disease process. In other instances a direct relationship of the autoncmic lesions to a disease process is not apparent. The data available in any given case usually do not indicate whether the histopathological alterations observed antedated the onset of the disease with which they are associated or arose as a result of the disease process. In either case they may play a rôle in the progress of the disease and its sequelæ. The autonomic nerves, furthermore, may play significant rôles in disease processes in the absence of recognizable neural lesions due to modified reflex activity or increased or decreased stimulation, inhibition or depression of central autonomic centers.

Lesions of the autonomic ganglia and ganglion cells that arise during the courses of certain diseases affect their progress due to their stimulating or depressing effects on the vasomotor nerves, the visceral muscles and certain glands. Vasomotor depression results in a fall in blood pressure and changes in the distribution of the blood in the organs. The volume of blood in the splanchnic area is greatly increased, while other parts of the body, including the central nervous system, the skin and the skeletal muscles are relatively ischemic. Infectious diseases in children frequently are accompanied by sympathetic hyperexcitability. Severe acute intoxication in children may be accompanied by sympathetic hypotonus which always indicates an unfavorable prognosis. The toxic effects of disease on the autonomic ganglion cells and the central autonomic centers result in modification of various visceral functions. Depression of the sympathetic or stimulation of the parasympathetic nerves results in gastrointestinal hypermotility, retardation of the cardiac rhythm, etc. On the contrary, stimulation of the sympathetic or depression of the parasympathetic nerves results in constipation, cardiac acceleration, etc. Stimulation or depression of the secretory nerves due to the toxic effects of disease, likewise, may result in far-reaching glandular dysfunction. Reflex vasoconstriction initiated and maintained by the stimulating effects of peripheral lesions, e.g., arthritis, not only retards recovery, due to limitation of the blood supply to the part in question, but also constitutes a causative factor in the production of pain. Modification of the autonomic status, due to the toxic effects of disease, frequently results in disturbances in metabolism due to changes in the permeability of the capillaries and the tissue elements and shifts in the acid-base balance.

(446)

Certain individuals exhibit excessive autonomic lability and an inability to achieve rapidly certain necessary autonomic adjustments, due to inherited constitutional factors. In these individuals, particular functional disabilities which form the focal points for certain diseases, such as migraine, urticaria, colitis, goiter, glaucoma, etc., frequently are precipitated by environmental changes to which the autonomic adjustment has been inadequate. More frequently the symptomatology is indefinite, involving vague pains and discomfort which may be referred to various organs, nausea, headache, respiratory distress, etc., in the absence of recognizable causative factors. These individuals range from organic well-being through periods in which organic discomfort is perceived subjectively to the acute episodes which the physician recognizes as clinically definable and objectively demonstrable disease, although he is able to recognize no causative factor other than autonomic dysfunction. In the presence of organic disease autonomic lability is manifested particularly in the vascular and the glandular reactions to the stimulating or the depressing effects of toxins and other irritating factors, resulting in far-reaching disturbances, particularly in tissue nutrition and endocrine balance, with unfavorable effects on the progress of the disease. Emotional behavior, as outlined in Chapter IV, is mediated at least in part through the hypothalamic centers that are concerned in the higher integration of autonomic reactions. The visceral components of emotional expression represent the responses of the organs in question to the discharge of impulses from these centers through both the sympathetic and the parasympathetic nerves. Hypothalamic integration also plays a significant rôle in emotional states associated with hypothalamic lesions, which include alternating moods of excitement and depression with associated alterations in visceral functions.

The most primitive components of emotional behavior spring from the vital requirements of the organism. The higher forms of emotional experience undoubtedly are derived from the same sources and never become entirely independent of their primitive prototypes. Autonomic reactions, therefore, play a part both in sensory experiences and emotional expression. The autonomic nerves thus exert a significant influence in the dynamics of the psychic life. Some of the data bearing on the relationship of the functional autonomic balance to personal behavior appear to support the assumption that adrenergic hyperactivity plays the dominant rôle in emotional reactivity. Other data indicate that cholinergic hyperactivity may dominate emotional behavior under certain conditions. The assumption that both adrenergic and cholinergic activity may be increased during emotional reactions has also been supported (Gellhorn et al., 1940).

On the basis of an extensive study of factors that indicate the functional balance of the autonomic nerves in children 6 to 13 years of age, Wenger and Ellington (1943) found that the factor scores remained constant in most of the children at least two years and that their distribution was continuous and highly symmetrical. On the basis of these studies and additional data obtained from children, Wenger (1947) advanced the opinion that children who exhibit sympathetic hyperactivity tend to be emotionally unstable, impetuous, tense and restless. They are more vigorous in activity but more apt to show fatigue, less secure in their emotional and social life and more dependent on approval and affection from others, and exhibit a stronger tendency to demonstrate compensatory behavior than children with normal autonomic balance. Children who exhibit an imbalance in the direction of parasympathetic predominance, on the contrary, exhibit emotional stability. They are deliberate and phlegmatic, socially independent and retiring. They also tend to be more self-sufficient and dominant than those with normal autonomic balance. The functional patterns of the autonomic nerves appear to be determined in a large measure by genetic factors. A dominant influence in behavior may be exerted through either the adrenergic or the cholinergic nerves, but, in general, personality is influenced more strongly through the sympathetic than through the parasympathetic nerves. Jost *et al.* (1952) have pointed out that in normal adults the physiological alterations that take place during physical and psychic stresses afford a reliable measure of the degree of emotional change.

The hypothalamic neural mechanisms, like other subcortical ones, are subject to inhibitory influences emanating from the cerebral cortex, but they are capable of independent activity in conformity with certain definite reaction patterns. Such activity in the hypothalamus and the thalamus plays an important rôle in the involuntary control of both somatic and visceral functions, such as bodily posture, facial expression, gastro-intestinal tonus, etc. During emotional stress the subcortical mechanisms involved are relatively free from cortical control; consequently, their influence in both somatic and visceral functions is exaggerated. In the somatic realm this results in the postures and facial expressions characteristic of the various emotions. In the visceral realm it results in functional disturbances in varying degrees, depending in a large measure on the nervous constitution of the individual. Although specific visceral reactions probably are not usually directly correlated with specific psychic or emotional states the visceral disturbances, under normal conditions, constitute an essential part of the emotional picture, but in many instances they become exaggerated to the point of positive visceral disorders.

The individual with a stable and well-disciplined nervous system is able to suppress the outward expressions of emotion in a high degree. His visceral responses to emotional excitation may be intense momentarily, but they usually do not result in serious visceral disorders. Persistent disorders of visceral functions due to emotional disturbances occur most commonly in association with psychic or nervous instability. They are none the less real and, since they are mediated through the autonomic nervous system, they are not subject to direct voluntary control and persist as long as the autonomic hyperstimulation prevails. Treatment of the visceral symptoms without reference to the emotional cause, therefore, must be regarded as futile. On the other hand, if the patient can be restored to emotional equilibrium, the visceral disorders of emotional origin soon subside.

ENDOCRINE DISORDERS

Chronic Adrenal Insufficiency (Addison's Disease).—Chronic adrenal insufficiency, first described by Addison in 1855, is a relatively rare disease which usually develops in the third or fourth decade of life. It is characterized by adynamia, gastro-intestinal disturbances (constipation alternating with diarrhea), pigmentation of the skin and mucous membranes and low blood pressure. Body temperature is often subnormal, particularly in the later stages of the disease. In some cases, the adrenal glands show no lesion, but adrenal hypofunction is brought about by pressure, inflammation or degenerative changes involving the celiac ganglia. The symptom-complex associated with adrenal insufficiency rests on a subnormal output of adrenin. Some of the dominant manifestations of the disease, *e.g.*, the gastro-intestinal disorders and low blood pressure, are directly referable to a functional autonomic imbalance. The dominant symptoms frequently indicate general depression of the sympathetic nerves.

Degenerative lesions involving the adrenals result not only in diminution of the functional tissue but also in impairment of the secretory function of the nerve fibers that supply these glands; consequently, the remaining secretory tissue is deprived of its normal stimulation. Diminution of the adrenin output in turn results in lowered sympathetic tonus. The low blood pressure, the subnormal body temperature and the asthenia associated with adrenal hypofunction are symptoms of sympathetic hypotonus.

On the basis of a critical study of the anatomy and the physiology of the pigmented portions of the skin, Bory (1926) advanced the opinion that the basal cells of the stratum germinativum act in close correlation with the adrenals and that, under certain physiological conditions, the skin either produces adrenin or stimulates the adrenals to secrete. He regarded the excessive pigmentation of the skin, in adrenal insufficiency, as the result of overproduction of melanin by the skin in its attempt to compensate for adrenal hypofunction. The implied correlation between the skin and the adrenals probably is brought about, at least in part, through the autonomic nerves.

In those cases of adrenal insufficiency in which the adrenal glands are neither involved in the primary lesion nor exhibit evidence of pressure atrophy due to lesions of adjacent tissue, the primary cause of the disease must be sought in autonomic dysfunction. Frequently such cases reveal pathological changes in the celiac plexus. Laignel-Lavastine (1924) recognized two types of the disease on the basis of etiology: (1) A type in which the primary lesion involves the adrenals, the autonomic system being involved secondarily, and (2) a type in which the adrenal insufficiency is the result of a lesion of the celiac plexus. The symptoms of both types of the disease are very similar.

Danisch (1928) reported symptoms similar to those of adrenal insufficiency in man, such as emaciation, general weakness and profound circulatory disturbances, in rabbits following extirpation of the celiac ganglia. He also pointed out that similar degenerative changes in the autonomic ganglia occur in various diseases in which there is no evidence of adrenal insufficiency. Many of the latter cases also exhibit profound circulatory and general secretory disturbances. On the basis of these considerations and his experimental findings, Danisch opposed the theory that lesions of the autonomic system alone can give rise to the symptom-

29

complex known as Addison's disease. He advanced the opinion that the full development of this symptom-complex depends primarily on dysfunction of the adrenal glands, including both the cortex and the medulla, even though the primary cause of such dysfunction is a lesion of the autonomic nervous system. Udaondao and Gonalons (1934) have described a syndrome of adrenal insufficiency, characterized by pigmentation of the skin and cardiac, digestive, thermoregulatory and kinesthetic disturbances, caused by emotional disturbances, either of intense and unexpected or depressive, slow and continuous type. In their experience, the administration of extract of adrenal cortex has consistently been followed by disappearance of the syndrome.

Adrenal Hyperfunction.—Hyperproduction of adrenin is commonly associated with alterations in the adrenal medulla. It profoundly affects the autonomic nervous system, particularly the vasomotor nerves. In experimental animals, it may result in death preceded by clonic muscular spasm, rapid respiration and vomiting. Postmortem examination reveals widespread hemorrhagic areas in the visceral organs and serous membranes and necrotic areas, particularly in the liver and the kidneys. These are essentially manifestations of increased blood pressure brought about by excessive stimulation of the vasomotor nerves. Continued moderate overproduction of adrenin in experimental animals gives rise to arteriosclerotic changes due to its stimulating effect on the vasomotor nerves.

Neoplasms involving the adrenal medulla or other chromaffine bodies, in man, commonly result in a marked increase in blood pressure and early arteriosclerosis accompanied by profound metabolic disturbances and frequently apoplexy. Although the rôle of the autonomic nerves in the symptom-complex associated with neoplasms of the chromaffine tissue has not been studied extensively, it may be assumed, on the basis of the results obtained in experimental hyperadrenalemia in animals, that these symptoms are mainly manifestations of sympathetic hyperstimulation due to excessive adrenin in the circulation. Chromaffine tumors involving both adrenals may give rise to grave diabetes mellitus. The production of glycosuria by injection of adrenin may be regarded as evidence that the hormone produced by one endocrine gland may, through its effect on the secretory neural mechanism, bring about dysfunction of another endocrine gland. Diabetes resulting from chromaffine tumors probably is brought about through the inhibitory effect of adrenin on the pancreatic islets.

Hyperthyroidism.—The thyroid gland cells are not directly innervated. Their secretory activity undoubtedly is influenced by regulatory changes in the blood supply to the gland brought about through the vasomotor nerves, but the functional regulation of the thyroid gland is predominantly hormonal (see Chapter XII). Since the production of the thyrotropic hormone is influenced by sympathetic nerve impulses sympathetic stimulation may indirectly exert an influence on thyroid function. The thyroid hormone exerts a stimulating influence on the sympathetic nerves due to its effect on the secretory activity of the adrenal medulla. In some instances symptoms of hyperthyroidism may be recognized in the absence of demonstrable lesions of the thyroid gland. Symptoms of hyperthyroidism brought about by stimulation of the sympathetic trunk in the cervical or the thoracic region have been reported. Association of hyperthyroidism with pathological changes in the autonomic ganglia and ganglion cells has also been determined by careful histopathological studies. A degree of parallelism between the severity and the duration of thyroid hyperactivity and the extent of the changes in the autonomic ganglion cells has also been recognized, but conclusive evidence that these changes play a rôle in the genesis of hyperthyroidism is not forthcoming. They probably are a result and not the cause of the disease. They frequently play an important rôle in its course, termination and sequelæ.

Hyperthyroidism undoubtedly is referable to underlying constitutional factors in many cases and may be regarded as a result of abnormal reactions to stimuli which in normal individuals would be met by physiological adaptation. Toxic thyroid adenomata obviously do not fall within this category. Exophthalmic goiter, on the other hand, is not invariably an indication of hyperthyroidism but may arise as a direct result of sympathetic dysfunction. Thyroid dysfunction associated with exophthalmos may be related to the same cause.

Petersen (1927, 1934) called attention to a striking increase in capillary permeability associated with exophthalmic goiter which he regarded as a basic factor in clinical manifestations. Dresel (1929) advanced experimental data on the basis of which he concluded that the active agent circulating in the blood of patients with exophthalmic goiter is far more active than any known thyroid preparation. Aub and his associates (1929) also have shown that the increased tissue permeability and associated increased metabolic activity in exophthalmic goiter patients result in a negative calcium balance. All these findings strongly suggest the existence of a parasympathetic status as defined by Petersen and Levinson (Chapter XX).

The dominant symptoms of hyperthyroidism, including tachycardia, exophthalamos, dilated pupils, perspiration and diminished gastric secretion, indicate sympathetic overstimulation. The autonomic nerves, consequently, plays an important rôle not only in the underlying physiological state of the body but also in the symptom-complex associated with hyperthyroidism. The nervous factors undoubtedly merit greater consideration in the treatment of this disease than has usually been accorded them, since the autonomic dysfunction associated with the disease in turn affects the thyroid gland unfavorably. Measures that tend to restore the autonomic functional balance, therefore, tend to remove one of the chief sources of irritation of the thyroid gland.

Parathyroid Disease. — A relationship between parathyroid extirpation and the symptoms of tetany that follow the removal of these glands in certain animals has long been recognized. Parathyroidectomy also gives rise to symptoms of tetany in man. Transplantation of parathyroids or injection of parathyroid extract ameliorates the symptoms and sometimes cures tetany. The metabolic disturbances following parathyroidectomy strongly suggest that the parathyroid hormone exerts an influence on the autonomic nervous system. According to certain investigators, it exerts an inhibitory influence on the sympathetic nerves and the adrenals. Parathyroid tetany may be aborted in certain cases by extirpation of the adrenals. On the other hand, active symptoms may be brought on by injection of adrenin in cases of latent tetany. The parathyroids also sustain an important functional relationship to the gonads. Parathyroidectomy is not followed by tetany in castrated animals. Subsidence of the symptoms of tetany in parathyroidectomized animals, following castration, furthermore, has been reported. The administration of parathyroid extract produces a fall in blood pressure in normal animals. Excessive or prolonged administration of this extract produces a very high calcium and phosphorus content in the blood serum and eventually results in convulsions and death.

The mechanism of parathyroid tetany is not fully known. On the basis of an experimental investigation carried out on dogs, West (1935) advanced the opinion that a circulatory factor acting peripherally upon some site in the muscles causes repeated contractions of individual muscle fibers and electric hyperexcitability. He also demonstrated the necessity of intact spinal reflex arcs for the conversion of essential or fibrillary tetany into its elaborate clonic and tonic forms and the independence of these forms of tetany of impulses emanating from central nervous centers higher than the spinal cord.

Hypophyseal Disorders.—The hypophysis is a complex gland which produces multiple hormones and subserves a variety of functions, some of which have no obvious relation to the autonomic nerves and others of which undoubtedly are influenced by nerve impulses. Much of its secretory activity is regulated through hormonal agents quite independently of the autonomic nerves (see Chapter XVI).

In view of the numerous hormones produced in the hypophysis and its complex interrelationships with other endocrine glands, including the gonads, hypophyseal dysfunction is expressed in a wide variety of disorders including abnormal growth and sexual development, disturbances in carbohydrate and water metabolism, thyroid and adrenal dysfunction, adiposity, somnolence, etc.

Many investigators have supported the theory that many of the disorders which have been attributed to hypophyseal dysfunction, such as changes in the osseous system, adiposity, diabetes insipidus, etc., even though associated with lesions of the hypophysis, are caused by hypothalamic lesions. This theory is supported, for certain disorders associated with hypophyseal lesions, by the results of extensive experimental studies, outlined in Chapter IV, of the effects of experimental lesions definitely localized in various parts of the hypothalamus.

The relief of disorders such as polyuria and obesity, in certain cases, by the administration of the appropriate hypophyseal hormones does not prove the independence of the hypophyseal dysfunction of a causative lesion in the hypothalamus. On the other hand, the results of certain experiments, particularly those reported by Smith and Engle (1927), in which transplantations of anterior hypophyseal tissue in immature mice and rats rapidly induced precocious sexual maturity strongly suggest that sexual precocity may result from hypophyseal dysfunction which is not necessarily related to a neural cause. Transplantation of anterior hypophyseal tissue in sexually mature animals also elicited marked reactions in the gonads and other genital organs. The effects of such transplants were not diminished by extirpation of the thyroid or the adrenal glands. Transplantations of endocrine gland tissue other than that of the anterior hypophyseal lobe neither retarded nor accelerated the development of the immature genital organs.

Hypophyseal tumors may give rise to diverse disorders. Some of these can be accounted for most satisfactorily on the basis of increased hormone production due to hyperplasia of certain constituents of the gland. Others obviously are due to the effects of pressure exerted by the tumor mass on adjacent neural structures, particularly the hypothalamus, or functional interruption of the hypothalamico-hypophyseal tract.

Disorders Referable to the Ovaries.—Our knowledge of the interrelationships of the ovarian hormone and the autonomic nerves has been greatly advanced particularly by the results of studies in metabolism during pregnancy, following parturition, and in the climacteric. The blood-sugar curve during pregnancy and parturition runs a very definite course. The sugar content of the blood is low at the close of pregnancy, rises abruptly during parturition and falls again before the end of the first week after parturition. Hyperglycemia antemenstrum also has been reported. This probably is to be regarded as the result of sympathetic stimulation. Disturbances in carbohydrate metabolism resulting in hyperglycemia also have been observed following castration.

The symptoms commonly associated with the menopause probably are results of cessation of the ovarian function. They are highly variable and, in a large measure, depend on constitutional peculiarities of the individual. In addition to changes in metabolism which are expressed primarily in the common tendency to increased deposition of fat, the vasomotor changes most clearly indicate disturbances in the functional state of the autonomic system.

The fact that sympathetic irritability is increased during the climacteric and following castration seems to indicate that the ovarian hormone exerts an inhibitory influence on the sympathetic nerves. Certain experimental data have an important bearing on this point. The glycosuria that commonly follows the injection of adrenin can be prevented by the simultaneous injection of ovarian extract. The removal of the sympathetic inhibitory influence of the ovarian hormone during the climacteric permits the sympathetic tonus to gain the ascendency, resulting in marked vasomotor disturbances. The sudden hot flashes, so common during this period, probably are the result of the shifting of large volumes of blood from the splanchnic area toward the periphery due to sympathetic stimulation. This at once explains the flushing of the skin as well as the sensation of warmth. The severe headaches associated with the menopause undoubtedly are related to vasomotor irritability. Certain symptoms associated with the menopause also suggest parasympathetic hyperirritability.

Disorders Referable to the Testes and the Pineal Body.—Our limited knowledge of the functional relationships of the testes and the pineal body to the autonomic nerves rests chiefly on anatomical and experimental data. Early castration results in eunuchoidism. Pineal neoplasms, in some cases, result in precocious sexual maturity. These results probably do not depend on the direct effects of modified secretory activity of the glands in question, since some of the symptoms are referable to modified function of other endocrine organs. The most striking effects of interstitial and pineal insufficiency involve metabolism and growth. They are expressed in the eunuchoid habitus in the one case and early sexual maturity and development and the secondary sexual characters in the other. Both clinical and anatomical data show clearly that the pineal gland exerts a regulatory influence in the development of the genital organs, particularly the testes. In this regard, its influence seems to be antagonistic to that of the posterior lobe of the hypophysis the destruction of which, under experimental conditions, commonly results in genital atrophy. To what extent testicular and pineal hormones affect the autonomic nervous system is not fully known. On the basis of the available data, it seems highly probable that their regulatory influence in the control of visceral functions is brought about, at least in part, through the autonomic nerves.

EMOTIONAL DISTURBANCES OF VISCERAL FUNCTIONS

Visceral Manifestations of Emotional Stress.—On the basis of common experience it may be stated that pleasurable emotions promote the visceral functions and painful or disagreeable emotions depress them. Strong emotional excitement invariably results in an immediate discharge of impulses through the autonomic nerves. The immediate reactions evoked tend to produce functional responses that are beneficial to the individual. For example, there may be a discharge of adrenin into the blood stream with consequent changes in the blood flow, or blood sugar may be mobilized. Izquierdo and Cannon (1928) reported that emotional excitement lasting one minute, in experimental animals (cats), is followed quickly by a marked rise in the number of red corpuscles in the blood. The maximal increase occurred immediately after the minute of excitement. Within one-half hour the number of red cells had returned to normal. Emotional polycythemia failed to occur, in their experiments, following extirpation of the rostral lumbar segments of the sympathetic trunks and section of the splanchnic nerves. Menkin (1928) reported that emotional excitement for ten to fifteen minutes, in normal cats, also resulted in a relative increase in mononuclear leukocytes that was maintained for a period of ten to fifteen minutes following the period of excitement. Within one-half hour the number of nononuclear leukocytes had returned to the former level. Emotional excitement of sympathectomized animals for ten to fifteen minutes resulted in no immediate changes in the relative number of mononuclear leukocytes. Emotional excitement for three minutes, in normal cats, as reported by Field (1930), resulted in a sudden increase in the number of blood platelets. The same excitement in sympathectomized cats usually resulted in a slight decrease in the number of blood platelets. Menkin advanced the opinion that sympathetic stimulation due to emotional excitement results in splenic contractions which force into the circulation an increased number of both erythrocytes and mononuclear leukocytes. In Field's experiments, splenectomized cats regularly exhibited a marked decrease in the number of blood platelets in the circulating blood after excitement for three minutes. These findings probably explain the emotional leukocytosis sometimes reported in patients while in a state of fear or apprehension preceding an operation.

Emotional excitement also exerts an influence on the basal metabolic rate. In a series of experiments on hypnotized persons, Grafe and Mayer (1923) found that the metabolic rate could be profoundly altered, in certain individuals, by the suggestion of various calamities, *e.g.*, death of relatives, amputation of limbs, etc. In 9 such tests, the metabolic rate was increased 5 to 25 per cent. In 4 experiments, no change or only a slight lowering of the metabolic rate was observed. In experiments made on psychasthenic war veterans, Ziegler and Levine (1925) found a marked rise in the metabolic rate as the result of emotional excitement in 11 cases, a slight fall in 3, and no change in 1 case. As reported by Landis (1925), anticipation of strong electrical stimulation caused a rise of 6, 17, and 37 per cent respectively in the metabolic rate in 3 persons tested. In studying the effect of the knowledge of an impending operation on the basal metabolic rate in three groups: (1) patients with nervous stability and a normal metabolic rate, (2) patients with hyperthyroidism who had received iodine according to preoperative routine, and (3) patients with hyperthyroidism who had not received iodine therapy. Segal *et al.* (1928) observed no marked change in the metabolic rate on the day of operation in the first two groups, but a marked rise in the third group on the morning of the expected operation.

The effect of the emotions on the digestive functions is most striking. Complete inhibition not only of gastro-intestinal motility but also of the secretory activity of the digestive glands in consequence of emotional stress has been observed frequently. Mental work without excitement exerts no marked influence on gastric secretion, but marked disturbances of gastric secretion in students due to anxiety over examinations have been reported (Miller *et al.*, 1920). Persistent worry frequently results in indigestion. Fear may inhibit salivary, gastric and pancreatic secretion. The entire digestive process may be profoundly disturbed by anxiety or distress. On the basis of a study of psychic and emotional factors in disorders of the digestive tract, McLester (1927) estimated that one-third of the patients with digestive disorders have no recognizable organic disease but are suffering because of lack of emotional balance.

Emotional excitement does not result in comparable digestive disorders in all persons. The gastro-intestinal reaction to an emotion, in a large measure, depends on the functional condition of the autonomic nerves, the endocrine glands and the acid-base balance. As observed by Lueders (1928), many patients with psychoses exhibit normal or increased gastro-intestinal function. He usually found no depression of gastro-intestinal motility or secretory activity in psychoses except when associated with somatic disorders or when the patient exhibited autonomic dysfunction. According to his findings, gastro-intestinal function is increased in psychotic patients that exhibit parasympathetic hyperactivity.

In a roentgen-ray study of gastric motility during emotional excitement, Todd and Rowlands (1930) described characteristic patterns of gastric activity which are correlated with the external manifestations of autonomic stimulation. When these external manifestations were suppressed, the pattern of gastric activity became markedly changed. After a period of training, certain definite gastric responses could be evoked by appropriate psychic stimulation.

In most patients with impaired digestion due to emotional excitement, the symptoms referable to the digestive organs are caused by inhibition of gastro-intestinal motility and secretion of the gastric juices due to sympathetic stimulation. Depressant or unpleasant emotions exert an inhibitory effect both on gastro-intestinal motility and secretory activity. Gastro-intestinal hyperactivity due to emotional stress is less common and, in most cases, less persistent. In these patients, the symptoms may be caused either by sympathetic inhibition or parasympathetic stimulation.

Mucous colitis probably is invariably associated with sacral parasympathetic hyperstimulation. Certain physiological and pathological conditions may be regarded as predisposing factors, but the most common cause of this disorder is emotional tension. The three emotions with which mucous colitis is most commonly associated are anxiety, guilt and resentment. Preoccupation with personal problems tends to prolong emotional tension and, consequently, the parasympathetic stimulation that causes the chronic state of colonic irritation. According to Menninger (1937), gastrointestinal neuroses can be adequately treated only as the dynamic aspects of the personality of the patient are understood. Therapy directed toward the stomach or intestine usually is ineffective. Rational therapy in these cases must be directed toward the total personality of the patient.

The sympathetic nerves of the heart and the blood vessels, unlike those of the digestive tube, convey excitatory impulses. The excitement that inhibits the digestive processes, consequently, results in increased heart-rate and elevation of blood pressure. Since sympathetic impulses both accelerate the heart-rate and constrict the arterioles, they bring about increased blood pressure by affecting both factors positively. The effect of even moderate excitement on blood pressure is unmistakable. The slight excitation incident to taking the blood pressure, in many cases, is sufficient to cause a marked rise in the systolic level. The first systolic reading, therefore, usually is higher than those taken later in the same subject. Schrumpf (1910) reported a case in which fear of a serious diagnosis caused a rise in blood pressure of 33 per cent. When reassurance was given, the blood pressure promptly returned to normal. Fright, anger or pleasure, in extreme cases, may cause a rise of 90 mm. of mercury (Cannon, 1928). In cases of so-called "soldier's heart" the slightest excitement or emotional stress usually results in a marked increase in the pulse-rate (130 to 150 beats per minute). The emotional stress incident to war may result in such sensitization of the sympathetic control of the heart, in these patients, that even mild stimulation produces extreme effects.

In an experimental study reported by Bond (1943), in which changes in the cardiac rhythm in unanesthetized cats and dogs startled by short, unexpected noises, were recorded electrically, it was found that these animals normally respond according to complex patterns of sudden high rises in heart-rate, beginning immediately after startle, followed by a sharp fall, a second rise of variable height and thereafter several undulations in rate until the response is terminated in two or three minutes. The response to adrenin appeared only after twelve seconds. The cardiovascular responses to startle in dogs with the vagus and the depressor nerves sectioned and the adrenals excluded were essentially similar to those of normal animals. Following section of the cardiac accelerator nerves and exclusion of the adrenals in both cats and dogs, startle was promptly followed by vagus inhibition that caused moderate cardiac acceleration. These results suggest that profound cardiovascular disturbances may result from emotional excitation even in normal individuals and that the cardiovascular responses are mediated chiefly through the sympathetic nerves.

Emotional disturbances tend to increase the output of sugar in diabetic patients. In many of them the degree of diabetes exhibited tends to vary in response to nervous and emotional influences. Emotional disturbances frequently are accompanied by low sugar tolerance and actual hyperglycemia even in the absence of diabetes. On the basis of quantitative determinations of the blood sugar in students before and after participation in intercollegiate athletic contests and scholastic examinations, Cannon (1915) pointed out that emotional disturbances exert a strong influence tending to bring about hyperglycemia in normal individuals. Inasmuch as the blood sugar is readily increased by sympathetic stimulation, it may be assumed that this influence of emotional stress is exerted through the sympathetic nerves. Although it is not clear that diabetes can be initiated through such sympathetic stimulation alone, the available data show clearly that any existing diabetes may be aggravated by emotional stress.

Psychic and emotional disturbances are commonly recognized as important etiological factors in hyperthyroidism in many cases. Any severe or unaccustomed emotional shock to the patient, furthermore, may aggravate the symptoms in a mild case and convert it into a severe one. Latent or potential cases of hyperthyroidism may be transformed into active ones by varying degrees of emotional shock. Although the thyroid gland cells are not innervated directly, sympathetic stimulation probably is a factor in producing the increased thyroid hyperactivity. The dominant symptoms associated with the disease also suggest the existence of autonomic dysfunction.

Many other visceral disorders brought about by the effect of psychic and emotional disturbances exerted through the autonomic nerves might be mentioned, e. g., disorders of menstruation, lactation, micturition, perspiration, etc. Indeed, every visceral function is subject to influences exerted by psychic and emotional states through the autonomic nerves.

The reactions of the visceral organs to an emotion may be regarded as the visceral contribution to the complete emotional state. Impulses emanating from the central autonomic centers in response to emotional stimulation result in excessive discharge of adrenin and other hormones into the blood and the liberation of sugar in sufficient quantity to cause transient glycosuria. Energy is thus supplied for the muscular exertion which may be called for in possible physical combat or flight, particularly in emotions like fear, anger or rage. Under existing social conditions, this autonomic defensive mechanism, in a large measure, is held in restraint. Some investigators have supported the assumption that its repeated activation, if unsatisfied by instinctive expression, may result in an irascible or a fearsome disposition. Thus, the visceral reactions to emotional stimuli, particularly in individuals with an unstable or hyperirritable autonomic system, would contribute to the causes of affective disorders. Cannon and his associates, however, have shown that the discharge of adrenin is increased by muscular activity. The visceral concomitants of emotional excitement also persist for some time after the stimulus has ceased to act. On the basis of results obtained in animal exepriments, Cannon and Britton (1927) attributed this to the continued discharge of adrenin due to the emotional excitement and its expression and emphasized the importance of limiting the expression of strong emotions, such as fear and rage, in order to avoid a persistent state of disquiet.

In view of the important rôle of the autonomic nervous system in visceral disorders, it is reasonable to assume that autonomic dysfunction, under certain conditions, may precipitate or maintain abnormal affectivity. On the basis of an extensive study of gastro-intestinal reactions to emotions in patients with psychoses, Lueders (1928) advanced the opinion that protracted chronic emotionalism and morbid moods affect the visceral functions less and less but exert their greatest damaging influence at higher levels. The mental and moral faculties, consequently, become impaired and dominated by uncontrolled emotionalism, obsessions, hallucinations, etc. Similar opinions have also been advanced by other investigators. In view of all the data available, psychoses cannot be regarded as merely abnormal functioning of the brain or the central nervous system. They represent changes in the entire individual. Even under normal physiological conditions, it may be assumed that the mind is influenced by the entire body; consequently, psychic processes are not limited to the cerebral cortex. Affective behavior must be regarded as a function of the whole organism. The emotional life of the individual is determined in a large measure by the functional reactivity and the balance of the autonomic nervous system.

Autonomic Factors in Psychoses.—Definition.—The psychoneurotic individual is one who is usually unable to achieve complete resolution of a tension or impulse without anxiety or inhibition and to execute the appropriate response, despite his possession of adequate equipment for successful mastery. Psychoneuroses probably are invariably associated with autonomic dysfunction in some degree. There probably is no advantage in attempting to correlate the specific nature of the problem with the specific autonomic symptoms. Any impulse or situation that cannot be normally mastered must give rise to some expression of this failure of mastery in the autonomic integration. The specific autonomic symptoms vary from individual to individual. For example, failure of mastery in similar situations may be accompanied in one individual by diarrhea, in another by salivation, in another by conjunctival congestion, etc. These differences may be related to constitutional factors or physiological states prevailing at the moment which not only play a part in determining whether mastery shall fail in a given instance but also in determining the nature of the autonomic response.

Schizophrenia.—In a study of autonomic integration in schizophrenia in which the autonomic status was determined by statistical analysis of the organic findings in 129 patients, Rheingold (1939) found the tendency toward a low oxygen consumption rate to be the most noteworthy abnormality. A state of general hypometabolism was prevalent in these patients, as indicated by low blood pressure, a slight increase in the cholesterol content of the blood, low normal carbon dioxide combining power and secondary anemia. The low oxygen consumption rate, probably due to faulty regulation of cell respiration, appears to be an integral feature of the disease. Hypothyroidism was present in a high percentage of the cases and probably represents a factor in the pathogenesis of schizophrenia. This concept is consistent with the fact that schizophrenics do not respond to thyroid feeding, since the thyroid hormone appears to act through hypothalamic mechanisms the dysfunction of which, in these patients, probably is a causative factor in the hypothyroid state.

Epilepsy.—The evolution of the epileptic seizure exhibits three phases: (1) the phase of prodromes or auras preceding the loss of consciousness; (2) the seizure proper attended by loss of consciousness, and (3) the phase of recovery. All of these phases are attended by marked disturbances in autonomic functions. Those observed in the first phase include vasomotor, pilomotor, pupillary, secretory, cardiovascular, visceral metabolic and emotional changes. The second phase, during which manifestations of widespread sympathetic stimulation are prominent, is essentially a catabolic phase. The heightened vasoconstrictor tonus in the peripheral areas, including the central nervous system, results in characteristic pallor, gradually giving way to a blush or frankly cyanotic discoloration of the face, with distention of the veins of the neck and the forehead. The body temperature is elevated without relation to the severity or the duration of the muscular spasm. Marked pilo-erection is also evident. These manifestations of sympathetic stimulation are most evident during the early part and at the acme of the seizure. The third phase, or phase of recovery, is essentially an anabolic phase characterized by cholinergic energy restoring activity and recovery of the cerebrospinal functions that were in abeyance during the seizure. Parasympathetic stimulation is evidenced by contraction of the pupils, salivation, retardation of the cardiac rhythm and frequently by evacuation of the urinary bladder and the rectum. Cholinergic stimulation is further indicated by peripheral vasodilatation, profuse perspiration, a fall in blood pressure and a return to normal body temperature.

The circulatory disturbance in the brain undoubtedly represents a fundamental factor in the causation of the convulsions during the epileptic attack. This conclusion, based on abundant clinical observations, is also supported by direct observation of the spasm of the cerebral vessels during the seizure. Changes in the CO_2 content of the blood as it affects the caliber of the arterioles and the capillaries, the acid-base balance and the respiratory exchange, all of which play significant rôles in the phenomena of epilepsy, are also closely related to the responses of the cerebral vessels to sympathetic stimulation. The most constant phenomena in epilepsy are the vasomotor manifestations in the pial and cerebral blood vessels.

Penfield (1933) reported the arrest of visible pulsations of the arteries of the brain, which usually was widespread, as the most constant vascular phenomenon associated with convulsive seizures induced by electric stimulation of the exposed surface of the brain during intracranial operations. In 4 of his cases the arrest of arterial pulsations was limited to a circumscribed area around the point of stimulation. The epileptic brain, according to Penfield, "is subject to vasomotor reflexes which have never been described in the normal brain." Inasmuch as sympathectomy failed to abolish epileptic seizures in certain of his patients, he concluded that the cerebral vasomotor spasm in these patients involved vasomotor reflexes which probably are not subserved by autonomic neurons located outside the cranial cavity. He advanced certain data which seem to support the hypothesis that some of these reflexes are subserved by neurons located along the cerebral vessels and by a local vascular nerve plexus which, on the basis of histological studies, he has reason to believe is significantly increased in some cases. He advanced the opinion that "where such a lesion exists, excision of the local scar with its vascular plexus is at present the most effective way of abolishing these malignant local reflexes." Conclusive evidence of the existence of local reflex mechanisms along the cerebral vessels is not forthcoming, but focal constriction of cerebral vessels due to local lesions undoubtedly occurs (Cobb, 1938). This phenomenon cannot be abolished by interruption of the cervical sympathetic trunks, but may be corrected in certain cases by excision of irritable areas in the cerebral cortex (White and Smithwick, 1941). Measurements of the flow of blood in the jugular vein before, during and after epileptic convulsions, reported by Gibbs et al. (1934), do not indicate widespread ischemia of the brain preceding or during the attack. In certain cases carotid sinus reflexes probably play a rôle in epileptic seizures.

Autonomic Factors in Headache.—The term, headache, as commonly used, may designate any one of a wide variety of aches and pains localized in the head. These symptoms are commonly associated with abnormal states of tension in the walls of the cerebral blood vessels. According to Pickering (1939), most headaches of intracranial origin are associated with tension around the intracranial arteries, as may occur when these arteries dilate. Tension around the venous sinuses, as might be produced by displacement of the brain or part of it, may also give rise to headache. The headaches of migraine and hypertension probably arise as a result of dilatation or stretching of arteries in the dura mater and the scalp (Sutherland and Wolff, 1940).

These points of view are supported by the results of experimental studies, particularly those of Schumacher and Wolff (1941), in which headaches induced by injections of histamine were abolished by increasing the intracranial pressure, thereby providing extramural support to the cerebral arteries at the base of the brain, whereas the headaches of migraine and hypertension were not abolished or reduced in intensity. The essential phenomena of migraine, according to their findings, are associated with dysfunction of the cranial arteries and represent contrasts in vascular beds. The preheadache disturbances, including vertigo, parasthesia and visual phenomena, follow marked constriction of cerebral arteries, whereas the headache of migraine results from dilatation and distention particularly of branches of the external carotid arteries. The preheadache visual phenomena usually subside before the headache arises, or there may be overlapping of these phenomena by at most a few minutes, indicating that the cerebral vasoconstriction has terminated before extracerebral vasodilatation has begun.

Postpuncture headache which frequently occurs following the withdrawal of cerebrospinal fluid through a lumbar puncture is commonly ascribed to the reduction in the intracranial fluid volume which removes the liquid cushion supporting the brain and allows it to settle in the cranial cavity, causing traction on blood vessels, nerves and dura. It is significant that this headache commonly appears soon after the patient has assumed the erect posture, which facilitates the drainage of the cerebrospinal fluid into the spinal canal. Postpuncture headache may be aggravated due to the escape of fluid from the subarachnoid into the subdural space through the puncture wound in the arachnoid membrane.

Certain so-called "relaxation" headaches, such as the Sunday morning headache of the business man, the day-off headache of the nurse and the postexamination headache of the student, appear to be causally associated with relaxation of peripheral vascular tonus. Migraine headaches of certain types also are associated with a marked hypotensive level of blood pressure at the time of onset and are relieved when the blood pressure is restored to its normal level. Headaches that fall into the latter category and the so-called "relaxation" headaches, according to Pfeiffer *et al.* (1943), can be definitely correlated with changes in peripheral vascular tonus and blood volume. They found no consistent blood electrolyte changes, but the migraine syndromes in question were accompanied by a relative hemoconcentration.

The vascular phenomena associated with headache, which may be regarded as its immediate cause, obviously do not constitute the primary cause but must be regarded as the results of more fundamental causes of disturbed vasomotor function. The latter include lesions of the mucous membranes, the eyes, the teeth and foci of irritation or inflammation in other parts of the head, and toxic stimulation due to metabolic disorders, infection or other causes. Frequently the cause of headache is purely emotional, particularly in patients who exhibit vasomotor lability in a high degree.

In view of its vascular substratum, it may be assumed that headache invariably involves vasomotor dysfunction in some degree. The frequency of headache and its severity are determined in part by the nature of the causative lesion and in part by the reactivity of the vasomotor nerves. It may be regarded as one of the commonest expressions of autonomic instability. In highly unstable individuals it may be precipitated by environmental changes, such as fluctuations in barometric pressure and atmospheric humidity, in the absence of other recognizable causes. Data reported by Stangl (1952) seem to support the assumption that most persons respond to changes in weather accompanied by marked changes in temperature by a shift in the functional balance of the autonomic nerves toward either sympathetic or parasympathetic predominance. Dysfunction of the vasomotor nerves due to autonomic imbalance, as has been pointed out by Goltz (1952), frequently constitutes a causative factor in allergic headache, migraine, cephalalgia, cervical myalgia, etc. Therapy should therefore be directed toward stabilizing the disturbed vasomotor mechanisms rather than toward relief of the symptoms alone.

Not infrequently the pain is referred from the site of the causative lesion in conformity with Head's theory of the localization of referred pain. For example, headache associated with an orbital lesion or eye strain may be localized in the occipital area. That vasomotor reactions in this area constitute a factor in the causation of the pain is indicated by the clinical observation that local massage or cold applications, in many instances, result in relief of the pain or reduction in its severity. Ciliary neuralgia differs from ordinary migraine in that the pain is referred forward into the temple, the eye, the cheek and the jaws (Harris, 1936). In a high percentage of these cases the eye becomes congested and lacrymation takes place.

Sjögren's Syndrome.—This syndrome is characterized by dryness of all mucous membranes due to deficient secretory activity of the glands, particularly the lacrimal and the salivary glands, the glands of the proximal portion of the respiratory tract, the gastric glands and the sweat glands. Cooperman (1950) has proposed the term, secreto-inhibitory syndrome as descriptive of this disorder. It occurs most commonly in women in the menopause or later and appears to be associated with an autonomic imbalance in which the adrenergic nerves are dominant. Cholinergic stimulation, therefore, is indicated.

THE SPLANCHNOPERIPHERAL BALANCE IN INFECTIOUS DISEASES

Nervous Regulation of Leukocyte Distribution and Permeability of Blood Vessels.—The important rôle of the leukocytes in all the local reactions connected with infection and inflammation is well known. The early experiments of Goldscheider and Jacob (1894) showed that marked changes in the number of leukocytes in the peripheral blood may take place almost instantaneously. In their experiments, the injection of a peptone solution into the circulation was followed immediately by a sharp drop in the number of leukocytes throughout the peripheral area. The ingestion of food usually is followed by a slight increase in the number of leukocytes in the peripheral blood. Widal and his associates (1920) observed a decrease in the number of leukocytes in the peripheral vessels in certain patients after taking milk into the empty stomach. Comparative studies also showed that while there was a decrease in the number of leukocytes in the peripheral blood, there was an increase in the splanchnic vessels and *vice versa*. Müller (1922) found that the injection of non-specific albumen preparations, minute amounts of salt solution, distilled water, or air also produced an immediate leukopenia throughout the peripheral area. The leukopenia produced by injection of albumen lasted thirty minutes. That produced by injection of physiological salt solutions and air lasted five to ten minutes. Müller and Myers (1924) found the peripheral blood almost devoid of leukocytes for about ten minutes following the injection of 10 cc. of a 20 per cent solution of peptone. During this period the leukocytes were concentrated in the vessels that are innervated by the splanchnic nerves, particularly those of the liver.

The peripheral leukopenia produced by the injection of solutions of peptone, non-specific albumen, etc., involves only the polymorphonuclear leukocytes and is apparent throughout the entire peripheral area. If one limb is deprived of its sympathetic innervation, blood taken from this limb, following injection of one of the above solutions, shows no marked reduction in the number of leukocytes, although the rest of the peripheral area exhibits leukopenia. This fact strongly supports the theory that the distribution of leukocytes is regulated through the autonomic nerves.

Data obtained by Müller (1926) in two cases of insulin shock in diabetic patients indicate that while the peripheral vessels are dilated, the number of leukocytes in the peripheral blood is markedly increased. The watery perspiration produced during this interval also indicates increased endo-thelial permeability. In these cases, the leukocytes in the peripheral blood reached 19,000 and 28,000 respectively in less than fifteen minutes and dropped to 7,000, the level which obtained before insulin treatment, in less than ten minutes following the administration of glucose by mouth. Simultaneously with the decrease of leukocytes in the peripheral blood, the alarming symptoms produced by peripheral vasodilatation subsided, thus showing that, under these conditions, the leukocyte curve runs paral-lel with the autonomic status at the periphery. In a further experimental study, Müller showed that general peripheral vasodilatation is accom-panied by sympathetic hypertonus in the splanchnic region. These data not only support the theory that the distribution of leukocytes is regulated through the autonomic nerves, but also indicate that endothelial permea-bility is modified by autonomic nerve impulses.

The observation of Martin (1932) that exercise results in a marked increase in the number of leukocytes in the peripheral blood and that of Morias (1933) that cervical sympathectomy is followed by leukocytosis in the affected area are in full accord with Müller's findings. In the counts made by Morias, the polymorphonuclear leukocytes showed a marked increase, whereas the other white cells showed no appreciable change in numbers. According to Roesler (1933), the administration of atropine or calcium results in a change in the white blood picture of normal men in favor of the neutrophils, and the administration of pilocarpine or cholin results in a change in favor of the lymphocytes. The administration of adrenin, in his experiments, resulted in the expected neutrophilia being marked by a preceding increase in the lymphocytes.

In a study of the white cell changes under a variety of conditions (infec-tion, vigorous exercise, pregnancy, diabetic acidosis, etc.), Hoff (1928) found that the distribution of leukocytes is subject to neural regulation and that the variations in the blood picture are closely correlated with other manifestations of changes in the functional balance of the autonomic nervous system, particularly variations in the acid-base balance. He also maintained that the output of myelocytes by the bone marrow is increased by experimental sympathetic stimulation, and that vagus stimulation results in relative lymphocytosis. According to Rosenow (1928), stab wounds in the corpus striatum and the hypothalamus cause neutrophilic leukocytosis, but the temperature and blood curves do not necessarily run parallel. In experiments on human subjects reported by Wossidlo (1935), diathermic stimulation in the region of the third ventricle resulted in leukopenia characterized by marked reduction in the number of polymorphonuclear neutrophils and little change in the numbers of other white cells.

According to Petersen and Müller (1930), practically every insult to the organism is followed by rhythmic changes in the functional activity of the organs, as is indicated by the leukocyte count and the chemistry of the lymph. For example, in their experiments carried out on dogs, external pressure on the eye sufficient to cause perceptible reflex cardiac inhibition applied for four minutes with repetition after five minutes was followed by a period of approximately seventy-five minutes during which the leukocyte count remained relatively low while the protein and calcium contents of the lymph were increased. After this, peripheral leukocytosis set in and the protein and calcium contents of the lymph were diminished. When ocular pressure was applied for two minutes and repeated at one-minute intervals, peripheral leukocytosis set in immediately with diminution in the calcium content of the lymph.

The results of experiments reported by Beer (1939) indicate a significant rôle of humoral transmission in the autonomic regulation of leukocyte distribution. In rabbits joined together parabiotically in pairs so that the peritoneal cavities were connected and only humoral transmission from one member of the pair to the other was possible, differences in temperature and in the numbers of white cells in the peripheral blood disappeared. The rhythmic changes in the numbers of leukocytes also became the same in both animals. Nerve stimulation which elicited leukocytosis in the animal to which the stimulus was applied resulted in a corresponding leukocytosis in the parabiotic partner.

Splanchnoperipheral Vasomotor Balance During Chill and Fever.—In experiments reported by Okinaka et al. (1952 a), the injection of penicillin in animals caused marked motility of leukocytes and phagocytosis, which was greatly reduced following extirpation of the carotid body. In immunized dogs splanchnic nerve stimulation resulted in a temporary increase in the antibody titer. The peripheral blood showed marked quantitative and qualitative changes with the development of immunization and after splanchnic stimulation in the immunized animal, but bilateral splanchnic stimulation no longer influenced the antibody titer or the lymphocyte count after ligation of the adrenal veins (Okinaka et al., 1952 b).

Examination of the skin of a patient in a chill reveals pallor, pilomotor stimulation, transient perspiration and lowered temperature. The arterioles and the capillaries are contracted. The muscles exhibit tremor which varies greatly in intensity. These phenomena cannot be explained as the direct effect of a bacterium or the toxin produced by it on the peripheral tissue, but must be regarded as secondary effects of the toxic agent mediated through the nervous system. The chill associated with the invasion of the blood stream by bacteria is not caused by the mere presence of bacteria in the blood, but takes place some time after the invasion, *i.e.*, when the organisms or their toxic products have made contact with the body cells.

Müller and Petersen (1926) showed that the injection of bacteria, like the injection of peptone, salts, etc., results in profound alteration in the tonus of the blood vessels both in the peripheral and the splanchnic areas, the splanchnic vessels being dilated and the peripheral vessels constricted. These diametrically opposite effects cannot be due to the direct influence of the same toxic agent on the vascular endothelium or the neurovascular elements in both regions. The tonic state of the blood vessels probably is determined by the effect of the toxic agent on the nervous system. The splanchnic vessels dilate in response to cholinergic stimulation in that region, and the peripheral vessels constrict in response to adrenergic stimulation in the peripheral region. Increased cholinergic activity in the splanchnic region during the interval of splanchnic vasodilatation is indicated by the increased production of lymph with the onset of the chill. The high protein content of this lymph indicates that it arises in the splanchnic region.

Petersen and Müller (1927) also pointed out that shock following perforation, acute pancreatitis, acute peritonitis, indeed every insult to the peritoneum, such as ordinary laparotomy, etc., leads to an alteration in the splanchnoperipheral autonomic balance with a redistribution of leukocytes resulting in splanchnic leukocytosis. In case of perforation, the peripheral sympathetic and splanchnic parasympathetic orientation[1] is so pronounced that the peculiar "facies" may be regarded as more or less pathognomonic.

A definite time relationship between altered tonus of the stomach and alteration in the peripheral leukocyte count has been demonstrated (Arquin, 1928). When the gastric musculature actually is contracting, the peripheral leukocyte count is increased. During periods of gastric dilatation the peripheral blood exhibits relative leukopenia. On the basis of this finding, Arquin suggested that in certain pathological conditions which involve chronic gastric congestion and delayed digestion, one should expect prolonged gastric dilatation to meet the physiological digestive requirements and, consequently, a prolonged peripheral leukopenia.

The findings of Müller and Petersen regarding the rôle of the autonomic nerves in the distribution of the blood volume in the peripheral and splanchnic regions is somewhat at variance with the so-called Dastre-Morat law, according to which the concentration of the blood in the splanchnic region due to paralysis of the splanchnic vasomotor mechanism, as had been assumed to occur in shock, is balanced by emptying of the peripheral blood vessels. They have pointed out that when a limb is deprived of its vasomotor innervation by sympathectomy, its blood supply is not depleted,

---

[1] Parasympathetic orientation, as used by Petersen and Müller, is not restricted to the functional state induced by stimulation of the parasympathetic nerves alone but indicates the functional state of organs in a region in which metabolism, permeability, blood supply, action currents, etc., are increased. Sympathetic orientation, as used by these authors, denotes the converse condition, *viz.*: tissue rest.

during shock, by drainage into the splanchnic region. They have also pointed out that the chill is not accompanied by paralysis in the splanchnic region but, on the contrary, by profound stimulation. The splanchno-peripheral balance has become "fixed" with the splanchnic and the peripheral regions oppositely oriented. The effect of such fixation becomes apparent in the change in body temperature coincident with the onset of rigor or following it.

Contrary to the current teaching, they do not admit that heat production due to muscle tremor plays any part in the increase in body temperature. The production of heat naturally is associated with an increased metabolic rate, indicating increased activity of the splanchnic organs, particularly the liver. According to Petersen and Müller (1927), all the measurable functions of the liver are accelerated during the chill. They found the output of bile and bile pigments measurably increased both in patients and experimental animals. The reticulo-endothelium of the liver also takes up fat from the blood in one-half the time normally required (Jaffe, 1927). Increased permeability of the capillaries and liver cells associated with this increased activity is evidenced by the fact that hemoglobin injected into the blood stream during shock passes into the lymph at an increased rate and that bile pigments also enter the lymph stream.

In further support of the theory that muscular tremor plays no part in the production of heat during the chill and that the rise in body temperature is due to heat generated by increased activity of the splanchnic organs, they advanced the results of animal experiments in which a condition approximating the normal human chill was produced by the injection of suspensions of living B. coli. Muscle and rectal temperatures were recorded both by means of clinical thermometers and delicate thermocouples. Constant leukocyte counts and observations on the lymph also were made. In no case in which an actual chill was produced did they observe an increase in muscle temperature, although there was a sharp rise in the rectal temperature during the same interval. A comparable, but greater, increase in temperature was noted in the liver. Frequently an actual reduction in muscle temperature took place during the rigor while the rectal temperature was rising. This occurred even when there was no actual increase in the rate of heat loss at the periphery. An abrupt rise in temperature of the muscles was observed only at the end of the chill, usually when a coincident increase in the number of leukocytes in the peripheral blood indicated some vasodilatation in the peripheral region. On the basis of these results, Petersen and Müller concluded that no increase in the production of heat takes place with the shortening of the muscle during rigor and that delay in the warming of the muscles, despite a rise in the temperature of the rest of the body, must be due to an autonomic fixation in the muscles which prevents the dilatation of the arterioles and capillaries.

The results reported by Petersen and Müller seem to indicate that profound alteration exists in the splanchnic and peripheral organs during the chill, brought about by the effects of a toxic agent on the nervous system which are exerted through the autonomic nerves. The splanchnic organs are hyperactive, while the peripheral tissues are relatively inactive. Peripheral vasoconstriction, due to increased sympathetic tonus, reduces the loss of heat from the skin. The work of Petersen and Müller seems to indicate that a similar condition obtains in the skeletal musculature during the chill. On this basis, the skin, muscles and the peripheral blood vessels may be regarded as a unit in their responses to the altered conditions of the body. Muscle tremor, therefore, may be regarded as indicative of increased splanchnic activity and heat production in the splanchnic organs. Conversely, increased splanchnic activity may produce muscle tremor. If the increase in temperature takes place gradually, without the intense autonomic fixation apparent in chill, the tremor may not appear. This probably explains why ordinary fever usually is not accompanied by chill.

Siedek (1951) has recognized three phases in infectious diseases: (1) preparation, (2) reaction, (3) restoration. In the first phase most of the autonomic functions are retarded. Blood pressure is low, the pulse is slow and body temperature is subnormal. In the second phase, as the fever rises, these functions are accelerated. In the third phase, as the fever subsides, they are again retarded. By experimental control of the autonomic balance the duration of the first and the second phases can be altered. The course of an infectious disease, therefore, depends not only on the causative agent but also on the functional state of the autonomic nerves. In cases in which the toxic stimulation causes shock, this condition may persist and result in the death of the patient unless the autonomic balance is restored. If shock is overcome, the autonomic imbalance will be shifted toward adrenergic dominance. In general, mild toxic stimuli cause a shift toward cholinergic dominance, and strong ones that produce shock cause marked cholinergic hyperactivity.

Autonomic Status of the Skin in Respiratory and Certain Other Infections.—In the general splanchnoperipheral interactions of the body the autonomic status of the abdominal and the pelvic organs is opposed to that of the extraperitoneal organs and tissues; consequently, the autonomic status of the buccal and the respiratory mucous membranes corresponds to that of the skin. Under physiological conditions, particularly during bodily rest, the abdominal and the pelvic organs are more abundantly supplied with blood than the extraperitoneal structures. During muscular exercise or increased external temperature, the autonomic status is reversed and the splanchnoperipheral blood volume ratio is shifted in favor of the peripheral structures. When the body is exposed to low temperatures, particularly in the absence of muscular exercise, peripheral vasoconstriction takes place and the skin becomes relatively ischemic. Since the buccal and respiratory mucous membranes are similarly oriented, they also become ischemic. Any measure, therefore, that produces marked reduction in skin temperature elicits nasal capillary constriction, and any measure that causes marked elevation in skin temperature elicits reflex nasal capillary dilatation. These reflex reactions undoubtedly possess temperature regulating value.

Under ordinary physiological conditions, infective organisms are present on the skin and mucous membranes, but, due to the local resistance, infection does not take place. Prolonged ischemia tends to reduce the local resistance and favors infection. This is well illustrated in infections of the upper respiratory passages following exposure to low temperature or drafts. That the reduction in the local resistance of mucous membranes is not a direct effect of exposure to cold is evidenced by the fact that if, during such exposure, peripheral vasoconstriction is prevented by muscular activity, infection does not take place. On the other hand, respiratory infections frequently take place in the absence of any appreciable lowering of the temperature of the mucous membrane beyond that which is directly attributable to the local ischemia.

Other infections of the mucous membranes, e.g., herpes during fever or conjunctivitis occasionally seen during a flare-up of a localized pulmonary tuberculosis, undoubtedly are to be explained on the same basis. They cannot be regarded as part of the primary infection, but arise as a result of reduced local resistance due to the temporary ischemia of the tissue. The exanthems of the acute exanthematous infections (scarlet fever, measles) undoubtedly also become possible because the resistance of the skin and the mucous membranes to the circulating toxin is reduced due to the autonomic status at the periphery (Petersen and Müller, 1930). Arsenical dermatitis following the administration of arsphenamine probably is to be explained in the same manner.

The reactions which serve for the protection of the tissues when toxic substances have entered the skin or the mucous membranes are characterized as inflammatory and depend on the autonomic status of the tissue as such. Since these reactions involve local vasodilatation, they are inhibited during the period of the general reaction to the infection which is characterized by peripheral vasoconstriction. Following this period, the tissues in the infected area become oppositely oriented, local vasodilatation takes place, leukocytes accumulate in the capillaries and infiltrate the tissues, tissue metabolism is accelerated and the local resistance is greatly increased. The inflammatory reaction, therefore, differs only in degree from the normal physiological response. The direction of the change at the outset is the same in both cases.

Autonomic Status of the Skin in Gastro-intestinal Infections.—The more frequent occurrence of gastro-intestinal infections in warm climates and during hot weather than under other conditions is a fact of common clinical experience. During hot weather the cutaneous blood vessels are dilated more or less constantly and the blood supply to the gastro-intestinal canal is correspondingly diminished; consequently, the local resistance of the gastro-intestinal mucosa is reduced. The bactericidal properties of the gastro-intestinal tract, particularly of the duodenum and upper jejunum, are materially diminished during periods of peripheral vasodilatation. Exposure to heat and high humidity, both in man and animals, results not only in diminished gastro-intestinal secretion but also in diminution in the normal response of the stomach and the intestine to food. As observed by Petersen and Levinson (1930), bacteria which under normal conditions are killed by passing through the stomach and the duodenum of the dog passed through these divisions of the digestive tube alive, in most cases, when the dogs were kept in a super-heated room. Animals kept in super-heated rooms usually died following the ingestion of meat poisoned with enteric toxins, whereas animals kept at normal or lower temperatures survived.

Man's susceptibility to gastro-intestinal infection, not only by fully virulent pathogenic organisms introduced into the digestive tube but also by the normal gastro-intestinal parasitic flora, always is notably increased at times of high external temperature. According to Arnold (1928), the gastro-intestinal flora undergoes a change in character as well as in range with increasing external temperature. The distal intestinal flora invades more proximal regions of the gastro-intestinal tract.

These changes do not necessarily depend on the actual level of the external temperature, but on the reactivity of the skin and the respiratory system at the time, as determined by their autonomic status. The splanchnoperipheral imbalance usually is most marked at the beginning of the warmer periods of the year and when persons enter a tropical region from a colder climate. Normal individuals usually are able gradually to become adapted to the higher temperatures. Such adaptation involves a readjustment of the splanchnoperipheral autonomic balance. This is of practical immunological importance for tropical diseases as well as for a wide variety of ordinary gastro-intestinal infections.

PULMONARY DISEASE

Tuberculosis.—Exaggerated tonus of the cholinergic components of the autonomic nerves is a common phenomenon during the second and the third stages of tubercular disease. The hectic flush so common in the later stages of tuberculosis, but which does not appear early in the disease, probably is an expression of cholinergic stimulation exaggerated during intervals of marked activity of the disease process. The relatively slow heart-rate often observed during periods of fever, as compared with the more rapid heart-rate in other diseases during periods of the same degree of fever, also indicates exaggerated cholinergic tonus. When the tuberculous process involves the intestinal tract, the discrepancy between the observed pulse-rate and that which would be expected with the degree of temperature present is still greater. According to Pottenger (1917), an unusual slowing of the pulse-rate in the course of pulmonary tuberculosis, coincident with an increase in temperature of 1° or 2° F., should be regarded as cause to suspect a complicating intestinal tuberculosis.

The gastric hyperacidity which commonly occurs relatively early in the course of tuberculous disease also is associated with exaggerated cholinergic activity. The patient's digestive powers may be above par at first, enabling him to utilize relatively large amounts of food. The increased gastro-intestinal motility associated with the hyperacidity frequently results in nausea and a tendency to vomit. In some cases, exaggerated cholinergic tonus also results in spastic constipation. During toxemia in pulmonary tuberculosis adrenergic activity is increased due to central stimulation and the reflex effect of the inflammation in the lung; consequently, sympathetic tonus may predominate. As soon as the acute toxemia subsides and central adrenergic stimulation is diminished or ceases, a condition of relative parasympathetic hypertonus again obtains in most cases. The patient's appetite is improved and his digestive powers are increased. As a rule, the associated gastric hyperacidity is not sufficient to cause discomfort. Sometimes it actually causes gastric distress. Digestion usually becomes impaired more and more and stasis and constipation become more pronounced as the disease advances and toxemia and depressive emotional states become more marked. The gastro-intestinal symptoms commonly observed during the later stages of tuberculosis are less suggestive of parasympathetic hypertonus than those usually observed earlier in the course of the disease. In those cases in which parasympathetic tonus clearly predominates during the later stages of the disease, it may be due to depression of the sympathetic tonus by the toxic effects of mixed infection on the sympathetic ganglion cells (Stämmler, 1923). Sympathetic atony indicates an unfavorable prognosis.

The data presented above indicate a succession of changes in the autonomic balance during the course of tuberculous disease which probably are in a measure conditioned by the constitutional tendency of the autonomic balance in the individual. According to Pende (1925), if a tuberculous patient first exhibits adrenergic and later cholinergic hyperirritability a grave prognosis is indicated, whereas if the patient exhibits primary cholinergic hyperirritability the disease usually runs a relatively benign course. Medowikov and Schenkmann (1932) have expressed the opinion that tuberculosis usually runs a benign course in children who, according to the pharmacodynamic criteria, exhibit cholinergic hyperreactivity, whereas it usually runs a graver course in children who exhibit adrenergic hyperreactivity. Nearly all the children with tuberculous meningitis, a highly fatal disease, in their series exhibited cholinergic hyperreactivity one or two weeks before death, as determined by the pharmacodynamic criteria.

Organs that have a direct neurolymphatic connection with the central nervous system react more intensely to local infection than those which do not. As observed by Pigalew and Epstein (1930), rabbits with abdominal tuberculous lesions showed increased capacity to combat the disease following section of both vagi below the diaphragm. In many instances, the lesions actually underwent regression. They, therefore, concluded that tuberculous tissue which is freed from nerve impulses develops increased resistance to the infection. This also is in keeping with the experience of laryngologists that cocainization of a tuberculous larynx to relieve pain frequently results in regression of the lesions. According to Ponomarew (1930), section of the vagus nerve on the infected side in rabbits with unilateral pulmonary tuberculosis retards the infectious process and tends to limit it to that side. It also tends to prevent intoxication of the vagus center. According to this author, the toxin produced in a tuberculous lesion poisons the nerve cells, resulting in trophic disturbances at the periphery and reduction in the capacity of the lungs to resist the infection. Trophic disturbances at the periphery in tuberculous patients also have been emphasized by Pottenger (1929, 1930) who described a large number of trophic reflexes arising in the pulmonary area and pointed out the significance of certain trophic disturbances in localizing tuberculous lesions in the lungs.

Petersen and Levinson have emphasized the importance of the reactions that take place in the zone of tissue stimulation that exists around every focus of tuberculous infection. Within this zone, the effects of the toxin produced vary from slight irritation to cellular fatigue and death. During the stage of stimulation, tissue acidity and cell permeability are increased, metabolic processes are accelerated, calcium leaves the tissue, sodium and potassium enter it and tissue cohesion is reduced. In general, this may be regarded as an abnormal status of the local functional balance in which the autonomic nerves, hormones, electrolytes and tissue metabolites all play their parts.

The local reactions of the blood vessels constitute one of the most important factors in the progress of a tuberculous lesion. The reaction of the tuberculous tissue is on the acid side (pH 7 to pH 7.3) which is the optimum for the growth of the tubercle bacillus. The toxin produced by the infection also causes dilatation of the blood vessels. In experiments reported by Preobraschewsky (1929), the dilatation produced by tuberculin in the vessels of uninfected animals was followed by contraction, but in the vessels of tuberculous animals the initial dilatation persisted indefinitely. The vessels of tuberculous animals also showed reduced reactivity to adrenin. This is in keeping with the fact that adrenin causes little contraction of the vessels in an irritated or inflamed area or none at all.

In the light of these experimental findings, it may be assumed that the tuberculin released at a focus of tuberculous infection causes local vasodilatation which, due to the failure of normal reversal to take place, becomes more or less permanent. The focal reactions, therefore, are closely associated with the increased permeability of the dilated capillaries. For the same reason, clinical activation of tuberculosis frequently coincides with biological processes, such as the menstrual cycle, the effects of the season, etc., which are associated with an increase in capillary permeability and autonomic imbalance.

Since clinically advancing tuberculosis is associated with increased capillary permeability and healed tuberculosis with decreased capillary permeability, it may be assumed that increased capillary permeability, regardless of its mode of production, must influence tuberculous lesions unfavorably, whereas diminished capillary permeability favors improvement. In view of the significant rôle of the vasomotor nerves in the regulation of capillary permeability, the importance of clinical measures designed to restore the autonomic functional balance in tuberculous patients is indicated.

Bronchial Asthma.—The passage of air through the respiratory tract in inspiration and expiration may be hampered by contraction of the bronchial musculature, edema of the mucous membrane or excessive secretory activity of the bronchial glands. All these phenomena are related to the functional autonomic balance. Spastic contraction of the bronchial musculature involves neuromuscular mechanisms which normally play a significant rôle in the defense reactions of the upper respiratory tract. The efferent nerves involved are parasympathetic. They may be activated reflexly from the respiratory mucous membrane by impulses conducted through vagus nerve fibers or from other parts of the body by impulses conducted through other visceral or somatic afferent nerves. Edema of the mucous membrane of the respiratory tract represents a vasomotor reaction which may be elicited reflexly by afferent impulses that arise in the respiratory tract or in other parts of the body. The bronchial glands are innervated through parasympathetic nerves and respond reflexly to afferent impulses that arise in other parts of the body as well as to impulses that arise in the respiratory tract. The efferent nerves through which bronchoconstriction or vascular or secretory reactions in the mucous membrane of the respiratory tract are brought about may also be activated by impulses that emanate from central autonomic centers. Asthmatic attacks associated with emotional states can be explained most satisfactorily on the assumption of hypothalamic stimulation. Bronchial asthma probably is invariably associated with cholinergic hyperreactivity. The significance of hyperirritability of the vagus reflex arcs in certain cases of intractable asthma, in the absence of recognizable etiological factors, is indicated by the beneficial effects of repeated bronchial relaxation brought about by means of adrenergic stimulation (Barach, 1943). The relief in these cases can be explained most satisfactorily on the assumption that a vicious cycle of bronchial spasm has been overcome by the repeated relaxation of the bronchial musculature.

In view of the important rôle of cholinergic hyperreactivity in the phenomena of bronchial asthma, adrenergic stimulation may be expected to afford temporary relief due to its tendency to counteract the effects of cholinergic stimulation. Removal of the adrenergic influence by interruption of the sympathetic pulmonary nerves obviously is an irrational procedure. Rational treatment of asthmatic patients should include measures designed to restore the normal functional autonomic balance.

Pulmonary Embolism.—Pulmonary embolism with consequent atelectasis or massive collapse of the lung is a common postoperative and posttraumatic complication. Various mechanisms have been suggested to explain these bronchial phenomena. Most of the data available support the assumption that they are essentially reflex. The pulmonary vascular bed is richly supplied with sensory receptors. It also possesses a potent sympathetic vasoconstrictor system. The reactivity of the bronchial musculature to the stimulus of pulmonary embolism is also striking (de Takats et al., 1942). The mortality and the morbidity of pulmonary embolism cannot be explained as the direct results of the mechanical plugging of the pulmonary artery, but they are due chiefly to reflex effects on other thoracic viscera elicited by the stimulating effects of distention of the vascular tree proximal to the obstructing embolus. Pulmonary embolism need not be regarded as the only cause of atelectasis. Extensive atelectasis, even massive collapse of the lung may be caused by peribronchial pressure produced by tumors or by swelling of the mucous sheaths around foreign bodies, etc. Most of the reflex bronchial phenomena associated with pulmonary embolism represent reactions carried out through the parasympathetic nerves. The vasoconstriction apparent in the lungs is mediated through the sympathetic nerves. The cardiac phenomena associated with pulmonary embolism suggest both parasympathetic and sympathetic reflex activity.

In view of the autonomic reflex activity involved in the phenomena associated with pulmonary embolism, it is apparent that pharmacological agents that increase the flow of blood to the pulmonary arterial bed by increasing the output of the right ventricle, such as adrenin and digitalis, may be harmful, since an increase in pulmonary hypertension would tend to accelerate impending failure of the right side of the heart. Digitalis also exerts a sensitizing effect on the vagus reflex mechanisms. Drugs like atropine and papaverine should be beneficial since they tend to counteract the autonomic reflexes which originate in the affected lung. The usefulness of oxygen must be obvious, particularly in cases in which cyanosis is marked but vasomotor collapse is absent.

NERVOUS REGULATION OF IMMUNE REACTIONS

Production of Immune Substances. — The data set forth above regarding the influences of the autonomic nerves in the distribution of leukocytes and the permeability of the vascular endothelium strongly suggest that immunity and bodily resistance are also influenced by the functional conditions of the autonomic nervous system. Specific immune reactions are subject to neural influences and may be initiated by specific reflex stimulation. As reported by Reitler (1924), the formation of antibodies was initiated in rabbits by injection of an antigen into the ear following ligation of its vessels. The ear also was amputated immediately (about three seconds) after the injection. This result shows clearly that the formation of antibodies may be initiated reflexly and that it may occur in the absence of antigen in the circulating blood. Bogendörfer (1927, 1932) reported the results of experiments, carried out on dogs, in which he demonstrated that the production of agglutinin is influenced by impulses emanating from a central nervous center. The injection of a specific antigen which resulted in active agglutinin production in normal animals was without effect, in his experiments, in animals in which the spinal cord was previously transected in the cervical region. If the cervical spinal cord was transected after the production of agglutinin was initiated, following injection of the antigen, the reaction continued. Transection of the spinal cord below the cervical region did not prevent the initiation of agglutinin production in response to the injection of antigen. These data support the theory that the production of immune substances represents specific reflex secretory reactions to specific stimuli. They also show that an immune reaction once initiated may continue in the absence of nervous influences.

In summarizing the results of investigations begun before 1925, carried out by his collaborators and himself, Belak (1939) proposed classification of the immune substances, with respect to their relationships to the autonomic nerves, in two categories: sympathergic and parasympathergic. The first category includes the essential nonspecific antibodies, such as alexins, opsonins, complement, etc., which are always present. Their production is augmented by sympathetic stimulation and inhibited by parasympathetic stimulation. The second category includes the essential specific antibodies, such as antitoxin, precipitin, agglutinin, lysine, etc. The production of these substances is augmented by parasympathetic stimulation and inhibited by sympathetic stimulation. It may be disturbed by psychic influences exerted through corticothalamo-hypothalamic mechanisms, perticularly in mentally ill persons (Loumos, 1952).

In experiments reported by Illenyi and Borzsák (1938) the hemolysin titer was increased by stimulation of the parasympathetic nerves, when the antigen was injected, and decreased by parasympathetic paralysis or stimulation of the sympathetic nerves. The effect on the hemolysin titer of sympathetic stimulation was more marked than that of parasympathetic paralysis. The onset of infectious disease, as indicated by fever, increased metabolism, leukocytosis, etc., is accompanied by sympathetic hypertonus, whereas during the period of recovery, as indicated by the return to normal body temperature, decreased metabolism, disappearance of leukocytosis, increased alkali reserve, etc., parasympathetic tonus gains the ascendency. At the beginning of an infectious process, therefore, resistance is decreased due to the increased sympathetic tonus which inhibits the production of the specific immune substances, whereas during the later phases resistance is increased due to increased parasympathetic tonus which augments the production of the specific immune substances (Frei, 1939; Hoff, 1942).

The non-specific immune substances, according to Belak, are related to the emergency functions of the sympathetico-adrenal system which responds automatically and promptly to psychic stimulation, pain, muscular exercise, blood pressure, cold and various other changes in the internal and the external environments. The relationship of the immediate reactions to infection, intoxication, etc., to the sympathetico-adrenal system, therefore, is biologically significant. The biological significance of the relationship of the production of specific immune substances to the parasympathetic system is less apparent.

The concept of the regulatory influence of the sympathetic nerves in the production of the non-specific immune substances and that of the parasympathetic nerves in the production of the specific immune substances, as formulated by Belak, undoubtedly expresses a fundamental biological relationship, but it cannot be regarded as strictly accurate in the light of our present knowledge of the anatomical distribution of the nerves of sympathetic and those of parasympathetic origin and the rôle of the neurohumoral mediators. Belak's conclusion that the non-specific immune substances are related to the emergency functions of the sympathetico-adrenal system is well founded. The specific immune substances undoubtedly are related to cholinergic nerves both of sympathetic and of parasympathetic origin which respond to cholinergic (parasympathetic) stimuli according to a common mode.

Allergic Disease.—The common manifestations of allergy, such as hay fever, asthma, eczema and diverse anaphylactic reactions, probably are invariably associated with abnormal functional states of the autonomic nerves. The latter may be induced by the tissue reactions to the sensitizing agent in question, but infrequently the modified functional status of the autonomic nerves is a factor in the etiology of allergic disease. The so-called "allergic state" probably does not exist in the presence of a normal functional status of the autonomic nerves.

Hereditary factors in the allergic state undoubtedly exist in many persons. Those with the more marked hereditary predispositions tend to show allergic symptoms earlier and in greater variety than those in whom the hereditary factors are less marked. The influence of heredity in the capacity of the organism to resist allergic disease has also been demonstrated. Strains of guinea pigs that are resistant to given allergens have been obtained by selective breeding (Landsteiner and Chase, 1940; Jacobs *et al.*, 1941). The hereditary factor may be concerned with the capacity of the organism to produce tissue antibodies, the permeability of the tissue elements, including the capillary endothelium, or the release of substances such as histamine and acetylcholine, all of which processes may be influenced through the autonomic nerves.

Emotional factors in the etiology of allergic disease have long been recognized. As Gillespie (1936) pointed out, an asthmatic attack may occur as the culmination of an anxiety, the expression of an emotional conflict, a protest against an unwelcome situation, a means of escape or as a conditioned response. Urticaria of emotional origin is not uncommon. Abramson (1942) reported the case of a woman 31 years of age who, while suffering from certain mental conflicts, developed giant hives after swimming in cold water. The application of ice to her arm also resulted in the development of an urticarial wheal. When later her mental conflicts were adjusted, her sensitiveness to cold disappeared. Numerous cases in which allergic symptoms of other types have been precipitated by emotional disturbances have been reported.

The emotional factors in allergic disease emphasize the rôle of the central autonomic centers, particularly those located in the hypothalamus. Milian (1936) advanced clinical data in support of the assumption that the itching associated with eczema is of central origin and that the associated capillary dilatation, edema and secondary vesiculation are related to abnormal vasomotor function due to the low threshold susceptibility of these nerves to itching. Implication of the sympathetic nerves in pruritis, erythema and vesiculation in the background of contact allergy has also been demonstrated. The cutaneous lesions concerned obviously are related to reflex activity mediated through autonomic centers.

The most spectacular of all allergic manifestations, protein anaphylaxis, undoubtedly represents the results of the antibody-allergen reactions of the tissue elements. Certain allergic manifestations, *e.g.*, those of physical allergy, cannot be explained on the same basis. A combination of heat, cold or sunlight with body proteins which could produce a new protein would be difficult to visualize. In either case the functional disturbances bear essentially the same relationship to the autonomic nerves. They involve primary tonic changes in the musculature of the visceral organs including the vascular system. Since the tonus of the visceral musculature is regulated through the autonomic nerves, deviations from the normal tonic level of the visceral organs imply deviations from the normal functional autonomic balance. The changes in smooth muscle tonus commonly associated with allergic disease, *e.g.*, the heightened tonus of the bronchial musculature in bronchial asthma and the increased gastro-intestinal tonus and motility associated with various allergic diseases, indicate heightened cholinergic nerve activity. The decreased vascular tonus, particularly in the shock tissue, commonly associated with allergic reactions are of the same order, although the efferent innervation of most of the blood vessels is mediated solely through sympathetic nerves. The decreased vascular tonus may be explained in part on the basis of decreased activity of the adrenergic vasoconstrictor nerves and in part on the basis of increased activity of the cholinergic vasodilators. The increased secretory activity associated with allergic catarrhal inflammation of the nasal, the pharyngeal and the bronchial mucous membranes, the gastro-intestinal mucosa and the conjunctivæ also indicate exaggerated cholinergic activity. The vaso-dilatation of the mucous membranes, indicating corresponding activity of the cholinergic vasodilator fibers, results in increased permeability of the capillary bed which facilitates the discharge of serous fluid and thus provides the substratum for increased secretory output of the glands. Increased capillary permeability due to vasodilator stimulation, in the absence of allergic disease, has been amply demonstrated. Activation of the glands in the mucous membranes, furthermore, is mediated through the parasympathetic nerves. Some of the most characteristic manifestations of allergic disease, therefore, are causally related to heightened parasympathetic or cholinergic reactivity.

Patients with allergic respiratory disease frequently exhibit excessive palmar sweating. This phenomenon also indicates cholinergic hyper-reactivity. As observed by Cohen and Wolf (1947), it cannot be explained on the basis of anxiety or other emotional stimulation alone. They found the incidence of intense palmar sweating significantly greater in allergic than in psychoneurotic patients. Excessive loss of water and sodium in the urine during allergic attacks has been interpreted as a defense mechanism on the part of the body to reduce its water content and thus favorably influence the edema of the shock tissue (Kern, 1940). It is significant to point out in this connection that water metabolism is regulated through hormonal mechanisms and that the production of the hormones concerned is influenced by nerve impulses that emanate from autonomic centers in the rostral portion of the hypothalamus.

The localization and the limitations of the shock tissue present intricate problems which probably will find their solution in a more complete understanding of the rôle of the cholinergic autonomic nerves in allergic reactions. The discharge of impulses through cholinergic nerves may be limited to a single organ or body region. This undoubtedly provides the physiological basis for the fact that allergic reactions, as observed clinically, commonly occur in localized tissues known as shock tissues. The cholinergic influence in these reactions is indicated by the fact that, regardless of which shock tissue is affected, adrenin affords relief. The general adrenergic reaction tends to counteract the effect of the local cholinergic stimulation wherever the disturbance may be. The experimental observation that the blood of rabbits in anaphylactic shock contains relatively large quantities of acetylcholine, whereas that of normal control rabbits contains none, supports this point of view.

CARDIOVASCULAR DISEASE

Factors in Abnormal Blood Pressure. — Blood pressure and the supply of blood to the tissues depend in part on the caliber of the blood vessels and the force and rate of the heart-beats. Both these factors are regulated through the autonomic nerves. Under normal conditions, an increase in blood pressure elicits reflex cardiac inhibition, tending to restore normal pressure. Under certain pathological conditions involving high blood pressure, the pressure may remain abnormally high and even mount still higher although the heart is failing and the pulse weak. The failure of the heart, under these conditions, has been regarded by some as due to the high blood pressure. If such were the case, lowering of the pressure would relieve the heart. This it fails to do. It has also been suggested that as the output of the heart diminishes the tonus of the blood vessels is increased, thus decreasing the size of the vascular bed to be filled. If this reaction actually took place it might account for the maintenance of blood pressure at the normal level but not for a further increase in blood pressure while the heart is failing. As is well known, one of the most powerful stimuli to the contraction of a muscle is its previous stretching. The profound disturbance of cardiac rhythm resulting from pericardial effusion probably is due in a measure to interference with diastolic filling and, therefore, with stretching of the cardiac muscle. The marked hypertrophy of the left ventricle in aortic regurgitation undoubtedly is the direct result of increased work. The stimulus for such increased work probably results from the increased stretching of the muscle due to the filling of the ventricle both from the atrium and the aorta. In like manner, the diastolic stretching of the cardiac musculature due to raising the blood pressure by stimulation of the vasoconstrictor nerves, in attempts to stimulate a flagging heart, probably is an important factor in bringing about the desired cardiac response. If the myocardium is diseased and the overstretched muscle fails to respond, such treatment must result in increased dilatation.

The work accomplished by the heart, even under normal conditions, is relatively enormous. On the assumption that the output of the heart is 2.5 ounces (usually it is more) at each contraction under conditions of normal blood pressure, the total output would amount to 7.5 tons of blood per day. The work accomplished would be equivalent to lifting a ton of blood 122 feet. In view of these figures, it must be apparent that any increase in blood pressure adds materially to the amount of work required of the cardiac musculature; consequently, anything which tends to maintain the blood pressure at an abnormally high level tends to deplete the cardiac reserve. The increased blood pressure associated with advancing age commonly plays an important rôle in shortening the remaining span of life due to the increased work required of the heart. The rise in blood pressure, nevertheless, must be regarded as a necessary conservative measure. Attempts to lower blood pressure by means of vasodilator drugs, without attacking the cause of the rise, therefore, must be fraught with some degree of danger.

Hypertension commonly is associated with structural vascular lesions. It often occurs in the absence of such lesions as a result of sympathetic stimulation. The cause of such sympathetic stimulation sometimes is traceable to hygienic or dietetic variations, sometimes to acute or chronic disease processes and frequently to psychic and emotional disturbances. Permanent arterial hypertension apparently of the idiopathic type is char-

acterized by hyperexcitability of the vasoconstrictor nerves and hypo-
excitability of the vasodilator nerves. Prolonged hyperactivity of the
sympathetic nerves, whether it results from the administration of adrenin
in physiological amounts or from the spontaneous emotional activity of the
pseudoaffective state results in a decrease in the volume of the circulating
blood involving both the liquid and the cellular elements. Prolonged
vasoconstriction of itself, therefore, probably results in a loss of blood from
the circulation.

In a study based on trained normal dogs, Wilhelmj *et al.* (1952) found that
some of the animals were well balanced and gave virtually no blood pressure response to emotional stimulation. Others were highly responsive.
Aside from the natural individual differences in responsiveness, the degree
of training appeared to be an important factor. A high degree of training
seemed to make the animals more emotionally unstable. In these animals,
common laboratory procedures incited considerable emotional tension that
was not always grossly apparent.

Hypotension frequently is more urgently dangerous than hypertension.
The rôle of adrenin deficiency in abnormally low blood pressure is well
known, particularly in Addison's disease. Adrenin deficiency probably always results in sympathetic hypostimulation. The cardinal symptoms of
Addison's disease can readily be explained on this basis. Hypostimulation
of the cardiac accelerator and the vasoconstrictor nerves, both of which are
sympathetic, must result in corresponding atony of the entire cardiovascular system. The profound asthenia associated with adrenal insufficiency
probably is due in part to vascular hypotension and in part to the relative
atony of the skeletal musculature.

Hypotension also plays an important rôle in the phenomena of shock,
but the various factors involved in this condition cannot be discussed in the
present volume. In view of the important rôle of the splanchnoperipheral
vasomotor balance in the distribution of blood volume and the permeability
of the vascular endothelium, it may be assumed that the vasomotor neural
mechanism plays an important rôle in the production of low blood pressure
in shock as well as in various other disease processes.

Carotid Sinus Reflexes in Disease. — The innervation of the carotid sinus
and the functional significance of the carotid sinus reflex mechanisms in the
normal physiology of circulation and respiration have been outlined in
Chapters VIII and IX. In certain individuals in whom these mechanisms
have become hyperirritable, stimulation of the carotid sinus frequently
results in dizziness and fainting. Such attacks may occur spontaneously
or they may be induced by external pressure on the hypersensitive carotid
sinus. In either case the symptoms are essentially identical. The same
mechanisms probably play a rôle also in fainting associated with emotional
disturbances in certain cases, a syndrome which Lewis (1932) designated
"vagovagal" syncope. Attacks of this kind frequently occur in apparently
healthy persons as a result of stimuli such as the sight of blood, overheated
and stale atmosphere or strong emotional reactions. They are accompanied
by pallor, perspiration, fall in blood pressure and frequently by bradycardia. If the carotid sinus is hyperirritable, external pressure on it may
cause a marked decrease in the heart-rate and the blood pressure and even

syncope. In some patients with high blood pressure it may result in a reduction of 25 per cent in the heart-rate and of 30 per cent or more in blood pressure (Greiwe, 1932).

On the basis of the results of extensive investigations, particularly those of Weis, Ferris, Capps and their collaborators (1933–1937), carotid sinus reflexes may be classified in three main categories: (1) asystole or sudden retardation of the cardiac rhythm with or without a decrease in arterial blood pressure; (2) marked decrease in blood pressure without marked retardation of the cardiac rate; (3) cerebral circulatory alterations, causing fainting and sometimes convulsions, with or without marked changes in the cardiac rhythm or blood pressure.

Of the patients studied by Ferris et al. (1935), a high percentage gave clinical evidence of vasomotor instability, such as palpation, moist palms, skin sensitivity, etc. The blood pressure tended to fluctuate spontaneously over a relatively wide range, and the basal metabolism was low. In some the hyperactivity of the carotid sinus mechanisms was associated with various functional and organic disorders such as emotional instability, cardiac disease and arteriosclerosis. If associated morbid conditions are relieved by appropriate treatment the hypersensitivity of the carotid sinus mechanisms usually is reduced (Weis et al., 1936). The carotid sinus, however, does not appear to play a major rôle in the regulation of autonomic tonus (Ferris et al., 1937).

In any given case of exaggerated activity of the carotid sinus mechanisms, reflexes of one of the three categories outlined above play the major rôle, but those of the other categories are active in some degree. Fainting in which reflexes of the cerebral type predominate, however, bears no obvious relationship to retardation of the cardiac rhythm or the reduction in blood pressure. Cerebral reflex vasoconstriction followed by compensatory vasodilatation has been demonstrated in such cases, but the vasoconstriction cannot be regarded as the actual cause of the fainting but only as a concomitant manifestation since the same or even a greater degree of cerebral vasoconstriction caused by adrenin does not result in fainting. Observations on the cerebral blood flow before and during syncope, furthermore, fail to indicate marked vasoconstriction. The failure of oxygen to diminish the tendency to faint also militates against the theory of anoxemia due to vasoconstriction.

The reflex activity of the carotid sinus mechanisms may be influenced by various pharmacological agents. Digitalis exerts a sensitizing effect on both the vagal and the cerebral reflex mechanisms. The routine preoperative use of this drug, particularly in elderly patients, therefore, is contraindicated (Ferris et al., 1935). Both the vagal and the depressor types of carotid sinus syncope can be controlled by adrenin or ephedrine. Atropine abolishes the vagal type but has no effect on the depressor type. Neither of these drugs exerts a marked effect on the cerebral type (Weis et al., 1936). Surgical denervation of the carotid sinuses abolishes both spontaneous and induced attacks in suitable cases but exerts no influence on unrelated accompanying symptoms.

Some Factors Involved in Pulmonary Engorgement and Hemorrhage. — The pulmonary blood vessels, like the systemic vessels, are subject to direct vasomotor control, but not in the same degree. The lungs also receive blood through the bronchial arteries which arise directly from the aorta. In cases of hemoptysis involving only the pulmonary vessels, any measure which constricts the systemic vessels, e.g., the administration of adrenin, may aggravate the bleeding by forcing blood from the systemic into the pulmonary vessels. On the other hand, measures which bring about vasodilatation, e.g., the administration of nitrates, tends to diminish the engorgement of the lung by diverting blood into the systemic vessels. Hemoptysis due to necrosis of lung tissue may involve both pulmonary and bronchial vessels. The former, being the more numerous, are more apt to be eroded. In case of hemorrhage from a bronchial artery the production of vasoconstriction by means of styptic drugs might be harmful because a general rise in blood pressure and consequent turgescence of the lungs would tend to bring about hemorrhage at other weak points. On the other hand, measures which produce wide-spread vasodilation might be beneficial because of their tendency to divert blood from the lungs, which would also counterbalance the risks of reopening the bleeding point. Lowered blood pressure would also favor the sealing of bleeding points by means of blood clots. The relief of asthmatic attacks by the administration of adrenin probably is due chiefly to its constricting effect on the vessels in the bronchial mucosa.

Regulation of Cerebral Blood Pressure and Cerebral Hemorrhage.— Since the cranial wall is rigid and the brain is incompressible, the liquid content of the cranium, consisting of blood and cerebrospinal fluid, is a constant volume. If the volume of blood in the cerebral vessels is increased, cerebrospinal fluid must be expressed from the cranium. This is the first effect of a rise in arterial pressure in the brain. The cerebral sinuses become compressed until the pressure in them equals that exerted against their walls by the brain substance. Since the medulla oblongata contains vital centers, its blood supply must be maintained at all hazards. If the blood supply to the medulla oblongata becomes inadequate, the resulting cerebral ischemia stimulates the vasomotor center to contract the splanchnic vessels. This results in forcing more blood to the brain. Dilatation of the splanchnic vessels, on the other hand, results in the withdrawal of blood from the brain. The blood supply to the brain is controlled, in a large measure, by the vascular reactions of the splanchnic region which in turn is controlled by the vasomotor center in the brain.

As shown by the results of animal experiments carried out by Cushing, the general blood pressure must be kept at a level somewhat higher than that of the intracranial pressure in order to avoid cerebral ischemia. When the intracranial pressure was increased by the introduction of a saline solution into the cranial cavity from a pressure bottle, no effects other than a slight increase in pulse- and respiration-rates were observed until the intracranial pressure exceeded the blood pressure. Even these effects could be avoided if the fluid did not affect the sensitive dura. When the intracranial pressure exceeded the blood pressure, the splanchnic vessels contracted and the blood pressure was raised until it again exceeded the intracranial pressure. By repeatedly increasing the intracranial pressure the blood pressure was forced to a level above 200 mm. of mercury before the vasomotor center showed signs of giving away. When the increased intracranial pressure was relieved, the splanchnic vessels dilated, bringing about a corresponding diminution of blood pressure. If the vagi were divided before the intracranial pressure was modified, the blood pressure corresponded even more closely to the intracranial pressure, but always remained slightly higher. The adjustment of the blood pressure to the intracranial pressure was brought about by vasoconstriction in the rest of the body, since no rise in blood pressure took place in response to increasing the intracranial pressure following section of both the vagi and the spinal cord.

These experimental data have a practical bearing on the treatment of cerebral hemorrhage. Measures designed to reduce the blood pressure to a level low enough to check the hemorrhage are fraught with danger because of the reduction of the blood supply to the medulla oblongata. Furthermore, since the blood pressure is automatically maintained at a higher level than the intracranial pressure a vicious cycle is established. The hemorrhage increases the intracranial pressure, and the increased pressure causes a rise in blood pressure which tends to increase the hemorrhage. In general, a rising blood pressure in cerebral hemorrhage indicates a grave prognosis because it shows that the bleeding has not ceased. Direct lowering of the intracranial pressure by means of a lumbar puncture tends to reduce blood pressure due to its effect on the vasomotor center; consequently, it tends to check the hemorrhage. On the other hand, such lowering of the intracranial pressure is not without danger, in certain cases, since it reduces the support of the cerebral arteries and renders them more liable to bleed. Since the blood pressure falls immediately following reduction of intracranial pressure the necessity for support of the arteries is also diminished.

On the basis of Cushing's experiments, it seems highly probable that, when more than one hemorrhage into the brain substance occurs, the smaller hemorrhages usually are caused by the effect of the larger primary one on blood pressure. The primary hemorrhage increases the intracranial pressure which, due to its stimulating effect on the vasomotor center, in turn raises the general blood pressure to a level at which the weakened arteries in other parts of the brain, particularly the pons, are unable to withstand the strain.

DISORDERS OF THE DIGESTIVE TRACT

Spastic Obstruction.—Since the digestive tube receives inhibitory impulses through the sympathetic and excitatory impulses through the parasympathetic nerves, sympathetic stimulation results in retardation and parasympathetic stimulation results in acceleration of gastro-intestinal activity. Any disturbance in the functional balance of the autonomic system, therefore, is reflected in gastro-intestinal activity.

The functional activities of the esophagus are dominated by its parasympathetic innervation. Under certain conditions it reacts to neural influences in a manner which affects the entire digestive system. In the case of a neoplasm near the cardiac orifice, the distal portion of the esophagus may become more or less permanently contracted and thus obstruct

31

the passage of food into the stomach, although the new growth, due to its small size, plays no mechanical rôle in the occlusion of the cardia. Globus hystericus also involves spasm of the distal portion of the esophagus. The patient is unable to swallow, although no organic disease is present. Constriction of the esophageal musculature is brought about by parasympathetic overstimulation. In the case of globus hystericus, the cause of esophageal spasm is to be sought in a psychic disorder. In most other instances, esophageal spasm must be regarded as a reflex response to afferent stimulation. For example, malignant disease of the stomach may give rise to reflex contraction of the esophageal musculature. In certain cases, esophageal spasm constitutes the earliest objective evidence of organic gastric disease.

The neural control of the cardiac sphincter, as Hurst and Rake (1930) pointed out, is subject to four abnormal conditions: vagus hyperactivity, vagus hypoactivity or paralysis, sympathetic hyperactivity and sympathetic hypoactivity or paralysis. Of these, the second and the third probably are the more important in cardiac sphincter dysfunction since vagus hypoactivity or paralysis may result in achalazia and sympathetic hyperactivity in cardiospasm. On the other hand, spasm of the cardiac sphincter may occur as a reflex result of acute inflammation or carcinoma of the distal portion of the esophagus, peptic ulcer and possibly duodenal ulcer and gall bladder disease. It probably does not occur as a purely functional disorder. Hysterical dysphagia probably is due to disturbances in the neuromuscular control of the voluntary mechanism of deglutition which does not involve the cardiac sphincter.

Pylorospasm may be brought about reflexly by a wide variety of causes, *e.g.*, gastric ulcer, appendicitis, renal calculus, pyelitis and sometimes disease of the gall bladder or the genitalia. Occasionally it occurs as a simple neurosis. If the spasm is slight and of short duration it may be relatively unimportant but, if marked and persistent, it results in gastric dilatation. In some cases dilatation may be delayed for a long time by the initial compensatory hypertrophy of the stomach wall.

Chronic appendicitis frequently is accompanied by mild ileal stasis which is due to spasm of the ileocecal sphincter brought about by local irritation of the diseased appendix. Gastro-ileal reflexes also play a rôle in the retardation of the passage of the contents of the small intestine into the cecum in chronic appendicitis. These reflexes may be elicited by the introduction of food into the stomach. In MacLean's (1932) study of 300 cases of chronic appendicitis, delay in the filling of the cecum was observed in about 50 per cent of the cases. In his opinion, this reaction is so characteristic that it may be regarded as a sign of chronic appendicitis.

Flaccid Obstruction.—Irritation of the peritoneum commonly results in reflex inhibition of gastro-intestinal motility. In acute general peritonitis the resulting sympathetic stimulation tends toward immobilization of the intestine and intestinal stasis. In certain individuals with unstable autonomic balance even slight splanchnic irritation elicits profound reflex inhibition of the intestine. Irritation of even a limited area of the peritoneum, therefore, may result in complete cessation of peristaltic activity and distention of the intestine due to loss of tonus of its musculature.

Paralytic ileus sometimes follows abdominal operations in the absence of marked trauma or injury to the peritoneum, probably due to reflex inhibition elicited by impulses that arise within the gastro-intestinal wall. Symptoms of flaccid intestinal obstruction, so-called ileus hystericus, arise in certain cases as part of the syndrome of hysteria. The intestinal inhibition in these cases undoubtedly is due to hypothalamic stimulation. Ileus of neurogenic origin, as observed by Chesterman (1946), involves local or general flattening of the intestinal gradients. It may either be spastic or distensive. The stimulating factors may excite the extrinsic nerves or act directly on the intramural neuromuscular mechanisms of the intestine.

Hypertrophies of Infancy.—The major cause of congenital hypertrophy of the pylorus, hypertrophic ileal obstruction and congenital hypertrophy and dilatation of the colon probably is dysfunction of the autonomic nerves. The essential lesion in congenital hypertrophy of the pylorus is a hypertrophy of the muscular coats of the pyloric canal and the antrum and, to a slight degree, of the distal portion of the corpus of the stomach. This is essentially the portion of the gastric musculature that is concerned with the expulsion of the stomach contents. Roentgen-ray examination shows ill-timed and abnormal forcible and prolonged contractions of the stomach, under these conditions, but the stomach content is not expelled. Hypertrophic ileal obstruction in infants usually involves the distal portion of the small intestine. It is similar in origin to congenital hypertrophy of the pylorus.

Congenital hypertrophy and dilatation of the colon resembles congenital hypertrophy of the pylorus and hypertrophic obstruction of the ileum both in pathology and in the fact that it involves a portion of the digestive tube on the proximal side of a sphincter. The lower limit of the change usually is at the junction of the colon with the rectum (O'Beirne's sphincter). Occasionally, the hypertrophy and the dilatation extend to the anal sphincter. The major etiological factor in this condition appears to be faulty development of the myenteric plexus in a limited zone of the hind gut. Taylor (1949) reported absence of intramural ganglia in the distal portion of the colon in 20 consecutive cases of congenital megacolon. In 20 per cent of the cases studied by Whitehouse and Kernohan (1949) the absence of myenteric ganglia extended oralward to the proximal portion of the sigmoid flexure.

Intussusception.—If the above interpretation of the rôle of the autonomic innervation in the gastro-intestinal hypertrophies of early infancy is correct, it may be assumed that the distinctive feature of autonomic dysfunction, during the early weeks and months of life, is localized hypertrophy. The autonomic dysfunctions of a later period are characterized by exaggeration of the normal functions of the gastro-intestinal musculature. Intussusception occurs most commonly during the period extending from the sixth month to the end of the second year but is not limited to childhood. Of 300 cases of intussusception operated upon in the Edinburgh Children's Hospital, according to Fraser (1926), 295 had their beginning in the lower end of the ileum where the original point of the invagination remained apparent after the reduction. The peristaltic rush consists of an advancing wave of contraction preceded by a wave of relaxation. As long as inhibition precedes contraction no harm can result, but if, when the wave of contraction reaches the lower end of the ileum, the inhibition phase is not transmitted, due to failure of the inhibitory mechanism, the strong contraction of the peristaltic rush may carry a portion of the gut into the distal segment as an invagination, thus initiating the intussusception. According to Fraser, intussusception occurs most commonly in cases in which the ileocecal segment has not become completely fixed to the posterior abdominal wall and is provided with a loose mesenteric attachment. There is no adequate reason to assume that this condition favors the initiation of intussusception, although it offers a mechanical explanation of migration of the intussuscepting segment. The evidence strongly suggests failure of the coördinating mechanism controlling the ileocecal segment. In some cases intussusception involves only the ileum and in some only the colon. Intussusception of the appendix occurs only rarely.

Additional evidence that intussusception has its cause in disturbed autonomic control of the intestine has been advanced by Fulton et al. (1934) and Watts and Fulton (1934). In monkeys and chimpanzees, stimulation of the cerebral cortex in the rostral portion of the premotor area or bilateral extirpation of the cortex in this area caused excessive motor activity of the gastro-intestinal tract and frequently resulted in intussusception. These gastro-intestinal reactions obviously represent responses to excessive parasympathetic stimulation. In many cases of gastric disorder, the stomach itself is not at fault, but is made irritable by the reflex effects of a lesion elsewhere. Whenever gastric symptoms are strikingly intermittent, it is safe to assume, in the absence of unmistakable evidence of a gastric lesion, that the lesion is located outside the stomach. In view of these considerations, it must be clear that if a patient can at times eat freely of any ordinary food without distress and at other times rejects all food or suffers pain regardless of what he eats, the stomach itself probably is not at fault. Such intermittent attacks commonly are due to lesions of the gall bladder or the appendix. Patients with gall stones commonly exhibit symptoms of intermittent gastric irritability. A slight alteration in the position of the stone or a slight increase in the associated cholecystitis may at any time elicit violent reflex irritation of the stomach and spasm of the pylorus.

In general, it may be stated that the nearer the lesion is to the stomach, the more probable is the occurrence of reflex gastric symptoms. Duodenal ulcer and gall bladder disease almost invariably cause marked reflex gastric symptoms. Pancreatitis not only gives rise to reflex disturbances set up by the pancreatic lesion, but also results in inadequate neutralization of the gastric juice in consequence of diminished pancreatic secretion. The symptoms associated with this condition, including those of intestinal obstruction, testify to the wide-spread sympathetic inhibition produced. Reflex gastric disturbances resulting from lesions farther removed from the stomach are less common but not infrequent.

Gastric and Duodenal Ulcers.—Autonomic nerve dysfunction has long been recognized as a factor in the etiology of gastric and duodenal ulcers. Some investigators have regarded peptic ulceration as a direct result of autonomic functional imbalance. On the basis of extensive clinical experience and a review of the literature, Cushing (1932) emphasized the rôle of the autonomic nerves in the genesis of peptic ulcers and pointed out the importance of influences that emanate from the diencephalic autonomic centers. Intracranial lesions that affect the hypothalamus, particularly the tuber cinereum, or the conduction pathways leading from the hypothalamus to the efferent nucleus of the vagus, according to Cushing, are prone to cause gastric ulcers presumably due to parasympathetic stimulation, possibly due to sympathetic paralysis. Intraventricular injections of pilocarpine or pituitrin in man, in his experience, caused an increase in gastric motility, hypertonus and hypersecretion leading to retching and vomiting with ultimate discharge of occult blood. Beattie (1932) also reported patches of hyperemia of the gastric mucosa in animals following direct electrical stimulation of the tuber cinereum. Pigalew (1932) advanced certain data which seem to support the view that gastro-intestinal lesions induced by lesions of the tuber cinereum occur most frequently in the pyloric portion of the stomach, the duodenum, the ileocecal region, and the rectum.

In a study of 18 resected stomachs of patients with gastric ulcers, Stöhr (1932) observed lesions of the enteric plexuses, particularly alterations in the ganglia and the ganglion cells, in every case in which the disease was chronic. The degenerative changes in the enteric plexuses were most marked at the sites of the ulcerative lesions, but they were apparent also in areas far removed from the ulcers. Whether the lesions of the enteric plexuses constitute a causative factor in the etiology of gastric ulcer or represent an accompaniment of the ulcerative lesions could not be determined. On the basis of these findings and extensive clinical observations, Stöhr (1934) advanced the opinion that the causation of chronic gastric and duodenal ulcers is intimately related to dysfunction of the entire autonomic nervous system.

Balint (1927) emphasized the constant association of hyperacidity with parasympathetic hyperirritability in ulcer patients and pointed out that most of these patients exhibit alkali retention, indicating an acid condition of the tissues. The opinion that hyperacidity is an important factor in the causation of gastric and duodenal ulcers is also supported by a large volume of experimental data bearing on the production and healing of chronic peptic ulcers in animals. Pepsin produced in the stomach probably also plays a significant rôle. In both acute and chronic experiments on cats, Schiffrin and Warren (1942) found that perfusion of a segment of the gastro-intestinal tract with pepsin in an acid medium resulted in more severe ulceration than perfusion with acid alone. They have emphasized the proteolytic action of the gastric juice as a factor in the etiology of gastric and duodenal ulcers.

Emotional factors in the etiology of gastric and duodenal ulcers have been emphasized by various investigators. In a study carried out on ulcer patients and normal subjects, Mittelmann and Wolff (1942) observed a rise in acidity and increased motility in the stomachs of all the ulcer patients and many of the normal subjects during periods of experimentally induced anxiety, hostility and resentment. On the contrary, gastric acidity and motility were decreased in the same subjects during periods of induced feelings of contentment and well-being. In reviewing the case histories of ulcer patients, they found that the patients had experienced prolonged emotional turmoil involving mainly conflict, anxiety, guilt, hostility and resentment. The occurrence of pain and in some cases hemorrhage was correlated with periods of special emotional stress.

In a subject with a permanent gastric fistula through which the gastric mucosa could be observed directly, Wolf and Wolff (1942) observed pallor of the mucous membrane and inhibition of gastric secretory activity and motility during emotions such as fear and sadness which involved a feeling of withdrawal. During emotional conflicts involving anxiety, hostility and resentment they observed increased gastric secretory activity, hypermotility and hyperemia and engorgement of the gastric mucosa. Intense sustained anxiety, hostility and resentment were accompanied by prolonged increased secretory activity, hypermotility and engorgement of the gastric mucosa. During these periods erosions and hemorrhages could be induced by the most trifling contractions. Bleeding points also appeared spontaneously due to vigorous gastic contractions. Direct contact of acid gastric juice with a small eroded area in the mucosa resulted in increased secretory activity and further engorgement of the entire gastric mucous membrane. Prolonged direct contact of the gastric juice with such a lesion resulted in a chronic ulcer.

In a study of personality factors in the etiology of duodenal ulcer, Brown et al. (1950) found that ulcer patients as a group tend to deal with environmental problems on an impulsive, emotionally immature level. In a study of ulcer patients treated by vagotomy, Szasz (1949) found that the more psychic energy is bound up by the organic illness and by the therapy employed before operation the greater is the probability of an unfavorable result of vagotomy, and the less psychic energy is bound up in this manner the better is the prognosis.

The pain associated with gastric and duodenal ulcers is mediated through visceral afferent components of spinal nerves. If the pain is abolished following vagotomy, the relief is not due to interruption of afferent vagus nerve fibers. Some patients with duodenal ulcer, as observed by Patterson and Sandweiss (1942), experience pain only when the duodenum is active regardless of the state of motility of the stomach. Other factors in the causation of ulcer distress are the site of the lesion, the acidity of the gastric and the duodenal contents, the relative abundance of pancreatic enzymes and bile and the potency of the gastric and the duodenal hormones, all of which are related to autonomic nerve function.

As reported by Bonney and Pickering (1946), roentgen ray examination of ulcer patients during pain revealed no localized contractions of the stomach or the duodenum that did not also occur in the absence of pain. The time relations of the pain also were compatible with the theory that it was caused by chemical stimulation of pain receptors located in the areas of ulceration. Data advanced by Smith et al. (1947) are not in full agreement with this point of view. In their experience, the relief of ulcer pain appeared to be due to decreased gastric and intestinal motility rather than to decreased acidity. Following vagotomy in the treatment of ulcer patients, both gastric secretory activity and gastric and intestinal motility are reduced. Introduction of acid into the stomach during the first few days after vagotomy, as reported by Dragstedt *et al.* (1948), resulted in pain of the same intensity as the ulcer pain before vagotomy. Although other factors may be concerned, chemical stimulation of local receptors appears to be a major factor in the causation of ulcer pain.

In certain cases of acute peptic ulcer, treatment directed to the ulcer itself may be efficacious, and the healing of the lesion may be regarded as terminating the disease. In view of the various factors in the etiology of gastric and duodenal ulcers, particularly the autonomic nerve dysfunction, treatment, particularly in chronic cases, should be directed to the patient as a whole since the ulcer is but a symptom of a more fundamental disorder. This is in full accord with the long-recognized clinical teaching that chronic peptic ulcers cannot be cured by resection of the ulcerative lesions.

Colitis.—Mucous colitis occurs most commonly in persons who exhibit other evidence of autonomic instability. Except in the presence of a primary infection, it is not an inflammatory condition but one which is fundamentally neurogenic. The colonic musculature is highly irritable and not infrequently spastic. Spastic contraction of one segment may result in distention of the more proximal parts due to the retention of gas under pressure and pain. The underlying cause of the pain may be either prolonged spasm of the musculature or stretching due to distention. Spasticity or stretching of the musculature results in limitation of the flow of blood in the mucous membrane with consequent ischemia and anoxemia of the tissue. The mucus-secreting cells are stimulated, and mucus is produced in large quantities. The resulting clinical picture is one of alternating periods of constipation, pain and distention followed by periods during which mucus appears in large or small quantities with reduced constipation and occasional diarrhea. The ischemic condition of the mucous membrane tends to lower its resistance to bacterial invasion; consequently, the bacterial flora present may penetrate the wall of the colon and produce an inflammation which dominates the picture, but which must be regarded as a secondary phenomenon.

In certain cases of mucous colitis in which infection arises as a secondary phenomenon the infection may result in ulcerative colitis. In many cases of ulcerative colitis due to a specific infection the local condition of an irritable or spastic colon undoubtedly represents an aggravating factor which plays a significant rôle in the progress of the disease. Nervous manifestations occur so frequently in ulcerative colitis that various investigators have recognized neurogenic factors as significant in the etiology of the disease. Others do not support this point of view but recognize the development of nervous manifestations in patients who gave no evidence of nervous instability previous to the onset of the disease. Colonic lesions undoubtedly may give rise to nervous disturbances which in turn affect the progress of the disease.

In view of the significance of autonomic nerve dysfunction in colitis, particularly in the absence of a specific infection, therapy directed toward the colonic lesions only is inadequate. Efficacious treatment must be directed toward the patient as a whole.

Constipation.—The propulsion of the intestinal content distad is influenced by various factors, including the character of the diet, the physiological state of the enteric nerves and the influence exerted upon them through the extrinsic intestinal nerves, and reflex stimulation arising in other parts of the body. Faulty propulsion in the large intestine usually is associated with overstimulation either of the sympathetic or the parasympathetic nerves. Depression of either division of the autonomic system may also result in motor dysfunction of the colon or the rectum or both.

Propulsion of the colonic contents may be retarded due to lack of stimulating material such as roughage in the diet or due to reflex sympathetic stimulation which inhibits intestinal motility. Constipation due to inhibition of intestinal motility frequently is associated with disagreeable emotional states.

Spastic constipation is a condition in which propulsion of the colonic contents is prevented or retarded by constriction of the lumen. It is commonly associated with an unstable or irritable condition of the colon. This obviously implies parasympathetic stimulation. The nerves in question may be activated reflexly due to stimuli that arise within the gastro-intestinal canal. The importance of certain foods, allergins, foreign proteins, etc., as common causes of reflex spastic constipation is generally recognized. Lesions in the anal area below the pectinate line, such as crypts, papillæ and low hemorrhoids, also give rise to impulses that elicit parasympathetic reflex activity of the colon. Fissures, hemorrhoids, etc., above the pectinate line more commonly give rise to sympathetic reflex stimulation which may result in inhibitory constipation. Reflex symptoms of anal pathology are not limited to the colon, but may involve more proximal segments of the gastrointestinal canal and adjacent viscera, particularly the urinary bladder.

Since inhibitory constipation implies sympathetic stimulation, and spastic constipation implies parasympathetic stimulation, chronic constipation of either type implies a functional autonomic imbalance. Parasympathetic stimulation or sympathetic inhibition tends to counteract constipation of the inhibitory type, and sympathetic stimulation or parasympathetic inhibition tends to counteract constipation of the spastic type. The importance of therapeutic measures directed toward restoration of the normal autonomic balance in the treatment of chronic constipation, therefore, is obvious.

CUTANEO-VISCERAL AND VISCERO-VISCERAL REFLEXES

The principle of counterirritation, long recognized and applied in medical practice, implies somato-visceral and viscero-visceral reflex activity. In general, local cooling of the skin elicits reflex vasoconstriction in the viscera with the same segmental innervation as the cutaneous area in question. The motility of the corresponding portion of the gastro-intestinal tract is also inhibited. Local warming of the skin elicits reflex vasodilatation in the viscera with the same segmental innervation and increased motility of the corresponding portion of the gastro-intestinal tract.

Ruhmann (1927) showed that visceral reactions similar to those elicited by localized thermal stimulation of the skin may also be elicited by localized mechanical and chemical cutaneous stimulation and that the visceral response comes about only after a change in the tonic condition of the cutaneous blood vessels in the area stimulated has taken place. The visceral organ affected, furthermore, undergoes a vasomotor change corresponding to the localized vasomotor change in the skin, *i.e.*, cutaneous hyperemia results in hyperemia, and cutaneous ischemia results in ischemia of the visceral organs in question. These findings are in full accord with the finding of Boas (1926) that bleeding of a gastric ulcer may be provoked by hot applications in the epigastric region.

Bing and Tobiassen (1935) pointed out that stimulation within delimited cutaneous zones elicits reflex tonic reactions in the corresponding abdominal viscera which can be demonstrated by percussion. Bing (1936) also described cutaneo-visceral reflex responses in the lungs which he regarded as the mechanisms involved in the therapeutic effect on these organs of hot applications to the skin. Viscero-cutaneous reflexes which may be of diagnostic value, elicited by the stimulating effects of pulmonary lesions, have been described particularly by Pottenger (1929).

In a study of the vascular reactions in the viscera elicited by localized cutaneous stimulation in decerebrated cats, Kuntz and Haselwood (1940) demonstrated that stimulation of the receptors involved in the cutaneo-visceral vasomotor reflexes is associated with changes in the tonic state of the cutaneous blood vessels. Kuntz (1945) demonstrated that somatic nociceptive stimulation also elicits reflex vasoconstriction throughout the gastro-intestinal tract. These reactions are carried out through segmental and intersegmental reflex arcs. They neither require suprasegmental centers nor involve parasympathetic nerves. The sympathetic innervation of the gastro-intestinal tract includes both vasoconstrictor, probably adrenergic, and vasodilator, probably cholinergic, fibers. In experiments on dogs Modlander (1941) observed that, in addition to the reflex effects expressed in visceral vasoconstriction and increased gastro-intestinal motility, cold applications also result in increased gastric acidity. He supported the opinion that ischemia in a visceral organ may give rise to pain due to the accumulation of a substance which stimulates the pain receptors and that the relief of visceral pain by the local application of heat to the skin may be explained on the assumption that the reflex vasodilatation produced in the viscus results in reduction in the concentration of the pain stimulating substance to a level at which it is no longer effective.

By the use of quick freezing and subsequent fixation of the tissues by the freezing-drying technic, Richins and Brizzee (1949) demonstrated, in white rats, that during the application of a warm pack to the appropriate cutaneous area, the arterioles in the subserosa and the submucosa of the duodenum were dilated and the capillary beds in the villi were engorged with blood. During the application of a cold pack in the same area the corresponding arterioles were constricted and the capillary beds were ischemic. The flow of blood through the capillary beds appeared to be determined chiefly by the arterioles in the submucosa. Reflex constriction of these arterioles appears to be a rigidly controlled response. It probably is the most significant neural factor in the regulation of the flow of blood through the capillary beds. The vasodilator reflexes appear to be less rigidly controlled.

In view of the facility with which cutaneous stimulation elicits reflex visceral reactions, particularly vasomotor changes and changes in the tonic state of the visceral musculature, it must be apparent that many visceral disorders, particularly of the gastro-intestinal tract, may be influenced beneficially by appropriate stimulation of the corresponding cutaneous area.

Reflex responses in one viscus elicited by impulses arising in another may be illustrated by the changes in the cardiac rhythm associated with the introduction of liquids into the stomach. Gastric distress associated with lesions in other viscera, e.g., the gall bladder, is a common phenomenon. Viscero-visceral reflexes are not limited to one or a few spinal segments, but may involve widely separated segments of the body. The inhibiting effect on one segment of the gastro-intestinal tract of distention of a more distal segment is well known. Impulses that arise in the urinary bladder also elicit reflex responses in the stomach. In dogs intravesical pressure of 38 mm. or more of mercury may give rise to one or more of the following reflex effects in the empty stomach: (a) reduction in the amplitude of the contractions, (b) complete cessation of motility, (c) diminution of tonus, (d) diminution of tonus with inhibition of motility, (e) occasional slight augmentation of motility. Most of the afferent impulses in question are conducted through the hypogastric nerves since the reflexes are not appreciably affected by section of the pelvic nerves.

A significant feature of the regulation of intestinal motility through extrinsic intestinal nerves, according to Youmans et al. (1942), is the reflex inhibition due to stimuli arising from excessively strong contractions which tends to keep the pressure within the intestine below the level at which it would block the flow of blood through the vessels in the intestinal wall. Other segmental and intersegmental intestino-gastric and intestino-intestinal reflexes are also mediated through centers in the spinal cord and the brain stem. In dogs in which the responses in one intestinal segment (Thiry loop) were recorded during distention of another segment (Thiry-Vella loop) with balloons inflated to various degrees of pressure, Peterson and Youmans (1945) observed that the minimal pressure required to elicit the reflex is decreased as the length of the jejunal segment distended is increased and that increasing the length of the segment distended augments the effectiveness of a given pressure to elicit reflex inhibition. These results can be explained most satisfactorily on the basis of spacial summation in the central nervous system or in the autonomic ganglia concerned. They also demonstrated sensitization of intestinal segments to redistention due to prolonged subthreshold distention or ineffective distention of any duration. Such sensitization probably occurs at the site of the distention.

Some intestino-gastric and intestino-intestinal reflexes are mediated solely through the enteric plexuses. Some are carried out through reflex arcs with synaptic connections in prevertebral ganglia (Kuntz and Saccomanno, 1944). Reflex inhibition of the flow of bile (Kuntz and Van Buskirk, 1941) and of the flow of pancreatic juice (Kuntz and Richins, 1949) mediated through the decentralized celiac plexuses in response to distention of a segment of the intestine or direct stimulation of mesenteric nerves has also been demonstrated.

Chapter XXII

AUTONOMIC NEUROSURGERY

Anatomical and Physiological Considerations

INTRODUCTION

Surgical intervention involving partial or complete sympathetic denervation of a part or parts of the body has become a recognized therapeutic procedure in the treatment of patients with diverse diseases, particularly abnormal conditions in which limitation of the blood supply to the part in question is a prominent factor and conditions characterized by dysfunction of the visceral musculature or glands. Autonomic nerve section is also carried out for the relief of intractable pain of visceral origin since the afferent conductors concerned and the autonomic nerves traverse common pathways.

In order to insure permanent physiological results by sympathetic denervation, the operation must be anatomically complete and carried out in such a way that regeneration cannot take place. If not all the efferent fibers concerned are interrupted, those that remain intact continue to conduct and the chemical mediator liberated at their terminations may activate not only the smooth muscle or gland cells with which they make functional contacts but also adjacent denervated muscle or gland cells. Preganglionic neurons possess the capacity for regeneration in a remarkable degree. The capacity of ganglionic neurons for regeneration is exceedingly limited. Experimental data bearing on this problem are set forth in Chapter XVIII (p. 389).

The physiological effects of sympathetic denervation by ganglionectomy and by preganglionic nerve section, particularly with reference to the circulation, are set forth in Chapter V. Data obtained primarily from animal experimentation seem to support the assumption that the vascular musculature becomes sensitized to adrenin in the circulating blood in a greater degree following degeneration of the postganglionic vasomotor fibers than following section of the preganglionic fibers, leaving the ganglionic neurons intact. Sympathetic denervation by means of interruption of the preganglionic rami would, therefore, be more advantageous than extirpation of the sympathetic ganglia. The prevention of regeneration is more difficult following preganglionic nerve section than following ganglionectomy. This applies particularly to operations carried out in the cervicothoracic region. Smithwick (1940) described an operative procedure in which, following section of the communicating rami of the second and the third thoracic nerves and division of the sympathetic trunk just caudal to the ganglion in the third thoracic segment, the decentralized ganglia are covered with a silk cylinder, the caudal end of which is drawn

(491)

laterad and sewed into the adjacent muscle. Various other methods of preventing the regrowth of preganglionic fibers into the ganglia have been attempted with varying degrees of success. The regrowth of preganglionic fibers into the superior cervical sympathetic ganglion can be effectively prevented by excision of a relatively long segment of the cervical sympathetic trunk. Sympathetic denervation of the lower extremity by means of extirpation of the rostral lumbar segments of the sympathetic trunk, as the operation is commonly carried out, is essentially preganglionic sympathectomy since the ganglia in which the sympathetic fibers to the extremity arise are left intact. The portion of the sympathetic trunk removed usually is long enough to render regrowth of preganglionic fibers into the caudal lumbar and the sacral sympathetic trunk ganglia improbable. Regrowth of preganglionic fibers into the celiac ganglia following section of the splanchnic nerves probably can be effectively prevented by excising segments of sufficient length or fixing the distal ends of the proximal segments into adjacent muscle.

In man removal of sympathetic trunk ganglia probably does not result in sensitization of the musculature of the affected blood vessels in the same degree as has been observed in other mammals including the monkey. Data advanced by Goetz (1949) fail to support the assumption that sensitization of the blood vessels to adrenin in the circulating blood following extirpation of the sympathetic trunk in man is of clinical significance. This operation, therefore, can be no less advantageous than preganglionic ramisection, and the risk of regeneration of the preganglionic fibers following preganglionic sympathectomy appears to be unwarranted. Data advanced by Reed and Kirgis (1952) indicate that following sympathetic denervation the periods of hyperactivity of smooth muscle, prior to the resumption of a flow of impulses from autonomic centers, are relatively infrequent. They regard the hyperactivity of smooth muscle that may follow regeneration of some sympathetic pathways as of greater practical significance than that which is dependent on sympathetic denervation.

With increasing knowledge of the anatomy and the physiology of the autonomic nervous system, surgery involving the autonomic nerves is emerging from its early uncertain and uncritical phase. Modern diagnostic methods afford adequate criteria for the discriminating selection of cases suitable for operation. Increasing knowledge of the type of operation required also is a significant factor in bringing about the desired physiological effects.

PERIARTERIAL SYMPATHECTOMY

The operation commonly known as periarterial sympathectomy consists of removing the adventitia with the nerve plexus contained in it from a segment of the vessel several centimeters in length. This operation has been employed in a wide variety of clinical conditions involving the blood supply of the extremities. The literature related to it is voluminous. A review of this literature, in the present connection, would be superfluous since the operation has quite generally fallen into disuse.

Jobulay attempted denervation of certain arteries by cutting as many as possible of the nerves which approach them as early as 1899. In 1901

Higier recommended tearing the nerve plexus around the femoral artery in cases of intermittent claudication. Priority in periarterial sympathectomy involving the removal of a segment of the adventitia commonly is accorded to Leriche. Early in 1917, Leriche and Heitz reported 2 cases of severe causalgia of the median nerve, following war wounds, in which pain was relieved by resection of the sheath of the brachial artery. Later in the same year, Leriche reported 37 cases of obstinate fractures and causalgia in which he divided the periarterial nerve plexus. He claimed complete success in 16 of these cases and fairly good results in some of the others in which the surgical treatment was followed by proper massage and muscle training. Since that time, Leriche employed periarterial sympathectomy in a wide variety of clinical conditions. Although it has not given relief in all cases, he has reported a high percentage of successes. According to published reports by himself and others, this operation, in his hands, has been followed by success in patients with causalgia, Raynaud's disease, trophic and post-traumatic ulcers, various edemas and skin diseases, and a variety of other clinical conditions. Beneficial results of periarterial sympathectomy have also been reported by numerous other surgeons, but the percentage of failures reported has been relatively high. Many have rejected this procedure on the basis of observed results and on the basis of our present knowledge of the innervation of the peripheral blood vessels.

The peripheral arteries, particularly those of the extremities, derive their nerve supply chiefly through branches of the peripheral nerves in proximity to which they lie. These branches, which include both fibers of sympathetic and spinal ganglion origin, join the peripheral arteries at intervals throughout their entire extent (Chapter VIII). Although the periarterial nerve plexuses on the brachial and the femoral arteries are continuous with the plexus on the aorta, offsets from the latter do not contribute materially to the innervation of the more distal portions of the peripheral arteries. Long fibers do not extend distad in considerable numbers even in the proximal portions of the periarterial plexuses associated with these arteries. Periarterial sympathectomy, consequently, does not accomplish sympathetic denervation of a peripheral artery.

In view of the anatomical relationships of the nerves of the peripheral arteries, numerous attempts have been made to explain the beneficial results reported following periarterial sympathectomy. The immediate result of this operation, as observed by various investigators, is a primary stage of local contraction of the denuded artery which is followed by a secondary stage of vasodilatation associated with increased pressure, as compared with that of the opposite side, and a local increase of several degrees in skin temperature. Later the vasomotor reactions revert to the preoperative state. Numerous investigators have supported the theory that all the beneficial results observed following periarterial sympathectomy are due to hyperemia resulting from partial sympathetic denervation of the artery. Others have maintained that periarterial sympathectomy results in a change in the tonic condition of the entire sympathetic system due to the reflex effect of stimulation of the sensory fibers distributed to the artery. Still others supported the opinion that the hyperemia following periarterial sympathectomy is due to stimulation of short duration caused by section of the small fiber bundles along the artery. On the basis of the results of microscopic studies of the capillaries, Magnus (1926) opposed the theory that the changes observed following periarterial sympathectomy are due to reflex effects of the operation and advanced the opinion that the local increase in temperature is a result of traumatic disturbance of the circulation. Brüning (1927) advanced the theory that interruption of the periarterial nerve plexus, which is made up largely of fibers that join the artery through branches of the spinal nerves and maintains a tonus which may be regulated through the vasoconstrictors, results in a lowering of this tonus and consequent hyperemia. Fraser (1931) supported the theory advanced by Leriche and Fontaine (1927) that the hyperemia is in part a result of incomplete denervation of the artery and in part the result of afferent impulses that induce a general vasodilatation.

The subsidence of pain following periarterial sympathectomy, as reported in certain cases, is no less difficult of explanation, on the basis of our present knowledge of the innervation of the peripheral arteries, than the occurrence of hyperemia. Like Leriche, certain other investigators have supported the theory that the subsidence of pain is a result of improved circulation and nutrition. Some have regarded it as a result of the absence of angiospasm. Attempts have been made to explain it on the basis of reflex inhibition of the vasoconstrictors in consequence of the removal of centripetal stimuli from the artery or raising of the threshold of stimulation of the sensory fibers supplying the artery or both. Experimental data have also been advanced in support of the theory that some sensory fibers supplying a peripheral artery run longitudinally in the periarterial plexus, and that the partial subsidence of pain following periarterial sympathectomy, in certain clinical cases, is due to the cutting of these sensory fibers.

None of the theories cited above seem adequate, in the light of our present knowledge, to explain either the occurrence of hyperemia or the subsidence of pain following periarterial sympathectomy. Some degree of peripheral vasodilatation undoubtedly is a fairly constant result of this operation. The reports of its beneficial results betray overenthusiasm in many instances, but the alleviation of pain in certain cases can neither be denied nor disregarded. It must be conceded, nevertheless, that there is no rational anatomical or physiological basis for this operation as a clinical procedure. The results reported in the literature, furthermore, do not justify its continued use.

SYMPATHETIC GANGLIONECTOMY AND RAMISECTION

Definition and Review.—Sympathetic ganglionectomy consists in the removal of one or more ganglia of the sympathetic trunk in order to insure complete interruption of all peripheral connections. Sympathetic ramisection consists in section of the communicating rami connecting one or more ganglia of the sympathetic trunk with the spinal nerves. Surgery of this type is not new. Alexander (1889) performed bilateral extirpation of the superior cervical sympathetic ganglion, Jacksh (1892) resected the vertebral plexus and divided the sympathetic trunk between the middle and the inferior cervical ganglia. Jaboulay (1896) divided the sympathetic trunk both above and below the middle cervical ganglion in cases of epilepsy and performed sympathetic ganglionectomy in a case of exophthalamic goiter. Jonnesco (1897) carried out a similar operation in a case of glaucoma. Ball (1899) extirpated the superior cervical ganglion in a case of glaucoma with atrophy of the optic nerve. The results of these early operations were unimpressive and did not stimulate interest in surgery involving autonomic nerve section or ganglionectomy. Stimulated by Franck's (1898) discussion of the incidence of angina pectoris in cases of acute exophthalmic goiter and his suggestion that anginal pain may be due to an overflow from the spinal cord of impulses from the cardiac plexus which reach the cord through the inferior cervical and the first thoracic sympathetic ganglia, Jonnesco, in 1916, first performed sympathetic ganglionectomy for the relief of anginal pain. Following his lead, many surgeons became interested in the surgical treatment of angina pectoris, with the result that sympathetic ganglionectomy became a recognized clinical procedure in the treatment of selected patients with angina pectoris.

The publication in 1924 by Royle and Hunter of their findings in experimental animals and the clinical results of sympathetic ganglionectomy and ramisection in patients with spastic paraplegia gave a tremendous impetus to the study of the functional relationships of the autonomic nervous system and led to the application of surgery involving the sympathetic system in a wide variety of clinical conditions. One of the most important results of this work, on the clinical side, is the extensive application of sympathetic ganglionectomy and ramisection in the treatment of diseases in which circulatory disturbances in the extremities are pronounced.

More recently surgical intervention has been carried out involving nearly all parts of the sympathetic division and certain parts of the parasympathetic division of the autonomic nervous system. Many and diverse surgical procedures have been described, a complete account of which cannot be included in the present volume. The parts most commonly involved in surgery are the sympathetic trunks, the splanchnic nerves, the celiac, the renal and the inferior mesenteric plexuses and the hypogastric nerves. Vagotomy, denervation of the carotid sinuses, partial extirpation of the pulmonary plexuses and section of the pelvic nerves have been carried out in many cases. In the light of present knowledge of the anatomy and the physiology of the autonomic nerves, the physiological results of a given surgical procedure can be anticipated with some degree of certainty.

SURGERY INVOLVING THE SYMPATHETIC TRUNKS.—Surgery involving the sympathetic trunk, as it has been practiced in the past, has usually consisted primarily of extirpation of one or more ganglia with the intervening internodes. This procedure insures complete sympathetic denervation of areas that receive sympathetic fibers solely from the ganglia in question. In certain areas there is sufficient overlapping of the distribution of sympathetic fibers that arise in adjacent segments that extirpation of the ganglia in the segments in question does not insure complete sympathetic denervation.

Equally complete functional sympathetic denervation can be obtained by section of the preganglionic fibers alone, leaving the ganglia and the sympathetic roots intact. Preganglionic sympathectomy of this kind is practiced by various surgeons in order to avoid sensitization of the sympathetically denervated structures to adrenin in the circulating blood. Preganglionic sympathectomy may be regarded as preferable to ganglionectomy wherever the regrowth of preganglionic fibers into the ganglia can be effectively prevented. This is particularly difficult in the segments concerned in the sympathetic innervation of the upper extremities.

Contrary to the current teaching, as has been pointed out in Chapter I, not all peripheral sympathetic conduction pathways traverse the sympathetic trunk. Ganglion cells, usually in small groups, occur in ventral

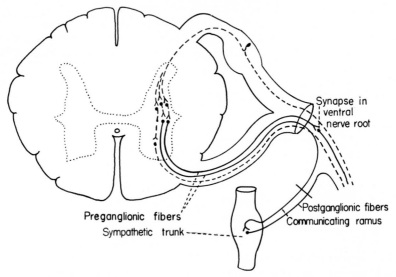

Fig. 90.—Diagrammatic illustration of a sympathetic conduction pathway with its synaptic connection in a sympathetic trunk ganglion and one that is independent of the sympathetic trunk and has its synaptic connection in a ventral nerve root. Section of the communicating ramus interrupts the former pathway, but leaves the latter intact

spinal nerve roots or adjacent to them, in communicating rami and in sympathetic roots. Ganglion cells that are located in ventral spinal nerve roots or adjacent to them or in the proximal portions of communicating rami are synaptically connected with preganglionic fibers that reach them directly through the ventral nerve roots. Most of them in turn send their axons distad in the spinal nerves and their peripheral rami. Conduction pathways formed in this manner, since they do not traverse the sympathetic trunk, are not interrupted by either extirpation of the corresponding segments of the sympathetic trunk or section of the communicating rami (Fig. 90).

In an extensive series of human dissections and histological examination of the proximal portions of the spinal nerves and the communicating rami accessory sympathetic ganglia were found in some segments in all the bodies examined (Alexander et al., 1949). They occur more frequently in the four rostral thoracic (Ehrlich and Alexander, 1951) and in the twelfth thoracic

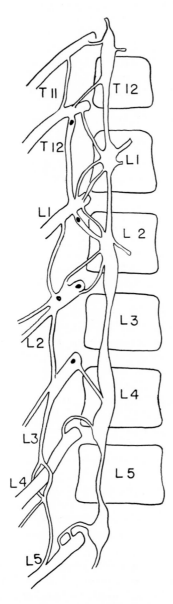

FIG. 91.—Diagrammatic drawing of the spinal nerves, the interconnecting and the communicating rami and the sympathetic trunk showing the approximate locations (solid black) of all the accessory sympathetic ganglia observed in the twelfth thoracic to the third lumbar segments inclusive on the right side in a single body.

to the third lumbar segments (Kuntz and Alexander, 1950) than in the intervening segments concerned with the preganglionic sympathetic outflow. Most of the accessory ganglia are located in relation to the spinal nerve trunks and their interconnecting rami. Some lie embedded in the nerves. Most of the ganglion cells in question, therefore, are synaptically related to preganglionic fibers that reach them directly through the ventral nerve roots and send their axons distad in the somatic rami usually of the nerve with which the ganglion is most closely associated. Some accessory ganglia receive preganglionic fibers from more than one ventral nerve root. They may also send fibers distad in more than one spinal nerve. In the caudal thoracic and the lumbar segments some postganglionic fibers derived from accessory ganglia join the plexus on the aorta and find their peripheral distribution through mesenteric nerves.

The accessory ganglia that are intimately associated with spinal nerve trunks are sufficiently numerous and of ample magnitude to account for relatively large numbers of sympathetic conduction pathways that do not traverse the sympathetic trunk. These pathways undoubtedly subserve much of the residual sympathetic activity that has been demonstrated in the corresponding dermatomes following extirpation of the sympathetic trunk. The locations of the accessory ganglia observed in the 12th thoracic to the 3rd lumbar segments on the right side in a single body are indicated in Figure 91.

Cervical Sympathectomy.—Resection of a segment of the cervical portion of the sympathetic trunk may be regarded as the procedure of choice to prevent the conduction of impulses from the superior cervical sympathetic ganglion. This operation probably insures complete sympathetic denervation of the eye. It does not insure complete sympathetic denervation of the cephalic area since sympathetic fibers that arise as far caudad as the inferior cervical or the stellate ganglion enter the head through the plexuses on the common carotid and the vertebral arteries. It also eliminates but a small portion of the sympathetic innervation of the heart. To insure complete sympathetic denervation of the head the operation must extend far enough to insure interruption of the conduction pathways from the inferior cervical or the stellate ganglion to the plexuses on the common carotid and the vertebral arteries or section of the corresponding preganglionic fibers.

Cervicothoracic Sympathetic Ganglionectomy, *i.e.,* extirpation of the inferior cervical and the rostral two or three thoracic segments of the sympathetic trunk, has been practiced extensively particularly for sympathetic denervation of the upper extremity. In operations of this type, it is desirable to include the third thoracic segment of the sympathetic trunk since in a large percentage of cases sympathetic fibers that arise in the ganglion in the second thoracic segment reach the brachial plexus through an intrathoracic ramus of the second thoracic nerve that joins the first (Kuntz, 1927), and in a somewhat smaller percentage sympathetic fibers that arise in the ganglion in the third thoracic segment reach the brachial plexus through the same ramus and a ramus that arises from the third thoracic nerve and joins the second (Kirgis and Kuntz, 1942).

In order to avoid the undesirable effects of extirpation of the inferior cervical or the stellate ganglion, particularly Horner's syndrome, and sensitization of the vascular musculature to adrenin in the circulating blood, due to degeneration of the postganglionic vasomotor fibers, and still obtain functional sympathetic denervation of the upper extremity, Telford (1935) advocated section of the communicating rami of the second and the third thoracic nerves and crushing and division of the sympathetic trunk caudal to the third thoracic ganglion, leaving the communicating ramus of the first thoracic nerve, the sympathetic trunk ganglia and the sympathetic roots that join the brachial plexus intact.   Smithwick (1936) advocated section of the roots of the second and the third thoracic nerves proximal to the communicating rami and removal of a short segment of each nerve and section of the sympathetic trunk caudal to the third thoracic ganglion, leaving all other connections intact.   These procedures are based on the assumption that preganglionic components of the first thoracic nerve play no significant part in the sympathetic innervation of the upper extremity.

This assumption has been supported by various investigators. According to Gask and Ross (1934), the preganglionic fibers concerned with the sympathetic innervation of the upper extremity traverse the thoracic nerves from the fourth to the ninth inclusive. With the aid of the plethysmograph, Foerster (1939) obtained data which he interpreted as indicating the presence of sympathetic preganglionic fibers for the upper extremity in the third to the sixth and possibly the seventh thoracic nerves. On the basis of results obtained in experiments on Rhesus monkeys in which action potentials of the peripheral nerves elicited by stimulation of the ventral nerve roots were recorded, Sheehan and Marrazzi (1941) reported limitation of the preganglionic outflow for the upper extremity to the fourth to the eighth thoracic nerves inclusive, with the major outflow in the fifth, the sixth and the seventh. Geohegan et al. (1942) found no preganglionic fibers for the hand in the ventral nerve roots rostral to the fourth thoracic in the monkey and none rostral to the third thoracic in the cat. On the basis of experiments on human subjects in which the changes in cutaneous resistance were recorded during stimulation of anterior nerve roots, Ray et al. (1943) reported preganglionic fibers for the hand commonly present in the second to the fifth thoracic nerves and in some instances as far caudad as the tenth. In one of 18 subjects they recognized evidence of such fibers in the first thoracic nerve. According to their findings, stimulation of the preganglionic fibers in any one nerve root elicits secretory activity of sweat glands in all the fingers. Failure to interrupt the preganglionic fibers in only one segment, therefore, would vitiate the clinical results in the treatment of peripheral vascular disease.

In an experimental investigation carried out on cats and dogs, Kuntz et al. (1938) found that stimulation of the ventral roots of the first thoracic nerve elicited vasoconstriction in the distal parts of the limb and activation of the sweat glands in the paw pads. With the stellate ganglion and the sympathetic roots connecting it with the brachial plexus left intact complete sympathetic denervation of the upper extremity could not be effected without interruption of the communicating ramus of the first thoracic nerve.

In experiments carried out on cats and Rhesus monkeys with the aid of the photoelectric plethysmograph, as reported by Kuntz and Dillon (1942), a stimulus (ice or faradic stimulation) was applied to one of the other extremities while the volume pulse waves in the finger or the toe pads were being recorded. With the animals under nembutal anesthesia, records were taken before operation, after removal of the second and the third thoracic segments of the sympathetic trunk, leaving the communicating rami of the first thoracic nerve and the stellate ganglion intact, and after removal of the stellate ganglion and the second and third thoracic segments of the sympathetic trunk (Figs. 92 and 93).

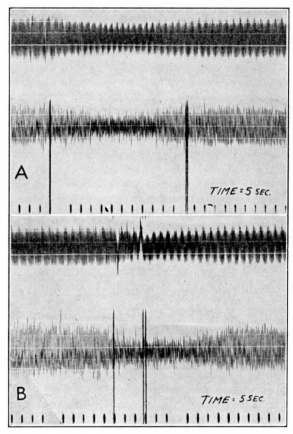

Fig. 92.—Photoelectric plethysmographic records from toe pads of the upper extremity of a cat under anesthesia induced with soluble pentobarbital made after unilateral extirpation of the second and third thoracic segments of the sympathetic trunk, leaving the cervicothoracic ganglion and its connections with the first thoracic nerve and the brachial plexus intact: *A*, upper record, from the side on which operation was done; lower record, from the other side. The stimulus was ice applied to the hind feet. *B*, upper record, from the side on which operation was done; lower record, from the other side. The stimulus was faradic stimulation in the femoral region. Stimulation was begun at the first marker and discontinued at the second (Kuntz and Dillon, courtesy of Arch. Surg.)

Application of ice to the soles of the feet or mild faradic stimulation of the femoral nerve, in both cats and monkeys, elicited marked vasoconstriction in the digits of the upper extremities with intact innervation. Following extirpation of the second and the third thoracic segments of the sympathetic trunk, ice applied to the soles of the feet sometimes, and faradic stimulation of the femoral nerve always, elicited vasoconstriction in the digits of the upper extremity on the operated side. Following

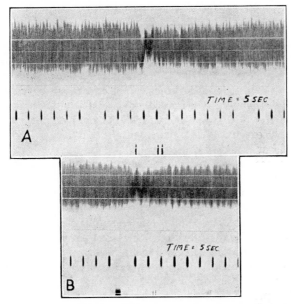

Fig. 93.—Photoelectric plethysmographic record from finger pads of a Rhesus monkey under anesthesia induced with soluble pentobarbital: *A*, before operation; *B*, after extirpation of the second and third thoracic segments of the sympathetic trunk. Faradic stimulation in the femoral region was begun at the first marker and discontinued at the second (Kuntz and Dillon, courtesy of Arch. Surg.)

extirpation of the stellate ganglion and the first two thoracic segments of the sympathetic trunk the same stimulation usually failed to elicit any change in the volume pulse waves in the digits of the affected extremity. In a few instances, particularly in the monkey, a slight degree of vasoconstriction could be elicited in certain of the fingers probably due to the presence of sympathetic fibers which join the brachial plexus from the nerves in the vertebral canal (Van Buskirk, 1941), which had not been interrupted, or to the presence of sympathetic pathways that do not traverse the sympathetic trunk.

The technic employed in these experiments obviates the criticism that may be raised against the results of experiments in which ventral nerve roots are stimulated directly. The recorded changes in the volume pulse waves, furthermore, cannot be due to increased output of adrenin, since no record of volume pulse changes in the digits could be obtained following complete sympathetic denervation of the extremity. The results of these experiments fully corroborate the earlier findings of Kuntz *et al.* cited above and seem to demonstrate conclusively the presence of some preganglionic fibers in the first thoracic nerve that are concerned with the sympathetic innervation of the distal parts of the upper extremity. If the distribution of the preganglionic fibers of the first thoracic nerve in the stellate ganglion in man is comparable to that in the monkey, complete sympathetic denervation of the upper extremity obviously cannot be accomplished by any operative procedure which leaves the preganglionic components of the first thoracic nerve, the stellate ganglion and the sympathetic roots that arise from it intact.

Cervicothoracic sympathectomy, including the rostral three thoracic segments of the sympathetic trunks, eliminates the major portion of the sympathetic innervation of the thoracic viscera. Complete sympathetic denervation of the heart and the lungs can be effected by extending the operation far enough to include the most caudal sympathetic trunk ganglia from which nerves enter the cardiac and the pulmonary plexuses. Except in rare instances, such extensive thoracic sympathetic denervation cannot be regarded as either practical or desirable.

In the presence in the rostral thoracic segments of accessory sympathetic ganglia and sympathetic conduction pathways that do not traverse the sympathetic trunk, cervico-thoracic sympathectomy as outlined above does not insure complete sympathetic denervation of the upper extremity. Since sympathetic pathways that are independent of the sympathetic trunk occur frequently in the rostral thoracic segments, it is pertinent to consider possible surgical procedures that will insure interruption of the independent sympathetic conduction pathways as well as those with synaptic connections in the sympathetic trunk.

An operative procedure has been described by Smithwick (1940) in which both roots of the second and the third thoracic nerves are severed and a segment of each nerve, including the site of origin of the communicating ramus, is removed. This procedure insures interruption of all preganglionic fibers in the second and the third thoracic nerves and removal of any accessory ganglion cells that may be closely associated with these nerves. Carried out in conjunction with extirpation of the rostral two or three thoracic segments of the sympathetic trunk, including the stellate ganglion, and interruption of the interconnecting rami between the adjacent rostral thoracic nerves, if such rami are present, it probably would insure complete sympathetic denervation of the upper extremity in most cases. The motor and the sensory defects caused by resection of the roots of the second and the third thoracic nerves are relatively slight. In the presence of accessory sympathetic ganglion cells that are closely associated with the first thoracic nerve the independent conduction pathways of which they constitute the distal link would remain intact. Their interruption would necessitate section of the ventral root of the first thoracic nerve which would result in extensive motor defects. The available data indicate less frequent occurrence of sympathetic conduction pathways that are independent of the sympathetic trunk in the first thoracic segment than in the second and the third. When present in the first thoracic segment, however, most of them appear to extend into the upper extremity.

Lumbar sympathectic ganglionectomy, as commonly carried out, involves extirpation of several lumbar segments of the sympathetic trunk. With respect to the lower extremity and the innervation of abdominal and the pelvic organs through postganglionic fibers that arise in the sacral sympathetic trunk ganglia it is essentially a preganglionic operation since no preganglionic fibers enter the sympathetic trunk caudal to the second or the third lumbar segment. As indicated by the extent to which the blood flow is increased and the duration of the vascular improvement, as reported by

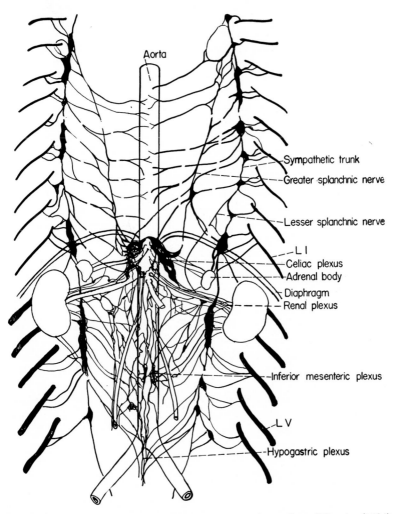

Aorta

Sympathetic trunk

Greater splanchnic nerve

Lesser splanchnic nerve

L I
Celiac plexus
Adrenal body
Diaphragm
Renal plexus

Inferior mesenteric plexus

L V

Hypogastric plexus

Fig. 94.—Dissection of sympathetic nerves in man, redrawn from Stiemens (1934), to illustrate origin from the sympathetic trunks of nerves to abdominal and pelvic viscera, with interruptions to indicate resections designed to eliminate sympathetic innervation of splanchnic vascular bed and lower extremities.

many observers, the results of this operation in the lower extremity have been more satisfactory than the results of cervicothoracic sympathetic ganglionectomy in the upper extremity, but residual sympathetic activity in the lower extremity following lumbar sympathectomy has been reported frequently.

As has been stated above, accessory sympathetic ganglia occur frequently in the twelfth thoracic to the third lumbar segments. Sympathetic conduction pathways that do not traverse the sympathetic trunk also occur frequently in these segments. Most of them reach their peripheral destinations through the somatic rami of the corresponding spinal nerves. Some join the plexuses associated with the aorta and its branches and are distributed through visceral nerves.

Residual sympathetic activity in the twelfth thoracic to the third lumbar dermatomes, following extirpation of the sympathetic trunk from the tenth or more rostral thoracic to the third lumbar segments inclusive, has been observed so frequently that it must be regarded as a common phenomenon. Such activity can be explained most satisfactorily on the assumption that sympathetic conduction pathways that are independent of the sympathetic trunks occur frequently in the segments in question. It is pertinent, therefore, to consider possible operative procedures by which these pathways can be interrupted. The advantage of dividing the communicating rami as near their origins from the nerve trunks as possible has been emphasized by Edwards (1951). Ray and Console (1949) have combined resection of the ventral roots of the twelfth thoracic and the first two lumbar nerves with thoracolumbar sympathetic trunk extirpation. Resection of the ventral roots of the twelfth thoracic and the first two lumbar nerves, according to their account, resulted in no recognizable motor defects in the lower extremity. The cremasteric reflex was abolished in male patients. They advanced the conclusion that most of the preganglionic fibers concerned in the residual sympathetic activity in the area affected, following thoracolumbar sympathectomy, emerge in the ventral root of the first lumbar nerve. This conclusion is also supported by data reported by Kuntz and Alexander (1950).

In view of the anatomical relationships of the sympathetic conduction pathways in the caudal thoracic and the lumbar segments that are independent of the sympathetic trunks, resection of the ventral roots of the twelfth thoracic and the first two lumbar nerves in conjunction with extirpation of the appropriate segments of the sympathetic trunk probably represents the nearest approach to complete surgical sympathetic denervation of the lower extremity that has as yet been accomplished. In the absence of sympathetic conduction pathways that are independent of the sympathetic trunk in the third lumbar segment, complete sympathetic denervation of the lower extremity probably can be accomplished by this procedure. If, in addition, the ventral root of the third lumbar nerve were resected, complete sympathetic denervation of the lower extremity probably would be achieved in nearly all cases. Resection of the ventral root of the third lumbar nerve, however, would result in extensive motor defects.

Sympathetic conduction pathways that are independent of the sympathetic trunk undoubtedly are more significant in the sympathetic innervation of peripheral areas than they are in the sympathetic innervation of splanchnic areas. Since some independent pathways reach their peripheral destinations through visceral nerves, section of the ventral roots of the twelfth thoracic and the first two lumbar nerves in conjunction with thoracolumbar sympathetic trunk extirpation probably results in more complete splanchnic sympathetic denervation than sympathetic trunk extirpation alone or in conjunction with splanchnicectomy.

Splanchnicectomy.—Splanchnicectomy consists in interruption of the preganglionic fibers to the ganglia of the celiac, the superior mesenteric and other plexuses associated with the abdominal aorta and its branches. Section of the splanchnic nerves that arise from the thoracic and the rostral two or three lumbar segments of the sympathetic trunk alone does not effect complete functional sympathetic denervation of the abdominal and the pelvic organs since numerous splanchnic rami comprising chiefly postganglionic fibers arise from the sympathetic trunk in the caudal lumbar and the sacral segments. In the cat, according to Harris (1943), approximately 3,000 postganglionic sympathetic fibers converge upon the inferior mesenteric plexus. Complete functional sympathetic denervation of the abdominal and the pelvic organs can be accomplished by section of the splanchnic nerves and extirpation of the caudal thoracic and the rostral two or three lumbar segments of the sympathetic trunks. Regrowth of preganglionic splanchnic fibers into the ganglia in question can be effectively prevented by resecting segments of the splanchnic nerves as long as possible, particularly those the roots of which arise rostral to the extirpated portion of the sympathetic trunk.

Presacral Neurectomy.—Resection of the hypogastric plexuses is carried out particularly for the relief of intractable pain of pelvic origin. This operation does not effect complete sympathetic denervation of the pelvic viscera since the sacral and some of the more caudal lumbar sympathetic rami join the pelvic plexuses directly. It probably interrupts all the visceral afferent fibers associated with the sympathetic nerves that reach the pelvic viscera. These obviously include most of the fibers which conduct impulses of pain from pelvic visceral receptors since pain of pelvic origin has been relieved in many instances following this operation. In cases of extensive pelvic disease, particularly malignancy which involves the cervix of the uterus, the prostate and the parietal peritoneum or other somatic tissues, the conduction of painful impulses is not limited to the hypogastric nerves.

Vagotomy.—Interruption or resection of the vagus nerve bilaterally can be safely carried out only distal to the origins of the recurrent larnygeal nerves. Bilateral vagotomy proximal to the roots of the lungs has been carried out for the relief of bronchospasm and in the treatment of patients with intractable asthma. Section of the vagus nerves distal to the roots of the lungs in the mediastinum or in the abdomen has become a recognized procedure in the surgical treatment of patients with peptic ulcers.

The anatomical relationships of the vagus nerves distal to the roots of the lungs have been studied in detail with particular reference to the most advantageous surgical approach. On the basis of 100 human dissections, Bradley et al. (1947) advanced the opinion that in more than 90 per cent of the cases the subdiaphragmatic approach for resection of the gastric rami of the vagus nerves is no less advantageous than the supradiaphragmatic one. At the level of the diaphragm most of the vagus nerve fibers usually are incorporated in a ventral and a dorsal trunk, but the gastric branches of each trunk vary in number. In 50 dissections, Jackson (1948, 1949) observed an average of 4 from the ventral trunk and an average of 6 from the dorsal one. On the basis of 50 dissections, Boyd (1949) concluded that complete vagotomy can be accomplished only by stripping the esophagus and the oral portion of the stomach of all obvious nerves and adventitious tissue to the muscular layer for at least 8 cm. This can hardly be accomplished except through the subdiaphragmatic approach. The opinion that vagotomy, as it is usually carried out through either the supradiaphragmatic or the subdiaphragmatic approach, usually is incomplete is concurred in quite generally by physiologists (Thomas and Komorov, 1948). Some vagus fibers become buried in the wall of the esophagus proximal to the level of the section. The intramural plexuses also are capable of longitudinal conduction. In some instances vagus fibers that lie buried in the esophageal wall for some distance again emerge at lower levels (Bradley *et al.*, 1947).

Peripheral Sympathetic Denervation.—Denervation in limited areas may be accomplished by crushing mixed nerves. This procedure has been developed particularly for the relief of severe pain in the lower extremities in certain cases of thrombo-angiitis obliterans and arteriosclerosis. The nerves in question should be crushed at a point sufficiently proximal to include all collateral branches that reach the painful area but far enough distal to avoid too extensive muscular paralysis. The immediate results include sensory paralysis, vasomotor paralysis, which in most cases results in some improvement in circulation locally, and motor paralysis in some degree. These effects subside with regeneration of the nerve which usually takes place in three to six months unless the nerves are crushed too far from their terminations.

Sympathetic Nerve Block.—Blocking of the sympathetic trunk ganglia or the communicating rami by means of paravertebral injection has become a valuable diagnostic and therapeutic procedure. The diagnostic value of paravertebral infiltration with procaine or other anesthetic agents depends on its temporary paralysis of the nerves which enables the surgeon to predict with accuracy the effect of their interruption on the peripheral circulation and on visceral pain. From the therapeutic point of view, repeated or even single injections of an anesthetic agent may result in lasting relief in certain clinical conditions. In general its effect is transitory. Destruction of the nerves in question by infiltration with alcohol has in many cases produced results quite comparable to those of sympathetic ganglionectomy. In patients who must be regarded as poor surgical risks, this method is safer than surgical sympathectomy.

Paravertebral injection of alcohol in the caudal cervical and the rostral thoracic segments commonly affects the spinal nerves to some extent due to their proximity to the sites of injection. This frequently results in an irritative neuritis which is one of the chief objections to the use of alcohol infiltration in this region. Other complications that have been encountered include reflex disturbances of respiration, pleuritic pain and pneumo-thorax. Complications resulting from paravertebral alcohol injections in the lumbar region are uncommon. Irritation of the spinal nerves occurs less frequently in this region than in the cervicothoracic region due to the greater distance of the sympathetic ganglia from the nerve trunks.

TESTS FOR COMPLETENESS OF SYMPATHETIC DENERVATION

Complete sympathetic denervation results in cessation of the secretory activity of the sweat glands and paralysis of the pilo-erector muscles in the area affected as well as in abolition of the neural regulation of vasomotor tonus. Cessation of perspiration affords a convenient and effective test of the completeness of sympathetic denervation. Heating of the body until the normally innervated skin shows profuse perspiration leaves a completely sympathectomized area dry. Pilocarpine nitrate injected sub-cutaneously in moderate dosage also elicits perspiration in the normally innervated area. This method is preferred by some, but it is unnecessarily disagreeable to the patient and frequently inaccurate since pilocarpine in large doses may cause perspiration in a completely sympathectomized area by direct stimulation of the sweat glands.

While moderate perspiration is visible or detectable by the sense of touch, the demonstration of slight perspiration may require more delicate methods. At least two simple chemical detectors are available: (1) Filter paper dipped in a cobalt chloride solution is blue when dry, but when even slightly damp its color changes to pink. Such paper in contact with the skin undergoes a change in color in the presence of very slight perspiration. (2) A mixture of 9 parts of 1.5 per cent tincture of iodine and one part of castor oil painted on the skin leaves a film of oil and iodine after evaporation. Starch powder dusted upon this area adheres to the oil and turns a deep blue-black color in the presence of moisture. An area of perspiration, therefore, stands out clearly and is sharply demarcated from areas free of perspiration. If sympathetic denervation is incomplete, patches of color may appear in an otherwise clear area.

Reflex changes in cutaneous resistance afford another method for demonstrating the completeness of sympathetic denervation. Since cutaneous resistance depends on the activity of the sweat glands it is increased following sympathetic denervation. As tested by means of the psychogalvanometer, the level of resistance is constant, following complete sympathetic denervation, and reflex responses to noises and psychic stimulation are abolished. This method is sufficiently sensitive to detect even slight perspiration, indicating incomplete sympathetic denervation or regeneration, but it is too complicated for general clinical use. A cutaneous resistance recorder, or "dermometer," has been devised by Richter (1946) that provides a means of outlining a sympathetically denervated area quickly without the coöperation of the patient and without the service of a trained observer. Richter and Whelan (1949) described a skin galvan-ometer that gives a graphic record of the activity of the sympathetic nerves indirectly through the changes in the electrical resistance of the skin.

Reflex vasomotor responses may be utilized to determine the completeness of sympathetic denervation, but the methods for inhibiting vasoconstriction or promoting vasodilatation previously referred to are not well adapted for the detection of minor variations in surface temperature. The finger plethysmograph (Bolton *et al.*, 1936) and the photoelectric plethysmograph (Hertzman, 1937, 1938; Smithwick, 1940) afford more effective means of detecting the presence of intact vasomotor fibers. These methods probably are more sensitive but less accurate in the localization of limited areas of incomplete sympathetic denervation within the larger area affected by the operation than the methods that depend on the detection of perspiration.

Chapter XXIII

AUTONOMIC NEUROSURGERY (CONTINUED)

PERIPHERAL VASCULAR AND CARDIAC DISEASES

PERIPHERAL VASCULAR DISEASE

Anatomical and Physiological Considerations.—Peripheral vascular disease is characterized by limitation of the blood flow through the peripheral vessels due to hypertonus or spastic contraction of the vascular musculature or partial occlusion of the vessels due to local lesions. In either case two major processes are at work: (1) obstruction of the arteries and (2) development of collateral circulation. Either of these processes may become dominant. The former is essentially damaging. The latter is reparative. Hypertonus or spasm of the vascular musculature is mediated through the vasomotor nerves which may be activated reflexly or by impulses that emanate from central autonomic centers. Since the peripheral vasomotor nerves are sympathetic, interruption of the peripheral sympathetic conduction pathways must effectively abolish responses of the vascular musculature to nerve impulses in the affected area. If limitation of peripheral circulation is due to organic obstruction of arterial vessels, the vascular musculature may exhibit hypertonus in some degree. Sympathetic denervation of such vessels results in increasing the flow of blood through them to the extent that the lumina are increased due to blocking of the tonic nerve impulses. If the collateral circulation is highly developed, the blood supply to the part in question may be markedly increased following sympathetic denervation even though the effective lumina of the partially occluded vessels are not appreciably enlarged.

Although complete sympathetic denervation of an extremity results in paralyis of its vasomotor nerves, the increase in the flow of blood observed immediately after operation is not maintained at the same level. Restoration of tonus in blood vessels following a period of relative atonicity immediately after sympathetic denervation is a common physiological phenomenon. Sensitization of the vascular musculature to adrenin in the circulating blood following degeneration of the postganglionic vasomotor fibers may result in a relatively high degree of tonus which, according to certain investigators, reaches its maximum in eight to ten days and then gradually subsides (Simmons and Sheehan, 1937). Studies involving measurements of the blood flow in extremities of experimental animals following sympathetic denervation do not support the assumption that it remains above the normal level except for a relatively short time. Data advanced by Goetz (1949), referred to in the preceding chapter, do not support the assumption that sensitization of the blood vessels to adrenin in the circulating blood following extirpation of the sympathetic trunk in man is of clinical significance.

In experiments carried out on dogs in which the volume flow of blood was approximately equal in both femoral arteries before operation, Herrick *et al.* (1932) found the minute volume in the femoral artery on the side of the operation approximately double that on the opposite side following unilateral lumbar sympathectomy. In experiments reported by Johnson *et al.* (1932), the blood flow in the extremity had returned to the preoperative level twenty-one days after sympathectomy. According to observations extending over a long period, as reported by Essex *et al.* (1943), the flow of blood in the left hind limb of a dog was approximately double that in the right hind limb eleven months after left lumbar sympathectomy, but after nine and ten years it was approximately equal in both hind limbs. The vessels in the left hind limb were profoundly sensitive to adrenin both nine and ten years after operation, whereas those of the right hind limb reacted normally to adrenin. Histological examination of the digital vessels ten years after operation revealed marked hypertrophy of the arteriolar muscle in the left limb, whereas the arterioles in the digits of the right limb showed no hypertrophy.

In experimental animals the temporary increase in circulation in a limb following its sympathetic denervation results in a rise in surface temperature and increased redness in any cutaneous area in which the color is not obscured by pigment. In man sympathectomy commonly results in a rise in surface temperature and increased redness of the skin in the areas affected. In a careful calorimetric study of the extremities following lumbar sympathetic ganglionectomy, Brown and Adson (1925) found a marked increase in the production and radiation of heat in the legs and the feet. Heat production and heat conduction in the feet were increased 200 to 900 per cent. The skin temperature of the feet was increased 2° to 6° C. Determinations of skin temperature of the legs and the feet before operation showed a decrease toward the periphery. After operation this condition was reversed. The feet became relatively warmer. Perspiration also was absent. Similar alterations in skin temperature and heat elimination following sympathectomy in cases in which the blood supply to the extremities was diminished before operation have been reported by many investigators.

In the animal experiments cited above the volume blood flow in sympathectomized extremities gradually returned to approximately the preoperative level. The vascular tonus regained after paralysis of the vasomotor nerves by sympathectomy obviously did not exceed the normal preoperative tonus. In man, if the vessels of an extremity are constricted before operation due to exaggerated vasomotor tonus, there is no reason to assume that they will contract beyond their normal calibers in the readjustment following removal of the vasoconstrictor influence; consequently, the blood supply to the extremity may remain permanently increased.

Preoperative Tests.—In the selection of patients for treatment by sympathetic denervation the determination of the capacity of the vascular bed to transmit more blood is one of the most important factors. Surface temperature determinations afford a useful index if interpreted with reference to the conditions of external temperature and humidity under which they are made. On very hot days or in the presence of fever the capacity for normal peripheral vasoconstriction is lost, and the skin temperature tests are of no value. At ordinary temperatures the normal vasoconstrictor gradient increases toward the periphery so that the fingers and the toes are the coolest points on the surface of the body. Removal of the tonic influence of the vasomotor nerves results in abolition of the temperature gradient in the extremities, and all parts of the body surface reach approximately the same temperature level. Morton and Scott (1930) have called the maximum vasodilator response of normal arteries "the normal vasodilatation level." In extremities in which the vasoconstrictor nerves have been released by elevating the body temperature or by regional or general anesthesia the lower limit of this level may be taken at 86.4° F. When the room temperatures is 68° F., the temperature at the tips of the fingers and the toes should rise to 90° F. or over. If this does not occur, organic vascular disease may be suspected (White and Smithwick, 1941). The total rise in the skin temperature of a given digit, following vasomotor inhibition, is less significant as an index of the capacity for vasodilatation than the proximity to which the rise approaches the normal vasodilatation level. The magnitude of the former response depends in part on the initial temperature of the extremity. The latter is a measure of the degree of arteriolar dilatation.

The preoperative tests that have been used most commonly to determine the capacity of the vascular bed in question for dilatation when deprived of its vasomotor innervation fall into three general categories: (1) nerve block, (2) general anesthesia and (3) heating of the body. Blocking of the sympathetic nerves with procaine or other anesthetic agents in a limited area produces the same effect relative to the capacity of the blood vessels in that area to dilate as interruption of the sympathetic nerves. It has no appreciable effect on the general blood pressure; consequently, the vasodilatation achieved in the blocked area will be approximately maximal. It affords a quantitative measure of the elevation of the peripheral temperature that can be expected following sympathetic denervation. General anesthesia is accompanied by vasodilatation throughout the entire cutaneous area comparable to that produced in a limited area by procaine block of sympathetic ganglia or peripheral nerves. Under general anesthesia, the vasoconstrictor gradient in the extremities is abolished as soon as the anesthesia reaches a stage which produces moderate muscular relaxation. The elevation of the skin temperature in the distal parts of the extremity, therefore, affords a reliable index of the vasodilator capacity. In spite of its effectiveness as a method for the quantitative estimation of the capacity for peripheral vasodilatation, the common use of general anesthesia for this purpose is unwarranted since its induction and after effects are more disagreeable to the patient than are other methods. Heating of the body by any convenient method, with the head and one or more of the extremities exposed, results in general cutaneous vasodilatation. In the absence of local arterial lesions, dilatation of the cutaneous vessels and elevation of skin temperature become apparent in a relatively short time in the exposed extremity as well as in the heated areas. The elevation of skin temperature in the exposed extremity is comparable to that produced by nerve blocking. These tests indicate whether the denervated vascular bed is capable of maximal dilatation, but they do not afford a measure of the degree of vascular tonus.

A method of study by which patients can be classified with respect to basal vascular tonus has been outlined by Naide and Sayen (1945). If, after 15 minutes' exposure to a constant room temperature of 20° C., clothed only with a light gown, the tips of the fingers cool to below 25° C., the subject is regarded as having high vascular tonus. If the finger tips do not cool to this level the subject is regarded as having low vascular tonus. Patients with low vascular tonus, according to these authors, usually develop adequate collateral circulation in the presence of obliterative vascular disease in the lower extremities and should not be subjected to sympathectomy. In the absence of contraindications, patients with high vascular tonus and satisfactory, demonstrated capacity for vasodilatation may be regarded as suitable for sympathectomy. The principle of this method of selecting patients has been used extensively. Certain patients whose peripheral circulation can be greatly reduced by vasoconstriction but cannot dilate maximally in the absence of neurogenic vasoconstriction can be benefitted by sympathectomy, but would not be regarded as suitable for operation on the basis of tests that indicate only the capacity of the denervated vessels for dilatation (Smithwick, 1949). Improved methods of study that indicate the degree to which the circulation can be reduced by vasoconstrictor activity, therefore, would be advantageous.

Goetz (1949) has advocated the use of plethysmography to determine the degree of vasospasm, the extent of organic occlusion and the amount of collateral circulation. He has pointed out that in certain patients, when skin temperature readings fail, plethysmographs may still indicate that, with the vasomotor tonus abolished, the collateral circulation will be adequate to insure good results of sympathetic denervation. In his experience, routine plethysmography has served to pick out the patients with organic occlusion who still have the capacity to respond satisfactorily to sympathectomy.

Smith *et al.* (1952) have pointed out three groups of patients with peripheral vascular disease for whom sympathectomy offers little hope of saving the extremity: (1) those with gangrene and occlusion of the femoral or the popliteal artery. (2) Those with intermittent claudication, marked edema, arterial occlusion and severe resting pain aggravated by elevation of the lower extremity. (3) Those who show a decrease in skin temperature of the extremity after sympathetic nerve blocking.

Raynaud's Disease.—The term Raynaud's disease has been loosely applied in the past to a wide variety of circulatory disorders. In order properly to limit this term, the Circulatory Clinic of the Massachusetts General Hospital has drawn up the following definition: "Raynaud's disease is a form of peripheral vascular disturbance caused by tonic contraction of the smaller arteries in the extremities without obvious pathological changes in their walls. It commonly involves symmetrical areas in the hands or feet causing excessive perspiration and circulatory stasis with periods of cyanosis or pallid asphyxia. The severe cases go on to dry gangrene of the phalanges. The spasm is intermittent and occurs on exposure to cold or emotional stimuli; it involves only the terminal arteries, while the main vessels continue their normal pulsations. The disease most commonly occurs in young individuals with hyperirritable nervous constitutions."

According to Raynaud's original account, this disease arises as a vasomotor neurosis. Most of the more recent investigators support this opinion. After a prolonged period of resulting circulatory stasis secondary changes take place in and around the digital arterioles. On the basis of an extensive study, Lewis (1929) concluded that the underlying cause of the circulatory disorder in Raynaud's disease is not vasoconstrictor hyperirritability but a local lesion involving the smooth muscle of the arterioles. According to his account, the digital arterioles themselves are hypersensitive to cold and respond to chilling by abnormal contraction. With this underlying hypersensitive mechanism, the normal variations in vasomotor tonus are sufficient to bring about all the circulatory changes observed in Raynaud's disease.

In a further study of the factors underlying the circulatory disturbances in Raynaud's disease, Simpson *et al.* (1930) found no abnormal changes in the digital arteries and arterioles in early and relatively mild uncomplicated cases, but the fault was wholly in the vasomotor nerves. Complete sympathetic denervation by operation or anesthesia completely removes the symptoms in these cases. In severe and complicated cases, they found abnormalities both of the vasomotor nerves and the digital arterioles. They interpreted the abnormality of the digital arterioles as a late effect of the disease. In their early experience, lumbar sympathectomy never failed to abolish the manifestations of the disease in the feet, but cervicothoracic sympathetcomy failed in some instances permanently to abolish all the circulatory manifestations of the disease in the hands. This may be due in part to the changes in the digital arterioles, but, in some cases, they also found evidence of residual sympathetic activity in the extremity following the operation, indicating incomplete sympathetic denervation.

On the basis of the responses to local cooling of the digital vessels in relatively advanced cases of Raynaud's disease, Lewis (1936) concluded that vasomotor tonus is normal in these patients and that the peripheral spasm is due to increased reactivity of the musculature of the digital arterioles to cold. According to his account, a typical localized vasospastic attack may be induced by cold stimulation applied at the base of a finger without causing a generalized reaction of the sympathetic nerves. He interpreted this reaction as due solely to a local fault in the digital vessels.

Lewis undoubtedly has made a notable contribution in pointing out that local lesions of the digital arteries may play a significant rôle in the manifestations of Raynaud's disease even in relatively early cases. The existence of such lesions, particularly in advanced cases, has been amply verified. Most of the data available fail to support his conclusion that the local vascular lesions constitute a primary factor but favor Raynaud's original conclusion that at the onset of the disease the recurrent vaso-spastic attacks are due to hyperreactivity of the vasoconstrictor nerves.

The relative frequency of Raynaud's syndrome in the hands of workers who use vibrating tools has been recognized by various investigators. Such workers, according to Agate *et al.* (1946), show manifestations of Raynaud's disease most frequently in cold weather. The vascular disturbance is bilateral and becomes more extensive the longer the occupation is continued.

Objective evidence of the occurence in some patients with Raynaud's disease of vasospasm in an extremity following sympathectomy has been interpreted as supporting the point of view that the disease is primarily a local vascular disorder (Hyndman and Wolkin, 1942). Such evidence cannot be regarded as conclusive in view of the frequent occurrence of residual sympathetic nerve activity in an extremity following sympathectomy due to failure to interrupt all the sympathetic conduction pathways, particularly those that do not traverse the sympathetic trunk.

In a study of digital capillary blood pressure in patients with Raynaud's disease and scleroderma both before and after sympathetic denervation, Eichna (1942) found that cessation of the blood flow through the capillary bed during vasospastic circulatory arrest induced by cold was caused by closure of the vessels proximal to the capillaries, while the capillaries, venules and veins remained patent. In fingers with intact circulation, the average capillary blood pressure was found to be 18.5 mm. Hg in the arteriolar limb, 22.4 mm. Hg at the summit and 19 mm. Hg in the venous limb. The gradient of fall in pressure through the capillaries usually was less than 3 mm. Hg. In the fingers of a sympathectomized extremity the average capillary blood pressure was found to be 27.8 mm. Hg in the arteriolar limb, 25.2 mm. Hg at the summit and 21.6 mm. Hg in the venous limb. The gradient of fall in pressure through the capillaries was still small (6 to 7 mm. Hg), but the greater pressure in the arteriolar limb indicated release of arteriolar tonus.

On the basis of an extensive clinical investigation, Blain *et al.* (1951) have classified patients with Raynaud's disease in three clinical groups: (1) those in whom cold alone will precipitate symptoms, (2) those in whom symptoms are precipitated by cold in conjunction with emotional stimulation and (3) those in whom the functional factors are predominant in precipitating attacks, although they are sensitive to cold. Patients in the first category can usually prevent attacks by avoiding exposure to cold. They usually do not progress to a point at which tissue is lost, providing reasonable care is exercised. Prognosis for patients in the second category depends on clinical appraisal of personality, capacity for variations in vasomotor activity in response to stress and capacity for intelligent coöperation in management. Therapy directed toward the relief of anxiety in these patients is indicated. Progression of the disease to the point of incapacitation or tissue loss is most apt to occur in patients in the third category. They are also the ones that show the least favorable results of sympathectomy regardless of whether sympathetic denervation is complete as indicated by tests for sudomotor and pilomotor activity.

The data obtained in this investigation, like many of those previously available, support the assumption that both abnormal vasomotor tonus and local fault of the digital arteries are factors in the etiology of Raynaud's disease, and that one or the other of these factors is predominant in any given case. Regardless of the cause of the disease, most patients in whom the operation is not contraindicated by preoperative tests are benefitted by complete sympathetic denervation of the affected extremities.

Marked improvement in patients with Raynaud's disease, after relatively long follow-up periods, has been reported by many investigators. Late postoperative reports are relatively few. In one patient, a girl who underwent bilateral lumbar sympathectomy at 16 years of age, as reported by Adson (1947), the circulation of the lower extremities was not impaired 22 years later, and the late results of the operation were regarded as highly satisfactory.

Scleroderma.—Scleroderma is characterized by diffuse or circumscribed hardening and rigidity of the skin. The musculature of the peripheral arterioles also becomes thickened and hypertonic. Since this condition frequently is associated with Raynaud's disease and other peripheral vascular disorders, diagnostic tests must be evaluated in the light of this fact. The assumption that autonomic dysfunction is a factor in the etiology of scleroderma is supported by abundant clinical data. Endocrine dysfunction undoubtedly is also an etiological factor in many cases.

In certain patients with Raynaud's disease and scleroderma, sympathectomy carried out for the relief of Raynaud's disease has resulted in definite improvement in the condition of the skin. In other cases, sympathectomy carried out for the relief of scleroderma has resulted in marked improvement in some patients and in no apparent benefit to others. Adson *et al.* (1930) reported excellent results in certain patients in which only moderate alterations in the skin had taken place. In more advanced cases, sympathectomy resulted in alleviation of pain and abolition of the vasomotor crises. Leriche *et al.* (1937) reported improvement in the condition of the skin in varying degrees in approximately two-thirds of a limited number of patients. In their experience, parathyroidectomy yielded somewhat better results. Since patients with scleroderma exhibit disturbances in calcium metabolism, and the calcium content of the skin is increased (Kaether and Schaefer, 1940), sympathectomy combined with parathyroidectomy should yield more satisfactory results than either operation alone, particularly in patients that exhibit marked vasospasm. Hämälänen and Sönderlund (1946) reported satisfactory results, after a follow-up period of 18 months, of sympathectomy alone in a limited series of patients that exhibited no apparent disturbances in calcium metabolism.

Thrombo-angiitis Obliterans.—As defined by Brown and Allen (1928), thrombo-angiitis obliterans "is fundamentally a chronic inflammatory condition of the vessels accompanied by proliferation of the intima and resulting in thrombosis with organization and canalization of the clot, fibrosis of the adventitia and an attempt on the part of the vasa vasorum and other vascular channels to establish a collateral circulation. At times acute inflammation is superimposed on the chronic process. The nerves are involved apparently by virtue of their relationship to the vessels and by ischemia in the distal portions." It frequently exhibits marked vasospasm; consequently, it may be quite impossible in the early stages to differentiate it from a primary vasomotor disorder.

In cases in which preoperative tests have indicated satisfactory capacity for increased circulation, sympathetic denervation has resulted in benefit even in the presence of organic occlusion in some degree. Brown and his associates have emphasized the importance of selecting patients with this disease for operation on the basis of their capacity for vasodilatation as indicated by diagnostic tests. During their earlier experience with sympathectomy in the treatment of patients with thrombo-angiitis obliterans, approximately one in seven was selected for this operation. Later the ratio increased to one in three (Adson and Brown, 1932). On the basis of their experience, they concluded that sympathectomy is indicated in all cases in which induced fever results in a rise in skin temperature of the digits twice as great as the rise in mouth temperature, or nerve block results in a rise in skin temperature of the digits of at least 3° C.

The possibility of improving the circulation in an extremity in the presence of thrombo-angiitis obliterans in many patients is generally recognized. The selection of patients in this category is highly important. The capacity for increased circulation in the extremity must be demonstrated, but the cardiovascular status of the patient should also be evaluated. Evidence of severe cardiac, cerebral or renal pathology contraindicates sympathectomy. Satisfactory results of sympathectomy in properly selected patients have been reported by many surgeons. Telford and Simmons (1946) have pointed out that sympathectomy is of little benefit to patients suffering from intermittent claudication. The occasional excellent results that have been reported appear to be obtained in patients with more proximal thrombosis. Satisfactory results have been reported in some patients in pregangrenous states, but sympathectomy can be of little benefit in the presence of extensive gangrene. Leriche (1949) reported excellent results of bilateral sympathetic ganglionectomy, adrenalectomy on one side and splanchnic nerve resection on the other side. He also advanced evidence of arrest of the development of symptoms in some patients following adrenalectomy alone.

In evaluating sympathectomy in the treatment of thrombo-angiitis obliterans, the progressive and disabling characters of this disease must be kept in mind. Arrest of the disease process is not to be expected, but, in selected cases, sympathectomy may be regarded as a warranted conservative measure to avoid or postpone amputation or to permit it to be carried out more distally.

Arteriosclerosis. — Arteriosclerosis may in certain cases be associated with sufficient vasospasm to warrant interruption of the vasoconstrictor nerves to the extremities. Atlas (1942) pointed out that surface temperature determinations do not, in all arteriosclerotic patients, afford a reliable criterion for evaluating the nutritive efficiency of the circulation through the feet since surface temperature apparently is controlled by the volume rate of blood flow through the arteriovenous anastomoses. In the presence of advanced arteriosclerosis in the feet, sympathetic denervation may actually produce disastrous results because, in the absence of an effective collateral circulation, elimination of the vasomotor tonus permits so much blood to flow through the arteriovenous shunts that the volume flow through the capillary bed is insufficient to supply adequate nutrition and oxygen to the tissues. In his experience, sympathetic denervation has been followed by gangrene in the foot in certain cases.

In the presence of extensive arteriosclerosis, according to Atlas, evaluation of the capacity of the arteriolar and capillary bed in the foot to dilate requires more than a single test. Constant and severe pain in the foot, extreme pallor on elevation, cyanosis and reddening on dependency, atrophy of the skin and subcutaneous tissue with loss of elasticity significantly delayed filling and emptying of the dorsal venous arch, and intensification of the pain and cyanosis on immersion of the foot in warm water indicate advanced involvement of the collateral circulation in the arteriosclerotic process. This combination definitely contraindicates sympathectomy. Its absence indicates an open and healthy collateral circulation. Only patients in which it is absent may be regarded as suitable for sympathectomy.

On the basis of data obtained from an extensive series of arteriosclerotic patients, Edwards and Crane (1951) have pointed out that many of them exhibit very little vasospasm and, consequently, respond unfavorably to the usual preoperative tests. In their experience, patients who responded poorly to anesthesia frequently were definitely benefited by sympathectomy. They reported good results of sympathectomy in some patients who showed no rise in skin temperature following sympathetic nerve blocking. In general, a good temperature response indicates a good result of sympathectomy, but a poor temperature response does not necessarily indicate a poor result of sympathetic denervation.

Chronic Ulceration of Extremities.—Deep thrombophlebitis, varicose veins or bouts of cellulitis, particularly in the lower third of the leg, may be followed by chronic indolent ulceration. This condition may be accompanied by vasospasm due to hyperactivity of the vasomotor nerves or induced reflexly by the peripheral irritation, particularly in cases in which pain is a significant factor. Improvement following sympathectomy has been reported particularly in cases in which preoperative tests revealed a large element of vasospasm. White and Smithwick (1941) reported beneficial results of sympathectomy in the treatment of certain cases of thrombosis of the brachial artery with chronically impaired circulation. Beneficial results of sympathectomy in the healing of both infected and uninfected wounds in the extremities have also been reported.

The production of reflex vasospasm in the extremities elicited by peripheral vascular irritation has been abundantly demonstrated. Ochsner and de Bakey (1939, 1940) have emphasized the importance of reflex vasospasm in the production of the clinical manifestations of deep thrombophlebitis, thus indicating the rationality of sympathectomy or nerve blocking in the management of these patients. The results of early and repeated blocking of the lumbar sympathetic ganglia with procaine, as summarized by Smithwick (1941), include improvement in circulation, reduction of swelling and prompt relief of pain. Untoward sequelæ such as swelling, superficial varices or ulceration where not observed.

In patients with acute interruption of the flow of blood in major arteries due to acute emoblism, ligation or laceration, prompt elimination of vasospasm by paravertebral nerve blocking or sympathectomy may materially reduce the incidence of gangrene. In the management of these and patients with certain other vascular lesions, supplementary treatment such as intermittent venous occlusion, passive vascular exercises, and the oscillating bed may be used to hasten the development of collateral circulation.

Erythromelalgia.—Erythromelalgia is a condition characterized by redness and burning pain in the extremities. The patient may be wholly incapacitated and unable to tolerate the slightest pressure or covering of the feet. Attacks may be brought on by the dependent position of the feet, heat or exercise. The vessels of the feet are greatly dilated, and arterial pulsations are present. Since active vasodilatation, like vasoconstriction, is mediated by the sympathetic nerves, the capacity for active vasodilatation as well as for vasoconstriction is abolished in a sympathectomized extremity; consequently, sympathetic denervation may be expected to yield beneficial results in cases of erythromelalgia. Proceeding on this assumption, Telford and Simmons (1940) have carried out lumbar sympathetic ganglionectomy in a few cases, in all of which the circulation in the feet returned to normal and the pain subsided.

Essential Hypertension.—The causes of essential hypertension as yet are not fully known, but certain etiological factors have been recognized. According to Whitelaw and Smithwick (1951), the major factors in the etiology of hypertension are (1) neurogenic, (2) humoral and (3) mechanical. It may be caused by either one of these factors or by a combination of two or all three of them. The neurogenic factors may be modified or in part eliminated by extensive sympathetic denervation. This may be expected to afford some measure of relief in cases in which vasospasm is a dominant factor. If the hormonal effect is exerted primarily through the central vasomotor control mechanism, as some experimental data seem to indicate, this effect may also be eliminated in a large measure. In the presence of occlusive vascular disease, sympathetic denervation can effect reduction in the blood pressure only to the extent permitted by the capacity for dilatation still retained by the blood vessels.

Various operative procedures have been employed in attempts to relieve hypertension. Those which have yielded the most satisfactory clinical results involve extensive splanchnic sympathetic denervation. Such operations insure not only removal of the vasoconstrictor innervation in extensive areas but also inhibition of adrenin secretion.

The flow of blood through the kidneys, the limitation of which has been recognized as an important factor in the experimental production of hypertension in animals, is not materially altered by splanchnic sympathetic denervation in hypertensive patients. The reduction in blood pressure observed in these patients following splanchnic denervation probably is due chiefly to the increased capacity of the vascular bed in the sympathectomized area.

The literature bearing on the surgical treatment of hypertension has become too voluminous to permit of a complete review in this connection.

The operative procedures, as most commonly carried out at present, involve splanchnic resection combined with extirpation of several segments of the sympathetic trunks in the caudal thoracic or the rostral lumbar region or in both. The aim of the operation is extensive vascular denervation. Splanchnic nerve resection and sympathetic trunk extirpation by which such extensive vascular denervation may be achieved are suggested in Figure 93.

According to an early report by Peet *et al.* (1940) relative to 350 consecutive cases operated during a period of 7 years, 86.6 per cent of the patients experienced postoperative relief of the major symptoms, especially headache, 81.3 per cent showed relief of incapacitation or improvement in this respect and 51.4 per cent showed significant reduction in blood pressure. The most favorable results were obtained in patients under thirty years of age. In older patients age appeared to be but a minor factor in the results of the operation. On the basis of the results obtained, which in many cases have continued over a period of years, they concluded that this form of surgical treatment offers a better prognosis in cases of severe hypertension than nonsurgical therapy. Of 300 hypertensive patients treated by bilateral subdiaphragmatic splanchnicectomy and extirpation of the two rostral lumbar sympathetic trunk ganglia, Allen and Adson (1940) listed the results in 224, with respect to reduction in blood pressure, as good in 13 per cent, fair in 18 per cent, temporary in 39 per cent and poor in 30 per cent. In their experience, clinical symptoms invariably disappeared with reduction in blood pressure, and in some instances the patient continued without clinical symptoms even though there was a gradual return of increased blood pressure. They emphasized the importance of early operative treatment before the renal and the cardiovascular tissues have suffered irreparable damage.

In discussing the results of splanchicectomy by the supradiaphragmatic and the subdiaphragmatic approaches, a combination of these two procedures, and splanchnicectomy combined with bilateral extirpation of the rostral two or three lumbar sympathetic trunk ganglia, White and Smithwick (1941) pointed out that the reduction in blood pressure becomes more significant as the splanchnic denervation becomes more complete, particularly when the patient assumes the upright position. This observation has been corroborated by various surgeons. In some cases which showed no appreciable reduction in blood pressure following splanchnicectomy alone by the supradiaphragmatic approach, a significant reduction was maintained, even in the horizontal position, after additional bilateral extirpation of the lumbar sympathetic trunk ganglia. This operation obviously effects sympathetic denervation of the lower extremities as well as of the splanchnic area.

DeTakats *et al.* (1946) emphasized the importance of rigid selection of hypertensive patients for sympathectomy and pointed out that patients with premalignant and malignant hypertension are unsuited for operation. Hinton and Lord (1946) advanced the conclusion that there is no test or series of tests that afford an adequate basis for the prognostication of the end results of sympathectomy in hypertensive patients. They recognized the eyes, the cerebral vessels, the heart and the kidneys as the four organs most concerned in hypertension. If the disease in each of these organs is graded from 1 to 4 plus, the probable benefit of sympathectomy can be predicted on the basis of the data obtained. If in grading the four organs the sum of the pluses exceeds 8, sympathectomy will probably result in no lasting benefit.

The hypothesis that the value of sympathectomy in the treatment of hypertensive patients consists in its physiological effects has been supported quite generally. Palmer (1947) advanced the opinion that the pooling of the blood in the dependent parts of the body and the presumed decrease in the venous return represent the major effects of thoracolumbar sympathectomy. Much of the favorable effect of the operation on the disease and the disability associated with it can be accounted for, in his opinion, by the relative postural hypotension produced. On the basis of the results obtained in an extensive series of patients, Peet (1947) pointed out that if sympathectomy is followed by a significant reduction in blood pressure, it may also result in improvement in the functional status of the heart, the eyes and the kidneys and, consequently, in the alleviation of symptoms, the relief of incapacitation and prolongation of life.

Undesirable side effects of such extensive sympathetic denervation as is commonly carried out in the treatment of hypertensive patients cannot be avoided. They include compensatory accentuation of vasomotor tonus and exaggerated sudomotor activity in the parts of the body in which the sympathetic nerves remain intact and alterations in the sensory and the motor innervation of the abdominal and the pelvic viscera. Complications due to cardiovascular, renal and cerebral lesions may also be anticipated in certain patients. If, in properly selected patients, inappropriate and too radical procedures are avoided, however, the beneficial effects of sympathectomy will usually outweigh the untoward ones (Smithwick, 1949).

Grimson et al. (1949) have carried out total thoracic and partial or total lumbar sympathectomy, splanchnicectomy and celiac ganglionectomy in an extensive series of hypertensive patients. According to their account, the disease apparently has been retarded in a substantial percentage of the patients and arrested in some. As reported by Ray and Console (1949), total sympathectomy from the stellate ganglion to the third lumbar segment resulted in somewhat greater lowering of blood pressure than was achieved by less extensive sympathectomy. Homeostasis was not abolished. This they regarded as due to the functioning of sympathetic conduction pathways that are independent of the sympathetic trunk and, consequently, were not interrupted by the operation.

Very extensive sympathectomy probably is neither necessary nor desirable in the treatment of most hypertensive patients that are suitable for operation. Hoobler et al. (1951) have reported the results observed in 338 patients over a period of 10 to 18 months following supradiaphragmatic splanchnicectomy. Orthostatic hypotension was not encountered in these patients, and postoperative disability was minimal, but symptomatic relief occurred no less frequently than in patients that had been subjected to more extensive sympathectomy. While reductions in blood pressure were less marked than have been reported following sympathetic surgery of other types, they have expressed the conviction that this less radical surgical procedure has a real place in the routine treatment of hypertensive patients.

The recognition of an adrenocortical factor in the etiology of hypertension has suggested to some surgeons that hypertensive patients could be benefited by surgery that is even more limited. This concept is consistent with the facts that destruction or removal of the adrenals results in marked lowering of blood pressure, and that hyperplasia of the adrenals is associated with elevation of blood pressure.

On the basis of experimental and clinical data, Heinbecker (1947) advanced the hypothesis that the primary cause of essential hypertension is humoral. The hormones concerned are derived from the anterior hypophyseal lobe and the adrenal cortex. Their combined effect causes constriction of the renal artery and, consequently, the production of renin. The production of the hormones in question is decreased following denervation of the adrenal glands due to the decreased output of adrenin. According to this hypothesis, which requires further confirmation, the causative factors in hypertension tend to limit the flow of blood through the kidneys. The aim of treatment, therefore, should be reduction in the intensity of the humoral mechanism that is responsible for limitation of the flow of blood through the kidneys. This aim can be accomplished by sympathetic denervation of the adrenal glands and the kidneys. More extensive sympathectomy than is required to denervate these organs might even be disadvantageous because the sympathetic denervation of an extensive vascular bed tends to divert blood from the kidneys.

On the assumption that adrenal cortical activity is a major factor in the etiology of hypertension, various surgeons have advocated subtotal adrenalectomy either alone or in conjunction with limited sympathectomy. In an attempt to discover as accurately as possible the effect of unilateral and subtotal adrenalectomy in hypertensive patients, Wolferth *et al.* (1951) observed no greater reduction in blood pressure following unilateral adrenalectomy in conjunction with sympathectomy than could be obtained by sympathectomy alone. Removal of approximately 90 per cent of the adrenal tissue either alone or in conjunction with sympathectomy yielded better results. Arterial blood pressure was reduced from an extremely high level to the normal level in some patients by adrenalectomy alone. These patients also showed symptomatic improvement, relief of heart failure, improvement in renal plasma flow and reduction in cerebral vascular resistance. Removal of so large a percentage of adrenal tissue creates an adrenal cortical deficiency that requires replacement therapy. The results of subtotal adrenalectomy in conjunction with sympathectomy appear to be more promising than those of adrenalectomy alone. As de Takats (1952) has pointed out, the neurogenic, the corticoadrenal and the renal factors form a vicious circle that can be broken by sympathectomy.

If subtotal adrenalectomy combined with sympathectomy should prove to be the most effective surgical treatment for hypertensive patients, depression of adrenal cortical function and sympathetic nerve activity should also be effective in the nonsurgical management of such patients. Since adrenalectomy results in Addison's disease, it is obviously contraindicated, as Green *et al.* (1950) have pointed out, unless the prognosis of the hypertensive disease is very grave. They do not recommend its use in the presence of either malignant hypertension or diabetes, but they concede that adrenalectomy in a limited number of patients with these diseases whose outlook is otherwise hopeless may lead to a better understanding of these two major diseases, which conceivably are closely related to one another, and to more rational treatment by the use of chemical blocking agents.

A complete evaluation of sympathectomy in the treatment of hypertensive patients can be made only on the basis of follow-up observations on large numbers of patients over relatively long periods. The data available at present cannot be regarded as adequate for this purpose. Peet and Isberg (1946) have given an account of observations on 437 patients over periods of 5 to 11 years following operation. Smithwick (1948) reported follow up observations on 256 patients over periods of 5 to 10 years. In both series the mortality rates compare favorably with those reported for nonsurgically treated hypertensive patients. In Smithwick's series, the mortality rates for patients grouped according to grade of eyegrounds were considerably lower than those reported by Keith et al. (1939) for nonsurgically treated patients. The progress of cardiovascular disease, as indicated by the electrocardiogram 5 years or more after sympathectomy, also compares favorably with that of nonsurgically treated patients in the same categories. Whitelaw and Smithwick (1951) have pointed out that when the neurogenic factor is dominant extensive sympathectomy results in lowering of blood pressure, reversal of the disease process and modification of hyperreactivity. If hypertension has been long sustained or severe, the effectiveness of sympathectomy in reversing the disease process will be in inverse ratio to the extent that humoral or mechanical factors or both are present. Life expectancy may be significantly prolonged following sympathectomy in many patients with slight or moderately advanced damage to the cardiovascular system even though blood pressure levels are not significantly altered.

Other Conditions Improved by Increased Circulation.—Anterior Poliomyelitis.—In view of the manifestations of inadequate circulation in extremities partially or completely paralyzed as a result of anterior poliomyelitis, benefit to the patient might be expected from sympathetic denervation of the extremity due to the increased circulation insured by interruption of the vasomotor nerves. The results of sympathectomy reported by various surgeons appear to indicate sympathectomy following poliomyelitis, particularly in children, if the residual motor function is sufficient to permit of some use of the limb. If the limb is completely paralyzed, lasting improvement in the circulation cannot be obtained, and sympathectomy is contraindicated. Collins et al. (1947) reported alleviation of vasomotor disturbances by paravertebral nerve blocking in a high percentage of patients with acute poliomyelitis and abolition of pain and muscle spasm in some.

Healing of Fractures.—Acceleration of bony union following sympathectomy, in cases in which union was delayed following fractures of bones of the extremities, has been reported. The results of experimental studies bearing on this point are not encouraging. In experiments reported by McMaster and Roome (1932) in which equal fragments (approximately

1.5 mm. in length) of the fibulæ were removed in dogs which had been subjected to unilateral lumbar sympathectomy, the healing process was completed earlier in the normally innervated leg than in the sympathectomized one. Key and Moore (1933) found no difference in the rate of bone repair on the sympathectomized and the control sides in cats. In experiments carried out on dogs in which the effects of sympathectomy both preceding and following fractures of the fibulae were observed, Zollinger (1933) found that in all but 2 of 17 experiments regeneration of the bone went on more rapidly on the sympathectomized than on the normally innervated side regardless of whether sympathetic denervation preceded or followed the fracture. This acceleration was not regarded as great enough to warrant the application of sympathectomy as a clinical measure designed to hasten bony union in patients with fracture.

In the rat, Zinn and Griffith (1941) found that the blood supply to the tibia was actually decreased five days after lumbar sympathectomy, probably due to disproportionately greater dilatation of the vessels in the soft tissues than in the bone. Increased vascularity of the periosteum at the site of a fracture and the resulting scar tissue undoubtedly is a factor in the healing process. This apparently is not materially increased following sympathetic denervation due to the compact character of the tissues in question. Injection of the arteries in specimens of old ununited fractures has shown that few large vessels actually penetrate through the dense scar tissue which surrounds the fracture.

CARDIAC DISEASE

Angina Pectoris.—Sympathectomy in the treatment of angina pectoris was carried out by Jonnesco as early as 1916. On the assumption that impulses of pain are conducted from the heart through visceral afferent spinal nerve fibers associated with the sympathetic cardiac nerves, the correctness of which has since been amply demonstrated, he removed the middle and the inferior cervical and the first thoracic sympathetic trunk ganglia on the left side. In later operations he also removed the superior cervical ganglion. Although the results of Jonnesco's early operations were most satisfactory, they did not stimulate widespread interest in the surgical treatment of patients with angina pectoris because his operation was regarded as too drastic.

Coffey and Brown (1923) reported 5 cases in which extirpation of the left superior cervical sympathetic ganglion alone or section of the superior cervical cardiac nerve and the sympathetic trunk caudal to the superior cervical ganglion sufficed to ameliorate the painful seizures of angina pectoris. These results seemed to demonstrate the feasibility of surgical intervention in patients with angina pectoris without interrupting the afferent conduction pathways from the heart. Following this lead, various surgeons carried out more or less extensive cervical sympathetic extirpation in the treatment of patients with angina pectoris with benefit to some and without benefit to others.

On the basis of our present knowledge of the innervation of the heart and the coronary vessels (see Chapter VII), the beneficial results of unilateral cervical sympathectomy which have been reported cannot be explained satisfactorily. Section of the left superior cervical cardiac nerve or extirpation of the superior cervical sympathetic ganglion interrupts only a minor portion of the sympathetic fibers to the heart and the coronary vessels and none of the afferents. Extirpation of the entire cervical portion of the sympathetic trunk, including the inferior cervical or stellate ganglion or extirpation of the inferior cervical or stellate ganglion alone interrupts a larger portion of the sympathetic innervation and the afferent spinal nerve components associated with the middle and the inferior cervical sympathetic cardiac nerves, but leaves a large percentage of the cardiac acelerator fibers and the afferent spinal nerve components associated with them in the thoracic cardiac nerves intact.

White (1930) demonstrated, by paravertebral injections of novocaine and procaine, that the afferent fibers that conduct impulses of pain from the heart in cases of angina pectoris enter the spinal cord through the communicating rami in the rostral thoracic segments, including the fourth. He, therefore, regarded the sympathetic trunk in these segments as the logical point of attack in the surgical treatment of patients with angina pectoris and recommended extirpation of the rostral two or three thoracic sympathetic trunk ganglia in order to interrupt the major portion of the pain-conducting fibers. If the pain radiates to the left, as it does in most patients, the operation should be carried out on the left side. If it radiates to the right side only, as it does in some patients, the operation should be carried out on the right side. White (1933) and Braeucker (1933) reported limited series of cases in which extirpation of the inferior cervical and the first and the second thoracic sympathetic trunk ganglia resulted in satisfactory relief of anginal attacks.

This point of view, which emphasizes interruption of the pain conduction pathways as the primary aim in the surgical treatment of angina pectoris, has been quite generally adopted. The occurrence in the rostral four thoracic spinal nerves of afferent fibers that conduct impulses of pain from the heart is amply demonstrated (White and Bland, 1948). Interruption of the sympathetic innervation of the coronary vessels undoubtedly is a significant factor in many cases since, according to the best available evidence, the sympathetic cardiac nerves include the coronary constrictor fibers (see Chapter VII). Unilateral section of the cardiac accelerator nerves, furthermore, results in no apparent damage to the heart or appreciable retardation of the cardiac rate. The operation, therefore, can be carried out without undue danger to the patient. It has been carried out successfully even in patients who had suffered recent coronary infarction or threatened cardiac failure (White and Smithwick, 1941).

Extensive interruption of the pain conduction pathways in the treatment of patients with angina pectoris has been regarded as dangerous by some on the assumption that in the absence of pain there would be no warning of an impending attack. This assumption is not supported by the result of studies carried out on patients following such treatment. In an extensive series of patients in whom all sensation of pain of cardiac origin had been removed, White and Smithwick (1941) found that anginal attacks always were recognized by the patient due to a sense of thoracic depression, palpitation, flushing or shortness of breath. According to White and Bland (1948), all patients with angina pectoris who are suitable for operation can be relieved by proper surgical measures without loss of warning signals against overexertion.

Certain data advanced by Danielopolu (1948) seem to indicate that sympathectomy in patients with angina pectoris is followed by myocardial infarction in approximately 15 per cent of the cases. He regards this relatively high incidence of myocardial infarction as related to sympathectomy. His assumption that sympathetic denervation of the coronary arteries is followed by permanent constriction is inconsistent with other physiological data.

Patients with severe cardiac pain who cannot safely be submitted to surgical treatment may be benefited by blocking the sympathetic nerves by paravertebral injection of procaine followed by alcohol. Employment of this method has been reported by various surgeons. Immediate relief of pain following injection of procaine in the early phases of myocardial infarction has also been reported (Fish and Grantham, 1952). Although complications such as intercostal irritation and neuritis occur frequently, this method of treatment involves a minimal risk and, if successfully applied, may be as effective as sympathetic ganglionectomy. If the alcohol is placed with sufficient accuracy to insure destruction of the sympathetic ganglia, the results are no less permanent than those of surgical intervention. Stubbs and Woolsey (1950) have reported relief of severe angina pectoris following injection of the stellate ganglia with a buffered solution of ammonium sulfate known commercially as dolamine. They regard this method of treatment as more advantageous than alcohol injection or surgery.

Cardiac Arrhythmias.—Various alterations of the cardiac rhythm undoubtedly are associated with autonomic dysfunction. A neurogenic factor in the causation of various ectopic cardiac rhythms is indicated by the fact that they are promoted by adrenin and abnormal excitation of the sympathetic cardiac nerves. Recurrent bouts of paroxysmal tachycardia and fibrillation also have been abolished by bilateral sympathectomy. On theoretical grounds it may be assumed that interruption of the accelerator fibers on the right side is of major importance in these cases since the pace-making mechanism is located in the walls of the right atrium.

Chapter XXIV

AUTONOMIC NEUROSURGERY (Continued)

Other Diseases With Autonomic Factors
Visceral Pain and Pain in Extremities

ARTHRITIS

Arthritis is frequently associated with exaggerated vasomotor tonus in the extremities and other evidence of heightened sympathetic activity such as perspiration in the presence of subnormal skin temperature. These conditions may be secondary to the inflammation around the joints, but the arthritic disease undoubtedly is aggravated by the limitation of the blood supply to the joint capsules and adjacent tissues due to the exaggerated vasoconstrictor tonus. The rationality of sympathectomy in the treatment of chronic arthritis, therefore, is indicated particularly in patients in whom it is associated with marked vasoconstriction.

Rowntree (1928) reported a single case of polyarthritis in which the improvement in the lower extremities following bilateral lumbar sympathectomy was very striking. The patient, a woman thirty-four years of age, had failed to respond to medical treatment for six years. A later operation in which bilateral extirpation of the inferior cervical and the first two thoracic sympathetic ganglia was carried out produced results in the upper extremities similar to those produced by lumbar sympathectomy in the lower extremities (Rowntree, 1929). Encouraged by these results, Rowntree advised sympathectomy in other patients with arthritis who failed to respond to medical treatment. In a review of 17 cases, Rowntree (1930) pointed out that the best results were obtained in patients with arthritis of the periarticular type associated with neurocirculatory alterations. According to his account, the operation alleviates the pain, relieves the excessive sweating and coldness of the extremities and supplies definite restorative influences to combat the trophic changes so that in many patients function is restored to a considerable degree. The most striking results were observed in the hands and the feet. The knee- and elbow-joints responded less rapidly, and the effect of the operation on the hip- and shoulder-joints was considerably retarded and not very marked. In the presence of osseous changes or ankylosis the results were less encouraging, but even in some of these cases the pain was greatly alleviated.

Favorable results of sympathectomy in the treatment of polyarthritis have been reported by certain other surgeons, particularly Flothow (1930) and Young (1936). In the experience of many, the results of this form of treatment have been disappointing. In many cases circulation in the sympathectomized extremities has been improved, the skin temperature elevated and perspiration abolished. In some patients pain was alleviated in a measure, at least temporarily. Others experienced no appreciable change with regard to pain. In certain patients, as reported by White and Smithwick (1941), the disease advanced more rapidly in the sympathectomized extremity than in the normally innervated ones.

In view of all the data available, the general application of sympathectomy in the treatment of chronic polyarthritis is unwarranted. This form of treatment undoubtedly is indicated in certain patients in whom the superimposed exaggerated vasoconstrictor and sudomotor activity cause serious discomfort, but the suitability of patients for operation cannot be determined on this basis alone.

Favorable results of sympathectomy in the treatment of traumatic arthritis (post-traumatic painful osteoporosis) have been reported by Fontaine and Hermann (1933). White and Smithwick (1941) reported satisfactory results in a limited number of patients treated by paravertebral nerve blocking. They recommended this form of treatment in most cases, reserving sympathetic ganglionectomy for patients in whom more conservative methods have failed. On the basis of a review of the literature and his own experience, Schumacher (1947) advanced the opinion that sympathectomy will yield gratifying results in most post-traumatic states in which nerve blocking affords temporary relief. Pretty (1947) has advocated more extensive use of sympathectomy in traumatic surgery, particularly in patients with a pre-existing autonomic imbalance.

Bayles *et al.* (1950) have described a neurovascular disorder of the upper extremity which they have called the hand-shoulder syndrome. The abnormal neurovascular reaction appears to be elicited by impulses of pain that arise in various locations such as the abdominal viscera, the cardiac muscles and skeletal muscles. It may be arrested by stellate ganglion block or sympathetic denervation of the upper extremity. The effectiveness of sympathetic denervation in the treatment of osteoporosis is significant since it is an incapacitating syndrome which is highly resistant to ordinary orthopedic measures.

HYPERHYDROSIS

Hyperhydrosis of neurogenic origin usually is most marked on the palmar and the plantar surfaces and the fingers and toes. It frequently is limited to the hands and the feet and usually is accompanied by vasospasm in some degree; consequently, the wet extremities frequently are cold and at times cyanotic. The common clinical observation that secretory activity of the sweat glands is abolished in the affected area following interruption of the sympathetic nerves demonstrates the rationality of sympathectomy in the treatment of hyperhydrosis. Obviously, such drastic treatment should be considered only in cases in which sweating is extreme and incapacitating.

The results of sympathectomy in the treatment of patients with hyperhydrosis that have been reported are consistently satisfactory. Nerve blocking by means of paravertebral infiltration of alcohol has also yielded satisfactory results. White and Smithwick (1941) regard surgical sympathetic denervation as preferable, except in exceptional cases, since its effects are certain and the operative risk is almost nil in this group of patients, most of whom are young and otherwise in good health. Tarlov and Herz (1947) reported circumscribed hyperhydrosis over the left side of the forehead that was relieved by section of the supraorbital nerve. The conclusion that sudomotor fibers are conveyed by this nerve, therefore, is confirmed.

CAROTID SINUS SYNDROME

The carotid sinus mechanism, which plays a significant rôle in the normal regulation of circulation and respiration (see Chapters VIII and IX), frequently becomes hyperirritable, giving rise to a characteristic syndrome. In its fully developed form this syndrome includes recurrent attacks of syncope and is easily recognized. Exaggerated carotid sinus reflexes of three types have been described: (1) asystole or sudden retardation of the cardiac rhythm with or without marked reduction in arterial blood pressure; (2) pronounced decrease in blood pressure without marked retardation of the cardiac rate; (3) alterations in the cerebral circulation that result in fainting and at times convulsions without marked change in heart-rate or blood pressure. The abnormal reflex responses may be entirely unilateral or much more pronounced on one side than on the other. Digital pressure on the hypersensitive carotid sinus may induce symptoms which are identical with those of spontaneous attacks. The carotid sinus syndrome sometimes resembles an anginal attack, but, as has been pointed out by Friedman (1945), it can be differentiated from angina by the fact that it is not brought on by exertion but by movements that stimulate the carotid sinus. Recovery is also more rapid than from an anginal attack, and the cardiogram is normal.

Hyperactivity of the carotid sinus reflex mechanism may induce abnormal reactions of the intracardiac conduction system, including complete heart block, temporary asystoles of the ventricles with continued contractions of the atria, ventricular extrasystoles, alterations in the form of the T-wave and complete inversion of the electrical cardiac axis. Carotid sinus irritability may be increased by light epival anesthesia, digitalis, etc. Manipulation of the hyperirritable carotid sinus or stimulation of the carotid sinus nerve during operations in the cervical region may result in alarming symptoms or even fatal collapse. Preoperative tests of the reflex excitability of the carotid sinus mechanism, therefore, are advantageous. In the presence of carotid sinus hyperirritability or when the field of operation is adjacent to the carotid sinus the use of anesthetics which, like ether, tend to depress this mechanism are more advantageous than the use of those which, like epival, tend to increase its reactivity.

Asystole or reflex slowing of the heart due to carotid sinus stimulation may be abolished by atropine since the reflex response is mediated through parasympathetic nerves. A marked decrease in blood pressure may in some instances be relieved by adrenin or ephedrine since these agents act not only to accelerate the heart rate but also to increase vascular tonus. Abolition of the primary attacks of syncope and convulsions may require complete blocking of the carotid sinus reflex mechanisms. This can be accomplished by infiltration of the tissues around the carotid sheath with procaine or resection of the carotid sinus nerve. Surgical denervation of the carotid sinus commonly abolishes all symptoms of reflex activity of the carotid sinus mechanism. Favorable results of carotid sinus denervation in the treatment of recurrent syncope and convulsions have been reported by various investigators.

EPILEPSY

A possible rôle of the carotid sinus and cardio-aortic nerves in epileptic seizures has been suggested by various investigators. Section of the carotid sinus nerves and partial section of the cardio-aortic nerves in the treatment of epileptic patients has been reported. On the experimental side Danielopolu and Marcu (1932) reported that clonic and convulsive movements induced by application of a strychnine solution to the motor cortex in dogs may be modified by stimulation or section of the cardio-aortic or the carotid sinus nerves. When clonic or convulsive movements were apparent, stimulation of the central end of the severed vagus nerve or increased pressure on the carotid sinus resulted in their exaggeration. In animals with the vagi intact, increasing blood pressure in the aorta, while the common carotid arteries were ligated, had but slight effect on the clonic movements, showing that the effects noted above were brought about reflexly, although increased pressure in the cerebral vessels may have played a minor rôle.

On the basis of these experimental results and the clinical data available, Danielopolu and Marcu advanced the opinion that if all the fibers of the carotid sinus and cardio-aortic nerves could be interrupted epileptic seizures might be abolished at least in some cases. Section of all these nerves obviously would be fraught with danger since the control of the cardiac rhythm and the blood pressure would be impaired. In animal experiments reported by Greiwe (1932), death usually followed section of both carotid sinus and the cardio-aortic nerves within twenty-four hours. Of the few animals that survived this procedure, some that were kept alive for six months by frequent blood letting exhibited extremely high blood pressure during the entire period and developed extensive and intensive arteriosclerosis. These findings fail to support the assumption that section of either the carotid sinus or the cardio-aortic nerves or both is a rational procedure in the treatment of epilepsy.

The hypothesis that cerebral vasoconstriction is a causative factor in epileptic seizures is supported by both experimental and clinical data (see Chapter XXI). On the basis of this assumption, cervical sympathectomy has been carried out in the treatment of epileptic patients without marked success. Since superior cervical sympathectomy does not interrupt all the sympathetic fibers that enter the cranial cavity along the vertebral arteries, Mixter and White, as reported by White and Smithwick (1941), carried out bilateral cervicothoracic sympathectomy in a series of patients suffering from frequent and severe epileptic seizures in order to effect complete sympathetic denervation of the cerebral vessels. The results obtained in 3 of 17 cases appeared to be encouraging at first, but the final outcome has been disappointing. These investigators have expressed the opinion that sympathetic denervation of the brain in epileptic patients has no significant effect on the convulsive state.

Blocking of the cervical sympathetic nerves in patients with epileptic seizures due to birth injuries and in patients with either genuine or Jacksonian epilepsy, as reported by Köhler and Langer (1950), has resulted in temporary alleviation of symptoms in a large percentage of the cases but in no marked lasting benefit. On the basis of limited experience with cervical sympathectomy in the management of patients with Parkinson's syndrome, Gardner and Williams (1949) concluded that sympathectomy is only of minor value in the treatment of patients with this disease.

TINNITUS AURIUM

A surgical technic, "tympanosympathectomy," for the relief of tinnitus aurium based on the assumption that in many patients this disorder is due to impulses transmitted to the inner ear through sympathetic nerves has been described by Lempert (1946). He recognizes that tinnitus aurium cannot in all cases be explained on this basis. In a series of 15 patients, all of whom, because of this disorder, were unable to concentrate on anything else, 10 were free of tinnitus following tympanosympathectomy. As reported by Passe and Seymour (1948), extirpation of the stellate ganglion, resection of the preganglionic fibers of the 1st and the 2nd thoracic nerves and stripping of the vertebral artery in a series of patients with Ménière's disease resulted in the relief of vertigo and the relief of tinnitus in varying degrees. Hearing was improved in most of the patients. Rosen (1949) described an operative technic for the relief of tinnitus and vertigo, in properly selected patients, that involves extirpation of the tympanic plexus and resection of the chorda tympani. Trowbridge (1949) reported relief of tinnitus aurium and secondary otalgia in properly selected cases by blocking of the tympanosympathetic nerves. The beneficial results of sympathectomy in disorders of the inner ear, according to Lewis (1951), probably are due to alterations in the blood supply, more particularly the prevention of vascular spasm rather than the production of vasodilatation.

SPASTIC PARALYSIS

The application of sympathetic ganglionectomy and ramisection in the treatment of spasticity of muscles of the extremities was advocated by Royle (1924) and Hunter (1924) on the assumption that the plastic component of the tonus of skeletal muscles is mediated through the sympathetic nerves and that this component may become exaggerated in the presence of impairment of the voluntary nervous mechanism, resulting in spasticity. If this assumption were correct, sympathetic denervation of a spastic extremity ought to relieve the spasticity and give the impaired voluntary nervous mechanism, if not completely destroyed, a chance, with the aid of passive manipulation and other means of reëducation, to regain control of the muscles. The anatomical and physiological data outlined in Chapter XVII fail to indicate a significant influence of the sympathetic nerves in the tonus of skeletal muscles. The assumption on which Royle and Hunter proceeded, therefore, is not well founded. It should be pointed out that Royle did not advocate sympathectomy as a cure for spastic paralysis but maintained that "it merely removes a factor which has been interfering with the normal physical education of the individual, and the essential treatment of spastic paralysis is education of the central nervous system."

The results of sympathectomy in Royle's early cases of spastic paraplegia, as set forth in his reports, were highly encouraging. Certain other surgeons also reported beneficial results in some cases. Later reports of the results of sympathectomy in the treatment of patients with spastic paralysis, of which there have been few during the past decade, are less optimistic than the earlier ones. In most instances the benefits derived, which probably can be explained most satisfactorily on the basis of increased cutaneous circulation and altered muscle metabolism, have not been regarded as sufficient to warrant such a drastic procedure.

BRONCHIAL ASTHMA

According to current teaching, based on adequate physiological data, stimulation of the sympathetic pulmonary nerves commonly results in inhibition of the bronchial musculature, and stimulation of the parasympathetic nerves commonly results in bronchoconstriction. Constriction of the bronchial vascular bed also is mediated through the sympathetic nerves (see Chapter IX). Sympathectomy in the treatment of bronchial asthma, therefore, is physiologically unfounded. A survey of the literature nevertheless shows that this form of treatment has been applied in many cases. In the hands of certain surgeons, according to their published reports, both unilateral and bilateral cervical sympathectomy resulted in benefit to the patient in a high percentage of cases. Others reported only failures.

In experiments reported by Braeucker and Kümmell, Jr. (1927), bronchial spasms simulating asthmatic attacks in man were induced in animals (rabbit, ape) by stimulating the medulla oblongata, vagus or sympathetic nerves and by certain other procedures. These spasms did not occur following section of the bronchial rami of the vagus nerves; consequently, it may be assumed that bronchial spasm induced by sympathetic stimulation may be due to reflex vagus excitation due to stimulation of the visceral afferent spinal nerve components associated with the sympathetic nerves of the bronchi. It seems probable, therefore, that the cessation of asthmatic attacks observed in certain cases following cervical sympathectomy may have resulted from interruption of the afferent conduction pathways from the bronchial mucosa to the spinal cord, thus reducing reflex stimulation of the vagus center. The bilateral effect of unilateral cervical sympathectomy, reported in certain cases, could be explained on the assumption that the distribution of the visceral afferent, like that of the sympathetic innervation of the bronchi, is not strictly unilateral, but some fibers cross over to the bronchi on the opposite side.

Although there is no rational physiological basis for sympathectomy in the treatment of bronchial asthma, and in spite of the high percentage of failures reported, this method of treatment has not been entirely abandoned. Carr and Chandler (1948) reported beneficial results of bilateral extirpation of the second to the fifth thoracic segments of the sympathetic trunk in a limited number of patients with intractable asthma. Blanchon (1951) also reported treatment of asthmatic patients by sympathectomy. Beneficial results of paravertebral injections of procaine and alcohol in patients with bronchial asthma have also been reported. These results can be explained with less difficulty than the beneficial results of sympathectomy since the infiltrating chemical substances undoubtedly block some of the pulmonary branches of the vagi as well as the sympathetic nerves.

From the physiological point of view, surgical intervention involving the parasympathetic pulmonary nerves in the treatment of patients with bronchial asthma appears to be more rational than sympathectomy. Phillips and Scott (1929) first reported surgical treatment of this kind. Reinhoff and Gay (1938) reported bilateral resection of the posterior pulmonary plexuses in 10 patients with intractable asthma. Four remained free of attacks two years after operation and had returned to work. Four others suffered occasional mild attacks all of which could be controlled by medical treatment. Only one showed no improvement. In a later report based on 21 patients that had been subjected to bilateral resection of the vagus nerve and the posterior pulmonary plexus and observed during postoperative periods of 4 to 8 years, Gay and Reinhoff (1942) regarded the results as satisfactory in 8 patients. They also pointed out that asthmatic attacks that occurred in the interval between operation on the two sides tended to be limited to the unoperated side, and that in some instances freedom from attacks was not achieved for several months after operation, but the attacks gradually became less severe. They found no adequate criteria for the selection of patients for operation. Blades *et al.* (1950) reported improvement in 22 of 38 asthmatic patients following unilateral vagus resection in some and bilateral vagus resection in others. Klassen *et al.* (1950) obtained equivocal results in three patients with bronchial asthma treated by vagus resection. They demonstrated by bronchography that bronchospasm had not been abolished. Clarke (1951) reported the results of vagus resection in 6 patients with intractable bronchial asthma as disappointing. In view of all the data available this method of treatment appears to merit further consideration particularly for patients with intractable asthma.

GASTRO-INTESTINAL DISORDERS

Cardiospasm.—The response of the cardiac sphincter to either sympathetic or parasympathetic stimulation is conditioned by the tonic state of the muscle (see p. 225). The effect of either nerve stimulation or partial denervation, consequently, cannot be predicted with certainty in any given case except as indicated by diagnostic tests. Since both the vagus and the sympathetic nerves may mediate either excitation or inhibition of the sphincter muscle, there is no reason to assume that cardiospasm can be abolished by interruption of either the vagus or the sympathetic nerves that innervate this muscle.

Knight and Adamson (1935) reported the results of surgical intervention involving resection of the left gastric artery and vein with the plexus of nerves associated with these vessels in the treatment of 5 patients with achalasia of the esophagus and cardiospasm. This procedure undoubtedly interrupts the major portion of the sympathetic and some of the vagus nerve fibers to the cardiac sphincter. In one patient the operation resulted in complete relief. Another showed marked improvement. The other three showed signs of recurrence. Craig *et al.* (1934) carried out bilateral cervico-thoracic sympathectomy with good immediate results in patients in whom preoperative nerve blocking with procaine afforded temporary relief. In other reported cases in which bilateral sympathectomy was carried out the results have been unimpressive. The results of surgical intervention directed toward the vagus nerves also have been disappointing.

In the selection of patients with achalasia and cardiospasm for surgical treatment directed toward the innervation of the cardia, it is important to differentiate between true cardiospasm and hypertrophic stenosis of the cardia. Certain patients in the former category undoubtedly may be bene-fited by nerve section, particularly if preoperative nerve blocking affords temporary relief. Beneficial results of nerve section in patients in the latter category are not to be expected.

Gastric Acidity.—Gastric acidity commonly is associated with para-sympathetic hypertonus. On the basis of this clinical observation and the fact that the parasympathetic innervation of the stomach plays a major rôle in the regulation of gastric secretion, interruption of the vagus branches to the stomach may be expected to result in reduced gastric acidity. The inhibitory effect of vagotomy on gastric secretory activity is amply demon-strated both experimentally and clinically. Reduction in the acidity of the gastric juice following vagotomy is also amply demonstrated in ex-perimental animals and in man. Certain clinical data have been inter-preted as indicating that incomplete vagotomy exerts no significant in-fluence on the neural phase of gastric secretion (Weinstein *et al.*, 1944), but Walters and Belding (1951) have shown that section of the dorsal vagus trunk alone results in reduction in the hydrochloric acid content of the stomach comparable to that observed after total vagotomy.

Peptic Ulcer.—Excessive gastric acidity is commonly regarded as a major factor in the etiology of gastric and duodenal ulceration. Since gastric secretory activity is regulated in large part through the parasympathetic nerves, impulses of central nervous origin that are conducted through the vagus nerves undoubtedly play a significant rôle in the production of gas-tric hyperacidity. Peptic ulceration may therefore be regarded as a psychosomatic disease. Vagotomy in the treatment of peptic ulcer patients is based on the theory that reduction of the acidity of the gastric juice facilitates healing of the ulcers and removes a major factor in the causation of recurrence of ulceration. It has become a recognized procedure in the surgical treatment of patients with peptic ulcers particularly in combina-tion with gastrectomy or gastroenterostomy.

The literature relative to vagotomy in the treatment of ulcer patients has become too voluminous to be reviewed in this connection. On the basis of this literature it is evident that gastric secretory activity and gastric acidity are reduced following vagotomy and that gastric tonus and gastric motility are greatly depressed. Emptying of the stomach is retarded, and the viscus may become dilated. Decompression of the stomach for several days after operation frequently is essential. Dragstedt *et al.* (1947) have pointed out that if obstruction of the pylorus is apparent gastroenterostomy should be done at the time of the vagotomy, but they found no indication for gastric resection either alone or in combination with vagotomy in the surgical treatment of patients with duodenal ulcers. In general vagotomy combined with gastroenterostomy is more effective than gastrectomy. The neural phase of gastric secretion appears to be permanently abolished following total vagotomy (Dragstedt, 1952). The physical and the chemical factors that normally protect the gastric mucosa, however, are rendered less effective following vagotomy due to the decreased production of mucus and mucoid combined with a decreased quantity of dissolved fractions, particularly mucoprotein (Kittle and Batchelder, 1952).

In comparing the early results of subtotal gastrectomy alone and in combination with vagotomy, Colp *et al.* (1948) found that morbidity was increased by the combined procedure, but it was much more effective in modifying both neurogenic and chemical secretory activity as indicated by the effect on gastric acidity. Various other surgeons have corroborated these findings. In view of the importance that has been attached to gastric acidity as a factor in the genesis and the perpetuation of peptic ulcers the combined procedure may be regarded as more advantageous than either gastrectomy or vagotomy alone.

Necheles and Jefferson (1952) have pointed out that crushing the left phrenic nerve in the neck in conjunction with vagotomy may be advantageous, since paralysis of the diaphragm permits the stomach to assume a higher position. The axis from the cardia to the pylorus tends to become more nearly perpendicular, and gastric emptying is facilitated. Some of the troublesome complications of vagotomy are thus minimized or eliminated.

Certain surgeons have abandoned vagotomy in the treatment of patients with gastric ulcer. The point of view that it should be applied in the treatment of patients with duodenal ulcer only after other surgical procedures have been found to be inadequate appears to be gaining ground. Warren and Meadows (1949) concluded, on the basis of 120 operations, that for the time being, the use of vagotomy should be restricted to patients with anastomotic ulcer and young patients without pyloric stenosis who exhibit strong emotional gastric secretory activity. Garlock and Lyons (1949) regard vagotomy as the operation of choice in the rare patients who develop gastrojejunal ulcer following gastrectomy for the relief of duodenal ulcer. Walters and Fahey (1949) also regard vagotomy as indicated in patients with recurring ulcers following adequate gastric resection. Beal and Dineen (1950) regard it as contraindicated in patients with gastric or obstructive duodenal ulcer, but as indicated in patients with marginal ulcer. That vagotomy affords protection in some degree against recurrence of ulcer is quite generally conceded. It is not to be regarded as a substitute for, but as an adjunct to gastric resection or other surgical procedures (Harth, 1951). The necessity of total vagotomy has been stressed by various surgeons, although Walters and Belding (1951) have pointed out that section of the dorsal vagus trunk alone results in reduction in gastric acidity comparable to that observed following total vagotomy. Recurrence or persistence of duodenal ulcer after vagotomy has been regarded as due to incomplete nerve section (Dragstedt and Woodward, 1951). Certain data seem to support the assumption that sympathetic dystonia is a significant factor in the recurrence of peptic ulcers. Nitsch (1949) found that recurrence of ulcers was usually preceded by evidence of increased sympathetic dystonia. Mason and Pollard (1949) also reported recurrence of peptic ulcers in a small percentage of patients following splanchniectomy for the relief of hypertension.

Although recent reports, including those of Grimson *et al.* (1952), Walters *et al.* (1952) and others, are encouraging, a complete evaluation of vagotomy in the treatment of ulcer patients cannot be made on the basis of the data available at present. Further postoperative studies of carefully selected patients over longer follow-up periods are required. The future of this method of treatment of ulcer patients probably will be determined by whether or not it produces serious, persistent side effects.

Congenital Megacolon (Hirschsprung's Disease).—Hurst (1919) advanced the theory that the underlying cause of congenital megacolon is an achalasia of the pelvi-rectal (O'Beirne's) sphincter or the internal sphincter ani. According to this theory, peristaltic waves passing down the descending colon, which should evacuate the bowel, are arrested at one or the other of these sphincters due to its inability to relax, resulting in distention and hypertrophy. Fraser (1926) also regarded failure of one or the other of these sphincters to relax as a primary condition of congenital megacolon. Constriction of the distal portion of the colon, with failure to relax, is now generally recognized as a factor in this disorder.

Certain data have been interpreted as indicating that in the presence of congenital megacolon the influence of the sympathetic nerves on the large intestine exceeds that of the parasympathetic nerves. On the basis of this assumption, sympathectomy has been carried out by many surgeons in the treatment of patients with congenital megacolon. The results of some of the early operations were reported as satisfactory, but in a high percentage of the cases the results were unsatisfactory. On the basis of known factors in the etiology and the pathology of this disease, sympathectomy as a therapeutic measure should be abandoned.

In histopathological studies of the large intestine in patients with congenital megacolon, the most constant finding is the absence of intramural ganglia and the presence of abnormal nerve bundles in the terminal undilated segment. The length of the aganglionic segment is somewhat variable. Most of the reports also indicate pathological changes in the rectum and part or all of the sigmoid colon. The aganglionic segment is constricted and lacks peristaltic activity; consequently, the evacuation of feces and gas is obstructed, and the portion of the colon proximal to the constricted segment becomes dilated. The most rational therapy consists in resection of the constricted segment of the colon.

VISCERAL PAIN

The afferent innervation of the thoracic and the abdominal viscera includes both vagus and spinal nerve components. From all except the esophagus and the respiratory tract impulses of pain are conducted only through spinal nerve fibers (see Chapter XIX). These pain-conducting fibers of spinal nerve origin reach the viscera via the sympathetic nerves. Most of those that are connected with receptors in the abdominal viscera reach the abdominal plexuses through the splanchnic nerves. The afferent innervation of the pelvic viscera includes spinal nerve components associated with the thoracolumbar and the sacral preganglionic outflows and some afferent components that are incorporated in the pudendal nerves. The pain-conducting pathways from the pelvic viscera are less clearly demarcated than those from the thoracic and abdominal viscera. Impulses of pain probably are conducted from the more distal pelvic viscera through both the hypogastric and the pelvic nerves. Whenever pelvic disease extends to parietal structures the pudendal nerves also play a prominent rôle in pain conduction.

Pain in Pulmonary Disease.—Nerve block by means of paravertebral injections of alcohol has been carried out for the relief of intractable pain due to pleural irritation in pulmonary tuberculosis and other diseases without marked success. Blocking of the sympathetic nerves with the afferent fibers associated with them obviously is inadequate to relieve this pain due to the fact that conduction from the parietal pleura involves somatic afferent nerve components. Conduction of impulses of pain from the respiratory tract through vagus afferent fibers has also been demonstrated. The lung and the visceral pleura are highly insensitive. Pain due to pulmonary disease, therefore, does not become severe unless the parietal pleura becomes involved in the disease process, giving rise to painful stimulation of somatic afferent components of the intercostal nerves. These fibers may be blocked temporarily by paravertebral alcohol injections, but they usually recover the capacity to conduct in a relatively short time. Bageant and Rapee (1947) reported immediate relief of pain, dyspnea, orthopnea and cyanosis following stellate ganglion block in patients with pulmonary embolism.

Pain from the Gastro-intestinal Tract.—Since the pain-conducting fibers from the gastro-intestinal tract traverse the sympathetic nerves they can be interrupted by sympathetic or splanchnic nerve section. The appropriate level for surgical intervention may be determined by diagnostic nerve blocking. The vagus nerves include some fibers that conduct impulses of pain from the esophagus. Spinal nerve fibers that are connected with pain receptors in the esophagus are associated with many sympathetic rami. Most of those from the distal thoracic portion of the esophagus traverse the fifth and the sixth thoracic segments of the sympathetic trunk. Extirpation or chemical blocking of these segments, therefore, may be expected to relieve pain due to disease of the distal portion of the esophagus.

Impulses of pain from the stomach are conducted into the spinal cord in the seventh and the eighth thoracic segments. Extirpation or blocking of these segments of the sympathetic trunks may be expected to abolish true gastric pain. Severe gastric pain of long duration, however, occurs only rarely unless the disease extends into the mesenteries and to the dorsal abdominal wall where somatic pain receptors are stimulated. The results of nerve blocking or sympathetic ganglionectomy for the relief of intractable gastric pain have not been impressive probably due to the involvement of somatic afferent fibers in most of the cases which have been subjected to this method of treatment.

Chronic intractable pain due to stimulation arising in the intestine alone occurs only rarely. The segments in which the afferent fibers stimulated in such cases traverse the sympathetic trunks can be determined by diagnostic nerve blocking. Permanent blocking or extirpation of these segments bilaterally may be expected to abolish the pain. Pain due to malignant disease of the intestinal tract is rarely amenable to this form of treatment since the discomfort usually is due either to obstruction or to involvement of the mesentery and somatic nerves.

Pain of Pancreatic Origin.—Impulses of pain that arise in the pancreas are conducted through the splanchnic nerves bilaterally, including the rostral lumbar splanchnics. The minimal operation found to be adequate to insure total analgesia of the pancreas, by Ray and Console (1949), included bilateral extirpation of the sympathetic trunk from the 11th thoracic to the 1st lumbar segments inclusive and interruption of the greater splanchnic nerves. Pain due to carcinoma of the body and the head of the pancreas, as reported by Trimble and Morrison (1952), was greatly relieved by bilateral paravertebral nerve blocking from the 9th to the 12th thoracic segments inclusive.

Pain of Biliary Origin.—Impulses of pain that arise in the gall bladder are conducted through the right major splanchnic nerve (Davis *et al.*, 1932). Most of the impulses of pain from the entire biliary system are conducted through this nerve. The left splanchnic nerve conveys relatively few pain-conducting fibers from this system. Resection of the right major splanchnic nerve or resection of both the major and the minor splanchnics, consequently, may be expected to abolish pain of biliary origin in most cases. The effectiveness of this method of treatment in patients with chronic biliary pain has been amply demonstrated (Craig, 1934; White and Smithwick, 1941). Mallet-Guy and Beaujeu (1948) reported relief of hypotonia of the common bile duct following splanchnicectomy in an extensive series of patients. They regarded the relief as due to removal of the inhibitory influence of the sympathetic nerves on the bile duct.

Abdominal Pains of Obscure Origin.—Abdominal pains, the causes of which could not be determined even by exploratory laparotomy, have been relieved in some patients by sympathetic ganglionectomy or ramisection. Scrimger (1934) reported 2 cases of this kind with well-defined referred somatic hyperalgesia in which both the visceral pain and the referred phenomena were relieved by sympathectomy in the segments indicated by paravertebral nerve blocking used as a diagnostic test. In cases of obscure abdominal pain with referred phenomena, the latter may indicate the appropriate segments for surgical intervention. In the absence of referred phenomena, nerve blocking by paravertebral injections of procaine affords a useful aid in determining the segmental level of the pain-conducting pathways involved.

Pain of Renal Origin.—In view of the anatomical arrangement of the innervation of the kidney, resection of the renal plexus or the splanchnic nerves may be expected to abolish pain of renal origin. Hess (1930) reported 10 cases of renal pain due to kinked ureters, small nephroses and movable or ptosed kidneys in which the renal plexus was resected. Nephrectomy was avoided in all these cases and in 6 cases the relief obtained was regarded as complete. Distention, of the renal pelvis during pyelography was no longer painful, and nausea and vomiting were eliminated. Relief of intractable pain of ureteral origin following sympathetic denervation has also been reported.

Pain from the Urinary Bladder.—Data bearing on the anatomical arrangement of the pain-conducting pathways from the bladder are not in full agreement. Afferent nerve fibers associated with the sympathetic innervation of the bladder traverse the hypogastric plexus. Afferent nerve fibers also reach the bladder through the pelvic and the pudendal nerves. Munro (1937) could detect no diminution in sensation following resection of the superior hypogastric plexus either on distending the bladder or on the application of tactile or thermal stimuli in the course of cystoscopy. Langworthy *et al.* (1940) have recognized evidence of vague sensations due to filling of the bladder in cases of sacral nerve paralysis, but they regard the conduction of actual pain impulses from the bladder through the hypogastric nerves as highly improbable. Conduction of impulses of pain from the bladder through the pelvic nerves appears to be amply demonstrated.

In spite of the data cited above, resection of the hypogastric plexuses has been carried out for the relief of pain of vesical origin in many cases. Favorable results of this operation have also been reported. Nesbit and McLellan (1939) have advanced the opinion that resection of the hypogastric plexus may relieve bladder pain of certain types, not by interrupting pain-conducting pathways, but by reducing spasm of the internal vesical sphincter. They reported a series of patients suffering from dysuria associated with various forms of chronic cystitis with marked vesical spasm in whom the results of resection of the superior hypogastric plexus were uniformly good. Facilitation of emptying of the bladder following this operation has been emphasized by Uebelhör (1951).

The results of resection of the hypogastric plexuses for the relief of pain due to malignant disease of the bladder have not been encouraging. Learmonth (1931) reported relief of pain in such cases following resection of the ganglia at the base of the bladder, thus effecting complete vesical denervation. This operation may be expected to abolish vesical pain except in cases in which the disease has extended too far into the perivesical area, but it is a drastic procedure which results in complete paralysis of the bladder, thus necessitating catheterization. Trimble and Morrison (1952) reported the pain due to carcinoma of the bladder with metastases greatly relieved by bilateral paravertebral nerve blocking from the 1st to the 4th lumbar segments inclusive.

Pain from Internal Genital Organs.—Most of the nerve fibers that conduct impulses of pain from the internal genital organs, except the gonads and the cervical portion of the uterus, reach the pelvis through the hypogastric plexuses. Interruption of these plexuses therefore may be expected to abolish pain arising in these organs. The relief of pain in dysmenorrhea and other uterine conditions following resection of the hypogastric plexuses has been most striking. Poliquin (1946) regarded 62 of 84 young women with essential or functional dysmenorrhea as cured after a follow-up period. Seven were not apparently benefited. In those that were regarded as cured, the general condition of the patient was also improved, particularly if there had been personality changes. On the basis of a study of 125 patients with intractable dysmenorrhea, Fertitta *et al.* (1950) advanced the opinion that presacral neurectomy is the treatment of choice in properly selected patients with primary uterine and secondary dysmenorrhea. Bickers (1950) regarded the relief of the pain of dysmenorrhea by presacral neurectomy as due primarily to the interruption of pain conducting fibers in the hypogastric plexuses. It is not followed by bowel or vesical complications and does not interfere with subsequent pregnancy.

Resection of the hypogastric plexus for the relief of pain in malignant disease of the uterus has been less successful, although encouraging results have been reported. De Sousa Pereira (1946) reported relief of pain in patients with cancer of the uterus following resection of the hypogastric plexus and the lumbar segments of the sympathetic trunks. He also pointed out that roentgen-ray and radium treatments of the pelvic organs are more effective following their sympathetic denervation due to the increased circulation. Relief of pain due to carcinoma of the cervix following presacral neurectomy should not be expected since the pelvic nerves include fibers that conduct impulses of pain from the cervix (White, 1952). According to White and Smithwick (1941), malignancy of the uterus usually does not give rise to intense pain until the disease has extended into the parametrial and paracervical tissues. In the latter case, impulses of pain are conducted through the sacral nerves. After the disease has extended into the pelvic wall, pain conduction through somatic nerves is more pronounced than through the visceral nerves.

PAINFUL DISORDERS OF THE EXTREMITIES

Disorders of the extremities such as causalgia, cryalgesia, traumatic arthritis and amputation stump neuralgia which are characterized by intractable pain frequently are associated with circulatory and sudomotor disturbances and trophic changes manifested by edema, glossy skin, muscular weakness and atrophy of the bone. These complications frequently follow relatively minor injuries to nerves, blood vessels or ligaments. The degree of disability caused by them and the difficulty of treatment frequently are disproportionate to the apparent minor significance of the primary injury. The causative factors in these conditions are not well known. The vasomotor changes undoubtedly play a significant rôle.

Most frequently there is hyperemia in the acute stage followed by cyanosis, coolness and excessive perspiration in the chronic stage. These phenomena emphasize the extent of sympathetic dysfunction and suggest that the trophic and other manifestations, including the pain, may be aggravated by the excessive sympathetic reflex activity. This hypothesis, furthermore, is supported by the fact that interruption of the sympathetic pathways by surgical intervention or by chemical nerve blocking has in many instances resulted in alleviation of the pain and improvement in associated symptoms.

Causalgia.—As defined by Mitchell, Morehouse and Keen (1864), who first described this condition in soldiers following penetrating wounds, causalgia is characterized by hyperalgesia of the hand or the foot following an injury in the region of a peripheral nerve. The sensory phenomena vary in intensity from a trivial burning sensation to excruciating pain. The pain is constant and exacerbations are brought on by the slightest physical or emotional stimuli. The skin in the affected area may become dry and scaly, but more frequently it is cold and moist. Trophic changes of the skin are not uncommon. Causalgia is most commonly associated with an incomplete injury of a peripheral nerve. Certain cases have been reported in which division of the nerve apparently was complete. The pain is usually limited to or most intense in the sensory distribution of the nerve injured, but it may spread beyond this area. In certain patients, as has been pointed out by Wan (1946), causalgia is purely a manifestation of dysfunction of the sympathetic nerves to the part affected. He therefore introduced the term "sympathetic causalgia."

Homans (1940) emphasized the rôle of the sympathetic nerves in causalgia. De Takats (1943) pointed out that painful vasodilatation accompanied by spreading neuralgia is a major factor in the causalgic state in many cases. As indicated by the results of plethysmographic studies, the flow of blood in the injured limb is persistently increased. Heat increases it still further in excess of the flow in the uninjured limb. Cold reduces the flow in a lesser degree in the injured limb than in the uninjured one. The painful, throbbing character of this chronic vasodilatation, which is abolished by sympathetic nerve block or by arterial compression and aggravated by venous stasis, indicates capillary hypertension; consequently, any treatment that results in reduction of capillary pressure and capillary dilatation should be beneficial.

The actual mechanisms of causalgic pain are not fully understood. The hypothesis that it is caused by the stimulation of somatic afferent nerve fibers at the point of peripheral nerve injury by impulses that are conducted through sympathetic fibers has been supported by Doupe *et al.* (1944), Nathan (1947) and Mayfield (1947). According to their point of view, the sympathetic fibers concerned make artificial synaptic contacts with the sensory fibers at the level of the injury. Because of the effectiveness of sympathectomy in the treatment of patients with causalgia, some have supported the assumption that the pain conducting fibers chiefly concerned traverse the sympathetic trunk. Data that seem to support this point of view are not wanting (Threadgill, 1947; Kuntz, 1951), but these data do not indicate that afferent nerve fibers that traverse the sympathetic trunk are distributed in the extremities in sufficient abundance to account for the conduction of all the impulses that are concerned in causalgic pain.

On the basis of the literature relative to sympathectomy in the treatment of patients with causalgia, which is too voluminous to be reviewed in this connection, it is apparent that this form of therapy is effective in a high percentage of cases. In mild cases, as reported by Smithwick (1949), paravertebral sympathetic nerve blocking with procaine applied once or oftener has resulted in apparent cure. In patients who obtained no permanent relief by repeated nerve blocking, sympathetic denervation of the limb has resulted in permanent relief. According to his account, the results obtained by sympathectomy have been excellent in approximately 75 per cent of the patients treated. In some patients the pain did not subside following sympathectomy until thrombosed segments of arteries or aneurisms had been removed. Bingham (1947) reported relief, following extirpation of the superior cervical sympathetic ganglion, of causalgia of the face associated with penetrating wounds. This operation could not effect interruption of any of the afferent pain conducting fibers concerned. Relief in these patients is consistent with the hypothesis that impulses conducted to the point of injury through sympathetic fibers are a factor in the causation of pain. Relief of causalgic pain in the foot following crushing of the peripheral nerves has also been reported.

Since advanced causalgic disease in many instances is not amenable to treatment either by sympathectomy or nerve crushing the selection of patients for such treatment is important. Those suitable for sympathectomy or nerve crushing can be readily differentiated from those that are not by diagnostic nerve blocking with procaine.

Cryalgesia.—In view of the nature of the damage caused by exposure to cold, no material benefit of sympathectomy should be expected in its early phases. On the basis of a histological study of the damaged tissues in cases of immersion foot, White and Warren (1944) advanced the opinion that the pain associated with the early phase of the inflammation is due to anoxemia of the injured superficial tissues and nerve endings, while the aching and burning pain which persists following the inflammatory phase is due to contraction of the newly formed interstitial connective tissue and collagen which affects blood vessels, muscle fibers and nerves. Pain of this type, according to their observations, tends to clear when the collagen surrounding the nerves ceases to contract, which may require six to eight months.

Sympathectomy has been employed successfully by various surgeons for the relief of late sequelæ of injury due to exposure to cold. Kirtley (1945) and Abramson and Schumacher (1945) reported the results of lumbar sympathectomy in patients with extensive damage representing sequelæ of trench foot. On the basis of their experience, this method of treatment appears to be adapted to patients whose feet exhibit marked hyperhydrosis with secondary infection and selected patients with gangrene of the toes or other portions of the foot. In those who exhibited extensive gangrene associated with vascular spasm, as reported by Schumacher and Abramson (1947), healing was accelerated. In those suffering from sensitivity to cold the severity of the symptoms was reduced. Sympathectomy also resulted in benefit in the presence of maceration of the skin and complicating secondary infections associated with marked hyperhydrosis. On the basis of their experience, they advanced the conclusion that sympathectomy is of definite but limited use in the treatment of selected patients for the sequelæ of trench foot, but it is of no value as a therapeutic measure in most cases.

Amputation Stump Neuralgia. — Alleviation or relief of amputation stump pain following sympathetic ganglionectomy and by paravertebral sympathetic nerve blocking has been reported. In many cases amputation stump pain is not amenable to treatment of this kind. In the selection of patients for treatment by sympathectomy or permanent nerve blocking, therefore, it is important to determine by diagnostic nerve blocking with procaine whether temporary abolition of the pain can be effected by functional interruption of the sympathetic rami.

Pain in Paralyzed Extremities. — The major pain-conducting pathways from the extremities are well known. In certain cases, as has been pointed out by White and Smithwick (1941), interruption of all the known sensory nerves has been followed by continued pain in an otherwise insensitive area. They also pointed out that in numerous cases section of the dorsal spinal nerve roots from the 3rd cervical to the 2nd thoracic inclusive has failed to relieve major amputation stump neuralgia in the upper extremity. Slaughter (1938) reported severe, burning, pricking pains in the legs of a man thirty-one years of age following complete transection of the spinal cord at the level of the first lumbar vertebra which subsided following bilateral extirpation of the lumbar segments of the sympathetic trunk and section of the hypogastric nerves. Hyndman and Wolkin (1941) reported 2 cases in which annoying sensory phenomena in the legs and the feet, following the complete paralysis of both lower extremities caused by fracture of the second lumbar vertebra, subsided following bilateral lumbar sympathectomy. The extremities of these patients were completely anesthetic to all tests for exteroceptive and proprioceptive sensibility up to the middle level of the thigh. Patency of the sympathetic innervation of the lower extremities was demonstrated by thermoregulatory and sweating tests.

The occurrence in the extremities of afferent spinal nerve fibers that traverse the sympathetic trunk and communicating rami has been amply demonstrated in experimental animals. Certain experimental data obtained from human subjects indicate the occurrence of such fibers also in man. Walker and Nulsen (1948) reported burning, tingling and pricking pains in the arm and the hand of some human subjects elicited by stimulation of the sympathetic trunk in the third thoracic segment by means of implanted electrodes. Echlin (1949) reported pain in the limb, including phantom pain in the foot, elicited by direct electrical or mechanical stimulation of the sympathetic trunk in the lumbar region exposed under local anesthesia. Following section of the sympathetic trunk rostral to the third lumbar ganglion, the same stimulation of the trunk rostral to the section caused similar pain, but its stimulation caudal to the section resulted in only mild discomfort probably due to the presence of some dorsal root fibers that reached the sympathetic trunk through a communicating ramus caudal to the section. In other patients, stimulation of the sympathetic trunk rostral to its section at the third lumbar level, while recovering from sodium pentobarbital anesthesia, resulted in pain of sufficient intensity to cause an outcry. The same stimulation of the sympathetic trunk caudal to the section elicited no pain response.

These experimental data indicate that the dorsal root fibers that reach the extremities through the sympathetic trunk are components of the same segmental nerves that convey the preganglionic fibers that are concerned in the sympathetic innervation of the corresponding portion of the limb. Certain data also support the assumption that they are not generally distributed to the skin and the muscles but chiefly in relation to blood vessels (Kuntz, 1951). They probably are concerned with the mediation of deep pain in the extremities, particularly pain of vascular origin. The relief of pain in paralyzed extremities following sympathectomy appears to be due to interruption of pain conducting dorsal root fibers that traverse the sympathetic trunk.

BIBLIOGRAPHY

ABEL, W., 1912. Further observations on the development of the sympathetic nervous system in the chick. J. Anat. and Physiol., **47**,35–72.

ABRAMSON, D. I., and SCHUMACHER, H. B., 1945. Sequelae of trench foot and their treatment by lumbar sympathectomy. Proc. Cen. Soc. Clin. Res., **18**, 24–25.

ABRAMSON, H. A., 1942. Physical and psychic allergy. J.A.M.A., **188**, 229.

ADAMS, R. J., 1952. Physiological hyperalgesia associated with the bladder distension reflex. A contribution to the question of the physiology of visceral pain. Acta Chir. Scandinav., **103**, 100–103.

ADDISON, W., 1855. On the Constitutional and Local Effects of Disease of the Suprarenal Capsules. London.

ADOLPH, E. F., 1946. The initiation of sweating in response to heat. Am. J. Physiol., **145**, 710–715.

ADSON, A. W., 1947. Raynaud's disease: report of case with late post operative results. Proc. Staff Meet., Mayo Clin., **22**, 450–452.

ADSON, A. W., and BROWN, G. E., 1932. Thrombo-angiitis obliterans. Results of sympathectomy. J.A.M.A., **99**, 529–534.

ADSON, A. W., O'LEARY, P. A., and BROWN, G. E., 1930. Surgical treatment of vasospastic types of scleroderma by resection of sympathetic ganglia and trunks. Ann. Int. Med., **4**, 555–568.

AGATE, J. N., DRUETT, H. A., and TOMBLESON, J. B. L., 1946. Raynaud's phenomenon in grinders of small metal castings. A clinical and experimental study. Brit. J. Int. Med., **3**, 167–174.

AGDUHR, E., 1919. Are the cross-striated muscle fibers of the extremities also innervated sympathetically? Proc. k. Akad. v. Wetensch., Amsterdam, **21**, 1231–1237.

ALEXANDER, W., 1899. The treatment of epilepsy. Edinburgh.

ALEXANDER, W. F., 1940. The innervation of the biliary system. J. Comp. Neurol., **72**, 357–370.

————1949. Inconstant sympathetic ganglia located in relation to upper lumbar nerves in man. Anat. Rec., **103**, 2–3.

ALEXANDER, W. F., and BACKLAR, B., 1951. Nucleic acid changes in rat nerve tissue after parenteral administration of Vitamin B$_{12}$. Proc. Soc. Exper. Biol. & Med., **78**, 181–184.

ALEXANDER, W. F., KUNTZ, A., HENDERSON, W. P., and EHRLICH, E., 1949. Sympathetic ganglion cells in ventral nerve roots. Their relation to sympathectomy. Science, **109**, 484.

————1949. Sympathetic conduction pathways independent of sympathetic trunks—their surgical implications. J. Internat. Col. Surg., **12**, 111–119.

ALLEN, E. V., and ADSON, A. W., 1940. The treatment of hypertension; medical versus surgical. Ann. Int. Med., **14**, 288–307.

ALLEN, W. F., 1932. Formatio reticularis and reticulospinal tracts, their visceral functions and possible relationships to tonicity and clonic contractions. J. Washington Acad. of Sci., **22**, 16–17.

ALVAREZ, C., 1931. Experiments on surgical treatment of pulmonary tuberculosis by means of thoracic sympathectomy. Rev. esp. de tuberc. (Madrid), **2**, 241.

ALVAREZ, W. C., 1929. The effects of degenerative section of the vagus and the splanchnic nerves on the digestive tract. Proc. Staff Meet., Mayo Clin., **4**, 205–206.

————1930. Conduction in the small bowel. Ibid., **5**, 245–247.

————1931. Abdominal pain: paths over which it travels and ways in which they may be blocked. Am. J. Surg., **14**, 385–394.

ANDERSON, B., 1951. Some observations on the neuro-hormonal regulation of milk ejection. Acta physiol. scandinav., **23**, 1–7.

————1951. The effect and localization of electrical stimulation of certain parts of the brain stem in sheep and goats. Ibid., **23**, 8–23.

————1951. Further studies on the milk ejection mechanism in sheep and goats. Ibid., **23**, 24–30.

ANREP, G. V., 1926. The regulation of coronary circulation. Physiol. Rev., **6**, 596–629.

ARNOLD, L., 1928. Passage of living bacteria through wall of intestine and influence of diet and climate upon intestinal auto-infection. Am. J. Hyg., **8**, 604–634.

ARQUIN, S., 1928. Stomach tonus and peripheral leukocyte count (splanchno-peripheral balance). Arch. Int. Med., **41**, 913–923.

ASHER, L., 1931. Der Einfluss des Sympathicus auf die Muskulatur und eine Analyse seines Mechanismus. Zentralbl. f. d. ges. Neurol. u. Phychiat., **61**, 453.

————1932. Wirkung des Sympathicus auf die Muskulatur. Klin. Wchnschr., **11**, 1292–1293.

————1937. Trophic function of the sympathetic nervous system. J.A.M.A., **108**, 720–721.

ASKANAZY, M., 1907. Ueber Arteriosklerose; Aetiologie und pathologische Anatomie. Therap. Monatschr., **21**, 443–449.

ASMUSSEN, E., CHRISTENSEN, E. H., and NIELSEN, M., 1939. Ueber die Kreislaufinsuffizienz in stehenden bei normalem arteriellen Druck und herabgesetztem Minutenvolumen. Skandinav. Arch. Physiol., **81**, 214–224.

ASMUSSEN, E., and KNUDSEN, E. O. E., 1942. On the significance of the presso-sensible and the chemo-sensible reflexes in the regulation of the cardiac output. Acta physiol. scandinav., **3**, 152–155.

ATLAS, L. N., 1942. Lumbar sympathectomy in the treatment of peripheral arteriosclerotic disease. II. Gangrene following operation in improperly selected cases. Am. Heart J., **23**, 493–497.

AUB, J. C., BAUER, W., HEATH, C., and ROPES, M., 1929. Studies of calcium phosphorus metabolism; effects of thyroid hormone and thyroid disease. J. Clin. Investigation, **7**, 97–137.

AUERBACH, L., 1864. Fernere vorläufige Mittheilung über den Nervenapparat des Darmes. Virchow's Arch. path. Anat., **30**, 457.

BABKIN, B. P., 1938. The triple mechanism of the chemical phase of gastric secretion. J. Dig. Dis. and Nutr., **5**, 467–471.

————1944. Secretory Mechanism of the Digestive Glands. New York.

————1946. Presidential address: antagonistic and synergistic phenomena in autonomic nervous system. Tr. Roy. Soc. Canada, **40**, Sec. V, 1–25.

BABKIN, B. P., and SAWITSCH, W. W., 1908. Zur Frage über den Gehalt an festen Bestandteilen in dem auf verscheidene Sekretionserreger erhaltenen pankreatischen Saft. Ztschr. physiol. Chem., **56**, 231.

BACQ, Z. M., and BROUHA, L., 1932a. Nouvelle demonstration du transport humoral des excitations nerveuses sympathiques chez le mammifere. Ann. de. physiol., **8**, 356–366.

————1932b. Recherches sur la physiologie du système nerveux autonome. I. La transmission humorale de excitations nerveuses sympathiques. Arch. Internat. physiol., **35**, 163–195.

BACQ, Z. M., BROUHA, L., and HEYMANS, C., 1932. Reflexes vasomoteurs d'origine sino carotidienne chez le chat sympathectomisé. Compt. rend. Soc. biol., **111**, 152–154.

BAETJER, Q. M., 1930. The relation of the sympathetic nervous system to the contraction and fatigue of skeletal muscles in mammals. Am. J. Physiol., **93**, 41–56.

BAGEANT, W. E., and ROPER, L. A., 1947. The treatment of pulmonary embolus by stellate block. Anesthesiol., **8**, 500–505.

BAIN, A., IRVING, J. T., and McSWINEY, B. A., 1935. The afferent fibers from the abdomen in the splanchnic nerves. J. Physiol., **84**, 323–333.

BALCHUM, C. J., and WEAVER, H. M., 1943. Pathways for pain from the stomach of the dog. Arch. Neurol. and Phychiat., **49**, 739–753.

BALFOUR, F. M., 1877. The development of elasmobranch fishes. Development of the spinal nerves and the sympathetic nervous system. J. Anat. and Physiol., **11**.

BALINT, R., 1927. Ulcusproblem and Säurebasengleichgewicht. Berlin.

————1928. Ueber die Ulkusschmerzen. Arch. Verdauungskr., **43**, 52–56.

BALL, J. M., 1899. Trans. Ninth Internat. Ophth. Cong., Utrecht.

BALLANCE, C., 1931. Anastomosis of nerves. Experiments in which the central end of the cervical sympathetic was anastomosed to the peripheral end of the divided facial nerve and the peripheral end of the divided hypoglossal nerve. Arch. Neurol. and Psychiat., **25**, 1–28.

BARACH, A. L., 1943. Repeated bronchial relaxation in treatment of intractable asthma. J. Allergy, **14**, 296–309.

BARBOUR, H. G., 1940. Hypothalamic control of water movement in response to environmental temperature. Tr. Assoc. Res. Nerv. and Ment. Dis., **20**, 449–485.

BARBOUR, H. G., McKAY, E. A., and GRIFFITH, W. P., 1943. Water shifts in deep hypothermia. Am. J. Physiol., **140**, 9–19.

BARCROFT, H., BOWMAN, W. McK., and EDHOLM, O. G., 1947. Reflex vasodilatation in human skeletal muscle in response to heating the body. J. Physiol., **106**, 271–278.

BARCROFT, J., 1932a. The effect of some accidental lesions on the size of the spleen. Ibid., **76**, 436–442.

————1932b. Alterations in size of the denervated spleen related to pregnancy. Ibid., **76**, 443–446.

BARCROFT, J., KHAUNA, L. C., and NISIMARU, Y., 1932. Rhythmical contraction of the spleen. Ibid., **74**, 294–298.

BARCROFT, J., and NISIMARU, Y., 1932. Cause of rhythmic contraction of the spleen. Ibid., **74**, 299–310.

BARD, P., and MOUNTCASTLE, V. B., 1948. Some forebrain mechanisms involved in expression of rage with special reference to suppression of angry behavior. A. Res. Nerv. & Ment. Dis., Proc., **27**, 362–404.

BARGMANN, W., 1949. Ueber die neurosecretorische Verknüpfung von Hypothalamus und Hypophyse. Klin. Wchnschr., **27**, 617–622.

BARRINGTON, F. J. F., 1914. The nervous mechanism of micturition. Quart. J. Exper. Physiol., **8**, 33–71.

————1921. Relation of hind-brain to micturition. Brain, **44**, 23–53.

————1931. The component reflexes of micturition in the cat. Parts I and II. Ibid., **54**, 177–188.

————1933. The localization of the paths subserving micturition in the spinal cord of the cat. Ibid., **56**, 126–148.

————1942. The component reflexes of micturition in the cat. Ibid., **64**, 239–243.

BARRON, D. H., 1934. Fortgesetzte Untersuchungen über Wärmebildung in normalen und sympathikuslosen Muskeln. Ztschr. f. Biol., **95**, 575–587.

BARRON, L. E., 1937. The influence of the extrinsic innervation on the human gastric motor mechanism. Am. J. Digest. Dis. and Nutr., **4**, 631–636.

BAYLES, T. B., JUDSON, W. E., and POTTER, T. A., 1950. Reflex sympathetic dystrophy of the upper extremity (hand-shoulder syndrome). J.A.M.A., **144**, 537–542.

BAYLISS, W. M., and STARLING, E. H., 1899. The movements and innervation of the small intestine. J. Physiol., **24**, 99–143.

BAZETT, H. C., 1951. A. theory of reflex control of temperature at rest and during exercise. Federation Proc., **10**, Part I: 152.

BAZETT, H. C., and McGLONE, B., 1928. Note on pain sensations which accompany deep puncture. Brain, **51**, 18–23.

BEAL, J. M., and DINEEN, P., 1950. A study of vagotomy. Arch. Surg., **60**, 203–222.

BEATON, L. E., and LEININGER, C. R., 1943. Spinal distribution of thermoregulatory pathways in the monkey. J. Neurophysiol., **6**, 37–38.

BEATON, L. E., LEININGER, C. R. and McKINLEY, W. A., 1943. Thermoregulatory pathways in the cat brain stem. Ibid., **6**, 29–35.

BEATON, L. E. and MAGOUN, H. W., 1941. Localization of the medullary respiratory centers in the monkey. Am. J. Physiol., **133**, 209.

BEATTIE, J., 1932. The relation of the tuber cinereum to gastric and cardiac functions. Canadian Med. Assn. J., **26**, 278.

BEATTIE, J., DUEL, A. B., and BALLANCE, C., 1932. Effects of stimulation of the hypothalamic pupillo-dilator center after successful anastomoses between the cervical sympathetic and certain motor nerves. J. Anat., **66**, 283–299.

BECK, T. S., 1846. On the nerves of the uterus. Phil. Tr. Roy. Soc., (1846), 213.

————1847. On the structure and functions of the sympathetic nervous system. Lancet, **1**, 615.

BEECHER, H. K., 1936. The active control of all parts of the capillary wall by the sympathetic nervous system. Scand. Arch. Physiol., **73**, 123–132.

BEER, A. G., 1939. Untersuchungen der vegetativen Regulation an Parabiosetieren mit besondere Berücksichtigung der humoral-nervösen Steuerung des weiszen Blutbildes. Ztschr. ges. exper. Med., **105**, 53–82.

BELAK, S., 1939. Schutzstoffbildung als vegetative Funktion. Klin. Wchnschr., **18**, 472–474.

BENETATO, G., BACIU, I., and VLAD, L., 1945. Zentralnervensystem und Abwehrfunktion. I Die Rolle der hypothalamischen vegetativen Zentren bei der phagozyten Tätigkeit experimentelle. Schweiz med. Wchnschr., **75**, 702–705.

BENNHOLD, H., and HAUPSTEIN, 1928. Kann die Pupille als Indikator des Gleichgewichtszustandes im vegetativen Nervensystem angesehn werden? Arch. exper. Path. u. Pharmakol., **130**, 89–110.

BENSLEY, R. R. and VIMTRUP, B., 1928. On the nature of the Rouget cells of capillaries. Anat. Rec., **39**, 37–55.

BERGH, G. S., 1942. The effect of food upon the sphincter of Oddi in human subjects. Am. Jour. Digest. Dis., **9**, 40–43.

BERGH, G. S., and LAYNE, J. A., 1940. A demonstration of the independent contraction of the sphincter of the common bile duct in human subjects. Am. J. Physiol., **128**, 690–694.

BERNARD, C., 1852. Influence du grand sympathique sur la sensibilité et sur la calorification. Compt. rend. Soc. biol., **3**, 161.

———1858. Leçons sur la physiologie due systéme nerveux. Paris.

———1887. Leçons sur le Diabete. Paris.

BERTEAU, B., and JONES, D. S., 1950. The dilator mechanism of the pupil. Anat. Rec., **106**, 98.

BETHE, A., 1903. Allgemeine Anatomie und Physiologie des Nervensystem, Leipzig.

BICHAT, N. F. X., 1800. Recherches physiol. sur la vie et la mort. Paris.

———1801. Traité Anatomie descriptive. Paris.

———1802. Anatomie générale, appliquée à la physiologie et à la médicine. Paris.

BICKERS, W., 1950. Dysmenorrhea and the pelvic autonomic system. South. M. J., **43**, 889–893.

BIDDER, F. H., and VOLKMANN, A. W., 1842. Die Selbstständigkeit des sympathischen Nervensystems durch anatomische Untersuchungen Nachgewiesen, Leipzig.

BING, H. I., 1936. Viscerocutaneous and cutovisceral thoracic reflexes. Acta. med. scand., **89**, 57–68.

BING, H. I., and TOBIASSEN, E. S., 1935. Viscerocutane und cutoviscerale Reflexe am Bauch. Hosp. tid. (1935): 1076–1084.

BINGHAM, J. A. W., 1947. Causalgia of the face: two cases successfully treated by sympathectomy. Brit. M. J., **1**, 804.

BIRCH, C. L., and BOYDEN, E. A., 1930. Reaction of gall bladder to stimulation of gastrointestinal tract. II. Response to faradic excitation to stomach, small intestine and cecum. Am. J. Physiol., **92**, 301–316.

BISGARD, J. D., 1931. A correlation of vasomotor and muscle tonus response to sympathetic ganglionectomy. Proc. Soc. Exper. Biol. & Med., **29**, 224–226.

BISHOP, G. H., and HEINBECKER, P., 1932. A functional analysis of the sympathetic nerve supply to the eye. Am. J. Physiol., **100**, 519–532.

BLADES, B., BEATTIE, E., JR., and ELIAS, W. S., 1950. Surgical treatment of intractable asthma. J. Thoracic Surg., **20**, 584–591.

BLAIN, A., COLLER, F. A., and CARVER, G. B., 1951. Raynaud's disease: a study of criteria for prognosis. Surgery, **29**, 387–397.

BLANCHON, P., 1951. Que pent-on attendre des interventions chirurgicales sur le systeme nerveux autonome au cours de l'asthme? La Revue du Practicien, (Suppl.), **5,**139–143.

BLISS, W. R., BURCH, B., MARTIN, M. M., and ZOLLINGER, R. M., 1950. Localization of referred pancreatic pain induced by electric stimulation. Gastroenterology, **16**, 317–323.

BLOCK, M. A., WAKIN, K. G., and MANN, F. C., 1952a. Circulation through kidney during stimulation of the renal nerve. Am. J. Physiol., **169**, 659–669.

————1952b. Renal function during stimulation of renal nerves. Am. J. Physiol., **169**, 670–677.

BLOTEVOGEL, W., 1927a. Sympathicus und Sexualzyklus. Ztschr. f. mikr.-anat. Forsch., **10**, 141–148.

————1927b. Das Ganglion cervicale uteri des normalen Tieres. Ibid., **10**, 149–168.

BOAS, I., 1926. Ueber provokatorische Erzeugung okkulter Blutungen. Deutsche med. Wchnschr., **52**, 349–351.

BOCHNIK, H. J., and MAGUN, R., 1950. Ueber den Einfluss des sympathischen Nervensystems auf die Tätigkeit der Skeletmuskulatur. Ztschr. ges. exper. Med., **116**, 117–137.

BOEKE, J., 1909. Die motorische Endplatte bei den höheren Vertebraten, ihre Entwickelung, Form und Zusammenhang mit der Muskelfaser. Anat. Anz., **35**, 193–226.

————1916. Studien zur Nerven Regeneration. I. Verhandl. d. kön. Akad. v. Wetensch., Amsterdam, **18**, 1–20.

————1917. Studien zur Nervenregeneration. II. Ibid., **19**, 1–69.

————1927. Die morphologische Grundlage der sympathischen Innervation der querestreiften Muskelfasern. Ztschr. f. mikr.-anat. Forsch., **8**, 561–639.

————1930. Some remarks on the papers by H. J. Wilkinson on the innervation of striped muscle fibers. J. Comp. Neurol., **51**, 299–309.

————1932a. Nerve endings, motor and sensory. Cytology and Cellular Pathology of the Nervous System. (W. Penfield), Sect. 6.

————1932b. Some observations on the structure and innervation of smooth muscle fibers. J. Comp. Neurol., **56**, 27–48.

————1933a. Innervationsstudien. III. Die Nervenversorgung des M. ciliaris und des M. sphincter iridis bei Säugern und Vögeln. Ztschr. f. mikr.-anat. Forsch., **33**, 233–275. IV. Die efferente Gefäszinnervation und der sympathische Plexus im Bindegewebe. Ibid., **33**, 276–328.

————1933b. Innervationsstudien. V. Der sympathische Grundplexus und seine Beziehungen zu den quergestreiften Muskelfasern und zu den Herzmuskelfasern. Ibid., **34**, 330–378.

————1935a. Die periphere Ausbreitung des sympathischen Systems. Nova Acta. N. F., **2**, 209–257.

————1935b. The autonomic (enteric) nervous system of Amphioxus lancolatus. Quart. J. Micr. Sci., **77**, 623–658.

————1936. Innervationsstudien. IX. Zur Nervenversorgung der Augenhäute. III. Die Beziehungen der Nervenfasern der Iris zu den Bindegewebszellen beim Affen Die interstitiellen Elemente des Irisstromas und der sympathische Grundplexus. Ztschr. f. mikr.-anat. Forsch., **39**, 477–520.

————1937. Ueber die Verbindugen der Nervenzellen untereinander und mit den Erfolgsorganen. Anat. Anz., Ergänzungsheft, **85**, 111–141.

————1939. Innervationsstudien. X. Sympathischer Grundplexus und Bindegewebsstrukturen (Reticulinfasern Sarkolemmas). Ztschr. f. mikr.-anat. Forsch., **46**, 488–519.

————1940. Problems of Nervous Anatomy. Oxford.

————1940. The sympathetic end formation, its synaptology, the interstitial cells, the periterminal network, and its bearing on the neurone theory. Discussion and Critique. Acta anat., **8**, 18–61.

BOEKE, J., and DUSSER DE BARENNE, G. J., 1919. The sympathetic innervation of the cross-striated muscle fibers of vertebrates. Proc. kön. Akad. v. Wetensch., Amsterdam, **21**, 1227–1230.

BOGENDÖRFER, L., 1927a. Ueber den Einfluss des Zentralnervensystems auf Immunitätsvorgänge. I. Mitt. Arch. exper. Path. u. Pharmakol., **124**, 65-72.

————1927b. II. Mitt. Die zeitlichen Verhältnisse. Ibid., **126**, 378–380.

————1932. Ueber Fragen des Zusammenhängen von Immunität mit Nervensystem, reticuloendothelialem und endokrinem System. Imm. All. u. Infk., **3**, 133–145.

BOLTON, B., CARMICHAEL, E. A., and STÜRUP, G., 1936. Vasoconstriction following deep inspiration. J. Physiol., **86**, 83–94.

BOND, D. D., 1943. Sympathetic and vagal interaction in emotional response of the heart rate. Am. J. Physiol., **138**, 468–478.

————1946. Observations on mechanism of pain in ulcer of stomach and duodenum; nature of stimulus. Ibid., **6**, 63–89.

BONNEY, G. L., and PICKERING, G. W., 1946. Observations on mechanism of pain in ulcer of stomach and duodenum; location of pain nerve endings. Clin. Sc., **6**, 91–111.

BORISON, H. L., 1948. Electrical stimulation of the neural mechanism regulating spasmodic respiratory acts in the cat. Am. J. Physiol., **154**, 55–62.

BOROS, B., and TAKATS, I., 1952. Die Frage der Doppleinnervation der Sphincter iridis im Lichte der Cannonschen Denervationgesetzes. V. Graefe's Arch. Ophthalmol., **152**, 319–334.

BORY, L., 1926. La glands pigmentaire de la peau. Prog. méd., **18**, 671–684.

BOUCKAERT, J. J., and HEYMANS, C., 1933. Carotid sinus reflexes. Influence of central blood pressure and blood supply on respiratory and vasomotor centers. J. Physiol., **79**, 49–66.

————1935. On reflex regulation of cerebral blood flow and cerebral vasomotor tone. Ibid., **84**, 367–380.

BOWING, H., 1924. Die Störungen der Blasenentleerung. Die Lebensnerven (L. R. Müller), 314–316.

BOYD, A. K., 1949. Vagotomy and the anatomic variations in the vagus nerve. Am. J. Surg., **78**, 4–14.

BOYDEN, E. A., 1925. The gall bladder in the cat, its development, its functional periodicity and its anatomical variation as recorded in 2500 specimens. Anat. Rec., **30**, 333–364; Am. J. Anat., **38**, 177–232.

————1928. Analysis of reaction of human gall bladder to food. Anat. Rec., **40**, 147–189.

BOYDEN, E. A., BERGH, G. S., and LAYNE, J. A., 1943. An analysis of the reaction of the human gall bladder and sphincter of Oddi to magnesium sulphate. Surgery, **13**, 723–733.

BOYDEN, E. A., and BERMAN, T. M., 1937. Evacuation of the gall bladder in peptic ulcer patients. Radiology, 28, 273–282.

BOYDEN, E. A., and BIRCH, C. L., 1930. Reaction of gall bladder to stimulation of gastro-intestinal tract. I. Response to substances injected into duodenum. Am. J. Physiol., **92**, 287–300.

BOYDEN. E. A., and GRANTHAM, S. A., 1936. Evacuation of the gall bladder in old age. Surg. Gynec. & Obst., **62**, 34–42.

BOYDEN, E. A., and RIGLER, L. G., 1934. Localization of pain accompanying faradic excitation of stomach and duodenum in healthy individuals. J. Clin. Investigation, **13**, 833–851.

BOYDEN, E. A., and VAN BUSKIRK, C., 1943. Rate of emptying of biliary tract following section of vagi or of all extrinsic nerves. Proc. Soc. Exper. Biol. & Med., **53**, 174–175.

BRACK, W., 1936. Sympathikus und Muskelermüdung, zugleich ein Beitrag zur Wirkung von Nebennierenrindenhormon und Askorbinsäure. Ztschr. f. Biol., **97**, 370–377.

BRADLEY, W. F., SMALL, J. T., WILSON, J. W. and WALTERS, W., 1947. Anatomic considerations of gastric neurectomy. J.A.M.A., **133**, 459–461.

BRAEUCKER, W., 1933. Die chirurgische Behandlung der Angina pectoris. Arch. f. klin. Chir., **177**, 664–679.

BRAEUCKER, W., and KÜMMELL, H., 1927. Ueber eine reine Vaguswirkung an den Bronchien. Pflüger's Arch. ges. Physiol., **218**, 301–309.

BRITTON, S. W., 1930. An apparent influence of sympathetic nerves on muscle glycogen. Am. J. Physiol., **93**, 213–218.

BRIZZEE, K. R., Histogenesis of the supporting tissue in the spinal and the sympathetic trunk ganglia in the chick. J. Comp. Neurol., **91**, 129–146.

BRIZZEE, K. R., and KUNTZ, A., 1950. The histologenesis of sympathetic ganglion cells. J. Neuropath. & Exper. Neurol., **9**, 164–171.

BROCHER, J. E., 1927. Isolierte Neurofibromatose im Sympathicus. Ztbl. f. allg. Path. u. path. Anat., **40**, 513–518.

BRONK, D. W., 1939. Synaptic mechanisms in sympathetic ganglia. J. Neurophysiol., **2**, 380–401.

BRONK, D. W., and STELLA, G., 1932*a*. Afferent impulses from single end-organs in the carotid sinus. Proc. Soc. Exper. Biol. & Med., **29**, 443–445.

———1932*b*. Afferent impulses in the carotid sinus nerve. I. The relation of the discharge from single end-organs to arterial blood pressure. J. Cell. and Comp. Physiol., **1**, 113–130.

BRONK, D. W., TOWER, S. S., SOLANDT, D. Y., and LARRABEE, M. G., 1938. Transmission of trains of impulses through a sympathetic ganglion and its postganglionic nerves. Am. J. Physiol., **122**, 1–15.

BROOKS, C. M., 1931. A delimitation of the central nervous mechanism involved in reflex hyperglycemia. Am. J. Physiol., **94**, 64–76.

BROOKS, C. McC., 1938. A study of the mechanism whereby coitus excites the ovulation-producing activity of the rabbit's pituitary. Ibid., **121**, 157–177.

BROUHA, L., CANNON, W. B., and DILL, D. B., 1939. Blood sugar variations in sympathectomized dogs. J. Physiol., **95**, 431–438.

BROUHA, L., NOWAK, S. J. G., and DILL, D. R., 1939. The role of the vagus in the cardioaccelerator action of muscular exercise and emotion in sympathectomized dogs. Ibid., **95**, 454–463.

BROWN, G. E., and ADSON, A. W., 1925. Calorimetric studies of the extremities following lumbar sympathetic ramisection and ganglionectomy. Am. J. M. Sc., **170**, 232–240.

BROWN, G. E., and ALLEN, E. V., 1928. Thrombo-angiitis Obliterans. Philadelphia.

BROWN, G. L., and McSWINEY, B. A., 1932. The sympathetic innervation of the stomach. IV. Reversal of sympathetic action by luminal. J. Physiol., **74**, 179–194.

BROWN, G. L., McSWINEY, B. A., and WADGE, W. J., 1930. Sympathetic innervation of the stomach. I. Effect on the stomach of stimulation of the thoracic sympathetic trunk. Ibid., **70**, 253–260.

BROWN, M., BRESNAHAN, T. J., CHALKE, F. C. R., PETERS, B., POSER, E. G., and TOUGAS, R. V., 1950. Personality factors in duodenal ulcer. A Rorschach study. Psychosom. Med., **12**, 1–5.

BROWN, W. H., and HIRSCH, E. F., 1941. The intrinsic nerves of the immature human uterus. Am. J. Path., **17**, 731–739.

BROWN-SEQUARD, C. E., 1852. Lectures on the physiology and pathology of the central nervous system. Philadelphia M. Examiner, 1852, p. 489.

BRÜCKE, F., 1950. Über Unterschiede zwischen zentraler und refleklorischer Sympathikuserregung. Deutsche med. Wchnschr., **75**, 1547–1549.

BRÜCKE, F. T. v., and STERN, P., 1938. Pharmachologesche Untersuchungen über die Innervation des Mageneinganges. Arch. exper. Path. u. Pharmakol., **189**, 311–326.

BRUGSCH, T., DRESEL, E., and LEWY, F. H., 1922. Experimentelle Beiträge zur Frage des hypophysären Diabetes. Vernandl. d. deutsch. Gesellsch. f. inn. Med., **34**, 347.

BRÜNING, F., 1927. Das Problem der Gefässinnervation. Deutsche med. Wchnschr., **53**, 962–963.

BUCK, C. W., CARSCALLEN, H. B., and HOBBS, G. E., 1951. Effect of prefrontal lobotomy on temperature regulation in schizophrenic patients. Arch. Neurol. & Psychiat., **65**, 197–205.

BUCY, P. C., HUGGINS, C., and BUCHANAN, D. N., 1937. Sympathetic innervation of external sphincter of human bladder. Am. J. Dis. Child., **54**, 1012–1018.

BURDENKO, N., 1933. Der Einfluss des Nervensystems auf pathologische Zustände des Magen-und Darmkanals. Ztschr. f. d. ges. Neurol. u. Psychiat., **148**, 343.

BURGET, G. E., and LIVINGSTON, W. K., 1931. Pathway for visceral afferent impulses from the forelimb of the dog. Am. J. Physiol., **97**, 249–253.

BURKART, A., 1936. Untersuchungen über den Einfluss des Nervus sympathicus auf die Temperatur der Nasen und Mundschleinhaut. Ztschr. Biol., **97**, 465–473.

BURN, J. H., 1925. The secretion of sweat and vasodilation produced by pilocarpine. J. Physiol., **60**, 365–378.

———1945. The reaction of adrenalin to acetylcholine in the nervous system. Physiol. Rev., **25**, 377–404.

BURN, J. H., and ROBINSON, J., 1952. Effect of denervation on amine oxidase in structures innervated by the sympathetics. Brit. J. Pharmacol., **7**, 304–318.

BURNS, B. I., 1935. Distribution of sympathetic nerve fibers to hind limb of a cat. J. Comp. Neurol., **61**, 191–219.

BURTON, A. C., 1939. The range of variability of the blood flow in the human fingers and the vasomotor regulation of body temperature. Am. J. Physiol., **127**, 437–453.

BÜTTNER, H. E., 1926. Über die Wirkung des Sympathicus auf den Kohlehydrastoffwechsel des Muskels. Ztschr. f. physiol. Chem., **161**, 282–299.

————1929. Sympathicuswirkungen auf die Muskulatur. Am. J. Physiol., **90**, 304–305.

BÜTTNER, H. E., and HEIMBRECHT, B., 1928. Ueber den Einfluss des Sympathicus auf den Verkürzungsrückstand des Muskels. Pflüger's Arch. ges. Physiol., **221**, 93–103.

CAJAL, S. R., 1908. Nouvelles observations sur l'évolution des neuroblastes, avec quelques remarques sur l'hypothèse neurogenetique de Hensen-Held. Anat. Anz., **32**, 1–25 and 65–78.

CAMPBELL, D. G., and PARSONS, C. M., 1944. Referred head pain and its concomitants. J. Nerv. & Ment. Dis., **99**, 544–551.

CAMPENHOUT, E. VAN, 1930a. Historical survey of the development of the sympathetic nervous system. Quart. Rev. Biol., **5**, 33–50.

————1930b. Contribution to the problem of the development of the sympathetic nervous system. J. Exp. Zoöl., **56**, 295–320.

————1930c. The autonomic nervous system in the light of recent research. Yale J. Biol. & Med., (1930), 223–228.

————1932. Further experiments on the origin of the enteric nervous system in the chick. Physiol. Zoöl., **5**, 333–353.

CANNON, W. B., 1912. Peristalsis, segmentation and the myenteric reflex. Am. J. Physiol., **30**, 114–128.

————1915. Bodily Changes in Pain, Hunger, Fear and Rage. New York and London.

————1928. The mechanism of emotional disturbance of bodily functions. New England J. Med., **198**, 877–884.

————1930. The sympathetic division of the autonomic system in relation to homeostasis. Proc. Assn. Res. in Nerv. and Ment. Dis., **9**, 181–198.

————1932. Recent studies on chemical mediation of nerve impulses. Endocrinology, **15**, 473–480.

————1933. Chemical mediators of autonomic nerve impulses. Science, **78**, 43–48.

————1939. A law of denervation. Am. J. M. Sc., **198**, 737–750.

CANNON, W. B., and BRITTON, S. W., 1927. The influence of motion and emotion on medulliadrenal secretion. Am. J. Physiol., **79**, 433–465.

CANNON, W. B., and DE LA PAZ, D., 1911. Emotional stimulation of adrenal secretion. Ibid., **28**, 64–70.

CANNON, W. B., and ROSENBLUETH, A., 1933. Studies on conditions of activity in endocrine organs. XXIX. Sympathin E and Sympathin I. Ibid., **104**, 557–573.

CANNON, W. B., and WASHBURN, A. L., 1912. An explanation of hunger. Ibid, **29**, 411–454.

CAPPS, J. A., 1932. An experimental and clinical study of pain in the pleura, pericardium and peritoneum. New York.

CARLSON, A. J., 1912. The character of the movements of the empty stomach in man. Am. J. Physiol., **31**, 151–168.

————1914a. Hunger contractions of the empty stomach during prolonged starvation (man, dog.) Ibid., **33**, 95–118.

————1914b. The nervous control of the gastric hunger mechanism. Ibid., **34**, 155–171.

————1916. The Control of Hunger in Health and Disease. Chicago.

————1930. The extrinsic nervous control of the large bowel. J.A.M.A., **94**, 78–79.

CARLSON, A. J., BOYD, T. E., and PEARCEY, J. F., 1922a. Studies on the visceral sensory nervous system. XIII. The innervation of the cardia and lower end of the esophagus in mammals. Am. J. Physiol., **61**, 14–41.

————1922b. Studies on the visceral and sensory nervous system; reflex control of the cardia and lower esophagus in mammals. Arch. Int. Med., **30**, 409–433.

CARMICHAEL, E. A., and WOOLLARD, H. H., 1933. Some observations on fifth and seventh cranial nerves. Brain, **56**, 109–125.

CARPENTER, F. W., 1906. The development of the oculomotor nerve, the ciliary ganglion and the abducent nerve in the chick. Bull. Mus. Comp. Zoöl., Harvard College, **48**, 141–228.

————1918. Nerve endings of sensory type in the muscular coat of the stomach and small intestine. J. Comp. Neurol., **29**, 553–560.

CARR, D., and CHANDLER, H., 1948. Dorsal sympathetic ganglionectomy for intractable asthma. J. Thoracic surg., **17**, 1–12.

CARRELL, A., and GUTHRIE, C. C., 1906. Anastomosis of blood vessels by the patching method and transplantation of the kidney. J.A.M.A., **47**, 648–650.

CAVAZZANA, P., and BORSELLO, P. L., 1948. Recherches sur l' aspect microscopique des plexus nerveux intramurax et sur les modifications morphologiques de leurs neurones dans les divers traits de l'intestin humain pendant la vie. Acta Anat., **5**, 17.

CHARLET, H., 1930. Fortegesetzte Untersuchungen über den Einfluss des Sympathikus auf den Kontraktionsablauf ermüdeter Skelettmuskeln. Ztschr. f. Biol., **90**, 299–312.

CHAUCHARD, A., CHAUCHARD, B., and BARRY, D. T., 1931. Effects of hemorrhage on the vascular nervous mechanism. Brit. J. Exper. Path., **12**, 190–199.

CHENG, CHI-PING, Sayers, G., GOODMAN, L. S., and SWINYARD, C. A., 1949. Discharge of adrenocorticotrophic hormone in the absence of neural connections between the pituitary and hypothalamus. Am. J. Physiol., **158**, 45–50.

CHERVET, N., 1936. Untersuchungen über den trophischen Einfluss des Nervus sympathicus auf die Hornhaut bei Kaninchen. Ztschr. f. Biol., **97**, 364–369.

CHESTERMAN, J. T., 1946. Neurogenic ileus. Brit. M. J., 830–832.

CHOROBSKI, J., and PENFIELD, W., 1932. Cerebral vasodilator nerves and their pathway from the medulla oblongata. Arch. Neurol. & Psychiat., **28**, 1257–1289.

CHRISTENSEN, K., 1934. The innervation of the nasal mucosa, with special reference to its afferent supply. Ann. Otol. Rhin. & Laryng., **43**, 1066–1084.

————1940. Sympathetic nerve fibers in the alveolar nerves and nerves of the dental pulp. J. Dent. Res., **19**, 227–242.

CHRISTENSEN, K., LEWIS, E., and KUNTZ, A., 1951. Innervation of the renal blood vessels in the cat. J. Comp. Neurol., **95**, 373–378.

CHRISTENSEN, K., POLLEY, E. H., and LEWIS, E., 1952. The nerves along the vertebral artery and innervation of the blood vessels of the hind brain of the cat. Ibid., **96**, 71–92.

CHUDOROSEVA, A., 1932. Die Wirkung der sympathischen Nervenfasern auf den Ermüdungsverlauf der Skelettmuskeln, welche von den degenererierenden motorischen Nerven ausgereizt werden. Physiol. Ztschr., **15**, 287–299.

CICARDO, V. H., 1951. Effect des ultra-sous sur le diencéphale. Compt. rend. Soc. biol., **145**, 1708–1709.

CLARK, E. R., and CLARK, E. L., 1925. The relation of Rouget cells to capillary contraction. Am. J. Anat., **35**, 265–282.

CLARKE, S. L., 1937. Innervation of the intrinsic muscles of the eye. J. Comp. Neurol., **66**, 307–325.

CLARK, W. E. LE G., 1940. The nervous and vascular relations of the pineal gland. J. Anat., **74**, 471–492.

CLARK, W. E. LE G., and MEYER, M., 1950. Anatomical relationships between the cerebral cortex and the hypothalamus. Brit. M. Bull., **6**, 341–344.

CLARKE, C. A., 1951. Bronchial asthma treated by bilateral resection of the vagus. A report of six cases. Lancet, **260**, 438–440.

CLELAND, J. P. G., 1933. Paravertebral anesthesia in obstetrics. Surg. Gynec. & Obst., **57**, 51–62.

CLELAND, J. P. G., and TAIT, J., 1927. Nervous connections of the mammalian spleen including an account of certain vasomotor and other abdominal reflexes. Quart. J. Exper. Physiol., **17**, 179–204.

COATES, A. E., and TIEGS, O. W., 1928. The influence of the sympathetic nerves on skeletal muscle. Australian J. Exp. Biol. and M. Sci., **5**, 9–46.

————1931. Are the skeletal muscles of the extremities directly innervated by sympathetic nerves? Ibid., **8**, 99–106.

COBB, S., 1918. Sympathetic regulation of muscle tone. Am. J. Physiol., **46**, 478.

————1938. Cerebral circulation: critical discussion of and symposium. A. Res. Nerv. & Ment. Dis., Proc., **18**, 719–752.

COFFEY, W. B., and BROWN, P. K., 1923. The surgical treatment of angina pectoris. Arch. Int. Med., **31**, 200–220.

COHEN, S., and WOLF, H. L., 1947. Studies of autonomic nervous system in atopic individuals; palmar sweating in allergic patients; cholinergic phenomenon. J. Allergy, **18**, 391–396.

COLFER, H. F., DE GROOT, J., and HARRIS, G. W., 1950. Pituitary gland and blood lymphocytes. J. Physiol., **111**, 328–334.

COLLINS, V. J., FOSTER, W. L., and WEST, W. J., 1947. Vasomotor disturbances in poliomyelitis with special reference to treatment with paravertebral sympathetic block. New England J. Med., **236**, 694–697.

COLP, R., 1948. Surgical treatment of gastric, duodenal and gastrojejunal ulcer; including the present status of vagotomy. Bull. New York Acad. Med., **24**, 755.

COMAN, F. D., 1926. Observations on the relation of the sympathetic nervous system to skeletal muscle tonus. Bull. Johns Hopkins Hosp., **38**, 163–188.

COOPERMAN, H. O., 1950. Sjögren's Syndrome: a secreto-inhibitory syndrome. Ann. West. Med. & Surg., **4**, 344–347.

COUJARD, R., 1951. Recherches sur les plexus nerveux de l'intestin. Arch. anat. micr. et morphol. exper., **39**, 110–151.

COX, J. W., RANDALL, W. C., ALEXANDER, W. F., FRANKE, F. E., and HERTZMAN, A. B., 1951. A method for the study of cutaneous vascular responses: Its application in mapping the pre- and post-ganglionic vasomotor supply to the foot. Bull. St. Louis University Hosp., **3**, 71–76.

CRAIG, W. McK., 1934. Surgical approach to and resection of the splanchnic nerves for relief of hypertension and abdominal pain. West. J. Surg., **42**, 146–152.

CRAIG, W. McK., MOERSCH, H. J., and VINSON, P. P., 1934. Treatment of intractable cardiospasm by bilateral cervicothoracic sympathectomy. Proc. Staff Meet., Mayo Clin., **9**, 749.

CRIDER, J. O., and THOMAS, H. E., 1944. Secretion of pancreatic juice after cutting extrinsic nerves. Am. J. Physiol., **141**, 730–737.

CRIDER, R. J., and WALKER, S. M., 1948. Physiologic studies on stomach of woman with gastric fistula. Arch. Surg., **57**, 1–9.

CRITTENDEN, P. J., and IVY, A. C., 1933. A study of cardiovascular reflexes. II. The experimental production of cardiac irregularities in icteric dogs with an analysis of the role played by nausea and vomiting. Am. Heart J., **8**, 507–518.

CROMER, S. P., and IVY, A. C., 1931. Physiological effects of denervating the carotid sinus in dogs. Proc. Soc. Exper. Biol. & Med., **28**, 565–566.

CROSS, B. A. and HARRIS, G. W., 1952. The role of the neurohypophysis in the milk ejecting reflex. J. Endocrinology, **8**, 148–161.

CSEPAI, K., HOLLO, J., and WEISS, S., 1925. Ueber den Einfluss der Blutreaktion und des Blutzuckers auf die wirkliche Adrenalinempfindlichkeit des Menschen. Wein. Arch. f. klin. Med., **10**, 213–222.

CUSHING, H., 1932. Peptic ulcers and the interbrain. Surg. Gynec. & Obst., **55**, 1–34.

CUSHNY, A. R., 1906. The action of drugs on uterus. Brit. Med. J., **2**, 1460.

DAHL, W., 1916. Die Innervation der weiblichen Genitalien. Ztschr. f. d. Geburtsh. u. Gynäk., **78**, 539–601.

DALE, H. H., 1906. On some physiological actions of ergot. J. Physiol., **34**, 163–206.

———1929. Some chemical factors in the control of the circulation. (Croonian Lectures). Lancet, **1**, 1179–1183; 1233–1237; 1285–1290.

———1933. Progress in autopharmacology. A survey of present knowledge of chemical regulation of certain functions by natural constituents of the tissues. Bull. Johns Hopkins Hosp., **53**, 297–347.

DALE, H. H., and LAIDLAW, P. P., 1912. The significance of the supra-renal capsules in the action of certain alkaloids. J. Physiol., **45**, 1–26.

DALY, M. DE B., and SCHWEITZER, A., 1951. Effects of sino-aortic nerve stimulation on the bronchi. Acta physiol. scandinav., **22**, 66–72.

———1951. Reflex bronchomotor responses to stimulation of receptors in the regions of the carotid sinus and arch of the aorta in the dog and cat. J. Physiol., **113**, 442–462.

———1952. The contribution of the vasosensory areas to the reflex control of bronchomotor tone. Ibid., **116**, 35–58.

DANIELOPOLU, D., 1948. L'infarctus du myocarde accident de la stellectomie dans l'angine de foitrine. Presse méd., **56**, 337.

————1948. Efficiency of stellectomy in angina pectoris. Causes of errors in appreciation of results. Acta cardiol., **3**, 175–188.

DANIELOPOLU, D., and MARCU, I., 1932. Ueber die Pathogenese der Epilepsie und über ihre chirurgische Behandlung. Einfluss der reflexogenen sinus-karotischen Zonen. Wein. klin. Wchnschr., **45**, 457–460.

DANISCH, F., 1928. Die sympathischen Ganglien und ihre Bedeutung für die Cholesterinsklerose des Kaninchens. Beitr. path. Anat., **79**, 333–399.

DARROW, C. W., 1943. Physiological and clinical tests of autonomic function and autonomic balance. Physiol. Rev., **23**, 1–36.

DASS, R., 1952. Sympathetic components of the dorsal primary divisions of human spinal nerves. Anat. Rec., **113**, 493–501.

DASTRE, A., and MORAT, J. P., 1883. Sur les nerfs vasodilateurs du membre inférieur. Arch. d. physiol., 1883, 549.

————1884. Recherches experimentales sur le systéme nerv. vasomoteur. Paris.

DAVIES, F., and FRANCIS, E. T. B., 1952. The conduction of the impulse for cardiac contraction. J. Anat., **86**, 302–309.

DAVIS, F., FRANCIS, E. T. B., and KING, T. S., 1952. Neurological studies of the cardiac ventricles of mammals. J. Anat., **86**, 130–143.

DAVIS, L., HART, J. T., and CRAIN, C. R. 1929. The pathway of visceral afferent impulses within the spinal cord. II. Experimental dilatation of the biliary ducts. Surg. Gynec. and Obst., **48**, 647–651.

DAVIS, L., and POLLOCK, L. J., 1932. Role of sympathetic nervous system in production of pain in head. Arch. Neurol. and Psychiat., **27**, 282–293.

————1936. The role of the autonomic nervous system in the production of pain. J.A.M.A., **106**, 350–353.

DAVIS, L., POLLOCK, L. J., and STONE, T. T., 1932. Visceral pain. Surg., Gynec. and Obst., **55**, 418–427.

DAVISON, C., and DEMMTH, E. L., 1946. Disturbances in sleep mechanism: a clinico-pathologic study. III. Lesions at the diencephalic level (hypothalamus). IV. Lesions at the mesencephalicometencephalic level. Arch. Neurol. & Psychiat., **55**, 111–133.

DE BOER, S., 1915. Die Bedeutung der tonischen Innervation für die Funktion der quergestreiften Muskeln. Ztschr. f. Biol., **65**, 239–353.

DE CASTRO, F., 1923. Evolución de los ganglios simpáticos vertebrales y prevertebrales. Connexiones y citoarquitectonia de algunos grupos de ganglios, en el niño y hombre adulto. Trab. d. Lab. de invest. biol., **20**.

————1932. Sympathetic ganglia, normal and pathological. Cytology and cellular pathology of the nervous system (W. Penfield), Sect. VII.

DEDERER, C., 1918. Transplantation of kidney. J.A.M.A., **70**, 6–9.

————1920. Successful experimental homotransplantation of kidney and ovary. Surg., Gynec. and Obst., **31**, 45–50.

DEMPSEY, E. W., 1939. The relationship between the central nervous system and the reproductive cycle in the female guinea pig. Am. J. Physiol., **126**, 758–765.

DEMPSEY, E. W., and UOTILA, U. U., 1940. Effect of pituitary stalk section upon reproductive phenomena in female rat. Endocrinology, **27**, 573–579.

DEMPSHER, J., BANG, F. B., and BODIAN, D., 1952. Functional and histological studies of sympathetic ganglia infected with pseudorabies virus. Fed. Proc., **11**, 33.

DENNING, H., 1924. Untersuchungen über die Innervation der Harnblase und des Mastdarmes. Ztschr. f. Biol., **80**, 239–254.

DENNY-BROWN, D., and ROBERTSON, E. G., 1933a. On the physiology of micturition. Brain, **56**, 149–190.

————1933b. The state of the bladder and its sphincters in complete transverse lesions of the spinal cord and cauda equina. Ibid., **56**, 397–463.

DETAKATS, G., 1952. Limitation of sympathectomy in treatment of diastolic hypertension. J.A.M.A., **148**, 1382–1389.

DE TAKATS, G., FENN, G. K., and JENKINSON, E. L., 1942. Reflex pulmonary atelectasis. J.A.M.A., **120**, 686–690.

DE TAKATS, G., FOWLER, E. F., JORDAN, P., and RISLEY, T. C., 1946. Sympathectomy in the treatment of peripheral vascular sclerosis. Ibid., **131**, 495–499.

DE TAKATS, G., GRAUPNER, G. W., FOWLER, E. F., and JENSIK, R. J., 1946. Surgical approach to hypertension: Second report. Arch. Surg., **53**, 111–163.

DEY, F. L., FISHER, C., BERRY, C. M., and RANSON, S. W., 1940. Disturbances in reproductive functions caused by hypothalamic lesions in female guinea pigs. Am. J. Physiol., **129**, 39–46.

DEY, F., GILBERT, N. C., RASKELLEY, R. C., and TRUMP, R., 1945. Effect of stimuli originating in the upper abdomen in the causation of reflex shortening of the esophagus. Proc. Cen. Soc. j. Clin. Res., **18**, 8–9.

DEYSACH, L. J., 1939. The comparative morphology of the erectile tissue of the penis with special emphasis on the mechanism of erection. Am. J. Anat., **64**, 111–132.

DILLON, J. B., and HERTZMAN, A. B., 1941. The form of volume pulse in the finger pad in health, arteriosclerosis, and hypertension. Am. Heart J., **21**, 172–190.

DIXON, W. E., and RANSOM, F., 1912. Broncho-dilator nerves. J. Physiol., **45**, 413–428.

DÖRING., 1949. Zur Klinik vegetativen Störungen bei Syringomyelie und über trophische Störungen im allgemeinen. Deutsche med. Wchnschr., **74**, 754–758.

DOGIEL, A. S., 1896. Zwei Arten sympathischer Nervenzellen. Anat. Anz., **11**, 679–687.

DOLLEY, D. H., 1911. Studies on the recuperation of nerve cells after functional activity from youth to senility. J. Med. Research, **24** (New series 19), 309–343.

————1913. The relation between functional activity and depression in nerve cells from anatomic analysis. Trans. Am. Med. Assoc., Sec. Path. and Physiol., (1913), 1–6.

————1917. The recovery from depression in the Purkinje cell and the decline to senility of depression; with the incidental histogenesis of abnormal pigmentation. J. Comp. Neurol., **28**, 465–493.

DOLLEY, D. H., and GUTHRIE, F. V., 1918. The pigmentation of nerve cells. J. Med. Res., **34**, 123–142.

DOUGLAS, D. M., and MANN, F. C., 1939. An experimental study of the rhythmic contractions in the small intestine of the dog. Am. J. Digest. Dis., **6**, 318–322.

————1939. The activity of the lower part of the ileum of the dog in relation to the ingestion of food. Ibid., **6**, 434–439.

————1940. The gastro-iliac reflex: further experimental observations. Ibid., **7**, 53–57.

DOUPE, J., CULLEN, C. H., and CHANCE, G. Q., 1944. Postraumatic pain and causalgic syndrome. J. Neurol. Neurosurg., and Psychiat., **7**, 33–48.

DOWNMAN, C. B. B., GOGGIO, A. F., MCSWINEY, B. A., and YOUNG, M. H. C., 1939. Reflex vaso-motor responses from the paws of the cat. J. Physiol., **96**, 14.

DRAGSTEDT, L. R., 1952. The surgical aspects of peptic ulcer. Rev. Gastroenterol., **19**, 286–293.

DRAGSTEDT, L. R., HARPER, P. V., JR., TOVEE, E. B., and WOODWARD, E. R., 1947. Section of vagus nerves to stomach in treatment of peptic ulcer complications and end results after four years. Ann. Surg., **126**, 687–708.

DRAGSTEDT, L. R., and WOODWARD, E. R., 1951. Appraisal of vagotomy for peptic ulcer after seven years. J. A. M. A., **145**, 795–802.

DRAGSTEDT, L. R., WOODWARD, E. R., and CAMP, E. H., 1950. Question of the return of gastric secretion after complete vagotomy. Arch. Surg., **61**, 775–786.

DRAGSTEDT, L. R., WOODWARD, E. R., HARPER, P. V., and STORER, E. H., 1948. Mechanism of the relief of ulcer distress by gastric vagotomy. Gastroenterology, **10**, 200–204.

DRESEL, K., 1929. Zum Basedowproblem. Deutsche med. Wchnschr., **55**, 259–261.

DUBOIS, F. S., and KISTLER, G. H., 1933. Concerning the mechanism of contraction of the gall bladder in the guinea pig. Proc. Soc. Exper. Biol. and Med., **30**, 1178–1180.

DUCCESCHI, V., 1922. Système nerveux sympathique et tonus muscularis. Arch. internat. de physiol., **20**, 331–339.

DUCCESSHI, V., and CAMPANANI, C., 1925. Sulla tonicità dei muscoli intrinseci della laringe. Arch. di fiscol Ferenze, **23**, 79–84.

DUNCAN, D., 1943. Roots of spinal nerves. Science, **98**, 515–516.

DU PETIT, F. P., 1727. Memoire dans lequel il est démontré que les nerfs intercostaux fournissent des rameaux qui portent de esprits dans le yeux. Hist. Acad. roy. d. Sc., 1727, 1.

DURAND, L., et DESCOTES, J., 1952. Étude expérimentale de l'innervation pyélourétérole. Lyon chir., **47**, 709–728.

DUSSER DE BARENNE, J. G., 1916. Ueber die Innervation und den Tonus der quergestreiften Muskeln. Pflüger's Arch. ges Physiol., **166**, 145–168.

EBBECKE, U., 1951. Arbeitsweise der Schweiszdrüsen und sudomotorische Reflexe bei unmittelbarer Beobachtung mit Lupenvergröszerung. Ibid., **253**, 333–350.

ECHLIN, F., 1949. Pain responses on stimulation of the lumbar sympathetic trunk under local anesthesia. J. Neurosurg., **6**, 530–533.

ECKHARDT, C., 1863. Untersuchungen über die Erektion des Penis beim Hunde. Beitr. z. Anat. u. Physiol., **3**.

ECONOMO, C. VON, 1931. Encephalitis Lethargica. London.

EDHOLM, O. G., 1942. The compensatory mechanism of the splanchnic circulation during changes of posture. J. Physiol., **101**, 1–10.

EDWARDS, E. A., 1951. Operative anatomy of the lumbar sympathetic chain. Angiology, **2**, 184–198.

EDWARDS, E. A., and Crane, C., 1951. Lumbar sympathectomy for arteriosclerosis of the lower extremities. New England J. Med., **244**, 199–204.

EHRFNBERG, C. G., 1833. Nothwendigkeit einer feineren mechanischen Zerlegung des Gehirns und der Nerven. Ann. d. Phys. u. Chem., **104**, 499.

EHRLICH, E. JR., and ALEXANDER, W. F., 1951. Surgical implications of upper thoracic independent sympathetic pathways. Arch. Surg., **62**, 609–614.

EITEL, H., KREBS, H. A., and LOESER, A., 1933. Hypophysenvorderlappen und Schilddrüse, Klin. Wchnschr., **12**, 615–617.

ELLIASSON, S., and STRÖM, G., 1950. On the localization in the cat of hypothalamus and cortical structures influencing cutaneous blood flow. Acta physiol. scandinav. **20**, Suppl. 70, 113–118.

ELLIOTT, T. R., 1905. The action of adrenalin. J. Physiol., **32**, 401–467.

EMMELIN, N., 1952. Paralytic secretion of saliva. An example of supersensitivity after denervation. Physiol. Rev., **32**, 21–46.

ENGEL, D., 1941. Influence of sympathetic nervous system on capillary permeability. Ibid., **99**, 161–181.

ENS, A., 1745. De Caussa vices cordis alternans producente. Utrecht.

EPPINGER, H., and Hess, L., 1909. Zur Pathologie des vegetativen Nervensystems. Ztschr. f. klin. Med., **66**, 345–351; **68**, 205–230.

ERICI, I., FOLKOW, and UVNÄS, B., 1951. Sympathetic vasodilator nerves to the tongue of the cat. Acta physiol. scandinav., **25**, 1–9.

ERICI, I., and UVNÄS, B., 1951. Efferent and antidromic vasodilator impulses to the tongue in the chorda lingual nerve of the cat. Ibid., **25**, 10–14.

ESSEX, H. E., HERRICK, J. F., BALDES, E. J., and MANN, F. C., 1943a. Effects of exercise on the coronary blood flow, heart rate and blood pressure of trained dogs with denervated and partially denervated hearts. Am. J. Physiol., **138**, 687–697.

————1943b. Observations on the circulation in the hind limbs of a dog ten years following left lumbar sympathetic ganglionectomy. Ibid., **139**, 351–355.

ESVELD, L. E. VAN, 1928. Ueber die nervösen Elemente in der Darmwand. Ztschr. f. mikr.-anat. Forsch., **15**, 1–42.

ETIENNE, S. C., 1545. De dissectione partium corporis humani. Paris

EULER, U. S. VON, 1951. Hormones of the sympathetic nervous system and the adrenal medulla. Brit. Med. J., **1**, 105–108.

————1951. The nature of adrenergic nerve mediators. Pharmacol. Rev., **3**, 247–277.

EUSTACHIO, B., 1563. Opuscula anatomica. Venice.

FABER, K., 1899. Reflexhyperastesier ved Fordojelsessygdomme. Hospitalstidende (1899): 315.

FAIK, S., GRINDLAY, J. H., MANN, C., 1950. Effect of vagotomy on intestinal activity. Surgery, **28**, 546–549.

FARRELL, J. I., and LYMAN, R. Y., 1937. Study of secretory nerves of and action of certain drugs on prostate gland. Am. J. Physiol., **118**, 64–70.

FAY, T., 1932. Atypical facial neuralgia, a syndrome of vascular pain. Ann. Otol. Rhin. & Laryng., **41**, 1030–1062.

FEINDEL, W. H., WEDDELL, G., and SINCLAIR, D. C., 1948. Pain sensibility in deep somatic structures. J. Neurol. Neurosurg., and Psychiat., **11**, 113.

FELDBERG, W., and GUIMARAIS, J. A., 1935. Effects of sympathetic impulses and adrenalin on salivary secretion. J. Physiol., **83**, 43–44.

FELDBERG, W., MINZ, B., and TSUDZUMARA, H., 1933. The mechanism of the nervous discharge of adrenalin. Ibid., **80**, 15–16.

FERGUSON, J. H., 1936. Effects of vagotomy on the gastric functions of monkeys. Surg., Gynec. and Obst., **62**, 689–700.

FERRIS, E. B. JR., CAPPS, R. B., and WEISS, S., 1935. Carotid sinus syncope and its bearing on the mechanisms of the unconscious state and convulsions. A study of 32 additional cases. Medicine, **14**, 377–456.

————1937. Relation of the carotid sinus to the autonomic nervous system and the neuroses. Arch. Neur., **37**, 365–384.

FERTITTA, J. J., FERTITTA, S., and MILLER, K. T., 1950. Presacral neurectomy in the treatment of dysmenorrhea. Surgery, **28**, 729–734.

FIELD, M. E., 1930. Effect of emotion on blood platelet count. Am. J. Physiol., **93**, 245–248.

FINKELMAN, B., 1930. On nature of inhibition in intestine. J. Physiol., **70**, 145–157.

FISCHER, E., and KAISERLING, G., 1939. Experimentelle Sympathicoganglionitis. Deutsche Ztschr. f. Chir., **251**, 525–538.

FISCHER, C., INGRAM, W. R., and RANSON, S. W., 1938. Diabetes insipidus and the neuro-hormonal control of water balance; a contribution to the structure and function of the hypothalamico-hypophyseal system. Edwards Bros., Ann Arbor, Mich.

FLOTHOW, P. C., 1930. Surgery of sympathetic nervous system. Fourteen sympathetic ganglionectomies. Am. J. Surg., **10**, 8–18.

FÖRSTER, W., 1939. Beitrag zur anesthesie des Plexus brachialis. Zentralbl. Chir., **66**, 1313–1316.

FOLKOW, B., 1951. Impulse frequency in sympathetic vasomotor fibers correlated to the release and elimination of the transmitter. Acta physiol. scandinav., **25**, 49–76.

FOLKOW, B., FROST, J., HAEGER, K., and UVNÄS, B., 1949. The sympathetic vasomotor innervation of the skin of the dog. Ibid., **16**, 195–200

FOLKOW, B., HAEGER, K., and UVNÄS, B., 1948. Cholinergic fibers in the sympathetic outflow to the muscles of the hind limbs of the cat. Ibid., **15**, 401–411.

FONTAINE, R., and HERMANN, L. G., 1933. Post-traumatic painful osteoporosis. Ann. Surg., **97**, 26–61.

FORBES, H. S., and COBB, S. S., 1938. Vasomotor control of cerebral vessels. Brain, **61**, 221–233.

FORD, F. R., 1933. Paroxysmal lacrimation during eating as a sequel of facial palsy (syndrome of crocodile tears). Arch. Neurol. & Psychiat., **29**, 1279–1288.

FORTUYN, J. D., 1941. Hypoglycemia and the autonomic nervous system. J. Nerv. & Ment. Dis., **93**, 1–15.

FRANCILLON, M. R., 1928. Zur Topographie der Ganglien des menschlichen Herzens. Ztschr. Anat. u. Entwchlngsgesch., **85**, 131–165.

FRANCKS, C., 1898. Adénite cervicale chromque; angene argus laryngete oedémateuse; laryngotomie intercrico thyroidienne: guérison. Arch. de med. et. pharm. mil. par., 1898, 417–420.

FRANKE, F. E., RANDALL, W. C., SMITH, D. E., and HERTZMAN, A. B., 1947. Vasomotor and sudomotor patterns in the skin of the finger and forearm. Federation Proc., **6**, Part II, 105.

FRASER, J., 1926. Surgical aspects of certain disturbances of the involuntary nervous system met with in the alimentary tract. Br. Med. J., **1**, 359–364.

————1931. The autonomic nervous system in relation to surgery. Edinburgh Med. J., **38**, 189–214.

FREED, H., 1936. A study of involvement of the autonomic nervous system in lesions of the midbrain and hypothalamus, with possible relationship to peptic ulcer. Arch. Neurol. and Psychiat., **36**, 884–888.

FREEDBURG, A. S., and SLOAN, LE R. H., 1937. Association of carotid sinus reflexes with syncope and convulsions. Report of four cases. Ibid., **38**, 761-774.

FREEMAN, N. E., and PHILLIPS, R. A., 1931. Studies on the conditions of activity in endocrine organs. XXVII. The question of reflex inhibitory action of the vagus on medulliadrenal secretion. Am. J. Physiol., **98**, 55–59.

FREI, W., 1939. Algemeine pathologische Physiologie des vegetativen Nervensystems bei Infektionskrankheiten und Immunstätsvorgängen. Erg. Allg. Pathol. u. path. Anat. I. Mensch. u. Tiere., **34**, 181–225.

FRIDMAN, A., 1931. Zur Frage über den Einfluss des sympathischen Nervensystems auf die quergestreifte Muskulatur. Rusch. physiol. Ztschr., **14**, 242–247.

FRIEDGOOD, H. B., BEVIN, S., and UOTILA, U. U., 1940. Augmentation of thyrotropic hormone activity by adrenin and pilocarpine. Am. J. Physiol., **129**, 724–734.

FRIEDGOOD, H. B., and PINCUS, G., 1935. Studies on conditions of activity in endocrine organs. XXX. The nervous control of the anterior hypophysis as indicated by maturation of ova and ovulation after stimulation of cervical sympathetics. Endocrinology, **19**, 710–718.

FRIEDMAN, M., 1945. The anginal syndrome as a manifestation of hyperreactivity of the carotid sinus. Am. Heart J., **29**, 37–43.

FRIESEN, S. R., and HEMINGWAY, A., 1952. The vascular response of the stomach to experimental alterations in the autonomic nervous system of the dog. Am. Surgeon, **18**, 195–200.

FRÖHLICH, A., and MEYER, H. H., 1922. Visceral sensibility. Klin. Wchnschr., **1**, 1368-1369.

FRORIEP, A., 1907. Die Entwickelung und Bau des autonomen Nervensystems. Medizinisch-naturwiss., Arch. **1**, 301–321.

FRUMIN, M. J., NGRI, T. H., and WANG., S. C., 1952. Mechanism of vasodilatation in the hind limbs of dogs. Federation Proc., **11**, 51–52.

FULTON, J. F., 1926. Muscular contraction and the reflex control of movement. Baltimore.

———1928. Vasomotor and reflex sequelae of unilateral cervical and lumbar ramisectomy in a case of Raynaud's disease, with observations on tonus. Ann. Surg., **81**, 827–841.

FULTON, J. F., KENNARD, M. A., and WATTS, J. W., 1934. Autonomic representation in the cerebral cortex. Proc. Am. Physiol. Soc., 1934:37.

GALEN, C., De usu partium corporis humani, **9**, 11.

GASPARINI, F., 1952. Morphologische Befunde an den Pyrenophoren der Ganglion cervicale uteri unter Berüchsichtigung des Alters und des Funktionszustandes der Geschlechsorgane. Acta Anat., **15**, 308–314.

GARDNER, J. H., 1952. Innervation of pineal gland in hooded rat. J. Comp. Neurol., (In Press).

GARDNER, W. J., and WILLIAMS, G. H. JR., 1949. Interruption of the sympathetic nerve supply to the brain: Effect on Parkinson's syndrome. Arch. Neurol. and Psychiat., **61**, 413–421.

GARLOCK, J. H., and LYONS, A. S., 1949. El tratamiento de la ulcera duodenal. Revista Medica del hospital general, Mexico, **12**, 602–609.

———The surgical therapy of duodenal ulcer. Surgery, **25**, 352–360.

GARVEN, H. S. D., 1925. The nerve endings in the panniculus carnosus of the hedgehog with special reference to the sympathetic innervation of striated muscle. Brain, **48**, 380–441.

GASK, G. E., and ROSS, J. P., 1934. The surgery of the sympathetic nervous system. William Wood & Co., Baltimore.

GASKELL, W. H., 1886. On the structure, distribution and function of the nerves which innervate the visceral and vascular systems. J. Physiol., **7**, 1–81.

GATENBY, J. B., and MOUSSA, A. A., 1950. The sympathetic ganglion cell, with Sudan black and the Zernike microscope. J. Roy. Micr. Soc., **70**, 342–364.

———1951. The neurone of the human autonomic system and the so-called "senility pigment." J. Physiol., **114**, 252–254.

GAY, L. N., and RIENKOFF, W. M., 1942. Further observations on treatment of intractable bronchial asthma by bilateral resection of pulmonary plexus. Bull. Johns Hopkins Hosp., **70**, 386–393.

GELLHORN, E., PARKER, A., and FELDMAN, J., 1940. Autonomic basis of emotion. Science, **92**, 288–289.

GEOHEGAN, W. A., WOLFE, G. A. JR., AIDAR, O. J., HARE, K., and HINSEY, J. D., 1942. The spinal origin of the preganglionic fibers to the limbs in the cat and monkey. Am. J. Physiol., **135**, 324–329.

GERSUNI, C., and CHUDOROSEVA, A., 1930. Ueber die Wirkung der Sympathicotomie auf die funktionellen Eigenschaften des Skeletmuskels des Frosches. Russk. fiziol. Zurnal., **13**, 408–420, und deutsche Zusammenfassung, 420–421.

GESELL, R., and HAMILTON, M. A., 1941. Reflexogenic components of breathing. Am. J. Physiol., **133**, 694–719.

GESELL, R., LAPIDES, J., and LEVIN, M., 1940. The interaction of central and peripheral chemical control of breathing. Ibid., **130**, 155–170.

GIBBS, F. A., LENNOX, W. G., and GIBBS, E. L., 1934. Cerebral blood flow preceding and accompanying epileptic seizures in man. Arch. Neurol. and Psychiat., **32**, 257–272.

GILDEA, E. F., and MAN, E. B., 1940. The hypothalamus and fat metabolism. A. Res. Nerv. & Ment. Dis., Proc., **20**, 501–524.

GILLESPIE, R. D., 1936. Psychological factors in asthma. Br. Med. J., **1**, 1285.

GINETZINSKY, A. G., 1924. The effect of the sympathetic on the function of muscle. Ibid., **2**, 534.

GINEZINSKY, V., 1926. Ueber den Einfluss des Sympathicus auf die Funktion des Skeletmuskels in anaeroben Verhältnissen. Russ. fisiol. Zurnal, **9**, 93–98.

GINSBERG, R. S., FELDMAN, M., and NECHELES, H., 1948. Effect of odor on appetite. Gastroenterology, **10**, 281–285.

GLASER, E. M., BERRIDGE, F. R., and PRIOR, K. M., 1950. Effects of heat and cold on the distribution of blood within the human body. Clin. Sci., **9**, 181–187.

GLASS, G. H. J., MERSHEIMER, W. L., and SVIGALS, C. S., 1951. Effect of vagotomy and subtotal gastric resection on the secretion of mucin in the human stomach. Arch Surg., **62**, 658–669.

GLEY, E., and QUINQUAUD, A., 1921. La fonction des surrenales. III. Variations de l'action vasomotrice due nerf grand splanchnique suivant diverses especes animales. J. de physiol. et de pathol. gen. **10**, 355–364.

GOETZ, R. H., 1949. The diagnosis and treatment of vascular diseases, with special consideration of clinical plethysmography and the surgical physiology of the autonomic nervous system. Br. J. Surg., **37**, 25–40; 146–156.

GOETZ, R. H., and AMES, F., 1949. Reflex vasodilatation by body heating in diagnosis of peripheral vascular disorders. Arch. Int. Med., **84**, 396–418.

GOLDSCHEIDER, A., 1923. Ueber die Bedütung der sensiblen Druckpunkte (Nervenpunkte) in der Pathologie. Deutsche med. Wchnschr., **49**, 839–843.

GOLDSCHEIDER, A., and JACOB, P., 1894. Ueber die Variationen der Leukocytose Ztschr. klin. Med., **25**, 373–448.

GOLTZ, F., 1892. Der Hund ohne Grosshirn. Pflügers Arch. ges. Physiol., **51**, 570–614.

GOLTZ, N. F., 1952. Head and face pain due to autonomic dysfunction. Ann. Ann. Otol. Rhin. and Laryng., **61**, 441–447.

GRABFIELD, G. P., and SWANSON, D., 1939. Studies on the denervated kidney. IV. The effects of unilateral denervation in acute experiments on sodium chloride excretion. Arch. internat. de Pharm. et de Therap., **61**, 92–98.

GRAFE, E., and MAYERS, L., 1923. Ueber den Einfluss der Affekte auf den Gesamtoffwechsel. Ztschr. ges. Neurol. u. Psychiat., **86**, 247.

GRANT, R. T., and BLAND, E. F., 1931. Observations on arteriovenous anastomoses in human skin and in the bird's foot with special reference to the reaction to cold. Heart, **15**, 385–411.

GRANT, R. T., and PEARSON, R. S. B., 1938. The blood circulation in the human limb; observations on the differences between the proximal and the distal parts and remarks on the regulation of body temperature. Clin. Sci. Inc. Heart, **3**, 119–139.

GRAY, D. J., 1947. Intrinsic nerves of the testis. Anat. Rec., **98**, 325–335.

GREAVES, D. P., and PERKINS, E. S., 1952. Influence of the sympathetic nervous system on the intraocular pressure and vascular circulation of the eye. Brit. J. Opthal., **36**, 258–264.

GREEN, D. M., NELSON, J. N., DODDS, G. A., and SMALLEY, R. E., 1950. Bilateral adrenalectomy in malignant hypertension and diabetes. J. A. M. A., **144**, 439–443.

GREENE, C. W., 1941. Coronary reflex dilatations accompanying contractions of voluntary muscles. Am. J. Physiol., **132**, 321–326.

GREGELEY, J., 1943. Beiträge zur Rolle der Schilddrüse und des Nervensystems bei der Chemischen Wärmeregulation. Arch. exper. Path. u. Pharmakol., **202**, 597–608.

GREGORY, R. A., 1946. Changes in intestinal tone and motility associated with nausea and vomiting. J. Physiol., **105**, 58–65.

GREIWE, J. E., 1932. The presso-receptory nerves and their functions. J. Med, **13**, 172–180.

GREVEN, K., and FEDERSCHMIDT, H., 1939. Untersuchungen zur Hamodynamik der kleineren und kleinsten Arterien. Pflüger's Arch. ges. Physiol., **242**, 617–643.

GREVING R., 1920. Die Innervation der Speiseröhre. Ztschr. f. angw. Anat. u. Konstit., **101**.

————1952. Histologische Studien am Plexus myentericus des Magens. 3. Ueber die Kontinaität von Ganglienzellen, das Terminalreticulum und das Synapse-Problem. Acta Neurovegetativa, **3**, 507–532.

GRIMSON, K. S., ALVING, A. S., and ADAMS, W., 1941. Total and subtotal sympathectomy in man, effect on blood pressure in hypertension. Am. J. Physiol., **133**, 305–306.

GRIMSON, K. S., ORGAIN, E. S., ANDERSON, B., BROOME, R. A., and LONGINO, F. H., 1949. Results of treatment of patients with hypertension by total thoracic and partial or total lumbar sympathectomy, splanchnicectomy and celiac ganglionectomy. Ann. Surg., **129**, 850–871.

GRIMSON, K. S., ROWE, C. P. JR. and TAYLOR, H. M., 1952. Results of vagotomy during seven years clinical observations and tests of gastric secretion. Ann. Surg., **135**, 621–636.

GRINDLAY, J. H., HERRICK, J. F., and BALDES, E. J., 1939. Rhythmicity of the spleen in relation to blood flow. Am. J. Physiol., **127**, 119–126.

GRUBER, C. M., 1933. The autonomic innervation of the genito-urinary organs. Physiol. Rev., **13**, 497–609.

GRÜNBERG, F. F., 1930. Zur Frage über morphologische Veränderungen im sympathischen Nervensystem bei experimenteller Bleivergiftung. Virchows Arch. path. Anat., **278**, 372–380.

GRUSS, W., 1932. Ueber Ganglien im Ramus communicans. Ztschr. Anat. u. Entwcklngsgesch., **97**, 464–471.

GUNN, J. A., and FRANKLIN, K. J., 1922. The sympathetic innervation of the vagina. Proc. Roy. Soc., London, Series B., **94**, 197–203.

GUTTMANN, L., 1931. Sweat secretion in human beings in its relation to the nervous system. Ztschr. ges. Neurol. u. Psychiat., **135**, 1–48.

GUYTON, A. C., 1952. Vasomotor waves due to oscillating blood pressure control mechanisms. Federation Proc., **11**, 61.

GUYTON, A. C., BATSON, H. M., and SMITH, C. M., 1951. Adjustments of the circulatory system following very rapid transfusion or hemorrhage. II. Method for studying competence of the body's blood pressure regulatory mechanisms and effect of pressoreceptor denervation. Am. J. Physiol., **164**, 351–368.

GUYTON, A. C., and HARRIS, J. W., 1951. Pressoreceptor-autonomic oscillation; a probable cause of vasomotor waves. Ibid., **165**, 158–166.

HÄMÄLÄINEN, M., and SÖDERLUND, B., 1946. Surgical treatment of scleroderma. Acta. chir. scandinav., **93**, 201–212.

HAIMOVICI, H., 1950. Evidence for adrenergic sweating in man. Applied Physiol., **2**, 512–521.

HALLER, T., 1932. Untersuchungen über den Einfluss des Sympathikus auf die Muskeltätigkeit unter natürlichen Bedingungen mit Hilfe von Aktionsströmen. Ztschr. f. Biol., **92**, 555–561.

HAMMOND, W. S., 1946. Reduction of sympathetic ganglia in the trunk of the chick following removal of neural crest. Anat. Rec., **94**, 23.

————1949. Formation of the sympathetic nervous system in the trunk of the chick embryo following removal of the thoracic neural tube. J. Comp. Neurol., **91**, 67–85.

HAMMOND, W. S., and YNTEMA, C. L., 1947. Depletions in the thoraco-lumbar sympathetic system following removal of neural crest in the chick. Ibid., **86**, 237–265.

HAMMOUDA, D. H., and WILSON, W. H., 1935. Further observations on the respiratory-accelerator fibers of the vagus. J. Physiol., **85**, 62–72.

————1943. The origin of the inflation and the deflation pulmonary reflexes. Ibid., **101**, 446–459.

HANDOVSKY, H., and SAMAAN, A., 1937. Observations on the renal circulation and secretion in the dog, with special reference to the effect of pituitary (posterior lobe) extract. Ibid., **89**, 14–31.

HARMAN, P. J., and DAVIES, H., 1948. Intrinsic nerves in the mammalian kidney. Part I. Anatomy in mouse, rat, cat and macaque. J. Comp. Neurol., **89**, 225–244.

HARRIS, A. J., 1943. An experimental analysis of the inferior mesenteric plexus. Ibid., **79**, 1–17.

HARRIS, W., 1936a. Ciliary (migrainous) neuralgia and its treatment. Br. Med. J. **1**, 457–460.

————1936b. Role of the sympathetic in sensory conduction and certain neuralgias., Ibid., **2**, 112–115.

HARRISON, F., 1940. The hypothalamus and sleep. A. Res. Nerv. & Ment. Dis., Proc., **20**, 635–656.

HARTH, H., 1951. Beitrag zur Vagotomiefrage. Wien. klin. Wchnschr., **63**, 508–509.

HARTING, K., 1929. Über die feinere Innervation der Tube. Ztschr. f. wiss. Biol., **9**, 544–560.

HASAMA, B., 1930. Pharmakologische und physiologische Studien über die Schweisszentren. III. Zur Frage nach der Beeinflussung der Schweissekretion und der Körper-temperatur durch die Medulla oblongata. IV. Ueber den Einfluss der anorganischen Kationen auf Wärme-sowie Schweisszentrum im Zwischenhirn. Arch. exper. Path. u. Pharmakol., **153**, 257–308.

HAXTON, H. A., 1948. Gustatory sweating. Brain, **71**, 16–25.

HEBB, C. O., 1940. Bronchomotor responses to stimulation of the stellate ganglia and to injection of acetylcholine in isolated perfused guinea pig lungs. J. Physiol., **99**, 57–75.

HEBB, C. O., and STAVRAKY, G. W., 1936. Presence of glucose in salivary secretion after administration of adrenalin. Quart. J. Exp. Physiol., **26**, 141–153.

HEGRE, E., and INGERSOLL, E. H., 1949. An analysis of regional variations in the response of the detrusor muscle to electrical stimulation of the hypogastric nerves. J. Urol., **61**, 1037-1047.

HEINBECKER, P., 1947. Factors limiting surgery for essential hypertension. Ann. Surg., **126**, 535–544.

HELSON, H., 1932. The part played by the sympathetic system as an afferent mechanism in the region of the trigeminus. Brain, **55**, 114–121.

HEMINGWAY, A., RASMUSSEN, T., RASMUSSEN, A. T., and WIKOFF, H., 1940. Effect of cutting the pituitary stalk on physiological temperature regulation. Endocrinology, **27**, 212–218.

HENDERSON, V. E., and ROEPKE, M. H., 1933. On the mechanism of salivary secretion. J. Pharm. and Exp. Therap., **47**, 193–207.

————1934. The role of acetylcholine in bladder contractile mechanisms and in parasympathetic ganglia. Ibid., **51**, 97–111.

HERMANN, H., 1949. Mikroskopische Beobactungen an den Herzganglien des Menschen bei Coronarsklerose. Virchow's Arch. path. Anat., **316**, 341–372.

————1952a. Das Nervensystem der menschlichen Gallenblase und seine Veränderungen bei Cholelithiasis. Arch. path. Anat., **322**, 17-48.

————1952b. Über einige Probleme der Histopathologie des peripheren vegetativen Nervensystems. Klin. Wchnschr., **30**, 196–199.

HERRICK, J. F., ESSEX, H. E., and BALDES, E. J., 1932. The effect of lumbar sympathectomy on the flow of blood in the femoral artery of the dog. Am. J. Physiol., **101**, 213–217.

HERRIN, R. C., and MEEK, W. J., 1931. Influence of the sympathetics on muscle glycogen. Ibid., **97**, 57–65.

HERRING, P. T., 1927. The pineal of the mammalian brain: its morphology and histology in relation to function. Quart. J. Exper. Physiol., **17**, 125–147.

HERTZMAN, A. B., 1937. Photoelectric plethysmography of fingers and toes in man. Proc. Soc. Exper. Biol. & Med., **37**, 529–534.

————1938. Comparative estimation of blood supply of skin areas from photoelectrically recorded volume pulse. Ibid., **38**, 562–564.

————1941. The relative responses of the dorsal metacarpal, digital and terminal skin arteries of the hand in vasoconstrictor reflexes. Am. J. Physiol., **134**, 59–64.

HERTZMAN, A. B., and DILLON, J. B., 1939. Selective vascular reaction patterns in the nasal septum and skin of the extremities and head. Ibid., **127**, 671–684.

————1940. Reactions of large and small arteries in man to vasoconstrictor stimuli., Ibid., **130**, 56–62.

HERTZMAN, A. B., and RANDALL, W. C., 1948. Regional differences in the basal and maximal rates of blood flow in the skin. Applied Physiol., **1**, 234–241.

HERTZMAN, A. B., RANDALL, W. C., and JOCHIM, K. E., 1946. The estimation of the cutaneous blood flow with photoelectric plethysmograph. Am. J. Physiol., **145**, 716–726.

HERTZMAN, A. B., and ROTH, L. W., 1942a. The vasomotor components in the vascular reactions in the finger to cold. Ibid., **136**, 669–679.

————1942b. The reactions of the digital artery and minute pad arteries to local cold. Ibid., **136**, 680–691.

————1942c. The absence of vasoconstrictor reflexes in the forehead circulation. Ibid., **136**, 692–697.

HERZOG, E., 1926. Beiträge zur normalen und pathologischen Histologie des Sympathicus. Ztschr. f. d. ges. Neurol. u. Psychiat., **103**, 1–41.

————1948. Principielles zur normalen und pathologischen Histologie des peripheren vegetativen Nervensystems. Klin. Wchnschr., **26**, 641–648.

————1950. Die Pathologie der peripheren vegetativen Ganglien. Verhdl. d. Deutsch Ges. f. Pathol., **34**, 52–86.

HERZOG, E., and SCHÜLER, E., 1941. Experimenteller Beitrag zur Frage der Ermüdung der sympathischen Ganglienzellen. Beitr. path. Anat., **8**, 178–193.

HESS, E., 1930. Renal sympathectomy. Penn. Med. J., **33**, 741–747.

HESS, W. R. VON., 1944. Hypothalamische Adynamie. Helvet. physiol. et pharmacol. acta **2**, 137–147.

HESSELMANN, J., 1932. Der Einfluss des Sympathikus auf den Gradienten der Permeabilität der Kapillaren. Ztschr. f. Biol., **92**, 287–292.

HESSER, C. M., 1949. Central and chemoreflex components in the respiratory activity during acid-base displacements in the blood. Acta physiol. scandinav., 18 Suppl. **64**, 5–69.

HETHERINGTON, A. W., 1943. Production of hypothalamic obesity in rats already displaying chronic hypopituitarism. Am. J. Physiol., **140**, 89–92.

HETHERINGTON, A. W., and RANSON, S. W., 1940. Hypothalamic lesions and adiposity in the rat. Anat. Rec., **78**, 149–172.

HEUSNER, A. P., 1946. Yawning and associated phenomena. Physiol. Rev., **26**, 156–168.

HEYMANS, C., 1929. The carotid sinus and other reflexogenic vasosensory zones. London.

————1938a. Role of cardioaortic and carotid-sinus nerves in the reflex control of the respiratory center. New England J. Med., **219**, 157–159.

————1938b. The pressoreceptive mechanisms for the regulation of heart rate, vasomotor tone, blood pressure and blood supply. Ibid., **219**, 147–154.

————1951. Chemoreceptors and regulation of respiration. Acta physiol. scandinav., **22**, 4–13.

HEYMANS, C., BOUCKAERT, J. J., and DAUTREBANDE, L., 1930. Sinus carotidien et réflexes respiratoires; influences respiratoires réfléxes et l'acidose, de l'alcalose, de l'anhydride carbonique, et l'ion hydrogène et de l'anoxémie. Sinus carotidiens et échanges respiratoires dans les poumons et au dela des poumons. Arch. internat. de pharmacodyn. et de therap., **39**, 400–449.

HEYMANS, C., BOUCKAERT, J. J., FARBER, S., and HSU, F. Y., 1935. Influences de l'acetylcholine sur les recepteurs chimio-sensitifs du sinus carotidien. Compt. rend. Soc. Biol., **120**, 1354–1356.

HEYMANS, C., BOUCKAERT, J. J., and WIERCNCHOWSKI, M., 1937. Réflexes vasomoteurs médullaires d'origine vasculaire barosensible. Arch. internat. de pharmacodyn. et de thérap., **55**, 233–256.

HEYMANS, C., and PANNIER, R., 1948. Presso-récepteurs du sinus carotidien et sensibilite du centre respiratoire au CO_2. Arch. Internat. pharmacodyn., **77**, 62–63.

HIGBEE, D., 1949. Functional and anatomic relation of sphenopalatine ganglion to the autonomic nervous system. Arch. Otolaryngol., **50**, 45–58.

HILL, C. J., 1927.   A contribution to our knowledge of the enteric plexuses.   Phil. Trans. Roy. Soc. London, Series B, **215**, 355–387.

HILLARP, N. A., 1946.   Structure of synapse and peripheral innervation apparatus of autonomic nervous system.   Acta anat. (supp. 4) **2**, 1–153.

————1947.   Innervation of the adrenal medulla in the rat.   Acta anat. (supp. 5) **3**, 153–161.

————1949.   Some critical remarks on the problem of the double innervation of the salivary gland cells.   Acta anat., **8**, 190–200.

HINES, M. J., and TOWER, S.S., 1928.   Studies on the innervation of skeletal muscle. Bull. Johns Hopkins Hosp., No. 5, 264–307.

HINSEY, J. C., 1927   Some observations on innervations of skeletal muscle of cat. J. Comp. Neurol., **44**, 87–195.

HINTON, J. W., and LORD, J. W., 1946.   Operative technic of thoracolumbar sympathectomy.   Surg., Gynec. and Obst., **83**, 643–646.

HINTZE, A. L., and SEAGER, L., 1929.   The tonus of the ear muscles in the rabbit after cutting the cervical sympathetic.   Am. J. Physiol., **89**, 400–402.

HIRANO, N., 1941.   Nervöse Innervation des Corpus ciliare des Menschen.   Arch. f. Ophthalmol., **142**, 549–559.

HIRSCH, S., 1952.   L'influence constrictive de l'adrénaline sur la coronaire.   Apport histologigue à l'étude de la contraction vasculaire.   Presse méd., **60**, 417–419.

HIRT, A., 1926.   Über den Faserverlauf der Nierennerven.   Ztschr. Anat. u. Entwcklngsgesch., **78**, 260–276.

HOEKSTRA, J., STEGGERDA, F. R., and TAYLOR, A. B., 1945.   Observations on pressure relationship between the proximal and the distal colon of dogs.   Federation Proc., **4**, 34.

HOFF, E. C., KELL, J. F. JR., HASTINGS, N., SHOLES, D. M., and GRAY, E. H., 1951. Vasomotor, cellular and functional changes produced in kidney by brain stimulation. J. Neurophysiol., **14**, 317–332.

HOFF, F., 1928.   Die vegetative Regulation des Blutes.   Deutsch. med. Wchnschr., **54**, 905–908.

————1942.   Infektionsabwehr und vegetatives Nervensystem.   Ibid., **67**, 417–420.

HOFFMANN, A., and WERTHEIMER, E., 1927.   Glykogenansatz beim künstlich gereizten entnerventen Muskel.   Pflügers Arch. ges. Physiol., **216**, 337–340.

————1928.   Der Glykogenbestand des Knorpels und seine Bedeutung.   Ibid., **220**, 183–193.

HOLLINGSHEAD, W. H., 1936.   The innervation of the adrenal gland.   J. Comp. Neurol., **64**, 449–467.

————1940.   The innervation of the supracardial bodies in the cat.   Ibid., **73**, 37–48.

HOLMES, G., 1933.   Observations on the paralyzed bladder.   Brain, **56**, 383–396.

HOMANS, J., 1940.   Minor causalgia; A hyperesthetic neurovascular syndrome.   New England J. Med., **122**, 870–874.

HONJIN, R., 1951.   Studies on the nerve endings in the small intestine.   Cytological and Neurological studies, U. of Kanazawa, **9**: 1–14.

HOOBLER, S. W., MANNING, J. T., PAINE, W. G., McCLELLAN, S. G., HELCHER, P. O., RENFEST, H., PEET, M. M., and COHN, E. A., 1951.   The effects of splanchnicectomy on the blood pressure in hypertension.   Circulation, **4**, 173–183.

HOSKINS, R. G., 1925.   Studies on vigor.   II.   The effect of castration on voluntary activity.   Am. J. Physiol., **72**, 324–330.

————1927.   The relation of the suprarenals to the sympathetic nervous system. J. A. M. A., **88**, 2011–2013.

HOSKINS, R. G., and McCLURE, C. W., 1912a.   The adrenal glands and blood pressure. Arch. Int. Med., **10**, 343–356.

————1912b.   The relation of the adrenal glands to blood pressure and intestinal pressure.   Am. J. Physiol., **30**, 192–195.

————1912c.   The adrenal glands and blood pressure.   Arch. Int. Med., **10**, 343.

————1912d.   The comparative sensitiveness of blood pressure and intestinal peristalsis to epinephrin.   Am. J. Physiol., **31**, 59–63.

HOSKINS, R. G., and WHEELON, H., 1914a.   Parathyroid deficiency and sympathetic irritability.   Ibid., **34**, 263–270.

————1914*b*. Ovarian extirpation and vasomotor irritability. Ibid., **35**, 119–123.

Houck, C. R., 1951. Lack of evidence of a Trueta shunt in dogs during electrical stimulation of renal artery nerves. Federation Proc., **10**, Part I, 66–67.

Houssay, Magedalena, Biasotti, and Mazzocco, 1932. Relationship between the hypophysis and the thyroid. J. A. M. A., **98**, 567–568.

Hunter, J. I., 1924*a*. The influence of the sympathetic nervous system in the genesis of the rigidity of striated muscle in spastic paralysis. Surg., Gynec. and Obst., **39**, 721–743.

————1924*b*. The postural influence of the sympathetic nervous system. Brain, **47**, 261–292.

————1925. Relationships of sympathetic innervation to tone of skeletal muscle. Am. J. Med. Sci., **170**, 469–480.

————1925. Sympathetic innervation of striated muscle. Br. Med. J., **1**, 197–201; 251–256; 298–301; 350–353; 398–403.

Hunter, J. I., and Latham, O., 1925. A contribution to the discussion of the histological problems involved in the conception of a somatic and sympathetic innervation of voluntary muscle. Med. J. Australia, **1**, 27–36.

Hurst, A. F., 1919. Physiology of intestinal movements, etc., in constipation and allied intestinal disorders, London.

Hurst, A. F., and Rake, G. W., 1930. Achalasia of the cardia. Quart J. Med., **23**, 491–504.

Hyndman, O. R., and Wolkin, J., 1941*a*. The autonomic mechanism of heat conservation and dissipation: I. Effects of heating the body; Evidence for the existence of capillary dilator nerves in anterior roots. Am. Heart J., **22**, 289–304.

————1941*b*. The sympathetic nervous system: Influence on sensibility to heat and cold and certain types of pain. Arch. Neurol. and Psychiat., **46**, 1006–1016.

————1941*c*. Sweat mechanism in man: Study of distribution of sweat fibers from the sympathetic ganglia, spinal roots, spinal cord and common carotid artery. Ibid., **45**, 446–467.

————1942. Raynaud's disease. A review of its mechanism, with evidence that it is primarily a vascular disease. Am. Heart J., **23**, 535–554.

Hwang, K., Essex, H. E., and Mann, F. C., 1947. Study of certain problems resulting from vagotomy in dogs with special reference to emesis. Am. J. Physiol., **149**, 429–448.

Illényi, A., and Borzsák, L., 1938. Der Einfluss des vegetativen Tonus auf die Bildung des Hämolysins. Ztschr. Immunitätsf. u. exp. Therap., **94**, 79–82.

Ingersoll, E. H., 1934. The effect of stimulation upon the coeliac ganglion cells of the albino rat. J. Comp. Neurol., **59**, 267–284.

————1936. Functional behavior of coeliac ganglion cells of the rabbit. Am. J. Physiol., **117**, 514–517.

Ingersoll, E. H., and Hegre, E. S., 1951. Spontaneous activity of the detrusor muscle in the cat. J. Urol., **66**, 758–764.

Ingersoll, E. H., Hegre, E. S., and Jones, L., 1951. Bladder activity of the cat in response to forebrain stimulation. Anat. Rec., **109**, 47–48.

Ingram, W. R., Ladd, L., and Benbow, J. T., 1939. The excretion of anti-diuretic substance and its relation to the hypothalamico-hypophyseal system in cats. Am. J. Physiol., **127**, 544–551.

Irwin, D. A., 1931. The anatomy of Auerbach's plexus. Am. J. Anat., **49**, 141–165.

Issekutz, B., Hetényi, G., and Diosy, A., 1950. The physiology of sweat secretion. Arch. internat. pharmacodyn., **83**, 133–134.

Ivy, A. C., and Bachrach, W. H., 1940. Abnormal mechanism for excitation of gastric secretion in dog. Am. J. Dig. Dis., **7**, 76–78.

Izquierdo, J. J., and Cannon, W. B., 1928. Studies on the conditions of activity in endocrine glands. XXIII. Emotional polycythemia in relation to sympathetic and medulliadrenal action on the spleen. Am. J. Physiol., **84**, 545–562.

Jabonero, V., 1951. Étude sur la morphopathologie des cellules interstitielles du systeme neurovégétatif périphérique. I. Biol. Latina, **4**, 323–356.

————1951. Études sur le systeme neurovégétatif périphérique III. Innervation de l'estomac humain. Acta anat., **11**, 490–532. IV. Innervation intermurale de la vesicule biliaire humaine. Ibid., **13**, 171–192.

————1951. La synapse plexiforme à distance du systeme neurovégétatif périphérique. Experientia, **7**, 471–475.

————1951. Innervation efférente des vaisseaux sanguins. Cardiologia, **19**, 209–247.

————1951. Observaciones sobre la innervación de la región carotídea humana. Arch. Med. Exper., **14**, 59–78.

————1951. Estudias sobre la histopathologia del sistema neurovegetativa periférico. Ibid., **14**, 32–58.

JABONERO, V., 1952. Études sur le système neurovégétatif périphérique. V. Innervation de l'oesophage humain. Nouveaux faits concernant la constitution du S. N. V. et de ses synapses. Acta Anat., **15**, 105–142.

JABONERO, V., GOMEZ BOSQUE, P., BORDALLO, F., and y PEREZ CASAS, J., 1951. Organización anatómica del systema neurovegetativo periférico. Instituto Nacional de Ciencias Medicas.

JABOULAY, 1899. Cited by BALL. Med. News, New York and Philadelphia.

JACKSCH, 1892. Wien med. Wchnschr., **42**, 617 and 660.

JACKSON, R. G., 1948. Anatomic study of the vagus nerves with a technic for transabdominal gastric vagus resection. Arch. Surg., **57**, 333–352.

————1949. Anatomy of the vagus nerves in the region of the lower esophagus and the stomach. Anat. Rec., **103**, 1–18.

JACOBS, J. L., KELLEY, J. J., and SOMMERS, S. C., 1941. Hereditary predisposition to sensitization in guinea pigs. Proc. Soc. Exper. Biol. & Med., **48**, 639–641.

JAFFE, R. H., 1927. Reticulo-endothelial system: its role in pathological conditions in man. Arch. Path. and Lab. Med., **4**, 45–91.

JAMIESON, R. W., SMITH, D. B., and ANSON, B. J., 1952. The cervical sympathetic ganglia. An anatomical study of 100 cervico-thoracic dissections. Quart. Bull. Northwestern Univ. Med. School, **26**, 219–227.

JANOWITZ, H. D., and GROSSMAN, M. I., 1949. Regulation of food intake in normal and esophagostomized dogs. Federation Proc., **8**, 81.

JANOWITZ, H. D., and HOLLANDER, F., 1951. Critical evidence that vagal stimulation does not release gastrin. Proc. Soc. Exper. Biol. & Med., **76**, 49–52.

JASCHWILI, D., 1928. Zur Frage der Wirkung des Sympathicus auf die Skeletmuskulatur. Ber. sächs. Akad. Math.-phys. K., **80**, 300–311.

JOHNSON, C. A., SCUPHAM, G. W., and GILBERT, N. C., 1932. Studies on peripheral vascular phenomena. II. Observations on peripheral circulatory changes following unilateral cervical sympathectomy and ramisection. Surg., Gynec. and Obst., **55**, 737–741.

JOHNSON, F. E., and BOYDEN, E. A., 1943. The effect of sectioning various autonomic nerves upon the rate of emptying of the biliary tract in the cat. Ibid., **76**, 395–410.

JOHNSTONE, J., 1764. Essay on the use of the ganglions of the nerves. Phil. Tr. Roy. Soc., **54**, 177.

JONES,C. M., 1938. Digestive tract pain. The Macmillan Co., New York.

JONES, C. M., and CHAPMAN, W. P., 1942. Studies on mechanisms of pain of angina pectoris with particular relation to hiatus hernia. Tr. A. Am. Physicians, **57**, 139—151.

JONES, D. S., 1937. The origin of the sympathetic trunks in the chick embryo. Anat. Rec., **70**, 45–65.

————1939. Studies on the origin of sheath cells and sympathetic ganglia in the chick. Ibid., **73**, 343–357.

————1941. Further studies on the origin of sympathetic ganglia in the chick embryo. Ibid., **79**, 7–15.

————1942a. The origin of the vagi and the parasympathetic ganglion cells of the viscera of the chick. Ibid., **82**, 185–197.

————1942b. The origin of the ciliary ganglia in the chick embryo. Ibid., **82**, 32–33.

JONES, T., 1927. Intramuscular nerve elements of the ventricular muscle. J. Anat., **61**, 247–260.

————1936. The structure and mode of innervation of capillary blood vessels. Am. J. Anat., **58**, 227–250.

JOST, H., RUILMANN, C. J., HILL, T. S., and GULO, M. J., 1952. I. Technics and control data. Central and autonomic nervous system reactions of normal adults to sensory and ideational (frustration) stimulation. J. Nerv. and Ment. Dis., **115**, 35–48.

JUNGMANN, P., 1922. Familiäre juvenile.Schrumpfniere. Klin. Wchnschr., 1, 444.

KABAT, H., 1940. Cardio accelerator fibers in vagus nerve of dog. Am. J. Physiol., 128, 246–257.

KAETHER, H., and SCHAEFER, K. W. P., 1940. Untersuchungen des Ca-Gehaltes normaler Haut verglichen mit den Befunden bei Sklerodermie. Klin. Wchnschr., 19, 353–354.

KAHN, R. H., and POLLAK, F., 1931. Die aktive Verengerung des Lumens der capillaren Blutgefässe. Pflügers Arch. ges. Physiol., 226, 799–807.

KAPLAN, S. A., FOMAN, S. J., and RAPAPORT, S., 1951. Effect of splanchnic nerve division on urinary excretion of electrolytes during mannitol loading in the hydropenic dog. Am. J. Physiol., 166, 641–648.

KASS, I. H., 1932. Neurofibromatosis of the bladder. Am. J. Dis. Child., 44, 1040–1047.

KATSURASHIMA, T., 1932. Ueber Nervenänderungen im Bereich des Magengeschwürs, resp. Ulkuskarzinoms. Mitt. u. allg. Path. u. path. Anat., 7, 285–322.

KATZ, L. N., and JOCHIM, K., 1939. Observations on the innervation of the coronary vessels of the dog. Am. J. Physiol., 126, 395–401.

KATZ, L. N., and SAPHIR, O., 1933. The nerve plexus between the aorta and pulmonary artery. I. Observations on its nature and function. Ibid., 104, 253–258.

KEHLER, E., 1949. Kritische Bemerkungen zur experimentellen Funktionsanalyse des vegitativen Systems. Med. Klin., 44, 753–755.

KEIL, F. C., and ROOT, W. S., 1941. Parasympathetic sensitization in the cat's eye. Am. J. Physiol., 132, 437–445.

————1942. The effect of the urethane of beta methylcholine chloride upon the parasympathectomized cat's eye. Ibid., 136, 173–176.

KEITH, N. M., ODEL, H. M., MORLOCK, C. G., ROSENBERG, E. F., and KERNOHAN, J. W., 1939. Pathologic studies of the arterial system in severe hypertension. Proc. Staff Meet., Mayo Clin., 14, 209–224.

KELLGREN, J. H., 1939. On the distribution of pain arising from deep somatic structures with charts of segmental pain areas. Clin. Sci., 4, 35.

KENNEDY, G. C., 1950. The hypothalamic control of food intake in rats. Proc. Roy. Soc., London, Series B., 137, 535–549.

KERN, R. A., 1940. Role of water balance in clinical manifestations of allergy. Am. J. M. Sc., 199, 778–789.

KERSLAKE, D. McK., and COOPER, K. E., 1950. Vasodilatation in the hand in response to heating of the skin elsewhere. Clin. Sc., 9, 31–47.

KEY, J. A., and MOORE, R. N., 1933. Healing of fractures, of defects in bones and of defects in cartilage after sympathectomy. Arch. Surg., 25, 272–279.

KING, A. B., 1939. Nerve endings in the cardiac musculature of the rat. Bull. Johns Hopkins Hosp., 65, 489–499.

KING, C. E., and ARNOLD, L., 1922. The activities of the intestinal mucosal motor mechanism. Am. J. Physiol., 59, 97–121.

KINMONTH, J. B., and SIMEONE, F. A., 1952. Motor innervation of large arteries. Brit. J. Surg., 39, 333–335.

KIRGIS, H. D., 1940. The cytological structure of the hypothalamic nuclei in relation to their functional connections. Tr. Acad. Sci. of St. Louis, 30, 69–84.

KIRGIS, H. D., and KUNTZ, A., 1942. Inconstant sympathetic neural pathways. Their relation to sympathetic denervation of the upper extremity. Arch. Surg., 44, 95–102.

KIRGIS, H. D., and OHLER, E. A., 1944. Regeneration of pre- and post-ganglionic fibers following sympathectomy of upper extremity; experimental study. Ann. Surg., 119, 201–210.

KIRGIS, H. D., and PEARCE, J. Y., 1950. The activity of the dilator pupillae of the cat following adrenalectomy and sympathectomy. Anat. Rec., 106, 41–42.

KIRGIS, H. D., REED, A. F., and PEARCE, J. Y., 1950. The relative effectiveness of sympathetic ganglionectomy and section of preganglionic fibers in inactivation of smooth muscle. Surgery, 28, 941–949.

KIRTLEY, J. A., 1945. Experiences with sympathectomy in peripheral lesions. Ann. Surg., 122, 29–38.

KISS, F., 1951. Results of research regarding the nervous system. Magyar Belawosi Archivum, 4, 79–87.

KITTLE, C. L., and BATCHELDER, T. L., 1952. Daily mucin secretion in normal and vagotomized total gastric pouches of dogs. Ann. Surg., 18, 217–223.

KJELLBERG, S. R., RUDHE, V., and SJÖSTRAND, T., 1951. The influence of the autonomic nervous system on the contraction of the human heart under normal circulatory conditions. Acta physiol. scandinav., **24**, 350–360.

KLASSEN, K. P., MORTON, D. R., and CURTIS, G. M., 1950. A physiologic evaluation of vagus section for bronchial asthma. J. Thoracic Surg., **20**, 552–570.

KLEYNTJENS, F., and LANGWORTHY, O. R., 1937. Sensory nerve endings in the smooth muscle of the urinary bladder. J. Comp. Neurol., **67**, 367–380.

KNAPP, M. E., 1929. Afferent nerve supply of blood vessels. Minnesota Med., **12**, 759–766.

KNIGHT, G. C., 1934a. The innervation of the esophagus and cardiac sphincter. J. Physiol., **81**, 6.

————1934b. The effects of sympathetic stimulation on the stripedmuscle of the esophagus. Ibid., **82**, 3.

KNIGHT, G. C., and ADAMSON, W. A. D., 1935. Achalasia of cardia. Proc. Roy. Soc. Med., **28**, 891–897.

KNOCHE, H., 1950. Ueber die feinere Innervation der Niere des Menschen. I. Mitteilung. Ztschr. Anat. u. Entwcklngsgesch., **115**, 97–114.

KOCH, E., 1931. Die reflektorische Selbststeuerung des Kreislaufs. Dresden und Leipzig.

KÖHLER, W., and LANGER, E., 1950. Die Halssympathikusausschaltung in der Epilepsiebehandlung. Deutsch. Med. Wchschr., **75**, 83–85.

KOMAROV, S. A., and STRAVRAKY, G. W., 1940. Nitrogenous constituents of cat's submaxillary saliva evoked by parasympathetic and sympathetic stimulation. Canad. J. Res., Sec. D, **18**, 233–247.

KOPPEN, K., 1950a. Histologische Untersuchungsergebnisse von der Nervenversorgung des Uterus. Arch. Gynäkol., **177**, 352–391.

————b. Histologische Untersuchungsergebnisse über die Nervenversorgung des Ovars beim Menschene. Zentralbl. Gynakol., **72**, 915–920.

KORR, I. M., 1949. Skin resistance patterns associated with visceral disease. Federation Proc., **8**, Part I, 87–88.

KOUNTZ, W. B., PEARSON, E. F., and KOENIG, K. F., 1934. Observations on the effect of vagus and sympathetic stimulation on the coronary flow of the revived human heart. J. Clin. Investigation, **13**, 1065–1078.

KRAUS, F., and ZONDECK, S. G., 1922a. Kurze vorläufige Mitteilung über Versuche betreffend die Rolle der Elektrolyte beim Herzschlag, die Wirkung des Kochsalzes bei Verblutung und den sogennannten Tonusstrom. Klin. Wchnschr., **1**, 996–998.

————1922b. Ueber die Durchtränkungsspannung. Ibid., **1**, 1773–1779.

————1924. Die Stellung der Elektrolyte im Organismus. Ibid., 707–710.

KRAYER, O., 1933. Ist die Integrität der sympathischen Schilddrüseninnervation notwendig für die thyreotrope Wirkung des Hypophysenvorderlappens. Arch. exper. Path. u. Pharmakol., **171**, 473–479.

KREDEL, F. E., and PHEMISTER, D. B., 1939. Recovery of sympathetic nerve function in skin transplants. Arch. Neurol. and Psychiat., **42**, 403–412.

KREMER, M., and WRIGHT, S., 1932. The effects on blood-pressure of section of the splanchnic nerves. Quart. J. Exp. Physiol., **21**, 319–335.

KRESTOWNIKOFF, A., 1927. Die Wirkung des Lichtes auf den Entfärbungsverlauf in einem Dehydrozenase-Methylenblausystem. Scandinav. Arch. Physiol., **52**, 199–208.

KROGH, A., 1922. The anatomy and physiology of capillaries. New Haven.

————1927. Die Capillarnerven und ihre reflektorische Tätigkeit. Bibliotek for Laeger, Copenhagen, **119**, 331–340; Klin. Wchnschr., **6**, 722–725.

KUBICEK, W. G., GULLICKSON, G., OLSON, M. E., and KOTTKE, F. J., 1952. Survival of sympathetic nerve fibers during chronic electrical stimulation. Federation Proc., **11**, 86–87.

KUHN, R. A., 1949. A note on identification of the motor supply to the detrusor during anterior dorsolumbar rhizotomy. J. Neurosurg., **6**, 320–323.

KULCHITSKY, N., 1924a. Nerve endings in muscles. J. Anat., **58**, 152–169.

————1924b. Nerve endings in the muscles of the frog. Ibid., **59**, 1–17.

KÜLENKAMPFF, D., 1923. Mesenteric and peritoneal appendicitis. Deutsch. klin. Wchnschr., **49**, 246–275 and 349–351.

Kuntz, A., 1909*a*. A contribution to the histogenesis of the sympathetic nervous system. Anat. Rec., **3**, 158–216.

————1909*b*. The role of the vagi in the development of the sympathetic nervous system. Anat. Anz., **35**, 381–390.

————1910. The development of the sympathetic nervous system in mammals. J. Comp. Neurol., **20**, 211–258.

————1920. The development of the sympathetic nervous system in man. Ibid., **32**, 173–229.

————1922*a*. Experimental studies on the histogenesis of the sympathetic nervous system. Ibid., **34**, 1–36.

————1922*b*. On the occurrence of reflex arcs in the myenteric and submucous plexuses. Anat. Rec., **23**, 193–210.

————1927*a*. On the distribution of unmyelinated fibers in muscles of the extremities following degeneration of the somatic nerves. Ibid., **35**, 17.

————1927*b*. Distribution of the sympathetic rami to the brachial plexus, its relation to sympathectomy affecting the upper extremity. Arch. Surg., **15**, 871–877.

————1934*a*. Nerve fibers of spinal and vagus origin associated with the cephalic sympathetic nerves. Ann. Otol. Rhin. & Laryng., **43**, 50–67.

————1934*b*. Sympathetic ganglions removed surgically. A histopathologic study. Arch. Surg., **28**, 920–935.

————1938*a*. Histological variations in autonomic ganglia and ganglion cells associated with age and diseases. Am. J. Path., **14**, 783–795.

————1938*b*. Structural organization of celiac ganglia. J. Comp. Neurol., **69**, 1–12.

————1940. Structural organization of inferior mesenteric ganglia. Ibid., **72**, 371–382.

————1945. Anatomic and physiologic properties of cutaneo-visceral vasomotor reflex arcs. J. Neurophysiol., **8**, 421–429.

————1951. Afferent innervation of peripheral blood vessels through sympathetic trunks. South. M. J., **44**, 673–678.

————1952. Origin and early development of the pelvic neural plexuses. J. Comp. Neurol., **96**, 345–358.

Kuntz, A., and Alexander, W. F., 1950. Surgical implications of lower thoracic and lumbar independent sympathetic pathways. Arch. Surg., **61**, 1007–1018.

Kuntz, A., Alexander, W. F., and Furcolo, C. L., 1938. Complete sympathetic denervation of the upper extremity. Ann. Surg., **107**, 25–31.

Kuntz, A., and Batson, O. V., 1920. Experimental observations on the histogenesis of the sympathetic trunks in the chick. J. Comp. Neurol., **32**, 335–345.

Kuntz, A., and Dillon, J. B., 1942. Preganglionic components of the first thoracic nerve. Their role in the sympathetic innervation of the upper extremity. Arch. Surg., **44**, 772–778.

Kuntz, A., and Farnsworth, D. I., 1928. Peripheral distribution of myelinated nerve fibers through gray communicating rami in dog. Proc. Soc. Exp. Biol. and Med., **25**, 808–809.

————1931. Distribution of afferent fibers via the sympathetic trunks and gray communicating rami to the brachial and lumbosacral plexuses. J. Comp. Neurol., **53**, 389–399.

Kuntz, A., and Haselwood, L. A., 1940. Cutaneo-visceral vasomotor reflexes in the cat. Proc. Soc. Exp. Biol. and Med., **43**, 517–519.

————1940. Circulatory reactions in gastro-intestinal tract elicited by local cutaneous stimulation. Am. Heart J., **20**, 743–749.

Kuntz, A., and Kerper, A. H., 1924*a*. The sympathetic innervation of voluntary muscle. Proc. Soc. Exp. Biol. and Med., **22**, 23–24.

————1924*b*. Experimental observations on the functional significance of the sympathetic innervation of voluntary muscles. Ibid., **22**, 25–28.

————1926. An experimental study of tonus in skeletal muscles as related to the sympathetic nervous system. Am. J. Physiol., **76**, 121–144.

Kuntz, A., and Main, L. R., 1940. The neural basis of certain syndromes associated with dental lesions. Arch. Clin. Oral Pathol., **4**, 333–344.

Kuntz, A., and Morris, R. E., Jr., 1946. Components and distribution of the spermatic nerves and the nerves of the vas deferens. J. Comp. Neurol., **85**, 33–44.

KUNTZ, A., and RICHINS, C. A., 1945. Innervation of the bone marrow. Ibid., **83**, 213–222.

———1946. Components and distribution of the nerves of the parotid and submandibular glands. Ibid., **85**, 21–32.

———1946. Reflex pupillodilator mechanisms, an experimental analysis. J. Neurophysiol., **9**, 1–8.

———1949. Effects of direct and reflex nerve stimulation on the exocrine secretory activity of the pancreas. Ibid., **12**, 29–35.

KUNTZ, A., RICHINS, C. A., and CASEY, E. J., 1946. Reflex control of the ciliary muscle. Ibid., **9**, 445–451.

KUNTZ, A., and SACCOMANNO, G., 1944*a*. The sympathetic innervation of the detrusor muscle. J. Urol., **51**, 535–542.

———1944*b*. Reflex inhibition of intestinal motility mediated through decentralized prevertebral ganglia. J. Neurophysiol., **7**, 163–170.

KUNTZ, A., and SULKIN, N. M., 1947*a*. Hyperplasia of peripheral neuroglia, a factor in pathologic changes in autonomic ganglion cells. J. Neuropath. and Exper. Neurol., **6**, 323–332.

———1947*b*. The neuroglia in the autonomic ganglia: cytologic structure and reactions to stimulation. J. Comp. Neurol., **86**, 467–477.

KUNTZ, A., and VAN BUSKIRK, C., 1941. Reflex inhibition of bile flow and intestinal motility mediated through decentralized celiac plexus. Proc. Soc. Exp. Biol. **46**, 519–523.

KURÉ, K., SHINOSAKI, T., and SHINAGAWA, F., 1925. Die morphologische Grundlage für die doppelte (cerberospinal und autonome) Innervation des quergestreiften Muskels. Ztschr. ges. exper. Med., **46**, 144–153.

KUSAKARI, H., 1930. Ueber die Beziehung der Nierenfunktion zum vegetativen Nervensystem. I, II, and III. Tohoku J. Exper. Med., **16**, 509–569.

KUSTER, H., 1905. Ueber Gliome der Nebennieren. Virchow's Arch. path. Anat., **180**, 117–129.

KWERCH, H., and LEIBESTEDER, F., 1951. Vegetatives Nervensystem und Blutsteuerung. Wein. klin. Wchnschr., **63**, 309–310.

LABHART, F., 1929. Fortgesetzte Untersuchungen über den Einfluss des Nervus sympathicus auf die Ermüdung des quergestreiften Muskels. Ztschr. f. Biol., **89**, 217–236.

LAIGNEL-LAVASTINE, M., 1905. Contribution à l'étude anatomo-pathologique du sympathique abdominal dans les infections. Rev. de Méd., **25**.

———1924. Le pathologie du sympathique. Paris.

LANDIS, C., 1925. Studies of emotional reactions-metabolic rate. Am. J. Physiol., **74**, 188–203.

LANDSTEINER, K., and CHASE, M. W., 1940. Breeding experiments in reference to drug allergy in animals. Proc. Int. Cong. Microbiol. (1940), 772.

LANGELAAN, J. W., 1915. On muscle tonus. Brain, **38**, 235–380.

———1922. On muscle tonus. Ibid., **45**, 434–453.

———1931. Influence du nerf sympathique sur les muscles striés chez le chat. Ann. de physiol., **7**, 469–471.

LANGLEY, J. N., 1898*a*. On the union of cranial autonomic (visceral) fibers with the nerve cells in the superior cervical ganglion. J. Physiol., **23**, 240–270.

———1898*b*. On inhibitory fibers in the vagus for the end of the esophagus and the stomach. Ibid., **23**, 407–414.

———1900*a*. Remarks on the results of degeneration of the upper thoracic white rami communicantes chiefly in relation to commissural fibers in the sympathetic system. Ibid., **25**, 468–478.

———1900*b*. On axon reflexes in the preganglionic fibers of the sympathetic system. Ibid., **25**, 364–398.

———1901. Observations on the physiological action of extracts of the suprarenal bodies. Ibid., **28**, 237–256.

LANGLEY, J. N., and ANDERSON, H. K., 1895. The innervation of the pelvic and adjoining viscera. Part I. The lower portion of the intestine. Ibid., **18**, 67–105. Part II. The bladder. Ibid., **19**, 71–84; Part III. The external generative organs. Ibid., 85–121; Part IV. The internal generative organs. Ibid., 122–130; Part V. Position of the nerve cells on the course of the efferent nerve fibers. Ibid., 131–139; Part VI. Histological and physiological observations upon the effects of section of the sacral nerves. Ibid., 372–384.

————1896. The innervation of the pelvic and adjoining viscera. Ibid., **20**, 372–406.

LANGLEY, J. N., and DICKINSON, W. L., 1899. On the local paralysis of the peripheral ganglia and on the connection of different classes of nerve fibers with them. Proc. Roy. Soc., London, Series B., **46**, 423.

LANGSTROTH, G. O., McRAE, D. R., and STAVRAKY, G. W., 1938a. A study of cat's submaxillary saliva under nerve stimulation or adrenaline administration. Arch. internat. de Pharmacodyn. et de Therap., **58**, 61–77.

————1938b. The secretion of protein material in parasympathetic submaxillary saliva. Proc. Roy. Soc., Series B., **125**, 335–347.

LANGWORTHY, O. R., 1924a. A study of the innervation of the tongue musculature with particular reference to the proprioceptive mechanism. J. Comp. Neurol., **36**, 273–292.

————1924b. Problems of tongue innervation: course of proprioceptive fibers, autonomic innervation of skeletal musculature. Bull. Johns Hopkins Hosp., **35**, 239–246.

LANGWORTHY, O. R., and KOLB, L. C., 1938. Histological changes in vesical muscle following injury of peripheral innervation. Anat. Rec., **71**, 249–263.

LANGWORTHY, O. R., KOLB, L. C., and LEWIS, L. G., 1940. Physiology of Micturition. Williams & Wilkins Co., Baltimore.

LANGWORTHY, O. R., and MURPHY, E. L., 1939. Nerve endings in the urinary bladder. J. Comp. Neurol., **71**, 487–510.

LANGWORTHY, O. R., and ROSENBERG, S. J., 1939. Control by the central nervous system of rectal smooth muscle. J. Neurophysiol., **2**, 356–360.

LAPICQUE, L., and LAPICQUE, M., 1930. Action des nerfs sympathiques sur la chronaxie des muscles striés. Compt. rend. Soc. biol., **103**, 875–877.

LAPICQUE, M., 1931. Excitabilité du sympathique en tant que modificateur de la chronaxie musculaire. Ibid., **107**, 961–963.

LARSELL, O., 1921. Nerve terminations in the lung of the rabbit. J. Comp. Neurol., **33**, 105–131.

————1922. The ganglia, plexuses and nerve terminations of the mammalian lung and pleura pulmonalis. Ibid., **35**, 97–132.

————1928. The nerves and nerve endings of the pleura and pulmonalis histologically and experimentally. Phi Beta Pi Quart., May, 1928 ((Volume in honor of the seventieth birthday of Dr. W. S. Miller).

————1950. The nervus terminalis. Ann. Otol., Rhinol. and Laryngol., **59**, 414–428.

LARSELL, O., and DOW, S., 1933. The innervation of the human lung. Am. J. Anat., **52**, 125–146.

LAWSON, H., and TEMPLETON, R. D., 1932. Studies in the motor activities of the large intestine. III. The longitudinal and circular activity of the distal colon. Am. J. Physiol., **100**, 362–373.

LEARMONTH, J. R., 1931a. A contribution to the neurophysiology of the urinary bladder in man. Brain, **54**, 147–176.

————1931b. Neurosurgery in the treatment of diseases of the urinary bladder. I. Anatomic and surgical considerations. J. Urol., **25**, 531–549. II. Treatment of vesical pain. Ibid., **26**, 13–24.

————1932a. Neurosurgery in diseases of urinary bladder. Am. J. Surg., **16**, 270–274.

————1932b. Operations on nerves of urinary bladder. Edinburgh M. J., **39**, 43–62.

LEARMONTH, J. R., and MARKOWITZ, J., 1930. Studies on the innervation of the large bowel. II. The influence of the lumbar colonic nerves on the distal part of the colon. Am. J. Physiol., **94**, 501–504.

LEHMAN, G., 1945. Gastric cardiospasm in the dog. Ibid., **143**, 163–167.

LEMPERT, J., 1946. Tympanosympathectomy: a surgical technic for the relief of tinnitus aurium. Arch. Otolaryng., **43**, 199–212.

LENNANDER, K. G., 1906. Leibschmerzen, ein Versuch einige von ihnen zu erklären. Mitt. a. d. Grenzgeb. d. Med. u. Chir., **16**, 24–46.

LERICHE, R., 1949. Des causes d'échec de la surrénalectomie et de la gangliectomie dans la thrombo-angéite, d'après 898 opérations. Presse Med., **57**, 539–540.

————1949. De la surrénalectomie secondaire a une ganglionectomie et une splanchnicectomie inefficaces chez les thrombo-angeitiques. Lyon chir., **44**, 513–515.

LERICHE, R., and FONTAINE, R., 1927. Experimental researches on vasomotoricity. Am. J. Surg., **85**, 641–646.

572   *BIBLIOGRAPHY*

LERICHE, R., and HEITZ, 1917. Des effets physiologiques de la sympathectomie périphérique. Compt. rend. Soc. de biol., **80**, 66–70.

LERICHE, R., JUNG, A., and DE BAKEY, M., 1937. The surgical treatment of scleroderma. Surgery, **1**, 6–24.

LEWIS, R. N., WERLE, J. M., and WIGGERS, C. J., 1943. The behavior of the spleen in hemorrhagic hypotension and shock. Am. J. Physiol., **138**, 205–211.

LEWIS, R. S., 1951. Sympathectomy and the internal ear. J. Laryng. & Otol., **65**, 825–842.

LEWIS, T., 1929. Experiments relating to the peripheral mechanism involved in spasmodic arrest of the circulation in the fingers, a variety of Raynaud's disease. Heart, **15**, 7–101.

————1932. Vagovagal syncope and carotid sinus mechanism, with comments on Gowers' and Nothnagel's syndrome. Brit. Med. J., **1**, 823–876.

————1936. Vascular disorders of the limbs. The Macmillan Co., New York.

LEWIS, T., and KELLGREN, J. H., 1939. Observations relating to referred pain, visceromotor reflexes and other associated phenomena. Clin. Sc., **4**, 47–72.

LEWIS, T., and PICKERING, G. W., 1931. Vasodilatation in the limbs in response to warming the body; with evidence for sympathetic vasodilator nerves in man. Heart, **16**, 33–51.

LI, P., 1940. The intramural nervous system of the small intestine with special reference to the innervation of the inner subdivision of its circular muscle. J. Anat., **74**, 348–359.

LILLIE, R. D., 1952. Ethylenic Reaction of Ceroid with Performic Acid and Schiff Reagent. Stain Tech., **27**, 37–45.

LIM, R. K. S., NOVAK, E. A., and WALSH, F., 1952. Further observations on the adenteric reflex and gastric inhibitors. Federation Proc., **11**, 95.

LINDE, S., 1950. On the behavior of electrolytes in gastric juice induced by histamine. Acta Physiol. scandinav., **21**, 54–60.

LINDSLEY, D. B., and SASSMAN, W. H., 1938. Autonomic activity and brain potentials associated with "voluntary" control of the pilomotors (M. M. errectories pilorum). J. Neurophysiol., **1**, 342–349.

LIPP, W., 1951. Studien zur Herzinnervation. I. Die Innervation der Pulmonalisklappen. Acta Anat., **13**, 30–62.

LIST, C. F., and PEET, M. M., 1938. Sweat secretion in man. I. Sweating responses in normal persons. Arch. Neurol. and Psychiat., **39**, 1228–1237. II. Anatomic distribution of disturbances in sweating associated with lesions of the sympathetic nervous system. Ibid., **40**, 27–43. III. Clinical observations on sweating produced by pilocarpine and mecholyl. Ibid., **40**, 269–290. IV. Sweat secretion in the face and its disturbances. Ibid., **40**, 443–470.

LIU, A. C., 1935. The coöperative action of sympathetic nerve impulses adrenine and sympathin on the nictitating membrane of the cat. Am. J. Physiol., **112**, 690–694.

LIVINGSTON, W. K., 1938. Phantom limb pain. A report of ten cases in which it was treated by injections of procaine hydrochloride near the thoracic sympathetic ganglions. Arch. Sur., **37**, 353–370.

LOBENHOFFER, W., 1913. Funktionsprüfungen an transplantierten Nieren. Mitt a. d. Grenzgeb. d. Med. u. Chir., **36**, 197–238.

LÖHR, H., 1950. Experimentelle Untersuchungen zur Physiologie des sympathektomierten Armes mit dem photoelektrischen Verfaren nach Kramer. Langenbeck's Arch. u. Deutsch z. Chir., **266**, 24–49.

LÖWENBURG, K., and ZBINDEN, T., 1936. Epidemic encephalitis (St. Louis Type) in Toledo, Ohio. Arch. Neurol. & Psychiat., **36**, 155–165.

LOEWI, O., 1921. Ueber humorale Uebertragbarkeit der Herznervenwirkung. I. Pflüger's Arch. ges. Physiol., **189**, 239–242.

LONG, C. N. H., 1940. Evidence for and against control of carbohydrate metabolism by the hypothalamus. A. Res. Nerv. & Ment. Dis., Proc., **20**, 486–500.

LÓRÁND, S., and ASBÓT, J., 1952. Ueber die durch Reizung der Brustwarze angeregten reflektorischen Uteruskontraktionen. Zentralbl. Gynäkol., **74**, 345–352.

LORBER, S. H., KOMOROV, S. A., and SHAY, H., 1949. Effect of sham feeding on gastric motor activity in the dog. Federation Proc., **8**, 99.

LOUMOS, S., 1952. The autonomic nervous system and immunity. Arch. Neurol. & Psychiat., **68**, 69–77.

LOURIE, R. S., 1943. Rate of secretion of the parotid glands in normal children. A measurement of function of the autonomic nervous system. Am. J. Dis. Child., **65**, 455–479.

LOWENSTEIN, O., and LOEWENFELD, I. E., 1950. Mutual role of sympathetic and parasympathetic in shaping the pupillary reflex to light. Arch. Neurol. & Psychiat., **64**, 341–377.

——————1952. Disintegration of central autonomic regulation during fatigue and its reintegration by psychosensory controlling mechanisms. I. Disintegration Pupillographic studies. J. Nerv. & Ment. Dis., **115**, 1–21. II. Reintegration Pupillographic studies. Ibid., **115**, 121–145.

LOWER, R., 1669. Tractatus de corde. London.

LOWSLEY, O. S., and BRAY, J. L., 1936. The surgical relief of impotence. J. A. M. A., **107**, 2029–2035.

LUCAS, A. M., 1935. Neurogenous activation of ciliated epithelium. Am. J. Physiol., **112**, 468–476.

LUEDERS, C. W., 1928. Gastro-intestinal reactions to the emotions: The role of the vegetative system. Arch. Int. Med., **42**, 282,–296.

LUETH, H. C., 1931. Studies on flow of bile into duodenum and existence of a sphincter of Oddi. Am. J. Physiol., **99**, 237–252.

LUNDBERG, H., 1925. Paralyzing action of hydrastinin on innervation of smooth muscles. Comp. rend. Soc. Biol., **92**, 644–653.

McCREA, E. E., and McSWINEY, B. A., 1928. The effect on the stomach of stimulation of the peripheral end of the splanchnic nerve. Quart. J. Exp. Physiol., **18**, 301–313.

McCULLAGH, G. P., McFADDEN, G. D., and MILROY, T. H., 1930. The effects produced by unilateral lumbar sympathectomy. I. Cutaneous temperatures and the limb musculature. J. Physiol., **69**, 353–363.

McDONOUGH, F. K., 1939. Homeostasis in sympathectomized dog. Am. J. Physiol., **125**, 530–546.

McLESTER, J. S., 1927. Psychic and emotional factors in relation to disorders of the digestive tract. J. A. M. A., **89**, 1019–1020.

McMASTER, P. E., and ROOME, N. W., 1932. Effect of sympathectomy on bone repair. Proc. Soc. Exp. Biol. & Med., **30**, 123–124.

MACFARLAND, W. E., and DAVENPORT, H. A., 1941. Adrenal innervation. J. Comp. Neurol., **75**, 219–234.

McGREGOR, I. A., 1952. The sweating reactions of the forehead. J. Physiol., **116**, 26–34.

MACKENZIE, J., 1910. Diseases of the Heart. London.

MACLEAN, A. B., 1932. The gastro-ileal reflex in chronic appendicitis. Br. Med. J., **2**, 1055–1056.

MAGNUS, R., 1926. Physiology of posture. Lancet, **2**, 531–536.

MAGNUS-ALSLEBEN, E., and HOFFMANN, P., 1922. Ueber den Einfluss der nervösen Versorgung auf die vitale Färbarkeit der Muskeln. Biochem. Ztzchr., **127**, 102–106.

MAIBACH, C., 1928. Untersuchungen zur Frage des Einflusses des Sympathicus auf die Ermüdung der quergestreiften Muskulatur. Ztschr. Biol., **88**, 207–226.

MAIN, L. R., 1938. Further roentgenographic study of mandibular third molars. J. Am. Dent. Assoc. and Dent. Cosmos., **25**, 1993–1997.

MALAMUD, N., 1937. Encephalomyelitis complicating measles. Arch. Neurol. & Psychiat., **38**, 1025–1038.

MALLET-GUY, P., and DE BEAUJEW, J., 1948. Résultats éloignés de la splanchnicectomie unilatérale dans le traitement des états d'hypotonie des voies biliaires. Lyon chir., **43**, 157–178.

——————1952. Bilan de la splanchnicectomie gauche dans le traitment des pancréatites chroniques récidivantes (d'après 52 observations personnelles 1942–51). Lyon chir., **47**, 531–552.

MALLET-GUY, P., EICHOLZ, L., and LATREILLE, R., 1952. Topographie ganglionnaire de l'innervation sympathique des voies biliares. Étude experimentale. Lyon chir., **47**, 75–88.

MALONE, E. F., 1913. The nucleus cardiacus nervi vagi and three distinct types of nerve cells which innervate the three different types of muscles. Am. J. Anat., **15**, 121–130.

MANSFELD, G., and HAMORI, A., 1938. Untersuchungen über die zentrale Regulierung der Atmung. Arch. internat. de pharmacol. et de therap., **60**, 179–194.

MARGUTH, H., MARGUTH, F., and SCHAEFER, H., 1952. Erregbarkeit und Reizerfolg bei elektrischer Reizung von Herznerven. Arch. ges. Physiol., **254**, 291–309.

MARGUTH, H., RAULE, W., and SCHAEFER, H., 1951. Aktionsströme in zentrifugalen Herznerven. Ibid., **254**, 224–245.

MARINE, D., and ROSEN, S. H., 1934. The effect of the thyrotropic hormone on auto- and homeotransplants of the thyroid and its bearing on the question of secretory nerves. Am. J. Physiol., **107**, 677–680.

MARINESCO, G., and KREINDLER, A., 1931. Les réflexes du sinus carotidien en pathologic nerveuse. J. de physiol. et de path. gén., **29**, 77–92.

MARK, R. E., 1951. Das Muskelfibrillieren ein Symptom der vegetativen Dystonie. Deutsche Arch. Clin. Med., **198**, 383–404.

MARRAZZI, A. S., 1939. Adrenergic inhibition at sympathetic synapses. Am. J. Physiol., **129**, 738–744.

MARSHALL, E. K., and KOLLS, A. C., 1919. Studies on the nervous control of the kidney in relation to diuresis and urinary secretion. Ibid., **49**, 302–343.

MARTIN, H. E., 1932. Physiological leucocytosis. The variations in the leucocyte count during rest and exercise, and after hypodermic injection of adrenalin. J. Physiol., **75**, 113–129.

MARTINEZ, C., and VISSCHER, M. B., 1945. Some observations on general skin temperature responses to local heating of human subjects in a cold environment. Am. J. Physiol., **144**, 724–734.

MASON, S. C., and POLLARD, H. M., 1949. Peptic ulcer following splanchnicectomy: a report of thirteen cases. Surg., Gynec. & Obst., **89**, 271–284.

MAUMARY, A., 1922. Zur Frage der Abhängigkeit des Muskeltonus vom sympathischen Nervensystem. Pflüger's Arch. ges. Physiol., **74**, 299–316.

MAYFIELD, F. H., 1947. Causalgia. West Virginia M. J., **43**, 201; Am. J. Surg., **74**, 522–526.

MECKEL, J. F., 1751. Observation anatomique avec l'examen physiologique du veritable usage des noeuds, ou ganglions des nerfs. Mem. Acad. roy. d. sc., **5**, 84.

MEDOWIKOV, P. S., and SCHENKMANN, D. O., 1932. Ueber die Einstellung des vegetativen Nervensystems bei der tuberkulösen Meningitis im Kindesalter. Ztschr. Kinderh., **52**, 325–330.

MEESMANN, A., 1952. Experimentelle Untersuchungen über die antagonistische Innervation der Ciliarmuskulatur. Graefe's Arch. Ophthal., **152**, 335–356.

MEIS, H., 1937a. Kurare und vegetative Innervation des Skelettmuskels. Ztschr. Biol., **98**, 70–80.

————1937b. Skelettmuskulatur und vegetatives Nervensystem. Klin. Wchnschr., **16**, 593–595.

MEISSNER, G., 1857. Ueber die Nerven der Darmwand. Ztschr. rat. Med., **8**, 364.

MELLANBY, J., and PRATT, C. L. G., 1940. The reactions of the urinary bladder of the cat under conditions of constant volume. Proc. Roy. Soc., Series B., **128**, 186–201.

MELTZER, S. J., and AUER, C. M., 1904. Studies on the "paradoxical" pupil-dilatation caused by adrenalin. I and III. Am. J. Physiol., **11**, 28–36, 40–51.

————1906. Vagus reflexes upon esophagus and cardia. Brit. Med. J., **2**, 1806–1807.

MENKIN, V., 1928. Emotional relative mononucleosis. Am. J. Physiol., **85**, 489–497.

MENNINGER, W. C., 1937. Functional disorders of the gastro-intestinal tract: the gastro-intestinal neuroses. Am. J. Dig. Dis. & Nutr., **4**, 447–453.

MENTHA, C., 1949. Étude sur les dermatomes sympathiques. Lyon chir., **44**, 401–418.

MEYER, G. W., and GRIMSON, K. S., 1950. Immediate increase in adrenaline sensitivity of the sympathectomized nictitating membrane of the cat following SC-1950. Federation Proc., **9** Part I, 88.

MEYER, J., SORTER, H., and NECHELES, H., 1945. Observations on anorexia. Gastroenterology, **5**, 283–289.

MICHOL, E., 1930. Fortgesetzte Untersuchungen zur Analyze der Wirkungsart sympathischer Nerven auf den quergestreiften Muskel. Ztschr. Biol., **90**, 313–326.

MIES, H., 1933a. Skelettmuskeltonus and Blutdruckzügler. Ibid., **94**, 108–118.

————1933*b*. Ueber den Tonus des roten und Weiszen Muskles. Ibid., **94**, 312–318.

MILIAN, G., 1936. Nature de l'exzéma. Rev. franc. Derm. Venereol., **12**, 388.

MILLER, R. J., BERGEIM, O., and HAWK, P. B., 1920. The influence of anxiety on gastric digestion. Proc. Soc. Exp. Biol. & Med., **17**, 97–98.

MITCHELL, G. A. G., 1938. The innervation of the ovary, uterine, tube, testis and epididymis. J. Anat., **72**, 508–517.

————1940. A macroscopic study of the nerve supply to the stomach. Ibid., **75**, 50–63.

————1949. The discoverers of the thoracic cardiac nerves. Edinburgh Med. J., **56**, 156–159.

————1950. The nerve supply of the kidneys. Acta Anat., **10**, 1–37.

————1951. The intrinsic renal nerves. Ibid., **13**, 1–15.

MITCHELL, S. W., MOREHOUSE, G. R., and KEEN, W. W., 1864. Gunshot wounds and other injuries of nerves. Philadelphia.

MITTELMANN, B., and WOLFF, H. G., 1942. Emotions and gastroduodenal function; experimental studies on patients with gastritis, duodentitis and peptic ulcer. Psychosom. Med., **4**, 5–61.

MOGILNIZCKY, B., 1923. Veränderungen der sympathischen Ganglien bei Infektionskrankheiten. Virchow's Arch. path. Anat., **241**, 298–318.

MOLANDER, C. O., 1941. Physiologic basis of heat. Arch. Phys. Therap., **22**, 335–340.

MOORE, F. D., CHAPMAN, W. P., SCHULZ, M. D., and JONES, C. M., 1946. Transdiaphragmatic resection of vagus nerves for peptic ulcer. New England J. Med., **234**, 241–251.

MOORE, R. M., 1938. Some experimental observations relating to visceral pain. Surgery, **3**, 534–555.

MOORE, R. M., and MOORE, R. C., 1932. Peripheral course of sensory nerves supplying arteries of lower extremity. Proc. Soc. Exp. Biol. & Med., **29**, 919–921.

————1933. Studies on the pain sensibility of arteries. I. Some observations on the pain sensibility of arteries. Am. J. Physiol., **104**, 259–266.

MOORE, R. M., and SINGLETON, A. O., 1933. Studies on the pain sensibility of arteries. II. Peripheral paths of afferent neurons from the arteries of the extremities and of the abdominal viscera. Ibid., **104**, 267–275.

MORGAN, L. O., and VONDERAHE, A. R., 1939. The hypothalamic nuclei in heat stroke. Arch. Neurol. & Psychiat., **42**, 83–91.

MORGAN, L. C., VONDERAHE, A. R., and MALONE, E. F., 1937. Pathological changes in the hypothalamus in diabetes mellitus. J. Nerv. & Ment. Dis., **85**, 125.

MORGAN, M. W., JR., OLMSTEAD, J. M. D., and WATROUS, W. G., 1940. Sympathetic action in accommodation for far vision. Am. J. Physiol., **128**, 588–591.

MORIAS, E., 1933. Variations leucocytaires consécutives a la résection du ganglion cervical du sympathique chez le lapin. Compt. rend. Soc. biol., **111**, 593–594.

MORISON, R. S., and ACHESON, G. H., 1938. Quantitative study of effects of acetyl choline and adrenaline on nictitating membrane. Am. J. Physiol., **121**, 149–156.

MORLEY, J., 1931. Abdominal Pain. New York, William Wood & Co.

————1937. Visceral pain. Brit. Med. J., **2**, 1270–1273.

MORRISON, L. M., and SPIEGEL, E. A., 1945. Demonstration of visceral pain by determination of skin potentials. Ann. Int. Med., **22**, 827–831.

MORTENSEN, O. A., FRIEDBACHER, K. F., and QUADE, R. H., 1928. Sympathectomy in the goat. Proc. Soc. Exp. Biol. & Med., **25**, 757–759.

MORTON, D. R., KLASSEN, K. P., and CURTIS, G. M., 1951. Clinical physiology of human bronchi: effect of vagus section upon pain of tracheobronchial origin. Surgery, **30**, 800–809.

MORTON, J. J., and SCOTT, N. J. M., 1930. The measurement of sympathetic vasoconstrictor activity in the lower extremities. J. Clin. Investigation, **9**, 235–246.

MOSELEY, R. L., 1936. Preganglionic connections of intramural ganglia of urinary bladder. Proc. Soc. Exp. Biol. & Med., **34**, 728–730.

MOUSSA, T. A., 1952. The cytoplasmic inclusions of the sympathetic neurons in the mouse. Am. J. Anat., **90**, 379–425.

MULINOS, M. G., 1927. Gastro-intestinal motor response to vagus stimulation after nicotin. Ibid., **25**, 49–53.

MÜLLER, E., 1920. Beiträge zur Kenntnis des autonomen Nervensystems. (1) Ueber die Entwicklung des Sympathicus und des Vagus bei den Selachiern. Arch. mikr. Anat., **94**, 208–247.

————1921. Ueber das Darmnervensystem. Upsala Lakaref. Forh., Ny foljd., **26**, 1–22.

MÜLLER, E., and INGVAR, S., 1923. Ueber den Ursprung des Sympathicus beim Hühnchen. Arch. mikr. Anat., **99**, 650–671.

MÜLLER, E. F., 1922. Leukozytensturz infolge unspezifischer Intrakutanimpfung. München. med. Wchnschr., **69**, 1506–1507.

————1926. Ueber eine gemeinsame Steuerung von Haut und Lebergebiet (Splanchno-peripheres Gleichgewicht). Ibid., **73**, 9–12; 71–74.

MÜLLER, E. F., and MYERS, C. N., 1924. Biochemical studies on the behavior of the leukocytes after intravenous administration of alkalinized salvarsan. Proc. Soc. Exp. Biol. & Med., **22**, 95–98.

MÜLLER, E. F., and PETERSEN, W. F., 1926. Ueber das splanchnoperiphere Gleichgewicht der Gefässpermeabilität und seine klinische Bedeutung. Klin. Wchnschr., **4**, 53–57.

MÜLLER, E. F., PETERSEN, W. F., and RIEDER, W., 1930. Functional pathology of the denervated kidney. Proc. Soc. Exp. Biol. & Med., **27**, 739–741.

MÜLLER, L. R., 1901. Klinische und experimentelle Studien über die Innervation der Blase, des Mastdarmes und des Genitalapparates. Deutsch. Ztschr. Nervenh., **21**.

————1911. Die Darminnervation. Deutsche Arch. klin. Med., **105**, 1–43.

————1931. Lebensnerven und Lebenstriebe, Berlin.

MÜLLER, R., 1908. Ueber die Nervenversorgung des Magen-Darmkanals beim Frosch durch Nervennetze. Pflüger's Arch. ges Physiol., **123**, 387–405.

MUNRO, D., 1937. Treatment of urinary bladder in cases with injury of spinal cord. Am. J. Surg., **38**, 120–136.

NAIDE, M., and SAYEN, A., 1945. Primary influence of basal vascular tone on development of post occlusive collateral circulation and in selecting patients for sympathectomy. Am. J. M. Sc., **209**, 478–483.

NAKANISCHI, M., 1927*a*. Ueber den Einfluss des sympathischen Nervensystems auf Skelettmuskeln. J. Biophysics, **2**, 19.

————1927*b*. Eine einfache Methode zur Bestimmung der Reizschwelle für die sympathischen Skelettmuskelnerven: Grütznersche innere Unterstützung. Ibid., **2**, 81–94.

————1928. Ueber den Einfluss des sympathischen Nervensystems auf Skelettmuskeln. 2. Die Wirkung der successiven Reizung des Sympathicus auf den tätigen Muskel. Akta med. Keijo, **11**, 1–4.

————1930*a*. Ueber den Einfluss des sympathischen Nervensystems auf die Skelettmuskeln. 3. Eine Methode zur Demonstration der sympathischen Wirkung auf den tätigen Muskel bei der Kröte. Keijo J. Med., **1**, 679–684.

————1930*b*. Ueber das Wesen des Skelettmuskeltonus. J. Chosen Med. Assn., **20**, 27–29.

————1932. Ueber den Einfluss des regulatorischen Nervensystems auf die Skelettmuskeln. VI. Die regulatorischen (sympathischen) Nervenfasern der Skelettmuskeln der Kröte. Keijo J. Med., **3**, 562–570.

NATHAN, P. W., 1947. On the pathogenesis of causalgia in peripheral nerve injuries. Brain, **70**, 145–170.

NATHAN, P. W., and SMITH, N. C., 1951. The centrepetal pathway from the bladder and urethra within the spinal cord. J. Neurol. Neurosurg. & Psychiat., **14**, 262–280.

NECHELES, H., and JEFFERSON, N. C., 1952. The role of the phrenic nerves in vagotomy and in gastrointestinal mechanism. Rev. Gastroenterol., **19**, 39–47.

NEDZEL, A. J., 1952. Effects of body chilling upon the blood vessels of denervated and intact kidneys in dogs and rabbits. J. Aviation Med., **23**, 49–53.

NEIL, E., 1951. Chemoreceptor areas and chemoreceptor circulatory reflexes. Acta physiol. scandinav., **22**, 54–65.

NESBIT, R. M., and McLELLAN, F. C., 1939. Sympathectomy for the relief of vesical spasm and pain resulting from intractable bladder infection. Surg. Gynec. & Obst., **68**, 540–546.

NETTLESHIP, W. A., 1936. Experimental studies on the afferent innervation of the cat's heart. J. Comp. Neurol., **64**, 115–131.

NEWTON, F. C., 1924. Researches on the alleged influence of sympathetic innervation on warmth production in skeletal muscles. Am. J. Physiol., **71**, 1–11.

NGAI, S. H., FRUMAIN, M. J., and WANG, S. C., 1952. Organization of the central respiratory mechanism in cats. Federation Proc., **11**, 112.

NIEMER, W. T., and VONDERAHE, A. R., 1940. Cyst of the pulvinar of the thalamus. Report of a case with obstructive internal hydrocephalus and diabetes mellitus of intermittent severity. Arch. Neurol. & Psychiat., **44**, 1086–1092.

NITSCH, K., 1949. Ulcusleiden und vegetatives Nervensystem. Med. Klin., **44**, 503–505.

NOLF, P., 1929. La systeme nerveux enterique. Essai d'analyse par la méthode à la nicotine de Langley. Arch. internat. physiol., **30**, 317–492.

NONIDEZ, J. F., 1931a. Innervation of the thyroid gland, the presence of ganglia in the thyroid of the dog. Arch. Neurol. & Psychiat., **25**, 1175–1190.

————1931b. Innervation of the thyroid gland; origin and course of thyroid nerves in the dog. Am. J. Anat., **48**, 299–329.

————1935a. Innervation of the thyroid gland. III. Distribution and termination of the nerve fibers in the dog. Ibid., **57**, 135–170.

————1936. The nervous "terminal reticulum." A critique. I. Observations on the innervation of blood vessels. Anat. Anz., **82**, 348–366.

————1937. The nervous "terminal reticulum." A critique. III. Observations on the autonomic ganglia and nerves with special reference to the problem of the neuroneuronal synapse. Concluding remarks. Ibid., **84**, 315–329.

————1939. Studies on the innervation of the heart. I. Distribution of the cardiac nerves, with special reference to the identification of the sympathetic and parasympathetic postganglionics. Am. J. Anat., **65**, 361–413.

————1946. Afferent nerve endings in the ganglia of the intermuscular plexus of the dog's esophagus. J. Comp. Neurol., **85**, 177–189.

NORCROSS, N. C., 1938. Intracerebral blood flow. An experimental study. Arch. Neurol. & Psychiat., **40**, 291–299.

NOTTER, H., 1936. Die Aktionsströme sympathischer Impulse in den Muskeln Während natürlicher reflextorischer Tätigkeit. Ztschr. Biol., **97**, 343–351.

NOWAKOWSKI, H., 1950. Zur Auslösung der Ovulation durch elektrische Reizung des Hypothalamus beim Kaninchen und ihre Beeinflussung durch Rückenmarksdurchschneidung. Acta. Neurovegetativa, **1**, 13–39.

OCHSNER, A., and DE BAKEY, M., 1939a. Rational consideration of peripheral vascular disease based on physiologic principles. J. A. M. A., **112**, 230–236.

————1939b. Treatment of thrombophlebitis by novocaine block of sympathetics; technique of injection. Surgery, **5**, 491–497.

————1940a. Peripheral vascular disease. A critical survey of its conservative and radical treatment. Surg. Gynec. & Obst., **70**, 1058–1072.

————1940b. Thrombophlebitis. The role of vasospasm in the production of the clinical manifestations. J. A. M. A., **114**, 117–124.

OCKERBLAD, N. F., and CARLSON, H. E., 1937. Ureteral pain as determined by faradic stimulation in man. Proc. Soc. Exp. Biol. & Med., **36**, 35–36.

O'CONNOR, W. J., and VERNEY, E. B., 1945. The effect of increased activity of the sympathetic system in the inhibition of water diuresis by emotional stress. Quart. J. Exp. Physiol., **33**, 77–90.

ODERMATT, W., 1922. Die Schmerzempfindlichkeit der Blutgefässe, und die Gefässreflexe. Bruns' Beiträge z. klin. Chir., **127**, 1.

OKINAKA, S., KITAMOTO, O., NAKAS, K., KUROYANAGI, T., and SHIBATA, S., 1952a. Studies on the defense mechanism of the body and neurohumoral regulation. Report II. On the role of N. splanchnicus and adrenal gland upon the antibody mobilization. Tohoku. J. Exp. Med., **55**, 389–393.

OKINAKA, S., KUBO, I., KUROYANAGI, T., and HAYASHI, T., 1952a. Studies on the defense mechanism of the body and neurohumoral regulation. Report I. On the neurohumoral influence upon the phagocytic function of the white blood cell. Tohoku. J. Exp. Med., **55**, 383–388.

37

OKINAKA, S., NAKAO, K., IKEDA, M., and SHEZUME, K., 1951. The cardio accelerator fibers in the vagus nerve. Tohoku J. Exper. Med., **54**, 393–398.

OKKELS, H., 1927. Pathological changes in the nerves of the stomach wall in cases of chronic gastric ulcer. Am. J. Path., **3**, 75–84.

OKKELS, H., and SAND, K., 1941. Morphological relationship between testicular nerves and Leydig cells in man. J. Endocrinology, **2**, 38–46.

OLMSTED, J. M. D., 1944. The role of the autonomic nervous system in accommodation for far and near vision. J. Nerv. & Ment. Dis., **99**, 794–798.

OLMSTED, J. M. D., and MORGAN, M. W., 1941. The influence of the cervical sympathetic nerve on the lens of the eye. Am. J. Physiol., **133**, 720–723.

ONUMA, T., 1929. Zur normalen und pathologischen Histologie des sympathischen Nervensystems. Tr. Jap. Pathol. Soc., **17**, 463–466.

ORBELI, L. A., 1924. Pavlov Jubilee Volume. Leningrad.

———1925. Die sympathische Innervation der Skelettmuskeln. J. Petrograd Med. Instit., **6**, 8–18.

OTIS, A. B., 1949. Application of Gray's theory of respiration control to the hyperpnea produced by passive movements of the limbs. Applied Physiol., **1**, 743–751.

OTTAVIANI, G., 1940. Histologisch-anatomische Untersuchungen über die Innervation des Mastdarmes. Ztschr. f. mikr.-anat. Forsch., **47**, 151–182.

OWEN, S. E., 1933. A study of viscerocardiac reflexes. I. The experimental production of cardiac irregularities by visceral stimulation. Am. Heart J., **8**, 496–506.

PALMER, A. J., 1947. Hyperhydrosis. Study of a case. Arch. Neurol. & Psychiat., **58**, 582–592.

PALMER, W. L., and HEINZ, T. E., 1934. Mechanism of pain in gastric and duodenal ulcers: VII. Further observations. Arch. Int. Med., **53**, 269–308.

PARKER, G. H., 1929. Neurofibril hypothesis. Quart. Rev. Biol., **4**, 155–178.

PARTRIDGE, R. C., 1933. Afferent impulses in vagus nerve. J. Cell. & Comp. Physiol., **2**, 367–380.

PASSE, E. R. G., and SEYMOUR, J. S., 1948. Ménières syndrome: Successful treatment by surgery on sympathetic. Br. Med. J., **2**, 812–816.

PATTERSON, T. L., and SANDWEISS, D. J., 1942. The relationship between gastro-duodenal motility phases and symptoms associated with duodenal ulcer in the human. Am. J. Dig. Dis., **9**, 375–383.

PAYNE, W. W., and POULTON, E. P., 1927. Experiments on visceral sensation; relation of pain to activity in human esophagus. J. Physiol., **63**, 217–241.

PEET, M. M., 1947. Results of bilateral supradiaphragmatic splanchnicectomy for arterial hypertension. New England J. Med., **236**, 270–277.

PEET, M. M., and ISBERG, E. M., 1946. Surgical treatment of essential hypertension. J. A. M. A., **130**, 467–473.

PEET, M. M., WOODS, W. W., and BRADEN, S., 1940. The surgical treatment of hypertension. Results of 350 consecutive cases treated by bilateral supradiaphragmatic splanchnicectomy and lower dorsal sympathetic ganglionectomy. Ibid., **115**, 1875–1885.

PEETERS, G., BOUCKAERT, J. H., and OYAERT, W., 1952. The influence of unilateral sympathectomy on the udder of the sheep. Arch. Internat. Pharmacol., **89**, 197–203.

PEISS, C. N., HERTZMAN, A. B., and RANDALL, W. C., 1951. Region rates of cutaneous insensible perspiration. Federation Proc., **10**, 103–104.

PEI-YEN CHANG, and FONG-YEN HSU, 1942. The localization of the intestinal inhibitory reflex arc. Quart. J. Exper. Physiol., **31**, 311–318.

PENDE, N., 1925. Vegetative innervation in diagnosis and treatment. Riforma med., **41**, 241–243.

PENFIELD, W., 1933. The evidence for a cerebral vascular mechanism in epilepsy. Ann. Int. Med., **7**, 303–310.

PENFIELD, W., and RASMUSSEN, T., 1950. The Cerebral Cortex of Man, Chapter IV. The Macmillan Company, New York.

PERMAN, E., 1924. Anatomische Untersuchungen über die Herznerven bei den höheren Säugetieren und beim Menschen. Ztschr. Anat. u. Entwcklngsgesch., **71**, 382–457.

PETERSEN, W. F., 1927. Permeability of skin capillaries in various clinical conditions. Arch. Int. Med., **39**, 19–44.

———1934. The Patient and the Weather. Edwards Bros., Ann Arbor, Mich.

PETERSEN, W. F., and LEVINSON, S. A., 1930. The Skin Reactions, Blood Chemistry and Physical Status of "Normal" Men and of Clinical Patients. Chicago.

PETERSEN, W. F., and MÜLLER, E. F., 1930. Lymph reactions following bulbous pressure in dogs. Proc. Soc. Exp. Biol. & Med., **27**, 345–348.

————1927. The splanchno-peripheral balance during chill and fever. Arch. Int. Med., **40**, 575–593.

PETERSON, C. G., and YOUMANS, N. B., 1945. The intestino-intestinal inhibitory reflex: threshold variations, sensitization and summation. Am. J. Physiol., **143**, 407–412.

PETERSON, L. H., 1952. Certain aspects of reflex and mechanical influences upon venous circulation. Federation Proc., **11**, 122.

PETREN, K., and THORLING, I., 1911. Untersuchungen über das Vorkommen von Vagotonus und Sympathikotonus. Ztschr. klin. Med., **73**, 27–46.

PFEIFFER, C., DREISBACH, R. H., ROBY, C. C., and GLASS, H. G., 1943. The etiology of the migraine syndrome. A physiological approach. J. Lab. & Clin. Med., **28**, 1219–1225.

PFLÜGER, E., 1903. Glykogen. Pflüger's Arch. ges. Physiol., **96**, 1–398. Bemerkungen zur Analyse des Glykogen. Ibid., 513–535.

PHILLIPS, E. W., and SCOTT, W. J. M., 1929. The surgical treatment of bronchial asthma. Arch. Surg., **19**, 1425–1456.

PHILLIPS, G., 1931. On posture and postural reflex action. The effect of unilateral lumbar sympathetic chain extirpation. Brain, **54**, 320–329.

PICKERING, G. W., 1939. Experimental observations on headache. Brit. Med. J., **1**, 907–912.

PICKERING, G. W., and HESS, W., 1933. Vasodilatation in the hands and feet in response to warming the body. Clin. Sc. Inc. Heart, **1**, 213–223.

PICKERING, R. W., 1950. Regional distribution of blood flow after hemorrhage with and without Dibenamine. Federation Proc., **9**, Part I, 100–101.

PIERI, G., 1928. Treatment of pain syndromes of viscera. Arch. ital. di chir., **20**, 487–540.

PIGALEW, I. A., 1932. Zur Frage der Genese geschwüriger Prozesse im Magen-Darmkanal. Ztschr. ges. exper. Med., **82**, 617–632.

PIGALEW, I. A., and EPSTEIN, G. S., 1930. Die Rolle des Nervensystems in der Entwickelung und den Verlauf des tuberkulösen Prozesses beim Kaninchen. Ibid., **70**, 417–437.

PINES, L., 1927. Ueber die Innervation der Epiphyse. Ztschr. f. d. ges. Neurol. u. Psychiat., **111**, 356–369.

PING, C., 1921. On the growth of the largest nerve cells in the superior cervical sympathetic ganglion of the albino rat from birth to maturity. J. Comp. Neurol., **33**, 281–311.

PIPER, H. F., 1952. Die Bedeutung von Augenhaltung und Akkommodation für die Klinik der vegetativen Dystonien. Med. Klin., **47**, 370–372.

PITTS, R. F., 1940. The respiratory center and its descending pathways. J. Comp. Neurol., **72**, 605–625.

————1942. The functions of components of the respiratory complex. J. Neurophysiol., **5**, 403–413.

PITTS, R. F., MAGOUN, H. W., and RANSON, S. W., 1939a. Localization of the medullary respiratory centers in the cat. Am. J. Physiol., **126**, 673–688.

————1939b. Interrelations of the respiratory centers in the cat. Ibid., **126**, 689–707.

————1939c. The origin of respiratory rhythmicity. Ibid., **127**, 654–670.

POILLEUX, F., GOIDIN and NICOLAIDUS, 1952. Dystonies biliaires Fonctionelles. Rôle du pneumogastrique droit (étude experimentale et déductions chirurgicales). Presse Med., **60**, 196–199.

POLIQUIN, P. A., 1946. Obstinate cases of dysmenorrhea and surgical removal of the superior hypogastric plexus. Union Med. du Canada, **75**, 671.

POLLAND, W. S., and BLOOMFIELD, A. D., 1931. Experimental referred pain from the gastro-intestinal tract. Part I. The esophagus. J. Clin. Investigation, **10**, 435–452.

POLLEY, E. H., 1951. An analysis of the nerves along blood vessels in skin and striated muscle of the hind limb of the cat. Anat. Rec., **109**, 78.

POLLOCK, L. F., and DAVIS, L., 1935. Visceral and referred pain. Arch. Neurol. & Psychiat., **34**, 1041–1054.

POLLOCK, L. J., BOSCHES, B., CHOR, H., FINKELMAN, I., ARIEFF, A. J., and BROWN, M., 1951. Defects in regulatory mechanisms of autonomic function in injuries of spinal cord. J. Neurophysiol., **14**, 85–93.

PONOMAREW, A. W., 1930. Zur Frage der Beteiligung des Nervensystems am Tuberkulösen Prozess. Ztschr. ges. exper. Med., **70**, 403–416.

POOL, J. L., and RANSOHOFF, J., 1949. Autonomic effects on stimulating rostral portion of cingulate gyri in man. J. Neurophysiol., **12**, 385–392.

POPA, G., and POPA, F., 1931. The influence of the sympathetic on the pigeon's wing. J. Anat., **65**, 407–410.

POPIELSKI, L., 1901. Ueber das peripherische reflektorische Nervenzentrum des Pankreas. Pflüger's Arch. ges. Physiol., **86**, 215–246.

POSTLETHWAIT, R. W., HILL, H. V., JR., CHITTUM, J. R., and GRIMSON, K. S., 1948. Effect of vagotomy and of drugs on gastric motility. Ann. Surg., **128**, 184–194.

POTTENGER, F. M., 1917. Clinical Tuberculosis. C. V. Mosby Co., St. Louis.

———1929. Ueber Lungenreflexe. Ztschr. ges. exper. Med., **68**, 316–336.

———1930a. Early diagnosis of tuberculosis. Am. Rev. Tuber., **21**, 159–182.

———1930b. Pulmonary tuberculosis; importance of clinical history in its diagnosis. California & West Med., **32**, 9–13.

PREOBRACHENSKY, A. M., 1929. Ueber die Veränderungen der funktionellen Eigenschaften der Gefässe und des Gefässtonus unter Einfluss der Tuberkuloseinfektion und des Tuberkulins nach Versuchen an isolierten Gefässen. Ztschr. Immunität. u. exp. Therap., **63**, 1–31; 32–45; 139–157.

PRETTY, H. G., 1947. Role of the sympathetic nervous system in traumatic surgery. Am. J. Surg., **74**, 527–529.

QUIGLEY, J. P., and LOUKES, H., 1952. Pyloric sphincter activity in normal dog. Federation Proc., **11**, 125.

QUINBY, W. C., 1916. A case of pseudohermaphroditism with remarks on abnormal functions of endocrine glands. Bull. Johns Hopkins Hosp., **27**, 50–53.

———1917. Experimental nephropathy. J. Urol., **1**, 139.

RAIFORD, T. S., and MULINOS, M. G., 1934a. Intestinal activity in the exteriorized colon of the dog. Am. J. Physiol., **110**, 123–128.

———1934b. The myenteric reflex as exhibited by the exteriorized colon of the dog. Ibid., **110**, 129–138.

———1936. Studies in gastro-intestinal motility. Arch. Surg., **33**, 276–296.

RANDALL, W. C., 1946. Sweat gland activity and changing patterns of sweat secretion on skin surface. Am. J. Physiol., **147**, 391–398.

———1946. Quantitation and regional distribution of sweat glands in man. J. Clin. Investigation, **25**, 761–767.

———1947. Reflex sweating responses and the influence of arterial occlusion upon sweat gland activity. Federation Proc., **6**, Part II, 183.

RANDALL, W. C., ALEXANDER, W. F., COLDWATER, K. E., HERTZMAN, A. B., and COX, J. W., 1952. Sweating patterns on the lower extremity of man elicited by stimulation of the sympathetic trunk. Ibid., **11**, 127.

RANDALL, W. C., DEERING, R., and DOUGHERTY, I., 1948. Reflex sweating and inhibition of sweating by arterial occlusion. Applied Physiol., **1**, 53–59.

RANDALL, W. C., HERTZMAN, A. B., and EDERSTROM, H. E., 1951. Dermatomal recruitment of sweating in response to heat. Federation Proc., **10**, Part I, 108.

RANDALL, W. C., and McCLURE, W., 1949. Quantitation of the output of individual sweat glands and their response to stimulation. Applied Physiol., **2**, 72–80.

RANDALL, W. C., SMITH, D. E., and HERTZMAN, A. B., 1948. Some cutaneous responses to reflex heating. Federation Proc., **7**, Part I, 99.

RANSON, S. W., 1916. New evidence in favor of a chief vasoconstrictor center in the brain. Studies in vasomotor reflex arcs. IV. Am. J. Physiol., **42**, 1–8.

———1940. Regulation of body temperature. A. Res. Nerv. & Ment. Dis., Proc., **20**, 342–399.

———1940. Functional and clinical significance of hypothalamus. Quart. Bull. Northwestern U. Med. School., **14**, 137–145.

RANSON, S. W., and MAGOUN, H. W., 1933. The central path of the pupilloconstrictor reflex in response to light. Arch. Neurol. & Psychiat., **30**, 1193–1204.

RASMUSSEN, A. T., 1938. Innervation of the hypophysis. Endocrinology, **23**, 263–278.

RAVEN, C. P., 1937. Experiments on the origin of sheath cells and sympathetic neuroblasts in Amphibia. J. Comp. Neurol., **67**, 221–240.

RAY, B. S., and CONSOLE, A. D., 1949. The relief of pain in chronic (calcareous) pancreatitis by sympathectomy. Surg. Gynec. & Obst., **89**, 1–8.

————1949. Evaluation of total sympathectomy. Ann. Surg., **130**, 652–673.

RAY, B. S., HINSEY, J. C., and GEOHEGAN, W. A., 1943. Observations on the distribution of the sympathetic nerves to the pupil and the upper extremity by stimulation of the anterior roots in man. Ibid., **118**, 647–655.

RAY, B. S., and WOLFF, H. G., 1940. Experimental studies on headache. Pain sensitive structures of head, their significance in headache. Arch. Surg., **41**, 813–856.

RAYBUCK, H. E., 1952. The innervation of the parathyroid gland. Anat. Rec., **112**, 117–124.

REED, A., and KIRGIS, H., 1952. Some problems of sympathectomy. Bull. Tulane Med. Faculty, **11**, 157–162.

REGELSBERGER, H., 1924. Vegetatives Nervensystem und Atmung. Jahresb. f. arztl. Fortbild., **15**, 15–21.

————1952. Der bedingte Reflex und die vegetative Rhythmik des Menschen dargestellt am Elektrodermatogramm. Acta neurovegetativa, Supp. **1**, 172.

REIL, J. C., 1887. Ueber die Eigenshaften des Ganglien-Symptoms und sein Verhältnis zum Cerebral-Systeme. Arch. f. d. Physiol., **7**, 189.

REIN, H., 1943a. Vasomotorische Schütreflexe aus dem Stromgebiet der Arteria hepatica. Pflüger's Arch. ges. Physiol., **246**, 866–879.

————1943b. Zur physiologischen Bedeutung des vasomotorischen Hepaticareflexes. Ibid., **246**, 880–885.

REIN, H., LIEBERMEISTER, K., and SCHNEIDER, D., 1932. Schilddrüse und Carotissinus als funktionelle Einheit. Klin. Wchnschr., **11**, 1636–1641.

REINHOFF, W. F., and GAY, L. N., 1938. Treatment of intractable bronchial asthma by bilateral resection of the posterior pulmonary plexus. Arch. Surg., **37**, 456–469.

REISER, K. A., 1933. Ueber die Endausbreitung des vegetativen Nervensystems. Ztschr. Zellforsch. u. mikr. Anat., **17**, 601–641.

REISS, E., 1950. Experimenteller Beitrag zur Frage der zentralnervösen Steuerung des Kohlehydratstoffwechsehs. Acta neurovegetativa, **1**, 40–50.

REITLER, R., 1924. Zur Kenntnis der Immunköperbildung im Organismus. Ztschr. f. Immunitätsf., **30**, 453–468.

REMAK, R., 1838. Observationes anatomicae et microscopicae de systemmatis nervosi structura. Berlin.

————1854. Ueber multipolare Ganglienzellen. Ber. d. Verhdl. k. Preuss, Akad. d. Wis., 1854, 26.

REMINGTON, J. W., HAMILTON, W. F., BOYD, G. H., JR., HAMILTON W. F., JR., and CADDELL, H. M., 1950. Role of vasoconstriction in the response of the dog to hemorrhage. Am. J. Physiol., **161**, 116–124.

REMINGTON, J. W., HAMILTON, W. F., CADDELL, H. M., BOYD, G. H., JR., WHEELER, N. C., and PICKERING, R. W., 1950. Vasoconstriction as a precipitating factor in traumatic shock in the dog. Ibid., **161**, 125–132.

REMINGTON, J. W., HAMILTON, W. F., CADDELL, H. M., BOYD, G. H., JR., and HAMILTON, W. F., JR., 1950. Some circulatory responses to hemorrhage in the dog. Ibid., **161**, 106–115.

RETIEF, P. J. M., 1950. Physiology of micturition and ejaculation. South African Med. J., **24**, 509–514.

RHEINGOLD, J. C., 1939. Autonomic integration in schizophrenia. Psychosomatic Med., **1**, 397–413.

RICE, H. V., and JOY, M. S., 1947. Modification of respiratory movements by vagal stimulation. Am. J. Physiol., **149**, 24–42.

RICHINS, C. A., 1945. The innervation of the pancreas. J. Comp. Neurol., **83**, 223–236.

————1950. The effect of sympathetic nerve stimulation on blood flow through the pancreas. Anat. Rec., **106**, 71–72.

RICHINS, C. A., and BRIZZEE, K., 1949. Effect of localized cutaneous stimulation on circulation in duodenal arterioles and capillaries. J. Neurophysiol., **12**, 131–136.

RICHINS, C. A., and KUNTZ, A., 1952. Effects of stimulation and depression of adrenergic and cholinergic nerves on salivary secretion. (Unpublished.)

RICHTER, C. P., 1946. Instructions for using the cutaneous resistance recorder or "dermometer" on peripheral nerve injuries, sympathectomies, and paravertebral blocks. J. Neurosurg., **3**, 181–191.

RICHTER, C. P., and LEVINE, M., 1937. Sympathectomy in man. Its effect on the electrical resistance of the skin. Arch. Neurol. & Psychiat., **38**, 756–760.

RICHTER, C. P., and OTENASEK, F. J., 1946. Thoracolumbar sympathectomies examined with the electrical skin resistance method. J. Neurosurg., **3**, 120–134

RICHTER, C. P., and WHELAN, F. G., 1949. Description of a skin galvanometer that gives a graphic record of activity in the sympathetic nervous system. Ibid., **6**, 279–284.

RICHTER, C. P., and WISLOCKI, G., 1928. Activity studies on castrated male and female rats with testicular grafts, in correlation with histological studies of grafts. Am. J. Physiol., **86**, 651–660.

RIJLANT, P., 1948. La drealité de la stimulation des neurones phréniques por le "centre respiratore." J. de physiol., **40**, 294a–295a.

RING, J. R., and RANDALL, W. C., 1946. Sweat glands in the rat and their response to prolonged nervous stimulation. Anat. Rec., **94**, 34–35.

RITCHIE, W. P., and BOYDEN, E. A., 1937. Evacuation of the gall bladder in patients with carcinoma of the stomach. Proc. Soc. Exp. Biol. & Med., **36**, 815–816.

RÖPER, C., 1951. Ueber die Innervation der lymphgefäage. Brun's Beitr. klin. Chir., **183**, 436–443.

ROESLER, G., 1933. Pharmakologische Untersuchungen am weissen Blutbild. II. Die Einwirkung vegetativer Gifte auf das Differentialblutbild des Menschen. Arch. exper. Path. u. Pharmakol., **174**, 28–44.

ROGOFF, J. M., WASSERMAN, P., and NIXON, E. N., 1946. Nervous system mechanism for epinephrine secretion. Proc. Soc. Exp. Biol. & Med., **61**, 251–257.

ROOT, W. S., and BARD, P., 1947. The mediation of feline erection through sympathetic pathways with some remarks on sexual behavior after deafferentation of the genitalia. Am. J. Physiol., **151**, 80–90.

ROSEN, S., 1949. Chorda tympani nerve section and tympanic plexectomy. New technic used in cases of deafness, tinnitus and vertigo. Arch. Otolaryngol., **50**, 81–90.

ROSENBLUETH, A., 1932. The chemical mediation of autonomic nervous impulses as evidenced by summation of responses. Am. J. Physiol., **102**, 12–38.

————1934. Central excitation and inhibition in reflex changes of heart-rate. Ibid., **107**, 293–304.

————1950. The transmission of Nerve Impulses at Neuroeffector Junctions and Peripheral Synapses. John Wiley & Sons, Inc., New York.

ROSENBLUETH, A., and BARD, P., 1932. The innervation and functions of the nictitating membrane in the cat. Am. J. Physiol., **100**, 357–544.

ROSENBLUETH, A., and CANNON, W. B., 1932. Studies on conditions of activity in endocrine organs; some effects of sympathin on nictitating membrane. Ibid., **99**, 398–407.

ROSENBLUETH, A., and SCHWARZ, H. G., 1935. Reflex responses of the nictitating membrane. Ibid., **112**, 422–429.

ROSENOW., G., 1928. Hirnstichleukocytose. Untersuchung über die zentralvegetative Blutregulation. Ztschr. ges. exp. Med., **64**, 452–461.

ROSS, J., 1887. On the segmental distribution of sensory disorders. Brain, **10**, 333–361.

ROUS, P., GILDING, H. P., and SMITH, F., 1931. The gradient of vascular permeability. II. The conditions in frog and chicken muscle, and in the mammalian diaphragm. J. Exper. Med., **53**, 195–218.

ROUX, G., 1926. Neuromas in cystic ovaries. Bull. de l'Acad. de Med., **95**, 295.

ROWNTREE, L. G., 1928. Results of bilateral lumbar sympathetic ganglionectomy and ramisectomy for polyarthritis of lower extremities—presentation of case. Proc. Staff. Meet., Mayo Clinic, **3**, 333.

————1929. Presentation of case of arthritis., Ibid., **4**, 91.

ROWNTREE, L. G., ADSON, A. W., and HENCH, P. S., 1930a. Results of resection of sympathetic ganglia and trunks in chronic "infectious "arthritis. Ann. Int. Med., 4, 447–454.

————1930b. Results of sympathetic ganglionectomy in periarticular arthritis. J. A. M. A., 94, 2090.

ROYLE, N. D., 1924a. A new operative procedure in the treatment of spastic paralysis and its experimental basis. Med. J. Australia, 1, 77; 1–86.

————1924b. The treatment of spastic paralysis by sympathetic ramisection. Surg. Gynec. & Obst., 39, 701–720.

ROYSTER, H. P., SLOAN, A. M., McCAIN, L. I., and SHOHL, T., 1949. The anatomy of the nerves supplying the common duct and proximal duodenum. Surgery, 26, 413–420.

RUHMANN, W., 1927a. Örtliche Hautreizbehandlung des Magens und ihre physiologischen Grundlagen. Arch. f. Verdauungskr., 41, 336–350.

————1927b. Der segmentäre Reflexablauf von der Haut zum Eingeweide. Ztschr. ges. exper. Med., 57, 740–767.

————1927c. Viscerale Schmerzlinderung durch die Wärme als Segmentreflex. Ibid., 57, 768–797.

RYLE, J. A., 1926. Gastric function in health and disease. Oxford University Press.

SACCOMANNO, G., 1943. The components of the upper thoracic sympathetic nerves. J. Comp. Neurol., 79, 355–378.

SAKUSSEFF, S., 1897. Ueber die Nervenendigungen im Verdauungskanal der Fische. Trav. de la Soc. des Natur. de St. Petersburg, 27.

SALEK, W., and WEITBRECHT, E., 1920. Zur Frage der Beteiligung sympathischer Nerven am Tonus der Skelettmuskulatur. Ztschr. Biol., 71, 246–254.

SALMON, A., 1952. Le rôle du système diencephalohypophysaire dans la physiologie du somneil. Presse med., 60, 54–57.

SANDERS, A. G., EBERT, R. H., and FLOREY, H. W., 1940. Mechanism of capillary contraction. Quart. J. Exp. Physiol., 30, 281–287.

SARTORIUS, O. W., and BURLINGTON, H., 1952. Effects of denervation on renal function in the dog. Federation Proc., 11, 137–138.

SAUER, M. E., and RUMBLE, C. T., 1946. The number of nerve cells in the myenteric and the submucous plexuses of the small intestine of the cat. Anat. Rec., 96, 373–381.

SAUTER, H., 1948. Beitrag zum Problem der Innervation des Uterus. Schweiz. med. Wchnschr., 78, 512–517.

SAWITSCH, W. W., and SOSHESTVENSKY, N. A., 1917. L'Influence d.n. vagus sur la secretion de l'intestin. Compt. rend. Soc. biol., 80, 508.

————1921. Der Einfluss eines Reizes des Nervus vagus auf die Sekretion der Darmfermente. J. Rus. de physiol., 3, 43.

SCHAPER, A., 1897. Die frühesten Differenzierungsvorgänge im Zentralnervensystem. Kritische Studie und Versuch einer Geschichte der Entwickelung nervöser Substanz. Arch. Entw.-Mech., 5, 81–132.

SCHARRER, E., 1937. Ueber ein vegetatives optisches System. Klin. Wchnschr., 16, 1521–1523.

SCHEER, P., 1940. Ueber den Einfluss des Nicotins auf die Knochenmarksfunktion. Ztschr. ges. Exp. Med., 107, 807–811.

SCHEINFINKEL, N., 1938. Thermoelectrische Untersuchungen über den Wärmebildenden Einfluss des Nervus sympathicus auf die quergestreifte Muskulatur. Schweiz med. Wchnschr., 68, 965–968.

SCHEUNERT, A., KRZYWANEK, F. W., and ZIMMERMANN, K., 1930. Zum Studium der Speichelsekretion. IV. Die Dauersekretion der Parotis des Schafes und ihre Bedeutung. V. Der Einfluss verschiedener Reize auf die Sekretion der Parotis des Schafes. VI. Ueber die an der Dauersekretion des Shafes beteiligten Drüsen und die Zusammensetzung des von ihnen gelieferten Sekretes. Pflüger's Arch. ges. Physiol., 223, 453–476.

SCHEUNERT, A., and TRAUTMANN, A., 1921. Ueber die Sekretion der Parotis und Mandibularis des Schafes. Ibid., 192, 33–80.

SCHIFFRIN, M. J., and WARREN, A. A., 1942. Some factors concerned in the production of experimental ulceration of the G-I tract in cats. Am. J. Dig. Dis., 9, 205–209.

SCHLESINGER, H., 1933. Der Bauchbecken-Austreibungsreflex der Harnblase. Ein bisher unbekannter therapeutisch verwertbarer Reflex. Med. Klin., **29**, 538–539.

SCHMID, M., 1936. Untersuchungen über den Einfluss des Sympathikus und von Adrenalin auf die Wärmebildung im Muskel. Ztschr. Biol., **97**, 493–504.

SCHNEIDER, K., 1929. Der Einfluss des Sympathicus auf die quergestreifte Muskulatur. Pflüger's Arch. ges. Physiol., **222**, 415–419.

————1930. Der Einfluss des Sympathicus auf die quergestreifte Muskulatur. Ibid., **227**, 293–300.

SCHNYDER, E., 1936. Ermüdung und Nichtermüdung der Muskulatur bei selektiver Reizung eines gemischten Nervenstammes: Ein Beitrag zur Lehre vom sympathikus. Ztschr. Biol., **97**, 505–511.

SCHÖNHOLZER, G., 1937. Über Störung des vegetativen Innervation bei der Poliomyelitis anterior acuta. Deutsch. Arch. klin. Med., **180**, 394–401.

SCHRUMPF, P., 1910. Ueber die durch abgetötete Tuberbacillen beim Menschen und beim Tiere hervorgerufene Pseudotuberkulose. Zentralb. Bakteriol., **4**, 216–218.

SCHULZE, J. W., and BOYDEN, E. A., 1943. The blood supply and innervation of the choledochoduodenal junction in the cat. Anat. Rec., **86**, 15–39.

SCHUMACHER, G. A., and WOLFF, H. G., 1941. Experimental studies on headache: A contrast of histamine headache with the headache of migraine and that associated with hypertension: B. Contrast of vascular mechanics in pre-headache and in headache phenomena of migraine. Arch. Neurol. & Psychiat., **45**, 199–214.

SCHUMACHER, H. B., 1947. Sympathetic interruption in cases of trauma and in post traumatic states. Surg. Gynec. & Obst., **84**, 739–749.

SCHUMACHER, H. B., and ABRAMSON, D. I., 1947. Sympathectomy in trench foot. Ann. Surg., **125**, 203–215.

SCHÜTZ, P. J., 1946. The causes and mechanisms of abdominal pain. Am. J. Dig. Dis., **13**, 299–307.

SCRIMGER, F. A. C., 1934. Further experience in the relief of pain by section of the rami communicantes and ganglionated sympathetic cord. Ann. Surg., **99**, 284–289.

SECKER, J., 1934a. The humoral control of the secretion by the submaxillary gland of the cat following chorda stimulation. J. Physiol., **81**, 81–92.

————1934b. The humoral control of the secretion by the submaxillary gland of the cat following sympathetic stimulation. Ibid., **82**, 293–304.

————1936a. On the alleged occurrence of acetylcholine and adrenaline in cat's saliva. J. Pharm. & Exp. Therap., **56**, 464–465.

————1936b. Further observations on the secretion by the submaxillary gland of the cat following sympathetic stimulation. J. Physiol., **86**, 22–28.

SEGAL, H. L., BINSWANGER, H. F., and STROUSE, S., 1928. The effect of emotion on basal metabolism. Arch. Int. Med., **41**, 834–842.

SHEEHAN, D., and MARRAZZI, A. S., 1941. The sympathetic preganglionic outflow to limbs of monkey. J. Neurophysiol., **4**, 68–79.

SHINGLETON, W. W., ANLYAN, W. G., and HART, D., 1952. Effects of vagotomy, splanchnicectomy and celiac ganglionectomy on experimentally produced spasms of sphincter of Oddi in animals. Ann. Surg., **135**, 721–729.

SIMENAUER, E., 1927. Die Sensibilität von Pleuren, Perikard und Peritonealüberzug des Diaphragma mit besonderer Berücksichtigung des Nervus phrenicus. Ztschr. Tuberk., **38**, 273–285.

SIMMONS, H. T., and SHEEHAN, D., 1937. An inquiry into "relapse" following sympathectomy. Lancet, **2**, 788–800.

————1939. The causes of relapse following sympathectomy on the arm. Brit. J. Surg., **27**, 234–255.

SIMPSON, S. L., BROWN, G. E., and ADSON, A. W., 1930. Observations on the etiological mechanism in Raynaud's disease. Proc. Staff Meet., Mayo Clinic., **5**, 295–298.

SINCLAIR, D. C., 1949. The remote reference of pain aroused in the skin. Brain, **72**, 364–372.

SINCLAIR, D. C., WEDDELL, G., and FEINDEL, W. H., 1948. Referred pain and associated phenomena. Ibid., **71**, 184–211.

SINIZIN, N. P., 1937. Der Sympathikus-Effekt während direkter Reizung des Skelettmuskels des Frosches. Fiziol. z., **22**, 150–154.

SKILLERN, P. G., 1947. Clinical observations on: (I) cutaneovisceral (somato-sympathetic) reflex arcs: (II) the role of hypermyotonia in bodily aches and pains. J. Nerv. & Ment. Dis., **105**, 449–464.

SKOOG, T., 1947. Ganglia in the communicating rami of the cervical sympathetic trunk. Lancet, **2**, 457–460.

SLAUGHTER, R. F., 1938. Relief of causalgic-like pain in isolated extremity by sympathectomy; case report. J. Med. Assoc. Georgia, **27**, 253–256.

SMITH, D. E., RANDALL, W. C., and HERTZMAN, A. B., 1948. Some cutaneous responses to reflex cooling. Federation Proc., **7** (Part I), 116.

SMITH, P. E., and ENGLE, E. T., 1927. Experimental evidence regarding the role of the anterior pituitary in the development and regulation of the genital system. Am. J. Anat., **40**, 159–217.

SMITH, R. C., RUFFIN, J. M., and BAYLIN, G. J., 1947. Effect of transthoracic vagus resection upon patients with peptic ulcer. South. M. J., **40**, 1–9.

SMITH, R. G., GULICKSON, M., and CAMPBELL, D. A., 1952. Some limitations of lumbar sympathectomy in arteriosclerosis obliterans. Early results in 100 consecutive cases. Arch. Surg., **64**, 103–107.

SMITHWICK, R. H., 1936. Modified dorsal sympathectomy for vascular spasm (Raynaud's disease) of the upper extremity. A preliminary report. Ann. Surg., **104**, 330–350.

————1940a. The rationale and technic of sympathectomy for the relief of vascular spasm of the extremities. New England J. Med., **222**, 699–703.

————1940b. Surgical intervention on the sympathetic nervous system for peripheral vascular disease. Arch. Surg., **40**, 286–306.

————1940c. The problem of producing complete and lasting sympathetic denervation of the upper extremity by preganglionic section. Ann. Surg., **112**, 1085–1100.

————1941. Medical progress: surgery of the sympathetic nervous system. The role of vasospasm in acute lesions involving major peripheral vessels. New England J. Med., **224**, 329–332.

————1948. Surgical treatment of hypertension. Am. J. Med., **4**, 744–759.

————1949. An evaluation of the surgical treatment of hypertension. Bull. New York Acad. Med., **25**, 698–716.

————1949. Surgery of the autonomic nervous system. New England J. Med., **240**, 543–551.

SMITHWICK, R. H., CHAPMAN, E. M., KINSEY, D., and WHITELAW, G. P., 1949. Human heart rate: some observations and deductions based upon effect of removing portions of the sympathetic nervous system in man. Surgery, **26**, 727–755.

SNAPE, W. J., 1948. Studies on the gall bladder in unanesthetized dogs before and after vagotomy. Gastroenterology, **10**, 129–134.

SOMOGYI, J. C., 1938. Experimentelle Beiträge über Rolle des sympathischen Nervensystems bei der Blutbildung. Ztschr. Biol., **98**, 464–472.

DE SOUSA PEREIRA, A., 1946. Abdominopelvic sympathectomy for relief of pain of cancer of the cervix. Arch. Surg., **52**, 113–134.

————1946. A basis for sympathectomy for cancer of the cervix uteri. Ibid., **52**, 260–285.

SPIEGEL, E. A., 1923. Zur Physiologie und Pathologie des Skelettmuskeltonus. Berlin.

SPIEGEL, E. A., and ADOLF, M., 1922. Die Ganglien des Grenzstrangs. Arb. a. d. neurol. Inst. Wein., **23**, 67–117.

SPIEGEL, E. A., and BERMIS, W. J., 1925. Die Rückenmarksbahn der Visceralsensibilität. Pflüger's Arch. ges Physiol., **210**, 209–214.

SPIEGEL, E. A., and WASSERMANN, S., 1926. Experimentelle Studien über die Enstehung des Aortenschmerzes und seine Leitung zum Zentralnervensystem. Ztschr. ges. exper. Med., **52**, 180–196.

SPINA, A., 1897. Experimentelle Beiträge zur Lehre von der Erektion und Ejakulation. Wein. Med. Blat., **10**.

SPOERRI, R., 1947. Histological studies on nerve elements and their endings at the epithelial cells of the gastric mucosa. Anat. Rec., **97**, 56; J. Comp. Neurol., **90**, 151–171.

SPYCHALA, V., 1932a. Untersuchungen über vegetative Beeinflussung der Muskeleigenreflexe. I. Einfluss quantitativ und qualitativ veränderter Blutversorgung auf den Quadrizepseigenreflex am Hunde. Ztschr. exp. Med., **83**, 192–198.

————1932b. Untersuchungen über vegetative Beeinflussung der Muskeleigen-reflexe. II. Einfluss der Sympaticusreizung und des Adrenalins auf den Quadrizep-seigenreflex am Hunde. Ibid., **83**, 199–202.

————1932c. Untersuchungen über vegetative Beeinflussung der Muskeleigen-reflexe. III. Einfluss der pressorezeptorischen Kreislaufnerven auf den Quadrizep-seigenreflex am Hunde. Ibid., **83**, 203–210.

STÄMMLER, M., 1923. Zur Pathologie des sympathischen Nervensystems; im beson-deren: Ueber seine Bedeutung für die Enstehung der Arteriosklerose. Beitr. path. Anat. u. allg. Path., **71**, 388–450.

STANGL, E., 1952. Das Föhnproblem in seiner Beziehung zum vegetativen Nerven-system. Wein., klin. Wchschr., **64**, 467–469.

STATE, D., and HIRSCH, E. F., 1941. Nerves of the adult human endometrium. Arch. Path., **32**, 939–950.

STEFANELLI, A., 1929. Le Piastre motorici a grappolo e loro significato con consider-azioni sulle espansioni motorici nel miocardio. Arch. ital. anat. e embriol., **27**, 180–194.

STELLA, G., 1939. The reflex response of the "apneustic" center to stimulation of the chemo-receptors of the carotid sinus. J. Physiol., **95**, 365–372.

STEWART, F. W., 1920. The development of the cranial sympathetic ganglia in the rat. J. Comp. Neurol., **31**, 163–217.

STÖHR, P., 1926. Mikroskopischer Beitrag zur Innervation der Blutkapillaren beim Menschen. Ztschr. Zellforsch u. mikr. Anat., **3**, 431–448.

————1934. Anatomische Betrachtungen über das vegetative Nervensystem und seine Veränderungen beim Magenulkus. Deutsch. med. Wchnschr., **60**, 45–49.

STÖHR, P., JR., 1930. Mikroskopische Studien zur Innervation des Magen-Darmkanales. Ztschr. Zellforsch u. mikr. Anat., **12**, 66–154.

————1932a. Microscopische studien zur Innervation des Magen-Darmkanales. II. Ueber die Nerven des Menschlichen Magens und Ihre Veränderungen Beim Ulkus. Ibid., **16**, 123–198.

————1932b. Die Nerven des Magens und ihre Veränderungen beim Ulkus chronicum. Klin. Wchnschr., **11**, 1214–1215.

————1934a. Anatomische Betrachtungen über das vegetative Nervensystem und seine Veränderungen beim Magenulkus. Ibid., **60**, 45–49.

————1934b. Mikroskopische Studien zur Innervation des Magen-Darmkanals. III. Ztschr. Zellforsch. u. mikr. Anat., **21**, 243–278.

————1935. Beobachtungen und Bemerkungen über die Endausbreitung des vege-tativen Nervensystems. Ztschr. Anat. u. Entwcklngsgesch., **104**, 133–158.

————1950. Bemerkungen über die Endigungsweise des vegetativen Nervensystems und über den Aufbau des Organismus. Acta neurovegetativa, **1**, 74–86.

STOTLER, W. A., 1937. Innervation of the intrinsic muscles of the eye: An experimental study. Proc. Soc. Exp. Biol. & Med., **36**, 576–577.

STOTLER, W. A., and McMAHON, R. A., 1947. The innervation and structure of the conductive system in the human heart. J. Comp. Neurol., **87**, 57–71.

STRAUSS, H., 1928. Achylia gastrica und Anaemia perniciosa. Arch. f. Verdauungsk., **43**, 450–458.

STRÖM, G., 1950. Vasomotor response to thermal and electrical stimulation of frontal lobe and hypothalamus. Acta physiol. scandinav., **20**, Suppl. 70, 83–112.

STRUDEL, G., 1952. Contribution expérimentale au problème de l'origine des ganglions rachidens et sympathiques chez l'embryon de poulet. Compt. rend. Soc. biol., **146**, 105–109.

STUBBS, J. B., and WOOLSEY, R. D., 1950. Angina pectoris. Treatment by injection of stellate ganglion with ammonium sulfate. South. M. J., **43**, 675–678.

SULKIN, N. M., and KUNTZ, A., 1948. The Golgi apparatus in autonomic ganglion cells and peripheral neuroglia and its modification following stimulation and induced hypertension. J. Neuropath. & Exper. Neurol., **7**, 154–161.

————1950. A histochemical study of the autonomic ganglia of the cat following prolonged preganglionic stimulation. Anat. Rec., **108**, 255–277.

————1952. Histochemical alterations in autonomic ganglion cells associated with ageing. J. Gerontol., **7**, 533–543

SUNDER-PLASSMANN, P., 1930. Untersuchungen über den Bulbus carotidis bei Mensch und Tier im Hinblick auf die "Sinusreflexe" nach H. E. Hering; ein Vergleich mit anderen Gefässtrecken; die Histopathologie des Bulbus carotidis; das Glomus caroticum. Ztschr. Anat. u. Entwcklngsgesch., **93**, 567–622.

SUTHERLAND, A. M., and WOLFF, H. G., 1940. Experimental studies on headache; Further analysis of the mechanism of headache in migraine, hypertension and fever. Arch. Neurol. & Psychiat., **44**, 929–949.

SWINYARD, C. A., 1937. The innervation of the suprarenal glands. Anat. Rec., **68**, 417–429.

SZABO, E., 1948. Innervation of the kidney and its practical significance. Acta Urologica, **2**, 1–11.

SZASZ, T. S., 1949. Psychiatric aspects of vagotomy. II. A psychiatric study of vagotomized ulcer patients with comments on prognosis. Psychosom. Med., **11**, 187–199.

SZASZ, T. S., KIRSNER, J. B., LEVIN, E., and PALMER, W. L., 1947. Role of hostility in pathogenesis of peptic ulcer; theoretical consideration with report of case. Ibid., **9**, 331–336.

SZEMZO, G., 1927. Der Schmerz als führendes Symptom. Theoretische Ueberlegungen und praktische Beobachtungen zum Schmerzproblem. Ztschr. klin. Med., **106**, 365–405.

TAKAHASHI, W., 1931. Zur Lokalizationsfrage der Zentren für die Epinephrinsekretion. Tohoku J. Exp. Med., **18**, 339–381.

TAKEDA, M., and ITO, A., 1951. Studies on motility of the cardiac and the pyloric regions by the electrical stimulation of the hypothalamus of rabbits. Med. J. Osaka Univ., **3**, 459–472.

TANTURI, C. A., and IVY, A. C., 1938. A study of the effects of vascular changes in the liver and the excitation of its nerve supply on the formation of bile. Am. J. Physiol., **121**, 61–74.

TARLOV, I. M., and HERZ, E., 1947. Unilateral frontal hyperhidrosis relieved by supraorbital nerve section. J. A. M. A., **133**, 476–477.

TAYLOR, J., 1949. Discussion on Hirschsprung's disease. Proc. Roy. Soc. Med., **42**, 221–228.

TCHENG, K. T., 1950. Innervation du myocarde et du faisceau de Hischez deux mammifèrs le mouton et le chat. Cardiologica, **15**, 227–265.

TELFORD, E. D., and SIMMONS, H. T., 1939. Treatment of gastro-intestinal achalasia by spinal anaesthesia. Brit. Med. J., **2**, 1224–1226.

————1940. Erythromelalgia. Ibid., **2**, 782–783.

————1946. Sympathectomy in peripheral arteriosclerosis. Ibid., **1**, 386–387.

TELFORD, E. D., and STOPFORD, J. S. B., 1933. The distribution of the vasoconstrictor fibers in the limbs. J. Anat., **67**, 417–419.

TERRACOL, J., 1932. L'intérêt diagnostique des "douleurs rapportées" dans le territoire des nerfs craniens. Rev. d'oto-neuro-opth., **10**, 246–252.

THALHAMMER, O., and JANICEK, L., 1951. Die unspezifische Therapie (chorea minor) im Lichte einer neuen vegetativ-regulalorischen Leukozytenreaktion. Wein. klin. Wchnschr., **63**, 198–200.

THAYSEN, J. H., SCHWARTZ, I. L., and DOLE, V. P., 1952. Fatigue of the sweat glands. Federation Proc., **11**, 161–162.

THOMAS, J. E., 1948. The functional innervation of the pancreas. Rev. Gastroenterol., **15**, 813.

THOMAS, J. E., and KAMAROV, S. A., 1948. Physiological aspects of vagotomy. Gastroenterology, **11**, 413–418.

THOMAS, J. E., and KUNTZ, A., 1926a. A study of the vago-enteric mechanism by means of nicotin. Am. J. Physiol., **76**, 598–605.

————1926b. A study of gastro-intestinal motility in relation to the enteric nervous system. Ibid., 616–626.

THOMAS, J. E., and WHEELON, H., 1922. The nervous control of the pyloric sphincter. J. Lab. and Clin. Med., **7**, 375–391.

THOMAS, P. E., and KARR, I. M., 1951. The automatic recording of electrical skin resistance patterns on the human trunk. Electroencephalography and Clinical Neurophysiol., **3**, 361–368.

THREADGILL, F. D., and SOLNITZKY, O., 1949. Anatomical studies of afferency within the lumbosacral ganglia. Anat. Rec., **103**, 96.

TIEGS, O. W., 1931. Note on the posture of the bird's wing and its supposed control by sympathetic nerves. Am. J. Physiol., **98**, 547–550.

————1934. The function of sympathetic nerves in relation to skeletal muscle—evidence of humoral action. Proc. Roy. Soc. London, Series B., **116**, 351–374.

TODD, T. W., and ROWLANDS, M. E., 1930. Emotional interference in gastric behavior patterns. J. Comp. Psych., **10**, 167–188.

TOURNADE, A., and CHABROL, M., 1919. Dissociation experimentale des effects vaso-constricteurs et adrenalino-secreteurs de l'excitation splanchnique. Compt. rend. Soc. biol., **85**, 651–654.

TOWER, S. S., 1926. A study of the sympathetic innervation of skeletal muscle. Am. J. Physiol., **78**, 462–493.

————1931. A search for trophic influence of posterior spinal roots on skeletal muscle, with a note on the nerve fibers found in the proximal stumps of the roots after excision of the root ganglia. Brain, **54**, 99–110.

TOWER, S. S., and HINES, M., 1929. Some observations on sympathetic innervation to skeletal muscles of goats. Am. J. Physiol., **87**, 542–552.

TOWER, S. S., and RICHTER, C. P., 1932a. II. The postganglionic neurons. Arch. Neurol. & Psychiat., **28**, 1139–1148.

————1932b. III. Evidence of activity of postganglionic sympathetic neurons independent of the central nervous system. Ibid., **28**, 1149–1152.

TRAVELL, J., BAKER, S. J., HIRSCH, B. B., and RINZLER, S. H., 1952. Myofascial component of intermittent claudication. Federation Proc., **11**, 164.

TRAVELL, J., and RINZLER, S. H., 1952. The myofascial genesis of pain. Postgraduate Med., **11**, 425–434.

TRIMBLE, I. R., and MORRISON, S., 1952. Treatment of intractable pain of visceral origin. J. A. M. A., **148**, 1184–1188.

TROWBRIDGE, B. C., 1949. Tympanosympathetic anesthesia for tinnitus aurium and secondary otalgia. Arch. Otolaryngol., **50**, 200–215.

UDAONDAO, C. B., and GONALONS, G. P., 1934. Insufficiency of the suprarenals caused by emotion. Prensa med. argentina, **21**, 1–9.

UEBELHÖR, R., 1951. Die Nerven der Blase nach klinischen Erfahrungen. Wein. klin. Wchnschr., **63**, 202–204.

UOTILA, U. U., 1939. The role of the cervical sympathetics in the regulation of thyroid and thyrotropic function. Endocrinology, **25**, 63–70.

UTTERBACK, R. A., 1944. Innervation of the spleen. J. Comp. Neurol., **81**, 55–68.

UVNÄS, B., 1947. Effect of frequency of hypothalamic stimulation upon bladder response. Proc. Soc. Exper. Biol. & Med., **64**, 181–185.

————1951. Activation of sympathetic vasodilator nerves by hypothalamic stimulation. Acta physiol. scandinav., **25** (Suppl. 89), 82–84.

VALENTIN, G. G., 1836. Ueber den Verlauf und die letzen Enden der Nerven. Nova. acta. phy. med. Acad. nat. curios., **18**, 51–541.

VAN BUSKIRK, C., 1941. The nerves in the vertebral canal and their relation to the sympathetic innervation of the upper extremity. Arch. Surg., **43**, 427–432.

VAN DIJK, J. A., 1930a. The part played by the sympathetic innervation in producing postural tone in the wing of the pigeon. Arch. Néerl. de Physiol., **15**, 114–125.

————1930b. The effect of stimulation of the cervical sympathetic cord upon the function of cross-striated muscle in the pigeon. Ibid., **15**, 126–137.

————1932. On the plastic component of postural tone in the bird's wing. Ibid., **27**, 268–278.

————1933. The influence of the sympathetic innervation upon the manifestations of the fore legs of decerebrated cats. Ibid., **18**, 105–138.

VAN DYKE, H. B., 1926. Action of small doses of ergotamine on muscular response to stimulation of sympathetic nerves. J. Pharmacol. & Exp. Therap., **27**, 299–317.

VOLOCHOR, A., and GERSUNI, G., 1933. Ueber die zentrale sympathische Regulierung der Tätigkeit des neuromuskulären Apparates. Physiol. Ztschr., **16**, 131–137.

VONDERAHE, A. R., 1937. Central nervous system and sugar metabolism, clinical, pathological and theoretical, with special reference to diabetes mellitus. Arch. Int. Med., **60**, 694–704.

————1939. Histopathologic changes in the nervous system in cases of peptic ulcer. Arch. Neurol. & Psychiat., **41**, 871–912.

————1940. Changes in the hypothalamus in organic disease. Res. Pbl. A. Res. Nerv. & Ment. Dis., **20**, 689–712.

von Siedek, Hans, 1951. Die vegetativenervosen Grundlagen des Infektgeschehens. Wien klin. Wchnschr., **63**, 907–909.

Voser, H., 1931. Untersuchungen über den Einfluss des Sympathicus auf die Muskeltatigkeit unter naturlichen Bedingungen. Ztschr. Biol., **91**, 86–98.

Wachholder, K., and Neuberg, H. J., 1950. Ueber den Einfluss des vegetativen Nervensystems auf das weisze Blutbild nach Untersuchungen am Ebbeckeschen Eintauchreflex. Arch. ges. Physiol., **253**, 91.

Wada, M., 1950. Sudorific action of adrenalin on the human sweat glands and determination of their excitability. Science III, 376–377.

Waddell, M. C., 1929. Anatomical evidence for existence of enteric reflex arcs following degeneration of extrinsic nerves. Proc. Soc. Exp. Biol. & Med., **26**, 867–869.

Walker, A. E., and Nulson, F., 1948. Electrical stimulation of the upper thoracic portion of the sympathetic chain in man. Arch. Neurol. & Psychiat., **59**, 559–560.

Walters, W., and Belding, H. H., 1951. Physiological effects of vagotomy. J. A. M. A., **145**, 607–613.

Walters, W., Belding, H. H., and Lillie, W. I., 1951. Vagotomie gastrique. Lyon chir., **46**, 775–783.

Walters, W., and Fahey, M. M., 1949. Vagotomy: Immediate results in 28 cases and later results in 68 cases. Proc. Staff Meet., Mayo Clinic, **24**, 501–506.

Walters, W., Priestley, J. T., and Belding, H. H., 1952. Vagotomy in the treatment of gastro jejunal ulceration. J. A. M. A., **148**, 803–808.

Wan, F. E., 1946. Sympathetic causalgia. Report of twenty cases treated by sympathectomy. Chinese M. J., **61**, 1–13.

————1946. Presacral neuralgia. Ibid., **61**, 14–16.

Wang, S. C., and Ranson, S. W., 1939. Descending pathways from the hypothalamus to the medulla and spinal cord. Observations on blood pressure and bladder responses. J. Comp. Neurol., **71**, 457–472.

Ward, A. A., 1948. Anterior cingulate gyrus and personality. Res. Pbl. A. Res. Nerv. & Ment. Dis., **27**, 438–445.

Warkentin, J., Huston, J. S., Preston, F. W., and Ivy, A. C., 1943. The mechanism of bile flow inhibition upon distention of the colon or stimulation of its nerve supply. Am. J. Physiol., **138**, 462–464.

Warren, R., and Meadows, E. C., 1949. Subtotal gastrectomy or vagotomy for peptic ulceration. New England J. Med., **240**, 367–372.

Wastl, H., 1925. The effect on muscle contraction of sympathetic stimulation and of various modifications and conditions. J. Physiol., **60**, 109–119.

Watkins, A. L., 1938. Reflex responses of the nictitating membrane and the blood pressure to distention of the bladder and rectum. Am. J. Physiol., **121**, 32–39.

Watts, J. W., and Fulton, J. F., 1934. Intussuseption: the relation of the cerebral cortex to intestinal motility in the monkey. New England J. Med., **210**, 883–896.

Weatherford, T., and Sulkin, N., 1952. A histochemical study of autonomic ganglia in scorbutic guinea pigs. Unpublished data.

Weber, E., and Weber, E. H., 1846. Experiences qui prouvent qui les nerfs vagues, stimules par l'appareil de rotation galvano-manétique, peuvent retarder et même arrêter le mouvement du coeur. Arch. gén. de med., Supp. 12.

Weinstein, V. A., Colf, R., Hollander, P., and Jemerin, E. E., 1944. Vagotomy in the therapy of peptic ulcer. Surg. Gynec. & Obst., **79**, 297–305.

Weiss, S., 1930. Ueber die vegetative Innervation des quergestreiften Muskels. Deutsch. Ztschr. Nervenh., **113**, 236–243.

————1935. Syncope and related syndromes. Oxford Medicine, **2**, 250(9)–250(66).

Weiss, S., and Baker, J. P., 1933a. Dizziness, fainting and convulsions due to hyperactivity of the carotid sinus reflex. Proc. Soc. Exp. Biol. & Med., **30**, 614–616.

————1933b. The carotid sinus reflex in health and disease: Its role in the causation of fainting and convulsions. Medicine, **12**, 297–354.

Weiss, S., and Benkovics, Z., 1925. Die Wirkung des Calciumions auf die Erregbarkeit des vegetativen Nervensystems. Ztschr. ges. exper. Med., **46**, 784–788.

WEISS, S., CAPPS, R. B., FERRISK, E. B., JR., and MUNRO, D., 1936. Syncope and convulsions due to hyperactive carotid sinus reflex. Diagnosis and treatment. Arch. Int. Med., **58**, 407–417.

WEISS, S., and DAVIS, D., 1928. The significance of the afferent impulses from the skin in the mechanism of visceral pain. Skin infiltration as a useful therapeutic measure. Am. J. M. Sc., **176**, 517–536.

WEISS, S., and FERRIS, Z., JR., 1934. Adams-Stokes symdrome with transient complete heart block of vagovagal reflex origin: mechanism and treatment. Arch. Int. Med., **54**, 931.

WELCH, P. B., 1937. Factors influencing the muscular activity of the normal colon. Am. J. Dig. Dis. & Nutr., **4**, 382–386.

WENGER, H., 1933. Nachweis der Wärmebildenden Funktion des Sympathikus im Skelettmuskel. Ztschr. Biol., **93**, 307–316.

WENGER, M. A., 1941. The measurement of individual differences in autonomic balance. Psychosom. Med., **3**, 427–434.

———1947. Preliminary study of the significance of measures of autonomic balance. Ibid., **9**, 301–309.

WENGER, M. A., and ELLINGTON, M., 1943. The measurement of autonomic balance in children. Ibid., **5**, 241–253.

WERNOE, T. B., 1920. Aestesioscopia abdominal. Ugesk, f. Laeger, **82**, 1415.

———1925. Viscero-cutane Reflexe. Pflüger's Arch. ges Physiol., **210**, 1–34.

WEST, R., 1935. Studies in the neurological mechanism of parathyroid tetany. Brain, **58**, 1–20.

WESTPHAL, K., 1923. Muskelfunktion, Nervensystem u. Pathologie der Gallenwege. II. Experimentelle Untersuchungen über die nervöse Beeinflussung der Bewegungsvorgänge der Gallenwege. Ztschr. klin. Med., **96**, 22–150.

WHEATLEY, M. D., 1944. Hypothalamus and affective behavior in cats: study of effects of experimental lesions with anatomic correlation. Arch. Neurol. & Psychiat., **52**, 296–316.

WHEELON, H., 1914. Extirpation of the testes and vasomotor irritability. Am. J. Physiol., **35**, 283–291.

WHITE, J. C., 1930a. Progress in the surgery of the sympathetic nervous system. New England J. Med., **203**, 226–231.

———1930b. Diagnostic blocking of the sympathetic nerves to extremities with procaine. J. A. M. A., **94**, 1381–1388.

———1930c. Angina pectoris. Am. J. Surg., **9**, 98–109.

———1933a. Progress in surgery of the sympathetic nervous system in 1932. New England J. Med., **209**, 843–850.

———1933b. Experimental and clinical studies in the surgical treatment of angina pectoris. Ann. Int. Med., **7**, 229–239.

———1940. Autonomic discharge from stimulation of the hypothalamus in man. Proc. A. Res. Nerv. & Ment. Dis., **20**, 854–863.

———1952. Conduction of visceral pain. New England J. Med., **246**, 686–691.

WHITE, J. C., and BLAND, E. A., 1948. Surgical relief of severe angina pectoris; methods employed and end results in 83 patients. Medicine, **27**, 1–42.

WHITE, J. C., and SMITHWICK, R. H., 1941. The Autonomic Nervous System. The Macmillan Co., New York.

WHITE, J. C., SMITHWICK, R. M., and SIMEONE, F. A., 1952. The Autonomic Nervous System: Anatomy, Physiology and Surgical Application. 3rd Ed. The Macmillan Co., New York.

WHITE, J. C., and WARREN, S., 1944. Causes of pain in feet after prolonged immersion in cold water. War Med., **5**, 6–13.

WHITEHOUSE, F. R., and KERNOHAN, J. W., 1949. Myenteric plexus in congenital megacolon. Arch. Int. Med., **82**, 75–111.

WHITELAW, G. P., and SMITHWICK, R. H., 1951. Effect of extensive sympathectomy upon blood pressure responses and levels. Angiology, **2**, 157–172.

WHITROCK, R. M., TRICHE, H. L., and SEEVERS, M. H., 1948. Influence of the extrinsic nerves on intestinal motility. Am. J. Physiol., **155**, 477–478.

WHYTT, R., 1751. An essay on the vital and other involuntary motions of animals. Edinburgh.

————1765. Observations on the nature, causes and cure of those disorders which have commonly been called nervous, hypochondriac or hysteric; to which are prefixed some remarks on the sympathy of the nerves. Edinburgh.

WIDAL, D., ABRAMI, P., and BRISSAUDE, 1920. Étude sur certains phénomènes de choc. Presse méd., **28**, 181–186.

WILHELMJ, C. M., and SACHS, A., 1939. The physiological control of the normal human gastric secretion curve. Am. J. Dig. Dis., **6**, 467–474.

WILHELMJ, C. M., WALDMANN, E. B., McGUIRE, T. F., and McDONNOUGH, J., 1952. Emotional blood pressure responses of trained normal dogs. Federation Proc., **11**, 173.

WILKINS, R. W., NEWMAN, H. W., and DOUPE, J., 1938. The local sweat response to faradic stimulation. Brain, **61**, 290–297.

WILKINSON, H. J., 1929. The innervation of striated muscle. Australian Med. J., **2**, 768–793.

————1930a. Observations on the sloe-plates of motor end-organs. J. Comp. Neurol., **50**, 133–135.

————1930b. Experimental studies on the innervation of striated muscle. Ibid., **51**, 129–151.

————1934. Further experimental studies on the innervation of striated muscle. Ibid., **59**, 221–238.

WILLIG, H., 1952. Untersuchungen über die Neuroregulation des Ovars. Zentralbl. Gynäkol., **74**, 17–20.

WILLIS, T., 1664. Cerebri anatome, cui accessit nervorum descriptio et usus. London.

WILSON, W. C., 1936. Observations relating to the innervation of the sweat glands of the face. Clin. Sc., **2**, 273–286.

WINSLOW, J. B., 1732. Exposition anat. de la structure du corps humain. Paris.

WOLF, G. A., JR., 1941. The ratio of preganglionic neurons to postganglionic neurons in the visceral nervous system. J. Comp. Neurol., **75**, 235–244.

WOLF, S., and WOLFF, H. G., 1942. Evidence on the genesis of peptic ulcer in man. J. A. M. A., **120**, 670–675.

————1948. Life situations, emotions and gastric function. Tr. & Studies, Col. Phys. & Surg., **16**, 97–115.

WOLFERTH, C. C., JEFFERS, W. A., LUKENS, F. D. W., ZINTEL, H. A., and HAFKEN-SCHIEL, 1951. Observations on the results of subtotal adrenalectomy in the treatment of severe, otherwise intractable hypertension and their bearing on the mechanism by which hypertension is maintained. Ann. Int. Med., **35**, 8–18.

WOOLLARD, H. H., 1926a. The innervation of the heart. J. Anat., **160**, 345–373.

————1926b. The innervation of bloodvessels. Heart, **13**, 319–336.

————1938. Listerian oration. Capillary endothelium. Australian Med. J., **2**, 134–140.

WOOLLARD, H. H., and CARMICHAEL, E. A., 1933. The testis and referred pain. Brain, **56**, 293–303.

WOSSIDLO, K., 1935. Ueber die vegetative Regulation des weiszen Blutbildes. Folia Haematol., **53**, 113–125.

WRETE, M., 1941. Die Entwicklung und Topographie der intermediären vegetativen Ganglien bei gewissen Versuchstieren. Ztschr. Zellforsch u. mikr. Anat., **49**, 503–515.

WRIGHT, R. D., JENNINGS, M. A., FLOREY, H. W., and LIUM, R., 1940. The influence of nerves and drugs on secretion by the small intestine and on investigation of the enzymes in intestinal juice. Quart. J. Exper. Physiol., **30**, 73–120.

WRIGHT, S., 1930. Studies of reflex activity in involuntary nervous system. II. Action of ergotamine on vasomotor reflexes. J. Physiol., **69**, 331–347.

WÜNCHE, G., 1949. Über segmentale Veränderungen des Haut und Unterhautbindegwebes bei Herdinfektion. Med. Klin., **44**, 800–801.

WYSS, O. A. M., 1947a. Respiratory effects from stimulation of afferent vagus nerve in monkey. J. Neurophysiol., **10**, 315–320.

————1947b. Separate localization in medulla oblongata of vagal inspiratory and expiratory reflex centers. Science, **106**, 322–323.

WYSS, O. A. M., and RIVKINE, A., 1950. Les fibres afferentes du nerf vague participant aux réflexes respiratoires. Helvet. physiol. et pharmacol. acta **8**, 87–106.

YAKOVLEV, P. I., 1948. Motility, behavior and the brain stereodynamic organization and neural coördinates of behavior. J. Nerv. & Ment. Dis., **107**, 313–335.

YI, C. L., 1938. Further evidence for existence of reflex sympatho-inhibitory center in medulla oblongata. Chinese J. Physiol., **13**, 411–416.

YNTEMA, C. L., and HAMMOND, W. S., 1945. Depletion of the cervical sympathetic trunks and ganglia following removal of the neural crest in the chick. Anat. Rec., **91**, 64.

————1947. The development of the autonomic nervous system. Biol. Rev. Cambridge Philos. Soc., **22**, 344–359.

————1952. Origin of intrinsic autonomic ganglia of trunk viscera in chick embryo. Anat. Rec., **112**, 102.

YOUMANS, W. B., 1940. Effect of denervation of the intestine on its motor responses at the site of distention. Proc. Soc. Exp. Biol. & Med., **45**, 420–424.

YOUMANS, W. B., KARSTENS, A. I., and AUMANN, K. W., 1942. Nervous pathways for the reflex regulation of intestinal pressure. Am. J. Physiol., **135**, 619–627.

YOUMANS, W. B., MEEK, W. J., and HERRIN, R. C., 1938. Extrinsic and intrinsic pathways concerned with intestinal inhibition during intestinal distention. Ibid., **124**, 470–477.

YOUNG, A., 1936. Ganglionectomy in the treatment of severe polyarthritis and osteoarthritis. Brit. Med. J., **2**, 375–381.

YOUNG, J. Z., 1939. Partial degeneration of the nerve supply to the adrenal. A study in autonomic innervation. J. Anat., **73**, 540–550.

ZAAIJER, J. H., 1914. Dauerresultat einer autoplastischen Nierentransplantation bei einem Hunde. Beitr. klin. Chir., **93**, 223–227.

ZIEGLER, A. M., and LEVINE, B. S., 1925. The influences of emotional reactions in basal metabolism. Am. J. M. Sc., **169**, 68–76.

ZINN, C. J., and GRIFFITH, J. I., JR., 1941. Effect of sympathectomy upon blood supply of bone. Proc. Soc. Exp. Biol. & Med., **461**, 311–312.

ZOLLINGER, R., 1933. Effect of lumbar ganglionectomy on repair of bone: Experimental study. Am. J. Surg., **20**, 70–76.

ZUCKERKANDL, E., 1893. Normale und Pathologische Anatomie der Nasenhölen. Wein-Leipzig.

INDEX

The principal references are indicated in **bold face** type.

38

The Art of the Shoe

The Art of the Shoe

Marie-Josèphe Bossan

Author: Marie-Josèphe Bossan

Translator: Rebecca Brimacombe

ISBN: 978-1-85995-694-6

Printed in China

Special thanks to the city of Romans, France, and Joël Garnier for his photographs.

Contents

Introduction

The Shoe: Object of Civilisation and Object of Art

Aside from noticing a shoe for its comfort or elegance, contemporaries rarely take interest in this necessary object of daily life. However, the shoe is considerable in the history of civilisation and art.

In losing contact with nature, we have lost sight of the shoe's profound significance. In recapturing this contact, in particular through sports, we begin its rediscovery. Shoes for skiing, hiking, hunting, soccer, tennis or horse-riding are carefully chosen, essential tools as well as revealing signs of occupation or taste.

In previous centuries, when people depended more on the climate, vegetation and condition of the soil, while most jobs involved physical labour, the shoe held an importance for everyone which today it holds for very few. We do not wear the same shoes in snow as in the tropics, in the forest as in the steppe, in the swamps as in the mountains or when working, hunting or fishing. For this reason, shoes give precious indications of habitats and ways of life.

In strongly hierarchical societies, organised by castes or orders, clothing was determinant. Princes, bourgeoisie, soldiers, clergy and servants were differentiated by what they wore. The shoe revealed, in a less dramatic manner than the hat, but in a more demanding way, the respective brilliance of civilisations, unveiling the social classes and the subtlety of the breed; a sign of recognition, just as the ring slips only onto the most slender finger, the "glass slipper" will not fit but the most delicate of beauties.

The shoe transmits its message to us by the traditions which impose and condition it. It teaches us of the deformations that were forced on the feet of Chinese women and shows us how in India, by conserving their unusual boots, the nomadic horsemen of the North sought to rule the Indian continent; we learn that sandals evoke the Turkish bath while Turkish slippers suggest the Islamic interdiction to enter places of worship with covered feet.

Sometimes the shoe is symbolic, evoked in ritual or tied to a crucial moment of existence. It is told that high-heels were to make the woman taller during the wedding day in order to remind her that it is the only moment when she will dominate her husband.

The boots of the shaman were decorated with animal skins and bones in order to emulate the stag; as the stag, he could run in the world of spirits. We are what we wear, so if to ascend to a higher life it is necessary to ornate the head, if it becomes an issue of ease of movement, it is the feet that are suited for adornment. Athena had shoes of gold, for Hermes, it was winged sandals. Perseus went to the nymphs to find winged sandals to be able to fly.

Tales echoes mythology. The Seven-league boots, which enlarged or shrunk to fit the ogre or Little Thumb, allowed them both to run across the universe. "You just have to make me a pair of boots," said Puss in Boots to his master, "and you will see that you are not so badly served as you believe."

Does the shoe therefore serve to transcend the foot, often considered as the most modest and least favoured part of the human body? Occasionally, without a doubt, but not always. The bare foot is not always deprived of the sacred and, thus, can communicate this to the shoe. Those who beg or venerate are constantly throwing themselves at the feet of men; it is the feet of men who leave a trace on humid or dusty ground, often the only trace of their passage. A specific accessory, the shoe can sometimes serve to portray who wore it, who is no more, of whom we do not dare to portray; the most characteristic example is offered by primitive Buddhism evoking the image of its founder by a seat or by a footprint.

Made of the most diverse materials, from leather to wood, from cloth to straw, whether plain or ornamented, the shoe, by its form and decoration, becomes an object of art. If the shape is sometimes more functional than esthetic - but not always, and one could explain many absurd forms - the design of the cloth, the embroidery, the inlays, the choice of colours, everything always closely reveal the artistic characteristics of their native country.

The essential interest comes from that which it is not; weapons or musical instruments are reserved for a caste or a determined social group, carpets are the products of only one or two civilisations, it does not stand up as a "sumptuous" object of the rich or a folkloric object of the poor. The shoe has been used from the bottom to the top of the social ladder, by all the individuals of any given group, from group to group, by the entire world.

Jean-Paul Roux,
Honorary Director of Research at the C.N.R.S.
Honorary Tenured Professor of the Islamic Arts
at the School of the Louvre

1. "Akha" sandal, dress of the Akha tribes of the Golden Triangle (box of recycled coca and jungle seed, 6 cm steel heel, leather). Trikitrixa, Paris.

2. Aviator Boots, c. 1914, France.

3. Clay model of shoe with upturned toe from an Azerbaijanian tomb,
13th-12th century B.C.E. Bally-Schuhmuseum, Schönenwerd, Switzerland.

4. Iron shoe. Syria, 800 B.C.E. Bally-Schuhmuseum, Schönenwerd, Switzerland.

From Antiquity to the Present

Prehistory

Prehistoric man evidently was unfamiliar with shoes: the Stone Age markings that are known to us all indicate bare feet. But the cave paintings discovered in Spain dating from the Upper Paleolithic period (around 14,000 B.C.E.) show Magdalenian man dressed in fur boots. According to the French paleontologist and prehistorian Father Breuil (1877-1961), Neolithic man covered his feet with animal skins as protection in a harsh environment. It seems that man has always instinctively covered his feet to get about, although there remains no concrete evidence of the shoes themselves. Prehistoric shoes would have been rough in design and certainly utilitarian in function. The well-preserved boots worn by Ötzi the Iceman discovered in an Alpine glacier are an excellent example. Their deerskin uppers and bearskin soles enabled him to travel long distances to trade. These materials were chosen primarily for their ability to shield the feet from severe conditions. It was only in Antiquity that the shoe would acquire an aesthetic and decorative dimension, becoming a true indicator of social status.

Antiquity

The Shoe in Ancient Eastern Civilisations

From the first great civilisations flourishing in Mesopotamia and Egypt in the 4th millennium B.C.E. arose the three basic types of footwear: the shoe, the boot, and the sandal. An archeological team excavating a temple in the city of Brak (Syria) in 1938 unearthed a clay shoe with a raised toe. Dating over 3,000 years B.C.E, it proves that this city shared features with the Sumerian civilisation of Ur in Mesopotamia: raised-tipped shoes are depicted on Mesopotamian seals of the Akkadian era around 2600 B.C.E. Distinguished from Syrian models by a much higher tip and embellished with a pom-pom, in Mesopotamia this type of shoe became the exclusive footwear of the king. The raised-toe form is attributable to the rugged terrain of the mountain conquerors that introduced it. After its adoption by the Akkadian kingdom, the form spread to Asia Minor where the Hittites made it a part of their national costume. It is frequently depicted in low-reliefs, such as the Yazilikaya sanctuary carvings dating to 1275 B.C.E. Seafaring Phoenicians helped spread the pointed shoe to Cyprus, Mycenae, and Crete, where it appears on palace frescoes depicting royal games and ceremonies. Cretans are also depicted wearing raised-tipped ankle boots in the painted decorations of Rekhmire's tomb (Egypt, 18th dynasty, 1580-1558 B.C.E.), indicating contact between Crete and Egypt during this era. The Mesopotamian empire of Assyria dominated the ancient east from the 9th to the 7th century B.C.E. and erected monuments whose sculptures depict the sandal and the boot. Their sandal is a simplified shoe composed of a sole and straps. Their boot is tall, covering the leg; a type of footwear associated with horsemen. From the middle of the 6th century to the end of the 4th century B.C.E., the Persian dynasty, founded by Cyrus the Great II around 550 B.C.E., gradually established a homogeneous culture in the ancient east. Processional bas-reliefs carved by sculptors of the Achaemenidian kings offer a documentary record of the period's costume and footwear.

In addition to images of boots, there are shoes made of supple materials and of leather shown completely covering the foot and closing at the ankle with laces. For a deeper understanding of how the shoe evolved from its origins to the present day, it is important to look at ancient civilisations in their historical context. Additionally, an analysis of the primary biblical texts will shed new light on the subject and give greater relevance to the history of the shoe.

5. Cylindrical seal and its stamp. Akkad Dynasty, Mesopotamia, around 2340-2200 B.C.E., H. 3.6 cm. Musée du Louvre, Paris.
6. "Lion put to death by the King," low-relief from the Palace of Assurbanipal at Nineveh, 638-630 B.C.E., British Museum, London.

Ancient Egypt

Ancient Egypt was the home of the first sandals. This form of flat shoe with straps arose in response to Egypt's climate and geography.

King Narmer's Palette from around 3100 B.C.E. reveals that a servant called a "sandal bearer" walked behind the sovereign carrying the royal sandals on his forearms, indicating the importance henceforth attached to the shoe in ceremonial garb.

Although often depicted barefoot in Egyptian wall paintings, men and women also wore sandals. Egyptian sandals were made of leather, woven straw, strips of palm or papyrus leaves or from the rushes and reeds that grew in the marshes. The Pharaoh and the socially prominent had them made of gold, though sandals were a luxury item for everyone. Tomb excavations have revealed that this object, originally strictly utilitarian, had a social function. The sandal maintained continuity of form throughout Pharaonic civilisation and lasted until the Coptic era of Christian Egypt. When the pharaoh entered the temple, or when his subjects celebrated the cult of the dead in funeral chapels, they removed their sandals at the sanctuary's entrance, a custom later adopted by Muslims upon entering a mosque. The ritual demonstrates the strong link that exists between the shoe and the sacred, a relationship that is also established by specific biblical passages, which will be discussed below. The advent in Egypt of the raised-tip sandal in the second millennium B.C.E. is probably a Hittite influence. It is the precursor of the poulaine, or pointed shoe, an eccentric medieval fashion introduced to Europe from the East by the Crusades. When sandals are among the items packed for the mummy's afterlife, they are placed in chests or illustrated on horizontal bands decorating the painted interior of the wooden sarcophagi. Evidently, their role was prophylactic.

Texts from the era of the pyramids allude to and reflect the wishes of the dead "to walk in white sandals along the beautiful paths of heaven where the blessed roam."

7. Sandal Maker, fresco relief, 18th dynasty, 1567-1320 B.C.E.
The Metropolitan Museum of Art, New York.
8. Wooden sandals inlayed with gold, treasure of Tutankhamen.
18th Dynasty, Thebes. Cairo Museum, Cairo.
9. Egyptian sandal of plant fibres. Bally-Schuhmuseum, Schönenwerd,
Switzerland.

The Bible: The Shoe in the Old Testament

The earliest written evidence of shoes can be read in the Bible, although research remains to be done with Chinese, Egyptian, and Mesopotamian texts.

As a rule, biblical characters wear sandals, whether they are God's chosen ones (the Hebrews), their allies, or enemies, which affirms the Near Eastern origin of this footwear type from earliest antiquity. The Old Testament rarely mentions the design and decoration of the sandal. Apart from its role as an invaluable aid to walking, which is mainly an issue concerning the lives of the Saints, the sandal plays an important symbolic role. Biblical shoe symbolism can be analysed in its different contexts, which include the removal of shoes in holy places, the shoe in military expeditions, legal actions, and everyday rituals, as well as the shoe as an accessory of seduction when dressing a female foot.

In the most famous example of removing one's shoes in a holy place, the vision of the burning bush, God orders Moses to take off his shoes: "Do not draw near this place. Take your sandals off your feet, for the place where you stand is holy ground" (The Pentateuch, Exodus, III, 5).

The situation repeats itself when the Hebrews arrive in the Promised Land, as recorded in the Book of Joshua: "And it came to pass, when Joshua was by Jericho, that he lifted his eyes and looked, and behold, a Man stood opposite him with His sword drawn in His hand. And Joshua went to Him and said to Him, 'Are You for us or for our adversaries?' So He said, 'No, but as Commander of the army of the LORD I have now come.' And Joshua fell on his face to the earth and worshipped, and said to Him, 'What does my Lord say to His servant?' Then the Commander of the LORD's army said to Joshua, 'Take your sandal off your foot, for the place where you stand is holy'" (Joshua, 5:13-15).

The order given to Joshua is identical to that given to Moses. Shoes figure in another story from Joshua. The kings, finding themselves beyond the Jordan river, formed a coalition to fight against Joshua and Israel, but the Gibeonites wanted to ally themselves with Israel at any price. So the Gibeonites planned a ruse that would make Israel think they came from a distant land:

"And they took old sacks on their donkeys, old wineskins torn and mended, old and patched sandals on their feet, and old garments on themselves" (Joshua 9:3). Dressed in this fashion they went to find Joshua, who asked them, "Who are you, and where do you come from?" They replied, "From a very far country your servants have come… And these wineskins which we filled were new, and see, they are torn; and these our garments and our sandals have become old because of the very long journey" (Joshua, 9:5, 8, 13).

These old sandals contrast with the ones mentioned in Moses' last sermon when he says to his people: "And I have led you forty years in the wilderness. Your clothes have not worn out on you, and your sandals have not worn out on your feet" (Deuteronomy, 29:5).

The Old Testament mentions footwear in a number of military contexts. The wars against the Philistines are the setting for the Books of Samuel. The rich iconography of the famous battle of David and Goliath, pointing to a much later date than the event itself, which took place between 1010 and 970 B.C.E., usually shows the Philistine giant wearing sandals and a leg armour,

but only the leg armour is mentioned in the Bible: "He had a bronze helmet on his head, and he was armed with a coat of mail, and the weight of the coat was five thousand shekels of bronze. And he had bronze armour on his legs and a bronze javelin between his shoulders" (Samuel, 17:5-6).

The sandal is part of the war imagery evoked in David's exhortations to Solomon, when the king reminds his son that his servant Joab had murdered two of Israel's army commanders: "And he shed the blood of war in peacetime, and put the blood of war on his belt that was around his waist, and on his sandals that were on his feet" (Kings, 2:5). And the messianic prophet Isaiah evokes the sandal when speaking of a military threat from a distant nation: "No one will be weary or stumble among them, No one will slumber or sleep; Nor will the belt on their loins be loosed, Nor the strap of their sandals be broken; Whose arrows are sharp, And all their bows bent" (Isaiah, 5:27-28). Shoes and the lack thereof also figure prominently in Isaiah's prophesy of Egypt's defeat against Assyria, its ancient rival for domination over the Near East: "In the year that Tartan came to Ashdod, when Sargon the king of Assyria sent him, and he fought against Ashdod and took it, at the same time the Lord spoke by Isaiah the son of Amoz, saying, 'Go, and remove the sackcloth from your body, and take your sandals off your feet.' And he did so, walking naked and barefoot. Then the Lord said, 'Just as My servant Isaiah has walked naked and barefoot three years for a sign and a wonder against Egypt and Ethiopia, so shall the king of Assyria lead away the Egyptians as prisoners and the Ethiopians as captives, young and old, naked and barefoot, with their buttocks uncovered, to the shame of Egypt. Then they shall be afraid and ashamed of Ethiopia their expectation and Egypt their glory'" (Isaiah, 20:1-5).

To cast or set down one's shoe in a place symbolised occupancy. In an image reminiscent of the Pharaoh Tutankhamen trampling his enemies underfoot, Psalms 60 and 108 celebrate preparations for a military expedition against Edam: "Moab is My wash pot; Over Edom I will cast My shoe; Philistia, shout in triumph because of Me." "Through God we will do valiantly, For it is He who shall tread down our enemies" (Psalm, 60:8; 12; Psalm, 108:9:13). In the kingdom of Israel, to tag a field with one's foot or to leave one's sandals there symbolised legal ownership. The fundamental text on this tradition is in the Book of Ruth: "Now this was the custom in former times in Israel concerning redeeming and exchanging, to confirm anything: one man took off his sandal and gave it to the other, and this was a confirmation in Israel. Therefore the close relative said to Boaz, 'Buy it for yourself.' So he took off his sandal. And Boaz said to the elders and all the people, 'You are witnesses this day that I have bought all that was Elimelech's, and all that was Chilion's and Mahlon's, from the hand of Naomi. Moreover, Ruth the Moabitess, the widow of Mahlon, I have acquired as my wife, to perpetuate the name of the dead through his inheritance, that the name of the dead may not be cut off from among his brethren and from his position at the gate. You are witnesses this day'" (Ruth, 4:7-10). The sandal's legal symbolism is also evident in the Hebrew law requiring a man to marry his brother's widow if the brother left no male heir. Deuteronomy provides an

10. Domenico Feti, *Moses before the Burning Bush*, 1613-14.
Oil on canvas, 168 x 112 cm.
Kunsthistorisches Museum, Vienna.

explicit commentary: "But if the man does not want to take his brother's wife, then let his brother's wife go up to the gate to the elders, and say, 'My husband's brother refuses to raise up a name to his brother in Israel; he will not perform the duty of my husband's brother.' Then the elders of his city shall call him and speak to him. But if he stands firm and says, 'I do not want to take her,' Then his brother's wife shall come to him in the presence of the elders, remove his sandal from his foot, spit in his face, and answer and say, 'So shall it be done to the man who will not build up his brother's house.'

"And his name shall be called in Israel, 'The house of him who had his sandal removed'" (Deuteronomy, 25:7-10). To walk barefoot also symbolised mourning. In one ritual, the deceased's relatives went bareheaded and barefoot with their faces partially covered by a type of scarf and bread offered by their neighbours. Ezekiel mentions the practice in reference to the mourning of the prophet: "Son of man, with one blow I am about to take away from you the delight of your eyes. Yet do not lament or weep or shed any tears. Groan quietly; do not mourn for the dead. Keep your turban fastened and your sandals on your feet; do not cover the lower part of your face or eat the customary food of mourners" (Ezekiel, 24:16-17).

In the 8th century B.C.E. Amos evoked the legal rights of the poor and the destitute and railed against the fairness of Israel's courts, corrupted by money. For example, judges of Israel would issue judgments on insufficient grounds in exchange for a modest gift, a practice the prophet denounced: "I will not turn away its punishment, Because they sell the righteous for silver, And the poor for a pair of sandals" (Amos, 2:6-8).

The sandal symbolises seduction in the Book of Judith, which recounts the occupation of a small Palestinian village called Bethulia by the armies of the Assyrian king Nebuchadnezzar: "I will cover all the land with the feet of my soldiers, to whom I will deliver them as spoils." (Judith, 2:7)

So Judith, who was a pious widow, got ready to leave town and give herself up to the enemy camp: "She chose sandals for her feet, and put on her anklets, bracelets, rings, earrings, and all her other jewellery. Thus she made herself very beautiful, to captivate the eyes of all the men who should see her." (Judith, 10:4) With her beauty the young woman aroused the passion of Holphernes, the army's leader, eventually taking advantage of his drunkeness after a banquet to cut off his head. In this way she diverted the attention of his armed forces, which included 120,000 infantrymen and 120,000 horsemen. In the hymn of thanksgiving sung by this biblical Joan of Arc, the victorious sandal counts among the accessories of feminine seduction: "Her sandals caught his eyes, and her beauty captivated his mind. The sword cut through his neck" (Judith, 16:9 New American Bible).

The Bible is mostly reticent concerning the aesthetics of the shoe. Ezekiel alludes to it in the guilty loves of Jerusalem: "I clothed you with an embroidered dress and put leather sandals on you. I dressed you in fine linen and covered you with costly garments" (Ezekiel, 16:10). And if the word boot only appears once in Isaiah ("Every warrior's boot used in battle" (The Birth of the Prince of Peace, Isaiah, 9:5, New International Version)), the sandal is primarily recognised as a symbol. This symbolism endures in the Muslim ritual of removing shoes before entering a mosque.

11. Sandals found in the fortress of Massada.

12. François Boucher, *Saint Peter Trying to Walk on Water*, 1766.
Cathédrale Saint-Louis de Versailles

The Shoe in the New Testament:
The Sandals of Jesus

The writings of the apostles Matthew, Mark, Luke, and John confirm the prediction John the Baptist made while baptising people with water in Bethania, beyond the River Jordan: each evoke Jesus' shoes through the voice of the prophet: "…but He who is coming after me is mightier than I, whose sandals I am not worthy to carry" (Matthew, 3:11). "And he preached, saying, 'There comes One after me who is mightier than I, whose sandal strap I am not worthy to stoop down and loose" (Mark, 1:7).

"I indeed baptise you with water; but One mightier than I is coming, whose sandal strap I am not worthy to loose" (Luke, 3:16).

"…but there stands One among you whom you do not know. It is He who, coming after me, is preferred before me, whose sandal strap I am not worthy to loose" (John, 26-27).

This statement (repeated four times) refers to sandals that were attached to the foot with a strap. These were typical during the Roman occupation of Palestine and were worn by Jesus' contemporaries. The New Testament mentions them on numerous occasions. If we look at the story of Matthew and Luke in the calling of the seventy-two disciples, Jesus advises them to walk barefoot: "Provide neither gold nor silver nor copper in your money belts, nor bag for your journey, nor two tunics, nor sandals, nor staffs… (Matthew, 10:9-10) And whoever will not receive you nor hear your words, when you depart from that house or city, shake off the dust from your feet" (Matthew, 10:14) "…behold, I send you out as lambs among wolves. Carry neither moneybag, knapsack, nor sandals…" (Luke, 10:3-4).

But Mark gives a different version: "He commanded them to take nothing for the journey except a staff – no bag, no bread, no copper in their money belts – but to wear sandals, and not to put on two tunics…" (Mark, 6:8-9).

Although it emphasises asceticism, Mark's version retains the shoe as a symbol of travel, as Jean-Paul Roux explains in an article in the journal of the Institute of Calceology entitled, "The symbolism of the shoe in the religions descended from Abraham: Judaism, Christianity, and Islam." In Luke's parable of the prodigal son, the father says of his newly found son, "Bring out the best robe and put it on him, and put a ring on his hand and sandals on his feet" (Luke, 15:22). Only free men could enjoy sandals, as slaves did not have the right to wear shoes. Elsewhere in the New Testament, the account of Saint Peter's deliverance in the Acts of the Apostles contains a story about sandals: "That night Peter was sleeping, bound with two chains between two soldiers; and the guards before the door were keeping the prison. Now behold, an angel of the Lord stood by him, and a light shone in the prison; and he struck Peter on the side and raised him up, saying, 'Arise quickly!'

"And his chains fell off his hands. Then the angel said to him, 'Gird yourself and tie on your sandals'; and so he did. And he said to him, 'Put on your garment and follow me'" (Acts, 12:6-8).

In the later iconography of Philippe de Champaigne's 17th-century painting, *Christ Nailed to the Cross*, sandals like the strapped versions evoked in the prophesy of Saint John the Baptist are depicted carelessly strewn on the ground. Finally, if we turn to the Gospel of Matthew, we read: "Now in the fourth watch of the night Jesus went to them, walking on the sea. And when the disciples saw Him walking on the sea, they were troubled, saying, 'It is a ghost!' And they cried out for fear. But immediately Jesus spoke to them, saying, 'Be of good cheer! It is I; do not be afraid.' And Peter answered Him and said, 'Lord, if it is You, command me to come to You on the water.' So He said, 'Come.' And when Peter had come down out of the boat, he walked on the water to go to Jesus. But

when he saw that the wind was boisterous, he was afraid; and beginning to sink he cried out, saying, 'Lord, save me!'" (Matthew, 14:25-30). This evangelical testimony was the subject of Boucher's 18th-century painting, *Saint Peter Walking on Water*, remarkable in that the apostle is shoeless, whereas Jesus is depicted wearing magnificent sandals based on the type worn by Roman patricians.

In conclusion, the simpler shoes (conceived for walking rather than for ceremonial use) discovered in the fortress of Massada built by Herod in the desert of the Dead Sea provide a good indication of the shoes worn by Christ and his contemporaries mentioned by the Apostles. These shoes are also more in keeping with Christ's spirit of poverty. Because of their surprisingly modern concept, their use will span the centuries, particularly in Africa, and they can be found in many third-world countries today, often reduced to a simple sole cut out from a salvaged tyre with a y-shaped thong. The sandal of Jesus moreover heralds the work of certain 21st-century designers who would take inspiration from the sandal and update its appearance.

Antiquity – The Copts

Coptic civilisation was a bridge between Antiquity and the Middle Ages. Direct descendants of the Pharaohs, the Copts were Egyptians who practised Christianity. Our knowledge of their shoes comes from archaeological digs undertaken in the 19th century, in particular at Achmin.

Additional information is available from mummy textiles and sarcophagi tops from the 1st to 4th centuries AD, which usually depicted people wearing sandals, although sometimes people appear barefoot. Funeral customs changed in the 4th century when the dead were buried dressed in their most precious clothing. From that time forward, painted textiles having disappeared, steles only offer rare images that show a type of shoe with a pointed toe.

As was the case throughout Egyptian antiquity, the heel was unknown to the Copts: shoes, boots and sandals were always flat-soled. The use of full boots and ankle boots remains exceptional and reserved for men. These forms of footwear show little variety, but Coptic shoemakers demonstrated imagination in the decorative techniques they employed, using red and brown leather, leather piping curled into spirals, geometric motifs cut out of gold leather, and even sculpted leather soles.

Greece

As in Egypt, the most popular shoe in Greece was the sandal. The Homeric heroes of the Iliad and The Odyssey wear sandals with bronze soles, while the gods wear sandals made of gold. Agamemnon, legendary king of Mycenae, protected his legs with the help of leg armour fastened with silver hooks.

Sandals figure in a story about the Greek philosopher Empedocles, born around 450 B.C.E. in Agrigentum. As the story goes, Empedocles wanted people to believe he had ascended into heaven, so he dove into the opening of Mt. Etna. The volcano swallowed him, but ejected his sandals intact, in this way revealing the suicide's hoax.

Archaeological discoveries in the tombs at Vergina confirm that wealthy Macedonians during the reign of Phillip II (382 B.C.E.-336B.C.E.) wore sandals with soles of gold or gilded silver. The Greek sandal, worn by men and women alike, had a leather or cork sole of variable thickness, differentiated right and left feet, and attached to the foot with straps. Originally simple shoes, sandals later displayed elegant complexity. Examples are found on sculptures from the period, such as the sandals worn by *Diana the Huntress* (Louvre, Paris). Attic vases show certain figures wearing laced boots called endromides, also known as embas when trimmed with a flap.

As for other models of Greek footwear, the pointed shoe of the Hittite variety, with which the Ionians were long familiar, never reached mainland Greece, although it was depicted by Greek vase painters who wanted to give an oriental character to their figures. Aeschylus (525 B.C.E.-456 B.C.E.) is credited with inventing the cothurne. Worn by the actors in Greek tragedies who played the roles of heroes and gods, the cothurne had an elevated cork sole that increased height at the expense of stability. This theatrical shoe adjusted equally to fit both feet, whence the expression "more versatile than a cothurne." It is interesting to note that the cothurne, because of its height, represents the beginnings of a heel, which would remain unknown to Antiquity, but would appear later in Italy at the end of the 16th century.

One Greek custom was reserved for courtesans: the wearing of sandals embellished with precious stones. It was said that their studded soles left an unambiguous message in the sand that said, "follow me." The rich variety of Greek footwear goes against the advice of Plato (428 B.C.E.-348 B.C.E.), who advocated walking barefoot.

13. Man's slipper, vamp decorated with motifs gilded with gold leaf. Egypt, Coptic era. International Shoe Museum, Romans.

14. Ivory statuette of a Greek actor wearing cothurnes. Petit Palais-Musée des Beaux-Arts de la ville de Paris, Paris.

15. *Artemis with a Hind*, called *"Diana the Huntress"*, Roman copy after an
original created around 330 B.C.E. by Leochares. Marble, H. 200 cm.
Musée du Louvre, Paris

The Etruscans

The Etruscans probably originated in Asia Minor, appearing in Italy in what is now Tuscany at the end of the 8th century B.C.E. Realistic paintings decorating their tombs and cemeteries (Triclinium, Tarquinia, Caere) portray gods and mortals dressed in raised-toe shoes of the Hittite variety. Strapped sandals, cut shoes, and laced boots emerged in Etruria in the 4th century B.C.E. and represent established contacts with other peoples around the Mediterranean basin.

Rome

Rome was the direct heir of the Greek civilisation and felt its influence in the area of footwear: Roman shoes are mainly imitations of Greek models.

In ancient Rome, shoes were indicators of social status and wealth. Some patricians wore shoes with soles of silver or solid gold, while plebeians were content to wear clogs or rustic footwear with wooden soles. Slaves lacked the right to wear shoes and walked barefoot, their feet covered in chalk or plaster. When high-ranking Roman citizens were invited to a feast, they had someone carry their sandals at the home of their host. The less fortunate had to carry their own shoes, because it was considered rude to keep one's walking shoes on. As a bed was used for dining in Rome, shoes were removed before the meal and put back on when leaving the table.

Roman shoes fall into two categories: the solea, a form of sandal, and the calceus, a closed toe shoe worn with a toga. Other types evolved with variation in colour, form, and construction. Magistrates wore strange-looking shoes with curved toes made out of black or white leather and decorated on the side with a gold or silver crescent. As in Egypt and Greece, the difference between the left and right foot was well differentiated. Shoemakers were citizens who worked in shops, rather than slaves. This is a crucial distinction in understanding the status of the shoe as an object.

In ancient Rome, the shoe began to acquire much importance in the military arena. The caliga, the Roman soldier's shoe, was a type of sandal. Strapped to the foot, it had a thick leather sole with pointed studs. It was up to the soldiers to acquire the studs; under certain circumstances, however, they were distributed free of charge as part of a ceremony called the clavarium.

It is said that as a child the Emperor Caligula was so fond of wearing the caliga he was named after the shoe, a delightful and telling anecdote. The mulleus, a closed shoe that was red in colour, differed little from the calceus. Worn by emperors, magistrates, and the children of senators, it got its name from the seashell from which bright crimson was extracted. The campagus took the form of a boot that exposed the foot. Trimmed in fur, and often decorated with pearls and precious stones, it was intended for generals to wear. A crimson version was exclusively reserved for emperors.

As in ancient Greece, the sandal and the slipper were mainly intended for women to wear indoors. The soccus, a type of slipper with a raised tip and identical for both feet, was apparently of Persian origin; it would become a traditional shoe in Turkey. These delicate little shoes aroused the concupiscence of the era's fetishists.

16. Attican cup with red figures, attributed to Epiktetos, around 500 B.C.E. Agora Museum, Athens.

17. Attica urn with black figures, representing a shoe repairer's workshop, around 520-510 B.C.E. Boston Museum of Fine Arts, Boston.

Suetonus (70-128) tells how the Roman senator Lucius Vitellus, who carried under his tunic the slipper that his mistress wore on her right foot, without the slightest embarrassment, would remove the shoe in public and cover it with kisses. Red shoes had long been the privileged attribute of Roman courtesans before all women dared to wear them.

After the emperor Aurelius (212-275) wore them, red shoes became an Imperial symbol, giving birth to a tradition that was later taken up by the Papacy, and subsequently by all the courts of Europe, which wore red-heeled shoes.

We know from the writings of Juvenal (55-140) that to give a spanking with a shoe was a serious punishment commonly administered to children and slaves.

Romantic Romans put their shoes to more gallant use by inserting amorous messages between the sandal and the foot of their confidant. In this way, sandals became a drop box for love notes as advocated by Ovid (43 B.C.E.-17 AD) in *The Art of Love*.

18. Low-relief of the Trajan column, soldiers of the Roman legions (military shoes), Rome, 113 C.E. Marble.

19. Colossal statue of Mars "Pyrrhus" (shod in *campagus*). End of 1st century C.E., marble, H. 360 cm. Musei Capitolini, Rome.

19

The Gallo-Romans

20. Funerary stele of a cobbler. Reims, Marne, faubourg Cérès, Gallo-Roman, 2nd century C.E. Collection of the Saint-Rémi Museum of Reims. Photo by Robert Meulle.

21. Silver sandal, Byzantine period. Bally-Schuhmuseum, Schönenwerd, Switzerland.

22. The Emperor Justinien and his servants, around 547 C.E. Mosaics from the churches of Saint Vital and Sant'Apollinare in Classe, Ravenna.

The Gallo-Romans wore various versions of flat shoes with rounded toes. The most popular were ordinary sandals for men and women based on Roman models.

The gallica was a closed shoe with a wooden sole and was the ancestor of the galoshes (a later overshoe with a wooden sole).

An 11th-century monument to a shoemaker confirms the existence of the shoemaker's industry and the respect these artisans enjoyed.

The Byzantine empire

Byzantine civilisation extended from the 5th to the 15th century, producing throughout this period a wealth of crimson leather shoes trimmed in gold reminiscent of embroidered Persian-style boots, as well as the Roman soccus and mulleus.

Byzantine mules and slippers were objects of luxury and refinement initially reserved for the Emperor and his court. Crimson or gold slippers were worn in the eastern Mediterranean basin, in particular in the area around Alexandria and in the Nile valley. Excavations at Achmin have brought many examples that belonged to women. The arrival of Christian shoemakers in this region revived the craft of shoemaking, as Christian symbols were added to the geometric decorative tradition. A silver sandal discovered in an Egyptian tomb and now in the collection of the Bally-Schuhmuseum is a good example. Dating to the 6th century C.E., it is embellished with the image of a dove symbolising Christ.

SAINT · REMY   BAPTISE · CLOVIS

LE·JOUR·TIE   NOEL   4·56

23

The Middle Ages

As the Middle Ages dawned in the West, footwear remained under the influence of ancient Roman models. The Francs wore shoes equipped with straps that rose to mid-thigh. Only their leaders wore shoes with pointed tips.

Thanks to the extraordinary degree of preservation of certain burial places, we get an idea of what Merovingian shoes looked like. The tomb discovered at Saint-Denis of Queen Arégonde, wife of King Clotaire I (497-561), has enabled us to reconstruct an image of her shoes as supple leather sandals with straps wrapped around the leg. Elsewhere, gilded bronze shoe buckles decorated with stylised animals discovered in a leader's tomb at Hordaim, are proof of the attention given to shoe ornamentation during this period. Shoes were very costly during the Middle Ages, which is why they appear in wills and are among the donations made to monasteries. Costliness also explains why a fiancé would offer his future wife a pair of embroidered shoes before marriage, a lovely tradition dating to Gregory of Tours (538-594). We can get a sense of the opulence of this gift from the shoes of this era preserved in the museum of Chelles near Paris.

The strapped or banded shoe continued into the Carolingian period, although the woman's model became more embellished. As for the wooden-soled gallique or galoche, it too remained in use.

From this time forward, soldiers protected their legs with leather or metal leggings called bamberges. In the 9th-century, a shoe called the heuse made out of supple leather extending high on the leg announced the arrival of the boot.

We known from the monk of the Saint Gall monastery that emperor Charlemagne wore simple boots with straps intertwining the legs, although for ceremonies he wore laced boots decorated with precious stones. But frequent contact between France and Italy helped develop a taste for regalia and increasingly the shoe became an object of great luxury.

At the same time, religious councils were ordering clerics to wear liturgical shoes while celebrating Mass. These ecclesiastical shoes or sandals were of cloth and completely covered the cleric's foot. Pope Adrian I (772-795) instituted the ritual of kissing feet. When some clergy members deemed this rite undignifing, a compromise was established. Henceforth, the papal mule would be embroidered with a cross. Kissing this cross was no longer a sign of servitude, but one of homage to Christ's representative on earth. Regarding shoemaking, the French word cordouanier (which became cordonnier or shoemaker) was adopted in the 11th century and signified someone who worked with Cordoba leather and by extension, all kinds of leather. As in Antiquity, shoes were patterned separately for the right and left foot. Shoes made out of Cordoba leather were reserved for the aristocracy, whereas those made by çavetiers, or cobblers (shoe repairmen) were rougher. The wearing of shoes began to expand in the 11th-century. The most common medieval type was an open shoe secured by a strap fitted with a buckle or button.

Other types included estivaux, a summer ankle boot of supple, lightweight leather that appeared in the second half of the 11th century; chausses with soles, a type of cloth boot reinforced with leather soles worn with pattens for outdoor use; and heuses, supple boots in a variety of forms originally reserved for gentlemen, but which became common under the reign of Philippe Auguste (1165-1223). In the early 12th century, shoes became longer. The pigaches were forerunners of the poulaine style introduced supposedly by the knight Robert le Cornu.

The Crusaders brought the exaggerated style with its inordinately long tip back from the East. It is based on the raised-toe model of Syrian, Akkadian, and Hittite culture, and reflects the vertical aesthetic of gothic Europe. When people of modest means imitated this eccentric fashion initially reserved for the aristocracy, the authorities responded by regulating the length of the shoe's points according to social rank: $1/2$ foot for commoners, 1 foot for the bourgeois, 1 and $1/2$ feet for knights, 2 feet for nobles, and 2 and $1/2$ feet for princes, who had to hold the tips of their shoes up with gold or silver chains attached to their knees in order to walk. The shoe length hierarchy led to the French expression "vivre sur un grand pied," (to live on a large foot), denoting the worldly status represented by shoe length.

The poulaine was made of leather, velvet, or brocade. The uppers could sport cutouts in the form of gothic church windows, although obscene images were sometimes used. A small round bell or an ornament in the shape of a bird beak often dangled from the tip of the shoe. There was even a military poulaine to go with a soldier's armour. Interestingly, during the battle of Sempach between the Swiss confederates and the Austrians in 1386, knights had to cut off the points of their poulaines because they interfered with combat.

Worn throughout Europe by men and women alike, as well as by certain clerics, the poulaine was condemned by bishops, excommunicated by religious councils, and forbidden by kings. But its immoral status only made the poulaine more seductive, and it was all the rage in the Burgundian court. Indeed, the poulaine would only disappear in the early 16th century, after a four century run.

Flat-soled shoes lasted the entire medieval period, but a heel was beginning to emerge as evidenced in Jan van Eyck's *Arnolfini Portrait*. The protective wooden pattens, depicted carelessly strewn on the floor in the left of the painting, exhibit an incline: the rear heel is higher than the front support.

Shoes were scarce and costly items in the Middle Ages, so protective wooden soles were used for going out in muddy backstreets. But the under soles made the shoes too noisy: it was strictly forbidden to wear them in church.

Previous pages:

23. Stained-glass window of the baptism of Clovis by Saint Remi (496). Sanctuary of Saint Bonaventure, Lyon 2nd, by L. Charat and Mrs. Lamy-Paillet in 1964. Photo by J. Bonnet, Imp. Beaulieu Lyon.

24. *Saint Mark Healing Aniane the Cobbler*, detail from a mosaic, 13th century. Basilica di San Marco, Venice.

25. Poulaine. Bally-Schuhmuseum, Schönenwerd, Switzerland.

26. Liturgical shoe of plain embroidered samite, Spain, 12th century.
Silk and gold thread. Historical Museum of Fabrics of Lyon, Lyon.

27. Poulaine style shoe. Bally-Schuhmuseum, Schönenwerd, Switzerland.

28. Martin de Braga, *Caton in the Company of Scipion and Lelius,
Standing Before Him*, third quarter of the 15th century.
The State Hermitage Museum, St Petersburg.

29. Jan van Eyck, *Portrait of Giovanni Arnolfini and his Wife*
('*The Arnolfini Portrait*'), 1434. Oil on oak panel , 82.2 x 60 cm.
The National Gallery, London.

30. *Philippe VI de Valois Receives Tribute from His Vassal Edward III of England*,
detail of an illumination from the Chronicles of Jehan Froissart, 15th century.
Bibliothèque nationale de France, Paris.

The Legend of Saint Crispin and Saint Crispinian

Crispin and Crispinian were two brothers from a patrician Roman family who converted to Christianity under the reign of Diocletian (245-313). Pope Caius (283-296) gave them the task of converting Gaul and in 285 AD they settled in Soissons to work as shoemakers and to preach the word of God. When the Roman general Maximianus Herculeus asked them to renounce their faith and to worship pagan idols, the brothers refused, which led to their frequent and cruel persecution. They were flagellated, pierced with awls, burned with boiling oil and molten lead, and finally thrown into the Aisne river with a millstone around their neck. Then a miracle occurred: the stone came loose and the shoemakers reached shore safe and sound, praising God. When Maximianus got the news, he had their heads cut off in 287.

Although their remains were left for vultures, the shoemakers' bodies remained intact; two old beggars gave the martyrs a proper burial. In 649, the Bishop of Soissons, named Ansérik, moved the two brothers' remains into the crypt of his basicala, which later came to be called the Abbaye Saint-Crépin-le-Grand. When the shoemakers' guild was established in the cathedral of Paris in 1379 by king Charles-le-Sage (1338-1380), the shoemakers chose Saint Crispin and Saint Crispinian as their patrons, whom they formally celebrate on 25 October. Many images of Saint Crispin and Saint Crispinian are still preserved in the chapels of parish churches where late medieval guilds paid tribute to their patron saints and dedicated altars.

31. Sign of shoemaker-bootmaker, "To Saint Crispin", 1593. Musée Carnavalet - musée d'histoire de Paris, Paris.

SAINCT CRESPIN

32. Retable of the "Master at the Eyelets"
(1500-1510):
two scenes in the life of Saint Crispin and
Saint Crispinian.
Schweizerisches Landesmuseum, Zurich.

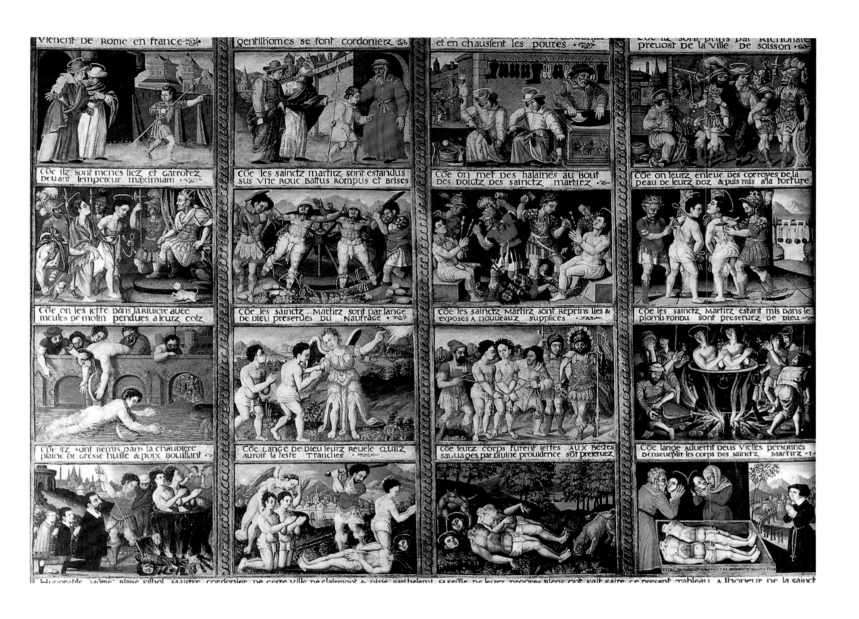

33. *The Martyrdom of Saints Crispin and Crispinian,*
votive offering of 1594 by painter Vital Despigoux.
Panel on wood. Clermont-Ferrand Cathedral, Puy-de-Dôme.

The Renaissance

At the end of the 15th century, poulaines fell victim to their own success and ended up popularised for common use. They were succeeded, without the slightest transition, by extremely wide, square-toe shoes designed for the fashion-conscious. As incongruous with fashion history as it may seem, this shoe was actually inspired by a congenital malformation: King Charles VIII had six toes on each foot, hence the very large toes of his custom-made shoes. The reaction against the previous fashion quickly went too far in the opposite direction. The Valois shoe worn during the reign of Louis XII (1462-1515) occasionally reached widths of thirty-three centimetres. The tip of the shoe, which was stuffed and decorated with animal horns, resembled a cow's head, leading to nicknames such as *mufle de vache* (cow muzzle), *pied d'ours* (bear foot), and *bec de cane* (duck bill). The shoe's eccentric form meant people had to straddle wide in order to walk, which naturally provoked sarcastic remarks.

During this same period, Venetians wore shoes called chopines, also known as *mules échasses* (mules on stilts) or *pied de vache* (cow feet). Attached to the foot with ribbons, these bizarre shoes displayed exaggerated platforms that could reach fifty-two centimetres high. The platforms themselves were of wood or cork and covered in velvet or richly decorated leather. Hidden under skirts, the shoes remained safe from scrutiny, but they resulted in a very comical walk. Hoisted upon such shoes, noblewomen had to support themselves between the shoulders of two servants in order to get around safely. This eccentric fashion certainly originated in Turkey, a country with which the Doges of the Republic traded. Turkish women were known to go to the bath on raised soles. Through the modified form of the chopine a Turkish harem shoe thus entered the palaces of Venetian aristocrats.

The wearing of chopines was banned in Spain by the archbishop of Talavera, who labelled women who wore them "depraved and dissolute." The more tolerant Italian church, on the other hand, failed to blacklist the shoe. Quite contrarily, the church, in association with jealous husbands, saw a way to immobilise flighty wives at home, and thereby stymie illicit affairs. Although all the courts of Europe were taken with the chopine, the shoe was never more than a limited fashion. It nevertheless managed to reach England, where Shakespeare's Hamlet says: "Your ladyship is nearer to heaven than when I saw you last by the altitude of a chopine" (*Hamlet*, Act II, Scene II).

The pantoufle, or mule, was a more moderate style imported from Italy that was first adopted in France in the early 16th century. Made of a thick cork sole without rear quarter, its lightness made it especially suitable for women to wear indoors.

From the reign of Francis I (1494-1547) to Henry III (1551-1589), men and women wore shoes called escarfignons. Also known as eschappins, these were flat slippers of satin or velvet with low-cut uppers and slashes. The horizontal and vertical slashes revealed the precious fabric of the stockings underneath. Rabelais (1494-1553) describes the shoes exactly in *Gargantua*, when he recounts the costumes of the Abbey of Thélème: "The shoes, slippers and mules of crimson, red, or purple velvet, resembled a jagged crayfish's beard." Like other articles of clothing during this period, shoes took after Germanic styles and were decorated with slashes called crevés. Nevertheless, the invention of the slashed shoe is credited to the soldiers of Francis I during the wars with Italy who, sustaining injuries from marching or from combat, had to adapt their shoes to fit their bandaged feet. As for protecting delicate shoes from filthy streets, wooden pattens remained popular for outdoor use.

Leonardo da Vinci is said to have invented the heel, but it did not appear until the end of the 16th century, when it began to rise, most likely in response to the flattering effect of greater height produced by the chopine. The first heels were attached to the sole by a piece of leather, as can be seen in the painting from the French School, entitled *A Ball at the Valois Court* (c.1580) in the Museum of Fine Arts, Rennes.

34. Vittore Carpaccio, *Two Venetian Ladies*, c. 1510.
Oil on wood, 94 x 64 cm. Museo Correr, Venice.

35. Chopine, Venice, 16th century. International Shoe Museum, Romans.

36. Wooden chopine covered in hide worn by the Venetians, Italy, 16th century.
H. 49 cm. Jacquemart Collection, depot of the Musée national
du Moyen Âge - Thermes et hôtel de Cluny in Paris,
International Shoe Museum, Romans.

37. Chopine with evidence of wear. Venice, Italy, around 1600.
Weissenfels Museum, with the authorisation of Irmgard Sedler.
38. Man's leather shoe, around 1530-1540.
Weissenfels Museum, with the authorisation of Irmgard Sedler.
39. Woman's shoe. Henri III period, France, 16th century.
International Shoe Museum, Romans.

Lois par la grace de dieu Roy
de france / Scauoir faisons a
tous presens et aduenir / Que
pour la tresparfaicte et singu
liere amour que auons au noble ordre

40. *King Louis XI Seated on a Throne, Surrounded by the Knights of the Order of Saint Michael*, 16th century. The State Hermitage Museum, St Petersburg.

41. Veronese (Caliari Paolo), *The Meal at Simon's House* (detail).
Oil on canvas, 454 x 974 cm.
Musée national du château et des Trianons, Versailles.

Following pages:

42. Anthony van Dyck, *Portrait of Charles I, King of England* (1600-1649), *Hunting*, c.1635. Oil on canvas, 266 x 207 cm. Musée du Louvre, Paris.

43. Frans Pourbus II, *Henri IV* (1553-1610), *King of France, in a black outfit*, c.1610. Oil on canvas, 39 x 25 cm. Museé du Louvre, Paris.

41

17th Century

The 17th century witnessed the export of French style throughout Europe. The fragile eschappins of the Renaissance began to disappear during the reign of Henry IV (1553-1610), replaced by sturdy shoes which uppers slightly exceeded the sole. The toe of 17th-century shoes, at first rounded, became square under Louis XIII (1601-1643). All shoes of the period revealed side openings. The method of fastening the shoe on top was hidden by a buckle or large bow. But the greatest novelty of the period was the heel, which imparted men and women with a form of bearing that would become the customary posture of European courts in the 17th century.

The new 17th-century shoe had an opening between the heel and the sole, from which it acquired the name *soulier à pont-levis* (drawbridge shoe). It was also called the *soulier à cric* (referring to a jack), a French onomatopoeia associated with the sound one made when walking in the shoe, according to Agrippa d'Aubigné's pamphlet (1552-1630), *Le Baron de Fenestre*. Around 1640, shoe length exceeded the foot, but the square toe was retained. Early in the 17th century, Henri IV sent a tanner named Roze to Hungary to study their method of leather preparation. His return heralded the rebirth of the Hungarian leather craftsmen and they began producing a soft leather used for boot making that clung to the calf and the thigh. In boot making, the boot's over foot, was held by a soulette, which was attached under the foot and held the spur. After 1608, when boots were permitted at court, salons, and balls, the spur was covered with a piece of cloth to prevent damage to ladies' dresses.

Beginning in 1620, boots called *bottes à entonnoir* or *bottes à chaudron* (cauldron boots) could be pulled up over the knee for horseback riding, or allowed to fall around the calf for other occasions. The purely utilitarian heel was positioned under the boot to better support the foot in stirrups. Special fabric boot stockings decorated with lace were worn to preserve the silk ones. Boot stockings were worn with entonnoir boots, which had the disadvantage of becoming a receptacle for water when worn in inclement weather. Lazzarines and ladrines were shorter, lighter boots with an ample cuff that were very popular during the reign of Louis XIII. But boots began to disappear from the salons and from court during the reign of Louis XIV (1638-1715), although they were still worn for hunting and in war. Even the heavy boot worn by soldiers until the beginning of the 19th century was gradually replaced in elegant surroundings by a softer version. In 1663, a shoemaker named Nicolas Lestage, established in Bordeaux under the trade name Loup Botté, presented the king with a pair of seamless boots. The shoemaker's masterpiece earned him great fame and prestige, including a coat of arms that contained a gold boot, a gold crown, and the lily of the house of France, but his trade secret would only be revealed much later: he worked from the skin of a calf's foot that remained intact. At Versailles, the royal residence since 1678, Louis XIV wore mules tended by the first valet during the ceremonial rising required by rituals of etiquette. The king's mules became the property of the outgoing chamberlain or the valet at the end of the year. A number of developments in footwear took place during the reign of Louis XIV: lateral openings were eliminated from shoes and wooden heels became the province of a specialised craftsman called *le talonnier* (heelpiece maker). The Sun King had his own heels trimmed in red leather and his courtiers hastened to imitate him. Red heels remained the mark of aristocratic privileges until the French Revolution, and were only worn by nobles admitted to the court. The height of these heels was noted as a symbol of society's vanity in a letter written to Cardinal Montalto by the disparaging courtier Marigny: "I wear pointed shoes with a pad under the heel making me high enough to aspire to the title Royal Highness."

44. Gerritsz van Brekelenkan, *A Gentleman Slipping on a Boot*, Dutch School, 1655. International Shoe Museum, Romans.

45. Musketeer boot, France, 17th century.

Following pages:

46. Rigaud, *Louis XIV, King of France*, 1702.
Oil on canvas, 276 x 194 cm.
Musée national du château et des Trianons, Versailles.

47. Anonymous, *The Count of Toulouse Dressed as a Novice of the Holy Spirit*, around 1694. Musée Condé, Chantilly.

45

Jean de la Fontaine (1621-1695) was well aware of the dilemma women faced walking on awkward high heels. In his fable called *The Milkmaid and the Jug of Milk*, he has Perrette the milkmaid wear flats so that she can take big steps, move with greater agility, and get to town without incident. Around 1652, the fashion was pointed shoes; later they became square. Women's shoes were based on masculine forms, but always utilised more refined materials, primarily silk brocade, velvet, and brocart, a rich silk brocade sewn with silver and gold thread. Leather on women's shoes was sometimes trimmed with fine silk embroidery. Overshoes called galoches were worn to protect these smart-looking and delicate shoes from muddy streets. Some shoes exhibited a unique feature whereby the quarter terminated with two tabs attached to the throat of the shoe with a buckle. The throat lay as a flap over the top of the shoe; in French it was called the oreille.

These shoes were originally decorated with a large ornament made out of two ribbon loops called *ailes de moulin à vent*, or windmill sails. This was the look Molière (1622-1673) derided in *The School for Husbands* when Sganarelle Scoffs, "Those little ribboned shoes make you look like you have big feathery pigeon feet."

Between 1670 and 1680, buckles embedded with a combination of real and fake pearls and diamonds replaced bows on tops of shoes. Unembellished bronze buckles were worn during mourning. Buckles were stored in jewellery boxes and adapted for use on different shoes. Children's shoes were smaller versions of adult models. Children of the wealthy wore shoes made of tripe blance, a type of wool velour.

Shoes worn by the lower classes exhibited little development. The masses wore wooded clogs or big leather shoes until they were completely deteriorated. Examples are depicted in paintings of the period by the Le Nain Brothers.

Regamey lith

F Séré direxit

ARMOIRIES

Concedées par LOUIS XIV, à son Cordonnier ordinaire,
Maître Nicolas LESTAGE de Bordeaux
Inventeur de la Botte incomparable sans couture.

Chromolih Engelmann & Graf, Cité Bergère, 1, à Paris

48. Woman's shoe in blue leather with decoration embroidered in silver,
Italy, 17th century. International Shoe Museum, Romans.

49. Coat of arms granted by Louis XIV to his standard shoemaker,
Master Nicolas Lestage, inventor of the incomparable boot without seams.

50. Woman's shoe, Italy, 17th century. International Shoe Museum, Romans.

51. Woman's shoe with its protective clog, Louis XIV period, 17th century. The fragility of these shoes necessitates the wearing of protective clogs to walk outside or face muddy grounds. The protective clog has a notch to place the heel. International Shoe Museum, Romans.

52. Woman's shoe in damask embroidered with threads of gold and silver, Louis XIV period, 17th century. International Shoe Museum, Romans.

53. Charles Le Brun, *Chancellor Seguier at the Entry of Louis XIV into Paris in 1660*, c. 1655-1661. Oil on canvas, 295 x 357 cm. Musée du Louvre, Paris.

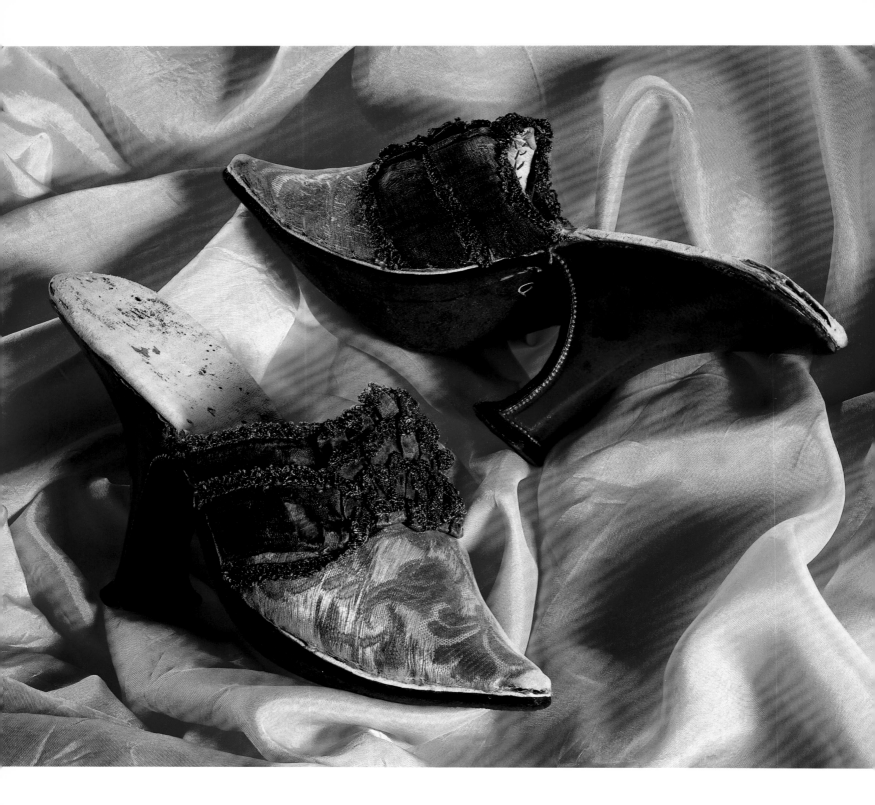

54. Woman's mules, around 1720-1730. Weissenfels Museum, with the authorisation of Irmgard Sedler.

55. François Boucher, *La Toilette*, 1742. Oil on canvas, 52.5 x 66.5 cm. Museo Thyssen-Bornemisza, Madrid.

56. William Hogarth, *Marriage A-la-Mode* : 2. The Tête à Tête. c. 1743. Oil on canvas, 69.9 x 96.8 cm. The National Gallery, London.

18ᵗʰ Century

At the beginning of the 18ᵗʰ-century, France still held sway over the world of elegance.

From the Regency to the French Revolution (1715-1789), there was little variation in shoe shapes. The toe could be round or pointed and was sometimes raised, but never square. A heel was named after Louis XV le Bien-Aimé (1710-1774). Elegant ladies favoured two different styles: the mule for indoors and high-heeled shoes for more formal outfits. Mules with heels of variable height had uppers of white leather, velvet, or silk, which was usually embroidered. Many models of mules and shoes are depicted in the work of the period's artists, including the prints of Beaudoin and Moreau le Jeune and the paintings of Quentin de Latour, Boucher, Gainsborough, and Hogarth, among others. Fragonard's *The Swing* shows a mischievous young woman in a wind-swept skirt carried high by her swinging, which sends her pink mule towards the nose of her suitor stretched out among the branches beneath the lovely creature.

The curved lines of the Louis XV style are also recognisable in the period's heeled shoes, which now attain their maximum height. The curved heel, positioned under the arch of the foot, served as a shank and stabilised the shoe's balance, although walking in them remained precarious – like walking in Venetian chopines during the Renaissance. To overcome this drawback, fashionable women began using canes in 1786, as the Count de Vaublanc noted in his memoirs: "If she wasn't holding her weight back with a cane, the doll would fall on her nose."

The pinnacle of 18th-century refinement would come to be nestled in diamond-encrusted heels, which in this instance were referred to as *venez-y voir* (take a look), although the coquetry was secret, due to the fact that dresses almost touched the floor. Restif de la Bretonne (1734-1806), whose glorification of the feminine foot and shoe is well known, is clearly referring to the shoe in the following description:

"It was a shoe of mother-of-pearl with a flower made of diamonds: the edges were trimmed in diamonds, as was the heel, which was quite slender in spite of this ornament. This pair of shoes cost two thousand écus, not counting the diamonds in the flower, which were worth three or four times this amount: it was a gift from Saintepallaire" (*The Pretty Foot*, p. 240). These enchanting shoes were of white embroidered leather or precious silks to match dresses and were finished with a buckle that could be changed for each outfit. As in the previous century, polished silver buckles, decorated with glass gems or precious stones, were stored in jewellery boxes and passed down through inheritance. Women continued to protect their shoes when going out by wearing the wooden pattens, which were now secured with two leather straps fastened to the top of the foot; the sole was fitted with a notch for the heel. Eighteenth-century France experienced a passion for the East, as evidenced in historical, economic, and cultural contexts. In the context of footwear, the taste for the exotic led to a craze for pointed shoes with raised toes, variously referred to as *shoes à la turque* (Turkish) *en sabot chinois* (Chinese), or *à l'orientale* (Eastern).

Men wore simple, flat-heeled shoes embellished with a buckle. Made of dark-coloured or black leather, these shoes emphasised the light-coloured stockings men wore with silk pants. Certain shoes of this type made of silk or velvet to match men's doublets enjoyed great popularity. A taste for imported English boots (and many other English fashion details) was revived around 1779. A new type of soft leather boot with cuffs to be worn with hunting outfits and court uniforms began to gain popularity during the last twenty years of the eighteenth century and would remain common until the 19ᵗʰ century.

Following pages:

57. Jean-Honoré Fragonard, *The Swing (Les hazards heureux de l'escarpolette)*. Oil on canvas, 81 x 64.2 cm. The Wallace Collection, London.

58. Woman's shoe, Louis XV period, France, 18ᵗʰ century. Silver buckle accentuated with rhinestones. International Shoe Museum, Romans.

59. Woman's shoe, toe upturned in the eastern style, Louis XV period, France, 18ᵗʰ century. International Shoe Museum, Romans.

60. Woman's shoes, Louis XV period. Jacquemart Collection, International Shoe Museum, Romans.

61. Man's shoe buckle and its original case, 18th century.

The return to greater simplicity and to straight lines preferred during Louis XVI's reign had its counterpart in footwear. For example, the buckle on men's shoes assumed greater prominence and women's heels became shorter. Additionally, women's heels were sheathed in white leather, while their shoe buckles were usually superceded by an ornament made of gathered fabric called a bouillonné, which was placed on the shoe's upper and matched the dress.

Shoemakers had stopped making shoes differentiated for the left and right foot during the Renaissance, but the practice made a limited comeback at the end of 18th century. By the second half of the 19th century it would become a standard manufacturing technique as shoemaking was industrialised.

In the years before the French Revolution, shoemakers managed thriving shops. The writer Sébastien Mercier records that, "in their black outfit and powdered wig, they look like Clerks of the Court." But when the Revolution came, shoemakers sympathised with the spirit of the new era: seventy-seven shoemakers participated in the storming of the Bastille.

In Arras, Robespierre drafted the shoe repairmen's official grievances, while in Vierzon, an appointee to the Public Safety Committee wrote to representative Laplance in September 1793 that he had replaced the court "made up of old wigged heads" and appointed a shoemaker to it. When the revolutionary Saint Just saw that ten thousand soldiers in the Rhine army were going barefoot, he ordered the city of Strasbourg to remove the shoes of ten thousand aristocrats with instructions to deliver the shoes to the soldiers before ten o'clock the next morning. To avoid the guillotine, everything reminiscent of aristocratic luxury had to be eliminated, making way for a simpler, but still elegant style. Even shoes sported a revolutionary cockade, the symbol of the new patriotic religion. Men dared not wear fine shoes with buckles out of fear of being labelled an aristocrat, although Robespierre himself risked wearing them. The masses generally wore clogs.

It was at this time that Antoine Simon was working as an obscure shoemaker on the rue des Cordeliers in Paris. A Jacobin and later a member of the Paris Commune, he was chosen by the Convention to look after the young heir in the Temple after the child was separated from his mother, Queen Marie-Antoinette, on 3 July 1793. Himself an illiterate, the new tutor to the Capet son had orders to make the child forget his social status. And with the help of his wife, the shoemaker succeeded in transforming the child into a perfect little sans-culotte, teaching his nine-year-old pupil a repertoire of invectives against God, his family, and the aristocracy, as well as revolutionary songs, such as "ça ira, ça ira" and "la Carmagnole."

Unlike the tormenter he is often depicted as, the coarse, uneducated shoemaker grew fond of little Louis XVII, as did Madame Simon. To amuse the child, Simon bought him a dog named Caster, followed by birds that he set up in a large aviary with seventeen bars where the child raised pigeons, a fact affirmed by the Temple's own accounts, which record the purchase of feed for the young Capet's pigeon. But in January 1794, by order of the Committee for Public Safety, Simon was relieved of his duties. It was against his will and against the will of the child, who begged the shoemaker to take him away and teach him how to make shoes. Alas, Simon the shoemaker was guillotined after 9 Thermidor (the fall of Robespierre on 27 July 1794).

From 1795 to 1799, footwear under the Directory began to evolve into the early neo-classical style favoured by Napoleon I. The light, flat, and pointed new style, for both men and women, confirmed the end of the former regime's heel. The most elegant and striking women of this period, known as les merveilleuses, wore sandals equipped with ribbons which they wore wrapped around their legs.

62. Embroided mules, France, early 18th century.
63. Woman's shoe, England, 18th century.
International Shoe Museum, Romans.

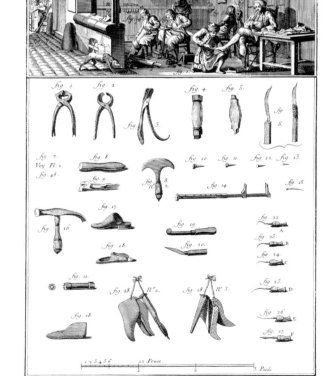

64. Carved, lacquered and painted wooden clogs, Louis XVI period,
France, 18th century. International Shoe Museum, Romans.

65. Plates from Diderot and Alembert's Encyclopaedia

Cordonnier et Bottier.

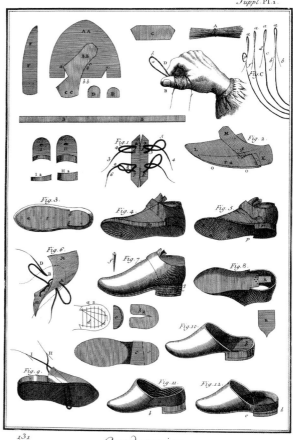

Cordonnier

66. Woman's mule, France, around 1789. Guillen Collection, International Shoe Museum, Romans.

SHOEING ASSES.
The Present Fashion of Making Boots Everlasting.

Publish'd Apr. 20. 1807. by LAURIE & WHITTLE. 53, Fleet Street, London.

466

67. Cruikshank, "Shoeing Asses". International Shoe Museum, Romans.

19th Century

Nineteenth-century women wore woollen ankle boots, but were especially known for their ballet shoes of fine glazed leather, satin, or silk. Ballet shoes fit a woman's foot closely like a glove and were held by ribbons crossed around the ankle. Very fragile, these ephemeral shoes scarcely lasted the duration of one ball.

An 1809 inventory of the wardrobe of Empress Josephine (1763-1814) listed seven hundred and eighty-five pairs of ballerinas made by the shoemaker Lalement. Dancing took place frequently during the Empire period, at court and elsewhere, during interludes between battles.

As for men's footwear, knee pants and silk stockings reintroduced by Napoleon showed off Empire-style escarpins, flat pumps made of patent leather and decorated with a buckle. The military-style boot was standard footwear for soldiers; it could be short or tall, with or without cuffs.

The Emperor, a shrewd strategist declared: "A well-equipped soldier requires three things: a good rifle, a military coat, and good shoes." Yet Napoleonic military shoes could be the subjects of humour, as in this story from the memoirs of an officer in the Great Army: "One day I went with General P… into an uninhabited house; it was pouring down and our clothes were soaking wet, so we lit a fire and warmed ourselves.

'Sit down,' the General said to me.

'Why?'

'I want to take your boots off.'

'This is a pleasantry!'

'No, it is not. Give me your foot.'

'General, I can't allow it.'

'Your boots are soaked and your feet are in water.

You're going to catch cold.'

'But I can take them off myself.'

'I want to take them off for you.'

Against my wishes, the General removed my boots, to my extreme astonishment. When he was finished:

'Now my turn,' he said, 'One good turn deserves another.

Take off my boots.'

'I'd be delighted.'

'It was in order to get you to do this that I acted as I did.'

During the Restoration and the reign of Louis-Philippe, men wore boots and escarpins made of black leather. Only soft half boots were allowed to be beige, tawny, or brown.

The British dandy George Brummell (1778-1840), better known as Beau Brummell, wore laced ankle boots with narrow pants. Nicknamed the "fashion king," his clothes become a standard of elegance that knew no boundaries. The Prince of Wales and King Georges IV of England (1762-1830) were among his admirers.

Women also wore flat ankle boots made of cloth and laced on the side. A taste for satin and silk escarpins tied with ribbons lasted until 1830.

The heel returned under Louis-Philippe (1773-1850), but it was not until 1829 that news of its astonishing reappearance was published in the fashion periodical *Le Petit Courrier de Dames*: "We dare risk reporting shoes with a high heel positioned mid-sole, raising the in-step and thereby lending grace to walking. At least if our heels are constructed this way, they will not be ridiculous like our grandmother's heels."

Another fashion publication, *Les Modes Parisiennes*, in 1850 reported: "Some women are wearing heeled shoes according to their whim; this shows a desire to succumb to fashion, because they are very uncomfortable for dancing; ankle-boots have also begun to have little heels; these can only be suitable for women who do not have to wear rubber overshoes." The Second Empire preferred luxury and had an appetite for parties.

68. Emperor's boots. Private collection.

69. Flat court shoes of Napoleon I for his coronation in 1804. Lost during World War II.

70. Louis Boilly, *Portrait de Monsieur d'Aucourt de Saint-Just* (Portrait of Monsieur
   d'Aucourt), 1805. Oil on canvas, 56 x 46 cm. Palais des Beaux-Arts, Lille.

71. Boots of Imperial Prince Jean-Joseph-Eugene-Louis Napoleon, only son
   of Napoleon III and Eugenie de Montijo. International Shoe Museum, Romans.

72. Woman's shoe in bronze kidskin, double attachment, Charles IX.
Buttoned on the side, embroidery with gilded metal beads, leather sole,
reel heel, 19th century. International Shoe Museum, Romans.

73. Pair of men's shoes in black leather and openworked black silk, around 1830.
Musée Galliera - musée de la mode de la Ville de Paris, Paris.
Photo by Pierrain, PMVP.

In contrast to the bourgeois court of Louis-Philippe, that of Napoleon III (1808-1873) proved to be extremely brilliant. Its salons and boulevards became a theatre of society life, while the operettas of Jacques Offenbach, in particular *La Vie Parisienne*, mirrored the period's joie de vivre with a sense of humour. The passion for crinoline born around 1850 led to a revitalisation of couture. The Empress Eugenie (1826-1920) brought fame to her couturier, Charles-Frederic Worth, who opened his salon in 1858, clothing the actresses and courtesans of the period, in addition to his imperial client. The bourgeoisie meanwhile accelerated their rise and pursued financial gain. The ankle boot reigned supreme, made of leather or cloth and very narrowly shaped. Decorated with embroidery and braids, it was either laced up or buttoned via a row of little buttons, whence the invention of the tire-bouton or buttonhook. The Second Empire also marks a decisive stage in the history of footwear, characterised by advances in mechanisation and large-scale industry. Traditional shoemaking, which changed in 1809 when a machine for tacking soles appeared in England, was transformed by the industrial revolution. In 1819, another new machine made wooden pegs for tacking soles. But the biggest change came from Thimonnier's invention of the sewing machine, patented in 1830. A perfect invention, the sewing machine made it possible to stitch uppers of soft materials and began to spread among shoemakers in 1860. The technique improved their production yields, as machines positioned the heel, stitched the upper, and attached the upper to the sole. After 1870, it became common to use a form for each foot, which enabled shoes to correspond to anatomy. Industrial development began to overtake hand-made shoes as factories were established and expanded, in particular the Rousset Company in Blois in 1851. François Pinet's career is a classic example.

74. Bride's shoe, bead design in heart shape. Marriage, 10 November 1896. International Shoe Museum, Romans.

75. Bride's shoe, detail, bead design in heart shape. Marriage, 10 November 1896. International Shoe Museum, Romans.

Shoes and Poverty

In the wake of the Second Empire's Fête Impériale or Imperial Celebration, the taste for magnificent clothing was matched with opulence in the art of the shoe. Examples of these styles, worn by the aristocracy and the increasingly wealthy bourgeoisie, can be seen today in public and private collections. Evidence of the fashions of their times, they are proof of the traditional expertise handed down from one generation to the next, revealing the individuality and the craftsmanship of their creators, whether famous or anonymous. On the other hand, the less well-dressed lower classes wore their shoes until thoroughly deteriorated; this reality was so common that these shoes are rarely preserved today. Nevertheless, images of these shoes survive, thanks to the art of painting. The writer Pierre-Joseph Proudhon (1809-1865), a friend of Gustave Courbet (1819-1877), taught that art should serve society and extol social demands. Although Napoleon III cared about improving the workers' hard lot, social conflicts remained and shook the traditional value system despite his efforts. Artists responded to what was going on around them by depicting in their painting the economic and social transformation brought on by the machine and industrialisation. German painter Adolph Menzel (1815-1905) first visited Paris in 1855. At the World Fair he discovered the pavilion devoted to Courbet's realism. Menzel was a court painter who commemorated ceremonies and celebrations, but he was also interested in factory labour, and looked at people with sincere and honest interest. This was important because an artist first had to consider the worker a worthy subject before the worker could become the painting's focal point. In *Steel Rolling Mill* (Alte Nationalgalerie, Berlin), dated 1872-1875, labourers are depicted busy at work dressed in crude, old shoes with worn-down heels, worn without stockings. The writer and art critic Champfleury, author of a book on popular imagery and contributor to the socialist journal *The People's Voice*, inspired the painter Gustave Courbet. Courbet depicted the modest shoes worn by the working classes in his socialist paintings, such as *The Stone Breakers*, which disappeared from the Dresden Museum during the World War II, and *The Burial at Ornans*. *The Stone Breakers* features a pair of clogs worn by the worker in right foreground, of which the left one is cracked inside. The worker moving rocks in the left foreground better protects his feet with rustic laced shoes of crude leather. *The Burial at Ornans* depicts poor and prominent villagers gathered for an indigent's burial in a communal plot. The sharp contrast between the different social classes is echoed by their shoes: the grave digger's simple laced shoes are worn out, whereas the elegant black shoes worn by the society figures look like new.

The son of a peasant, Jean-François Millet (1814-1875) painted scenes of rural life, each one a testament to the peasant's humble labour and the nobility of man on earth. Farm hands, who were day workers, are usually depicted in simple clogs, as seen in *The Angelus* (1857-1859), *The Wood Splitter*, and *The Gleaners* (Salon of 1857).

The painter Jules Breton was also interested in peasant life and painted lively scenes. In the *Call of the Gleaners* (Salon of 1859), he depicts young women in clogs or bare footed. A lack of shoes was a sign of abject poverty, symbolised by the French expression *"va-nu-pieds"* which literally means, "who goes barefoot." As Jean-Paul Roux explains: "During the middle ages wearing shoes became one of the primary indicators a person was well born. It was of such importance that for a long time the feudal lord sometimes carried peasant shoes alongside leather ones! This is but a survival. The man with shoes was everything, the shoeless person was nothing. Va-nu-pieds! This expression, now a fixed label, has no real meaning today and it is rarely used. Yet quite recently, hundreds of years or more, in the unequivocal testimony of 19th-century novelists, the phrase carried its full weight as a synonym of the word beggar, and signified a man so poor he could not even pay for a pair of shoes."

76. Adolph Menzel, *Steel Rolling Mill*, 1872-1875.
Oil on canvas. Alte Nationalgalerie, Berlin.

77. Jules Breton, *Calling in the Gleaners,* 1859.
Oil on canvas, 90 x 176 cm. Musée d'Orsay, Paris.

78. Gustave Courbet, *The Sifters*, 1854-1855.
Oil on canvas. Musée des Beaux-Arts, Nantes.

Jean Béraud

From Shoemaker to Company Manager

François Pinet was born in Château la Vallière (Indre-et-Loire) on 19 July 1817. The son of a shoemaker, he was introduced to the trade by his father. When his father died in 1830, Pinet was thirteen and was placed in the home of a master shoemaker to complete his professional education. He embarked on his Tour de France and in 1836 was declared a professionally accredited journeyman (*Compagnon Cordonnier Bottier du Devoir*, or Shoemaker-Boot maker Companion of Duty) under the name "Tourangeau la Rose d'Amour."

At age sixteen, with a total of twelve francs to his name, young François found work in Tours earning a weekly wage of five francs. Living on this modest salary, he saved to buy his own tools and to acquire his independence by working. He spent three years in Bordeaux, and then moved to Marseille, becoming the head of the *Société des Compagnons Cordonniers* (Workers' Association of Shoemaker Companions). In 1844, he went to Paris where he continued his training in large-scale manufacturing. An intelligent observer, Pinet was able to grasp the usefulness of manufacturing's division of labour and to see how its various components were combined to increase quality production.

In 1845, he became a travelling salesman and started learning about business practices. In 1854, he took out a patent for a new heel manufacturing method that produced lighter and more solid heels than those composed of superimposed layers. In 1855, he opened a shoe factory to produce women's styles at 23 rue du Petit Lion Saint Sauvent. When the company grew, it moved to a larger spot (number 40) on the same street. Pinet got married in 1858. His wife brought the qualities of heart, charm, grace, and vivacious spirit to the marriage. Quickly focusing her intelligence and sound education on the company, she became an enlightened collaborator.

François Pinet waited until 1863 to build new workshops and offices at 44 rue Paradis Poissonnière. The premises were constructed according to his own plans and under his management. In this new model business, functional for the era, workers felt appreciated and respected. Pinet employed 120 people in his workshops and 700 men and women who worked from home. The creations of François Pinet attracted a wealthy clientele in France and abroad. In Pinet's large shoe store on the boulevard de la Madeleine, elegant ladies rushed to buy ankle boots, escarpins, and derbies that encased the foot in the softest of leathers. Pinet's shoes came in shining fabrics and in radiant colours, and were hand-embroidered and hand-painted. As a proprietor, Pinet also established in 1864 the first employers' association of federated shoe manufacturers and became its leader.

Pinet received many awards for his work, including a superb medal from the 1867 Paris World Fair that would thenceforth be engraved under the soles of his shoes as a sign of his talent. That same year, he invented a machine that could form Louis XV heels in one piece. Composed of a press and a dye, the machine's technology was awarded a new patent. Technological advancements of this kind marked the transition from craft industry to industrial manufacturing during the period. During the events of 1870-1871 that shook France, and especially Paris, Pinet provided financial assistance to the wounded and established a 20-bed mobile hospital unit at his own expense.

In 1892, during a traditional St. Crispin's banquet, he became a member of a new journeyman's society called the Union Compagnonnique. François Pinet died in 1897. A humble shoemaker from the provinces, he succeeded in dressing the feet of the world's most elegant women. In the process he made a valuable contribution to spreading haute couture's international influence. There were other 19th-century developments.

79. Jean Beraud, *Parisian, Place de la Concorde*, 1890.
Oil on canvas. Musée Carnavalet - musée d'histoire de Paris, Paris.

80. Hand embroidered woman's bottine in satin. Executed by Pinet, Paris, around 1875. International Shoe Museum, Romans.

81. Miniature bottine in glossy kidskin, openworked upper, remarkable stitching producing the effect of leather lace, laced on the side. Leather sole, reel heel. Executed by Rousselle, Second Empire. International Shoe Museum, Romans.

82. Miniature woman's shoe in black kidskin, scalloped vamp, upper laced by a brown silk ribbon ending in a bow, leather sole, Louis XV heel. France, around 1880. International Shoe Museum, Romans.

83. Woman's shoe. Oxford in white satin, embroidered patterns in silver, tasselled laces. Leather sole, covered reel heel. Executed by Pinet, Paris, around 1897. Guillen Collection, International Shoe Museum, Romans.

The advent of department stores in 1852 made a wide range of shoes readily available. The return of the heel, after being unsuccessfully revived under Louis-Philippe, become standard and took the demi-bobine or half-roll form. The arch of the foot being thenceforth supported by the shoe's shank, the heel could be positioned at the back edge of the sole. An aura of mystery surrounded the ankle boot hidden under crinoline. According to the notes and memoirs of Madame Jules Baroche, there came from England a more revealing fashion: "This year court ladies adopted a very English fashion: an ankle-revealing skirt of multi-coloured wool worn with a Louis XIII hat, a mischievous eye, a turned-up nose, and patent-leather ankle boots with heels. This outfit unfortunately requires a slender leg and a delicate foot. Otherwise it is smart, daring, casual, and better suited than any other for a walk in the woods."

But prince Napoleon found fault with the trend: "Women betray themselves in the morning with indiscrete skirts and in the evening with indiscrete blouses; what is to become of us?" The Empress wore tasselled boots to the races at Longchamp.

During this period, the female foot was much written about. Literature of the 19th century abounds with descriptions of feet dressed in mules d'appartement (slippers) and bottines (ankle boots).

Honoré de Balzac (1799-1850), Emile Zola (1840-1902), and Guy de Maupassant (1850-1893) were among the many writers who dwelled on this fashion accessory.

In *Madame Bovary*, Gustave Flaubert (1821-1880) describes more than one hundred pairs of shoes. Marc Constantin wrote the following description in the *The Almanac of Fine Manners* (1854): "The ankle boot has deposed the shoe and reigns victorious; nothing is prettier than a supple laced boot clasping the foot, which it makes look even smaller! It has a slimming effect on the lower leg and creates an elegant step."

For evenings or for a ball, women wore extremely sophisticated escarpins of tapestry or silk, which often matched their gowns. Gustave Flaubert refers to them in *Madame Bovary*: "Her beautiful outfit will be stored in the closet with pious respect, right down to her satin shoes whose soles were yellowed from the slippery wax on the floor." These styles were based on the open shoes with heels of the Louis XV and Louis XVI periods.

The mule d'appartement (slipper) in silk or velvet was another standard shoe. Men wore black boots or ankle boots. Children wore ankle boots that were smaller versions of the adult models.

From 1870 to 1900, shoes competed with ankle boots for in-town wear. The low-cut pump continued to be worn for evening. Round toes became pointed. Shapes were slowly changing, but the very recent revolution in dress caused by Paul Poiret, would have the foot in modern shoes thenceforth available for all to see.

84. Oxford style man's shoe by A. Biset in light brown kidskin. Elongated and upturned toe with perforated design, France, around 1890. International Shoe Museum, Romans.

85. Pump in embroidered calfskin, Paris, 1855. Guillen Collection, International Shoe Museum, Romans.

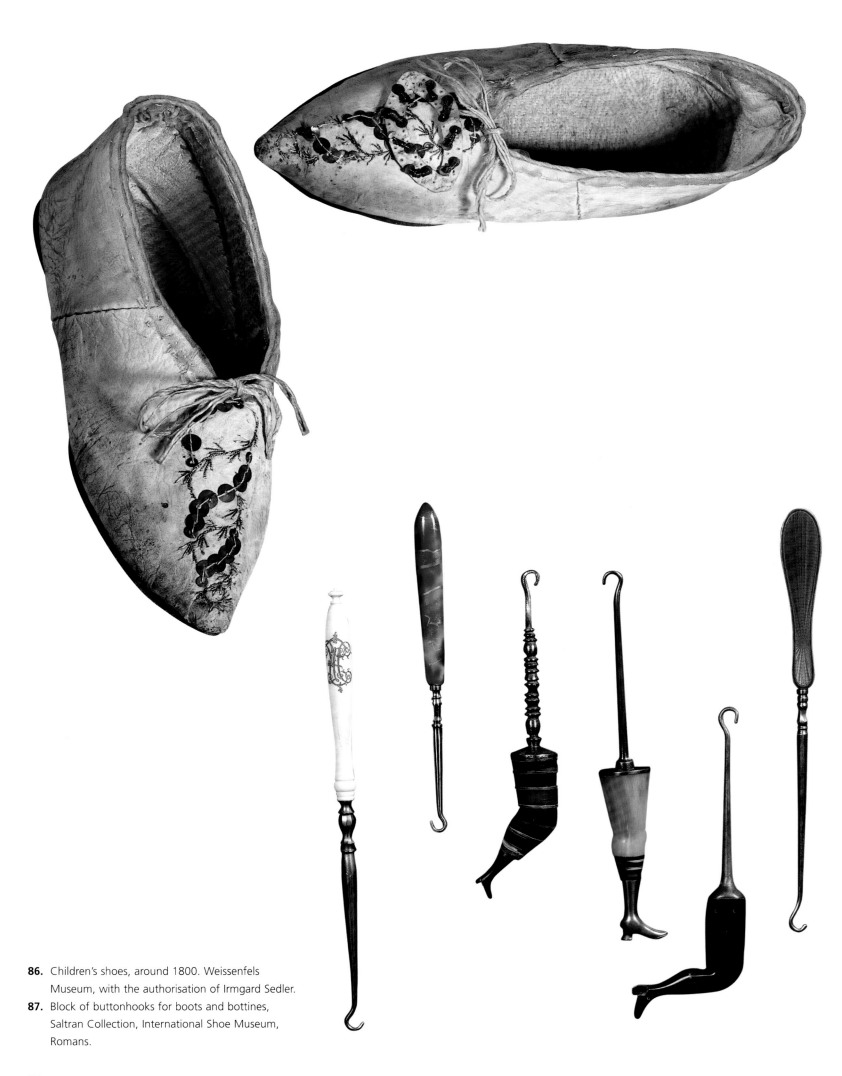

86. Children's shoes, around 1800. Weissenfels
Museum, with the authorisation of Irmgard Sedler.

87. Block of buttonhooks for boots and bottines,
Saltran Collection, International Shoe Museum,
Romans.

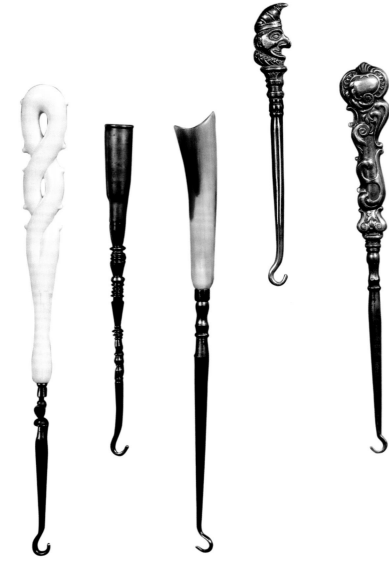

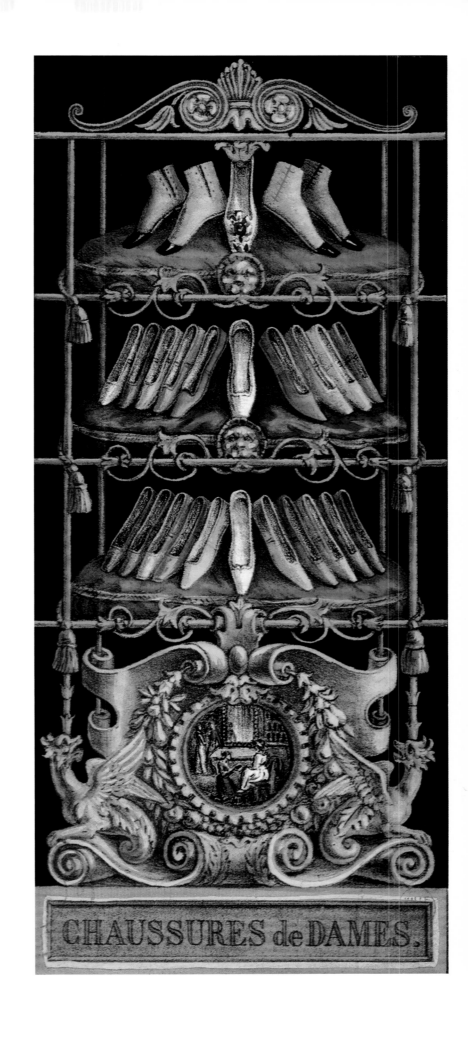

88. Painted shoe shop display, around 1840. Lithograph.
Musée Carnavalet - musée d'histoire de Paris, Paris.

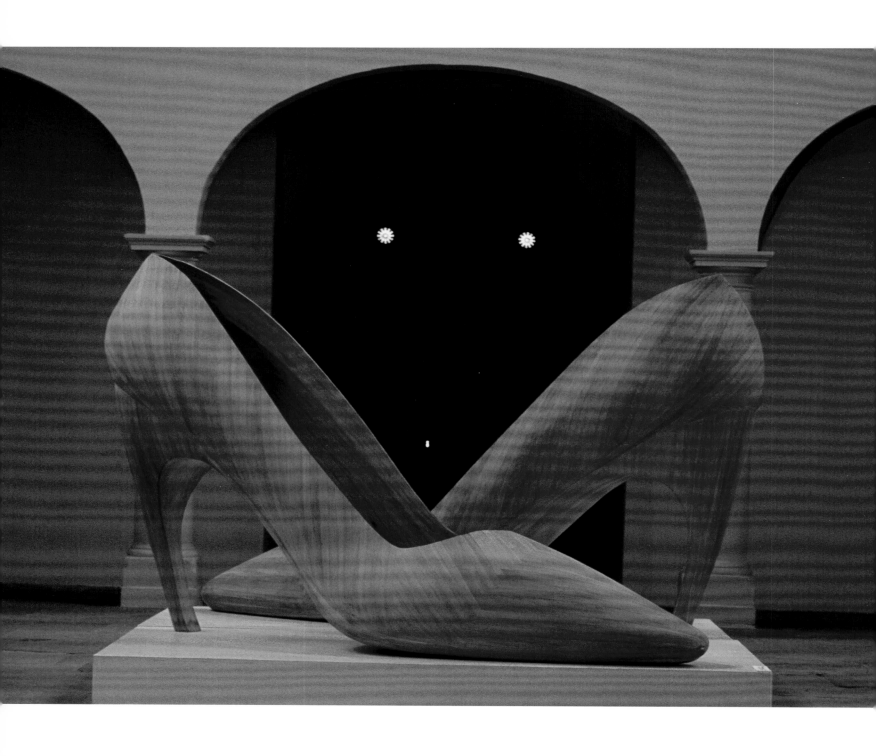

89. "Shock heel" shoes, Paris, 1987. Created by Roger Vivier,
International Shoe Museum, Romans.

The Shoe in the 20ᵗʰ Century

The shoe's history and evolution in the 20ᵗʰ century can only be understood in relation to the personalities and the older firms that paved the way to our understanding of traditional and industrial fabrication. True "dynasties," some of these custom shoemakers and manufacturers are still growing into the 21ˢᵗ century. Many names are cited here taken from among the talented designers and prestigious firms, but many are absent, as this book cannot pretend to be exhaustive. All deserve greater recognition, not only for their contribution to the rise of fashion in France and the world, but also for passing their traditional know-how on to the next generation.

It is also impossible to understand 20ᵗʰ-century footwear in isolation from its closely related historical, economic, and artistic contexts. These underlying factors would lead to a revolution in clothing that would produce the versatile functionality of modern apparel. To fashion designers who deemed shoes a fashion accessory these factors were rich sources of inspiration.

Many historical factors contributed to the evolution of 20ᵗʰ-century shoes. First, the rise of international relations promoted foreign influences, while large world fairs, in which French couture participated, facilitated artistic exchange. Second, Haute Couture fashion shows and the informative role of fashion magazines, spread by photography and film, were among the principal agents of change. To these factors must be added the growth of sports and the introduction of the automobile. Additionally, a wealthy French and foreign clientele that only wore custom-made clothing and shoes continued to exist alongside the booming apparel industry, a phenomena that enabled mass production of Couture-inspired fashions accessible to the largest number of consumers at lower prices, which in turn promoted the growth of the shoe business. In this way names like André and even Bata became the pride of footwear's mass-market. The impact of the two world wars would also be considerable. Finally, the advent of Designer Fashion and technological innovations in footwear would carry shoes into the 21ˢᵗ century.

A number of events marked the years around 1900: the advent of the lady's suit revolutionised fashion; the English craze for sports and fresh air established itself in France; and a bathing suit that included cloth ankle boots with rubber soles was transported to Etretat and Trouville. Women who risked bicycle riding dared to wear baggy pants inspired by bloomers (also a rage on the other side of the Channel) and caused a sensation by showing their feet in shoes, as observed in the painting *The Bicycle House in the Bois de Boulogne* (Carnavalet Museum, Paris), painted by Jean Béraud circa 1900. From 1900 to 1914, couturiers proliferated, riding the wave of la Belle époque and the house of Worth. There were Paquin, the Callot Sisters, Doucet, and Lanvin, among others. Ladies of society and courtesans sunk fortunes into their outfits. The nouveaux riches strutted about, arrayed in their most beautiful finery, trying to project an image of their newly acquired affluence. Until 1910, the button or lace-up ankle boot of "gold," beige, or black was standard for winter, whereas the covered shoe was worn in summer. Deep-cut shoes with Louis XV heels and a pointed toe box were the height of sophistication for evening, worn with matching dress and stockings. Elegance for men amounted to wearing button ankle boots, but low, top-laced shoes accompanied outfits for sports and casual wear. Most of these shoes were made by artisans scattered around Paris working in anonymity, making shoes rapidly, but skilfully, on demand, before the flowering of renown custom shoemakers became commonplace. The revolution in dress triggered by Paul Poiret eliminated corsets and shortened skirts. The wearing of straight skirts with soft, fluid lines inspired by the Orient cast a spotlight on shoes, which previously had enjoyed little visibility. The new style was reminiscent of the light clothes from the Directoire and Empire periods when shoes were worn exposed, revealing most of the foot.

90. Stitching factory, "Sigle & Co" in Kornwestheim
(which will later be called "Salamander") around 1910.

91. Last factory, "Sigle & Co" in Kornwestheim
(which will later be called "Salamander") around 1910.

74

92. Woman's pump from shoemaker A. Gillet in the Charles IX style in garish green silk with gold kidskin appliqué, Louis XV costume heel, Paris, around 1928, 1930. International Shoe Museum, Romans.

93. Woman's town sandal in kidskin coloured cream and red by A. Gillet. Platform sole covered with red kidskin, Paris, Summer 1935. International Shoe Museum, Romans.

94. Woman's pump in silver kidskin. Design of pink dots and small green rectangles in geometrical spaces largely leaving visible the silver background. Covered Louis XV heel, leather sole, Paris, around 1925. International Shoe Museum, Romans.

95. Mule, unsuitable for walking, in black kidskin and sky blue satin, small cabochon in porcelain. Height of the heel: 20 cm. Vienna, Austria, around 1900. Guillen Collection, International Shoe Museum, Romans.

96. Man's bottine with buttons, France, from 1895 to 1910. International Shoe Museum, Romans.

97. Man's bottine, around 1912. International Shoe Museum, Romans.

Paul Poiret's straight dresses also created a look that required a shoe with a more refined profile. World War I (1914-1918) disrupted the whole society's living conditions. Women, for example, found themselves having to cover for men in the most diverse jobs. In this way they experienced a need to dress more practically in a fashion that allowed their feet unrestricted movement. Now highlighted, the shoe quite naturally acquired a new elegance. The Roaring Twenties succeeded the terrible war years. Women cut their hair and the short skirt claimed a definitive victory. Long boots and black stockings gave way to light-coloured stockings to set off new shoes available in all the colours of the rainbow. The Charles IX style began its long reign. The low-cut shoe with the Louis XV heel came to be worn mainly in the afternoon. For evening, it was either of a matching fabric to go with the gown, or of gold lamé or silver.

Men's top-laced shoes, often covered with a small gaiter of black or grey wool, gave the illusion of an ankle boot. In the 1930s, Elsa Schiaparelli and Coco Chanel set the tone for fashion, and with the added influence from Madeleine Vionnet, evening gowns descended in length, emphasising the figure's lines with a bias cut. In response, shoes became more slender, heels became higher, and shoe buttonholes tended to be hidden. Flats and crepe-sole shoes were worn with outfits for sport. At the same time, at the dawn of the World War II, wedge soles appeared. Wartime leather restrictions imposed on the entire population turned wedge soles into a standard style. Unfortunately, wood (brightly painted or covered in fabric) and cork wedges were uncomfortable and ugly, although the innovation of the articulated wooden heel would provide some extra ease in walking. Designers also used substitute materials such as raffia and felt to make the uppers.

These heavy wedged shoes became pedestals for a straight silhouette with broad shoulders, until after the Liberation in 1947, when Christian Dior launched his "New Look." A very Parisian style, the New Look was characterised by a cinched waist and a large skirt that fell below the calf, worn with slender heels in perfect harmony with the silhouette. Henceforth, in the mind of designers, an elegant women's outfit would be unthinkable without high-heeled shoes. The stiletto heel was thus born in reaction to the heavy shoes associated with the war. A metal core guaranteed the heel's stability, but the stiletto left perforations in the floors of public places until a protective tip was invented. The heel survived until the 1960s, although its profile became slightly curved underneath the sole. The popularity of the mini-skirt led to its disappearance and shoes with round toes (succeeding pointed toes) replaced the stiletto. Two styles dominated store shelves: the Richelieu (the front upper sewn over the back upper) and the Derby (the back upper sewn over the front upper), while the moccasin, a shoe without laces, attracted a young clientele.

According to Sylvie Lefranc, head of the Bureau de Style de la Fédération de l'Industrie de la Chaussure de France (Fashion Office of the French Shoe Industry Federation) consumers lacked access to a wide range of shoe styles and products in the early 1960s. A malaise of sameness pervaded all the product lines, except for those of prestigious custom shoemakers, which were only available to the privileged few. Enter Roger Vivier, who had the innovative genius to pave the way to modern consumerism. In a manufacturing partnership with the Société Charles Jourdan, Vivier launched a ready-to-wear line of fine shoes that were expensive but still affordable to a large number of consumers. Vivier was able to express his personal talent for bold silhouettes and the use of sophisticated materials in the line. The democratisation of elegance gathered momentum as a trend and marked the advent of Designer Fashion footwear: new products were henceforth the subjects of aesthetic research, and contours and volumes were stylised to reflect the personality of their designer.

Among the designers who had the ability to impart their own unique and identifiable look to their shoes were Roland Jourdan, following in the footsteps of Roger Vivier with his stylistic exercises focused on heels; Robert Clergerie, who lent his prestige to masculine and feminine style by creating new shapes; Stéphane Kélian, the inventor of the feminine braid and riding boot wizard; and finally, Walter Steiger, who handled line with a true designer's meticulousness. This new generation of fashion designers strongly influenced the 1970s and triggered a real craze among female consumers, who were passionate about shoes elevated to the full status of fashion object.

Alongside the phenomena of sophisticated urban fashion that had developed in reaction against the banality of standard shoes, there appeared a new trend generated by lifestyle. Originating in the United States and winning over Europe, the trend amounted to the advent of sportswear and jeans, or the casual look. Kicker's founder Daniel Raufast recognised the significance of the trend (it was especially marked in the youth and children's markets starting in the early 1970s) and developed a casual, playful product in response. During the same period, Mr. Helaine of Arche introduced a small, super-soft, and colourful boot that was distributed around the globe. The world of adventurers and nostalgia for pioneers and soldiers attracted a new generation of young men, as footwear with a history – Clark's Desert Boots, Pataugas, and Palladium's Pallabrousse – was adopted for leisure and weekend wear. New milestones in technical performance were reached in the 1970s with the successful introduction of rubber soles moulded on fabric uppers; once the movement was launched, there was no turning back.

Beginning in the 1980s, sportswear ceased to be the only source of inspiration for new styles, as the active sports themselves dictated the rules. The Girbauds were among the pioneers in this area, co-opting specific items from various sports contexts and giving them the right to be cited. The major specialised brands followed suit by going after the youth market: Adidas, Reebok, Converse, Puma, and Superga became fashion players in their own right. Events happened quickly in this industry segment, but it should be noted that Nike played an important role in developing new lines featuring modernist design.

Other fashion trends arose from an openly ecological approach – before anyone had ever heard of the Greens. These currents persisted over the decades, ever faithful to the cult of the natural, ergonomics, and authenticity. Bama, Birkenstock, and even Scholl were among the leaders to whom the contemporary Camper is heir.

Fashion's 360-degree turn toward more intimate and primary values privileged the person over appearances and is especially evident in footwear, which is an accurate reflection of contemporary lifestyles.

Sportswear now "contaminates" the world of elegance as well. What couture house does not have running shoes and high-tops in their collection? Even men have been seduced by the casual chic of Tods and Hogan, after experiencing the sturdy comfort of Paraboots.

But Cinderella's slipper still inspires fantasy, and elegance and glamour exist now more than ever. Sophisticated women's shoes today have new defenders. New designers carry the torch of the great artists of seduction, redesigning new contours and original heels, playing with materials and decoration: Rodolphe Ménudier, Michel Perry, Manolo Blahnik, Pierre Hardy, and Benoît Méléard are among the most visible.

The rapid change in footwear, from both a design and manufacturing perspective, is perfectly illustrated by the careers of the most illustrious custom shoemakers: Andrea Pfister, Berluti, Ferragamo, Massaro, and Yantorny. Each name represents a different trajectory, but all stand for devotion to excellence. Here are their biographies, which offer a behind-the-scenes look at the art of the shoe.

98. Man's shoe. Black suede and black veneer. UNIC Romans, around 1923. Man's shoe in white perforated calfskin and black calfskin. UNIC Romans, around 1938. International Shoe Museum, Romans.

99. Evening shoes in navy blue velvet, steel bead design,
    celluloid heel inlayed with strass. Created by shoemaker Hellstern,
    around 1925. International Shoe Museum, Romans.

100. Double heeled sandals worn with stockings of black kidskin. Fastening
    by thirty white buttons, scalloped sides with gold edging. Extremities
    resembling toes with toenails of strass. Height of the back heel: 24 cm.
    Creation of shoemaker Hellstern, Paris, around 1950.
    International Shoe Museum, Romans.

101. Thigh boots in pink kidskin mounted on a winged shoe with volutes in
    gilded bronze. Fastening at the front by seventeen buttons.
    Creation of shoemaker Hellstern, Paris, around 1950.

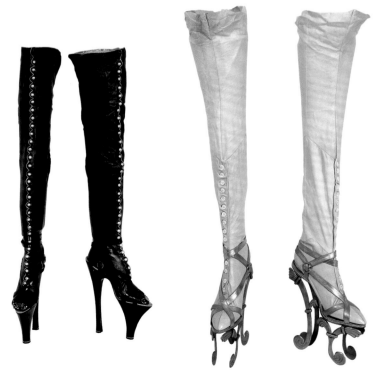

Shoemakers of Yesterday and Today

The history and evolution of the shoe in the 20th century cannot be discussed without reference to the prominent figures or time-honoured companies whose preceding role helps the understanding of the traditional and industrial design.

True "dynasties," some shoemakers and manufacturers are still booming in the 21st century. Amongst the talented designers and renowned houses many names are mentioned, although even more are missing. In no way does this study claim to be exhaustive. On the contrary, all deserve to be better known for their contribution to the prestige of fashion in France and the world as well as for handing down their knowledge of the masters to future generations.

Hellstern

Hellstern, which initially specialised in men's shoes, was founded in about 1870 in Paris on rue du 29 juillet and later moved to place Vendôme around 1900. Together, the three Hellstern sons (Maurice, Charles, and Henri) actively worked to develop the company, which at its peak (1920-1925) employed over one hundred workers, a considerable amount in those days. From home, jobbing workers assured an up-market output: in the Loire where the Cavalry School gave rise to a labour force skilled in shoemaking, in the Midi where were established highly talented Italian workers.

The company's influence was significant for that time: a branch was maintained in Brussels until 1949, another in London closed its doors in 1965, and in Cannes a shop directed at ready-to-wear lasted until 1970. But Hellstern's repute was in essence Parisian. The company took part in the haute couture fashion shows, which drew in French and foreign clientele seeking luxury products. It dressed the famous feet of its time: princes and princesses of the European courts, stars of stage and screen, society women and demimondaines.

Some clients were real devotees ordering up to three pairs a week - more than five hundred and fifty annually - payable by the month, trimester, or year. Veritable fortunes, a pair of HELLSTERN shoes cost on average about 525 French francs in 1919, 250 French francs in 1924, and 1000 French francs in 1929!

The three brothers divided the work among themselves. Henri, who after World War II became the president of the National Union of French Shoemakers, was the man responsible for public relations. Charles was the designer and involved in the creation of female footwear fashion essentially characterised during this period (1920-1930) by three styles: "the Charles IX" flat or heeled shoe, fastened at the instep by a strap passing from the interior to exterior quarter where it attaches by a button or buckle; "the Salomé" by-product of the Charles IX, fastened around the ankle by a T-shaped strap; "the court shoe" flat or heeled thin soled shoe revealing the instep, without fastening.

The International Shoe Museum of Romans possesses more than two hundred and fifty pairs marking Hellstern's production once belonging to just one woman. This exceptional collection, acquired by the association of the friends of the Romans museum, is suggestive of all the moments in the life of a posh bourgeois woman of her times. It was between the World Wars,

the wild joie de vivre explosion after the terrible ordeal: the woman must be beautiful and flaunt it, day, evening, and in private.

Of course, these three styles of fashionable shoes are found in the Hellstern collection, town as well as evening shoes.

For the Charles IX and the Salomé models, the same styles by form and design are replicated in a variety of colours, up to thirteen, and realised in suede, kid, lizard, snake, and crocodile skin. The shades are brilliant: purple, green, fuchsia, yellow, red, blue, white, et cetera. The last are generally elongated with the toe slightly rounded. Leather appliqués of a colour contrasting to that of the upper often form a design of geometric lines of a superior quality of execution, highlighting virtuosity in the art of stitching with a very fine needle, allowing for stitches measuring less than one millimetre. This technique is no longer employed in our time. Most heels are in the Louis XV style, measuring a height of about five to eight centimetres, always of wood covered with leather or celluloid inlayed with strass or glass of various colours. Ornamentation comes essentially from the variety of buckles, which serve only a decorative purpose. They personalise each pair, whatever the style. Here, the buckle is jewellery and even a jewel: some are solid silver, of jet, or more simply of pearls, painted metal, strass, or marcasite. Others, older, dating to the 19th century, illustrate imagination commonly used by the shoemaker.

For evening shoes, the styles use velvet, lamé, embroidered silk, gold or silver kidskin, kidskin cut away to form a veritable lace of leather, with scintillating adornments that recall the fox trot and the Charleston.

The court shoe, in kidskin trimmed with coarse-grained silk, is distinguished by its elegant simplicity while the Salomé and especially the Charles IX are embellished far more.

During the World War II, Hellstern used no other material but leather, yet its creations have the look of the thick-soled shoes of that period.

One of the unusual highlights of this collection:

Ninety-nine pairs of in-town boots. These boots are of kidskin, rise to the knee, sport a high Louis XV heel, and close towards the outside by a fancy-edge-trimmed buttoning that hugs the leg. A few styles are laced.

This terrific uniqueness of form is offset by the terrific variety of colour; some variation can be seen in the buttoning, which can be either at the back or double on each side. The buttons, always twenty-four, are of mother-of-pearl, jet, or strass.

Finally, the most outstanding ensemble of the collection is twenty or so styles unfit for walking, touching on foot fetishism: sandals, shoes, and boots of the "boudoir" in the most extravagant designs. These always sport a very high heel, reaching up to twenty-six centimetres, while the front of the foot is fitted with a slim pad of a sole towards the base. In certain designs, shoe and heel are one. The arch is exceptionally accentuated. The shades of the leather, always kidskin, are limited to black, red, gold, or silver. The heels are at times "paved" with strass, the uppers are perforated.

Among the most curious pieces, a pair of thigh boots in pink hand leather mounted on a shoe winged with volutes in gilded bronze as well as a pair of black and gilt thigh boots with a double heel fitting the foot like a glove whose fingers are graced with nails of strass.

The ensemble of this collection can be summed up as wild and wise.

102. Masterpiece by P. Yantorny: shoe of feathers.
International Shoe Museum, Romans.

Pierre Yantorny

The Most Expensive Shoes in the World

The veil of mystery around Pierre Yantorny, who called himself the "most expensive shoemaker in the world," has finally lifted, thanks to the release of his personal journal, photographs, papers, and shoes left to the International Shoe Museum, Romans, by the artist's nephew. These records will allow us to revise his biography and to dispel the myths about his Indonesian origins and his role as Conservator at the Cluny Museum in Paris.

Pierre Yantorny was an Italian, born on 28 May 1874, in Marasso Marchesato, Calabria. He only attended school from age eight to eight and a half, at which time he began his working life in a macaroni factory where he earned twenty cents a day, working from six in the morning until six in the evening. He subsequently went to work for an individual as the caretaker and exerciser of a horse. When his father settled in Chicago, the twelve year old went to Naples and apprenticed with another apprentice shoemaker; his only payment consisted of the knowledge he acquired.

Six months later, hired by a real boss, he was able to save some money, enabling him to set off for Genoa. After a short stay, he went to Nice where he perfected his craft, but already he was dreaming of Paris. To finance his trip and save forty-two francs to pay for a train ticket, another shoemaker suggested that Yantorny apply to the Marseille slaughterhouse to work with sheep.

As Yantorny writes in his journal:

"And so I arrived in Paris on 13 June 1891, after travelling for three days, because it was not a fast train; at four in the morning I made my triumphant entry into the French capital. I had been given the address of a shoemaker's workshop on the rue Saint-Honoré where I might be able to find tradesmen who could help me get work. But damn! The workshop had disappeared five years ago."

Thanks to the kindness of an Italian restaurant owner on the rue Traversière, Yantorny found a tradesman who worked for the major Paris houses and who agreed to take him on. The workday began at four in the morning and lasted until ten in the evening. Hard work and talent quickly led to his wielding the knife and the awl like a pro. But, alas, his benefactor disappeared without leaving an address.

Yantorny took a job washing dishes in a restaurant for three months so he could afford to buy his own tools.

However, unable to find work, he returned first to Genoa and then to Nice on 17 January 1892, with twenty cents in his pocket. He spent the winter there further perfecting his craft then returned to Paris where he stayed until 1898, presenting himself as a tradesman worthy of the top firms – a designation that pops up constantly in his journal.

Two years in London introduced him to a new aspect of shoemaking, for it was there he learned the art of making shoe trees, which he deemed an indispensable complement to that of shoemaking and form making. This experience moreover presented an opportunity for Yantorny to learn English, a considerable asset in terms of his future American clientele.

Upon returning to Paris for the World Fair, he temporarily abandoned his shoemaker's craft in order to learn form making. His small room on the rue Saint-Dominique became the scene of his personal investigations. As he notes in his journal:

"This is where I began my study of form making, all by myself; I worked long hours, going days without eating; experience itself fed me, because I saw that I was making progress in what I was trying to do."

Four years later, he rented an old bakery at 109 rue du Faubourg Saint-Honoré, and established himself as a maker of forms for shoemakers. The perfecting of four different models with, in his own words, "all the necessary lines to charm the eye" brought him a tremendous amount of work. But he continued to entertain the idea of acquiring a wealthy clientele:

"I wanted to make shoes for people who wore shoes to coordinate their outfits and naturally many more sacrifices had to be made to acquire this clientele…"

A few years later, he set up shop above 26 place Vendôme, where the jeweller Boucheron is currently located. When he failed to receive orders and fell under criticism from the shoemakers' corporation, he said: "actions speak louder than words and time will be the judge of the rest."

To attract customers, Yantorny placed a sign in his window that read, "the most expensive shoes in the world." The expression served as a trade name. A master of his craft, he sought the wealthiest of clients who had the taste, the time, and above all the means to put down a deposit of three thousand francs and submit to the six to eight fittings required to produce the perfect shoe.

In his journal, Yantorny stresses the art of fitting a pair of ankle boots: the process had to result in a perfect correspondence between form, foot, and shoe. According to Yantorny, negligence on the part of the shoemaker could lead to ingrown toenails, calluses, corns, and even enlarged toes, which brought him to the conclusion that:

"If the client purchases from the shoemaker all these ailments, he will have them for the rest of his life and no doctor or surgeon on Earth will be able to heal him. This is why individuals who care about their health and well-being must take care and not entrust their feet to the first shoemaker that comes along."

Yantorny goes on to humourously survey the effects of wearing ill-fitting shoes in various circumstances:

"If you have poorly made shoes and they get wet, you'll catch a cold and other illnesses" (which is confirmed by Pasteur);

"If you are in business negotiations and your feet hurt because of your shoes, you'll be in a bad mood and you'll be unable to properly conduct your business";

"If you go to the theatre to see a production you like and you wear shoes that hurt your feet, you won't have any fun"; and finally,

"If you go out to dinner, no matter how fine the food and no matter how pleasant the company, if your feet hurt you won't enjoy yourself at all."

This is why Yantorny insists the foot be dressed in the perfect comfort produced from a quality shaped shoe and foot mould.

Packed with technical advice, Yantorny's journal provides information about the perfection of his craft. The shoemaker shares with us his love for his trade, which extends to the smallest details:

"For women's shoes, eyelets must be handmade like we do for button holes; but to be pretty, the eyelet must be very round and the points flat enough that they don't damage the grain of the leather, and so that they can be very close together." As for aesthetics, just open his journal and see how much it concerns him:

"My only concern is to constantly combine tradition with artistic creativity.

1) The traditional side is doing no harm to the foot.

2) The artistic side involves giving the foot an illusion of being as small and as thin as possible and even correcting natural defects.

103. Duke of Guise shoe by P. Yantorny. Crimson silk velvet embroidered with
gold and silver thread. Inspired by liturgical cloths of the 17th century;
Louis XV heel, Paris, around 1912. International Shoe Museum, Romans.

104. Duke of Guise shoe by P. Yantorny. Black satin background with red satin appliqué, buckle adorned with strass and Louis XV heel. Paris, around 1912. International Shoe Museum, Romans.

105. Extract from the journal of shoemaker P. Yantorny.
International Shoe Museum, Romans.

106. Receipt from P. Yantorny, "the most expensive shoemaker in the world".
International Shoe Museum, Romans.

107. Trunk from P. Yantorny, made for Rita Acosta Lydig. Leather and silk.
The Metropolitan Museum of Art, New York.

Example: for a shapeless foot, make shoes that give the foot all the lines and balance needed to be eye-catching."

The expression "to be eye-catching" punctuates the journal in which he also comments on industrialisation:

"Industrial shoe manufacturing has poor shoe forms and makes little boxes for feet that one calls shoes. Handcrafted shoes must be made according to the client's aesthetics" and

"It is very difficult to make shoes that conform to a person's feet and individual aesthetics";

"If there is a seam behind the vamp, very often it is done badly and throws the heel off, as well as the leg, when you look at a person from behind."

Although Yantorny says in his journal that getting rich was not his goal, his creations were expensive. Before 1914, the first order came to thirty-five thousand francs, probably in recognition of his talent and strong personality. A sumptuous leather-bound order book with parchment pages confirms the high price of this first order, which comprised the creation of several different shoe forms, a traditional and artistic study of the foot, fifty pairs of shoes without trimming at the price of one hundred and twenty-five francs each, fifty shoetrees, two trunks for boots and shoes, six pairs of stockings for each pair of shoes (amounting to three hundred pairs of stockings), and finally buckles, shoe horns, button hooks, and all the accessories needed for upkeep.

Who were his clients? Few in number and seen by appointment only, they were Russian and French, but above all American women, like the wealthy Rita de Acosta Lydig. One of the most elegant and prominent woman in New York, Lydig ordered over three hundred pairs of shoes. True works of art, they were kept in Russian leather trunks with velvet panne interiors that could hold twelve pairs. The Metropolitan Museum in New York has an example of one of these extraordinary trunks. Each shoe came with its own shoetree engraved with the name Rita. Some of these shoes were made in vintage fabrics: Yantorny was a connoisseur of textiles and obtained velvets, brocart, satin, and lace from collectors in order to produce his creations.

This tireless worker eventually felt the need to step back and gave himself a two-year sabbatical in India around 1930. Those closest to him remember the story well:

"One day I realised that I was starting to pay attention to things which did not interest me.

So I took the train to Marseille and the boat to Bombay. I didn't stop until I reached Darjeeling. There I walked until I reached a spot where I could contemplate Mount Everest without anyone bothering me; and I stayed there for five days, just staring at the Himalayas in their tranquillity. This is what most people need to do: to stop and look at something outside their ordinary experience."

He returned from this lengthy Asian interlude a vegetarian and devotee of silence and meditation. Nevertheless, his Italian temperament quickly re-asserted itself and at his home in the Valley of Chevreuse, the shoemaker became a farmer. He sowed seed behind a plough drawn by two oxen, harvested his own wheat, and made his own bread.

When going to work, Yantorny always got upset at the sight of passers-by in the street wearing imperfect shoes. From his meditations, he came up with the idea of establishing a new school for shoemaking. His dream of leaving behind a complete codification of his craft, for instructional purposes, held an important place in his journal:

"We need a school and the students in this school need to pass examinations and to be awarded the prizes based on their level of intelligence; in other words, first-place shoemaker; second-place shoemaker, and third-place" and "The young people selected must be taken to the mountains, far away from large towns, so they can learn well without big-city distractions."

Yantorny recommended admitting students at age fourteen, he believed mastery of the craft required eight years, five of which were devoted to forms and shoetrees. The examination would consist of measuring the feet of three different people and making forms, shoes, and shoetrees for each person. The successful candidate would receive the title master shoemaker and as Yantorny adds:

"If he gets first prize, he will have the right to make shoes for the most elegant and richest people on earth and will garner high prices for his shoes."

Yantorny's school was never created. On the other hand, his own research was awarded. In 1924, he registered a shoe-lacing patent in the United States. Eleven years later, Cardinal Pacelli, the future Pious XII, thanked him in the name of Saint Peter for his generous offering to the works and needs of the Holy See, with a special apostolic benediction from the Pope for Yantorny and his family.

This man who was fluent in three languages (his maternal Italian,

French, and English) could neither read nor write. His companion therefore had to lend a hand and record his journal as he dictated. The journal ends with Yantorny's description of his feathered shoe, now preserved in the International Shoe Museum, Romans:

"The masterpiece I wanted to present to the public was the feathered shoe made with small Japanese bird feathers each measuring around one and one-half millimetres. It took six months to make one pair. I didn't make it with the intention of selling it, only as an art object and to show just how far I could push the envelope of shoemaking."

Then he concludes:

"My only aim is to leave something to a museum of the shoe that future generations could admire, not a financial legacy, but the artistry found in shoes."

The most significant creations of this atypical shoemaker, who died on 12 December 1936, are divided between the Metropolitan Museum of Art, New York, and the International Shoe Museum, Romans.

85

André Perugia,

Last of the Great Renaissance Artists, First of the Moderns

Considered one of the 20th-century's greatest custom shoemakers, André Perugia was born in 1893 in Tuscany, the son of a shoe repairman. The family fled poverty by emigrating to Nice, where the father set up shop as a shoemaker.

His apprenticeship began in his father's workshop and continued with a boot maker in Nice when he was sixteen. Perugia quickly realised that he knew as much as his boss and decided to take over his father's shop. There he felt the limitations of the shoemaker's trade, already demonstrating a strong inclination towards invention.

Perugia's shoe styles attracted the interest of the wife of the head of the Negresco hotel, who offered him a window to display his shoes to hotel patrons. Paul Poiret came upon them during a trip to Nice, where he had gone to show his collections to Hindu princesses and to a wealthy clientele vacationing on the Riviera. Poiret wanted to enhance the splendour of this fashion show with colourful accessories and only André Perugia agreed on such short notice to produce the models sought by the couturier. After a triumphant showing, Poiret offered to set up Perugia in Paris, but the war disrupted the plans, which did not come off until 1920.

Poiret effectively introduced Perugia to his elegant clientele at his fashion show. Perugia did not have to wait for success and he returned home with a full order book. But he was still in his small family shop, and he dreamt of making shoes for the glittering world of Parisian high society.

One year later, the dream became a reality with the opening of a boutique at 11 rue du Faubourg Saint-Honoré. The shoes of famous customers displayed along with their names and a few extravagant styles captured journalists' attention. It was easy for Poiret to promote the young man; Perugia's talent did the rest.

The shoemaker created a number of models for the couturier, including the "Arlequinade" and "Folie," which corresponded to names of Poiret perfumes. Meanwhile, a top-drawer clientele filed into the house of Perugia, including Mistinguett (French music-hall idol), Josephine Baker (exotic dancer of the Roaring Twenties), queens, princesses, stars of stage and screen, and aristocrats. Perugia only made women's shoes, although he would good-naturedly make masculine models as an exception, for Maurice Chevalier, for example.

Beginning in 1927, Perugia crossed the Atlantic to capture a wealthy American clientele. Success in America was also by appointment only to "Monsieur Perugia," which became "Mister Perugia." In 1933, established at 4 rue de la Paix, he introduced the "Padova" brand distributed in the United States by Saks Fifth Avenue.

His foreign sales network grew with RAYNE in England. Additionally, in 1936, the Queen of England paid him the honour of an order during a visit to Paris. In 1937 he would establish himself once and for all at 2 rue de la Paix until the end of his career.

Perugia left a vast body of work. To interpret and understand his œuvre the observer must consider its technical aspects, its themes of inspiration, and Perugia's collaboration with couturiers. The work of a custom shoemaker is similar to that of a haut couturier. The shoemaker takes an impression of the foot (by making a plaster cast or a drawing) and takes measurements. The style and the height of the heel determine the form. From these elements an initial frame without ornament is made, which the shoemaker can open at the top, on the side, and at the heel during the fitting. When the frame was perfectly adjusted to the customer's foot, the shoe was ready for fabrication. A portion of Perugia's orders was executed in his workshops; the remainder was made by shoemakers working at home.

For Perugia, difficulty in execution and expense mattered little, whereas the shoe's suitability for walking and its proper fit were paramount.

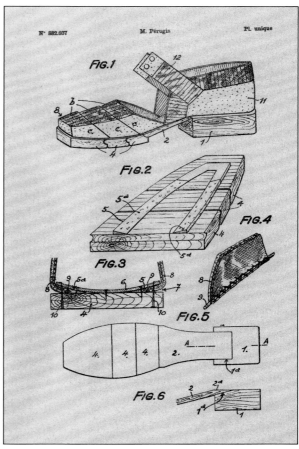

108. Print: *The House of Perugia or the Fashionable Shoemaker.* Guillen Collection, International Shoe Museum, Romans.

109. Patent awarded to Perugia in 1942. International Shoe Museum, Romans.

110. Perugia. War shoe, vamp made up of strips of cloth and skins, fitting of
boiled hide, square heel, wooden sole of blades attached to canvas, 1942.

111. Print: *Consultation — Perugia Shoes*. International Shoe Museum,
Romans. Photo by Joël Garnier.

112. Display window of Perugia shop, Faubourg Saint Honoré, Paris.

Perugia's customers ordered nearly forty pairs per season at an approximate unit price of fifty thousand francs, which amounted to a significant annual sales figure in the 1920s. Perugia's œuvre shows the use of an extraordinary diversity of materials: exotic and often surprising leathers (including llama stomach skin and antelope skin, which was painted and embroidered with purl), fabrics, laces, vegetable fibres, and horsehair, among others.

He did not hesitate to completely transform traditional leathers: snakeskin became gold and alligator skin sported cheerful colours. To this was added the opulence of embroidered and enamelled ornamentation, which transformed the shoe into an exclusive design. Perugia was a perfect master of his craft.

Perugia was also perfectly aware of his limitations, which motivated him to keep raising the bar through technical research. He never stopped devising new processes, forty of which bear registered and meticulously illustrated patents. These patents punctuate his entire career from 1921-1958. To Perugia we owe in particular not only the 1942 invention of the articulated wooden heel, which thrived during the World War II, but also the 1956 invention of the clever interchangeable heel system. Additionally, Perugia invented a metal instep; iron craftsmen made his heels for him. Perugia shoes defied the laws of balance by changing the established structure of the heel.

His interest in bare footedness led him to launch a sandal for evening. Without making the shoe inappropriate for walking, he eliminated as much of the upper as possible and used a transparent vinyl to create the illusion of a bare foot. Mindful of improving the fit of shoes, he thought of the foot in movement rather than in repose as was customary.

For Charles Jourdan, to whom he was a technical advisor from 1962 to 1966, Perugia adapted his patented inventions and his know-how to an industrial scale, but he was not involved in the creative process strictly speaking.

Perugia displayed originality in the art of the shoe from his very first creations. Times changed and different cultures nourished his design themes. The oriental theme appears throughout his oeuvre and is seen in shoes for evening, town, apartment, and even the beach. Perugia's oriental style was part of a fashion movement generated by the craze for the Ballets Russes. From 1909, Diaghilev's company performed in Paris. The ballet Shehezerade flaunted the sensuality of harem women in a commotion and explosion of colours and pleasantly distracted the public with the charms of the Orient. On 24 June 1911, Poiret organised a Persian celebration called *The Book of One Thousand and One Nights* and met his guests dressed as a sultan. His trip to Morocco in 1918 also enriched his imagination. It was surely under Poiret's influence that Perugia immersed himself in orientalism, which became a favourite theme. The effect is seen in Perugia's Chinese-inspired motifs, such as the apartment mule with raised heels. Perugia then looked towards Japan and made notched soles in imitation of the gaiter spat; closer to home, he found inspiration in Venetian mules that displayed masks.

Turning to history for inspiration, Perugia took the Greek cothurne and Roman campagus as models. The medieval period inspired his taste for the rustic shoes of the 10th and 11th centuries, made of a tall upper held by a thin cord. He succeeded in making an elegant version of this type: the "Dagobert." In addition to an evocative name, the Dagobert had an upper held by a thin cord hidden by a small cuff. The Charles IX, the Salomé, and the court pump known as the escarpin followed. Some of these shoes, with their tall uppers of beige antelope skin printed in gold and with openwork diamond patterns, were reminiscent of the cut windows of gothic churches.

But the shoemaker's own artistic milieu had a considerable impact on him. Poiret, who was a patron of painters, writers, and designers, turned Perugia into a connoisseur and enlightened art collector. The geometric ornaments of his shoes express a cubist aesthetic. Between 1925 and 1930 Art Deco motifs were everywhere. Perugia's wood heels, first sculpted and then gilded with gold leaf, reveal true artistic labour. This exclusive shoemaker was the first to exhibit in the Salon's Decorative Arts.

CONSULTATION

CHAUSSURES, DE PÉRUGIA

113. Perugia. Pump in blue kidskin printed with gold, heel and quarter from a single piece of wood carved and gold leaved, around 1950 (copy of a style created in 1923). International Shoe Museum, Romans.

114. Perugia. Style created for Arletty. Evening sandal in gold kidskin, cork platform sole covered with gold, 1938. International Shoe Museum, Romans.

115. Perugia sandal in gold kidskin and strass, metal heel inlayed with strass, 1952. International Shoe Museum, Romans.

116. Perugia. Heelless shoe in purple velvet calfskin, lace of gold kidskin, base of polished cork coloured gold, 1950. International Shoe Museum, Romans.

Around 1955, he reached the pinnacle of his career with a collection created in the United States. Each shoe was meant to be a homage to a 20th-century painter: Picasso, Braque, Matisse, Fernand Léger, Mondrian, et cetera. But Perugia's shoe as an art object still fulfills its primary function for walking. In addition to these bold creations, Perugia made many models for couturiers. As Paul Poiret's official shoemaker, he created pointed shoes with rich ornamentation and in various bright colours, that perfectly harmonized the couturier's long, straight silhouettes.

A long collaboration from 1930 to 1950 with Elsa Schiaparelli, with whom he shared a complementary competence, gave birth to new and original forms that were especially remarkable in their extraordinary modernity. After the World War II, Perugia placed his talent in the services of Dior, Jacques Fath, Balmain, and Hubert de Givenchy. During this period he continued to divide his time between France and the United States, where he collaborated with I. Miller, one of America's most famous custom shoemakers. His superb career came to an end with Charles Jourdan, to whom he left his extraordinary personal collection. An inspiring artistic resource, it is on view today at the International Shoe Museum, Romans. André Perugia died in Nice on November 22, 1977. Even though some of his designs were drawn from the past and mined orientalism for inspiration, this exclusive shoemaker's status as an innovator is confirmed by the results of his technical and aesthetic research.

Perugia's place in the world of fashion elevates the beauty of the shoe and affirms its modernity. His perfection of new materials, new forms, and new fabrication processes remain valid today. "Last of the great Renaissance artists and first of the moderns," Baudelaire's apt description of Delacroix can also be applied to this shoemaker for the excellence of his art of the shoe.

117. Perugia. Pump in kidskin, black glaze, upper shaped as a fish, heel composed of a metal blade enamelled black, style modeled after a painting by Braque, around 1955. International Shoe Museum, Romans.

118. Perugia. Mule in cream coloured kidskin and brown velvet with gold embroidery, heel covered with black and gold discs, 1949. International Shoe Museum, Romans.

119. Perugia. Evening sandal in red satin and gold kidskin, style created for Jacques Fath, around 1953. International Shoe Museum, Romans.

120. Bronze leather replica, 1985, after a style created in 1923 by Salvatore Ferragamo
in Hollywood for the film *The Ten Commandments*,
directed by Cecil B. DeMille. Ferragamo Museum, Florence.

121. Salvatore Ferragamo and Emilio Schubert during the first exhibition of fashion
in Florence in 1951. They presented their latest invention, "The Kino".

122. The Ferragamo workshop in Florence, after the return of Salvatore Ferragamo
in 1927. These photos were taken for the magazine *Gran Bazar* and published
in the end of the 1920s. Ferragamo Museum, Florence.

Ferragamo

Salvatore Ferragamo was born in 1898 in Bonito, a poor village in southern Italy. The son of a peasant, he made his first pair of shoes at age nine. Salvatore made these shoes as a gift to his sister in honour of her first communion, because he did not want her going to church on that day wearing clogs. Encouraged by this initial experience, he embarked on an apprenticeship with a shoemaker in Naples. In 1914 he immigrated to the United States, where he lived for thirteen years, working primarily for the motion picture industry and making shoes for the biggest names in cinema to wear on screen and in town. Concerned about comfort and elegance, he studied anatomy at the University of California. This education taught him the fundamental role the arch of the foot played in distributing the weight of the body. He then perfected a steel arch support that he thenceforth included in all his designs. Returning to Italy in 1927, he established himself definitively in Florence in 1935 near the district where traditional craftsmen had their shops. He then purchased the Palazzo Spini-Feroni, which remains the home of the world-renowned family business today. Economic problems in Italy during this period, followed by the war, prompted Salvatore Ferragamo not only to use inexpensive materials, such as braided paper, straw, and hemp, but also to replace his famous shank with cork. These difficulties did not hinder his remarkable creative imagination. Quite the contrary, because it was then that he made his most famous creation: the wedge sole, which was wildly successful and glorified the shoemaker's genius. New inventions marked the 1940s, such as the invisible sandal with upper made of nylon thread and heels sculpted in the form of an "F."

The exhilarating atmosphere of Italy in the 1950s made Rome, Amalfi, and Portofino tourist destinations for the wealthy, who never failed to make a stop in Florence to buy the famous shoemaker's latest creations. One day Greta Garbo bought seventy pairs in one fell swoop. The Duchess of Windsor stocked up on bi-coloured shoes each spring. Ferragamo's creativity, originality, and imaginativeness combine harmoniously with extraordinary technical knowledge. These qualities won him the 1947 Neiman Marcus Award. Twenty years later, his daughter Fiamma repeated this achievement. Salvatore Ferragamo died in 1960. He still speaks to us through his most beautiful creations exhibited in the museum that bears his name, which is established in the Spini-Ferroni palace for the delight of all visitors.

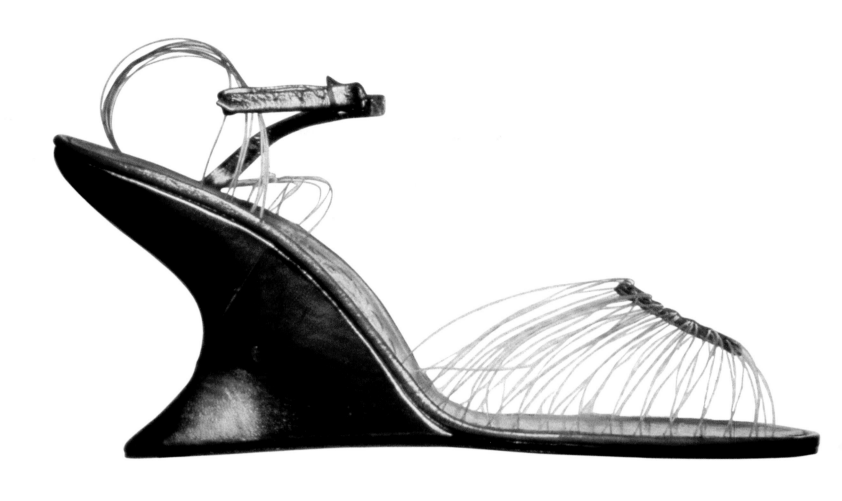

123. Ferragamo, sandal in nylon and gilded leather. Ferragamo Museum, Florence.

124. Ferragamo, style created for Sophia Loren, beads and motifs embroidered in satin. Ferragamo Museum, Florence.

Alfred Argence

Established in 1900, Argence first opened its doors in Paris at 89 rue du Faubourg Saint-Honoré, before moving to the rue des Pyramides, where it remained until it closed. This prestigious firm, which focused on elegant women's shoes, was a member of the Syndicat des Bottiers de Paris, and attracted an elegant and famous clientele, including Sarah Bernhardt and Cléo de Sérode. Argence received many awards in the context of international exhibitions, such as the 1908 general labour exhibition in Florence and the 1908 international exhibition of modern industry and decorative and commercial arts in Rome. Alfred Victor Argence succeeded his father and worked in collaboration with Haute Couture. He was awarded many prizes at various exhibitions, such as "Artisans of Paris" in October 1942 and the "Exhibition of Shoemaking Firms" organised by the National Federation of French Shoemakers and the Union of France in the framework of the Congress of the International Leather Bureau in Paris in September 1948. The firm's business gradually declined before closing down in the early 1980s.

125. Evening shoe. Mary Jane in black suede, applications of gold kidskin, stass embroidery, silver filigree buckle. Louis XV heel covered with gold celluloid and strass. Pump realised by Julienne.
International Shoe Museum, Romans.

Julienne, Woman Shoemaker

The daughter of a master shoemaker, Julienne started learning the secrets of the trade at a very young age.

In 1919, she set up shop in Paris at 235, rue Saint-Honoré; a boutique in Biarritz followed later. Her imaginative skill as a model-maker and her technical knowledge of traditional French craftsmanship positioned her at the forefront among the best.

Julienne specialised in fine shoes for distribution, attracting a clientele of elegant women with limited budgets who could not afford custom shoes.

Julienne's shoes were pretty replicas of custom-made styles; the excellence of their materials and forms sharply distinguished Julienne's shoes from banal, mass-produced brands. Always ahead of new trends, Julienne assimilated the exotic influences of the colonial exhibition and adapted them for Parisian taste. Julienne stopped working before World War II.

126. Pump realised by Julienne. Large bakelite buckle decorated with white beads, application in red kidskin. International Shoe Museum, Romans.

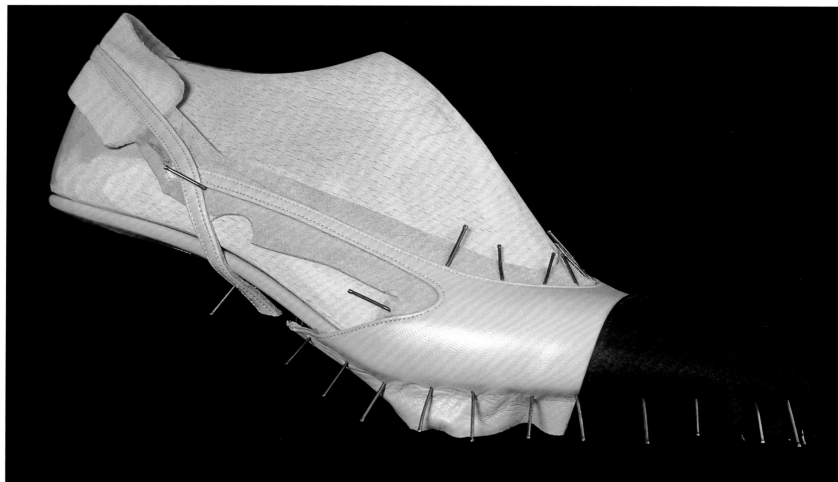

La Maison Massaro

A Shoemaking Dynasty

Sébastien Massaro founded the firm that bears his name in 1894, setting up shop at 2 rue de la Paix in Paris. His four sons, François, Xavier, Donat, and Lazare learned the trade under their father's supervision.

Lazare's son, Raymond Joseph Massaro, was born on 19 March 1929. His career led him to the Ecole des métiers de la chaussure (a French trade school for shoemakers) on the rue de Turbigo in Paris, where he obtained vocational training qualification (C.A.P) in Louis XV women's shoes in 1947. The young Raymond finished his training in the family workshop. He remembers his father at the time making shoes for Elsa Schiaparelli, the Duchess of Windsor, Countess Von Bismarck, the millionaire Barbara Hutton, Shirley MacLaine, and Elizabeth Taylor, all of whom were regulars of the boutique on the rue de la Paix, along with other celebrities.

The Massaro family designed mainly for individuals, but it was developing closer ties with Parisian Haute Couture firms. In 1954, Lazare Massaro created a ballerina shoe for Madame Grès that would influence the entire period. This was followed by his invention of the famous bi-coloured sandal in beige and black for Coco Chanel in 1958.

Raymond Massaro took over the firm's management and continued his the work of his father and grandfather. Many celebrities called upon his talent, including King Hassan II, to whom he became shoemaker, the actress Romy Schneider, and more recently the private Haute Couture collector Mouna Ayoub.

Raymond Massaro also filled some unusual requests for shoes that were quite humourous. Once there was a maharajah, a regular resident at a luxury hotel in Paris, who came to the capital with his personal secretary. The Asian secretary was so used to his country's ancestral tradition of going barefoot inside the palace, that he was unable to walk in shoes inside the expensive hotel without great difficulty. The Indian vassal prince wanted to respect French customs out of courtesy. So he asked his shoemaker to make a pair of shoes without soles that would allow his secretary's feet to come into direct contact with the ground. The clever shoes allowed the secretary to bow to both French and Indian traditions.

Major couture firms also came calling to Raymond Massaro, including: Emmanuel Ungaro, Guy Laroche, Gianfranco-Ferré, Christian Dior, Thierry Mugler, Ocimar Versolato, Christophe Rouxel, Olivier Lapidus, Jean-Paul Gaultier, and Dominique Sirop. He produced various styles for Karl Lagarfeld at Chanel, and made resin heels that looked like women's legs for Azzedine Alaïa. Constantly innovating, this designer is totally committed to originality.

In 1994, the French Minister of Culture exclusively awarded Raymond Massaro the title Master of Art for combining consummate craftsmanship with a creative spirit. The shoemaker also belongs to the "Committee Signé Paris," established in 1997 to promote in France and abroad firms dedicated to excellence that represent Paris fashion through the quality of their artistic know-how. In 1999, Raymond Massaro exhibited his shoes in Tokyo as part of Japan's Year of France.

Raymond Massaro is also devoted to the science of foot orthopedics.

Previous pages:

127. Massaro in his workshop.

128. Shoe in production for Chanel by Massaro.

129. Elastic pump created for Madame Grès (beachwear) by Massaro, 1955.

130. Shoe created by Massaro for Chanel, 1958.

131. Shoe created by Massaro, 1992.

132. Black-varnished sandal with platform sole in cork created by Massaro for Chanel in summer 2001. On the cork heels, the inscription "Château Chanel" can be read.

133. Massaro, "legs" platform shoes for Azzedine Alaïa, 1991. Black glaze, red kidskin and red base. Achieved using resin, the "leg heel" was hand carved.

134. Shoe created by Massaro, 1991.

135. Massaro, white mule painted entirely by hand with the Parisian coat of arms. 1997. Creation for the Signé Paris committee.

MERGITUR FLUCTUAT NE

103

Sarkis Der Balian

The Immortal Shoemaker

Sarkis Der Balian was an Armenian born in the early 20th century in Aïtab Cilicia, Little Armenia. He showed an early interest in shoes. Orphaned at age seven, he was taken in by a regional shoemaker, who gradually taught the craft to Balian while the child went to school. He soon detected within his young apprentice a gifted student and a hard worker who had unusual manual dexterity, so he encouraged the boy to continue.

Full of love for his craft, the child embraced an Armenian saying that "knowing a traditional craft is like having a gold bracelet on your wrist." He arrived in France on 7 March 1929, to practice his craft in the various workshops of Parisian custom shoemakers. Around 1934, he went to work for Enzel, a shoemaker on the rue Saint-Honoré, where he managed a team of forty workers. The famous Charles Ritz managed the firm and he admired Balian's work. During this period he made shoes for Marie Curie, the aviator Hélène Boucher, and Mistinguett, among others.

Balian complemented these productive years designing for Enzel with independent work as a model maker, which allowed him to assert himself more individually. Among the clients he created models for were Max Bally, the factories of Unic-Fenestrier in Romans, the Fougères factories, and the firm Besson, a small Parisian maker of women's shoes. He also technically perfected certain models made for the large couturiers.

In 1935, he toured Italy, taking away from that country an image of perfected beauty that would constantly guide and illuminate his work designing pumps, sandals, booties, and shoes. The events of 1936 led to Enzel being closed down. His journey then led him to the corner of the rue Rivoli and the rue Renard to "Cecile," a firm specialising in footwear for men, women, and children where he obtained the job of Technical Manager. He turned down an invitation from Delman who offered him the opportunity to make shoes in the United States in 1939. Attached to his adopted country of France, he set up shop on the rue de la Sourdière in Paris from 1943 to 1945. The rococo interiors of his first store, which he designed himself and made with his own hands, remains in place today. Success led him to move into a much larger store at 221 rue Saint-Honoré in 1947. Once again, he left his stamp on the architectural interior and decoration and designed a setting to welcome and seduce a demanding clientele, interested in elegance and comfort. The comfort of his shoes merited the label "Der Balian comfort fit" for this consummate craftsman, shoemaker, boot maker, model maker, and designer, as he described himself.

His need to constantly achieve new heights led him to produce masterpieces such as the history of Cinderella. A true miniature painting, it is made of over five hundred thousand tiny bits of leather. The same technique is found on a shoe depicting the city of Zurich viewed from the windows of the Town Hall. At the time, the city of Zurich persistently tried to purchase the shoe, but Balian refused. The piece represented over a year's work for this craftsman of art objects who never looked at his watch, and who was ready to undo and redo as often as necessary, the result being the only thing that mattered to him.

Throughout his long career Balian made shoes for a wide range of celebrities, including the painters Salvador Dali and Dunoyer de Segonzac; sculptor Paul Belmondo; actors Claude Dauphin, Gaby Morlet, Greta Garbo, and Laurent Terzieff; boxer Georges Carpentier; the artists Henri Salvador and Yehudi Menuhin; the writers Jean Anouilh, Aragon, and Elsa Triolet; and the aviator Jean Mermoz.

Internationally known since 1930 he received many prizes and the highest awards in all the national and international exhibitions. In 1955, he won footwear's world cup in Bologna for his masterpiece called "floralie," an extraordinary shoe with a hollow silver heel that was inlaid. The jury was so impressed with this shoe that they named Balian the "Michelangelo of the shoe." For this honour, the city of Paris presented him with the médaille de vermeil. Best worker in France in 1958, his appointment as technical advisor for technical training was renewed five times by the French Ministry of National Education.

Balian's generosity led him to spontaneously transmit his knowledge to the younger generation. He moreover knew how to recognise and admire quality work with total impartiality; doing so was his greatest pleasure. Assisted by his wife and daughter, Astrid, he kept his business going until 1995 and died on 29 March 1996.

This virtuoso of shoemaking, about which he was absolutely passionate, still speaks to us if we stop to contemplate his work preserved and displayed at the International Shoe Museum, Romans.

136. Sarkis Der Balian at his workbench.

Following pages:
137. Zurich, creation of Sarkis Der Balian, Paris, 1950. Shoe made of parchment inlayed with naturally coloured leather, representing the view of Zurich from the city hall.

138. Charles IX in maroon satin, platform sole, straight heel, gold kidskin design imitating paintwork, creation of Sarkis Der Balian, around 1940.

139. Flora, creation of Sarkis Der Balian, Paris, for the World Cup, won in 1955. Upper composed of piped and interlaced straps, hallow heel silver-plated and inlayed with iridescent leather.

140. Cinderella, creation of Sarkis Der Balian, Paris, 1950. Fairytale realised on a velvet upper inlayed with tiny, multicoloured sequins.

Berluti

Three Generations of Artists

A native of Senigallia, Italy; Alexandre Berluti began his apprenticeship in woodworking as an adolescent. This initial craft cultivated his love of finely worked wood that he would later rediscover in the art of form making for shoes. Possessing great manual dexterity, he acquired knowledge of leather craft that his descendants would inherit. The gripping tales of Ilebrando, an old shoemaker who emigrated to Marseille, reached Berluti's village and put the notion of travel in his head. So, around 1887, carrying Ilebrando's shiny tools as his luggage, he departed for new horizons. Once on the road, he encountered a company of street acrobats whom he accompanied for several years, making the shoes for the players in the company.

Arriving in Paris in 1895, he practised the craft of shoemakers, creating exclusively custom shoes, a tradition maintained today by the Berluti firm. The 1900 World Fair offered him a chance to make himself known to a larger public. Upon his return to his native country, he ran a workshop until his death and transmitted the secrets of his art to his son Torello.

Torello apprenticed in his father's workshop where he showed a predilection for hard work and a desire to get ahead. With a sculptor's skill, his hand measured, cut, polished, and assembled shoes. During the Roaring Twenties, he settled in Paris, opening a boutique in 1928 on the rue du Mont Thabor under the trade name Berluti, exclusive custom-made shoes.

The house style was established by three emblematic types: lace-up pumps (or pope's shoe, a pure form made from a single piece without seams), the flat or moccasin of a single piece called the "Renaissance princess shoe" and finally the Napoleon III, a tall style with elastic on the side, which would one day elicit the following comment from the Duke of Windsor: "Something simultaneously modest and mischievous."

From this time forward, Berluti had a reputation, and attracted a lot of attention from the international clients of the surrounding luxury hotels, resulting in the store's relocation to 26 rue Marbeuf. This elite location became a temple to the shoe and of masculine elegance, decorated in wood and leather, in homage to the family's dual crafts.

In the early 1950s, a variety of celebrities were to be seen at Berluti's: James de Rothschild, Alain de Gunzburg, Sacha Distel, Eddy Constantine, Bernard Blier, Gaston and Claude Gallimard, Charles Vanel, Fernand Gravey, Marcel l'Herbier, Pierre Mondy, Yul Bryner, Marcel Achard, Jules Roy, and André Hunnebelle. These names demonstrate how well Berluti's fame attracted the Jet Set in 1958.

In the early 1960s, the firm was successfully established and Torello's son Talbino took the reigns. Talbino had been introduced to the shoemaker's craft at age fourteen, but he subsequently pursued architectural studies. The roles were immediately shared between the father and son. Talbino, whose talent was rather intellectual and imaginative, had the vision and made the designs, whereas Torello fabricated the stuff of his son's dreams. From this close collaboration was born the laced moccasin in the early 1940s. But in 1959, Talbino disrupted the firm's tradition by inviting exclusive ready-to-wear into the world where the custom-made reigned with its production delays. This new direction satisfied demanding and impatient clients. Immediately available, these "exclusive ready to wear" shoes permitted lower prices, an expanded client base, and the growth of the firm.

But how did one get a perfect fit if measurements were not taken? Talbino and his cousin Olga solved the problem by playfully perfecting five morphological foot types: the pretentious, the intellectual, the fragile, the masochist, and the unpleasant. These portraits corresponded to a "visual chart" that allowed one to visualise the most suitable model once the client's shoes were off.

141. Men's shoes executed by Berluti.
142. Photograph of Olga Berluti.

Between 1960 and 1980, Talbino tirelessly developed the firm. He and his father gave clients a warm welcome into a world of refinement.

As for Olga Berluti, Italian by birth, she spent her childhood in Parma and Venice, but became Parisian at heart and in culture. During university she leaned toward philosophy before devoting herself to the art of custom shoemaking. Her arrival to rue Marbeuf in 1959 marked the beginning of ten years of intense and productive apprenticeship in addition to study with surgeons who were clients of the firm. Together, they examined how shoes are used as well as posture and the form of the foot, enabling them to diagnose foot and back problems some people suffered from. This truly "clinical research" led to the physiological line called "Comfort." New ideas were in the air. Olga responded by offering to clients used to wearing classic shoes new designs that had the forms and colours they were dreaming about. Unusual shades of green, grey, and yellow appeared attracting such customers as François Truffaut, Andy Warhol, Roman Polanski, and Jacques Lacan. The boutique became a salon, with hurried people stopping in their tracks to exchange pleasantries with Olga. The shoemaker had become artist and poet. Even the moon's magic, through its whitening effect on shoe leather exposed to moonbeams, cooperated with Olga, who achieved deep tones and a previously unknown shine. As the ambassador of this prestigious brand, the exceptional, exciting, and passionate Olga was in charge of promotion and decoration of Berluti boutiques, which opened throughout the world. The firm's current designs reflect the fashion phenomenon of urban sports shoes, as can be seen in the styles offered in the recently opened boutique on the boulevard Saint-Germain. But our century's changes are unlikely to alter the time-honoured methods of hand-fashioned shoes, for three generations the symbol of the Berluti.

143. Berluti boutique in Paris, 26 rue Marbeuf.
144. Men's shoes executed by Berluti.

Following pages:
145. Men's shoes executed by Berluti.
146. Men's shoes executed by Berluti.

147. Men's shoes executed by Berluti.

148. Shape of shoes created for Gaston Gallimard.

149. Shoe created for Gallimard by Berluti.

150. Men's shoes, Tatoues Collection, House of Berluti.

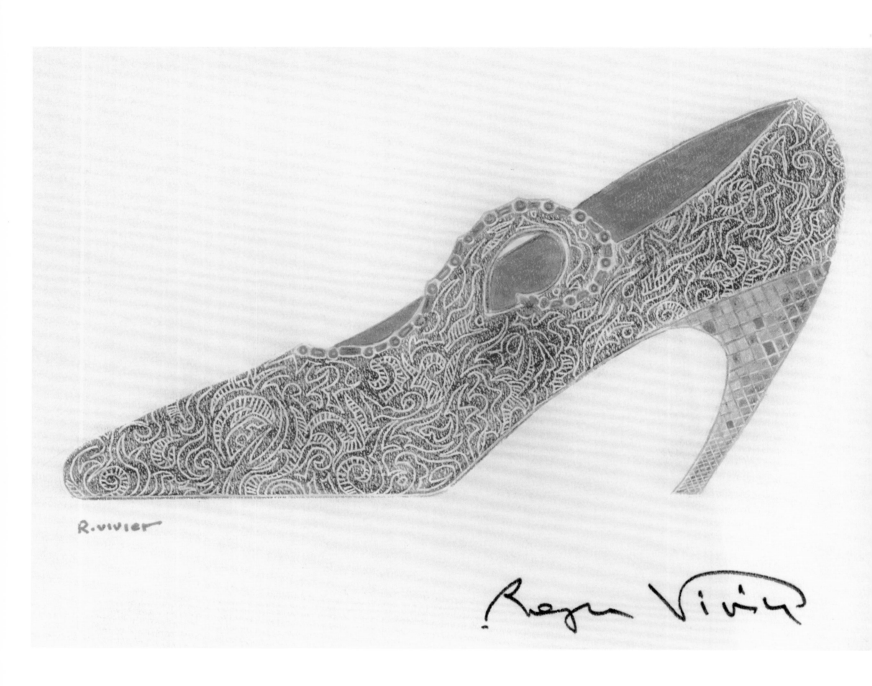

R.VIVIER

Roger Vivier

Roger Vivier

Couturier of the Shoe

Roger Vivier was born in Paris in 1907. At age thirteen he went to work in a shoe factory owned by family friends where he learned technical basics and the different stages of fabrication.

His artistic abilities naturally led Vivier to the Ecole des Beaux-Arts in Paris where he studied sculpture. Between 1926 and 1927, at age twenty, he decided to devote himself to shoe design. His meeting with theatre decorator Paul Seltenhammeur was decisive; with Seltenhammeur, Vivier visited Venice and Berlin, turning his attention to a world closely linked to the artistic and literary avant-garde of his time. Mistinguett ordered Vivier shoes, as did Josephine Baker and Marianne Oswald, who sang Cocteau. Vivier navigated all the avant-garde trends with eclectic taste, immersing himself in the great artistic movements of the time: the decorative arts in France, the Bauhaus in Germany, the Wiener Werkstätten in Austria. His assimilation to this culture was expressed in the decoration of the successive apartments he lived in.

Hired in 1936 as an exclusive designer and maker of shoe patterns for Laborémus, the French division of a major German tannery located under the eaves of 16 place Vendôme, Roger Vivier was responsible for producing a highly Parisian shoe line that would win over buyers and facilitate the quantity sale of leather skins.

In 1937, Roger Vivier opened his first store on rue Royale where his styles, made by his own workshop, were sold to a large French and American clientele. He also designed shoes for the largest manufacturers in the world such as Delman who guaranteed the exclusivity of his designs in America. Vivier also attracted the attention of the fashion world, especially Elsa Schiaparelli.

The war necessitated the closing of his studio on the rue Royale when he joined the army. Discharged in 1940, he was invited by Delman to continue his work in the United States. In 1941, he left for New York on the transatlantic ship *L'Exeter*. On board he met Suzanne Rémy, the top milliner at Agnès, who was emigrating with her mother. When the United States entered the war, the use of leather was drastically restricted to be able to meet the priority demands of the army. Short on raw materials, Roger Vivier turned to a complementary activity and becoming the assistant to photographer Georges Hoyningen-Huene, who was working for Harper's Bazaar. There he came in contact with the fashion world and met Carmel Snow, Harper's Bazaar's editor at the time. He also formed a close friendship with Fernand Léger and associated with other European artists in exile such as Max Ernst, Calder and Chagall. At the same time, he was working for Bergdorf Goodman and making hats in the evening with Suzanne Rémy. The celebrated milliner from Agnès taught him the art of hat making. A hat store under the name of "Suzanne et Roger" opened in 1942 at the corner of Madison Avenue and 64th Street. Within a year, the store had become the most Parisian destination in New York. In 1947, he went back to Paris where he made the acquaintance of Michel Brodsky, his future collaborator, and Christian Dior. He created all the custom-made shoes for Dior's collections after 1953. That same year he made shoes for the Coronation of Queen Elizabeth II of England.

Two years later, Christian Dior and Roger Vivier had the ingenious idea of establishing a department for "prêt-à-porter" shoes. It was the first time a Parisian couturier associated his label with that of a shoemaker for the purpose of promoting a mass-market line. In 1954, a shoe with a slender heel of seven to eight centimetres deposed the draped shoe and reigned until the appearance and victory of the stiletto heel in 1956, also one of Vivier's inventions. Shoes were adorned with sumptuous 18th-century style embroidery by Rébé. Vivier's collaboration with Yves Saint-Laurent always showed the most innovative forms.

For example, the 1959 choc heel, so named because at first glance it was shocking, was nevertheless a brilliant success. In 1960, the Punchinello heel and the stem heel drew attention. The success of the square toe was confirmed in 1961 when the following women adopted it: Queen Elizabeth II, the Empress of Iran, the Duchess of Windsor, Jacqueline Kennedy, Olivia de Havilland, Marlene Dietrich, Elizabeth Taylor, and Sophia Loren.

In 1963, Roger Vivier opened his own boutique with Michel Brodsky at 24 rue François 1ᵉʳ. The comma-shaped heel was his personal signature on sumptuous shoes. In 1965, he created a shoe with a stacked heel for Yves Saint-Laurent; square, decorated with a buckle of gold metal, this design sold tens of thousands of pairs. The use of synthetic materials, such as transparent vinyl, also aroused great interest.

In 1970, the hippie style inspired Vivier to make thigh-high boots, which were appreciated by Brigitte Bardot and mini-skirt wearers. Vivier made shoes for many celebrities: the Empress of Japan, Princess Grace of Monaco, Claude Pompidou and Romy Schneider, among others. The list of royal highnesses, princesses and actresses is impressive. His international reputation as a virtuoso of shoemakers put him at the feet of clients from all four corners of the globe. One of them even ordered shoes for her toy poodle, Bonbon. Although somewhat surprised by this most unexpected order, Vivier accepted. On the day of the fitting, the shoemaker brought out two models that were fit to the animal's paws; the woman's little "toutou" began to run around the store while his mistress's eyes filled with wonder at the models. However, her look then changed to consternation and she turned to her shoemaker and said, "But my dog has four paws." Roger Vivier hastily amended this oversight to the great pleasure of his faithful client.

Vivier gave his shoes the volume of a sculpture and the contours of a drawing. They can sport daring heels, like the stem heel, or malicious heels, like the Cancan, Guignol, and Punchinella; sometimes they rest on the ground like a scintillating paste sphere, a favourite style of Marlene Dietrich. The variety of materials used created surprise: shoes were adorned with pheasant feathers of gold edged in black, guinea fowl feathers, kingfisher feathers and were even wrapped in panther.

Some of his shoes were covered in pearls, brightly coloured paste, sequins, and sumptuous embroidery from the dazzling collaboration between Roger Vivier and the embroiderer François Lesage. His collaboration with Paris couture ended in 1972, but foreign contracts gave him the opportunity to create relentlessly until the end of his life. His son, Gérard Benoît-Vivier assisted him. The elder Vivier died on 1 October 1998. He was at home in his townhouse in Toulouse, still at his worktable. The most important collections of his shoes (Vivier preferred the French word *soulier* over *chaussure* to signify the general category of all shoes) affirming his talent, virtuosity, and tireless work are preserved in the following museums: Fashion and Textile Museum (Paris), Galliera Museum (Paris), the International Shoe Museum (Romans), Victoria and Albert Museum (London) and the Metropolitan Museum of Art (New York). Vivier's timeless shoes were and continue to be the subject of many international exhibitions that pay tribute to the shoe's great couturier.

151. Shock heel by Roger Vivier, 1955.

119

152. Evening sandal. Organza and strass. Created by Roger Vivier, Paris, 1985.
International Shoe Museum, Romans. Photo by Joël Garnier.

153. Poulaine style shoe. Velvet, pendants and beads. "Clown" heel.
Created by Roger Vivier, Paris, 1987. International Shoe Museum, Romans.

154. Poulaine style shoe. Velvets, pendants and beads. "Clown" heel.
Created by Roger Vivier, Paris, 1987. International Shoe Museum, Romans.

155. Evening sandal. Blue satin, sequin embroidery. "Comma" heel.
Created by Roger Vivier, Paris, 1963. International Shoe Museum, Romans.

156. Kidskin shoes shown in eleven shades, straight heel, around 1980, creations of François Villon. International Shoe Museum, Romans.

François Villon (1911-1997)

His real name was Benveniste. François Villon was a pseudonym the shoemaker borrowed because he admired the great French poet of the Middle Ages.

After a close collaboration with the firm Perugia, of which he was the chief executive, François Villon created his own design house in 1960. He set up shop at 27 rue du Faubourg Saint-Honoré and worked on the custom-made shoe concept he had already experimented with at Perugia, but adapting it to a larger scale of production. The François Villon label was highly successful around 1965, attracting a refined and famous clientele.

The styles of François Villon did not always keep up with the vagaries of fashion and were sometimes out of step with the times. He made various versions of boots, such as leather thigh-high boots (a red leather version was worn by Sheila for her televised series in 1968), cowboy boots for city dwellers, and riding boots. He also introduced the cut boot in 1970, which coordinated with the dresses of Louis Féraud.

Beginning in 1969, his ballerinas were shown in the same couturier's fashion shows. He created shoes for sport, for town, and for evening with equal enthusiasm. His research led him to create a spiral heel constructed with great complexity.

François Villon quickly opened a number of boutiques abroad in Milan, New York, Singapore, and Hong Kong.

Among the couture firms that chose his shoes for their fashion shoes were Hermès, Chanel, Ted Lapidus, Jean Patou, Nina Ricci, Jean-Louis Scherrer, Louis Féraud, and Lanvin.

François Villon pursued his career tirelessly until his death in 1997.

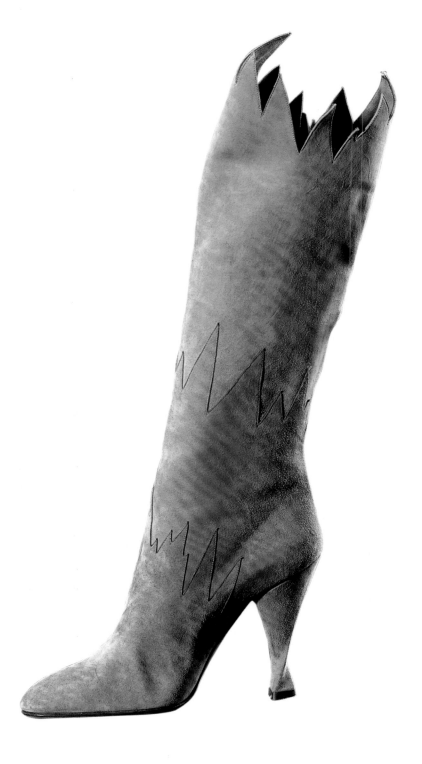

157. Suede boot with tendril heel, creation of François Villon, Paris, 1980-1981. International Shoe Museum, Romans.

Andrea Pfister

Happy Feet

Born in 1942 in Pesaro, Italy, in the region of the Marches, Andrea Pfister was age eighteen when he entered the University of Florence to study art history. A graduate at age twenty from the Ars Sutoria of Milan, he won first prize in the 1963 international competition for best shoe designer held in Amsterdam, thus beginning a surefooted career marked by the following key dates:

1964: Pfister settles in Paris where he designs shoe collections for the couture firms Jean Patou and Lanvin.

1965: Pfister launches his first collection under his own name.

1967: Pfister meets Jean-Pierre Dupré, who becomes his partner. Together they open the first Andrea Pfister boutique on the rue Cambon in Paris.

1974: Pfister buys his own factory, which produces two hundred pairs of shoes a day and introduces a new development with the creation of bags, belts, and scarves.

1987: Pfister inaugurates a second boutique with a highly symbolic address: via San Andrea in Milan.

1988: Once again Pfister is consecrated best shoe designer, winning the Grand Fashion Medal of Honour from the Fashion Footwear Association of New York and the Fashion Media Association.

1991: Pfister begins collaboration with Anaconda tanneries (specialists in reptile skins) and Stefania (specialists in kid leather and suede) to create a chromatic line of his design. The styles he envisions combine reptile and kid leather with suede in perfect harmony.

1993: The International Shoe Museum, Romans, gives him a retrospective. The exhibit travelled to the Bata Shoe Museum in Toronto in 1996 and the FIDM in Los Angeles and San Francisco in 1998.

Always interested in the alliance of aesthetics and comfort and known for his research on shoe shapes and heels, Pfister improvises on diverse themes with great panache: fruits, flowers, animals, the starry night, the ocean, music, the circus, Las Vegas, et cetera.

Classic and baroque, opulent and unusual, daring and visionary, decorated with multi-coloured glass pearls, paste, sequins and even embroidery, Pfister's shoes seduce his clients. Among his clientele one can find such stars as Ursula Andress, Candice Bergen, Jacqueline Bisset, Claudia Cardinale, Cher, Catherine Deneuve, Bo Derek, Linda Evans, Madonna, Lisa Minelli, Diana Ross, Barbara Streisand, Elizabeth Taylor, and Sylvie Vartan.

As Jean-Claude Carrière has so aptly written: "Feet in Andrea's shoes have style. To walk in Pfister, is to wear always-smiling shoes; it's to invent a look everyday. It's to walk lightheartedly even under grey skies. It's near bliss."

158. "The North Pole" farandole of penguins in snake skin on suede ankle boot. Andrea Pfister. Winter 1984-1985. International Shoe Museum, Romans.

159. "Tomato" mule by Andrea Pfister, Spring-Summer 2002. International Shoe Museum, Romans.

160. "Carrot" sandal by Andrea Pfister, Spring-Summer 2002. International Shoe Museum, Romans.

161. Mules by Robert Clergerie, Spring-Summer 1998.
International Shoe Museum, Romans.

162. Photograph of Robert Clergerie.

The Rise of the Shoe Industry;
Romans is the city of fine shoes

The two great names of the 20th century:
Joseph Fenestrier
Robert Clergerie

In the Middle Ages, the tanners of Romans were highly prosperous. Around 1850, François Barthélemy Guillaume got the idea of using the city's tanneries that were already in place to create the first factory for shoes mounted on wood.

Beginning in the 19th-century, Romans shoes acquired a certain fame. The train station, open since 1864, permitted long-distance shipping. At the same time, industries related to shoes were being established and expanded, especially factories for shoe forms. The great industrial revolution, beginning in 1890, gathered momentum with the use of electrical-powered engines and propelled breathtaking expansion of mechanisation, completely changing the face of the industry.

But Romans had a significant reservoir of highly qualified labourers who knew how to perform each stage of production by hand. These workers did not welcome the arrival of technical modernisation. They feared this change would eliminate work for a certain number of workers in the profession.

Early in the century, large shoemaking centres like Limoges and Fougères adopted machines that increased production more cheaply and with fewer workers. Romans suffered from this extra-muros factor, but continued to stand for quality production.

After putting a lot of effort into development, around 1900 all the factories of Romans (thirty-five factories and three thousand workers) were equipped with finishing machines and produced one hundred thousand pairs of shoes a month. Out of the three thousand workers, one-third worked in the factory, while the others performed their jobs at home. During this period there were three kinds of workers:

– Preparation men and women included the workers who cut the uppers and soles, those who stitched the uppers, buttonhole makers and eyelet and button fitters;
– The workers involved in making the shoe itself were divided into assemblers and finishers;
– The workers who trimmed the shoes, prepared shoes for boxes and were responsible for steaming and shipping.

The average salary for workers in these categories came to about three francs per day for men and two francs for women. However, highly skilled seamers working on pieces in the fabrication process earned twenty francs a week; other less skilled workers, even though more hardworking, could not earn more than ten francs a week.

Those working at home were also involved with their household. Their workday was therefore not as productive as a factory worker's.

The First World War disrupted the city's economy and production had to be increased to met the needs of the military. Men called to the front were replaced by women labourers who demonstrated their adaptation to manual dexterity. Many a small business came into being at the impulse of a skilled and adventurous labourer, sometimes assisted by a travelling salesman, with one managing the workshop and the other managing sales.

In 1920, many firms were like families and were still structured like traditional craft organisations rather than industrial companies. But the workers of Romans defended and always produced quality articles. Firms such as Sirius, Bady, Will's, and Barnasson had considerable reputations and knew how to create a true brand image for their shoes. But the most typical Romans-style factory was the work of a pork butcher called to a higher destiny and fame.

In 1895, Joseph Fenestrier, age twenty-one, bought a small rubber boot factory near the train station. A novice to the industry, he partnered with M. Pervillat. The business had a very craft-based structure, and despite an unfavourable business climate, it produced eighty pairs of shoes a day. From 1890-1901, the industrial sector slowed down and during this period many factories closed their doors. But from 1901, lack of space on the premises justified the construction of a new factory on the boulevard Gambetta, with immense possibility of future expansion. Joseph Fenestrier launched the then innovative idea of specialisation and made expensive men's shoes, an idea that would remain the foundation of his future concepts. To this end, he introduced a new assembly technique: Goodyear Stitch construction. To do this, he set up the most modern machine available, which he leased from the United Shoes Machinery Company, an American trust. Well aware that abundant skilled labour was located in situ, Joseph Fenestrier proceeded to risk mechanising. In 1904, he launched the first advertising campaign in the history of the shoe throughout France under the following brand names:

UNIC
CHAUSSURES D'HOMMES
CINQUANTE ANS D'HONNEUR COMMERCIAL ET D'EXPERIENCE PROFESSIONNELLE
PRODUCTION DES USINES FENESTRIER _ ROMANS (DRÔME-DAUPHINE)

HISTOIRE CONTEMPORAINE DE LA CHAUSSURE _ 2 _ 1910

163. Advertisement UNIC, 1910. International Shoe Museum, Romans.

– Excelsior chaussures moderne
– Good Taste American Fashion
– Chaussures supérieures Fenestrier

The Unic brand established in 1907 crowned his career. Posters of six square metres in size displaying six legs dressed in Unic carried this prestigious brand to the height of its glory. Then, in 1910, Unic was awarded a true victory with the grand prize from the World Fair in Brussels. Joseph Fenestrier nevertheless expressed the following motto: "In ten years, ten times better, ten times bigger."

Shortly after the Brussels World Fair, production exceeded five hundred pairs a day. New extensions were made to the factory. Fenestrier constantly fanned the flames of Unic's loyal following among an elegant clientele with intelligent advertising, the creation in Paris of an independent sales division, and by the inauguration in 1912 of a sales system based on imposed prices. Throughout this period, the firm shone most brightly in all the international sales exhibitions. Between 1910 and 1914, Unic won the highest awards at the World Fairs. The prizes came one after another: 1911 (Turin), 1912 (London), 1913 (Ghent), and 1914 (Lyon). Unic became a member of the exhibition's jury (outside of the competition) in the 1915 San Francisco World Fair. The brand expanded throughout continental Europe, Russia, Egypt and the Middle East.

Just like French cities, major cities in Germany, Belgium, Italy, and Switzerland had an elite Unic retail store. After the premature death of its founder in 1916, at age forty-two, his widow took over managing the firm. In 1917, a fire destroyed the factory. A second factory established in Saint-Marcellin the year before enabled production to continue while the factory in Romans was rebuilt.

In 1922, the couple's son, Joseph Emile-Jean Fenestrier, took over. In 1926, eight hundred workers working in two factories produced one thousand two hundred pairs of shoes per day.

Exports grew in the countries still free of protectionism: Australia, the Netherlands, India, and the Far East. Alongside increased sales, the company developed internal social programs: a mutual aid society, allocations to families with more than two children, playgrounds and fields for sports. The factory had its own autonomous division of fully equipped fire engines, which sometimes reinforced the town's numbers. The firm also had its own maintenance division, which included shops for spare parts and wood working, among others.

An office of design and testing came up with the new styles. The first collection of women's sports shoes came out in 1930. Joseph Fenestrier briefly considered making Louis XV shoes, but abandoned the idea for technical reasons.

From 1935, Sarkis Der Balian, talented Parisian custom shoemaker established at 221, rue Saint-Honoré, lent his experienced hand to the design of certain styles and often travelled to Romans. Unic called on the best artists and artisans for advertising, including Cappiello, Cassandre, Laure Albin-Guillot, and Van Moppès. The company's motto summed up the guarantee it gave to its clientele: Unic uniquement (exclusively unique). In 1938, a new-patented design called the "new crêpel" appeared for men and women. Its immense success lasted thirty years.

During the World War II, designers and technicians used their ingenuity to make "portables," shoes out of wood, felt and raffia. In 1945, Joseph-Emile-Jean Fenestrier was appointed president of the Fédération Nationale de l'Industrie de la Chaussure de France, a French shoe industry group. He died in 1961. The company remained in existence and merged with Maison Sirius in 1967.

In 1969, the André group bought Unic, which became Société Romanaise de la Chaussure. Robert Clergerie took over the company in 1977, giving it new life.

Robert Clergerie graduated from the École Supérieure de Commerce of Paris and came to shoes from the government sector. He took over the

management of Xavier Danaud (a Charles Jourdan subsidiary) in 1971 and his work there with Roland Jourdan gave him solid experience. While continuing to make men's shoes in the tradition of the Goodyear Stitch construction and distributing under the name of Joseph Fenestrier, Clergerie launched his own line of ankle boots and boots. At the same time, he made even more sophisticated styles by studying volume and heels. His shoes took on the look of sculpture, true accessories to feminine elegance. But in this approach, Clergerie always remembered the words of André Perugia, who told him one day: "Young man, never forget that although someone may wear an article of clothing, a shoe wears you: therein lies the whole problem."

Clever public relations with a network of press attachés contribute to the international reputation of Clergerie's designer label. He collaborates with couturiers and creates styles for Thierry Mugler, Anne-Marie Beretta, Chantal Thomas, and Yohji Yamamoto. The leader's talent has three times earned him the Award for best designer from F.F.A.N.Y. in the United States. Many boutiques under the sign of Robert Clergerie were opened in France and around the world between 1981 and 2002. He established his first boutique in 1981 in Paris at 5 rue du Cherche Midi, followed in 1982 by a shop at la place des Victoires (a symbolic location for a successful product). Additional boutiques opened in Tokyo, New York, Madrid, London, Brussels, Los Angeles, and most recently Chicago in 2001.

164. Sandal by Robert Clergerie, Spring-Summer 1998. International Shoe Museum, Romans.

165. Pump in lilac satin with metal heel by Robert Clergerie, Spring-Summer 1995. International Shoe Museum, Romans.

Charles Jourdan

From a workshop on Côte Macel (Butchers' Hill) in Romans to the Empire State Building in New York

Charles Jourdan undoubtedly ranks among the most accomplished individuals in the world of shoes. His stellar rise began in 1917 at the age of thirty-four. Cutting-room foreman at Etablissements Grenier, he lacked the necessary capital to set up his own business. His workday done, Jourdan would withdraw into his tiny workshop on côte Macel where he made women's shoes. His wife Augusta and two colleagues lent him a hand until late into the night. The results of these nocturnal creations were already worthy of the Jourdan quality label.

When the war ended in 1919, Jourdan's customers became numerous enough to enable him to leave his employer and go into business for himself in a larger studio with ten workers. His diligence as a craftsman paid off, resulting in a large volume of orders. In 1921, he relocated his workshop to the boulevard Voltaire and hired thirty workers.

By 1928, the business had outgrown the small factory and new buildings were constructed. During the 1930s, Jourdan expanded his products' distribution throughout France by deploying "official sales reps." He also launched his new label Séducta, which was promoted by a national advertising campaign that appeared in *L'Illustration* magazine.

The name Séducta sprang from Jourdan's imagination and derives from the French word for seduction. The emblem is a type of doe, a hybrid animal with the coat of a deer and the antlers of a stag. This leaping animal, reproduced under the soles and on the boxes of the shoes, symbolises the beauty of the elegantly shod foot, with the accent on the doe's light-footed nature.

The metaphor is found in the Bible in the Second Book of Samuel where David addresses the Lord in a Psalm of Thanksgiving: "God is my strength and power, and He makes my way perfect. He makes my feet like the feet of deer, and sets me on my high places." This image of the female foot is also found in the 7th-century Buddhist legend of Padmavati. The daughter of a Brahmin and a doe, she was born with doe hoofs hidden inside silk wrappings. How interesting to note that from Antiquity to the 1st-century of our era, beauty and lightness of foot were compared to that of a doe. In our case, the biblical and Buddhist connection evokes Jourdan's refinement in the art of dressing the foot in charming heeled pumps, emblematic accessories of feminine seduction.

The stock market crash in New York cast a shadow over the 1930s. Parisian haut couture was hit hard by the world economic crisis and Jourdan was affected as well. Nevertheless, he responded by creating two sub-brands, Feminaflor and Qualité garantie. Three hundred workers produced four hundred pairs of shoes.

When World War II broke out, Jourdan, like other manufacturers, had to make use of alternative materials such as felt, raffia, rubber, wood, and cardboard due to the leather shortage. After 1945, Jourdan, assisted by his three sons René, Charles, and Roland, expanded the firm, which thenceforth had one thousand two hundred workers. Nine hundred pairs of shoes were leaving the factory daily in 1948.

In 1950, Roland set out to capture the American market and opened a sales office in the Empire State Building in New York. In 1957, the first Charles Jourdan boutique opened in Paris on the boulevard de la Madeleine. An instant hit, sales clerks had to give out numbered admission tickets to customers in the long waiting line. This extraordinary success was the starting point for the creation of an international chain of Charles Jourdan boutiques.

Recognition was at a zenith when Charles Jourdan signed a licensing agreement with Christian Dior. During the 1960s the brand went international

as boutiques were opened in London, Munich, New York, Los Angeles, Miami, and Tokyo. Charles Jourdan directed a series of advertising campaigns with photographs by Guy Bourdin that changed the art of advertising. No longer was the shoe the main subject, but portrayed in a strange, even surrealist situation.

In 1971, Roland Jourdan was appointed Chairman of the group, while his brothers sold their shares. Karl Lagerfeld entrusted Roland with the production of his shoes in 1980. That same year, the Séducta label was revived. When Roland Jourdan stepped down in 1981, the Swiss group Frantz Wasmer assumed the honour. The 1990s saw the launch of the Charles Jourdan Bis line for men and women and collaboration with the designers Michel Perry and Claude Montana.

With Emile Mercier at the helm and Hervé Racine as the current CEO, Charles Jourdan's star continues to shine in Paris and throughout the world. Its global prestige is based on the following: a production system invested with exceptional Expertise and engineered to respond effectively to the needs of the marketplace, marketing communications in sync with trends set by the stylists, a network of seventy boutiques under the Charles Jourdan trade name, and over a thousand loyal retailers. But above all, the firm continues to offer its customers products continually renewed in the spirit of its founder, Charles Jourdan.

166. Seducta pump, 1954. International Shoe Museum, Romans.
167. Seducta logo, taken from a 1949 advertisement.

168. Charles Jourdan in his factory.

169. Evening shoes created by Patrick Cox in honour of the Golden Jubilee of
Queen Elizabeth II of England in 2002. Creation limited to fifty copies.
Gift of Patrick Cox. International Shoe Museum, Romans.

Following pages:

170. Hand woven boot, Winter 1994. Hand woven shoe, Winter 1998.
Hand woven sandal. Stéphane Kélian.
International Shoe Museum, Romans.

171. Sandal by Stéphane Kélian, Summer 2001.
International Shoe Museum, Romans.

Stéphane Kélian

Specialist in Elegant Hand Braiding

In 1920, there were one hundred and twenty factories in Romans. Many companies that flourished between the wars gradually disappeared over the years. Others sprang up, such as the firm Kélian, founded in 1960 by Georges and Gérard Kéloglanian, men's footwear specialists. Stéphane, the brother of the two founders, launched in 1978 the first women's collection under the label Stéphane Kélian. Talented specialists in elegantly braided styles, their superb quality shoes quickly acquired an international reputation. Listed on the stock exchange since 1985, the company has two factories (Romans and Bourg-de-Péage) and employs four hundred.

Jean Tchilinguirian

Tradition and Expertise

Léon Tchilinguirian, an Armenian immigrant, worked in Romans' shoe factories before opening his own workshop in 1945. In 1955, his son Jean joined the family business, which included his two brothers and sister. This compact manufacturing unit combines tradition and expertise.

Additionally, several large ready-to-wear designers, including Agnès B, have eagerly entrusted the manufacture of part of their collection to this small company with big league status. Today, Jean Tchilinguirian produces designs under his own label "Tchilin" and markets them in his own boutique in Romans.

172. Shoe by John Lobb. Ledermuseum, Offenbach.

173. Shop of shoemaker John Lobb, 24 rue du Faubourg Saint-Honoré, Paris.

174. Shop of shoemaker John Lobb, 9 St James's Street, London.

140

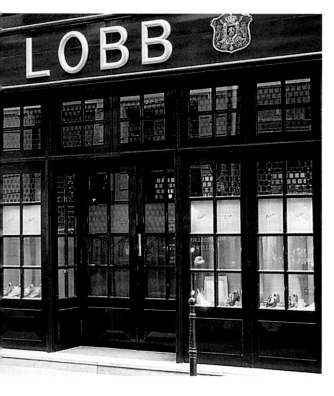

John Lobb

This firm, founded by John Lobb in 1849, is based in London on Saint James Street. During the Victorian era, the custom shoemaker won the highest honours in international exhibitions.

In 1901, John Lobb formed a Paris division. The firm remains a family business. It can take up to six months to achieve the exceptional quality of these made-to-order shoes, which are hand sewn.

Lobb primarily appeals to a wealthy and famous masculine clientele, for whom he makes golf shoes (brogues), Oxfords (Richelieu), and moccasins (loafer).

Official supplier to Her Majesty Queen Elizabeth II, His Royal Highness the Prince of Edinburgh, and His Royal Highness the Prince of Wales, this family firm upholds tradition and quality.

Weston

In the early 20th century, the Blanchard company was making expensive men's shoes in Limoges. Eugène Blanchard travelled to the United States in 1904 to learn the "Goodyear Stitch" construction process and other American manufacturing methods. His idea was to adapt his newly acquired methods to the business in Limoges, but the project did not materialise until after the war of 1914-1918. The year 1926, however, marked a significant step: the Weston brand was launched based on the techniques and philosophy of custom shoemaking. Many of the mechanical tasks went back to being done manually and styles were offered to customers in five widths.

The change in fabrication method thenceforth limited production, which went from six hundred to sixty pairs a day. This is how the brand acquired the characteristics that make it famous even today.

The first Weston store opened in Paris at 98 boulevard de Courcelles. Because of its English identity, the brand was an immediate success. A second store opened in 1932 at 114 avenue Champs Elysées.

In the 1960s, Weston shoes were mainly aimed towards an older clientele. But eventually young people came to appreciate the exceptional quality of the shoes and were willing to pay for it. The shoes stood out from machine-made varieties through the attention given to the following: proper fit and shape, a range of full-grain leathers, a leather inner lining, welt construction, cork filling and leather tanning of hand-crafted soles. Clients were also offered personalisation of their orders and repair service. In 1994, Weston had seven stores in France and stores in the following three cities: Geneva, New York, and Tokyo.

Babybotte Baby Booties

In 1949, the Bidegain company located in Paris launched a revolutionary model called the Babybotte bootie becoming the baby shoe specialist. The company made the shoes for Princess Caroline of Monaco, as well as for Margotte, the heroine of the French animated children's film *The Magic Merry-Go-Round*.

The company became known for the advanced technology of its products, which were designed in close collaboration with pediatricians and chiropodists.

Around 1954, the rear guard was invented, giving better support to the baby's ankle.

It also manufactured and marketed "Le loup blanc," the leading brand of children's medical shoes established in 1959.

It has manufactured and developed children's shoes for its "Kenzo Jungle" line since the summer of 2000, when it entered into a licensing agreement with Kenzo.

Pompeï, Shoemaker for the Stage and Screen

The Pompeï workshop was a family affair

Born in 1912 in Fermo, Italy, Ernesto Pompeï received professional training to work in the shoe industry. The central Italian town of Fermo, located in the region of the Marches, was home to skilled leatherworkers. In 1930, he left his native village for the capital where he became shoemaker for the theatre of Rome, specialising in stage shoes. After that, Ernesto's career would take a new direction.

In 1932, with his brother Luigi, he founded the firm Société Pompeï on the via Cavour, close to Saint Mary Major Basilica in Rome.

At the outset, the brothers supplied theatres before entering the cinema world with the celebrated film Scipio Africanus (Scipio the African) by Carmine Gallone, produced in Italy in 1937. Pompeï's workshop soon was Cinecitta's regular shoemaker, as evidenced by Pompeï's dazzling history of collaboration with great costume designers like Sanilo Donati (favoured by Federico Fellini) Piero Tosi (for Luchino Visconti), Lila de Nobile, Marcel Escafier, and Alberto Verso.

Ernesto's son Carlo was born in Rome in 1938. A graduate of Rome's political science university, nothing had indicated that he would enter the family business. Nevertheless, he was deeply involved in the world of theatre as well as becoming an assistant film director from 1963-1970 and working on American films such as Otto Preminger's *The Cardinal*. In 1971, Carlo joined Société Pompeï and collaborated closely with his father until his father's death in 1973.

From 1974 to 1990, the firm grew and established branches in London, Brussels and the United States. In 1988, Société Pompeï's takeover of the Galvin firm (rue Meslay in the third arrondissement in Paris), which had worked for everyone in the world of Paris entertainment, led to a new development: thenceforth known as Société Pompeï-Galvin, the new firm moved to the boulevard Bourdon in the fourth arrondissement in 1993.

For theatre, opera and cinema, the house of Pompeï designed styles ranging from the simplest to the most extravagant; from Ancient Rome to the Court of Versailles, passing through the First World War and the barbarian invasions in the process.

All of these designs involved the cooperation of talented and demanding costume designers. As shoemaker to the stage and screen, Carlo Pompeï received an encouragement award for theatrical crafts in 1995 and the gold medal for craftsmen in the arts in Munich. These distinctions awarded Carlo's specialties as a shoemaker: professionalism and preservation of traditional craftsmanship. These qualities are the same as those of a shoemaker for town shoes: both are preoccupied with historical accuracy. It should be noted that extraordinary care was given to making shoes that only had to give the

175. Baby booties, 1954.

176. Shoes worn by Monica Belluci in *Astérix and Obélix: Mission Cleopatra*. Created in the Pompeï workshop in 2001.

177. Shoes worn by Anita Ekberg in the role of Sylvia in Federico Fellini's *La Dolce Vita*, 1960. Shoes created at the Pompeï workshop. International Shoe Museum, Romans.

Following pages:

178. Shoes for movie extras created by the House of Pompeï.

illusion of period fashion. Unfortunately, the morphology of the foot had changed. Longer and larger, it could not wear the short shoes from the time of Louis XVI, or the long, pointed ankle boots from the beginning of the century. Still, it is always possible to the lower the heel, to round the upper, to reduce the leg, without necessarily changing the shoe's appearance.

In addition to being concerned about historical accuracy, Carlo Pompeï was also concerned with the comfort of the actor's feet. Some celebrities received special treatment: custom-made styles of which Carlo Pompeï tried to keep a few copies for his collection. Sometimes the shoes needed for a film, a musical or theatrical entertainment were chosen from among existing stock and adapted as needed. After being used, the loaned shoes were returned to the studio where they were checked and arranged according to period and style. There were close to eight hundred thousand. Before being re-used, the shoes were "refreshed," dyed if necessary, and always fit with an inner sole worthy of Pompeï's nickname, "number one in cleanliness." When it is a matter of supplying hundreds of pairs of shoes, the shoes are not actually fitted; selections are made from the sizes provided by the costume maker. It also happened that the production company retained ownership of the shoes and costumes. Who knows why the actors sometimes kept their shoes: personal attachment, a souvenir, or in the spirit of collecting?

Carlo Pompeï's Paris studio was for receiving, conservation, and fabrication. Approached by individual clients, but most often by costume designers or the theatre artists themselves, the shoemaker responded to extremely varied requests. Fabrication was often done in a rush. If the Paris studio was overwhelmed, the Rome studio took over for it. There were also Carlo Pompeï workshops in London, Brussels, and Avignon, where Carlo Pompeï supplied the operas of Aix, Orange, and Marseille.

Famous actors put themselves in the hands of this shoemaker. But Carlo Pompeï was also shoemaker for the following companies in the performing arts: the Opéra Garnier (Paris), the Opéra Bastille (Paris), the Comédie Française (Paris), and la Scala (Milan). To these should be added many other theatres and opera companies in Paris and in France (Lyon, Marseille, Toulouse, Nancy, Montpellier, Reims, Metz, Rennes, Limoges, Tours, Angers, and Villeurbanne), as well as in other European countries and the United States.

Finally there is one other specialty among Carlo Pompeï's activities that deserves mentioning: making shoes for fashion shows, including those of Thierry Mugler. For the 100th anniversary of the cinema, the International Shoe Museum, Romans, devoted an exhibition to the Maison Pompeï, which was re-shown and updated by the Bon Marché on the left bank in Paris.

143

179. Manufacture of Tod's treaded moccasins: the tools.

180. Manufacture of Tod's treaded moccasins: the cutting out.

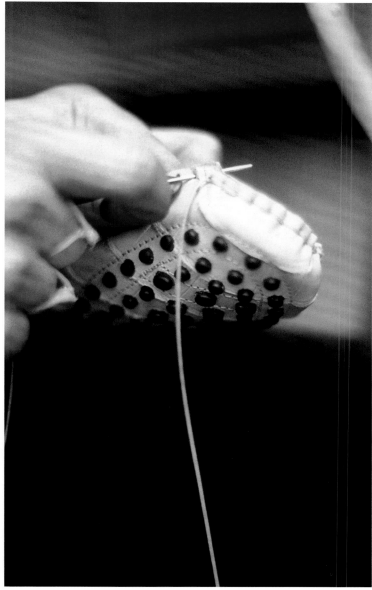

181-182. Manufacture of Tod's treaded moccasins.

183. Giraffe shoe and zebra shoe in kidskin and velvet painted entirely by hand.
Heels of carved wood covered with hide evoking the hind legs of a giraffe
and a zebra. Created by Stéphane Couvé Bonnaire, winner of the competition
under the category for the stiletto heel organised by the Style Bureau of
the National Federation of the Shoe Industry in 1995.
International Shoe Museum, Romans.

184-185. Leopard shoe and gaiter.

186. Children's boots, Kickers, 1971.
International Shoe Museum, Romans.

187. Child's mule decorated with a daisy, synthetic sole.
Summer 2002. International Shoe Museum, Romans.

Le Salon Midec

International Footwear Fashions

Salon Midec-Paris, a fashion showing entirely devoted to shoes, is held at the Porte de Versailles in March and September. Established by a French industry group called the Bureau de Style Chaussure, Maroquinerie, Cuir and aimed at promoting design, Midec exhibits the collections of young international designers inside a "Fantasy" space. It also organises the annual competition "Exercises de Style" which is open to budding fashion designers to nurture new talent and a fresh approach to the future.

L'Escarpin de Cristal (The Crystal Pump)

An initiative of the magazines Hebdo Cuir and Chausser, in partnership with professional sponsors, the escarpin de cristal (the crystal pump) has rewarded creativity and originality since 1999. It looks for footwear innovation in the following areas: image, design, technology, performance, communication, and distribution. This event promotes excellence and unites the profession.

The C.I.D.I.C. Grant

188. "Opium" mules, dress of the Akha tribes of the Golden Triangle. Trikitrixa, Paris. Box of recycled coca and jungle seed, 6 cm steel heel, leather.

Creativity in footwear is also honoured by the C.I.D.I.C. (The French interprofessional development committee for the leather, leather goods

152

and shoe industries). Each year it selects an especially innovative leather accessory designer to receive a grant from ANDAM (National Association for the Fashion Arts). The European Grand Prize in Shoe Design was instituted by the Saint Crispin association. The purpose of the prize is to stimulate creativity. The award also aims to discover and promote young talent entering the professions of shoe and fashion design. The young applicants are asked to design a fashion illustrating a given theme. Twenty finalists selected by a jury make a prototype from their design. The five winners are awarded during the festivities honouring Saint Crispin, patron saint of shoemakers. The work of all the participants is exhibited at the International Shoe Museum, Romans. This competition is under the aegis of the Romans firms Charles Jourdan, Robert Clergerie, and Stéphane Kélian, with the support of the Conseil National du Cuir (French national leather council), the C.I.D.I.C. (Comité interprofessionnel de développement des industries du cuir, de la maroquinerie et de la chaussure, or the French interprofessional development committee for the leather, leather goods and shoe industries), and the C.T.C. (centre technique cuir, chaussure, maroquinerie, or the French technical centre for leather, shoes and leather goods). The city of Romans and the International Shoe Museum jointly organise the event. All of these different awards have allowed many, now internationally recognised, talents to emerge in France, mother of the avant-garde. They are steps in the right direction that need to be continued and applauded.

189. "Gall" heeled sandals with rooster feathers and steel heel of 6 cm. Trikitrixa, Paris.

190. "Look" shoes, Summer 2002.
191. "Rosette" sandals with pheasant feathers. Trikitrixa, Paris.
192. "Double T" shoes. Created by Tod's, Spring-Summer 2003.

Following pages:
193. Shoes created by Sara Navarro, Summer 2002.

Shoes from Around the World

The Ottoman Empire

An avid traveller, Jean-Etienne Liotard set sail for Constantinople in 1738. His carefully observed paintings and drawings of the individuals he encountered earned him a reputation as the Enlightenment's "Turkish painter." In this portrait of almost photographic detail, the woman's pattens are accurately depicted being used to protect her from the damp. Note also that the painting depicts the slave without shoes, in contrast to the mistress: the slave must make do with henna-painted feet.

It was common for women in Turkey and many other oriental countries to wear pattens of variable height inside the bath. Women's pattens were of wood, inlaid with mother-of-pearl or ivory and covered with silver; the strap was richly embroidered with silver and gold thread. Such pattens carried a comprehensive range of the opulent ornamentation found in these countries. As Jean-Paul Roux rightly emphasises, the inlaid decoration found on these shoes is quite similar to the decoration found on door and window casements, furniture, and Muslim pulpits.

In the early 19th century, the Ottomans formed one of the world's largest empires, encompassing the whole Balkan Peninsula, all of western Asian to Persia, Africa, Egypt, and Tripolitania, and the suzerainties of Algeria and Tunisia. Situated at the crossroads of three continents, between the Mediterranean and the Indian Ocean, the Ottoman Empire occupied a key position. This vast geographical area sometimes produced an interactive synthesis of decorative styles that is perceptible in the ornamentation of shoes from its different countries.

In some oriental countries, women enjoyed an "elevated" status – for a day. To remind them of their superiority to their husbands for one day, brides were hoisted onto excessively high pattens such as these, but the women had to come down from their pedestals the very next day. This way of thinking is confirmed by the Koran: "Men are superior to women, due to the fact that Allah has raised many of them above the others" (Montet translation, Payot, 1954). On the other hand, the woman ruled the home and the presence of a pair of men's babouches at the door forbade any other man from entering.

194. Marriage shoes of wood inlayed with windows of mother of pearl and metal, Middle East, 19th century.
Cruller Collection, International Shoe Museum, Romans.

195. Jean-Etienne Liotard, *Turkish Woman and Her Slave*, 18th century.
Art and History Museum, Geneva.

Persia

After the death of Alexander in 323 B.C.E., Iranian culture entered a period of dormancy. The breakdown of the Sassanian and Byzantine empires paved the way for Islam's takeover.

During the golden age of the Safavid dynasty (1501-1736), Persia still dazzled western travellers. The French painter Chardin (1699-1779), who spent ten years in Persia around 1660, was among those impressed. According to Chardin, even the poor were well dressed and wore silver ornaments on their arms, feet and neck.

Unlike shoes in the Hellenised West, the shoes of oriental countries exhibit a continuity of forms whose decorative grammar was transmitted from one century to the next. For example, 17th- and 19th-century ceremonial boots from Persia display on their soles the same stylised floral motifs found on garments worn by Ashurbanipal in the 7th century B.C.E.

The motifs are visible on a narrative relief from Ashurbanipal's palace entitled, "The King Killing a Lion," now in the British Museum.

Another significant example of continuity is the similarity between the 16th-century heeled shoes with raised tips now in the International Shoe Museum, Romans, and the mules worn by the Persian Emperor Fath' Alī Chāh in his portrait painted around 1805, now in the Louvre. These shoes were worn to best advantage with stockings richly embroidered with gold motifs based on those shown on Ashurbanipals's clothing.

According to Jean-Paul Roux, the babouche, a slipper without a rear quarter or heel worn by men in the orient, probably originated in Iran. The Persian word papoutch comes from the words pa (foot) and pouchiden (to cover). This form of footwear was especially suited to the Islamic custom of removing shoes before entering a mosque or a private home.

196. Persian miniature: *Khosrow organises a reception during a hunt*. Folio 100, *The Five Poems of Nizgâmi*, 1620-1624.

197. Attributed to Mihv' Ali Iran, *Portrait of Fath' Ali Shah*, c. 1805, oil on canvas.

198. Man's shoe in black distressed leather, upturned pointed toe, studded soul, claw heel. Persia, 15th-16th century. International Shoe Museum, Romans.

199. Rider's boot. Steel-tipped, claw heel. Persia, 17th century. International Shoe Museum, Romans.

India

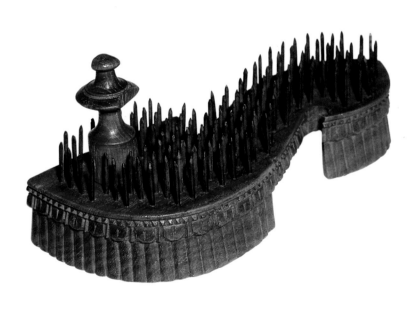

A great civilisation developed in the Indus valley around 2500-2000 B.C.E. Excavations at Harappa (Punjab) and Mohenjodaro (Sindh) have yielded seals contemporary with the Akkadian period of King Sargon's reign, proof of cultural links between Indian and Sumerian towns well before the Buddhist period. Does this mean the traditional raised tip shoe originated in India? The question remains unanswered. We do know, however, that wearing a raised tip shoe with a pompon became a privilege reserved for the king in both Mesopotamia and India.

Ancient Indian literature makes frequent reference to shoes, but there is little Indian shoe iconography, perhaps because the lower portions of narrative reliefs, standing sculptures and wall paintings are often deteriorated. Additionally, visual images generally illustrate events taking place in locations where wearing shoes is either prohibited or unnecessary. In India, as in many Asian countries, shoes were not worn inside private homes, palaces, or temples.

Valmiki, the legendary author of the Ramayana, tells how King Rama (one of the incarnations of Visnu in Hindu mythology) was exiled to a forest and had his gold-incrusted shoes represent him in his capital. During his three-year absence, the shoes presided in his place. All the decisions delivered by his regent brother were proclaimed before these shoes. A Buddhist variation of the same theme adds an additional detail: when the decisions pronounced before the royal shoes were just, the shoes remained still, but when the decisions broke the law, the shoes rose up in protest.

When the king moved in a procession outside his capital, he was preceded by a servant who carried in her hands the royal sandals, which were the sovereign's emblem. This is affirmed by Buddhist iconography, in particular the Great Stupa (No.1) at Sanchi, which dates from around the Christian era. The material of traditional Indian shoes varies according to historical period and region. Basket makers made sandals out of rush, date palm leaves, and lotus leaves.

In northern India, kings, noble warriors, hunters, and stable boys wore boots and sandals made of leather from the tanned skins of oxen, cow, buffalo, ram, and sheep.

The priestly Brahmin caste considered leather impure and who thus wore wooden sandals instead. Literary descriptions indicate that sandals were made in a variety of colours in shades of blue, yellow, red, brown, black, orange, and sorrel; there were even "multi-coloured" sandals.

Boots, which were sometimes laced, had cotton linings that likewise came in a variety of colours. Boots could be pointed, decorated with ram horns, embellished with scorpion tails, or even have peacock feathers sewn on. To prevent Buddhist monks from giving in to the temptation of these novelty shoes, Buddha was quoted in religious texts as strictly forbidding monks to wear them. Only sandals with simple soles or used shoes received as an offering were approved.

Indians often walked barefoot. The age-old Hindu craft tradition was handed down for generations and stifled innovation.

Men, women, and children continued to wear a type of leather slipper with a raised tip and an exposed heel. Often highly ornate, it displays the Hindu preference for filling. Finally, Islam's influence in India even touched footwear where Turkish-Persian borrowings are evident in certain decorative motifs.

200. Sandal of carved wood. India, 19th century. Collection of the Musée national du Moyen Âge - Thermes et hôtel de Cluny, Paris. allocated to the International Shoe Museum, Romans.

201. Fakir's sandal, India. International Shoe Museum, Romans.

202. Hooked toe shoes, India. Bally-Schuhmuseum, Schönenwerd, Switzerland.

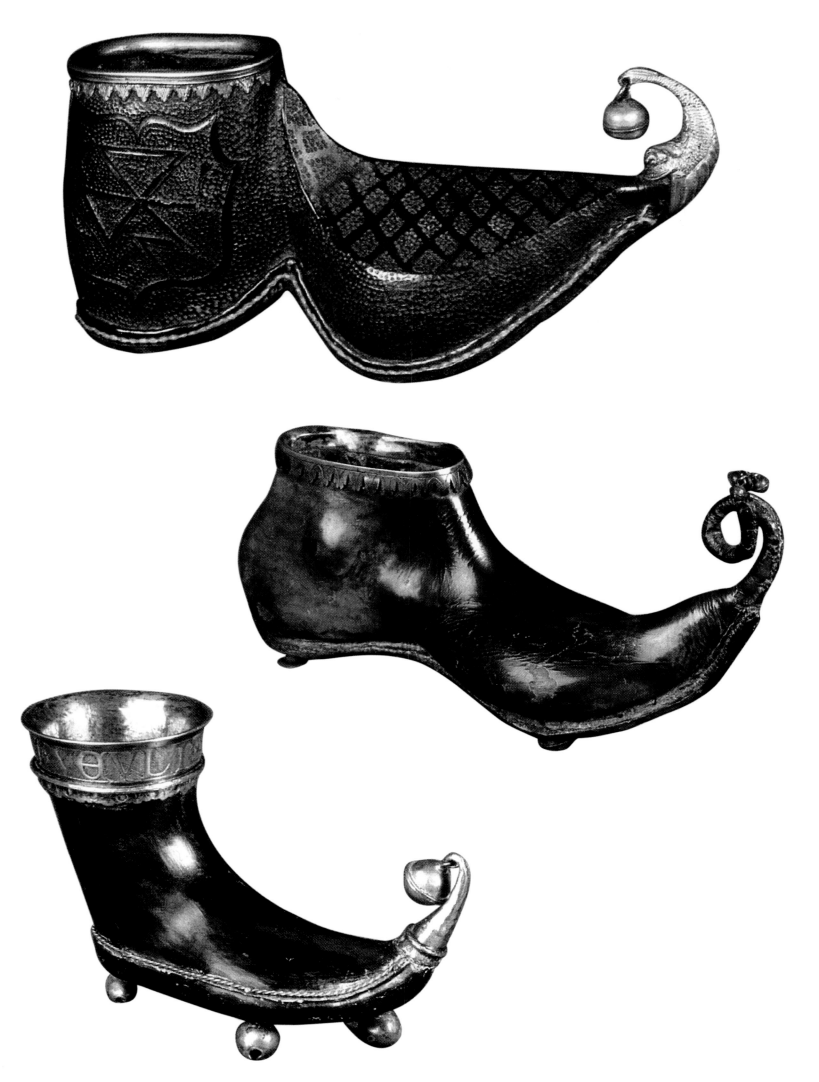

China

Surely the most unique aspect of Chinese footwear is the tradition of binding women's feet. This ancient Chinese practice deserves specific analysis. Foot deformation is said to have been invented in an aristocratic milieu. According to a Chinese historian, in 1100 B.C.E., the Empress Ta Ki had a clubfoot. She convinced her husband to order the compulsory compression of all little girls' feet so that they would resemble those of their sovereign, who had become the standard for beauty and elegance.

Five hundred years before Christ, during the era of Confucius (555 B.C.E.-479 B.C.E.), the beauty of small feet was already being praised as proof of a wellborn status, whereas large feet were synonymous with low birth. Other sources attribute the invention of foot binding to the courtesan Pan Fei, a favourite of Emperor Xiao Bao Kuan (ruled 499-501). Reality was nothing of the sort, although we do owe the expression "golden lotus" to this Emperor.

One day, while Pan Fei was dancing over a floor inlaid with gold lotus flowers for the enjoyment of her imperial lover, the ruler cried out in astonishment: "Look, a golden lotus springs up from her every step!" This metaphor has since come to stand for small Chinese feet.

Another tradition attributes this custom to the 10th century C.E. in Beijing where the Emperor Li Yu (937-978) held his court. Yao Niang, the Emperor's favourite, was famous for her talented dancing. The Emperor gave her a splendid lotus decorated with pearls and then he asked her to wrap her feet in white silk in such a way that their ends came to a point like a crescent moon and dance around the lotus. All the men there watched in rapture as this elegant silhouette twirled on the points of her feet. This lotus dance and the expression "golden lotus" probably originated in a Buddhist legend in which Padmiavati, the daughter of a Brahmin and a doe, made a lotus flower bloom wherever she stepped. In yet another version dating to the 7th century, the story specifies that the young girl had doe hoofs concealed under silk wrappings. The influence of this Indian legend in China was no doubt due to the spread of Buddhism in the early 5th-century. Europeans who began arriving in China in the 13th century showed great discretion concerning the custom of foot binding.

All the same, Marco Polo (1254-1324) noticed the peculiar walk of Chinese women and wrote in his memoirs that:

"Young women always walk so docilely that one foot follows the other by no more than a half-finger length…"

Young girls in very poor families shared the chores of a difficult material existence; having bound feet was a luxury they could ill afford. Scorned, these girls with "big feet," a distinct sign of their modest origin, were called "barefooted" in the Guang Dong. Only girls with bound feet could serve the mistress of the house in her apartments; the others were condemned to the most humble kitchen jobs. In the 13th-century, during the last years of the Song dynasty, it was customary to drink out of a special shoe whose heel contained a small cup.

Later, under the Yuan dynasty, one drank directly from the shoe. This strange custom is attributed to Yang Tieai, a wealthy man of loose morals, who amused himself by planning banquets where guests drank out of the shoes worn by prostitutes attending the party. This practice was called "toasts to the golden lotus," by its author and it had enthusiasts until the end of the 19th century. This is why lotus lovers consider Yang Tieai the patron saint of the brotherhood of drinkers from the little shoe.

203. Silk mandarin boots, from the reign of Kangxi (1662-1722). Gugong Museum, Beijing.

204. G. Castiglione, *Equestrian Portrait of Emperor Qianlong Passing the Troops in Review*, Gugong Museum, Beijing.

205. Photo of four Chinese prostitutes.
Collection of Beverley Jackson.

206. Man's boot in ribbed black satin. Thick sole with
sewn leather. Guillen Collection,
International Shoe Museum, Romans.

207. Woman's boot in pink satin, embroidery of gold and
black thread tracing a dragon, China, 19th century.
International Shoe Museum, Romans.

208. Marriage shoes, China. Collection of Beverley Jackson.

168

During the Ming dynasty (late 16th-mid 17th century), foot deformation was an integral part of Chinese culture; this custom became prevalent, circulating through all levels of society. It was beginning with the Ming dynasty that the practice was adopted for clearly erotic or aphrodisiac purposes in the art of hiding and revealing the foot. A Chinese woman who showed a bare foot in public was committing an indecent assault. This is why Catholic missionaries caused a scandal in the late 19th-century when they spread images of the Virgin with bare feet, Our Lady of Lourdes.

To avoid a clash of civilisations, they had to order more appropriate iconography from the West. In 1664, imperial edicts forbid women of the Manchurian dynasty to deform their feet under penalty of death. The emperor Kangxi (1662-1722) imposed a total ban on foot binding for girls born after 1662. A father or husband who broke this law would be punished by eighty blows with a stick, and then exiled three thousand lilies (about one thousand five hundred kilometres). Nevertheless, the decree was ineffectual and Kangxi had to repeal it. When the same prohibition was reintroduced in 1694, Manchurian women responded by adopting a different shoe style.

Under the soles of their shoes made for normal feet, they attached a two-inch high support covered in silk, a trick barely visible under their pants. In this way they were able to imitate the unsteady, but charming walk of deformed feet, creating the perfect illusion. Foot binding led to a number of private superstitions and beliefs among the Chinese.

Above all, for the wellborn, foot binding was necessary preparation for a good marriage; failure to perform this custom condemned a girl to being single. The initial binding was usually performed with some ceremony. The child's mother would place a pair of embroidered shoes and some strips on an altar to Zaojun, "god of the hearth." An experienced and virtuous woman would be invited to come officiate several days later.

After god's help was invoked, the first wrapping was applied while the young girl held in her hands a small water chestnut or a little brush and recited her prayer. She asked for feet as sweet and as smooth as the water chestnut and as fine as the brush. On her wedding day, the bride wore shoes embroidered with sayings such as "one hundred years of happiness" or "health and wealth until white-haired."

In northern China, husbands were given miniature shoe-shaped cookies symbolising concord and harmony. Lotus-shaped shoes for the wives meant "a succession of sons." In central China, engaged couples took their vow of "until death do us part" by exchanging their shoes.

Finally, four pairs of embroidered slippers were part of a bride's dowry, a guarantee of a lasting marriage. After the wedding, the young woman carefully put them away. The most surprising beliefs are associated with women's shoes used as treatments by Chinese doctors to cure various illnesses.

For example, an effective cure for tuberculosis consisted of wearing three pairs of a young bride's slippers until they were totally worn out. For a daughter-in-law to offer her slippers to her sick mother-in-law was a very thoughtful gesture; in particular it demonstrated great filial piety, which her husband would never forget if he later wanted to repudiate his wife.

According to Tan Sivy, in his thesis, "The golden lotus, or little Chinese feet," in the late 19th-century there was a doctor in Huang named Song You who healed the sick by using shoes as a remedy. Many students followed his teachings. The writer Yao Lingx affirms it:

"Fevers: apply a small slipper firmly over the patient's navel. The fever will leave the patient through this orifice and go into the shoe. Cholera: boil the sole of a young virgin's slipper until the liquid becomes thick. Have the patient drink the beverage while it is still hot."

At the start of the Ming dynasty, in the late 14th century, the town of Datong in Shanxi carved out a reputation for itself throughout the Empire for having women with beautiful feet.

Under the Qing, a new style of binding was introduced that became standard until the waning of the Empire. Lévy describes it clearly in his book, *Chinese Footbinding*, the history of a curious erotic custom: "…smooth and soft at once, tiny and pointed, the very mention of the Datong foot stirred the soul of aesthetes."

Beginning in the 19th-century, the town organised an annual foot beauty contest that quickly spread to most other large towns, usually taking place within Buddhist pagodas. The contest drew several hundred candidates and attracted a crowd of admirers who came from afar. Old Chinese who were eyewitnesses at the beginning of the-century, describe the scene:

"The competitors were seated with their legs extended on small stools. Their shoes were decorated with pearls, little bells, and silk butterflies. Spectators came and went in groups, criticising, admiring, and making their preferences known out loud, but they weren't allowed to touch the feet or the shoes."

Winners, according to witnesses, merrily joined the harems of wealthy and powerful men. And it is even said that some women over age sixty, with ugly, wrinkled faces, surpassed much younger contestants. Practised until the end of the Empire, these contests disappeared after the prohibition of foot binding declared by the republican government in 1913. How was mutilation achieved?

Deliberately induced, irreversible deformation was inflicted upon little girls from childhood. Their feet were bound in a progressive and continuous manner. At first the binding would be rather loose, but then the tension would be gradually increased. The binding was replaced at least every two days, and each time the foot was left bare for a few moments in order to wash it and rub it with sorghum alcohol to prevent infection. To obtain a foot in greater conformity to the fashion's canonical version, a semi-cylindrical metal piece sized in proportion to the foot was placed under the arch before bandaging was applied. The young girl continued to bind her feet with regularity at the risk of losing the effects of the treatment. When adulthood was reached, each foot measured approximately thirteen to sixteen centimetres.

The term "golden lotus" was reserved for feet less than nine centimetres; feet longer than ten centimetres only rated a "silver lotus."

The deformity achieved by foot binding lead to the creation of special shoes; courtesans especially wore red shoes. Catholic missionaries later helped put an end to foot binding, although in 1900 Chinese women of all social classes still observed the custom, more frequently in the town than in the country. The fashion still lingered in 1948 in spite of prohibitions.

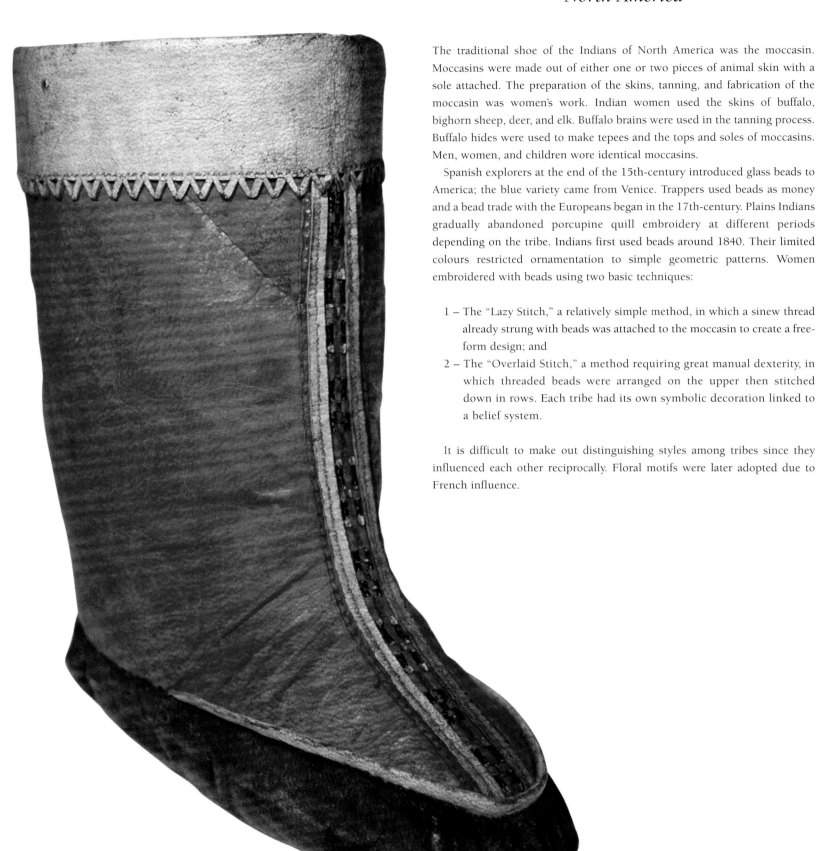

North America

The traditional shoe of the Indians of North America was the moccasin. Moccasins were made out of either one or two pieces of animal skin with a sole attached. The preparation of the skins, tanning, and fabrication of the moccasin was women's work. Indian women used the skins of buffalo, bighorn sheep, deer, and elk. Buffalo brains were used in the tanning process. Buffalo hides were used to make tepees and the tops and soles of moccasins. Men, women, and children wore identical moccasins.

Spanish explorers at the end of the 15th-century introduced glass beads to America; the blue variety came from Venice. Trappers used beads as money and a bead trade with the Europeans began in the 17th-century. Plains Indians gradually abandoned porcupine quill embroidery at different periods depending on the tribe. Indians first used beads around 1840. Their limited colours restricted ornamentation to simple geometric patterns. Women embroidered with beads using two basic techniques:

1 – The "Lazy Stitch," a relatively simple method, in which a sinew thread already strung with beads was attached to the moccasin to create a free-form design; and

2 – The "Overlaid Stitch," a method requiring great manual dexterity, in which threaded beads were arranged on the upper then stitched down in rows. Each tribe had its own symbolic decoration linked to a belief system.

It is difficult to make out distinguishing styles among tribes since they influenced each other reciprocally. Floral motifs were later adopted due to French influence.

209. Sealskin child's boot, Greenland, 19th century.
International Shoe Museum, Romans.

210. Woman's moccasin decorated with stylised flowers, Canada, 19th century.
Musée national du Moyen Âge - Thermes et hôtel de Cluny, Paris.

211. Men's shoes, seal and walrus skin. Alaska, beginning of the 20th century.

Shoes Worn by Celebrities

Shoe of Henry II de Montmorency

Henry II de Montmorency was the grandson of Anne de Montmorency, supreme commander of the French army, Marshall of France, and advisor to kings Francis I and Henry II. The last representative of this illustrious family's older branch and the nephew of king Henry IV, Henry II de Montmorency added to his family's prestigious appointments: Admiral of France and Brittany, viceroy of New France, and finally, governor of Languedoc after his father's resignation in 1613. The sceptre of Marshall awarded his military victories. But Gaston d'Orléans convinced him to rise up against Languedoc; his impudent revolt against Cardinal Richelieu led to his imprisonment at Castelnaudary. Abandoned by Monsieur, the king's brother, as Gaston d'Orléans was called, de Montmorency was condemned to death and beheaded in Toulouse in 1632. His leather shoe, preserved at the International Shoe Museum, is monogrammed and decorated with a fleur-de-lis on top of the upper. It is evidence of the type of virtuoso shoemaking that existed during the first half of the 17th century.

Madame de Pompadour's Shoes

Or the triumph of the heel under Louis XV

These low-heeled shoes in yellow silk embroidered with silver thread and with a slightly raised toe have lost their buckles and show some wear. They come from the estate of Madame de Pompadour who left them to her personal maid.

The seated portrait of Madame de Pompadour, painted by François Boucher in 1758 and now in the Victoria and Albert Museum, shows her crossed feet dressed in new shoes embellished with a substantial buckle, probably of silver. In Boucher's standing portrait of Madame de Pompadour in the Wallace Collection, her right foot is hidden by her yellow dress, but the left foot, dressed in a heeled shoe fastened with a buckle, is similar to the example found in the International Shoe Museum, Romans. A third portrait by Boucher, in the collection of Maurice de Rothschild, highlights Madame de Pompadour's sumptuous pink mules. These shoes have raised tips in the oriental style and are enhanced by elaborate decoration on the upper, which is also trimmed with a meridian coil running lengthwise and bordered with shirred fabric. The high heel covered in white leather is a typical example of a Louis XV heel. These pink shoes create a visual echo of delightful harmony with the pink ornaments on Madame de Pompadour's green dress. Quentin de la Tour's pastel portrait preserved at the Louvre depicts beautiful pink mules that are rather similar, but the ornamentation is simplified.

As she displays her own shoes in these four portraits, Madame de Pompadour, who was famous for her elegance, perfectly illustrates which women's shoes where fashionable during the reign of Louis XV: shoes fastened with a buckle and mules. Mules with Louis XV heels (still a commonly used term) would experience a considerable vogue and are still fashionable in the 21st century. The technical dictionary of the shoe industry written by Louis Rama, an authority in the matter, defines the Louis XV heel as follows: "Louis XV heel: a high heel, much knocked down by a concave profile; the throat is covered by an extension of the sole obtained by splitting called the heel breast flap." Although methods of heel manufacture and styles have definitely evolved over time, the concept of the Louis XV heel, elaborated in the 18th century, remains unchanged. It is still a heel with an evocative name, whose very mention calls forth the symbol of eternal femininity.

212. Shoe having belonged to Henri II de Montmorency. Leather decorated with a fleur de lis on the vamp. Initials of the duke on the flap, France, 17th century. International Shoe Museum, Romans.

213. Shoe of the Marchioness of Pompadour. International Shoe Museum, Romans, dépôt of Musée national du Moyen Âge - Thermes et hôtel de Cluny, Paris.

214. François Boucher, *Portrait of the Marquise de Pompadour*, 1756. Oil on canvas, 201 x 157 cm. Alte Pinakothek, Munich.

The Shoe of Marie-Antoinette

Attributed to the Queen, this shoe was found at the base of a guillotine at the place de la Révolution in Paris on 16 October 1793. It was sold the same day for one louis to the Count of Guernon-Ranville, who immediately turned it into a relic.

The interior bears a handwritten inscription inserted like an innersole:

"Shoe worn by Queen Marie-Antoinette on that horrible day she mounted the scaffold, this shoe was picked up by an individual the moment the queen died and immediately purchased by Monsieur le Comte de Guernon-Ranville."

As André Castelot writes in his book on Marie-Antoinette (1):

"She hurried and climbed the steep ladder with such haste (with bravado said one witness) that she lost one of her little plum Saint Huberty shoes."

According to the account of Rosalie Lamorlière, the Queen's personal maid at the Temple, Marie-Antoinette went to her execution wearing plum shoes with two-inch heels (they measured two pouces or about six centimetres) in the Saint Huberty style. The style was named after the opera performer who started the trend. This shoe could be of silk or leather.

215. Shoe of Marie-Antoinette collected the 10 August 1792.
Anonymous, Musée Carnavalet - musée d'histoire de Paris, Paris.
216. Shoe of the parish priest of Ars. International Shoe Museum, Romans.

Shoes of Saint-Jean-Marie Vianney,
Parish Priest of Ars

Jean-Marie Vianney, the fourth child in a humble farming family, was born on 8 May 1786, in Dardilly in the vicinity of Lyons. As a child he tended flocks with other peasant children his age, but stood out through his kindness and devotion. Responding to God's call, he entered the seminary. Threatened with being sent back because he lacked an aptitude for study, Jean-Marie Vianney was finally ordained at age twenty-nine.

Appointed parish priest of Ars, a small village located thirty-five kilometres from Lyon, he practised his ministry there until his death. People came rushing from all over France to confess to Father Vianney and to listen to his catechisms and sermons, which were delivered straightforwardly with examples from everyday life. He often spent sixteen hours a day behind the confessional and said the rosary every evening. His tireless zeal for charity and kindness was coupled with great austerity in living. Sleeping four hours at night, contenting himself with a frugal diet, and wearing a patched cassock, the priest imposed the severest penance upon himself.

Like many saints, he engaged in heroic combat against the Devil, who shook his doors, knocked around his furniture, tried to throw him out of his bed, and even set upon his shoes and tore them apart.

A crude, worn leather shoe preserved in a private collection affirms this, as we read on a document written by the shoe repairman: "Repaired shoe of the actual Priest of Ars. It had been torn apart by the Devil, as he himself said. I certify it in Lyon, 21 February 1875."

This extremely modest cleric, long scorned by his brethren, was promoted against his wishes to the dignity of Canon. Napoleon awarded him the Legion of Honour, again against the priest's wishes.

The Bishop of Belley started the canonical proceedings in 1866. Pius X declared him blessed in 1905. In 1925, Pope Pius XI proclaimed him Saint and Patron of Parish Priests. This humble country priest is now world famous. On 5 October 1986, Pope Jean-Paul II personally visited Ars as a formal tribute to Saint-Jean-Marie Vianney.

Goethe's Slippers

Marianne de Willemer secretly prepared a Christmas present that she was saving to give her friend Goethe on 25 December 1816. Two letters addressed to the writer's son, Auguste, which she signed by the fitting pseudonym, "the baby Jesus," reveal the playful way in which she went about it.

"I intend to send your father a pair of slippers from above. Saint Catherine and Saint Theresa are ready to take on the work, but they must be absolutely sure about his size. Would you kindly have your father's shoemaker cut an exact pattern of the upper and send it to me in Frankfurt where I am attending to business?

"If the shoemaker is unskilled and does not know how to draw, a slipper your father doesn't wear anymore or which no longer suits him will do just as well, as long as it still fits him. I will ask Saint Crispin to make a new pair. I hope that you will keep my secret and that you will reveal nothing of my plan to your father or anybody else."

On 20 December 1816, she sent Auguste a package accompanied by another letter. "Thank you for handling my errand so well and best wishes for your birthday, which is the same day as mine. Please open the small box that will probably arrive in Weimar Monday evening or Tuesday morning and give your father the slippers and the little picture it contains on Christmas Eve and light a few candles (because light is my element)." In a letter dated 31 December, Goethe replied to Marianne de Willemer:

"Admittedly Jesus has been especially well disposed towards me this year, but he couldn't stop himself from making some mischief. Although a man must kiss the Pope's slipper because it bears a cross and caress the feet of his beloved to symbolise his complete abandonment to her will, it is incredible that someone can use magic symbols to make a decent person venerate his own shoes, in this way forcing him into uncommon moral and physical contortions."

The band around the uppers on these famous slippers bore the name Suleika in Persian script, behind which was hidden the name Marianne de Willemer, the poet's muse who inspired his poems in the *West-Eastern Divan*. This literary figure's real attraction to the female foot and its accessory, the shoe, was no secret. As he wrote to one of his girlfriends: "Send me your last pair of shoes as soon as possible so that I can have something of yours to press against my heart."

217. Slipper of Emperor Franz-Joseph of Austria. Ledermuseum, Offenbach.
218. Slippers of Goethe. Bally-Schuhmuseum, Schönenwerd, Switzerland.

Sissi's Shoes

The life of Elisabeth von Wittelsbach, princess of Bavaria better known by her first name Sissi (immortalised in film by actress Romy Schneider), took on a fairy tale quality the moment she became engaged to her cousin, German Emperor Franz-Joseph of Austria. Almost immediately, the First Lady of the Empire came up against the hostility of her mother-in-law, Archduchess Sophie. Stuck in the restraints of a rigid and old-fashioned protocol dating back to Charles V, Sophie imposed this manner of dress on the princess. This etiquette required the Empress to wear a new pair of shoes everyday. She refused. The domestic supplier was outraged, losing an important revenue source. (Nevertheless, at one time an inventory listed one hundred and thirteen pairs of shoes in the Empress's wardrobe!) Meanwhile, sharp-tongued ladies-in-waiting criticised the Empress for going horseback riding too often, repeating their concerns to the ladies of the court, and even to the despised maids, that grooms and passers-by could not keep their eyes off her Majesty's ankles when she mounted a horse. The Empress's radiant beauty and her agile walk made her one of the most attractive women of her era. It was while walking with a quick step on the quai du Mont Blanc in Geneva on her way to the steam ship line that Sissi met her fate at age sixty-one, struck down by an assassin named Luigi Lucheni, an Italian anarchist.

219. Bottines of Sissi, Empress of Austria, 19th century. Ledermuseum, Offenbach.

Shoes of the Countess of Castiglione

(Florence 1837 — Paris 1899)

Born in Florence in 1837, Virginia Oldani came from an old, noble Genoese family. In 1854 she married Count François Verasis, equerry to the Sardinian King Victor Emmanuel II. Her beauty soon made her Turin's idol. The king's minister Cavour got the idea of using her beauty for diplomatic purposes and sent her the court of Emperor Napoleon. Her mission was to seduce Napoleon into joining the cause of Italian unity and obtain the support of the French government. She became his mistress in 1856 and facilitated the Emperor's decision to form an alliance with the Piedmontese. This beautiful woman, who was also a strange narcissist, sat for the photographers Mayer and Pierson. Both prominent photographers in the capital, they excelled in the art of flattering portraiture through a highly perfected technique, which they used to photograph the Second Empire's political, artistic, and social elite.

The Countess also asked Pierson to photograph her legs and feet. The resulting photograph sent an erotic message in no uncertain terms. It was an image perfectly consistent with the male fantasies of the period, which were fixated on this part of the female anatomy, normally protected from lustful glances under crinoline.

220. Slippers of Prince Imperial Jean-Joseph-Eugene-Louis Napoleon. International Shoe Museum, Romans.

A photograph by Disderi shows her with her legs in clingy white stockings, her right foot dressed in a buttoned ankle boot with a bobbin heel placed on a footstool. Virginia moreover liked to take her shoes off in public and offered her bare feet for her admirers' contemplation. This eccentric figure went so far as having casts made of her feet, of which two examples exist. These terra cottas may be the work of Carrier-Belleuse, a sculptor especially known for his casts.

The International Shoe Museum, Romans, has a pair of sumptuous apartment mules attributed to the Countess. They are of purple velvet embroidered with gold thread and fine pearls with a gold lamé heel; the shoes bear the following label: J.A. Petit women's shoes, 334 rue Saint-Honoré Paris, 134 Regent Street London. These shoes are a good example of Second Empire style, although their excessive decoration brings to mind the embroidery on Ottoman babouches from the same period.

221. Boots of William I of Prussia, 19th century. Ledermuseum, Offenbach.

Shoes Worn by Louis Pasteur

The son of an artisan tanner, Louis Pasteur was born in Dole, the administrative centre of the Jura, in 1822. An illustrious French chemist and biologist, this great scientist is internationally known for discovering the vaccine for rabbies.

As Annick Perrot, Conservator of the Pasteur Museum, explains, Pasteur was a revolutionary in science, but led a conventional private life. His artistic tastes and lifestyle were typical for a 19th-century bourgeois. His clothing habits are telling.

For example, at age eighteen, a boarder at the Collège of Besançon, Louis Pasteur wrote the following to his parents on 28 October 1840:

"Take care of my little case Huguenet made for my boots."

During a trip to Strasbourg, he sent his wife a letter dated 7 October 1852:

"If I have any good shoes bring them to me. My shoes and my gaiters especially. Idem: patent leather shoes and boots…"

Another letter to his father dated 29 January 1856, contains an interesting anecdote:

"I have been very well since the beginning of winter wearing the clogs you sent me in Strasbourg. Apart from this head cold, which should pass in a couple of days or so, I have not been sick at all, especially with the type of stomach upset to which I am so prone; the slightest damp feet gives me a sudden case of diarrhoea. I haven't had any attacks since coming back from vacation and I am sure that it's because I am wearing clogs."

Having dry feet will definitely keep you from getting sick, but this statement is amusing coming from the pen of a scientist like Pasteur.

The last seven years of his life Pasteur lived in a huge apartment within the Institute that bore his name. In 1937, it became a museum housing the scientist's furniture, personal possessions, art works, photographs, and even his shoes. The context of his life faithfully preserved in an emotionally charged atmosphere allows us to imagine Pasteur padding back and forth from his room to the bath in slippers made entirely of fine black felt: a testament to his last days? They appear to have been hardly used.

A second pair of solid burgundy, embroidered slippers may be the work of Madame Pasteur, who, like many young girls and women of her era, was an expert in needlework. Needlepoint on canvas in the shape of slippers was moreover very popular in the 19th-century. We can picture Madame Pasteur seated near the fireplace in the small third-floor sitting room pulling her needle, while her husband played cards with his friend Bertin.

The museum also has a pair of black woollen gaiters that fasten with seven small side buttons in addition to three pairs of black leather ankle boots, which Pasteur seems to have worn exclusively at the end of this life, even to the beach.

Two seemingly similar pairs of button ankle boots in black kid actually differ in several details. The first, fastened by six buttons, has the following label in the interior cloth lining near the leg:

"12 boulevard Saint-Michel 12 Marquer. Custom Shoemaker Paris."

These ankle boots match the ones shown in a photograph of Pasteur seated in the garden at the Institute. The second pair, without a label, is noteworthy for its seven-button closure.

222. Photograph of Louis Pasteur.

Ankle Boots of La Belle Otéro,
a Belle Epoque Beauty

Beautiful women abounded in the decade before 1900 and the one that followed. But three famous courtesans in particular competed for star status during La Belle Epoque: Emilienne d'Alençon, Liane de Pougy, and La Belle Otéro, whose first name was Caroline.

A Spanish beauty, La Belle Otéro debuted at age twelve on the ramblas of Barcelona and then conquered Marseille where she danced at the Palais de Cristal. Her beauty caused a sensation provoking fights between audience members. Her career continued in Paris where her charms earned her a multitude of passionate admirers who ruined themselves to obtain her favours. Rather like a grasshopper among men, she gambled at the roulette table and recovered her losses by spending the night with old casino stooges who were as rich as they were ugly. She returned from one amorous escapade in Saint Petersburg with the necklaces of two empresses and one queen as souvenirs.

At her peak, she walked into Maxim's dressed to kill, while her rival Liane de Pougy, to mock her ostentation, arrived at the fashionable establishment, where it was tasteful to dine after the show, without a speck of jewellery, escorted by her personal maid bending under the weight of a cushion they all carried.

La Belle Otéro slummed at the Bal Mabille (a dance hall), lunched at Armenonville, paraded the Bois de Boulogne, and counted her conquests. Among the vanquished were William II, whom she fascinated, and other admirers who squandered fortunes on her beautiful eyes. Some men killed themselves after being ruined or rejected which led to the unfortunate honour of her being called the "suicide siren."

Yet, this woman from Andalusia who led the dumbest and most consuming lifestyle of all the Belles could actually sing and dance with talent. Mindful of maintaining her artistic reputation, before each opening she would run to light a candle in Notre-Dame-des-Victoires. After a triumphant music-hall version of Carmen, she turned down a contract with the Opéra Comique and retired while still beautiful at age forty-five.

Her fortune, estimated at five million in 1922, melted like snow on a summer day from gambling, putting an end to her expensive lifestyle. From her small mansion built in Nice, she downsized to average rooms in luxury hotels, sold off her "surplus" (for which she received almost nothing), and finally retired to a small room where she lived on a meagre pension from the casino.

At age ninety-three, the elderly La Belle Otéro was still courted by a few old men who would come to dine in her room, bringing with them champagne and caviar.

Caroline Otéro died penniless in April 1965, despite several articles in the press that had attempted to bring her out of the shadows of anonymity. Today her ankle boots preserved in the International Shoe Museum, Romans, have rescued her from oblivion. They are fine examples of the art of the shoe during La Belle Epoque.

Additionally, these ankle boots have two five-centimetre pull-tabs in the front and rear of the opening so they could be pulled on with ease. Hemiplegic since the age of forty-six, it was difficult for Pasteur to dress and put his shoes on. A last pair of ankle boots, closed on both sides of the ankle by panels of elastic fabric, clearly represents the tone of fashion at the time and was certainly easier to get on than button ankle boots. As one approaches the stairs in the apartment often climbed by Pasteur, one notices the double handrails that were needed because of the scientist's paralysis and one can almost sense the echo of a slow-footed silhouette moving with difficulty. Carefully placed inside an armoire, his shoes are there to remind us of the "steps" taken by a great man at various moments in his life.

Having died in 1895, Pasteur now rests in the Institute's specially constructed funeral chapel on the first floor designed in the characteristic Byzantine style of the Symbolist period. A cartouche in the centre of the vault contains a sentence extracted from Pasteur's acceptance speech to the Académie Française:

"Happy are they who carry God and an ideal of beauty within themselves and who live up to the ideals of art, science, country, and the teachings of the Gospel."

223. Shoes and slippers of Louis Pasteur.

181

224. Bottines of the Belle Otéro. Brown and beige kidskin, silver kidskin inlays.
    Paris, around 1900. International Shoe Museum, Romans.

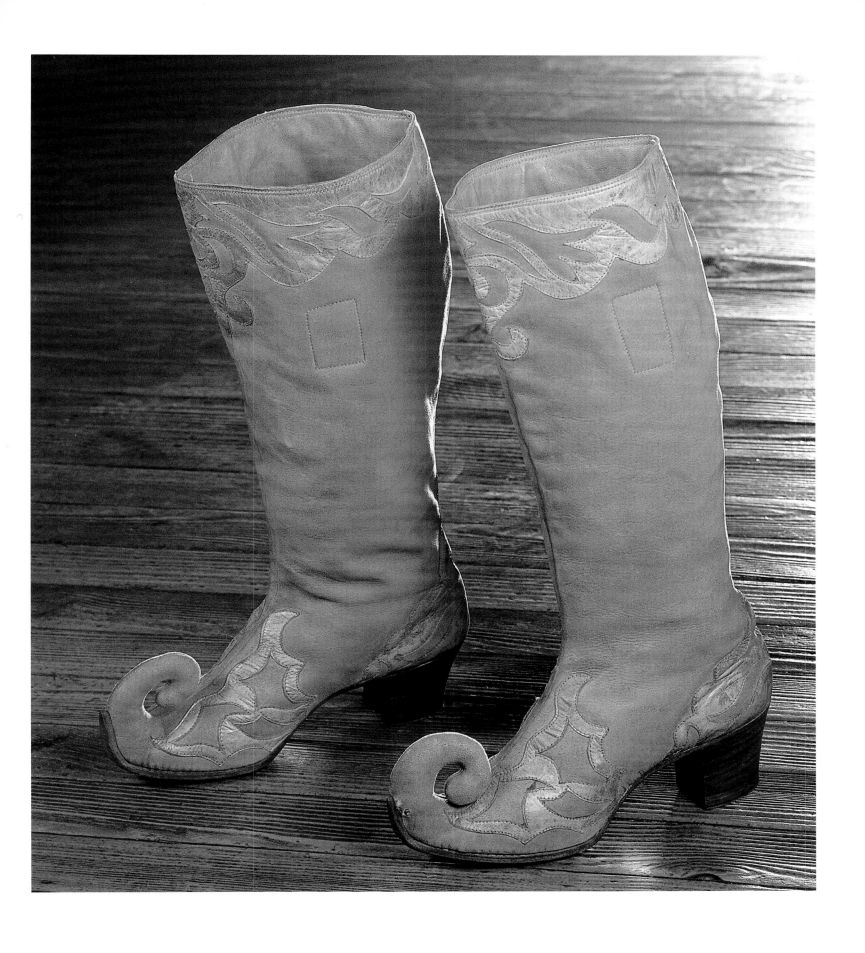

225. Boots of Ninon Vallin worn in *Marouf, the Shoemaker of Cairo*.
Brown suede, applications of turquoise kidskin, eastern style roll at
the end of the vamp, around 1917. International Shoe Museum, Romans.

Boots Worn by Opera Singer Ninon Vallin

Once upon a time, there was a voice: "Mârouf, the Shoemaker of Cairo"

Born in 1886, in Montalieu, a village in the Dauphiné, Eugénie Vallin devoted herself to singing from a very young age. The child's talent quickly revealed itself in the choir of the parish church in the small community of Grand-Serre, located in the territorial division of the Drôme, where her father, a notary-lawyer, had just acquired an office in 1906. The Conservatory of Music in Lyon awarded her four prizes in 1910. Her soprano voice of exceptional range permitted her to have a spectacular and triumphant international career performing on the world's most prestigious stages. The International Shoe Museum, Romans, has a pair of oriental style boots worn by the famous opera singer at la Scala in Milan, 1917, in the opera "Mârouf, the Shoemaker of Cairo," by Henri Rabaud; she sang the role of Princess Saamcheddine.

Created by the Opéra Comique in Paris on 15 May 1914, this opera in five acts takes us to Cairo, to Khaïtan, and to the desert. It is the tale of the legendary adventures of a shoemaker practising his craft in Egypt's capital.

Mârouf, predisposed to laziness, is unhappy at home. His wife, Fatimah, is unattractive, ill-natured, and beats him, so Mârouf decides to go away. He comes through a shipwreck, and his friend, Ali, picks him up from the shore and takes him to Khaïtan, a legendary big city somewhere between China and Morocco. The humble shoemaker passes himself off as the world's richest merchant expecting a caravan full of marvels.

The Sultan himself invites him to the Palace and, in spite of the suspicions of the vizier, offers him the hand of his daughter, Princess Saamcheddine. Mârouf is living in luxury, frittering away his brother-in-law's money, when he confesses his hoax to his wife. The two lovers decide to flee and take refuge with a poor peasant at an oasis. As a way of thanking him for his hospitality, Mârouf then starts to work, helping the peasant with his field labour.

While pushing the plough, Mârouf strikes an iron ring, which raises up a trap door giving access to an underground chamber. What's more, the ring has magic powers; when the princess strokes it, the peasant turns into a genie who immediately places himself at the young couple's service and introduces them to an incredible treasure. When the Sultan and his guards catch up with the fugitives, the noise of an approaching caravan can be heard in the distance. Mârouf and the princess triumph, whereas the vizier is condemned to one hundred blows with a stick.

Hailed in the world's major capitals, Ninon Vallin was nothing like a diva. She regularly visited her native region and participated in the festivals of her village with a total lack of pretension.

This princess of singing died in Millery on 22 November 1961, on the day of Saint Cecilia, patroness of musicians.

226. Shoes of Maurice Chevalier. Derby in navy blue suede, worn at the Théâtre des Champs-Elysées at the time of his farewell to the stage. International Shoe Museum, Romans.

Shoes Worn by Maurice Chevalier

"The Symphony of the Wooden Soles"

Maurice Chevalier's famous boater may have been an integral part of his character and repertoire (in the joyful refrain "with my boater hat"), but his shoes mostly went unnoticed. Nevertheless, his heirs donated a pair to the International Shoe Museum, Romans, in 1984 through the intermediary, photographer Jacques-Henri Lartigue. Derbies of navy blue suede labelled Bally Suisse, the artist last wore these shoes on stage; a photograph confirms this, showing Maurice Chevalier taking a bow on the stage of the Théâtre des Champs Elysées, on 1 October 1968, in the same shoes.

Born in Paris in 1888, the screen actor and popular singer was Mistinguett's partner at the Folies Bergères and triumphed at the Casino of Paris. A great boardwalk and music hall professional, he successfully interpreted many songs, such as the *Symphony of the Wooden Soles*, from 1945:

"I love the tap tap of wooden soles
It makes me gay, it makes me oh how can I say
When I hear this rhythm so strong
Into my heart comes a song
Tap tap says good morning
Little shoes from fir trees
Tap tap tap time to wake up, get out of bed, and go to work,
Romantic young things seem to tap dance as they walk
And all day long we hear the eloquent sound
What a charming racket thousands of little shoes make
Now women are charming
To the tip of their toes
I love the tam tam of the wooden soles
It makes me happy it makes me so oh how can I say
When I hear this rhythm so strong
Into my heart comes a song
Tap tap tap is the refrain
Of the busy street
Tap tap tap the symphony
Of beautiful days with less patent-leather
It clacks, it vibrates, and it sounds more joy than a honking horn
It's the Parisian rhythm of the happy shoe
Its sings of life full of vigour and fun
It's euphoria gets under your skin
I love the tap tap of the wooden soles
It makes me happy, it makes me so oh how can I say
When I hear this rhythm so strong
Into my heart comes a song
It's wonderful! How wonderful!
It's really wonderful!"

Through his carefully chosen vocabulary the songwriter recreates the echo of the very specific noise made by the wooden-heeled shoes worn during World War II. Maurice Chevalier's gift for rhythmic cadences makes the song amusing and playful. It's a big tip of the hat to the ingenuity of shoemakers; they substituted raw materials in the face of a leather shortage during this period of our history and in the process launched a new style adapted to the circumstances.

Shoes Worn by Charles Trenet

"Y'a d'la joie!" ("Life is good!")

When Charles Trenet gave a recital in Romans on 7 October 1990, he promised to donate his stage shoes to the International Shoe Museum, Romans. After his death on 21 June 2001, the executors of his estate made the official presentation the day of the music festival.

They are unlabelled, comfortable shoes that aided and supported his sensitive feet, concealing the scar from a wound to his right foot dating to the World War II. A Richelieu model with a black box, the style has a classic elegance that brings back memories when we look at it; the shoes seem to hum his songs, such as *La mer* (Beyond the Sea), *Douce France* (Sweet France), *Que reste-t-il de nos amours?* (What's Left of Our Love?), *Route Nationale 7* (Highway 7), *Revoir Paris* (To See Paris Again), *Le jardin extraordinaire* (The Amazing Garden), *Boum Boum* (Bang Bang), *Y'a d'la joie!* (Life is Good) and others.

Now museum pieces, these shoes are back on stage as physical evidence of an immensely talented artist's career. They remind visitors that Charles Trenet, giant of the French chanson and immortal genius of international renown, created a hymn of life out of happiness.

Studio Shoes Worn by César (1921–1998)

Donated to the International Shoe Museum, Romans, by the artist.

The sculptor called "the Vulcan of modern times" by Edmonde Charles Roux, César Baldaccini was a member of Picasso's circle at a very young age. He wore clogs with wooden soles in his studio to weld and assemble the pieces of junk metal he found.

A private visit to the International Shoe Museum, Romans, captivated the sculptor, who marvelled at shoe machines built from all different kinds of metal. The artist signed the visitor's book in a manner commensurate with his talent and his art: first, with a vigorous and rapid stroke of the pencil he drew a structure, then he drew the pump that appears on the ground behind a metal gate. The overall drawing has a sense of space and form.

In the adjoining office to his studio, on shelves next to his art books and mementos, the sculptor kept women's shoes. When a journalist who had come to interview him noticed the shoes, César explained, "I've just discovered a wonderful thing: the International Shoe Museum in Romans."

Shoes Worn by Jacques-Henri Lartigue

Painter and photographer (1894-1986)

The photographer who took Valéry Giscard d'Estaing's official portrait as President of the Republic, Jacques-Henri Lartigue was involved in photography at a very young age and exhibited as a painter from 1918. He illuminated his paintings with the sign of a painted sun in addition to his signature.

The same sun is reproduced on his rubber-soled canvas studio shoes donated to the International Shoe Museum, Romans, in 1983.

227. Shoes of Charles Trenet. International Shoe Museum, Romans.
Photo by Joël Garnier.

228. Shoes of Jacques-Henri Lartigue, photographer, 1980.
International Shoe Museum, Romans.

229. Shoes from the César workshop, clog in thick brown leather.
International Shoe Museum, Romans.

Mouna Ayoub:

The journey of an Haute Couture collector

Born in the Lebanese mountains, Mouna Ayoub became interested in the world of fashion at a very young age. As a child, she accompanied her mother to "Madame Juliette," a French couturier established in Sid El Bauchrié. Flipping through magazines at this design studio, she discovered the most beautiful styles of Dior, Paquin, Schiaparelli, Vionnet, and Saint Laurent.

At Madame Juliette's, Mouna also learned how to make clothes for her doll. It wasn't long before she shared her mother's unconditional admiration for Coco Chanel and began to dream of Paris, the international capital of elegance that set the tone for fashion and good taste.

After being educated by the Sisters of the Sacred Heart of Bikfaya, where she perfected her French, her studies lead her to Aix-en-Provence, Marseille, and Paris. She quickly developed an eye for fashion before the shop windows of avenue Montaigne and rue Cambon.

On 1 February 1978, she married a rich Saudi. For the occasion she wore a wedding gown designed by Jean-Louis Scherrer. Thenceforth she became a regular attendee of Haute Couture showings. Faithful to the most prestigious Paris firms, her watchful and expert eye also followed the young designers showing on Haute Couture's runways. Her significant and intelligent purchasing policy has made Mouna Ayoub the greatest private collector of Haute Couture. The sumptuous clothes she has collected with wonderful enthusiasm for over twenty years illustrate couture's superb craft traditions.

This extraordinary, ever expanding legacy also includes over one thousand pairs of shoes. During the 2001 autumn/winter season, a selection of her collection was the subject of an exhibition at the International Shoe Museum, Romans; mules, sandals, Charles IX, boots, bootees, ankle boots, Louis XV pumps, all entirely hand-made, represented ten years (1990 to 2000) of Raymond Massaro's work for Chanel. These shoes were shown to the cultural and sensory delight of visitors.

The exemplary patron, Mouna Ayoub, a true supporter of artistic creativity, facilitates the transfer of expertise from one generation to the next. As the talented embroiderer François Lesage explains: "If there were fifteen others like her, the future of Haute Couture would be absolutely assured."

230. Shoe of Mouna Ayoub,
International Shoe Museum, Romans.

Shoes Worn by Paul Bocuse
and Pierre Troisgros

These two ambassadors of world-renown French gastronomy never cease innovating within their great culinary tradition.

Paul Bocuse wore black kid moccasins to chair the jury for the 1961 Meilleur Ouvrier de France (Best Worker in France) award. He decided to keep wearing them in his famous restaurant in Collonges-Au-Mont-d'Or where he warmly greets customers who come to savour his Bresse fowl cooked in a pig's bladder, one of his many famous dishes.

Pierre Troisgros, however, when not in front of the stove in his Roanne restaurant preparing sorrel salmon, slips on his wooden clogs and surveys the vineyards at his estate in Blondins in the Loire.

Several years ago these two great chefs gave these shoes to the International Shoe Museum, Romans. Visitors discover a feast for the eyes!

On the surface, most shoes appear extraordinarily banal, even trivial. Some shoes, however, have transcended their everyday reality through the human story they tell and the themes they embody.

231. Shoes of Paul Bocuse worn for the competition for the Best Worker in France in 1961. Moccasin style in black kidskin. International Shoe Museum, Romans.

232. Clogs of Pierre Troisgros in wood and leather. Executed by Daniel Drigeard, clog maker in Renaison. Worn in the vineyard, "Les Blondins", that the chef in the kitchen cultivates.

233. Salomé, Shoes of Mistinguett, Musée Galliera - musée
de la mode de la Ville de Paris, Paris.

234. Pair of indoor mules of Sacha Guitry by shoemaker Camille Di Mauro, Paris, 1940. Musée Galliera - musée de la mode de la Ville de Paris, Paris. Photo by Lifermann, PMVP.

235. Pair of shoes of Lana Marconi for her marriage with Sacha Guitry by shoemaker Camille Di Mauro. Musée Galliera - musée de la mode de la Ville de Paris, Paris. Photo by Lifermann, PMVP.

236. Marriage shoes of Queen Elizabeth II. Bally-Schuhmuseum, Schönenwerd, Switzerland.

237. Joan Crawford in the "Hollywood Boot Shop" that Ferragamo opened in 1923. Ferragamo Museum, Florence.

238. Shoes of Princess Grace of Monaco. Beige cloth embroidered with multicoloured flowers, Louis XV heel. Exclusive model conceived by Evins and realised by Miller. International Shoe Museum, Romans.

239. Dance slippers of Wilfride Piollet. 1998-1999.
International Shoe Museum, Romans. Photo by Joël Garnier.

240. Boots worn by Meryl Streep in the role of Karen Blixen and aviator boots
worn by Robert Redford in the role of Denys Finch Hatton in Sydney
Pollack's *Out of Africa* in 1986, created by Pompeï Companie

241. "Low-cut" pumps of Marilyn Monroe decorated entirely with red Swarovski strass, strass covered heel. Created by S. Ferragamo for the film *Let's Make Love*, directed by George Cukor in 1960. Ferragamo Museum, Florence.

242. Sandals of Elizabeth Taylor in *Cleopatra*, 1963.

243. "Pull-Over" style created for Brigitte Bardot in 1966. Bottine covered in velvet. Ferragamo Museum, Florence.

244. Shoes worn by Romy Schneider in the role of Marthe Hanau in Francis
Girod's *The Banker*, 1980.

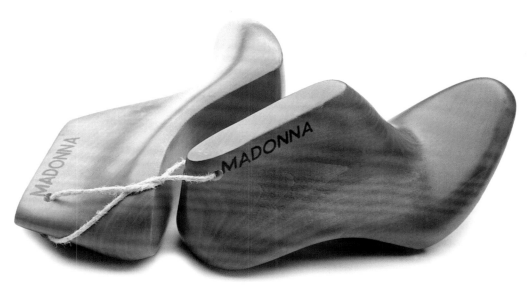

245. Mule of Madonna by Dolce and Gabbana. Ledermuseum, Offenbach.
246. Wooden lasts of Madonna's feet preserved at the Spini Feroni Palace.

247. Ankle boots worn by Leonardo DiCaprio as Jack in *Titanic*, created by the House of Pompeï, 1996.

248. Charles IX style shoe worn by Kate Winslet as Rose in the film *Titanic*, shoe created by the House of Pompeï, 1996. Vamp varnished black, quarters and attachments in violet velvet calfskin.

249. Bottines for the doll Rosalie in black leatherware, around 1889.
Given by a shoemaker to his granddaughter for Christmas.
International Shoe Museum, Romans.

250. The boots of the well-digger. International Shoe Museum, Romans.
Photograph: Joël Garnier.

Following pages:

251. Shoes of Zoya. Pumps in beige kidskin, heel and buckle in amber, Russia,
around 1920-1925. The heels are exceptional and highly representative
of the country's resources. Zoya played the piano in the concert circle.

252. Bottines of Mathilde, winter 1920. International Shoe Museum, Romans.

The Stories Shoes Tell

On the surface, most shoes appear extraordinarily banal, even trivial. Some shoes, however, have transcended their everyday reality through the human story they tell and the themes they embody.

Theresa's Doll Shoes

At age eight Theresa played with a doll just like other little girls her age. Theresa's doll wore a gathered blue dress and had porcelain eyes, but she lacked shoes. This was a serious omission because Theresa was the granddaughter of a master shoemaker.

On her way home from school, Theresa never forgot to stop at her grandfather's workshop to give him a kiss. There, with the help of a few workers, shoes were custom made and "hand sewn." On Thursdays, when there was no school, the little girl often spent the afternoon in the workshop where a mingled scent of leather, glue, and polish emanated. Theresa nosed about every nook and cranny, between the workbench and the shelves full of wooden forms and boxes of nails, while the steady sounds of the workshop resounded around her; the sound of the lasting pliers pushing in nails to fit the leather on the last and the sound of the hammer pounding out the leather.

One cold and gloomy November afternoon in 1889, the little girl, with doll in arms, pushed open the door, as was her custom, and entered the shop like a stream of sunlight, filling the place with joy. In that same instant, the grandfather's eyes fell upon the doll's bare feet. Now Theresa, who could not stop herself from thoroughly exploring the world of the shoemaker's workshop, placed her "daughter" on a stool. Taking advantage of the moment, her grandfather rapidly measured the doll's feet. When his workday was done, and with the utmost secrecy, the master craftsman put his heart into skilfully crafting miniature ankle boots for the doll. On Christmas Eve, he wrapped them in tissue paper and, while the child lay asleep, placed the doll shoes inside her own shoes left in front of the fireplace.

Christmas morning, Theresa discovered her shoes stuffed with the little doll shoes. Her eyes blazed with delight as she turned to her grandfather and said, "Look Grandfather what Father Christmas brought me. He knows how to make shoes just like you and you did not even teach him how."

Theresa carefully preserved the little ankle boots as a memento of the deep affection she shared with her beloved grandfather. Years passed. Christmas time was approaching when Theresa decided to donate the shoes to the International Shoe Museum, Romans. She was age ninety-five. In offering them, the elderly woman said, "Grandfather is watching from above. How happy he must be to see his ankle boots join the thousands of pairs gathered here and made by men practicing his craft from over four thousand years ago to the present day."

As the holidays approached, the Museum could not have asked for a more wonderful gift than Theresa's doll shoes.

The Well-Digger's Boots

In 1880, many dwellings, farms in particular, only had one source of water: the well, a source of life in the broadest sense. Jules was a well-digger in the

northern region of the Drôme in the Dauphiné. It was arduous and dangerous work. To descend forty or fifty metres under ground, this digger, a specialist in sinking wells with small diametres, wore protective boots of his own design crafted by an artisan in his village. Made of a thick wooden sole with cut zinc encasing the foot and the leg, each boot weighed two kilos.

As his grandson explains: "When my grandfather performed maintenance on a well, he had to descend to the bottom and splash about in icy water. So the thick wool socks knit by my grandmother and these big boots pulled on over them protected him from the cold. And then to sink a well, he had to go at the wall before he reached the water layer, using an iron pick on the marl or clay; there was always the risk of being hit by a rock."

The primary function of these boots was therefore to protect Jules's feet and legs in his struggle against a hostile environment. They foreshadow the work shoes that became standard for many high-risk professions after 1950. The industrialisation of work shoes owes its development to public health and safety committees, which led to the appearance of protective shoes in civil engineering, firemen's fireproof boots and the clogs worn in food chains and hospitals. The wearing of clogs in hospitals arose as an antiseptic measure in the operating room, instead of covering their town shoes with cloth boots, it is now mandatory for surgeons to wear clogs with surgical scrubs.

Zoya's Shoes

Zoya came from a noble family of Russian landowners. Born in Crimea around 1900, she learned to play the piano as a child, like many girls her age in her social class. An exceptionally gifted student, she continued her training at the conservatory in Simferopol. Despite her country's major social and artistic upheavals, Zoya kept up her studies at the Petrograd conservatory. While historical events lead many of her fellow countrymen to emigrate abroad, Zoya refused to leave, deeply attached to her Russian roots and her friends with whom she shared a love of music.

Exiled to the interior, her talent made her an appreciated and recognised concert pianist, while her charm, elegance, and sublime beauty caught the attention of filmmakers who offered her a screen test and implored her to take up acting. Zoya, nevertheless, declined the offer. The irresistible call of music, her happiness interpreting it, and the immaterial, almost supernatural joy it gave her and those who listened to her play, was much stronger.

Thenceforth, Zoya devoted herself completely to her art with an audience of Leningrad's upper classes. It was the 1920s and her country was anaemic, devoid of vitality in the aftermath of the war of 1914 and the Bolshevik revolution of October 1917. Lenin then launched his New Economic Policy (NEP) that allowed private enterprise, deeming that the country needed to take a breather. During this period, Zoya wore a fabulous pair of beige kid pumps made by a Petrograd shoemaker. What elevated these shoes to the category of masterwork were the buckles and heels cut from single pieces of amber, evidence of the imagination and know-how of Russian craftsmen during a difficult period of scant luxury. Her talent in full bloom, terrible experiences awaited Zoya who was taken prisoner in 1937; she died in the Gulag.

For many years Zoya's niece lived in France. In the 1960s, during a trip to Russia, the niece met her cousins and they offered her the gift of their most precious possession: Zoya's shoes. In 2000, the family heirloom's new owner donated the shoes to the International Shoe Museum, Romans, where they are preserved on display. For all that they embody, these shoes invite silence, reverence, and meditation.

Mathilde's Ankle Boots

It was 1920 and Mathilde was twenty years old when she boarded a train one winter morning with her cousin. The two young women were going on vacation to visit their grandparents. Thin and elegant, Mathilde was a charming brunette. This morning, she wore laced ankle boots in glazed brown calfskin, showing off her shapely legs. Georges was already seated by the window when the two cousins settled into the compartment. Mathilde's arrival struck him like a bolt of lightning. For a split second, he saw nothing but the young woman's ankle boots and legs because the conductor stood in front of her like a screen, but her figure quickly emerged in its full glory, blinding Georges who could not take his eyes off her appearance. Mathilde sensed she was the subject of intense observation, but her upbringing did not permit her to give the slightest regard to the stranger, whom she noticed was quite distinguished, all the same. While the landscape rolled by like pictures of happiness, the two cousins chatted softly. Georges strained his ears to take in all he could of the conversation, which was sometimes muted by the locomotive's loud cries, revolving around the work of Johan Sebastian Bach and a church rehearsal of "Jesus Joy of Man's Desiring." Arriving at her destination, Mathilde exited the compartment leaving Georges two clues with which to undertake a proper investigation to find the beautiful stranger: her first name and, better yet, the name of the town where she played organ for a collegiate church at Sunday mass.

Days passed, but Georges' memory of the encounter refused to recede into the impenetrable fog of oblivion. On the contrary, Mathilde's image was permanently etched on his mind; the image of her pretty legs in ankle boots was foremost among his thoughts while her silhouette marked by a combination of elegance and vulnerability occupied the rest. Georges ended up confiding the wonderful secret in his heart to his mother who was offended by this unexpected revelation, especially in the way it went against the accepted behaviour of his milieu. Yet, his heart, a little later, filled with a strange joy he had never felt before, when he decided to travel the five hundred kilometres that separated him from Mathilde. When he entered the church to attend eleven o'clock high mass, the organ resounding at full volume matched his own emotions. The sonorous rush of the music sustained his feelings and touched his innermost soul, transporting him to another realm where he had a momentary glimpse of eternity. When the service was over, Georges was as much in contemplation as he was on the look out. He hid behind a pillar by the small wooden spiral staircase that connected the organ gallery to the nave. Suddenly, as if a signal, he heard the sound of Mathilde's footsteps coming down the steps. It echoed in his ears, regulating his heartbeat like a metronome. Finally he caught sight of her. Wearing the famous ankle boots he had so admired on the train, she was surrounded by friends and acquaintances, radiating an inner beauty that exalted her.

The memory of love at first sight on the train and future plans leapt into his head; his heart beat in double-time. A silent lover observing from afar, Georges came and went for three consecutive Sundays, travelling a total of four thousand kilometres in an era when slow transportation methods made travelling difficult. Unable to get his mind off Mathilde, the young man located the parish priest, who spoke of his organist in the most laudatory terms. And so it happened that in this church, a few months later, the priest united them before God and man in the sacrament of marriage.

The love the couple shared steadily grew as a result of the countless attentions they paid each other and, from these daily little nothings which amount to so much, the ordinary was transformed into the extraordinary; it was the art of producing happiness, but also a way to overcome trials. The rest was chemistry; the union produced four children.

Near the end of his life, after forty-five years of marriage, Georges still had the strength to tell Mathilde what an exceptional wife she had been and how deeply he had loved her with unparalleled devotion. He said it was because she knew how to be all the different women he needed at different times over the course of their lives. He told her again how, on that winter morning in 1920 on the train, he had instantly known that this person, as beautiful as a spring day, would change his life. Mathilde replied that she too, at the very same moment, was affected by an inexplicable feeling before the stranger and had expected nothing but happiness. Georges had always had a weakness for women's legs in lovely shoes and bought his wife beautiful ones. However, it was the ankle boots of their first meeting that were carefully preserved like relics, protected in their original brown and beige canvas bag and stored on the top shelf of the closet in the couple's bedroom.

One day, shortly before Georges died, Mathilde had a premonition as to how she would like to remember him after his passing into eternal life; she decided to present her ankle boots to the International Shoe Museum, Romans, sharing the story attached to them with great candour and emotion. Today, in this vault of preserved memory, the ankle boots represent mutual love shared between a man and a woman elevated to the sublime, expressed through the reciprocal gift of oneself.

Toine's clogs

Toine owned a small family farm he inherited from his father. At the break of dawn, he would put on his clogs and start such daily chores as opening the hen house door, climbing the hayloft to empty hay into the trough with the two mules, milking the goats, giving an alfalfa ration to the rabbits in their hutch and cleaning the pig pen.

Constantly coming and going from the well (sole source of water for the house) to the kitchen garden, to the cellar (where large vats for the grape harvest were lined up), and passing through the kitchen (where the food the land produced was prepared and eaten), Toine needed to wear sturdy shoes.

As the seasons changed, he wore the same shoes across the fields to harvest the corn, and in high summer, to harvest peaches. During the period of heavy labour that followed, Toine ploughed the fields behind a mule named Negro.

His clogs lefts tracks in the furrows of loose earth he sank his feet into as the village church bell chimed the hours and signalled when it was time to return to the farmhouse. And when autumn's wind bared the trees along the road near the stables, Toine's clogs made the leaves crackle underneath.

There was a boot scraper, a thin, timeworn iron strip supported by two segments of weather-beaten vine stakes and raised fifteen centimetres off the ground, near Toine's main door. Its only purpose was to remove the mud still stuck on his wooden soles.

Toine's "all terrain" clogs are a good illustration of agricultural practice between the wars in the small rural community of Génissieux located in the Drôme des Collines. Donated to the International Shoe Museum, Romans, by his nephew in 1978, their presence memorialises the bond between man and his land.

253. Clogs of Toine, farmer, 1950. International Shoe Museum, Romans. Photograph: Joël Garnier.

The Shoe in Literature

Literary descriptions of shoes have abounded since Antiquity. Valuable backups to iconographic sources, often the only meaningful reference for lost shoes and archaeological fragments of ancient shoes, literary descriptions are also an indispensable source for dating shoes before the advent of fashion journalism.

Additionally, literature is a source of reference for shoe manufacture. However, among literary images of the shoe, the most sublime, symbolic and poetic image is indisputably that evoked in Paul Claudel's masterpiece, *The Satin Slipper*. It tells the story of Doña Prouhèze who is guilty of an illicit love for Don Rodrigue. After removing her shoes and entrusting her satin slipper to the Virgin Mary as a symbol of a solemn vow, she offers the following prayer:

Take my heart in one hand and my slipper in the other while there's still time. I put myself in your hands! Virgin Mother, I give you my slipper! Virgin Mother, hold my miserable little shoe in your hand! I warn you, soon I won't be seeing you anymore; I'm about to completely turn from you! But when I try to leap into sin, let it be with a crippled foot! When I desire to clear the barrier you've set up, clip my wings! I've done what I could; it's up to you to protect my poor little shoe, hold it against your heart…

Restif de La Bretonne

Restif de La Bretonne had a gift for glorifying the foot and the shoe in his literary works. He leaves no doubt as to his predilection through the thoughts of the "anti-Justine": "More than anything else I have a weakness for pretty feet and pretty shoes."

In his "contemporary" novel, the hero Saintepallaire is a young husband with a foot fetish. As the author writes: "Nothing imaginable was more distinguished and valuable than his young wife's shoes. They were covered up to the heel with pearls and brilliant diamonds. They had cost over ten thousand crowns and had been a gift from Saintepallaire.

At night, when they were alone in their bedroom, the young husband knelt down and with a trembling hand removed the beautiful shoes from her pretty feet. Then he dressed them in slippers, which were no less beautiful, although less expensive. The shoes were placed in a small glass temple made up of a round base atop crystal ionic columns with gold capitals. The shoes were kept in this box as the evidence and guarantee of an immortal love. Ten years had passed since then with the young wife never forgetting on each wedding anniversary to wear the shoes. The husband's erotic passion did not diminish. Perhaps this ritual always renewed his love. Or perhaps his wife, under the advice of her admirable mother-in-law, used methods unknown to other women. Or perhaps men like Saintepallaire are more loving and more sensitive to many and often repeated stimuli…"

During the first year of marriage, the shoemaker delivered a new pair of shoes everyday to Saintepallaire, who did the ordering and selected the colours and ornaments himself.

His wife only wore them for one day and then put them away in a wall cabinet. During the second year, he only ordered white shoes. His wife successively wore all the shoes she had but once, including a few pairs that he had bought her before the marriage. Thanks to this activity, he was always occupied with his wife and her charms.

In novels such as *Le Pied de Fanchette* (The Foot of Fanchette) and *Monsieur Nicolas*, to name only the most famous, the shoe is much more than a discreet accessory. In these books, clogs, pumps, slippers, and mules are described in detail worthy of a whole catalogue of 18th-century women's shoe styles.

It should be noted that, although the symbolism of these shoes harks back to the 17th century through their resemblance to Cinderella's slipper, they also announce the foot and shoe fetishism examined by Octave Mirbeau in his *Diary of a Chambermaid*.

Chateaubriand, *Atala*

"The Moccasins of Chactas"

Chateaubriand set sail for America in 1791. The story of Atala, published in 1801, tells of the love between Chactas and Atala.

This swamp idyll plunges the reader into the exoticism of America. As Chateaubriand writes: "Atala made me a coat from the inner bark of an ash tree, because I was almost naked. With porcupine quills she embroidered moccasins for me made out of muskrat skin." The author's description of the moccasins demonstrates his gift for meticulous observation that he exercised when in contact with the Indians.

For example, that moccasin production was in fact women's work and porcupine quill embroidery was commonplace in the 18th-century. It is interesting to note that the author does not put shoes on Atala for her funeral, whereas the painter Girodet's discrete brush depicts her feet covered by a shroud. "Atala was laid upon a bed of mimosa; her feet, her head, her shoulders, and part of her breast were uncovered. A wilted magnolia was visible in her hair… Her lips like a pink bud picked two mornings ago seemed to languish and smile. In her astonishingly white cheek one could make out a few blue veins. Her beautiful eyes were closed; her humble feet were together."

254. Detail by Pierre Julien, *Jean de La Fontaine*.
Marble. H. 1.73 m, L. 1,10 m. Musée du Louvre, Paris.

255. Anne Louis Girodet, *The Entombment of Atala*,
also called *"Funérailles d'Atala"*, 1808. Oil on canvas, 207 x 267 cm.
Musée du Louvre, Paris.

Emile Zola, *Au Bonheur des dames*

(Ladies' Delight)

The advent of large department stores during the Second Empire changed domestic trade in France. The concept was to present departments, carrying all kinds of everyday items, to hundreds of customers. The terms of sale were also new; the store would take only a small profit on each item sold at a fixed price, but would make up the difference through volume. When Aristide Boucicaut came to seek his fortune in Paris, he started out as a humble employee before heading a department in a general store. In 1852 he bought a small boutique of thirty metres called Le Bon Marché located in a popular neighbourhood.

From 1863 the store's sales reached seven million; by 1877 Le Bon Marché comprised of a variety of shops. The store inspired Émile Zola to write *Au Bonheur des dames* (Ladies' Delight), which was published in 1883. The novel recounts how Octave Mouret successfully reinvents modern commerce when artisan boutiques are replaced by large department stores. The department store inspires Mouret to exanimate feminine vanity. Among the store's various departments, a position of privilege was accorded the shoe department:

"But Madame Marty became especially feverish over new departments; a new department could not be opened without her inaugurating it. She rushed in and bought something all the same... Then she went down to the shoe department in the back of a ground floor gallery, behind neckwear, to a counter opened just that day, where she wreaked havoc on the cases, swooning before the white silk mules decorated with swan feathers, shoes, and white satin ankle boots with high Louis XV heels."

" 'Oh! Dear,' she stammered, 'make no mistake. They have an incredible selection of great coats. I picked out one for myself and one for my daughter... And Valentine, what about the shoes?' " " 'It's unprecedented!' added the young girl, with her feminine bravado. 'There are boots for twenty francs fifty. Oh! The boots!' "

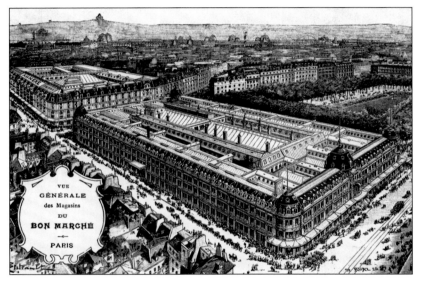

Gérard de Nerval, *Sylvie*

Alain Fournier, *Le Grand Meaulnes*

(The Wanderer)

"Shoes of Yesterday"

Sylvie and *Le Grand Meaulnes* (The Wanderer) were published sixty years apart, but the two writers are united by two descriptions of shoes. The 1853 novel *Sylvie* evokes the author's cherished memories of the Valois. Nerval is torn between his feelings for his childhood friend Sylvie and Adrienne's mysterious seductiveness; Adrienne's magical attraction is the stronger.

Searching for an old style of lace, Sylvie rummages in her aunt's drawers: "She rummaged again in the drawers. Oh! What riches! How wonderful this item felt; how that one shined, how another shimmered with bright colours and modest beading! Two slightly broken pearl fans, tins with Chinese motifs, an amber necklace, and tons of frills and flounces, among which shone forth two little shoes of white drugget with buckles incrusted with Irish diamonds! 'Oh! I want to put them on if I can find the embroidered stockings!'"

"Just then we unfolded silk stockings of pale pink with green patches; but the Aunt's voice accompanied by the chattering stove suddenly brought us back to reality."

256. Illustration of the Bon Marché.
257. Illustration of the Bon Marché.

"'Go downstairs quick!' said Sylvie, and regardless of what I said, she would not allow me to help her with her shoes."

Like Gérard de Nerval, Alain Fournier places his novel in the beloved landscapes of his childhood. Meaulnes mysteriously disappears for three days and gets lost in the most isolated corner of the Sologne. He comes upon an estate, goes inside an abandoned room, and falls asleep. In the morning he wakes to find old-fashioned clothes nearby that seem to have been left for him.

"They were outfits worn by young men a long time ago, frock coats with high velvet collars, fine, very open vests, countless white ties and patent leather shoes from the turn of the century. He dared not touch anything With his fingertips, but after cleaning himself up as he shivered, he put one of the great coats on over his schoolboy's blouse, turning up the pleated collar, exchanged his steel-tipped shoes for the fine patent leather pumps, and prepared to go downstairs bareheaded" (*Le Grand Meaulnes* (The Wanderer), Ch. XIII, "La fête étrange" (The Strange Celebration) p.67, Le Livre de poche Brodard et Taupin).

What these two writers have in common is a continuous back and forth movement from dream to reality. Both delightfully conjugate the past with the present; the surprise and pleasure of discovering old-fashioned shoes experienced by both Sylvie and the *Grand Meaulnes* highlights this. Gérard de Nerval and Alain Fournier revive the worlds of childhood and adolescence, which reappear even today in the joyful and playful art of dress up, by allowing the reader to plunge into fantasy for a moment's pleasure.

Pierre Loti, *Madame Chrysanthème*

"In Japan: Introductions…"

"I could make out the rear view of a beautiful young thing all fixed up, who was finishing being rigged out in the empty street: there was a final maternal glance at the waistband's enormous shells and at the pleating around the waist. Her dress was of pearl grey silk; her obi (1) in mauve satin; a sprig of silver flowers trembled in her black hair; she was lit by one last melancholy ray of the setting sun; five or six people were with her…"

"Yes, it was definitively her, Miss Jasmine… my fiancé that was being brought to me! … I hurried downstairs where my landlord, the old Mrs. Prune lived with her husband. They were praying before the altar of their ancestors."

"'They're here, Mrs. Prune,' I said in Japanese, 'they're here! Quick, the tea, the stove, the embers, the small pipes for the women, the little bamboo spitting pots! Bring all the items necessary for the reception with haste!' I heard the door being opened and I went back upstairs. Wooden clogs were left on the floor; the stairs creaked under bare feet…"

Pierre Loti's travels took him to countries that were poorly understood during his time. His literary work reflected his attraction to exotic countries. He visited Japan in 1886 and published *Madame Chrysanthème* a year later. The novel transports the reader to the country of the rising sun where the author is introduced to a fiancée. The author faithfully observes the ancestral custom of taking off one's wooden clogs before entering the house and uses the staircase to recreate the sound of bare feet.

258. "Getta", wood and straw core, Japan, 19th century.
Traditional shoes whose shape remains unchanged for several centuries. International Shoe Museum, Romans.

259. Child's shoes resembling a cat's head, embroidered silk, China, 19th century. Guillen Collection, International Shoe Museum, Romans.

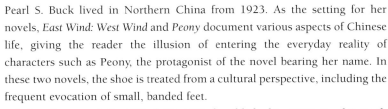

Pearl S. Buck, *East Wind: West Wind*,

"Peony"

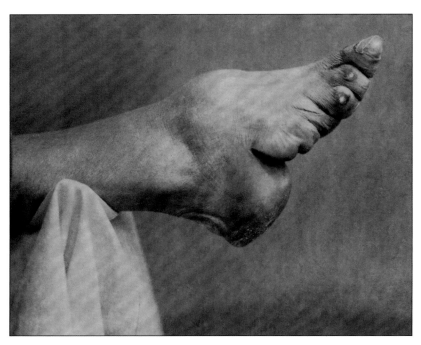

Pearl S. Buck lived in Northern China from 1923. As the setting for her novels, *East Wind: West Wind* and *Peony* document various aspects of Chinese life, giving the reader the illusion of entering the everyday reality of characters such as Peony, the protagonist of the novel bearing her name. In these two novels, the shoe is treated from a cultural perspective, including the frequent evocation of small, banded feet.

In her first novel, *East Wind: West Wind*, published in 1929, Pearl S. Buck shows how important foot banding was to Chinese women and the pride they took in this custom. However, by showing no less respect for the West, Buck denounces the cruelty of such a tradition though defended by the torturers themselves.

On the verge of marrying the man to whom she was promised even before she was born, Kwei-Lan listens to her mother's advice: "'The manners and etiquette of aristocratic life... these things you know... the cunning of shoes upon your little feet – ah, me, those feet of yours and all the tears they have cost! But I know of none so small in your generation. My own were scarcely more tiny at your age. I only hope that the family of Li have paid heed to my messages and have bound as closely the feet of their daughter, the betrothed of your brother, my son'" (*East Wind: West Wind*, pages 10-11, Moyer Bell, 1993). At the dawn of the Communist Revolution, Kwei-Lan remains attached to her parents' traditions and authority, but her husband, a young doctor, persuades her to renounce foot binding.

"'I have wished ever since our marriage to ask you if you will not unbind your feet. It is unhealthful for your whole body. See, your bones look like this.' He took a pencil and sketched hastily upon the leaf of his book a dreadful, bare, cramped foot.

How did he know? I had never dressed my feet in his presence. We Chinese women never expose our feet to the sight of others. Even at night we wear stockings of white cloth.

'How do you know?' I gasped.

'Because I am a doctor trained in the West,' he replied. 'And then, I wish you to unbind them because they are not beautiful. Besides, foot-binding is no longer in fashion. Does that move you?' He smiled slightly and looked at me not unkindly.

But I drew my feet hastily under my chair. I was stricken at his words. Not beautiful? I had always been proud of my tiny feet! All during my childhood my mother herself had superintended the soaking in hot water and the wrapping of the bandages – tight and more tight each day. When I wept in anguish she bid me remember that some day my husband would praise the beauty of my feet.

I bowed my head to hide my tears. I thought of all those restless nights and the days when I could not eat and had no desire to play – when I sat on the edge of my bed and let my poor feet swing to ease them of their weight of blood. And now after enduring until the pain had ceased for only a short year, to know he thought them ugly!

'I cannot,' I said, choking as I rose, and, unable to keep back my weeping, I left the room.

It was not that I cared over-much about my feet. But if even my feet in their cunningly embroidered shoes did not find favour in his sight, how could I hope to win his love?

Two weeks later I left for my first visit to my mother's home, according to our Chinese custom. My husband had not spoken of unbinding my feet again. Neither had he addressed me by my name" (*East Wind: West Wind*, pages 55-57, Moyer Bell, 1993).

260. Photo of women and a little girl with bound feet, China.
The Peabody & Essex Museum, Salem, Massachusetts.

261. Photo of a mutilated foot.
The Peabody & Essex Museum, Salem, Massachusetts.

262. Shoe cloisonné, gift offered between spouses, China. 18th century.
Collection of Gérard Lévy.

263. Shoes for bound feet, China.
International Shoe Museum, Romans.

Kwei-Lan's husband, through his medical studies in Europe, has abandoned the law of the ancestors and does not respect his country's customs or rituals. The poor little wife tries in vain to seduce her husband using all the resources of her meticulous and refined education, but the young doctor responds with indifference to all these attentions, making the young woman an exile in her own country.

The husband's point of view reappears in *Peony* in a passage describing how Peony, a young slave, is happy with her condition of servitude, because it allows her to escape foot binding, giving her the ability to run:

"How she loved to run! It was her luck to be bondmaid in this house of foreigners. Had she been in a Chinese house her feet would have been bound small as soon as it was sure she was to be pretty, so that if a son of the house were to love her and want her for a concubine, she would not shame the family by having feet like a servant's" (*Peony*, pages 28-29). Kwei-Lan's opinion of a Western woman's feet says a lot about the persistent attachment Chinese women had to foot mutilation: "I looked at

her feet and saw that they were like rice-flails for size." (*East Wind: West Wind*, p. 105, Moyer Bell, 1993). This issue marks a cultural divide between East and West. On the other hand, Buck often mentions shoes furtively in descriptions of costume or uses shoes to describe movement. These indications are always under the sign of lightness and silence, because the shoes were made of black satin or velvet:

"So saying she tripped away, her satin-shod feet silent upon the stones of the court" (*Peony*, p.65). The descriptions always emphasise the simplicity of Chinese shoes, slippers, and sandals, but the author also lingers over children's shoes adorned with animal heads that were embroidered by mothers for their sons:

"I have made him a pair of shoes with tiger faces" (*East Wind: West Wind*, p.110, Moyer Bell, 1993).

With this description of pretty shoes for little boys, Pearl S. Buck juxtaposes the sad privilege reserved for young girls in great Chinese families who have little feet.

Charles Perrault

The countless adaptations of these three fairytales for children have overshadowed Charles Perrault's original works intended for adults. A trilogy of the shoe, the stories offer the following perspectives: *Cinderella*, or the slipper of seduction; *Puss in Boots*, or the boots of appearances and rediscovered dignity; and *Little Thumb*, or the boots of power. One has only to return to the originals to be convinced.

Cinderella

Cinderella's glass slipper is the story's centrepiece:

"Her fairy godmother merely tapped her with her wand … then she gave here a pair of glass slippers, the most beautiful in the world."

At the ball, "The young lady was having so much fun she forgot her fairy godmother's advice; as a result, she was surprised when she heard the first stroke of midnight, having thought it was only eleven o'clock: she stood up and ran out as nimbly as a doe. The prince followed her but was unable to catch her. She dropped one of her glass slippers, which the prince picked up with great care. Cinderella arrived home completely out of breath without a coach and footman and wearing her old clothes: nothing remained of her former magnificence except for one of her little slippers, which matched the one she had allowed to fall off." This scene recalls the story of Rhodopis told by Strabo in the 1st century B.C.E. (which Perrault probably knew), as well as the Chinese tale of Sheh Hsien mentioned previously. As for Cinderella's lightness of foot, compared to that of a doe, the image has its source in a number of Biblical passages, such as in Habaquq III:19 (… he makes my feet like doe feet and makes me walk on my high places…), the Psalms, and the Book of Samuel. One also thinks of the Buddhist story of Padmavati, daughter of a Brahmin and a doe whose hooves are hidden in silk wrappings, which leads us to the Séducta label created by Charles Jourdan, its lively mark shows a doe-like creature in a leaping pose. Returning to Cinderella's lost slipper:

"When her two sisters returned from the ball, Cinderella asked them if they had fun and if the beautiful lady had been there; they replied yes, but that she had fled at the stroke of midnight and so hastily that she had dropped one of her little glass slippers, the most beautiful in the world; that the prince had picked it up and did nothing but stare at it for the remainder of the ball and that he had definitely fallen in love with the beauty to whom the little slipper belonged. They were right, because a little later the prince announced through his herald that he would marry the woman whose foot fit the little slipper.

Fittings started with princesses, followed by duchesses, then the entire court, but it was a waste of time. The prince was taken to the home of the two sisters, who did everything they could to get their feet into the slipper, but they were unable to pull it off. Cinderella, who was watching, recognised the slipper and said, while smiling:

"I can tell it wouldn't look bad on me!" (…) The gentleman who was doing the fitting regarded Cinderella attentively and found her to be very beautiful, and said that it would be fair, as he had been ordered to try it on every young woman. He made Cinderella sit down and, as soon as he brought the slipper to her little foot, he could tell that it would naturally fit and it slid right on like wax. The two sisters were dumbfounded, but they were even more shocked when Cinderella drew from her pocket the matching little slipper, which she put on her other foot."

And we all know the happy ending:

"She was taken to the young prince dressed just as she was. He found her more beautiful than ever and a short time later he married her" (Extracts from Charles Perrault's original text published in Paris in 1697).

These large extracts from Charles Perrault's original text, published in Paris in 1697, are explicit enough for us to catch the allusion to the sexual act. The symbolism of Cinderella's "glass" slipper in this way makes clear the popular expression "to find a shoe for one's foot." In the early 19th-century, Jakob Ludwig Grimm offered a variation on this tale:

Cinderella had two very ugly sisters. Their mother ordered the eldest to cut off her big toe so she could wear the prince's slipper; the other sister cut off half of her heel.

"The next morning the prince went to see his father the king and told him, 'The only one who can be my wife is the one who can wear this beautiful slipper.' The two sisters rejoiced then, because they had pretty feet. The eldest took the slipper into another room to try it on. But the slipper was too small and she couldn't get her big toe in. Her mother who was nearby said, 'Take the knife and cut off your big toe. You won't be walking on foot when you're queen.' The young girl cut off her big toe, forced her foot into the slipper, overcame her pain, and returned to the prince and the king. He then mounted her on his horse and took off with her as his fiancé."

The prince discovered the deception when he saw blood flowing across the shoe. He returned the girl to her mother who gave him her second daughter. Yet, once again, blood put an end to the ploy. Finally enters Cinderella with her slender foot formed exactly in the shape of the slipper, allowing her to reign in the prince's court happily ever after.

Puss in Boots

"From the Mill to the Castle"

In this fairytale, Perrault puts words in the mouth of a talking cat in the manner of Jean de la Fontaine:

"Don't worry master, all you have to do is give me a sack and make me a pair of boots for going into the brush and you'll see that you're not as bad off as you think you are."

The sole inheritance of the miller's youngest son, this mouse and rat eater assumes the appearance of a man by dressing in boots.

"When the cat received what he had asked for, he bravely put the boots on, threw his sack over his shoulder, grabbed the strings with his two front paws, and set off for a hunting ground where there were a large number of rabbits."

The boots were intended for the cat's hunting expeditions and to protect him from the brush, but proved to be a hindrance when climbing roofs to escape an ogre who turned himself into a lion.

"The cat was so terrified to see a lion in front of him that he immediately jumped into the gutters, which was a difficult and dangerous thing to do on account of his boots, which were not suited for walking on roof tiles."

Unlike Little Thumb's functional seven-league boots, designed for leaving at a moment's notice to cover great distances, the clever cat's boots were instead suited for to his role as a skilled strategist, which resulted in his impoverished master becoming the Marquis of Carabas, a rich landowner, lord, and moreover, the king's son-in-law.

264. Sir Edward Coley Burne-Jones, *Cinderella*, 1863.
Transparent and opaque watercolour on paper, 65.7 x 30.4 cm.
The Museum of Fine Arts, Boston.

265. Postilion's boot also called, "seven league boot". Weight: 4.5 kg, France, end of the 17th century. The seven leagues represent the distance covered by postilions between two posts. International Shoe Museum, Romans.

Petit Poucet

(Little Thumb)

One of Perrault's most popular fairytales, *Little Thumb* was widely published with many different variations and omissions beginning in the 18th century. The author's text gives a precise itinerary for a pair of seven-league boots, the indispensable accessory to a giant ogre's magic power, which Little Thumb will acquire through exceptional ingenuity.

The ogre's house is the starting point for the itinerary of the boots. When he learns that his seven daughters have ruined him, the ogre tells his wife, "Quick, give me my seven-league boots so I can catch them."

This is how Little Thumb and his brother discover the power of the ogre's seven-league boots: "They saw that the giant was going from one mountain to the next and that he crossed rivers as easily as if they were tiny streams."

The ogre's magic boots correspond to the winged sandals of Hermes, the Greek messenger of the gods who could instantaneously cross the sky. While the ogre sleeps, the audacious Little Thumb takes off his boots and takes hold of their power.

"Little Thumb drew near to the giant, gently pulled off his boots, and immediately put them on. The boots were extremely wide and long, but since they were magical, they could expand or shrink according to the leg they clothed; so it happened that they fit his feet and legs as if they had been made for him."

"Dressed in these magical boots, he returned to the giant's house to seize his gold, telling the giant's wife: "It is such a pressing matter he wanted me to take these seven-league boots and carry on post haste…""

Little Thumb returned to his father's home with all the giant's riches. But Perrault leaves the end of the story up in the air: "Many people disagree with this last detail… They attest that when Little Thumb put the giant's boots on he went to court where he knew that an army two hundred leagues away was desperately needed, as was news from the front. He sought the King, they say, to whom he offered to bring news of the army before the end of the day. The King promised Little Thumb a large sum of money if he was successful. Little Thumb returned that very evening with the news and this first run brought him attention and he had all the work he needed. The King paid him handsomely to carry his orders to the army and countless women would pay any price for news of their lovers, and this was his greatest profit. Some wives gave him letters to carry to their husbands, but they paid him so little and it was such a small thing that he dared not reveal what he earned from that side of the business. After working as a courier and having amassed a fortune he returned to his father's house where he was received with unimaginable joy."

Coachmen's boots, also called "seven-league boots" in the 17th century are connected with Little Thumb and his role as the King's courier. In the last paragraph, ignored in the versions adapted for children, beautiful 17th-century women imitate their ancient Roman counterparts by entrusting amorous letters to Little Thumb.

Ovid's *The Art of Love* sanctioned the role of confidants carrying gallant messages in their sandals for their mistresses, and Perrault allows himself the same privilege with the seven-league boots. Charles Perrault pictures the power of the seven-league boots making Little Thumb the King's best courier and saves the child and his family from poverty.

Much later, Marcel Aymé based his *Contes du chat perché* on these stories. By placing the seven-league boots in a Parisian setting in Montmartre where dream and reality are combined he gives the story a contemporary, urban twist.

In these three fairytales, Perrault makes the shoe an emblematic accessory in the search for happiness, glory, power, and fortune.

266. Engraving by Gustave Doré, *Puss in Boots*, tales by Perrault, 19th century.
267. Henri Terres, *Puss in Boots*, 1995. International Shoe Museum, Romans.
268. Engraving by Gustave Doré, *Little Thumb*, tales by Perrault, 19th century.

Un rire général salua cette chute.... (Page 79.)

The Countess of Ségur, *Good Little Girls*

"The Shoe of Madame Fichini"

The Countess of Ségur, born Sophie Rostopchine, was a children's book writer of Russian decent. Her trilogy of Sophie, *Les Petites Filles modèles* (Good Little Girls), followed by *Les Malheurs de Sophie* (Sophie's Troubles) and *Vacances* (Vacations) are crown jewels among children's book collections and have a Second Empire ambiance.

The 1857 publication of *Petites Filles modèles* (Good Little Girls) details the showy elegance of an upstart named Madame Finchini right down to the shoes when she arrives at Madame de Fleurville's country house: "Here I am Dear Ladies,' she said stepping out of the car and revealing her big foot dressed in lilac satin shoes that matched her dress and had lace ornaments" (Ch. IX, p.76, Hachette).

A lilac faille ankle boot preserved in the Galliera Museum in Paris resembles this description as does Bertall's illustration reproduced in the 1857 edition, showing Madame Fichini's spectacular fall with her leg in the air and her foot in the shoe.

269. *The Little Girl Models: Fall of Madame Fichini*, illustration by Bertall,
  former publishing house of Hachette booksellers.
270. Pair of lilac bottines by Camille Di Mauro, around 1860.
  Musée Galliera - musée de la mode de la Ville de Paris, Paris.
  Photo by Lifermann, PMVP.

222

The Shoe and Art

Conceived for walking, the shoe is an essential everyday object, but its aesthetic qualities can elevate it to the status of art. As art objects, shoes say a lot about their creator's personality, but above all they express the ideas and manual skill of the shoemaker, whether famous or anonymous. Shoes are also inexhaustible sources of iconography that have nourished the imagination of artists throughout the world, throughout time, in drawing and sculpture and in the decorative and plastic arts. This part of the book is therefore primarily visual, devoted to the contemplation of selected works from the countless examples of shoes transformed by artistic inspiration.

In 1832, Delacroix travelled to North Africa, a major episode in his career that transformed his vision, his technique, and his aesthetic. Maurice Serullaz, in his book on Delacroix, lists the various items the artist brought back, as indicated by the notes in Delacroix's travel journal:

"Five pair of slippers; eleven pairs of slippers with double soles; two small pairs; one small women's pair; common woman's slipper; man's slipper without quarter; four pairs of boots" (Maurice Serullaz, Delacroix, Ch. VII, "Living Antiquity", Light and its Coloured Reflections, p.173).

Delacroix shared his shoe observations in a letter he wrote to Félix Grullemardet as he approached Tangiers on 24 January 1832:

"After a lengthy crossing of thirteen long days, dear friend, I am damp facing the African river and with a view of this town, the first in the Moroccan empire with which we communicate. This morning I had the pleasure of watching a boatload of Moroccans come aside our corvette to bring over our consul whom we had contacted. These people exhibit a mélange of fascinating costumes: several were a little like the Barbary coast outfits one sees in Paris, except the men have bare legs and feet: only the lords wear slippers" (Maurice Serullaz, Delacroix, Ch. VIII, "Living Antiquity" Light and its Reflections, p.145).

Delacroix hardly considered shoes a superfluous accessory. According to what he wrote to George Sand in 1838, he felt quite the contrary:

"I had to run to both ends of Paris all day… I will try to come see you tonight and put on your shoes; I love the slippers, stockings, and legs (in the Arab fashion). Send word if I cannot see you and kindest regards."

As Maurice Serullaz points out: "And he signed with a visual pun he rarely used: Eugène 2, the musical note la, and a cross," which sounded out his name when spoken in French: deux, la, croix. (Maurice Serullaz, Delacroix, Ch. X, Les bibliothèques du Palais-Bourbon et du Palais du Luxembourg 1838-1848, p.203).

271. François Bonvin, *Shoemaker's Workshop*, 19th century.
Beres Gallery Collection.

272. Court shoe in Dresden china, 19th century,
International Shoe Museum, Romans.

273. Clog-shaped snuffbox. Rural Museum of Popular Arts, Laduz.

223

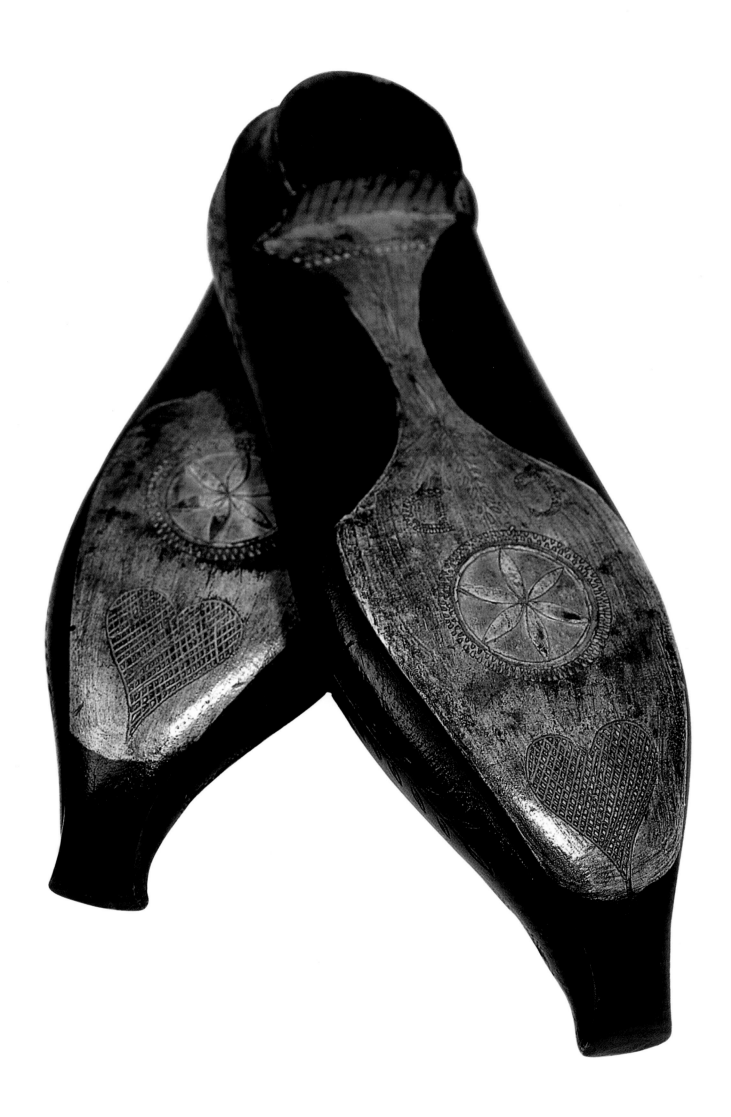

274. Marriage clogs, 19th century. Rural Museum of Popular Arts, Laduz.
275. Eugène Delacroix, *Babouches*, 1832. Musée du Louvre, Paris.

276. Vincent van Gogh, *A Pair of Shoes*, 1885.
Oil on canvas, 37.5 x 45 cm. Van Gogh Museum, Amsterdam.

280. René Magritte, *Le modèle rouge* (The Red Model), 1935.
Oil on canvas, mounted on cardboard, 56 x 46 cm.
Musée national d'art moderne, Centre Georges-Pompidou, Paris.

281. René Magritte, *Love Disarmed*, 1935. Private collection.

282. René Magritte, *Philosophy in the Boudoir*, 1947.
Private collection, Washington.

283. Schiaparelli Studio, drawing, winter 1937. Shoe-shaped hats.
French Association of Costume Arts.

284. Salvador Dalí, *Cannibalism of Objects. Head of a Woman with Shoe*, 1937.
Gouache and ink, 63.5 x 48.2 cm. Private collection.

232

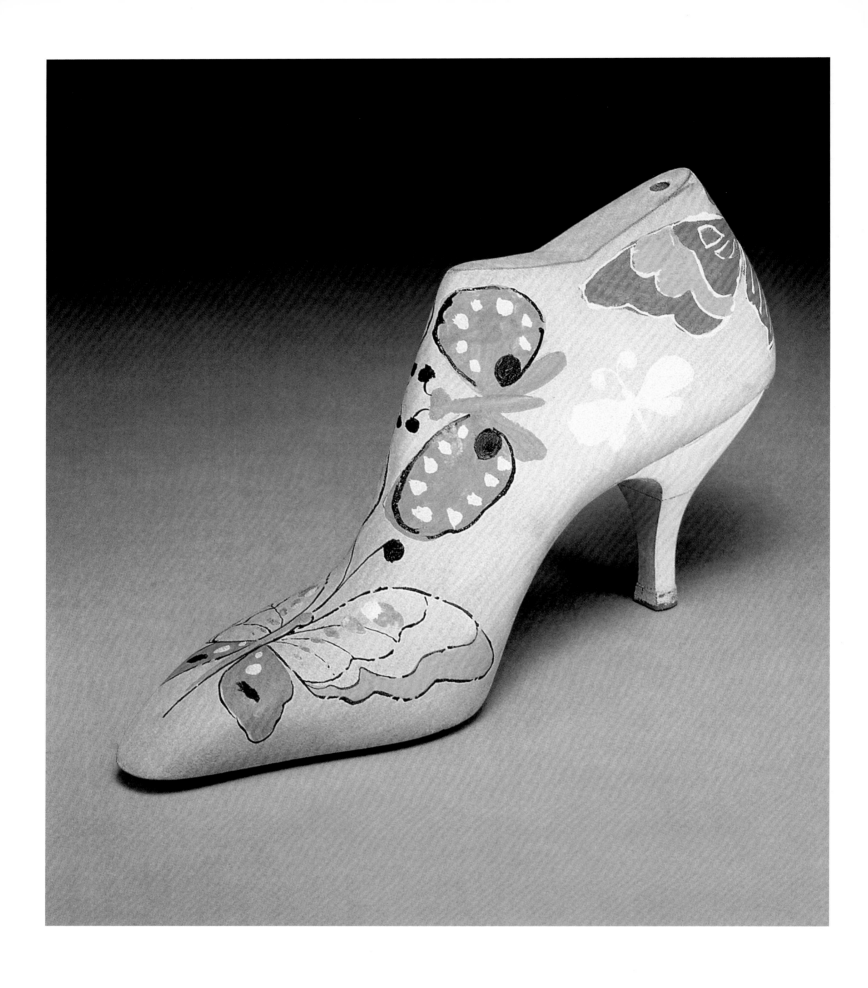

285. Warhol, *Shoe*, 1950-1953. Collection of José Mugrabi.

234

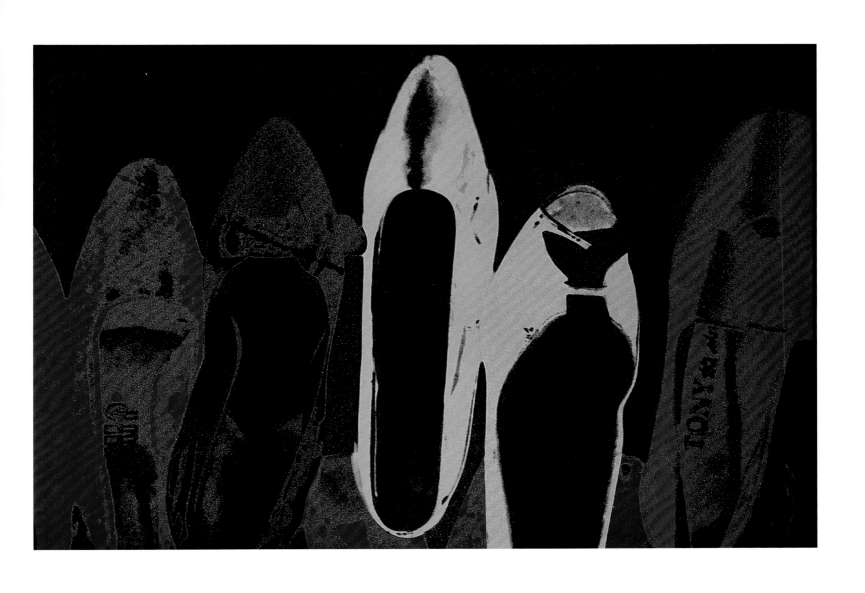

286. Warhol, *Tony Shoes*, 1980. Collection of José Mugrabi.

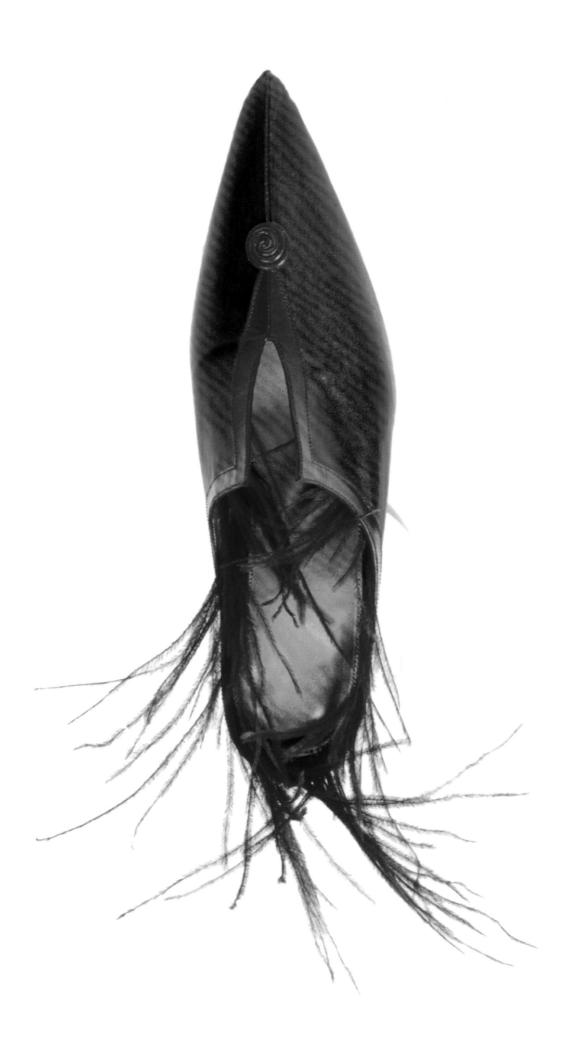

287-288. Shoes of Zita Attalaï. Ledermuseum, Offenbach.

289. Shoe of Zita Attalaï. Ledermuseum, Offenbach.

290. Ex-voto executed by Berluti.

Henri Terres

Henri Terres was born in Oran in 1948 and devoted himself to drawing and lithography under the influence of surrealism before exhibiting his first sculptures in 1990. Primarily metal works (iron, steel, and bronze), these sculptures were decidedly figurative. At first the artist assembled his pieces by welding recycled materials that he had re-cut and polished. An important final stage involving polychrome resulted in truly painted sculptures. When recycled materials seemed to offer him a limited and repetitious formal vocabulary, Terres abandoned their use in 1992, turning instead to thick slabs of sheet metal. The two themes most frequently depicted are the human face and bestiaries.

291. Glass bottillons by Christine Crozat, Paris 1997-1998. International Shoe Museum, Romans.

292. Henri Terres, "Paleontology" or "pump's skeleton," 1995. International Shoe Museum, Romans. Photo by Joël Garnier.

In 1995, Terres exhibited a sculpture series at the International Shoe Museum, Romans. Humourously entitled "Fancy Shoes," the theme was the seven deadly sins. The exhibition consisted of bas-reliefs made from a mixture of crushed stone and resin, which had been patinated with polychrome or painted with acrylics before receiving a final polish. Frames, formed during the first stage of the work and painted along with the bas-relief, were an integral part of each sculpture.

That year Terres also participated in a group exhibition called "Roger Vivier and his world," at Galerie Enrico Navarra in Paris. This exhibit brought together the work of a number of artists, including César.

The Berluti firm retains over three thousand wood forms crafted for famous and anonymous clients.

Today, Olga is restoring and adorning them with fabric and embroidery chosen to match the personality of each client represented. The shoe forms have been transformed into votive offerings by her inspired hand. Art objects in their own right, they tremble with life.

For twenty years a costume designer for the film industry (another facet of her great talent) Olga Berluti, finds her inspiration to immortalise the uniqueness of these individuals constantly renewed.

293. Mules in suede by Anne-Marie Beretta. Metal heel shaped
   as a crouched Titan. International Shoe Museum, Romans.

294. Shoe in white velvet calfskin and calfskin glazed black by Perugia, emphasised relief of toes, metal wheel, twisted metal heel, style created after a painting by Fernand Léger, around 1955. International Shoe Museum, Romans.

295. Perugia style after a painting by Picasso. Sandal in red and blue kidskin, forepart in the shape of toes, metal arch, geometric heel, around 1955. International Shoe Museum, Romans.

E Jour de la
nature entra
li rois en leulr
se saint piere
droit en ce pon̄t
que on debuoit celebrer la grant
messe ainsi comme il se fu encli
nez deuant lautel li apostoles le
ons li assist la couronne impial
sour le cief · Lors commanca li
peuplez a cryer en tel maniere
au grant charlemaine auguste

couronne de dieu · puisible empeor
des komains soit vie et victoire
Apres les soenires de peuple li papes
le courona et vesti des harnimens
empiaus selonc la coustume des
anciens princes · et fu apelez dilluec
en auant emperes auguistes · Pou
de jours fu apres que il manda q̄
ceulx qui lapostole leon auoient
depose fussent deuant lui amenez
et puis furent iuires selonc les
lois de romme des ciefs pere

Appendix

The Story of Rhodopis

A beautiful courtesan named Rhodopis was bathing in the Nile when an eagle swooped down and carried off in its beak a sandal that she had left nearby. Flying towards Memphis, the bird dropped its prey on the knees of the Pharaoh, who was busy dispensing justice. Pleasantly intrigued by the sandal's delicacy and elegance, the Pharaoh ordered a search be immediately undertaken throughout Egypt to locate its owner. He eventually found her and made her his wife. This ancient legend, told in the first-century of our era by Strabo predates the famous fairytale of Cinderella written by Charles Perrault in the 17th century.

Empress Foot

Any young woman could compete for the title Empress of the Byzantine Court. Candidates were judged on their beauty, charm, intelligence, and smallness of foot. In a tradition that endured until the 11th century, a pair of winged crimson shoes embroidered with pearls were handed over to the lucky woman "with great solemnity" by a court princess.

The Outlawed Poulaine

1 – The order of Charles V prohibiting the king's secretaries and notaries from wearing the shoes.

2 – Letters patent of Charles V (1368)

The letters patent prohibited "any person of any status or position whatsoever from the future wear of the shoe known as the poulaine, at the risk of paying a fine of ten florins, because this ostentation goes against good manners and disrespects God and Church with its worldly vanity and foolish presumption." In France, the Cardinal Curson prohibited a Université de Paris professor from wearing these scandalous shoes in 1215.

3 – Papal bulls (Urban V)

The papal bulls contained severe admonitions to priests and monks about the insolent luxury displayed in their costume and in particular their shoes. Pope Urban V was especially critical of their wearing the poulaine.

4 – The Council of Lavaur

The Council prohibited clerics from wearing long-tipped boots and prohibited their servants from wearing poulaines.

Bertrade with the Big Feet

Bertrade, mother of Charlemagne (742-814), had one foot that was much larger than the other, hence her nickname, "Big-foot Berthe."

Charlemagne's foot measured thirty-two centimetres, four millimetres and corresponded to a size 48 shoe, which was also General de Gaulle's size. By imperial order Charlemagne's foot become an official unit of measure, remaining in use until the metric system was adopted in 1795.

296. Coronation of Charlemagne, *The Grand Chronicles of France*, mid 15th-century. The State Hermitage Museum, St Petersburg.

297. *Story of Noah's Arc* (detail), from a mosaic from the 13th century. Basilica di San Marco, Venice.

The Legend of Bethmale's Clogs

(from the Saint Girons area, county Foix in Ariège)

The Bethmale Valley in Ariège was a centre of Christian resistance during the Moorish invasion in the 12th century. It was at that time that Boedbit, the Moorish leader, became enamoured with Esclarelys, who was engaged to a young man named Dannaert. Dannaert rallied opponents to fight the invaders and they took up position in the mountains; one of them was captured by the enemy, strung up by his feet, and beaten senseless with clogs. Meanwhile, the carefree and superficial Esclarelys, whose name meant *étoile de lis*, a reference to the Lily, had given into temptation and run off with her seducer, and was happily whiling away the hours cheating on her fiancé, and to a certain degree, collaborating with her country's enemies. A little later, Dannaert and his comrades captured the Moorish camp, taking the Moors prisoner and placing them in chains. Dannaert then ordered all the unmarried girls to be lined up for his review, and when he inspected them he was wearing strange clogs with long, pointed tips held up vertically and from which dangled two pieces of skewered flesh. These were the hearts of the two lovers Boedbit and Esclarelys, removed from their bodies by the scorned fiancé. He had just tossed their remains to wild mountain lions in a fit of vengeance.

Ever since then, engaged couples in the Bethmale valley have made similar clogs for themselves and their betroved decorated with brass tacks arranged in the shape of a heart: it is said the deeper the love, the more finely sharpened the nail. The ancestral tradition of this engagement gift reminds the future couple of the value of engagement, commitment, and faithfulness in marriage.

298. Clogs from the Bethmale Valley, Ariège.
Wood, nail decoration in heart shape,
18th century. Guillen Collection.

299. Clogs typical of the Bethmale Valley, Ariège.
Gift from fiancé to the young woman;
the higher the toe, the bigger the love.
Rural Museum of Popular Arts, Laduz, Yonne.

246

Shoemaker Brothers after Saint Crispin

In the footsteps of Saint Crispin and Saint Crispinian

Three men from three very different worlds came together in 1645 against the backdrop of 17th-century Paris to found the brotherhood of the shoemakers after the example of Saint Crispin and Saint Crispinian.

The three men were:

– Henri Buch. Born in 1598 to a poor family in Arlon, Belgian Luxembourg, he learned the shoemaker's trade training in his uncle's workshop.

– Gaston de Renty. Born in 1611 in Bessy Bocage, Normandy. Surrounded by luxury, this wealthy gentleman (godson of Gaston d'Orléans, Louis XIII's brother) led a life of abstinence in the spirit of the Gospel's Beatitudes.

– Jean-Antoine le Vachet. Born in 1601 to a bourgeois family in Romans-sur-Isère, a town in Dauphiné where tanners and mégissiers (tanners who used a special alum-based preparation) enjoyed great prosperity, this highly educated priest conducted his ministry in Paris, following the example of Vincent de Paul, with whom he was a close friend.

The workshop, which was located on the rue de la Tixanderie, at the crossroads between the rue de Rivoli and the rue Lobau, was close to the sumptuous town houses then coming under construction, and resembled a devoted secular brotherhood within the world of 17th-century Paris labour. The three founders shared a common objective: to eradicate the deep-rooted causes of extreme poverty. To achieve this goal, the volunteers embraced the social problems of their time, dividing the job among them as follows.

The one nicknamed "le bon Henri" or "Wise One," due to his knowledge of the trade, became the superior and was in charge of the workshop. Gaston de Renty, the community's patron, thought it insufficient to provide for the immediate needs of the poor and the marginalised in hospitals and in prisons; instead, he became a proponent of reintegration by promoting the value of work, an innovative concept at the time. Jean-Antoine le Vachet, the advisor and spiritual guide was part-contemplative, part-apostle, and he too lent his support to these artisan models of personal and communal piety. At the outset they numbered seven; later, an alliance with married laity and former community members would help spread the movement to Toulouse, Lyon, and other countries.

Dressed modestly (the costume of the era's labourers consisted of a smock and an apron), the Frères Cordonniers took no vows and lived uncloistered. They worked six days a week from five to eight following a fixed daily schedule that began with the day's offering, prayers being read aloud, and a meditation. After that they headed for the workshop thinking of Jesus working with Joseph. One of them would take turns going to mass on behalf of the whole community. At mealtime, in accordance with convent regulations, the reading was read aloud. Short breaks allowed them to converse before they picked up their hammers and awls amidst the smell of new leather, dye, and polish. These humble artisans dedicated their work to God and worked under his watchful eye, which was enough to make them happy. And their behaviour at work confirmed it: they sang canticles while beating the leather, producing quality shoes and maintaining their good reputation at the same time.

The priest, the artisan, and the gentleman directed their combined efforts towards the neediest cases, attending to the poor, the sick, and the imprisoned. They made themselves poor among the most impoverished. The Thirty Years War and the Fronde had resulted in soaring destitution: from 1648 to 1651 there were over one hundred thousand beggars and vagrants in the capital and its outskirts. Many confined in the general hospital of Paris were considered a volatile force to be feared. And the 17th-century prison environment was hellish for both guilty and innocent.

Prison cells unfit for human habitation held men eaten away by vermin, their feet wearing nothing but heavy chains for shoes. Father Vachet made

every effort to obtain the just release of many. The active ministry of the Frères Cordonniers in the face of so much adversity enabled some caught in the flood of despair to rebuild their lives by apprenticing to the trade. In the interest of hospitality and sharing, the community obtained work for handicapped and homeless people reduced to indigence.

The Frères Cordonniers knew that goodness never attracted attention. Today we owe our knowledge of their exemplary conduct to Eugénie Debouté and his remarkable book, *Without hearth or home: The story of Jean-Antoine le Vachet*, a spiritual leader during the Fonde.

The Origin of the Godillot Shoe

Born in Besançon in 1816, Alexis Godillot became an army supplier in 1854 and developed the equipment necessary to manufacture shoes by machine. He owned factories in Saint-Ouen, Bordeaux, and Nantes, as well as in Paris on the rue Rochechouart. Godillot shoes weighed three kilos, so they did not make things any easier for the soldiers, who covered twenty-five to thirty kilometres a day. Sold commercially for seven francs, the army paid eight francs twenty-five for them. After making his fortune and being decorated by the Legion of Honour, Godillot retired to Hyères where the Palm-lined avenue running from the train station is named after him.

300. David Ryckart, *Cobbler and his Companions in his Workshop*, 1864. Museum der bildenden Künste, Leipzig.

Shoemakers and Shoe Repairmen

A Brief History

In all likelihood, shoemaking has existed ever since prehistoric man thought of protecting his feet with the aid of primitively cut and assembled animal skins. But the ancient Egyptians were probably the first to ply the trade, as attested by a reconstructed fresco from the XVIII dynasty (1567-1320 B.C.E.) depicting a sandal maker at work in the collection of the Metropolitan Museum, New York.

Shoemaking flourished in Greece, supporting entire villages, such as Sicyon, where very expensive shoes were made. A painted Greek vase dating to 500 B.C.E. now in the Ashmolean Museum, Oxford, is decorated with the image of a shoe repairman in his workshop. In ancient Rome, emperor Numa Pompilius (715-672) divided citizens into nine colleges; shoemakers, called sutores in Latin, were ranked fifth. Roman shoemakers therefore were not slaves, but citizens and they worked in shops. A bas-relief from Ostia dating to the 2nd century B.C.E. in the National Museum of Rome depicts a shoemaker at work.

Although many images in painting, pottery, and sculpture portray shoemaking in Antiquity, the etymology of the French word cordonnier (shoemaker) only dates back to the Middle Ages. Originating in the 11th-century adoption of cordouannier (it would become cordonnier in the 15th century), cordonnier signified a person who worked leather from Cordoue (Cordoba), as well as the artisans authorised to use this leather to make shoes, which were generally reserved for the aristocracy. Shoes made by savetiers (shoe repairmen) were less refined. In the Middle Ages, shoes reached exorbitant prices. This explains why shoes appear in medieval wills and notary deeds, and were part of the general bequest a feudal lord made to his vassal and donations made to monasteries.

Beginning in the 12th century, shoemaking expanded in France and provided work to no less than four corps of tradesmen, each with its own specialty and bylaws. These were the *cordonniers* (shoemakers), *sueurs* (leather sweaters), *savetonniers* (shoemakers who worked with basane, a tanned lamb's skin they prepared themselves), and the *savetiers* (shoe repairmen).

The *cordonniers*, who alone knew the secret of making cordouan, produced expensive shoes and had the right to affix their mark. The *sueurs* applied the final treatments to the leather and sewed the soles previously cut by the shoemakers. The *savetonniers* or basaniers made soft shoes in small sizes and were prohibited from using any type of leather except basane, a tanned lamb's skin that they prepared themselves. As for the *savetiers*, they contented themselves with mending old shoes, by replacing or repairing the soles and the uppers. The general public gave them colourful nicknames, such as: *carreleurs de souliers* (shoe masons), *orfèvres en cuir* (shoe smiths), *courvoisiers*, and *bobelineurs*.

During the 10th and 11th centuries, these artisans formed guilds, which were labour organisations that brought together merchants, artisans, and artists. Prevalent in northwestern Europe up to the 13th century, the guilds transformed themselves into corporations at the end of the 11th century, whence they enacted their own rules and monitored compliance in the following areas: pricing; quality control, production control, work time, and the acceptance of apprentices, later called compagnons. After apprenticing with a master, the apprentice had to make a "tour" meant to expand and improve his knowledge by working alongside other masters. This education lasted from six to nine years but came to be limited to eighteen months beginning in the 17th century. After this training period, the young man executed a masterpiece to prove his craft before a jury of examiners. Upon passing the examination, the apprentice obtained the title of master and the right to membership in the corporation.

King Charles the Wise established the brotherhood of shoemakers in the Cathedral of Paris in 1379. The shoemakers took Saint Crispin and Saint Crispinian as their saints. The corporation loosened its regulations in the 17th and 18th centuries, which explains how a shoemaker was able to have his shop in the same town where he apprenticed. Eventually, the profession was divided into groups according to categories of shoes, with each group restricted to producing the type of shoes they had been designated to make. Thus there were men's shoemakers, women's and children's shoemakers, boot makers, shoemakers who only worked in lambskin, and finally, the shoe repairmen, also known as cobblers.

A special craftsman called le talonnier made wooden heels. Form makers (formiers) made the shoemaker's forms and shoetrees, but had neither standing nor oath. Working without a master, many were themselves poor master shoemakers. Nevertheless, the jurors of the shoemaker community tried in vain to gain control over them. Out of all these groups, it was the cobbler, whose lifestyle was immortalised by Jean de la Fontaine in his famous fable, *The Cobbler and the Financier*. Prints from the 17th century depict the blatant distinction between shoemakers and their customers when they illustrate scenes of shoe shops. It is usually a cavernous space where masters and journeymen measure the feet of a customer whose elegance indicates his class. In reality, the sale took place in the street: the shoe shop, backed up against a house, could only contain two people. As for the didactic plates in the Encyclopaedia of Diderot and d'Alembert featuring tools of the shoemaker's trade accompanied by explanatory notes, they give us a valuable introduction to the art of fabrication in the 18th century. In the years before the French Revolution, shoemakers managed thriving shops. The writer Sébastien Mercier records that, "in their black outfit and powdered wig, they look like Clerks of the Court." In the 19th century the profession became organised, leading to the formation of la société des Compagnons Cordonniers Bottiers du Devoir du Tour de France (the Workers' Association of the Shoemaker and Boot maker Companions of Duty). The Tour de France sponsored by the Compagnons du Devoir was an itinerate work-study program that enabled an apprentice to successively acquire mastery of his trade in a number of French towns called *villes du devoir*, or towns of service.

In 1829, Thimonier invented the sewing machine, which gradually established itself in the workshops and transformed traditional shoemaking. In today's shops, shoemakers continue to uphold the cobbler's tradition by repairing shoes and boots, and making custom shoes like the shoemakers of old.

The shoe shop: Its appearance remained unchanged for a long time. The centre of the room held a workbench upon which various tools lay about. These tools fall into three main categories: Pattern-cutting tools and other cutting tools: punch, compass with points, cutter's knife, triangular file for sharpening the leather knife, sharpening stone, and a type of mechanic's file for forming or adjusting patterns. Tools used for assembling and execution: awl, working cutter, lasting pincers, joiner's pincers, nails, steel tack claw, nail hammer, peen hammer, hand protector, rand cutter, rasp, and stirrup. Tools used for finishing: a tool for polishing and smoothing soles, various leather polishing tools, and wooden mallets.

A glass globe enclosing a candle or oil lamp provided the workshop's dim lighting and was called a *boule de cordonnier* or shoemaker's globe. Under the table was a bucket of water used to soak the leather called the *baquet de la science*. The shoemaker and the shoe repairman usually worked seated on a stool. The shop always seemed to have a birdcage called the *cage aux serins* or canary cage. Tradition required a shoe repairman to have a pot of basil or an orange tree called the *oranger du savetier* to mask the smell of old shoes. An artisan could refer to himself as *cordonnier en vieux et en neuf*, or maker of shoes old and new, indicating that he made new shoes and repaired shoes already worn.

The paintings in the International Shoe Museum, Romans, apart from their pictorial interest, enable us to visualise the world of shoe fabrication from the 17th to the end of the 19th century. Above all, they teach us about the permanence of the specific tools used to create shoes over the centuries, tools that visitors can still recognise in contemporary workshops.

301. Théodore Rivière, *The Cobbler*,
19th-century. Bronze.
International Shoe Museum, Romans.

302. Members of the Swann Club during a polishing session at Paul Mincelli in 1996.

The Swann Club

Olga Berluti's Lessons in Polishing

The very special art of polishing shoes by moonlight invented by Olga Berluti sheds some light on her research into the art of polishing. Aficionados of beautiful shoes, during stops outside rue Marbeuf, would listen to Olga impart her knowledge in such romantic terms that they were swept away to another world. These meetings, at once professional, friendly, and animated, gave birth to the Swann club, in memory of the refined atmosphere in the works of Marcel Proust.

The one hundred members admitted to this circle of privileged aesthetes met once a year for a light-hearted lesson in polishing that was orchestrated by Olga's magic.

Always under moonlight, the faithful removed their shoes and placed them on a table. The table was covered with a white damask tablecloth whose brilliance was enhanced by the light from candelabras illuminating the ceremony's main event. Fingers were swaddled in squares of Venetian linen, immersed in wax, to massage the leathers. Then came buffing, at first using water but followed by champagne.

The entire Swann Club never came together at one time. Some lived far away, but eagerly made the trip. The location of the get togethers would change. Boredom was unheard of at these unique evenings, which provided a blissful moment of escape.

René Caty

Among the most famous names in fashion, Adolphe Carraz's shoe factory for expensive women's shoes opened in 1909 and employed thirty-two workers. Around 1931, through a family alliance, the firm became the company known as "Carraz et Caty." In 1948, it brought a new article to the market called the "ballerina," which quickly became a smashing success, peaking at the end of the 1950s.

The Continuity of Myths

Cinderella in China

Well before Charles Perrault and after Strabo, the 9th-century Chinese text relates an Asian version of the Cinderella myth. There once was a powerful man with two wives, each of whom had a daughter. One daughter was named Sheh-Hsien. When her parents died, Sheh-Hsien continued to live with her stepmother, who used to send her to draw water. One day Sheh-Hsien withdrew a fish with red fins and gold eyes. She carried the fish to a pond where everyday the fish would come when she called.

Taking advantage of Sheh-Hsien's absence, the stepmother killed the fish, ate it, and hid the fishbone under a manure heap. The young girl cried when she could no longer find her fish. Then a figure descended from the sky and told her to remove the fishbone from the manure heap and place it in her room where it would allow her to obtain her heart's desire. In this way, Sheh-Hsien obtained gold, pearls, and food.

Now her half-sister and her stepmother had gone to the village celebration leaving Sheh-Hsien to watch the house. While they were gone, she put on a blue dress and gold shoes and went to the celebration herself where her appearance left everyone speechless. In her haste to get back to the house before her stepmother and half-sister, she lost one of her gold shoes. The powerful king of a neighbouring island purchased the shoe. In vain he tried it on all the young girls in his kingdom. In the end, he found the other shoe at Sheh-Hsien's house and married her.

Glossary

Ankle boot

Woman's shoe very fashionable in winter since 1940. Strictly speaking, it is a short boot with a fur-lined interior, the fur-lining peeking out and serving as decoration.

Babouche

The babouche, "slipper of coloured leather with neither quarter nor heal" (Littré), is probably of Iranian origin as proved by the Persian word PAPOUTCH (from *pa*, "foot" and *pouchiden*, "to cover").

Blake

Lyman Reed Blake (1835-1883), American technician who, in 1858, invented a machine to sew right through the insole to the sole using a chain stitch. His patents were acquired and subsequently perfected by Gordon Mackay.

Boot

Shoe covering the foot and the leg at the same time and rising to various heights.

Boot hook

1- Hook that one passes through the bootstrap to help slip it on.
2- Sort of small plank having a notch in which one wedges one's shod foot to help remove one's boot.

Bottine

Small boot, of which the upper rises above the ankle to cover the calf at various heights, closed by lacing or buttoning. During the Middle Ages, bottines were called boots without soles that were slipped over the shoe like gaiters or houseaux.

In the 19th century, from the end of the Restoration, women wore bottines, whether of fine leather or fabric with or without heal, in following the mode. One found laced bottines and bottines with buttons, for which came the invention of the buttonhook.

At the beginning of the 20th century, women wore very elegant bottines with a high upper rising to the calf. The vogue of bottines began to disappear after the war of 1914-1918.

Buckle

Generally metallic accessory, with or without a tongue, which serves to fasten the shoe.

Ornamental buckle: buckle strictly for decoration.

During the 17th century, shoe buckles were most often made of precious metals. In 1670 and 1680, buckles replaced bows on top of shoes. They were decorated with an entourage of real or fake pearls and diamonds. For mourning, buckles were bronzed and without precious stones. Buckles, kept in jewellery cases, adapted to different shoes. Small and rectangular, they became round and oval in the 18th century, following the fashion. Their dimensions increased at the end of the reign of Louis XV and appeared square under Louis XVI. The buckles of men's shoes covered the foot under Louis XVI.

Buckle attachment strap

Short tie, sewn to a piece of the upper and folded in such a way as to form a part receiving a buckle

Campagus

Ancient shoe worn in Rome. The campagus takes the shape of a bottine leaving the foot uncovered. Trimmed with fur, often decorated with pearls and precious stones, it is the shoe of generals. When crimson in colour, it is reserved exclusively for emperors.

Chiquet

Small, not very high heel generally on flat, women's shoes.

Chopine

Woman's shoe worn in Venice in the 16th century, also called "stilted mule" or "cow's foot". These strange shoes, held to the foot by ribbons, demonstrate pedestals of an excessive height reaching up to fifty-two centimetres.

Clog

Derived from the ancient soccus, shoes made of a wooden sole attached to the foot with straps.

Worn from the Middle Ages under leather soled chausses and shoes, they stay in use until the 17th century under town boots.

Drawing bridge shoe (pont-levis)

Before Henri IV, men's shoes were heelless. At the end of the 16th century and the beginning of the 17th century, they were made heeled, leaving an empty space beneath the sole, which causes these shoes to be called drawbridge shoes (pont-levis).

Espadrille

Cloth shoe with a braided rope sole worn throughout Spain and the Midi of France.

Eyelet

Hollowed out, metal piece used to reinforce a perforation. Sometimes one places it in the lacing holes.

Floral toe

Toe adorned with perforations of different sizes. The origin of this name goes back to the beginning of the 20th century for the motif represented was most often of flowers.

Goodyear

Name of the patent (from the patronymic of the inventor) originally naming the method known as the Goodyear Welt.

In 1862, a patent is awarded to Auguste Detouy for a machine for sewing the leather sole by means of a curved needle. Charles Goodyear Junior (son of Charles Goodyear, American inventor of the process of the vulcanisation of rubber) improves the method and registers a patent for a machine to sew the welt in 1869.

Louis Rama, in the *Technical Dictionary of Leather* gives the following technical definitions:

1 - hand-sewn welt:

type of manufacture in which the welt and the upper are hand-sewn on the wall of a plated insole.

2 - machine-sewn welt:

type of manufacture producing mechanically all of the operations of hand-sewing the welt on the wall of a plated insole.

Lacing

The most elegant horizontal lacing is typical of the oxford while lacing in the form of a cross is often used for derbies.

Ladrine

In the time of Louis XIII, when the wearing of boots was broad, this one rose to mid-leg and fell back like a funnel on the calf. It was called a ladrine or lazarine. The boot was decorated with useless spurs even worn to the ball and for which one made leather wheels to avoid tearing dresses.

Last-maker

Technician who creates or develops the lasts.
Manufacturer of lasts in industrial series.

Mule

Light house shoe without quarter leaving the heel exposed.

Pieds noirs (French settlers in North Africa)

It is not by chance that the descendants of North African settlers themselves (ah yes!) created this nickname for themselves that, supposedly, should have been given to them by the Arabs: Pieds noirs. So called for their solid shoes of "civilized" material as compared to the precarious babouches of the unworthy.

Pigage or Pigache

Shoe of the 12th century, with a pointed and hooked toe, sometimes decorated with a little bell and whose style goes back to antiquity.

Platform sole

Thick mid-sole, whose edge can be coated or decorated, inserted between the upper and the sole itself.

Polishing brush

Horsehide brush used for shining shoes.

Quarter

One of the two pieces symmetrically arranged that form the back of the upper and continue to the instep or thereabouts to close the shoe.

Rose

Under Louis XIII, to decorate men's and women's shoes, bows and ribbons are placed on the instep hiding the tie or buckle. Thus are formed shoe roses, often very big, gathered or goffered, resembling dahlias. Under Louis XIV, this mode is replaced by buckles.

Sable

Extremely fine method of weaving beads used in the 18th century for shoes and small objects: buckles, ornaments, etc…

Saint Crispin and Saint Crispinian

Patron saints of shoe repairers, 1660. In *La Vie Parisienne*, operetta by Jacques Offenbach: "By Saint Crispin, we arrive, and the way so as to dine put us in good spirits, by Saint Crispin…" (Final chorus Act II)

Sandal

Worn since Egyptian, Greek and Roman antiquity, this simplified shoe is made up of a sole and straps or strips of various widths and assembled in a variety of ways, between which the foot remains visible. Several religious orders still keep with the use of sandals.

Shankpiece

Elongated piece of leather, wood, steel or plastic placed in the shank to give firmness to the arch of the shoe and support the arch of the foot.

Shoe

Covering for the foot but stopping at the instep.

Shoehorn

Strip of metal, horn or plastic used to aid the foot in entering the shoe. According to the *Historical Dictionary of Arts, Trades and Professions Exercised in Paris since the 13th Century*, by Alfred Franklin, in the 16th century, a leather strap or a horn is used. A royal account of 1570 contained the following two notes: "for having cut a quarter of morocco leather hide, to make shoehorns to put in the wardrobe…", "for three horn shoehorns to serve the pageboys…"

Trévoux's dictionary (1704-1771) reproduced this passage almost word for word and added: "In the past one made it of horn and even of iron."

In a word, the Academy, in its 1778 edition, pointed to this proverb: It is inside without shoehorn, which means: "It succeeded with no trouble and more easily than one believed."

Size

Interior dimension of a shoe expressed in points and taking into account the length of the foot and its lengthening in a walk. Shoe size is expressed in points:

English point, sometimes also called wrongly American point: $1/3$ of an inch or 8.466 mm. French point or Paris point: $2/3$ of a centimetre or 6.666 mm.

Slipper

Light and supple shoe suited to various uses: house slippers, ballet slippers, fencing slippers, bootees.

Interior, removable part of a ski boot or walking shoe assuring the tight and supple contact between the foot and the outer shell of the shoe.

Soccus

Kind of slipper or shoe without any lacing entirely enclosing the foot. Worn in Greece by both sexes, in Rome it is reserved to women and comic actors, as opposed to the tragic cothurnus.

Solea

Roman sandal of the simplest form made up of a wooden sole with a string passing over the top of the foot.

Solleret

The solleret, formerly called pédieu, was, in the suit of armour, the part that imprisoned and protected the foot. First, it was a sort of steel gutter only protecting the instep and leaving the rest of the foot under the mail. This piece was then divided into several articulated lames forming a series of arches or a scorpion tail pointed toe in the 14th century and poulaines in the 15th century. Under Charles VIII, the solleret was spoon-billed, bear's footed until François I, then duckbilled. It disappeared under Charles IX.

Stirrup strap

Leather strap that fixes the foot in the process of manufacture or repair to the knees.

Stivali

In the 14th century, one called a stivali a light summer shoe. They were tall boots of supple hide or cloth, dyed in red or black and worn by both sexes.

Throat

In shoe manufacture, the throat of a shoe is the extension of the vamp on the instep.

Tongue

Until the end of the 15th century, shoes have tongues on the instep, usually tied by a string and which are called liripipes.

On an oxford or derby, instep's protective flap situated under the lacing.

On a loafer or moccasin without laces, part of the upper being an extension of the vamp that covers and hides the tightening elastic.

Upper

As opposed to the sole, the superior part of the shoe, designed to dress and protect the top of the foot.

Vamp

Top of a shoe, from the instep to the toe.

Welt

Small strip of leather sewn the length of the edge of a shoe's vamp to strengthen the sole.

Bibliography

Marie-Josèphe Bossan, *Livre guide du musée international de la chaussure de Romans édité par l'association des amis du musée de Romans*, 1992.

François Boucher, *Histoire du costume*, Paris, 1965.

Eugénie Debouté, *Sans feu ni lieu un maître spirituel au temps de la Fronde – Jean-Antoine le Vachet*, Châtillon 1994

Yvonne Deslandres, *Le Talon et la mode*, 1980.

Catherine Férey – Simone Blazy, *Des objets qui racontent l'histoire*, Saint-Symphorien-sur-Coise, December 2000.

Paul and Jacqueline Galmiche, *La Saga du pied*. Erti, Paris 1983.

Victor Guillen, "La légende des sabots de Bethmale", in *Chausser*, Spezialausgabe.

Paul Lacroix, *Histoire des cordonniers*, Paris, 1852.
D. Pfister, "Les chaussures Coptes", in *Revue de l'Institut de Calcéologie n° 3*, 1986.

William Rossi, *Érotisme du pied et de la chaussure*, Cameron Sait Amand Montrond, 1978.

Jean-Paul Roux, *La Chaussure*, Paris, 1980.

Marie-Louise Teneze, "Cycle de Cendrillon", in *Bulletin n° 1 de l'Institut de Calcéologie*, 1982.

Marie-Louise Teneze, "Le Chat botté", in *Bulletin n° 2 de l'Institut de Calcéologie*, 1984.

Marie-Louise Teneze, "Le Petit Poucet", in *Bulletin n° 3 de l'Institut de Calcéologie*, 1986.

Jean-Marc Thévenet, *Rêves de Pompes, Pompes de Rêves*, Paris 1988.

Gabriel Robert Thibault, "L'exaltation d'un mythe: Rétif de La Bretonne et le soulier couleur rose." in *Bulletin n° 4 de l'Institut de Calcéologie*, 1990.

Loszlo Vass and Magda Molnar, *La chaussure pour homme faite main*, Germany, 1999.

Correspondance de Pasteur, gesammelt und mit Anmerkungen versehen von Pasteur Vallery-Radot, Flammarion, 1951.

Le Musée, la Chapelle funéraire, Institut Pasteur.

Dictionnaire de la Mode au XXe siècle, Paris 1994.

La Mode et l'enfant, 1780-2000, Musée Galliera, Musée de la Mode de la ville de Paris, April 2001.

Le Soulier de Marie-Antoinette,
Caen – Musée des beaux-arts, Caen 1989.

XVIIᵉ siècle, Lagarde and Michard, Bordas.

XIXᵉ siècle, Lagarde and Michard, Bordas.

XXᵉ siècle, Lagarde and Michard, Leonard Danel Loos (Nord), 1962.

Grammaire des styles
– *Le costume de la Restauration à la Belle époque.*
– *Le costume de 1914 aux années folles.*
– *4000 ans d'histoire de la chaussure*, Château de
Blois, 1984.

Index

Acknowledgements

Association des amis du musée de Romans, Véronique Auroux, Association Charles Trenet, Mouna Ayoub, Muriel Barbier (Musée Galliera), Laure Bassal, Guy Blazy (Conservateur en chef du Musée des Tissus et des Arts Décoratifs de Lyon), Simone Blazy, (Conservateur en chef du Musée Gadagne, Lyon), Docteur Jean Bénichou, Galerie Berès, Paris, Olga Berluti, Henri Bertholet (Maire de Romans), Georgy Bidegain, Paul Bocuse, Bon Marché Rive Gauche, Olivier Bouissou (Délégué général de la Fédération française de la chaussure, Commissaire général du MIDEC et de Mod'Amont), Docteur Simon Braun, Pierre Brissot, Stéphanie Busuttil, Marie-Noëlle de Cagny (Bureau de style, chaussure maroquinerie cuir, Paris), Jean-Claude Carrière, Professeur Jean-Paul Carret, Pierre Caty, Charles Jourdan, Centre historique de la résistance en Drôme et de la Déportation, Centre Technique du Cuir, Lyon, Professeur Guy Chouinard, Robert Clergerie, Le Conseil National du Cuir, Patrick Cox, Astrid Sarkis Der Balian, Kegetzique Sarkis Der Balian, Sophie Descamps (Conservateur au département des antiquités grecques et romaines, Musée du Louvre), Henri Ducret, Thierry Dufresne, Jean-Pierre Dupré, Pierre Durand, Françoise Durand, Fabienne Falluel (Conservateur au Musée Galliera, Paris), La Fédération française de la chaussure, Ferragamo, Marc Folachier, Elisabeth Foucart (Conservateur en chef au département des peintures, Musée du Louvre), Jacques Foucart (Conservateur général au département des peintures, Musée du Louvre), Jean-Paul Foulhoux, Ginko, Pascal Giroud, Dominique Goberthier, Bernard Gouttenoire, François Gravier, Cécile Guinard (Musée de Romans), Nicole Hechberg (chargée du Centre de documentation du musée de Romans), Claude James, Véronique Jeammet (Conservateur au département des antiquités grecques et romaines, Musée du Louvre), Claudette Joannis (Conservateur en chef du Patrimoine, Adjoint au Directeur du Musée de Malmaison et Bois-Préau), Roland Jourdan, Daly Jourdan-Barry, Isabelle Julia (Conservateur à l'Inspection Générale des Musées), Stéphane Kélian, Geneviève Lacambe (Conservateur général du Patrimoine), Christiane Laffont (Adjointe chargée de l'urbanisme, du patrimoine et des arts plastiques), Françoise Laigle (journaliste), Karl Lagerfeld, Lydie Laupies, André Laurencin (Conservateur honoraire du Musée Denon), Bénédicte Leblan, Christian Lebon, Sylvie Lefranc (Fondatrice et ancienne Directrice du Bureau de style chaussure maroquinerie cuir, Paris), Éric Le Marec, Jeannie Longo, Françoise Maison (Conservateur en chef chargé des collections du Second Empire, Château de Compiègne), Christiane Marandet (Conservateur général honoraire du patrimoine), Suzanne Marest (Styliste conseil au Bureau de style chaussure maroquinerie cuir, Paris), Laurence Massaro, Raymond Massaro, Docteur Jacques Mazade, André Meunier, Docteur Jean-Jacques Morel, Comte et Comtesse Moussine-Pouchkine, Musée d'art et d'histoire, Genève, Musée Bally, Schoenenwerd (Suisse), Musée de l'Homme, Paris, Rosita Nenno (Conservateur Musée Allemand du Cuir et de la Chaussure, Offenbach), Catherine Perrochet (Musée de Romans), Anne Rondet, Annick Perrot (Conservateur du Musée Pasteur), Andrea Pfister, Patrick Pichavant, Pascal Pitou, Hervé Racine, Stefania Ricci (Conservateur du Musée Salvatore Ferragamo), Huguette Rouit, Joël Roux, Jean-Paul Roux (Directeur de recherche honoraire au CNRS, Professeur titulaire honoraire de la chaire des Arts Islamiques à l'École du Louvre), Le Service Communication de la Ville de Romans, Brigitte et Jean Schoumann, Alexandre Siranossian (Directeur de l'École nationale de musique et de danse), Docteur Tan Sivy, Jean Tchilinguirian, Henri Terres, Françoise Tétart-Vittu (Chargée du Cabinet des arts graphiques au Musée Galliera, Paris), Olivier Thinus, Tod's, Pierre Troisgros, Gérard Turpin, Gérard Benoît-Vivier.